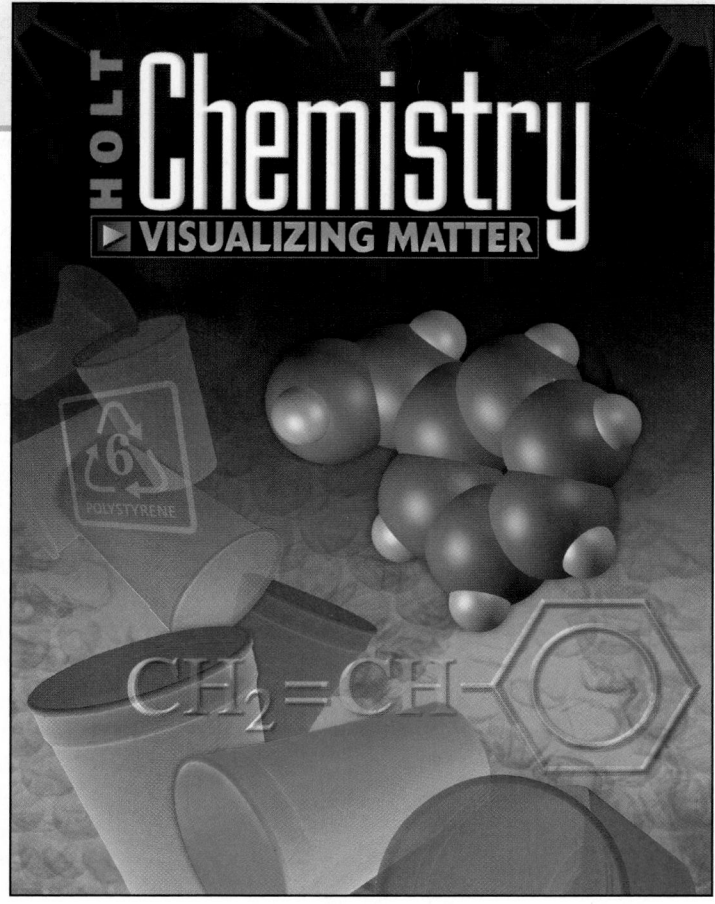

Annotated Teacher's Edition

*A*UTHORS

▼

R. Thomas Myers, Ph.D.
Professor Emeritus of Chemistry
Kent State University
Kent, Ohio

Keith B. Oldham, Ph.D.
Professor of Chemistry
Trent University
Peterborough, Ontario, Canada

Salvatore Tocci
Science Writer
East Hampton, NY

HOLT, RINEHART AND WINSTON
Harcourt Brace & Company

Austin • New York • Orlando • Atlanta • San Francisco
Boston • Dallas • Toronto • London

▼ Contributing Writers

Jeffrey D. Bracken
Chemistry Teacher
Westerville North High School
Westerville, OH

Robert Davisson
Science Writer and Editor
Delaware, Ohio

Dave Jaeger
Chemistry Teacher
Will C. Wood High School
Vacaville, CA

Mary Ellen Teasdale
Chemistry Reference Librarian
Texas A&M University
College Station, TX

Suzanne Weisker
*Science Teacher and
Department Chair*
Will C. Wood High School
Vacaville, CA

Jay A. Young, Ph.D.
Chemical Safety Consultant
Silver Spring, MD

▼ Staff Credits

Managing Editor
David F. Bowman

Editorial Staff
John Benner
Derika Hatcher
Cecelia B. Schneider
Amanda Tinsley

Copyediting Supervisor
Steve Oelenberger

Copyeditors
Suzanne Brooks
Brooke Fugitt
Denise Haney
Tania Hannan

Senior Book Designer
Marta Kimball

Book Design Staff
José Garza
Cathy Jenevein
Amanda Marks
Bob Prestwood

Editorial Permissions
Jan Harrington

Director Image Services
Debra Schorn

Image Services Staff
Elaine Tate
Sherry France
Linda Wilbourn
Leroy Dee Golden II

Photo Research Manager
Peggy Cooper

Photo Researchers
Jeannie Taylor
Diana Suthard
Jennifer Guidry

Senior Staff Photographer
Sam Dudgeon

Photo Studio
Victoria Smith
Lauren Eischen

*Media Design
Art Director*
Joe Melomo

Media Design Staff
Shawn McKinney

New Media Design Art Director
Susan Michael

Senior Production Manager
Mimi Stockdell

Production Coordinator
Beth Sample

*Production
Senior Secretary*
Sara Downs

Media Senior Production Manager
Kim A. Scott

Media Production Coordinator
Nancy Hargis

Production Assistant
Adriana Bardin

Manufacturing Coordinator
Jevara Jackson

*New Media
Associate Director*
Kate Bennett

*New Media
Project Manager*
Stacy Doolittle

Researchers
Mike Tracy
Joyce Herbert
Patty Kolar
Jennifer Swift

► **Cover:** Design by Lawrence R. Didona. **Photos:** John Langford/HRW Photo. **Art Credits:** All art, unless otherwise noted, by Holt, Rinehart & Winston. **Photo Credits:** Circuit board (border) - Image Copyright © 2000 Photodisc, Inc.; Snow Flake (border) © Image Copyright © 2000 Photodisc, Inc. Abbreviated as follows: (t) top; (b) bottom; (l) left; (r) right; (c) center. 18T-19T (border) Douglas Struthers/Tony Stone Images; (bkgd) Sam Dudgeon/HRW; 19T (br) Sam Dudgeon/HRW; (bc) Image copyright © 2000 Photodisc, Inc.; 21T (all) Charlie Winters; 24T (tl) Tony Freeman/PhotoEdit; 26T (tr) Charlie Winters; 27T (br) Sergio Purtell/Foca; 28T (tr), (cr), Sam Dudgeon/HRW; (bl) Image Copyright © 2000 Photodisc, Inc.; 33T (tr) Sam Dudgeon/HRW; 37T (br) Dennis Fagan/HRW; (bc) Charlie Winters; 46T (tr) Sam Dudgeon/HRW; (bc) Charlie Winters; 51T (bc) Charlie Winters; 690 (tl) Image copyright © 2000 Photodisc, Inc.; 691 (tl) Image copyright © 2000 Photodisc, Inc.

For permission to reprint copyrighted material, grateful acknowledgment is made to the following sources:
sciLinks is owned and provided by the National Science Teachers Association. All Rights Reserved.
Flinn Scientific, Inc., Batavia, IL: From *Latex, The Preparation of a Rubber Ball*, Publication Number 430.00. Copyright © 1993 by Flinn Scientific, Inc. All Rights Reserved. No part of this material may be reproduced or transmitted in any form or by any means, electronic or mechanical, including, but not limited to photocopy, recording, or any information storage and retrieval system, without permission in writing from Flinn Scientific, Inc.

Printed in the United States of America

ISBN 0-03-053837-8
12345678 048 03 02 01 00 99

▼ Content Reviewers

G. Lynn Carlson, Ph.D.
Chemistry Department
University of Wisconsin-Parkside
Kenosha, WI

Michael J. Costello, Ph.D.
Professor
Chemistry and Chemical Engineering
    Technology
Broome Community College
Binghamton, NY

Wendy L. Keeney-Kennicutt, Ph.D.
Department of Chemistry
Texas A&M University
College Station, TX

Charles Scaife, Ph.D.
Professor
Department of Chemistry
Union College
Schenectady, NY

Hari D. Sharma, Ph.D.
Professor Emeritus
Department of Chemistry
University of Waterloo
Waterloo, Ontario, Canada

Richard S. Treptow, Ph.D.
Professor of Chemistry
Department of Chemistry and Physics
Chicago State University
Chicago, IL

Martin VanDyke, Ph.D.
Professor of Chemistry, Emeritus
Front Range Community College
Westminster, CO

Charles M. Wynn, Sr., Ph.D.
Professor of Chemistry
Department of Physical Science
Eastern Connecticut State University
Willimantic, CT

▼ Teacher Reviewers

Elizabeth M. Dabrowski
Science Department Chair
Magnificat High School
Rocky River, OH

Diego Enciso
Lecturer
Natural Sciences Department
Lawrence Technological University
Southfield, MI

Jeffrey L. Engel
Chemistry Teacher
Madison County High School
Danielsville, GA

Thomas F. Fetter
Department Head
Science Department
West Delaware High School
Manchester, IA

Cheryl Kurosky
Chemistry Teacher
Duluth Central High School
Duluth, MN

Jack Markham
Chemistry/Physics Teacher
Laconia High School
Rosendale, WI

Gerald L. Shoemaker, Ph.D.
Research Chemist/Chemistry Teacher
Roosevelt High School
Kent, OH

Samuel Vicchy
Chemistry Teacher
Belleville High School
Belleville, MI

Catherine Williams
Chemistry Teacher
Waseca High School
Waseca, MN

Linda L. Wohlever
Mathematics Teacher
Hathaway Brown School
Shaker Heights, OH

Contents

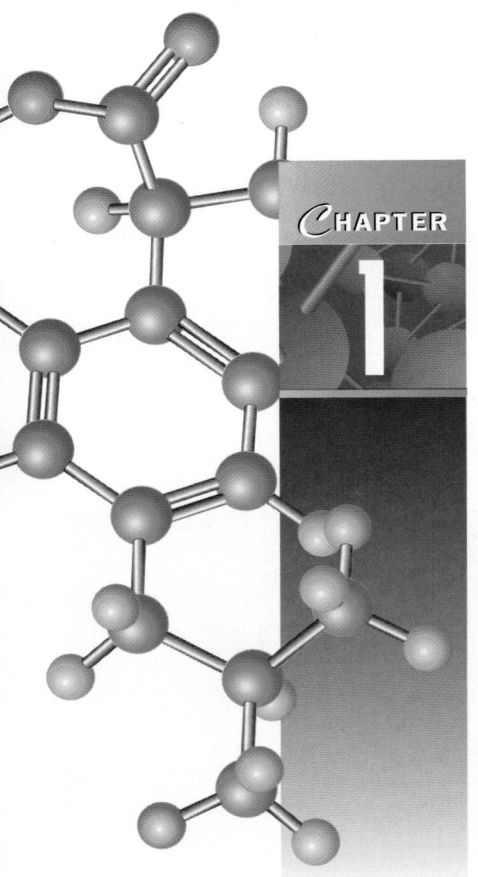

CHAPTER 1

The Science of Chemistry 2

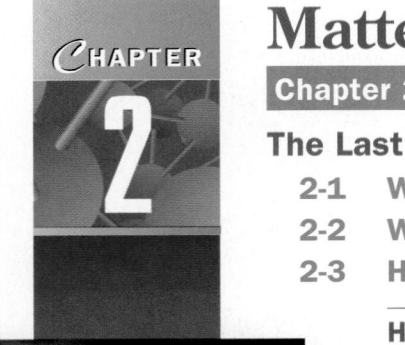

CHAPTER 2

Matter and Energy 38

Copper-65

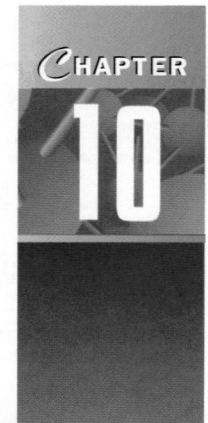
1997 American League Batting Average

Player	Team	Average
Frank Thomas	Chicago	.347
Edgar Martinez	Seattle	.330
David Justice	Cleveland	.329
Bernie Williams	New York	.328
Manny Ramirez	Cleveland	.328

Solutions 466

Chemical Equilibrium 510

Appendices

Answers for Appendix B are found in Appendix C. Appendix C also includes student answers for all PRACTICE PROBLEMS within chapters.

*A*PPENDIX **A**

*A*PPENDIX **B**

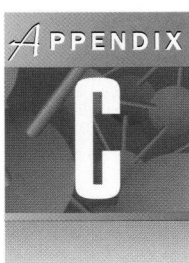

*A*PPENDIX **C**

Laboratory Program 688

Teacher's Notes for all Labs are found in the margins.

Sample Problems

Mass-Mass Stoichiometry

| Mass of *given* substance (g) | → | Amount of *given* substance (mol) | → | Amount of *unknown* substance (mol) | → | Mass of *unknown* substance (g) |

Use the molar mass of *given* to convert to amount of *given* (use the periodic table).

Use the mole ratio of coefficients from balanced equation to convert to amount of *unknown*.

Use the molar mass of *unknown* to convert to mass of *unknown* (use the periodic table).

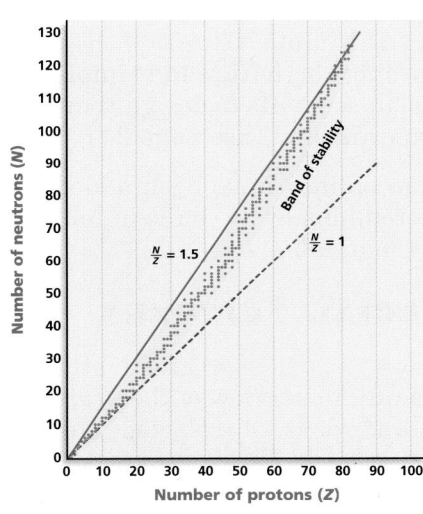

WHAT'S NEW AND DIFFERENT

Holt Chemistry Visualizing Matter

Now correlated to the National Science Education Standards (See pages 36T-39T)

STUDENT TEXT

CHAPTER SEQUENCE

The streamlined course sequence emphasizes core concepts and applications and can be completed within the standard school year.

The text retains its focus on applications using a balance of examples from organic and inorganic chemistry.

NEW • **Chapter 7**, Carbon and Organic Compounds, provides a more thorough foundation in the naming, structural features, and classes of organic compounds. (See page 232.)

NEW • **Chapter 8**, The Mole, puts all of the introductory coverage of the mole concept together in one chapter. (See page 272.)

NEW • **SciLinks Internet** links provided through the National Science Teachers Association (NSTA) help students use the Internet in a safe and structured environment. (See page 30T.)

NEW • **Study Skills** tips in the chapters are supported by a new Reading and Study Skills appendix that provides useful strategies for reading in the content area. (See page 20T.)

NEW • **Reading and Study Skills Appendix** provides research-based techniques for increasing reading comprehension and for developing useful study strategies. (See page 806.)

LABORATORY PROGRAM

A revision of the laboratory program gives you more structured experiments in the built-in laboratory manual in the back of the book.

NEW • **QuickLabs and InquiryLabs**, provide short activities and simple options for students to design their own experiments. (See page 24T.)

NEW • **CBL** lab options have been added to selected labs in the built-in laboratory manual.

SPECIAL FEATURES

NEW • **Element Spotlight** gives students a quick overview of the properties and uses of selected elements.

NEW • **Science & Technology** gives students insights into areas of research and related careers in science.

• **Consumer Focus** relates chemical principles to commonly used products.

FOR THIS EDITION?

TEACHER'S EDITION

A revision of the margin wrap gives you more teaching and assessment options. New features for this addition include: Reading Strategies, Lesson Warm-Ups, Resource Links, Internet links, and a wide range of Alternative Assessments. (See page 34T.)

SUPPLEMENTS

- **Study Guide** revisions include more directed reading activities to enhance reading comprehension.

- **NEW** • **ChemFile Supplements** increase your teaching options.

    Lab A Laboratory Experiments— structured labs (See page 26T.)

    Lab B Microscale Experiments— low cost alternatives (See page 26T.)

    Lab C Technique Builders and Problem-Solving Experiments— student-designed inquiry (See page 27T.)

    Lab D Consumer Experiments— analyzing familiar materials (See page 27T.)

- **Mini-Guide to Problem Solving**— further review and practice (See page 29T.)

- **Teaching Resources CD-ROM**— time-saving resources (See page 32T.)

- **Teaching Transparencies**— instructional support for visual learners (See page 33T.)

- **Test Generator**—more questions and improved software capabilities (See page 23T.)

- **NEW** • **Technology** components enhance your instructional effectiveness.

 ChemFile Interactive Tutor-CD-ROM (See page 28T.)

 CNN Presents Science in the News: Chemistry Connections (See page 31T.)

19T

CHAPTER STRUCTURE

It is simple and easy to follow!
Because students succeed when given readable text that is interesting, engaging, and relevant.

• • •

SOMETHING TO THINK ABOUT

Students are drawn into the chapter with an interesting, relevant introduction.

STUDY SKILLS

USING THE ILLUSTRAT

The illustrations throughout this text w you make the connections between wh you see in the macroscopic world and r models. To practice thinking on the pa level, draw your own pictures to repre concepts or problems.

HIGHLIGHTS

Every chapter closes with a listing of the key terms, concepts, and problem-solving models.

SECTION 3-1

How do we know atoms exist?

OBJECTIVES ▸ **State** the three laws that support the existence of atoms. ▸ **Calculate** the masses of atoms in amu and gram units. ▸ **List** the five principles of Dalton's atomic theory. ▸ **Describe** how the atomic mass unit was chosen.

STUDY TIPS

Students get advice for improving their organizational and study skills.

SECTION STRUCTURE

Short, bite-sized sections start with concept heads that highlight important content.

THERE'S MORE...

Appendix B Reading and Study Skills

▸ HOW TO Make power notes
▸ HOW TO Make KWL notes
▸ HOW TO Make concept maps
▸ HOW TO Make pattern puzzles
▸ HOW TO Make two-column notes

Reading Strategies in your Annotated Teacher's Edition (See page 156 for an example.)

ILLUSTRATIONS

It's visualizing matter and making connections!

Students need concrete visual models, so the program is built around an illustration program of unequaled instructional value.

• • •

Molar Enthalpy Versus Temperature for Water

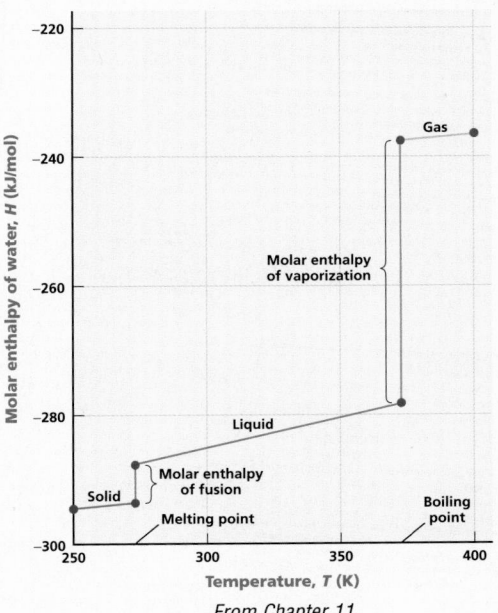

From Chapter 11

GRAPHS AND DATA ANALYSIS

Students see how data are pictorially represented by graphics.

SYMBOLIC CONNECTIONS

Graphic connections expose students to the variety of ways that chemists represent compounds.

$C_8H_9NO_2$
Acetaminophen

From Chapter 1

Hydronium ion, H_3O^+
Magnesium ion, Mg^{2+}
Magnesium metal, Mg
Chloride ion, Cl^-
Water molecule, H_2O

MACRO-MICRO CONNECTIONS

Concrete models help reinforce abstract principles.

From Chapter 16

PROBLEM SOLVING

It's the process that counts!

Students can solve mathematical problems with ease when they receive step-by-step instruction. No program offers better problem-solving support.

• • •

HOW TO Write the polya...

A fertilizer shown in Figure 5-12 has calcium dihydrogen phosphate as an ingredient. What is the formula for this salt?

1 Use Table 5-7 to determine the formula and charge for the polyatomic ion
Dihydrogen phosphate is H_2PO_4. Notice that dihydrogen phosphate has seven atoms from three different elements, plus one extra electron.

2 Determine the formula and charge for the cation
Because the calcium ion is Ca^{2+}, we clearly need two dihydrogen phosphate anions for each calcium cation. The diagram below shows how we can assemble this information to create the formula $Ca(H_2PO_4)_2$
Notice the use of parentheses to show that *everything* inside the parentheses is doubled by the subscript 2 outside. The formula written without the parentheses, CaH_2PO_{42}, would imply 42 oxygen atoms. Sometimes we need two sets of parentheses, such as in the case of mercury(I) phosphate, $(Hg_2)_3(PO_4)_2$.

For every calcium cation in calcium dihydrogen phosphate... Ca^{2+} $H_2PO_4^-$ $H_2PO_4^-$ ...there must be two dihydrogen phosphate anions.

$$Ca(H_2PO_4)_2$$ The two anions are shown in parentheses and designated by the subscript 2.

SAMPLE PROBLEM 10G Air-bag stoichiometry and density

Assume that 65.1 L of N_2 gas is needed to inflate an air bag to the proper size. What mass of NaN_3 must be included in the gas generant to generate this volume of N_2? (Hint: The density of N_2 gas at this temperature is about 0.916 g/L.)

1 List what you know
- Volume of N_2: 65.1 L N_2
- Density of N_2: 0.916 g/L
- Mass of reactant: ? g NaN_3

2 Set up the problem
- Write and balance the chemical equation.
  balanced chemical equation: $2NaN_3(s) \rightarrow 2Na(s) + 3N_2(g)$
- Calculate molar masses using the periodic table.
  molar mass of NaN_3: 65.02 g/mol
  molar mass of N_2: 28.02 g/mol
- First the product amount must be converted from a volume to a mass using density. Then it must be converted from a mass to an amount in moles using molar mass. Next the mole ratio is used to determine moles of reactant needed. Then the mass of reactant is calculated using molar mass as a conversion factor.

$$mL\ N_2 \rightarrow g\ N_2 \rightarrow mol\ N_2 \rightarrow mol\ NaN_3 \rightarrow g\ NaN_3$$

$$65.1\ L\ N_2 \times \frac{0.916\ g\ N_2}{1\ L\ N_2} \times \frac{1\ mol\ N_2}{28.02\ g\ N_2} \times \frac{2\ mol\ NaN_3}{3\ mol\ N_2} \times \frac{65.02\ g\ NaN_3}{1\ mol\ NaN_3} = ?\ g\ NaN_3$$

3 Calculate and verify
- Calculate, and round to the correct number of significant digits.
  Calculator answer: 92.2495035 g NaN_3
  Answer to three significant figures: 92.2 g NaN_3
- Verify your answer by rounding the numbers in the se...
  estimating.

PRACTICE PROBLEMS

1. Calculate the number of grams of Fe_2O_3 that must be generant for this mass of NaN_3.
2. Calculate the mass of sodium hydrogen carbonate pr... bag reaction.
3. The density of $NaHCO_3$ is 2.20 g/mL. What volume ... duced by the reaction?
4. What mass of water and of sodium acetate would be ... reaction of $NaHCO_3$ and CH_3COOH to fill the above ... Recall the volume of the air bag is 65.1 L. (Hint: T... room temperature is 2.68 g/L.)

CONCEPT CHECK

1. In what ways are polyatomic ions like simple ions? In what ways are they different?
2. Identify and name the cations and anions that make up the following ionic compounds and indicate the charge on each ion:
   a. $NaClO_3$ c. $(NH_4)_2CrO_4$
   b. K_2SO_3 d. $Al_2(SO_4)_3$
3. Name the compounds represented by the following formulas:
   a. Na_3AsO_4 c. $Ca(NO_3)_2$
   b. NH_4ClO_4 d. $Fe(OH)_3$
4. Write formulas for the following compounds:
   a. mercury(II) sulfate   e. potassium dichromate
   b. calcium cyanide   f. potassium chromate
   c. rubidium oxalate   g. sodium azide
   d. lithium thiosulfate   h. methylammonium sulfide

IONIC COMPOUNDS 179

REVIEW & ASSESS

TERM REVIEW

1. A formula expressing the simplest ratio of cations to anions in an ionic compound is known as a(n) _____.
(empirical formula, formula unit)

2. The number of particles in 1 mol of a substance is known as _____.
(Avogadro's constant, molar mass)

3. _____ is the mass in grams of 1 mol of a substance. (Average atomic mass, Molar mass)

4. The simplest ratio among the elements represents the compound's _____.
(empirical formula, percentage composition)

5. _____ represents the number of atoms in exactly 12 g of carbon-12.
(One mole, Avogadro's constant)

CONCEPT & SKILLS REVIEW

RELATING MOLES TO NUMBER OF ATOMS

1. Relate the mole to two other coun... ... units.

2. How would you determine the num... ... of atoms in 2 mol of gallium?

3. How is Avogadro's constant related ... ...moles?

4. Why are moles used to represent th... ...umber of atoms in a sample of a given subs...an...?

Practice Problems

5. How many atoms of oxygen enter your lungs when you inhale 5.00×10^{-2} mol of oxygen atoms? (Hint: See Sample Problem 8A.)

6. How many atoms are in the 6.75×10^{-2} mol of mercury within the bulb of a thermometer? (Hint: See Sample Problem 8A.)

7. Assume that you have 2.59 mol of aluminum foil. How many atoms of aluminum do you have? (Hint: See Sample Problem 8A.)

8. How many moles of gold are in 1.00 L of sea water if there are 1.50×10^{17} atoms in the sample? (Hint: See Sample Problem 8B.)

9. How many moles are in a copper penny containing 1.80×10^{21} atoms? (Hint: See Sample Problem 8B.)

AVERAGE ATOMIC MASS

10. How is the carbon-12 atom used to define atomic mass units?

11. Why ... close to whole number ...0067 likely cause?

Practice Problems

13. The lithium found in a hearing-aid battery has two naturally occurring isotopes. Lithium-6 has a mass of 6.015121 amu and an abundance of 7.42%. Lithium-7 has a mass of 7.016003 amu and an abundance of 92.58%. Calculate the average atomic mass of lithium. (Hint: See Sample Problem 8C.)

14. Silver found in most jewelry has two naturally occurring isotopes. Silver-107 has a mass of 106.905092 amu and an abundance of 51.35%. Silver-109 has a mass of 108.904757 amu and an abundance of 48.65%. Calculate the average atomic mass of silver. (Hint: See Sample Problem 8C.)

RELATING AMOUNT TO MASS

15. ...

16. How is mole... moles related average atomic mass?

17. Describe h... ...you would determine the number ... moles present in a given mass of a known substance.

THE MOLE 301

ASSESSMENT

There's all the variety that you need!
You can easily create your own a multifaceted assessment plan from a wide range of options.

● ● ●

EVALUATION WITHIN THE CHAPTER

Concept Checks provide quick reviews of a topic and practice for "How To" skills.

Section Reviews provide a thorough review of a section with two levels of questions and practice problems.

EVALUATION AT THE END OF THE CHAPTER

The Assignment Guide in your Annotated Teacher's Edition correlates all end of chapter items by text section for easy assignment.

Term Review focuses on key vocabulary and relationships among terms.

Concept & Skills Review contains both questions and problems organized by topic.

Linking Chapters items tie concepts students have just learned to concepts learned in previous chapters.

Alternative Assessments provide options for projects and reports. Some items are keyed directly to *sciLinks* Internet sites. (See page 30T for more information on *sciLinks*.)

Test Prep is the quick quiz you can give to identify gaps in students' understanding before the final chapter test.

EVALUATION IN THE ANNOTATED TEACHER'S EDITION

Alternative Assessments provide another range of options for assessing student knowledge using a variety of modalities and methods. (See page 18T for an example.)

EVALUATION SUPPLEMENTS

Chapter Tests blackline masters provide an objective- based assessment for the complete chapter using the following item formats: multiple choice, short answer, essay, and problems.

Test Generator with TestBuilder Software allows you to construct your own chapter tests from data files containing over 1300 items correlated with the text objectives. Questions can be changed to match your teaching emphasis. The ***Assessment Item Listing*** is a complete printout of the data files. Questions are coded by item type and level of comprehension.

PORTFOLIO ASSESSMENT

Holt Chemistry: Visualizing Matter and *Holt ChemFile* contain a variety of materials that can be used to build portfolios.

STUDENTS CAN MAKE SELECTIONS FROM THE FOLLOWING AREAS:

▶ **Content** One concept map from the chapter. See the rubric Evaluating Concept Maps* for evaluation criteria.

▶ **Outside Reading** One or more Supplemental Reading Guides*.

▶ **Writing** A research paper related to material covered in a chapter. See the Science Research Paper* worksheets and Internet Activities*.

▶ **Performance Assessment** One lab report for an in-text lab or a student-designed investigation from the ChemFile Technique Builders and Problem-Solving Experiments manual.

TEACHERS CAN MAKE SELECTIONS FROM THE FOLLOWING AREAS:

▶ **Formal Assessment** A chapter exam from the *Chapter Tests* booklet or test constructed using the *ChemFile Test Generator with TestBuilder Software.*

▶ **Informal Assessment** Use the Informal Assessment Direct Observation Checklist* during a laboratory or other cooperative learning experience.

▶ **Performance Assessment** Use a student-designed investigation from the *ChemFile Technique Builders and Problem-Solving Experiments* manual or a performance assessment item from the Alternative Assessment section of the chapter review.

*Denotes material found on the *Holt ChemFile Teaching Resources CD-ROM*. See page 32T for a description of this product. For more background on portfolio assessment, see the scoring rubrics section on the *Holt ChemFile Teaching Resources CD-ROM*.

IN-TEXT LABORATORY PROGRAM

It's got the variety you've asked for!

A revised in-text laboratory program meets the demands of your curriculum, by recognizing the limits placed on equipment and supplies, and your desire to motivate and challenge students.

• • •

CHAPTER LABS...

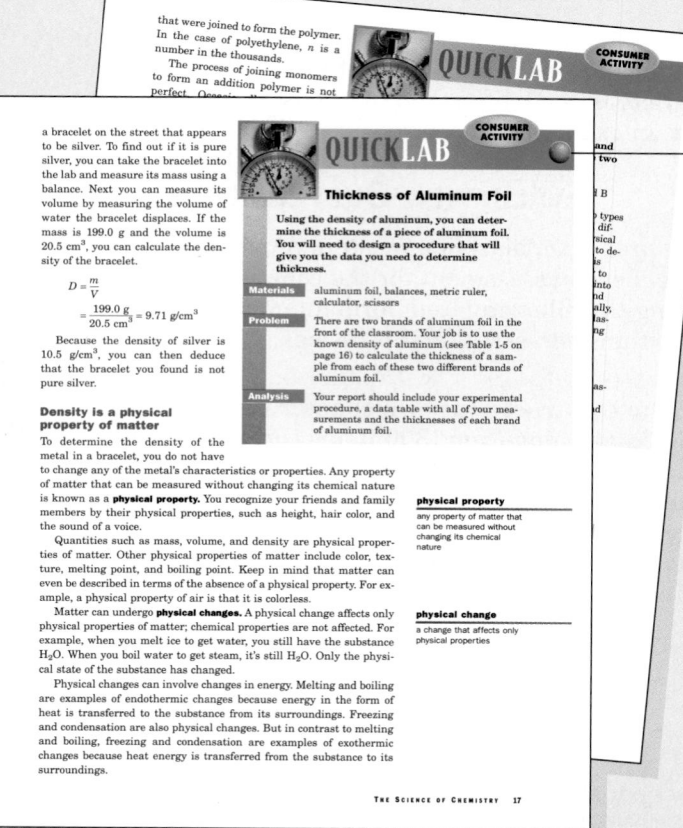

that were joined to form the polymer. In the case of polyethylene, n is a number in the thousands.

The process of joining monomers to form an addition polymer is not perfect. Occasio...

QUICKLAB
CONSUMER ACTIVITY

a bracelet on the street that appears to be silver. To find out if it is pure silver, you can take the bracelet into the lab and measure its mass using a balance. Next you can measure its volume by measuring the volume of water the bracelet displaces. If the mass is 199.0 g and the volume is 20.5 cm³, you can calculate the density of the bracelet.

$$D = \frac{m}{V}$$

$$= \frac{199.0 \text{ g}}{20.5 \text{ cm}^3} = 9.71 \text{ g/cm}^3$$

Because the density of silver is 10.5 g/cm³, you can then deduce that the bracelet you found is not pure silver.

Density is a physical property of matter

To determine the density of the metal in a bracelet, you do not have to change any of the metal's characteristics or properties. Any property of matter that can be measured without changing its chemical nature is known as a **physical property.** You recognize your friends and family members by their physical properties, such as height, hair color, and the sound of a voice.

Quantities such as mass, volume, and density are physical properties of matter. Other physical properties of matter include color, texture, melting point, and boiling point. Keep in mind that matter can even be described in terms of the absence of a physical property. For example, a physical property of air is that it is colorless.

Matter can undergo **physical changes.** A physical change affects only physical properties of matter; chemical properties are not affected. For example, when you melt ice to get water, you still have the substance H₂O. When you boil water to get steam, it's still H₂O. Only the physical state of the substance has changed.

Physical changes can involve changes in energy. Melting and boiling are examples of endothermic changes because energy in the form of heat is transferred to the substance from its surroundings. Freezing and condensation are also physical changes. But in contrast to melting and boiling, freezing and condensation are examples of exothermic changes because heat energy is transferred from the substance to its surroundings.

physical property
any property of matter that can be measured without changing its chemical nature

physical change
a change that affects only physical properties

THE SCIENCE OF CHEMISTRY 17

From Chapters 1 and 7

QUICKLAB

Thickness of Aluminum Foil

Using the density of aluminum, you can determine the thickness of a piece of aluminum foil. You will need to design a procedure that will give you the data you need to determine thickness.

Materials aluminum foil, balances, metric ruler, calculator, scissors

Problem There are two brands of aluminum foil in the front of the classroom. Your job is to use the known density of aluminum (see Table 1-5 on page 16) to calculate the thickness of a sample from each of these two different brands of aluminum foil.

Analysis Your report should include your experimental procedure, a data table with all of your measurements and the thicknesses of each brand of aluminum foil.

QUICKLABS

These short activities are easily completed in less than a full class period.

INQUIRYLABS

In these problem-based experiments students build their own experimental procedures.

Stockroom chemicals may be mixtures

When is a substance pure? That's a difficult question to answer. When you drink water from the tap, you may think you are drinki...

Chromatography is widely used in industry and research

Chromatography may be used to separate the components of a liquid or gaseous mixture so that they may be isolated or identified. The method works because different dissolved substances are attracted differently to solvents and other media, such as solid surfaces.

Paper chromatography is a powerful separation technique. It can be used to separate the dyes in ink. Water or some other solvent dissolves the ink. The solvent containing the ink travels up the paper by *capillary action*, the attraction of the surface of a liquid to the surface of a solid. The dissolved dyes from the ink travel at different rates according to the attraction that they have for the solvent or the paper, as shown in **Figure 13-4.** Those most attracted to the paper travel the slowest. They remain in a rather low position on the paper. The dyes that have the least attraction for the paper travel fastest and farthest. The resulting chromatogram displays bands of different colors.

Laboratories use chromatography to isolate and identify the agents that give foods their flavor and give perfumes their aroma. Law enforcement officers use chromatography to determine the blood alcohol level of motorists suspected of drunk driving.

INQUIRYLAB
CONSUMER ACTIVITY

Using Physical Properties

The Color of M&M® Candies

In this activity you will investigate whether the colors of candies are single dyes or whether these candies are colored with a mixture of different dyes.

Materials M&M candies, chromatography paper, developing solution (0.1% NaCl)

Problem Design an experiment that will determine whether M&M candies contain mixtures of dyes or whether they are single dyes. For example, is the orange color a result of mixing two primary colors? What about the other colors?

Analysis
1. Summarize your results in a report that includes your experimental procedure, a data table that summarizes your results, and the experimental evidence.
2. Be sure to answer the questions posed in the problem statement.

chromatography
a technique for separating components of a mixture by placing the mixture in a mobile phase that is passed over a stationary phase

FIGURE 13-4

a In chromatography, ink marks are made on absorbent paper, which is then suspended in contact with a solvent.

b The finished chromatogram, shown at right, displays different dyes found in the ink sample.

SOLUTIONS 477

CONSUMER ACTIVITY

Labs throughout the program marked with the Consumer Activity logo use some supplies that can be found in the home.

24T

From Chapters 13 and 1

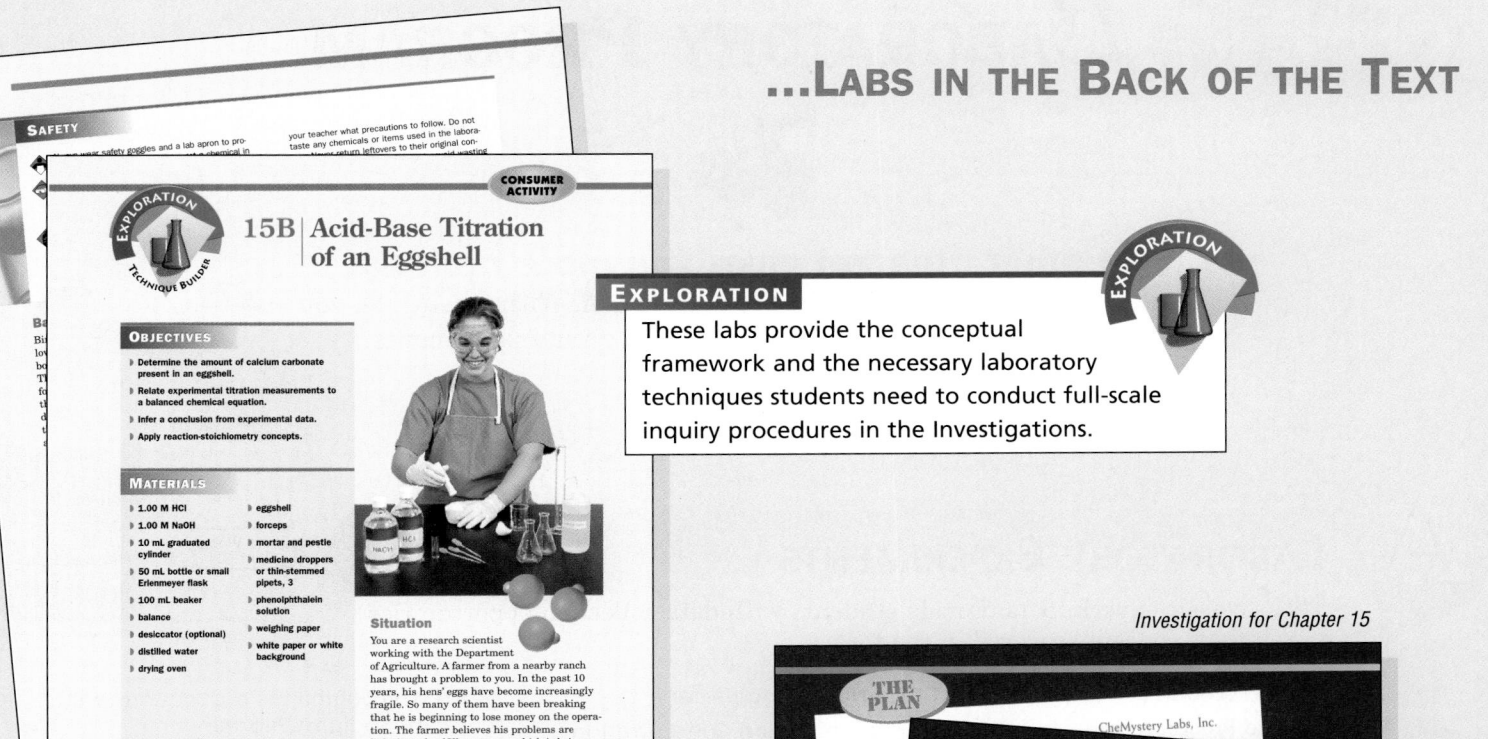

SAFETY

EXPLORATION

15B | Acid-Base Titration of an Eggshell

CONSUMER ACTIVITY

OBJECTIVES

▶ Determine the amount of calcium carbonate present in an eggshell.

▶ Relate experimental titration measurements to a balanced chemical equation.

▶ Infer a conclusion from experimental data.

▶ Apply reaction-stoichiometry concepts.

MATERIALS

▶ 1.00 M HCl
▶ 1.00 M NaOH
▶ 10 mL graduated cylinder
▶ 50 mL bottle or small Erlenmeyer flask
▶ 100 mL beaker
▶ balance
▶ desiccator (optional)
▶ distilled water
▶ drying oven

▶ eggshell
▶ forceps
▶ mortar and pestle
▶ medicine droppers or thin-stemmed pipets, 3
▶ phenolphthalein solution
▶ weighing paper
▶ white paper or white background

Situation

You are a research scientist working with the Department of Agriculture. A farmer from a nearby ranch has brought a problem to you. In the past 10 years, his hens' eggs have become increasingly fragile. So many of them have been breaking that he is beginning to lose money on the operation. The farmer believes his problems are linked to a landfill upstream, which is being investigated for illegal dumping of PCBs and other hazardous chemicals. Your job is to find out if the PCBs are the cause of the hens' fragile eggs.

Exploration for Chapter 15

EXPLORATION

These labs provide the conceptual framework and the necessary laboratory techniques students need to conduct full-scale inquiry procedures in the Investigations.

Investigation for Chapter 15

THE PLAN

CheMystery Labs, Inc.

MEMO

Date: Ap
To: Cice
From: M

This is
three t
priorit

First
wheth
stand
vise
need

Bec
for

INVESTIGATION

15B | Acid-Base Titration Industrial Spill

THE PROBLEM

BLEACHEX

Vacaville Bleachex Production Facility
3617 Industrial Parkway
Vacaville, CA 90627

DELIVER BY OVERNIGHT COURIER
Date: April 21, 1999
To: EPA National Headquarters
From: Anthony Wong, Plant Supervisor
Re: Vacaville Bleachex Corp. Plant Spill

As a result of last night's earthquake, the Bleachex plant in the industrial park south of Vacaville was severely damaged. The safety control measures failed because of the magnitude of the earthquake.

Bleachex manufactures a variety of products using concentrated acids and bases. Plant officials noticed a large quantity of liquid, believed to be either sodium hydroxide or hydrochloric acid solution, flowing through the loading bay doors. An Emergency Toxic Spill Response Team attempted to determine the source and identity of the unknown liquid. A series of explosions and the presence of chlorine gas forced the team to abandon their efforts. The unknown liquid continues to flow into the nearly full containment ponds.

We are sending a sample of the liquid to you by overnight courier and hope that you can quickly and accurately identify the liquid and notify us of the proper method for cleanup and disposal. We need your answer as soon as possible.

Anthony Wong

Anthony Wong

References

Review titration methods using a buret. Before filling the buret, be sure it is clean. Then rinse the buret three times with 5 mL of the standard solution each time before filling the buret. The equivalence point of the titration can be determined using an indicator or pH probe. This is a simple titration, not a back-titration, in which the unknown reacts with an excess of acid and the excess acid is titrated to determine how much must have reacted.

780 INVESTIGATION 15B

INVESTIGATION

These labs give students the opportunity to design their own experiments and conduct analyses for fictitious clients.

THERE'S MORE...

CBL™ System (Texas Instruments, Inc. Calculator Based Laboratory) options are included for some experiments in the text. You can find program files for the use of Vernier probes written by Vernier Software on the *Holt ChemFile Test Generator CD-ROM.* For further information on the use of Vernier Software's CHEMBIO programs see the teacher's margin on page 689.

HOLT ChemFile *L*ABORATORY **P**ROGRAM

No other program gives you more options!

Time, equipment, and facilities are a premium. With ChemFile, you have more choices than ever before for great experiments.

• • •

LABORATORY EXPERIMENTS

These classic experiments provide students with data collection opportunities to reinforce concepts covered in the text.

A1   Laboratory Procedures
A2   Accuracy and Precision in Measurements
A3   Reactivity of Halide Ions
A4   Test for Iron(II) and Iron(III)
A5   Evidence for Chemical Change
A6   Calcium and Its Compounds
A7   Water of Hydration
A8   Boyle's Law
A9   Molar Volume of Gas
A10   Molar Heat of Fusion of Ice

A11   Ice-Nucleating Bacteria
A12   Hydronium Ion Concentration and pH
A13   Titration with an Acid and a Base
A14   Energy and Entropy
A15   Heat of Crystallization
A16   Temperature of a Bunsen Burner Flame
A17   Heat of Solution
A18   Heat of Combustion

A19   The Solubility Product Constant of Sodium Chloride
A20   Buffering Capacity
A21   Oxidation-Reduction Reactions
A22   Cathodic Protection: Factors Affecting the Corrosion of Iron
A23   Carbon
A24   Oil-Degrading Microbes
A25   Polymers
A26   Radioactivity
A27   Detecting Radioactivity

MICROSCALE EXPERIMENTS

These low-cost options for some of your favorite experiments will require some specialized equipment, but they pose less danger, produce less waste, and they involve shorter experiment times.

B1   Laboratory Procedures
B2   Accuracy and Precision: Calibrating a Pipet
B3   Relative Solubility of Transition Elements
B4   Periodicity of Properties of Oxides
B5   Reactivity of Halide Ions
B6   Chemical Bonds
B7   Conductivity as an Indicator of Bond Type

B8   Test for Iron(II) and Iron(III)
B9   Colored Precipitates
B10   Simple Qualitative Analysis
B11   Generating and Collecting O_2
B12   Generating and Collecting H_2
B13   Testing Reaction Combinations of H_2 and O_2
B14   Reacting Ionic Species in Aqueous Solution
B15   Hydronium Ion Concentration, pH

B16   Titration of an Acid with a Base
B17   Percentage of Acetic Acid in Vinegar
B18   Clock Reactions
B19   Equilibrium
B20   Oxidation-Reduction Reactions
B21   Cathodic Protection: Factors that Affect the Corrosion of Iron
B22   Determination of Vitamin C in Fruit Juices

TECHNIQUE BUILDERS AND PROBLEM-SOLVING EXPERIMENTS

Explorations have a standard format to build the fundamental skills for a procedure or technique. **Investigations** emphasize scientific inquiry and give your students the opportunity to solve analytical problems.

CONSUMER EXPERIMENTS

Students apply concepts from the textbook when performing experiments using materials generally found around the home. Some of these experiments link the world of chemistry with other areas of science.

0.5M FeCl₃

HOLT ChemFile INTERACTIVE TUTOR CD-ROM

GIVE YOUR STUDENTS THEIR OWN PRIVATE CHEMISTRY COACH!

This interactive CD-ROM brings the particle world of chemistry to life. In the "virtual laboratory" students see the motion and interaction that occurs in chemical systems. The *Holt ChemFile Interactive Tutor* was created to model chemical systems in ways that students can readily comprehend.

Modules are divided into the following lesson types:

• Topic tutorials
• Topic practice
• Problem-solving tutorials
• Problem-solving practice

Students develop problem-analysis skills as the Tutor graphically displays problems in ways that help students plan effective solutions. The Tutor guides students every step of the way by providing encouragement for correct choices and gently pointing out errors or misunderstandings resulting from incorrect choices.

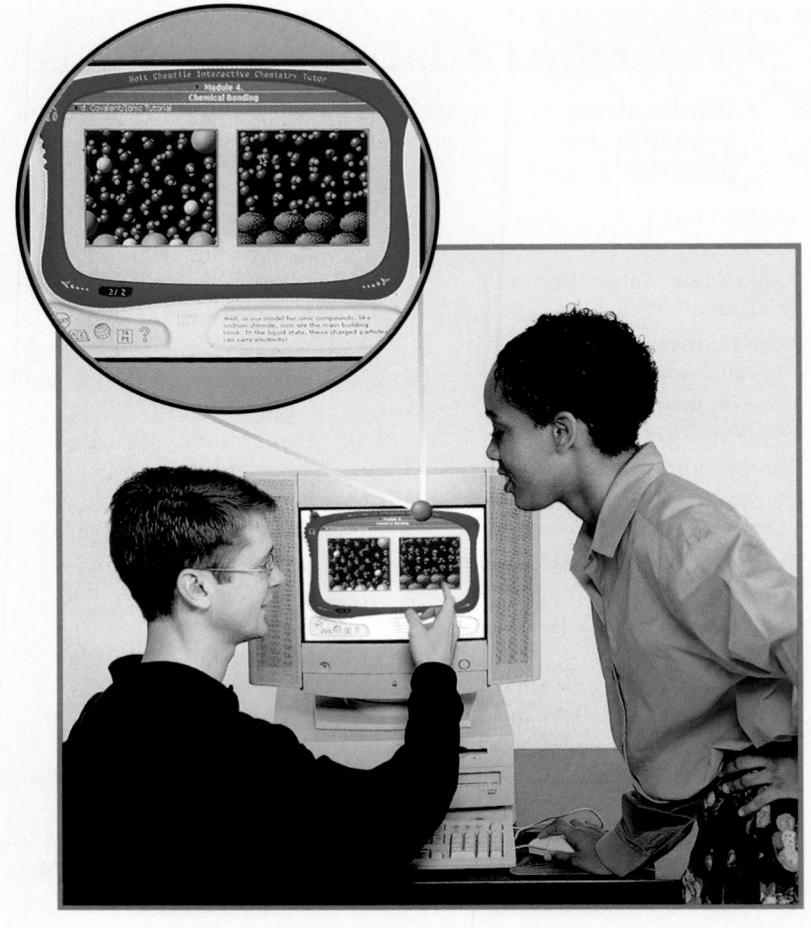

CD MODULES

1 States of Matter/ Classes of Matter

2 Models of the Atom

3 Periodic Properties

4 Chemical Bonding

5 Equations and Stoichiometry

6 Gas Laws

7 Equilibrium

8 Strong and Weakly Ionized Species, pH, and Titration

9 Thermochemistry

10 Electrochemical Cells

Resource File: Additional Practice Worksheets

The interactive periodic table makes the data needed for calculations readily available.

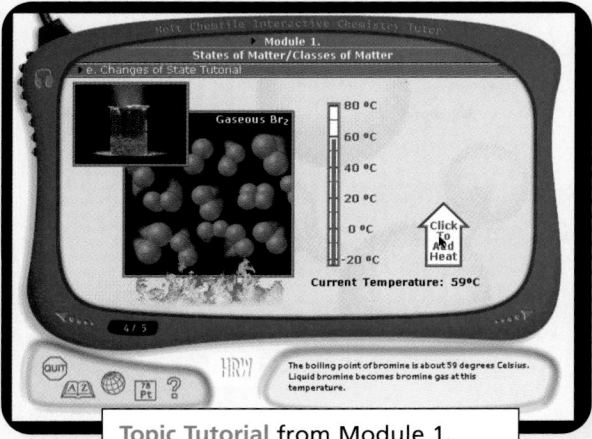

Topic Tutorial from Module 1, States of Matter/Classes of Matter

Problem-solving tutorial from Module 5, Equations and Stoichiometry

Topic practice from Module 1

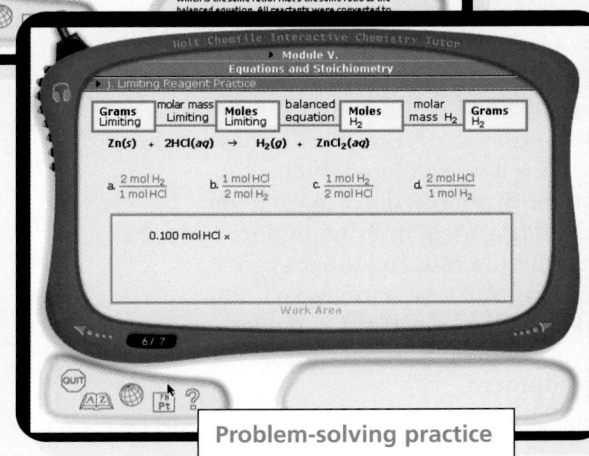

Problem-solving practice from Module 5

THERE'S MORE...

TUTOR PRACTICE WORKSHEETS

The Tutor package also provides you with a file of practice worksheets for each module. They emphasize the major concepts of the module and provide additional problem-solving practice.

HOLT ChemFile

MINI-GUIDE TO PROBLEM SOLVING

This paperback volume is a must for students that need extra help and practice with chemistry problems. The guide moves students through the same quantitative concepts as the text, but at a slower pace. Visual algorithms along with lots of practice reinforce the consistent logic patterns students need to be successful.

1 Conversions
2 Significant Figures
3 Scientific Notation
4 Four Steps for Solving Quantitative Problems
5 Mole Concept
6 Percentage Composition
7 Empirical Formulas
8 Stoichiometry

9 Limiting Reactants
10 Percent Yield
11 Gas Laws
12 The Ideal Gas Law
13 Stoichiometry of Gases
14 Concentration of Solutions
15 Dilutions
16 Colligative Properties

17 pH
18 Titrations
19 Thermochemistry
20 Equilibrium
21 Equilibrium of Acids and Bases, K_a and K_b
22 Equilibrium of Salts, K_{sp}
23 Redox Equations
24 Electrochemistry

INTERNET CONNECTIONS

www.scilinks.com

Your Safe Passage to the Internet
Together, HRW and NSTA take the worry out of using Internet resources.

● ● ●

HOW CAN I BE SURE STUDENTS ARE ACCESSING APPROPRIATE MATERIAL?

How Long Will Sites Stay Active?

All links are managed and monitored by National Science Teachers Association staff. Sites are continually added and deleted from the system. Students don't go to dead ends, dark sites, or sites under construction and links between sites are constantly reviewed and updated. Using *sciLinks*, students explore concepts in a dynamic, safe environment.

SciLinks
Students go to the *sciLinks* address to find out more about the topic shown. When students type in a specific keyword for that topic, they access a system that provides a variety of appropriate links.

Links to find out more about **lesson content**

Links to find out more about **special features**

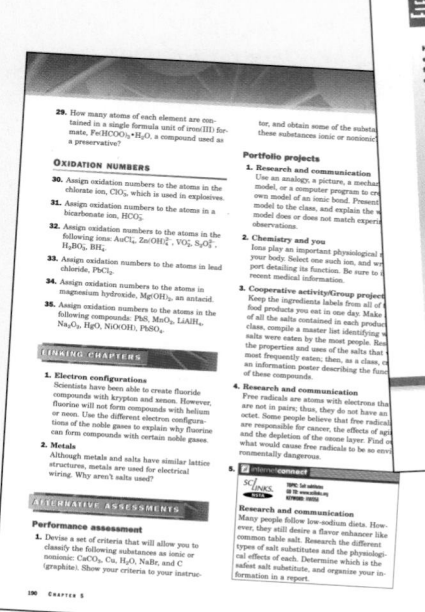

Links for **student research activities**

THERE'S MORE...

You can find **additional teaching resources** on the HRW Web site. New materials are continually added to keep you updated on content, methodologies, and resources.

GO TO: go.hrw.com

30T

CNN PRESENTS SCIENCE IN THE NEWS

Turner Le@rning

Build critical thinking and listening skills

Science news stories show practical uses of chemistry principles.

• • •

HOLT RINEHART WINSTON   Turner Le@rning

FEATURE STORIES

Each segment is correlated with *Holt Chemistry: Visualizing Matter* in the Annotated Teacher's Edition.

The video package includes a Teacher's Guide with instructional strategies and a student worksheet for each segment. Student worksheets focus on segment analysis, critical-thinking skills, and listening skills.

Student worksheet

Teacher's Guide page

TEACHING RESOURCES CD-ROM

The most comprehensive file of resources you can find.
It's compact, well organized, and easy to access.
• • •

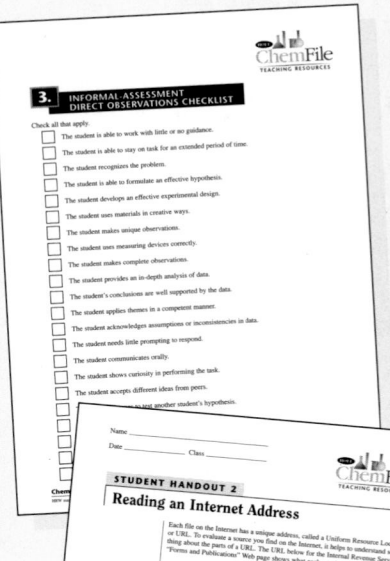

Rubrics and Checklists
You can use these rubrics and classroom checklists to successfully manage performance-based and portfolio assessments. Word-processing documents for the rubrics on the CD-ROM can be altered to meet your standards for evaluation.

Internet Activities
These worksheets provide the introductory framework students need before they attempt to navigate the Internet.

Basic Skills Worksheets
Students get the critical additional practice they need in key skill areas such as graphing and making measurements

Lab Contract and Safety Quiz
Students receive the necessary background and demonstrate their commitment to safety before they begin working in the lab.

Occupational Applications Worksheets
These worksheets provide insights into careers that relate to chemistry.

Math Skills Worksheets
These worksheets bridge the gap between student's math instruction and the application of math concepts to chemistry.

Science Research Paper Worksheets
Students use a structured format to develop a complete research paper.

Supplemental Reading Guides
The worksheets cover selections from popular authors, popular literature, and interesting contemporary topics. Use the worksheets to build reading comprehension and critical-thinking skills.

CHEMISTRY VIDEODISCS

The best technology format for large group instruction

Emphasize macro/micro connections with graphics and video clips.

• • •

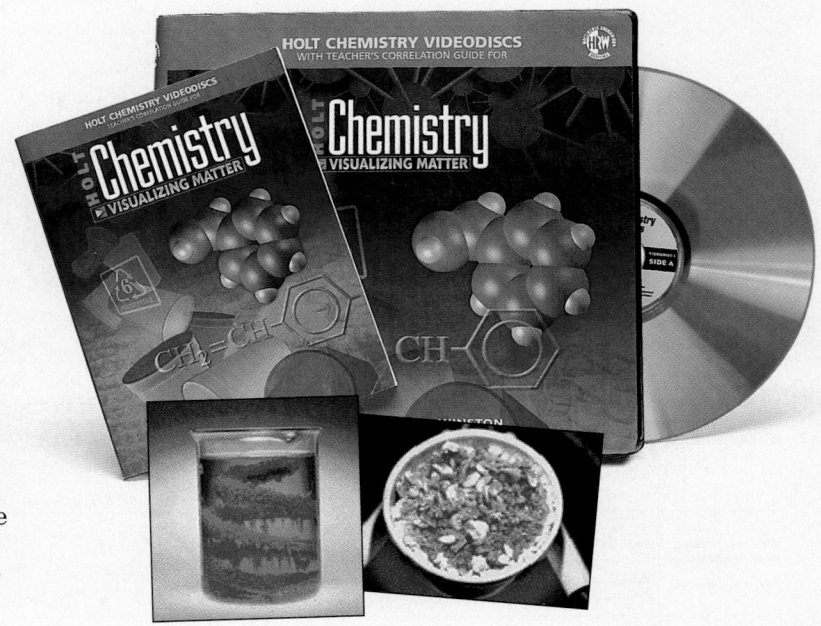

The two-disc set contains hundreds of still-frame images, video clips, animation sequences, and molecular rotations. Special question screens help you show students the link between the images and the text. All media are bar-coded and correlated to the text chapters in the *Holt Chemistry: Visualizing Matter Videodisc Correlation Guide.*

HOLT ChemFile TEACHING TRANSPARENCIES

146 Teaching Transparencies 146

Lab Technique: Filtration Setup

Vacuum filtration

Gravity filtration

56 Teaching Transparencies 56

Diffusion

Water molecule
Dye molecule

Like gases, the two liquids in this beaker diffuse over time. The green liquid food coloring from the drop will eventually form a uniform solution with the water.

16 Teaching Transparencies 16

Solving Mole Problems

Amount of element in moles

Mass of element in grams

Number of atoms of element

Highlight key concepts in the text with this collection of 150 color transparencies and 91 blackline-master images that you can use for large-group instruction. Strategies for using the transparencies in daily lessons are provided in the *Holt ChemFile Transparency Directory.*

ANNOTATED TEACHER'S EDITION

YOU'VE GOT AT-A-GLANCE PLANNING AND POINT-OF-USE SUPPORT!

CHAPTER 12 PLANNING GUIDE

Gases and Liquids

CLASSROOM RESOURCES

SECTIONS	TEACHER'S DEMONSTRATIONS	PROBLEM SOLVING ● ■ Text ◆ ChemFile Mini-Guide	LABORATORIES ● ■ Text ◆ ChemFile Manuals: A, B, C, D
12-1 **What are the characteristics of gases?** Section Review, p. 432	**Demo 1** Elastic and Inelastic Collisions, p. 424 **Demo 2** Atmospheric Pressure, p. 428		
12-2 **What behaviors are described by the gas laws?** Section Review, p. 444	**Demo 3** Volume Changes with a Vacuum Pump, p. 434 **Demo 4** Amount of Oxygen in Air, p. 438	■ **Sample Problem 12A:** Solving pressure-volume problems, p. 435 ■ **Sample Problem 12B:** Solving volume-temperature problems, p. 440 ■ **Sample Problem 12C:** Comparing molecular speeds, p. 443 ◆ **Chapter 11** Gas Laws	■ **QuickLab:** Pressure Relief, p. 437 ◆ **Exp. C10** Gas Pressure–Volume Relationship ◆ **A8** Boyle's Law ◆ **Inv. C10** Gas Temp Relationship: Balloo ◆ **Exp. C11** Masses of Gases ◆ **A9** Molar Volume of
12-3 **How do the gas laws fit together?** Section Review, p. 451		■ **Sample Problem 12D:** Using the ideal gas law, p. 447 ■ **Sample Problem 12E:** Using the combined gas law, p. 448 ■ **Sample Problem 12F:** Using the ideal gas law to solve stoichiometry problems, p. 450 ◆ **Chapter 12** The Ideal Gas Law ◆ **Chapter 13** Stoichiometry of Gases	◆ **B11** Generating and ◆ **B12** Generating and ◆ **B13** Testing Reactio H_2 and O_2 ◆ **D11** Factors Affecti Yeast
12-4 **What conditions will cause a gas to condense?** Section Review, p. 458	**Demo 5** Boiling Water in a Vacuum, p. 454		

422A

TECHNOLOGY RESOURCES
See page 422 for a listing of Internet resources.

SECTIONS	VIDEOS/VIDEODISC *Holt Chemistry Videodisc* **CNN** *Science in the NEWS*	CHEMFILE CD-ROMS ●*Teaching Resources* ◆*Interactive Tutor*	OVERHEADS ●*Color Transparencies* ◆*Transparency Masters*
12-1	States of matter Gas molecular speeds Ozone **CNN** Segment 21 **PRESENTS** Global Warming	● Skills Review: SI Conversions ● Supplemental Reading: *Ultraviolet Reflections: Life Under a Thinning Ozone Layer*	● **58** Sodium as a Solid, Liquid, and Gas ● **48** Relationship Between Pressure, Force, and Area ◆ **48A** Units of Pressure ● **49** Mercury Barometer
12-2	Gas laws and bicycle pumps Gas volume change Gases: Charles's law data and graph Gas pressure–temperature relationship Avogadro's law Gas diffusion: ammonium chloride ring	● Skills Review: Graphing ● Skills Review: Isolating Variables in Equations ● Supplemental Reading: *The Same and Not the Same*, "Static/Dynamic" ◆ **Module 6:** Gas Laws **Topic:** Behavior of Gases	● **50** Gas Mixtures and Dalton's Law ● **52** Avogadro's Law ● **54** Graham's Law ● **56** Diffusion ◆ *See also* **49A, 50A, 51A, 52A.**
12-3	Gas pressure–number of moles relationship		● **53** Gas Law Calculations ◆ **53A** Numerical Values of the Gas Constant
12-4	Evaporation of liquids Vapor-liquid equilibrium Boiling point of water Sublimation of iodine crystals **CNN** Segment 22 **PRESENTS** Belching Cows	● Occupational Application: Pest-Control Technician ● Occupational Application: Air Quality Specialist	● **59** Liquid-Vapor Equilibrium System ● **61** Change-of-State Models for Water ● **62** Exothermic and Endothermic Changes of State ● **63** Phase Diagram for Water

ASSESSMENT RESOURCES

ALTERNATIVE ASSESSMENTS	CHAPTER TESTING	SCORING RUBRICS *Holt ChemFile Teaching Resources CD-ROM*
Student Text Performance assessment, p. 464 Portfolio projects 1–2, p. 464 **Teacher's Edition** Group Strategies, pp. 432, 440, 442 **Study Guide** Sections 12-1 to 12-4	**Student Text** Test Preparation, p. 465 **Holt Chemistry: Visualizing Matter Chapter 12 Test** (blackline masters) **Holt ChemFile Test Generator for Macintosh and Windows**	**Lab Work** Student-Designed Experiments Rubric Performance-Tasks Scoring Rubric Assessment for Structured Inquiry Assessment for Open-Ended Inquiry **Portfolio Projects** Evaluating Concept Maps Assessing Portfolios Portfolio Assignment Student Evaluation Form

422B

NATIONAL SCIENCE EDUCATION STANDARDS CORRELATION

Physical Science Content Standards *Titles shown in red represent the categories from the standards that fit a high school chemistry course. Each category is further broken down to show the topics from the chapters and the accompanying labs that fit each standard.*

STANDARDS	CHAPTER 1	CHAPTER 2	CHAPTER 3	CHAPTER 4
Physical Science				
Structure of atoms	particle nature of matter		atomic theory, cathode rays, gold-foil experiment, atomic orbitals, nuclear forces, isotopes, electron configurations	radioactive isotopes, atomic radii, ion formation
Structure and properties of matter	defining characteristics of elements and compounds, physical properties as a consequence of structure, models for solids, liquids, and gases, density	structural models	conservation of mass, laws of definite and multiple proportions, atomic mass and moles	periodicity of properties; physical properties as a consequence of structure; metals, nonmetals, and semiconductors; plasmas; crystal packing
Chemical reactions	characteristics of reactions, activation energy			periodicity and reactivity, nuclear transmutations
Motions and forces		chemical bonds	coulombic force	metallic bonds
Entropy and conservation of energy		conservation of energy, chemical energy		
Interactions of matter and energy	endothermic vs. exothermic processes	states of matter, specific heat capacity, potential and kinetic energy, heat and temperature	wave characteristics, electromagnetic spectrum, quanta, spectral analysis	conductors, insulators, semiconductors
History and Nature of Science				
Nature of scientific knowledge	scientific research, chemical industry, history of aluminum	scientific methods, peer review, chance discoveries, history of helium	evolution of scientific thought: atomic structure; history of beryllium	evolution of scientific thought: periodic table; history of oxygen
Science as Inquiry				
Abilities to do scientific inquiry	mathematical tools: SI measurement **Lab:** use technology and mathematics in investigations, formulate hypotheses, design and conduct investigations	mathematical tools: significant figures **Lab:** communicate and defend a scientific argument, use technology and mathematics in investigations, formulate hypotheses, design and conduct investigations	**Lab:** use technology and mathematics in investigations, design and conduct investigations	**Lab:** formulate hypotheses, design and conduct investigations, formulate and revise explanations, recognize alternative explanations
Science in Personal & Social Perspectives				
Personal and community health	aspirin warnings		essential elements	mercury poisoning
Natural resources	aluminum, chemical industry	helium	beryllium	oxygen
Environmental quality; and natural and human-induced hazards		explosives		
Science and technology challenges			fireworks	superconductors
Science and Technology				
Abilities of technological design		scientific methods, discoveries of Teflon and cisplatin	**Lab:** identify problems, design solutions, implement designs, evaluate designs, communicate processes	superconducting devices

CHAPTER 5	CHAPTER 6	CHAPTER 7	CHAPTER 8	CHAPTER 9
ion formation	covalent molecules, bond length, molecular orbitals	structure of carbon		
ionic bonding, physical properties as a consequence of structure, models for solids, liquids, and gases	covalent bonding, physical properties as a consequence of structure, catenation of carbon, electronegativity	covalent bonding, physical properties as a consequence of structure, catenation of carbon, functional groups	mole relationships for single substances	
oxidation numbers, polyatomic ions	formation of molecules	organic reactions		conservation of mass and reactions, types of reactions
coulombic force	bond character, hydrogen bonding, London forces	network solids		
				energy transfers
conductors, insulators, semi-conductors; lattice energy	bond energy, VSEPR theory	bond strength		enthalpy
history of sodium, nomenclature	Lewis dot models, nomenclature	polymer discoveries, history of silicon, nomenclature		
Lab: use technology and mathematics in investigations, design and conduct investigations, formulate and revise explanations, communicate and defend a scientific argument		**Lab:** formulate hypotheses, use technology and mathematics in investigations, formulate and revise explanations	mathematical tools: composition stoichiometry	mathematical tools: proportional reasoning
		saturated fats	fire extinguishers	
sodium	nonrenewable resources	silicon, recycling codes		
		biodegradable substances		
	Mars exploration	landfills and waste	protease inhibitors	
Lab: identify problems, design solutions, implement designs, evaluate designs, communicate processes				

STANDARDS	CHAPTER 10	CHAPTER 11	CHAPTER 12	CHAPTER 13
Physical Science				
Structure of atoms			particle nature of matter	hydronium ions; electrolytes and nonelectrolytes
Structure and properties of matter			models for solids, liquids, and gases; kinetic molecular theory, vapor pressure	models for solids, liquids, and gases; solutions and suspensions; separating mixtures
Chemical reactions	mass relationships in reactions, limiting reactants, reaction efficiency	thermodynamic properties of reactions, photosynthesis, metabolism	free radical reactions	
Motions and forces		elastic collisions	elastic collisions, pressure, ideal gas concept, diffusion, effusion, condensation	solubility, emulsions, surfactants
Entropy and conservation of energy		conservations of energy; energy transfers; heat vs. temperature; entropy, enthalpy, Gibbs energy	average kinetic energy	
Interactions of matter and energy		changes of state	pressure, volume, temperature relationships; phase diagrams	conductors, insulators, semiconductors; colligative properties
History and Nature of Science				
Nature of scientific knowledge		history of hydrogen	history of nitrogen	history of lead
Science as Inquiry				
Abilities to do scientific inquiry	mathematical tools: reaction stoichiometry **Lab:** formulate hypotheses, use technology and mathematics in investigations, design and conduct investigations, recognize alternative explanations, communicate and defend a scientific argument	mathematical tools: thermodynamics **Lab:** use technology and mathematics in investigations, design and conduct investigations, formulate and revise explanations, communicate and defend a scientific argument	mathematical tools: gas laws	mathematical tools: concentration **Lab:** use technology and mathematics in investigations, design and conduct investigations, formulate and revise explanations, communicate and defend a scientific argument
Science in Personal & Social Perspectives				
Personal and community health	automobile air bags	energy and nutrition	greenhouse effect, ozone hole, caffeine	sports drinks, vitamins
Natural resources		hydrogen	nitrogen	
Environmental quality; natural and human-induced hazards	automobile pollution control		greenhouse effect, ozone hole, pollution, chlorofluorocarbons, non-CFC air conditioning	
Science and technology challenges	air-bag design		supercritical fluids	
Science and Technology				
Abilities of technological design	engine efficiency **Lab:** identify problems, design solutions, implement designs, evaluate designs, communicate processes		removing caffeine	

CHAPTER 14	CHAPTER 15	CHAPTER 16	CHAPTER 17	CHAPTER 18
	proton donors and acceptors		electric charge	particle nature of matter
complex ions	properties of acids and bases, pH	collision theory, catalysts, inhibitors, antioxidants	oxidizing and reducing agents	nuclear stability, half-life
reversible reactions, equilibrium systems, precipitation reactions, common ion effect	acid-base reactions, buffers	reaction rates	oxidation/reduction reactions	nuclear reactions, decay of radioactive isotopes
		elastic collisions energy transfers	coulombic force	nuclear forces
		reaction mechanisms	electrosynthesis processes	mass defect, binding energy
Le Chatelier's principle		activation energy, catalysis	electrochemical cells, galvanic cells	nuclear fission and fusion
Bosch and Haber processes	history of magnesium		history of chlorine, Faraday's experiments	discovery of radioactivity
mathematical tools: equilibrium constants	mathematical tools: solution stoichiometry and equilibrium constants **Lab:** use technology and mathematics in investigations, formulate hypotheses, formulate and revise explanations	mathematical tools: reaction rates **Lab:** use technology and mathematics in investigations, design and conduct investigations, formulate and revise explanations	mathematical tools: electrochemical processes **Lab:** use technology and mathematics in investigations, formulate and revise explanations, communicate and defend a scientific argument	
lead poisoning	antacids and health	enzyme supplements		radiation exposure
	magnesium		chlorine	
fertilizers and explosives	acid precipitation	red tides	corrosion	fission reactors
ammonia and World War I		enzyme technologies	fuel cells, batteries	radioactivity, nuclear energy
	Lab: identify problems, design solutions, implement designs, evaluate designs, communicate processes		electrosynthesis, fuel-cell technologies **Lab:** identify problems, design solutions, evaluate designs, communicate processes	dating techniques, radiological technologies

SAFETY IN THE CHEMISTRY LAB

The direct cause of most lab accidents is doing something that is unsafe or disregarding a known safety principle. ("I knew I was supposed to read the label."), The fundamental cause of every accident is not recognizing the importance of a precaution that could have prevented the accident. ("I didn't know that paying attention to the label was that important.")

The following is a list of several possible unrecognized causes of accidents and suggestions for accident prevention. Of course, the list is not complete; no such list can be. Use it to help you identify some of the hazards in your laboratory. Once the potential causes of accidents are identified, you can then begin to work on their elimination.

Some causes of accidents can be eliminated by considering the following alternatives.

1. Some classic experiments can be altered to use small-scale or micro-scale techniques. Your favorite labs should be dropped if they pose known hazards.
2. Some procedures that are unsafe for students can be performed by the teacher as demonstrations.
3. Many dangerous but popular chemical demonstrations are available on videotape.

Your guiding philosophy should be that there is nothing that can be learned from a lab that justifies someone getting hurt.

ACCIDENTS WAITING TO HAPPEN	PRECAUTIONS FOR PREVENTION

Attitudes About Safety

▶ There is an attitude that precautions are optional if you are pressed for time.	▶ Practice zero-tolerance for unsafe conditions and practices. There is nothing that can be accomplished in your lab that is worth the risk of a serious accident.
▶ There is no assessment of students' knowledge and attitudes regarding safety.	▶ Conduct frequent safety quizzes. Students with perfect scores should be the only ones allowed to work in the lab.
▶ Neither you nor your supervisors have established a comprehensive safety plan.	▶ Include regular safety inspections and detailed recordkeeping in your safety plan.
▶ The most recent safety inspection or audit was conducted more than six months ago.	▶ Conduct regular in-house safety and health inspections with an emphasis on improvement rather than placing blame.

Fires and Other Emergencies

▶ Fire and other emergency drills are infrequent, and no records or measurements are made of the results of the drills.	▶ Have actions preplanned in case of an emergency (e.g., establish what devices should be turned off, which escape route to use, where to meet personnel outside the building, who is designated to count people at that meeting place, who is authorized to reenter).
▶ Students are unsure what to do when the fire alarm or another alarm sounds.	▶ Inform everyone in the lab about any alarms and what to do if they sound.
▶ There are items stored in hallways along escape routes. Fire doors are propped open for ventilation.	▶ Keep escape routes clear. Do not prop open fire doors or block them for any reason.
▶ You know your escape route but no alternatives.	▶ Always plan alternative escape routes in case of unforeseen problems.
▶ The emergency phone numbers are kept at the main switchboard only.	▶ Post current emergency phone numbers next to all phones.

| ACCIDENTS WAITING TO HAPPEN | | PRECAUTIONS FOR PREVENTION |

Fires and Other Emergencies CONTINUED

▶ Fire extinguishers are placed at "dead ends" so they will not be in the way along escape routes.

▶ Place fire extinguishers near escape routes so that they will be of use to those escaping.

▶ You have no idea how many fire extinguishers there are or when they were last charged. You've never used an extinguisher, and neither have the other teachers.

▶ Regularly maintain fire extinguishers and train supervisory personnel in the proper use of extinguishers by having them extinguish real fires.

▶ Students believe that if a fire breaks out they should run for the nearest fire extinguisher and use it to put out the fire as quickly as possible.

▶ Instruct students (who should not use fire extinguishers because they have not been trained in their use) that in case of a fire they should call a teacher (who should be trained).

▶ You don't know who in the building has had CPR or first-aid training.

▶ Get trained in CPR or first aid by your local chapter of the American Red Cross. Be sure to take frequent refresher ourses. Post lists of trained staff.

▶ The investigation conducted after a serious accident was superficial; it did not identify any previously unrecognized cause or causes and did not result in the implementation of safer procedures.

▶ Record all details of the accident, even those that may seem insignificant, to allow meaningful retrospective studies of accidents. Analyze accidents to prevent reoccurrence and not for any other reason.

Facilities and Equipment

▶ Eyewash fountains are present, but no one knows anything about their specifications.

▶ Ensure that eyewash fountains and safety showers meet the requirements of the ANSI standard (Z358.1).

▶ Eyewash fountains are checked and cleaned once at the beginning of each school year. No records are kept of routine checks and maintenance on the safety showers and eyewash fountains.

▶ Flush eyewash fountains for 5 min every month to remove any bacteria or other organisms from pipes. Test safety showers (measure flow in gallons per minute) and eyewash fountains every six months and keep records of the test results.

▶ Chronic contamination of breathing air is dealt with by keeping windows propped open at all times.

▶ Ensure that laboratory ventilation and fume hood performance and use conform to the requirements of the ANSI standard (Z358.1).

▶ Spills are handled on a case-by-case basis with whatever materials happen to be on hand.

▶ Have the appropriate equipment and materials available for spill control; replace them before their expiration dates.

▶ Labs are opened in the morning and locked after school is out.

▶ Lock all laboratory rooms whenever a teacher is not present.

▶ Compressed gas cylinders are carried by hand and set up in a corner of the laboratory.

▶ Secure all compressed gas cylinders when in use, and transport them secured on a hand truck.

Safety Wear

▶ Instead of goggles, you prefer to wear safety glasses with hard plastic lenses. You do not use a face shield when preparing solutions from concentrated acids. Students or teachers who wear contact lenses use regular lab goggles.

▶ Wear eye protection in the laboratory at all times; use safety goggles, ANSI Type G or H. When circumstances require, wear face, neck, and also ear protection (face shield, ANSI Type N). For details, see the ANSI standard (Z87.1) Require ANSI Type K cupped goggles for students or teachers who wear contact lenses.

▶ Gloves are reused to save money. They are discarded only after they begin to fall apart.

▶ Check gloves routinely for pin holes, tears, or rips. Because gloves cannot resist penetration by a chemical after being handled for long periods of time, replace them before that time period expires.

▶ You wear old clothes in the lab instead of a laboratory coat or apron so that spills won't be a problem.

▶ Wear a laboratory coat or apron to protect skin and clothing from chemicals.

▶ You assume that your lab coat or apron offers the appropriate protection.

▶ Wear a long-sleeved shirt or blouse and slacks that extend to the ankles under the lab coat or apron.

▶ You allow students to wear sandals in the laboratory.

▶ Do not allow any footwear in the lab that does not cover feet completely; including open-toed shoes.

▶ Observers are allowed into the lab but told to stay away from the lab benches.

▶ Keep a spare set of protective equipment on hand for visitors.

Work Habits

▶ New lab procedures are used with students without a pre-lab session or demonstration.

▶ Analyze new lab procedures in advance to pinpoint potential hazards.

▶ You work alone during your preparation period to organize the day's labs.

▶ Never work alone in a science laboratory or storage area.

▶ Honor students do independent study alone in the laboratory.

▶ Never allow students to occupy a science laboratory unless a teacher is present.

▶ Although students do not eat or drink in the lab, you sometimes drink a soda or coffee in the storage area.

▶ Never eat, drink, smoke, or chew gum or tobacco in a science laboratory or storage area. Do not store food or beverages in the laboratory environment.

▶ After work, you're in a hurry to get home, so you don't wash your hands.

▶ Always wash hands after work in a science laboratory and after spill cleanups.

▶ Sometimes you leave the room while a hot water bath is warming up.

▶ Never leave any heat sources (such as gas burners, hot plates, heating mantles, sand baths, etc.) unattended.

▶ The storeroom is too crowded, so you decide to keep some equipment on the lab benches.

▶ Do not store reagents or equipment on lab benches, and keep lab shelves organized. Never place reactive chemicals (in bottles, beakers, flasks, wash bottles, etc.) near the edges of a lab bench.

ACCIDENTS WAITING TO HAPPEN	PRECAUTIONS FOR PREVENTION

Work Habits CONTINUED

▶ When you work in the fume hood, you put your head inside so you can see what you are doing. Reagents are kept in the fume hood because you lack appropriate storage areas.	▶ Never lean into the fume hood. Do not use the fume hood as a storage area.
▶ Students who have finished their lab work take off their goggles when they begin writing up their results.	▶ Make sure protection is used not only by the lab worker but also by anyone working nearby.
▶ You pipette by mouth because you know how to do it properly.	▶ Never pipette by mouth.
▶ No extra precautions are taken when handling liquid nitrogen.	▶ Tape all Dewar flasks.

Purchasing and Using Chemicals

▶ You prepare your solutions from concentrated stock to save money.	▶ Reduce risks by ordering diluted instead of concentrated substances.
▶ You purchase plenty of chemicals to be sure that you won't run out. You purchase chemicals in large quantities to save money.	▶ Purchase chemicals in class-size quantities, if at all possible. Do not purchase or have on hand more than one year's supply of each chemical.
▶ Each year you have some excess chemicals, but you reorder more so that you don't run out.	▶ Dispose of or use up any chemicals leftover at the end of one year before the next year is over.
▶ When chemicals arrive, you unpack them and place them in your storage room.	▶ Label all chemicals accurately with the date of receipt, and write the initials of the person responsible for unpacking that chemical on the label.
▶ You don't generally read labels on chemicals when preparing solutions for a lab.	▶ Read each label to be sure it states the hazards and describes the precautions and first aid procedures (when appropriate) that apply to the contents in case someone else has to deal with the chemical in an emergency.
▶ You never read the Material Safety Data Sheets (MSDSs) that come with your chemicals.	▶ Always read the Material Safety Data Sheet (MSDS) for a chemical before using it. Follow the precautions described in that Material Safety Data Sheet. File and organize MSDSs for all chemicals where they can be found easily in case of an emergency.
▶ You put a copy of the warnings from the concentrated acid label on a bottle of the diluted acid.	▶ Label the diluted acids and bases with the hazards, precautions, and first aid procedures that apply specifically to them.
▶ Large reagent bottles of flammable chemicals are kept on the open shelves of the laboratory for days at a time.	▶ Store no more than one day's supply of flammable liquids or solids on the open shelves of the laboratory. At the end of the day, store any such unused chemical in a flammable-liquid storage cabinet.

Purchasing and Using Chemicals CONTINUED

▶ The main stockroom contains chemicals that haven't been used for years.

▶ Do not leave bottles of chemicals unused on shelves in the lab for more than one week or unused in the main stockroom for more than one year.

▶ No extra precautions are taken when flammable liquids are dispensed from their containers.

▶ When transferring flammable liquids from bulk containers, ground the container, and before transferring to a smaller metal container, ground both containers.

Chemical Storage

▶ Students are told to put their broken glass and solid chemical wastes in the trash can.

▶ Have separate containers for trash, for broken glass, and for different categories of hazardous chemical wastes.

▶ Students obtain their chemicals and equipment from stockrooms or storage areas.

▶ Lock all storage spaces; only permit teachers to enter.

▶ You haven't updated your chemical inventory in years.

▶ Keep an accurate and up-to-date inventory of chemicals on hand.

▶ You keep mutually reactive chemicals stored by hazard class, but flammable liquids and solids are stored on the shelves of the storage area.

▶ Keep incompatible classes of mutually reactive chemicals (e.g., acids and bases, oxidizers and reducers, nitric acid and glacial acetic acid) separate from each other in the storage area. Store bulk quantities of flammable liquids and solids in a flammable materials storage cabinet or in a separate room specifically designed and designated to be used for such storage only.

▶ Corrosives are kept above eye level, out of reach from anyone who is not authorized to be in the storeroom.

▶ Always store corrosive chemicals on shelves below eye level.

▶ Chemicals are kept on the floor of the stockroom on the days that they will be used so that they are easy to find.

▶ Never store chemicals or other materials on floors or in the aisles of the laboratory or storeroom, even for a few minutes.

▶ A second-hand refrigerator is used for lab storage.

▶ Use only an "explosion-proof" refrigerator for lab storage.

▶ You're not sure which chemicals are incompatible. Chemicals are stored without consideration of possible emergencies (fire, earthquake, flood, etc.), which could compound the hazards.

▶ Use MSDSs to determine which chemicals are incompatible. Store chemicals that are incompatible with common fire-fighting media like water (such as alkali metals) or carbon dioxide (such as alkali and alkaline-earth metals) under conditions that eliminate the possibility of a reaction with water or carbon dioxide if it is necessary to fight a fire in the storage area.

▶ Batteries are stored with no extra precautions.

▶ Cover both terminals of dry cells and rechargeable batteries with insulating tape when storing them.

DISPOSAL OF CHEMICALS

Only a relatively small percentage of waste chemicals is classified as hazardous by EPA regulations. The EPA regulations are derived from two acts (as amended) passed by the Congress of the United States: RCRA (Resource Conservation and Recovery Act) and CERCLA (Comprehensive Environmental Response, Compensation, and Liability Act).

Some states have enacted legislation governing the disposal of hazardous wastes that differs to some extent from the federal legislation. Disposal procedures in this book comply with the federal legislation as described in the EPA regulations.

▶ If a particular disposal procedure does not comply with your state requirements, ask your state's environmental office to assist you in devising a procedure that is in compliance.

The following general practices are recommended in addition to the procedures identified above.

▶ Except when otherwise specified in the disposal procedures, neutralize acidic and basic wastes with 1.0 M sodium hydroxide, NaOH, or 1.0 M sulfuric acid, H_2SO_4, which you add slowly while stirring.

▶ In dealing with a waste-disposal contractor, prepare a complete list of the chemicals you want to dispose of.

▶ Classify each of the chemicals on your disposal list as a hazardous or nonhazardous waste chemical. Check with your local environmental agency office for the details of such classification.

▶ Unlabeled bottles must be identified to the extent that they can be classified as a hazardous or nonhazardous waste. Some landfills will analyze an unknown waste for a fee. It must be labeled as an unknown sample and shipped to the landfill in a separate package with instructions to analyze the contents sufficiently to allow proper disposal.

ELECTRICAL SAFETY

The following safety precautions to avoid electric shocks must be followed any time electrical equipment is present in the lab.

▶ Each electrical socket in the laboratory must be a three-hole socket and must be protected with a GFI (ground-fault interrupter) type circuit.

▶ Check the polarity of all circuits with a polarity tester from an electronics supply store before use. Repair any incorrectly wired sockets.

▶ Use only electrical equipment equipped with a three-wire cord and three-prong plug.

▶ Be sure all electrical equipment is turned off before it is plugged into a socket. Turn off electrical equipment before it is unplugged.

▶ Wiring hookups should be made or altered only when the apparatus is disconnected from the power source and the power switch is turned off.

▶ Do not let electric cords dangle from work stations; dangling cords are a tripping and shock hazard. Do not use electrical equipment with frayed or twisted cords.

▶ The area under and around electrical equipment should be dry; cords should not lie in puddles of spilled liquid. Hands should be dry when using electrical equipment.

▶ Do not use electrical equipment powered by 110-115 V alternating current for "conductivity" demonstrations or for any other use in which bare wires are exposed, even if the current is connected to a lower voltage AC or DC connection.

▶ Use dry cells or Ni-Cad rechargeable batteries as direct current sources. Do not use automobile storage batteries or AC to DC converters; these two sources of DC current can present serious shock hazards.

EYEWASH FOUNTAIN

Do you know how to operate an eyewash fountain?

Be certain to instruct anyone working in the lab in the proper use of the eyewash fountain, as outlined below.

▶ If your eyes are exposed to chemicals, walk immediately to an eyewash fountain, preferably within 15 seconds of exposure.

▶ Immediately start flushing your eyes; continue for at least 15 minutes while someone else calls a doctor.

▶ Keep your eyes wide open; with your fingers, lift your upper and lower lids away from the eyeball so that the flowing water washes across it.

▶ Move your eyes continuously up, down, left, right, across, and around. This will help the flowing water get inside the eyeball socket and wash out any chemicals.

Prepared by Jay A. Young, Consultant, Chemical Health and Safety, Silver Spring, MD

REFERENCES

1. Budavari, Susan, ed. The Merck Index. 12th ed. Rahway, NJ: Merck and Co., 1996. Use this reference for reliable general information about a chemical instead of using a less reliable chemical dictionary or one of the many books with the words "Dangerous Properties" as part of the title.

2. Council Committee of Chemical Safety. Safety in Academic Chemistry Laboratories. 5th ed., Washington, DC: American Chemical Society, 1995. This is the authority if you wish a brief treatment. Single copies are free. For a more extensive treatment, see Young, below.

3. "Fire Protection for Laboratories Using Chemicals" (also known as "NFPA-45") Current edition. National Fire Protection Association. Batterymarch Park, Quincy, MA This is the national safety code for laboratory fire protection and prevention.

4. Gerlovich, J. A., et al. School Science Safety. Batavia, IL: Flinn Scientific, Inc., 1984. This is a practical guide in two volumes for teachers.

5. Pipitone, D. A., and D. Hedberg. "Safe Chemical Storage." Journal of Chemical Education. Vol. 59 (1982), A159. A discussion on the proper storage of chemicals. Also see Pipitone, D. A. Safe Storage of Laboratory Chemicals. 2nd ed. New York: Wiley-Interscience, 1991 and the current edition of the Flinn Scientific Catalog, Flinn Scientific, Inc., Batavia, IL.

6. "Practice for Occupational and Educational Eye and Face Protection, Z87.1," "Emergency Eyewash and Shower Equipment, Z358.1," "American National Standard for Laboratory Ventilation, Z9.5." Current editions. American National Standards Institute. New York. These standards are recognized worldwide as reliable. Safety goggles and face shields that meet Z87.1 requirements are marked Z87.

7. Reese, K. M. Health and Safety Guidelines for Chemistry Teachers. Washington, DC: American Chemical Society, 1980. This source contains several useful tips on enhancing safety in your laboratory.

8. Standard First Aid and Personal Safety, American Red Cross. Your local Red Cross chapter probably gives a short course in first aid. This book summarizes the content of that course.

9. Young, Jay A. "Risk Assessment and Hazard Evaluation for Undergraduate Laboratory Experiments," Journal of Chemical Education, 59 (1982), A265. This provides some suggestions on teaching your students how to practice safety in the lab.

10. Young, Jay A., ed. Improving Safety in the Chemical Laboratory: A Practical Guide. 2nd ed. New York: Wiley-Interscience, 1991. The details of this topic are fully discussed.

Master Materials List

Chemical List For Explorations And Investigations

This listing shows the amounts needed for 15 lab groups to perform all of the Investigations (Inv) and Experiments. Solution preparations are found in the Teacher's Edition margin for that lab and in the comprehensive list of solution preparations on page 50T.

Chemical	Amount	Experiment
Acetic acid	87 mL	10C
Bromine sample	10 g	4A
$CaCl_2$	55 g	3A
Calcium sample	10 g	4A
Copper sample	10 g	4A
$Cu(NO_3)_2 \cdot 3H_2O$	180 g	Inv 2B
$CuSO_4 \cdot 6H_2O$	75 g	5A
Denatured alcohol	80 mL	15B
Ethanol solution, 50%	45 mL	7A
$FeSO_4 \cdot 7H_2O$	50 g	17A
Germanium sample	10 g	4A
H_2SO_4, concentrated	75 mL	15A, 16A, 17A
HCl, concentrated	315 mL	3A, 11A, 15A, 15B
Helium sample	500 mL	4A
Iodine sample	10 g	4A
K_2SO_4	87 g	3A
KIO_3	5 g	16A
$KMnO_4$	5 g	17A
KNO_3	600 g	2B, Inv 2B
$Li_2SO_4 \cdot H_2O$	64 g	3A
Liquid latex	150 mL	7A
Lithium sample	10 g	4A
Magnesium sample	10 g	4A
$MgSO_4 \cdot 7H_2O$	300 g	13 B
Na_2CO_3	60 g	10B
$Na_2S_2O_5$	1 g	16A
Na_2SO_4	71 g	3A
NaCl	650 g	1A, 2B, 3A, 13A
$NaCl-KNO_3$ solution	750 mL	2B
$NaHCO_3$	50 g	10C
NaOH pellets	200 g	11A, 15A, 15B, 15C
Neon sample	500 mL	4A
Phenolphthalein	5 g	15B
Potassium sample	10 g	4A
Silicon sample	10 g	4A
Sodium silicate solution	185 mL	7A
$SrCl_2 \cdot 6H_2O$	215 g	3A, 10B
Sucrose	300 g	13B
Water-soluble starch	5 g	16A

Equipment

The scenario price listing for the equipment and laboratory apparatus needed for the Investigations can be found on page 692.

Equipment	Amount	Experiment
Balance, centigram or triple-beam	15	1A, Inv 2B, 5A, Inv 5A, 10A, 10B, Inv 10B, 10C, Inv 10C, 11A, 11B, 13A, 13B, 15B
Beaker, 2 L or plastic bucket	15	7A
Beaker, 100 mL	30	15B
Beaker, 150 mL	60	2B
Beaker, 250 mL	30	1A, Inv 1A, 2A, Inv 2B, 3A, Inv 3A, 10B, Inv 10B, Inv 10C, 13A, Inv 15B, 17A, Inv 17A
Beaker, 400 mL	60	17A, Inv 17A
Beaker tongs	15	2B, 10B, Inv 10B, 10C, 13B
Bottle, 50 mL	15	15B
Büchner funnel	15	2B, 10B
Bunsen burner with gas tubing and striker	15	1A, Inv 1A, 2B, 3A, Inv 3A, 5A Inv 5A, 10A, 10C, Inv 10C, 13B
Buret	30	15A, Inv 15B, 17A, Inv 17A
Buret clamp, double	15	15A, Inv 15B, 17A, Inv 17A
CBL™	15	2A, 2B, 11A, 13B, 15C
Chemical handbook	1	2A
Chromatography paper, 12 cm	60 sheets	13A
Cobalt glass plate	15	3A, Inv 3A
Copper wire, 18 gauge	150 cm	1A
Crucible tongs	15	1A, 3A, Inv 3A, 5A, Inv 5A, 10A
Crucible and lid (metal or ceramic)	15	5A, Inv 5A, 10A
Desiccator (optional)	15	5A, Inv 5A, 15A
Distilled water	500 mL	2A, 2B, 3A, 5A, 7A, 10B, 11A, 11B, 13B, 15B, 15C, 16A, 17A
Dropper bottle	15	5A
Dropper or pipet	15	10C

EQUIPMENT	AMOUNT	EXPERIMENT
Drying oven	2-3	10B, Inv 10B, Inv 10C, 15B
Evaporating dish	15	1A, 10C
Filter funnels	15	2B
Filter paper	200 sheets	2B, 10B
Fine-tipped dropper bulb	45	16A
Flame-test wire	150 cm	3A, Inv 3A
Flask, Erlenmeyer; 125 mL	60	13B, 17A, Inv 17A
Flask, Erlenmeyer; 250 mL	30	Inv 15B
Flask, small Erlenmeyer	15	15B
Forceps	15	15B
Glass funnel	15	2B, 10B
Glass plate or microchemistry plate with wells	15	3A, Inv 3A
Glass stirring rod	15	2B, 5A, 10B, 11A
Gloves		All Labs
Graduated cylinder, 10 mL	15	7A, 15B
Graduated cylinder, 25 mL	30	2A, 7A
Graduated cylinder, 100 mL	30	1A, 2A, 2B, Inv 2B, I2, 10B, Inv 10B, Inv 10C, 11A, Inv 17A, 17A
Graphing calculator	15	2A, 2B, 11A, 13B,15C
Heat-resistant mat	15	1A
Hot plate	15	Inv 2B, 13A
Medicine dropper	60	15B
Metal shot, 5 g	15	2A
Meter stick	2-3	7A
Metric ruler	15	13A
Mortar and pestles	15	Inv 5A, 15B
pH probe, Vernier	15	Inv 15B, 15C
Pipe-stem triangle	15	5A, Inv 5A, 10A, 10B, Inv 10B
Pipets, graduated	30	15A
Pipets, microtip	45	15C, 16A
Pipets, thin-stemmed	60	15B
Plastic ruler, cm	15	2A
Ring, iron	15	Inv 1A, 2B, Inv 2B, 5A, Inv 5A, 10A, 10B, Inv 10B, 10C, Inv 10C, 11B, 13B, Inv 17A
Ring clamp	15	Inv 1A, 2B, Inv 2B, 5A, Inv 5A, 10A, 10B, Inv 10B, 10C, Inv 10C, 11B, 13B

EQUIPMENT	AMOUNT	EXPERIMENT
Ring stand	15	Inv 1A, 2B, Inv 2B, 5A, Inv 5A, 10A, 10B, Inv 10B, 10C, Inv 10C, 11B, 13B, 15A, Inv 15B, 17A
Rubber policeman	15	2B, Inv 2B, 10B
Rubber stopper (one-hole)	15	2B, 10B
Spatula	30	1A, 2B, Inv 2B, 5A, Inv 5A, 10A, 10B, 10C, 11A
Spectroscope	1	3A, Inv 3A
Temperature probe, Vernier	15	2A, 2B, 11A, 13B
Test tube, small	30	1A
Test tube, large	100	15A, 15C
Test-tube rack	15	15A, 15C
Thermometer (alcohol-filled)	15	2A, Inv 2B, 11A, 11B, 13B
Thermometer clamp	15	13B
Tray, tub or pneumatic trough	15	2B, Inv 2B
Vacuum flask (sidearm flask) and tubing	15	2B, 10B
Wash bottle	15	10B, Inv 15B, 15C, 17A, Inv 17A
Watch glass	15	10C, 11A
Water, tap	60 mL	15C
Weighing boat	30	10A, 11B
Weighing paper or wax paper	box	1A, 5A, 15B
8-well microstrip reaction strip	30	16A
Wire gauze (nonabestos) with ceramic center	15	Inv 1A, 2B, Inv 2B, 10C, Inv 10C, 13B

MISCELLANEOUS MATERIALS

MATERIAL	AMOUNT	EXPERIMENT
Aluminum foil	1 roll	Inv 1A
Apple juice	1 L	15C
Baking soda	300 g	10A, 15C
Clock with second hand	1	2A, 16A
Colored markers	15 sets	13A
Cooking oil	50 mL	1A
Drain cleaner	1 L	15C
Eggshells	30	15B
Empty soda can	15	11B

MATERIAL	AMOUNT	EXPERIMENT
Food samples peanuts, pecans, potato chips, tortilla chips, walnuts	small bag	11B
Ice	22.5 L	2B
Large cork	15	11B
Large paper clips	30	11B
Lemon juice	16 oz	15C
Lightbulb	5	4A
Liquid detergent	16 oz	15C
Litmus paper, blue	200 strips	15C
Litmus paper, red	200 strips	15C
Matches	15 small boxes	11B
Milk	60 mL	15C
Note cards, 3 × 5 in.	30 packs	4A, Inv 15B
Paper, white	45 sheets	15B
Paper towels	5 rolls	7A, 10B
Pencils	15	13A
Periodic table, blank	30	4A
pH paper	1 roll	Inv 15B
Popcorn	1 large bag	Inv 1A
Rock salt	600 g	2B, Inv 2B
Scissors	15	13A
Small nails	30	11B
Soft drink, clear	1 L	15C
Stopwatch	15	2A, Inv 15B, 16A
Tape dispenser	15	13A
Tape, transparent	1 roll	13A
Vinegar, white	1 L	7A, 15C
Wooden splints	60	3A, Inv 3A

MATERIALS LIST FOR QUICK LABS AND INQUIRY LABS

MATERIAL	AMOUNT	LAB	PAGE
Alligator clips	30	Q17	pp. 637
Aluminum foil	large roll	Q1	pp. 17
Aquarium, 5 gallon	2	Q14	pp. 524
Balance, centigram or triple-beam	15	Q1 I2 Q17	pp. 17, pp. 61, pp. 590
Balloon, latex	20	Q12	pp. 437
Beaker, 50 mL	15	Q15	pp. 564
Beaker, 250 mL	15	I2	pp. 49
Beaker, 500 mL	15	Q15	pp. 564
Blender	1	Q15	pp. 564

MATERIAL	AMOUNT	LAB	PAGE
Box, sealed container holding one or more objects	15	Q12	pp. 53
Bunsen burner and related equipment	15	I2	pp. 49
Cabbage, red	1	Q15	pp. 564
Calculator	15	Q1	pp. 17
Chromatography paper	30 sheets	I13	pp. 477
Colored pencils	15 sets	I2	pp. 61
Copper strip	15 strips	Q17	pp. 637
Crystalline solid	2 different samples	Q5	pp. 168
Developing solution, 0.1% NaCl	1 L	I13	pp. 477
Distilled water	1 L	I1, I2	pp. 31, 61
Earphones	15 pair	Q17	pp. 637
Effervescent tablet	15	Q16	pp. 590
Electrical tape	roll	Q17	pp. 637
Filter funnel	15	I1, I2	pp. 31, 61
Filter paper	30 sheets	I1, I2	pp. 31, 61
Food products	assorted	Q15	pp. 564
Graduated cylinder, 25 mL	15	I2	pp. 49
Graduated cylinder, 100 mL	15	I2	pp. 61
Graph paper	30 sheets	I2	pp. 61
Household cleaners	assorted	Q15	pp. 564
Iron filings	90 g	I1	pp. 31
M&M's™ candies	large bag	Q13	pp. 477
Magnet	15	I1	pp. 31
Measuring cups	2 sets	Q14	pp. 524
Microscope	1	Q5	pp. 168
Nylon hair comb	15	Q6	pp. 220
Paper, white	30 sheets	I1	pp. 31
Paper towel	1 roll	I1	pp. 31
Pennies, pre-1982, and post-1983	2 sets of 100	I2	pp. 61
Pet bottle	15	Q12	pp. 437
Plastic cup, clear	30	I1 Q17	pp. 31 pp. 590
Plastic pieces, 2 × 2 in.	30	Q7	pp. 257
Plastic spoon	15	I1	pp. 31
Playing cards, 3 different sets	15 of each set	Q11	pp. 386
Potato, raw	15	Q17	pp. 637
Poppy seeds	90 g	I1	pp. 31
Ring clamp	15	I2	pp. 49

MATERIAL	AMOUNT	LAB	PAGE
Ring stand	15	I2	pp. 49
Rubber band	30	Q12	pp. 437
Ruler, metric	15	Q1	pp. 17
		I2	pp. 61
Salt	90 g	Q2	pp. 31
		I2	pp. 49
Sand	90 g	I2	pp. 31
Scissors	15	Q1	pp. 17
Spatula	15	Q15	pp. 564
Stopwatch	15	Q16	pp. 590
Sugar	200 g	I2	pp. 49
Tap water	1 L	Q6	pp. 220
		Q14	pp. 524
		Q15	pp. 564
		Q16	pp. 590
Thermometer	15	I2	pp. 49
Zinc strip	15 strips	Q17	pp. 637

SOLUTION PREPARATION FOR EXPLORATIONS AND INVESTIGATIONS

SOLUTION/EXPERIMENT	PREPARATION
0.001 M $CaCl_2$ Inv 10B	Dissolve 0.147 g of $CaCl_2 \cdot 2H_2O$ in enough distilled water to make 1.00 L of solution.
0.0200 M $KMnO_4$ 17A, Inv 17A	Dissolve 3.16 g of $KMnO_4$ in enough distilled water to make 1.00 L of solution. For best results, this solution must be prepared shortly before the lab.
0.10 M H_2SO_4 15A	Dissolve 5.6 mL of concentrated H_2SO_4 in enough distilled water to make 1.00 L of solution.
0.10 M HCl 15A	Dissolve 8.3 mL of concentrated HCl in enough distilled water to make 1.00 L of solution.
0.15 M $FeSO_4$ 17A	Dissolve 41.70 g of $FeSO_4 \cdot 7H_2O$ in enough distilled water to make 1.00 L of solution.

SOLUTION/EXPERIMENT	PREPARATION
0.20 M HCl Inv 15B	Observe the required precautions. Add 16.5 mL of concentrated HCl to enough distilled water to make 1.00 L of solution. Add the acid slowly and stir the solution to avoid overheating.
0.25 M $FeSO_4$ Inv 17A	Dissolve 69.51 g of $FeSO_4 \cdot 7H_2O$ in enough distilled water to make 1.00 L of solution.
0.30 M NaOH 15A	Dissolve 12 g of solid NaOH in enough distilled water to make 1.00 L of solution.
0.3 M $SrCl_2$ 10B	Dissolve 80.0 g of $SrCl_2 \cdot 6H_2O$ in enough distilled water to make 1.00 L of solution
0.5 M $CaCl_2$ Inv 10B	Dissolve 73.5 g of $CaCl_2 \cdot 2H_2O$ in enough distilled water to make 1.00 L of solution.
0.5 M HCl 11A	Observe the required precautions. Add 42 mL of concentrated HCl to enough distilled water to make 1.00 L of solution. Add the acid slowly, while stirring the solution to avoid overheating.
0.5 M K_2SO_4 3A	Dissolve 87 g of K_2SO_4 in enough water to make 1.00 L of solution.
0.5 M Li_2SO_4 3A, Inv 3A	Dissolve 64 g of $LiSO_4 \cdot H_2O$ in enough water to make 1.00 L of solution.
0.5 M Na_2CO_3 10B, Inv 10B	Dissolve 53.0 g of Na_2CO_3 in enough distilled water to make 1.00 L of solution
0.5 M Na_2SO_4 3A	Dissolve 71 g Na_2SO_4 in enough water to make 1.00 L of solution
0.5 M NaOH 15B, Inv 15B	Dissolve 20.0 g of NaOH pellets in enough distilled water to make 1.00 L of solution. Add a few pellets at a time, while stirring the solution to avoid overheating.

SOLUTION/EXPERIMENT	PREPARATION
0.5 M SrCl$_2$ **3A**	Dissolve 133.3 g of SrCl$_2$• 6H$_2$O in enough distilled water to make 1.00 L of solution.
1.0 M CH$_3$COOH **10C**	Observe the required precautions. Add 87 mL of glacial CH$_3$COOH to enough distilled water to make 1.00 L of solution.
1.0 M HCl **3A, Inv 3A,** **Inv 10C, 11A, 15B**	Observe the required precautions. Add 83 mL of concentrated HCl to enough distilled water to make 1.00 L of solution. Add the acid slowly, while stirring to avoid overheating.
1.0 M H$_2$SO$_4$ **16A**	Observe the required precautions. Add 0.6 mL of concentrated H$_2$SO$_4$ to 9.4 mL of distilled water. Add the acid slowly, while stirring to avoid overheating.
1.0 M H$_2$SO$_4$ **17A**	Observe the required precautions. Slowly add 56 mL of concentrated H$_2$SO$_4$ to enough distilled water to make 1.00 L of solution, Add the acid slowly while stirring the solution to avoid overheating.
1.0 M NaOH **11A**	Dissolve 40.0 g of NaOH in enough distilled water to make 1.00 L of solution
Cu(NO$_3$)$_2$–KNO$_3$ **Inv 2B**	Add 300 g of KNO$_3$ and 150 g of Cu(NO$_3$)$_2$•3H$_2$O to 900 mL of distilled water. Slowly heat the solution while stirring until the two salts are dissolved. Each 50 mL sample should contain approximately 15 g of KNO$_3$ and 7.5 g of Cu(NO$_3$)$_2$.

SOLUTION/EXPERIMENT	PREPARATION
Mixture **I2**	Mix 5 g of the four components in a large resealable plastic bag for each lab group: sand, salt, iron filings, and poppy seeds.
NaCl solution **13A**	Dissolve 10 g of NaCl in enough distilled water to make 1.00 L of solution
NaCl–KNO$_3$ **2B**	Dissolve 140 g of NaCl and 320 g of KNO$_3$ in enough distilled water to make 1.00 L of solution. Gently heat the solution while stirring to completely dissolve the salts.
Phenolphthalein **15B, Inv 15B**	Dissolve 1.00 g of phenolphthalein in 50.0 mL of denatured alcohol, and add 50.0 mL of distilled water.
Solution A **16A**	Make a paste of 1 g of water-soluble starch and 10 mL of water. Add 225 mL of boiling distilled water. Reheat and boil for a few minutes. After the solution has cooled, add 0.05 g of Na$_2$S$_2$O$_5$ (sodium metabisulfate) and 1.3 mL of 1.0 M H$_2$SO$_4$. Dilute with enough distilled water to make 250 mL of solution. (Note: This solution should be prepared no more than two months prior to use.)
Solution B **16A**	Dissolve 1.07 g KIO$_3$ in enough distilled water to make 250 mL of solution.

The Science of Chemistry

CLASSROOM RESOURCES			
SECTIONS	TEACHER'S DEMONSTRATIONS	PROBLEM SOLVING ■ Text ◆ ChemFile Mini-Guide	LABORATORIES ■ Text ◆ ChemFile Manuals: A, B, C, D
1-1 **What is chemistry?** Section Review, p. 9	**Demo 1** Changes in Matter, p. 4 **Demo 2** Evidence of Chemical Change I, p. 6 **Demo 3** Evidence of Chemical Change II, p. 8		◆ **A1** Laboratory Procedures ◆ **B1** Laboratory Procedures
1-2 **What is matter?** Section Review, p. 19	**Demo 4** Mass, Volume, and Density, p. 16	■ **How To** Use conversion factors, p. 14 ◆ **Chapter 1** Conversions	■ **Exp. A1** Laboratory Techniques, p. 702 ■ **Inv. A1** Conservation of Mass—Percentage of Water in Popcorn, p. 706 ■ **QuickLab** Thickness of Aluminum Foil, p. 17
1-3 **What is the nature of matter?** Section Review, p. 24	**Demo 5** Observing Elements, p. 20		◆ **D1** How Sweet It Is!
1-4 **How is matter classified?** Section Review, p. 32	**Demo 6** Litmus in Acid and Base, p. 27 **Demo 7** Separating a Compound into Elements, p. 28 **Demo 8** Separation by Distillation, p. 30		◆ **Exp. C2** Separation of Mixtures ◆ **Inv. C2** Separation of Mixtures—Tanker Truck Spill ■ **InquiryLab** Using Physical Properties to Separate a Mixture, p. 31 ◆ **D2** What's So Special about Bottled Drinking Water?

SECTIONS	VIDEOS/VIDEODISC *Holt Chemistry Videodisc* **CNN** *Science in the NEWS*	CHEMFILE CD-ROMs ● *Teaching Resources* ◆ *Interactive Tutor*	OVERHEADS ● *Color Transparencies* ◆ *Transparency Masters*
1-1	Mercury(II) oxide decomposing **CNN** Segment 1 Chemical Industry Report Segment 2 Chemicals Unknown and Untested	◆ **Module 1:** States of Matter **Topic:** Defining the States and Classes of Matter	● **1** Particle Models for Water
1-2	**CNN** Segment 3 Chemicals in the Home	● Basic Skills: Using Your Calculator, SI Conversions ● Internet Activities: Student Handouts 1–9 Introduction to the Internet and Web Browsers ● Internet Activity 2: Using a Browser ● Internet Activity 3: Searching the Web ● Internet Activity 4: Evaluating Web Sources	◆ **3A** SI Base Units ◆ **4A** SI Prefixes ◆ **1A** Properties of Matter ◆ **6A** Densities of Some Familiar Materials ● **2** Comparison of Physical and Chemical properties
1-3	**CNN** Segment 4 Student Superconductors Segment 5 Making Fullerenes	● Supplemental Reading: *The Same and Not the Same* "What Are You?" ● Internet Activity 9: Buckminster Fullerene	● **6** Regions of the Periodic Table ● **5** Abundance of Elements in Earth's Crust
1-4	pH change during acid neutralization Acetaminophen molecular rotation Benzene molecule rotation **CNN** Segment 6 Cleaner Gas	● Internet Activity 6: Chemistry Web Pages ◆ **Module 1:** States of Matter **Topic:** Defining the States and Classes of Matter	● **3** Classifying Matter ● **4** Electrolysis of Water ◆ **2A** Grades of Chemical Purity

ASSESSMENT RESOURCES

ALTERNATIVE ASSESSMENTS	CHAPTER TESTING	SCORING RUBRICS *Holt ChemFile Teaching Resources CD-ROM*
Student Text Performance assessments, p. 36 Portfolio projects, p. 36 **Teacher's Edition** Group Strategies, pp. 14, 18, 32 **Study Guide** Sections 1-1 to 1-4	**Student Text** Test Preparation, p. 37 **Holt Chemistry: Visualizing Matter Chapter 1 Test** (blackline masters) **Holt ChemFile Test Generator for Macintosh and Windows**	**Lab Work** Student-Designed Experiments Rubric Performance-Tasks Scoring Rubric Assessment for Structured Inquiry Assessment for Open-Ended Inquiry **Portfolio Projects** Evaluating Concept Maps Assessing Portfolios Portfolio Assignment Student Evaluation Form

1

The Science of Chemistry

READING STRATEGY

Assimilating Knowledge

Before students read this chapter, have them write a short list of all the things they know about the structure of matter and the changes in matter.

When students have finished their lists, ask them to contribute their entries to a group list on the board or on an overhead projector. Then have students list the things they might want to know about the nature of matter.

If students are having trouble coming up with questions, you can offer these suggestions to get them on track: What properties of liquid water change when it freezes? What properties do not change? How do you know that air is matter? How can you tell a block of aluminum from a block of steel if both are painted the same color? What causes the difference between the two blocks? What differences account for the fact that iron rusts in air while gold does not?

ABOUT THE ILLUSTRATION

Chemistry is of vital importance in today's world. The chemical industry is responsible for an enormous fraction of our national economy. Chemical processes simplify the production of consumer goods and services by offering more efficient and less costly production paths.

---

internetconnect

Holt Chemistry: Visualizing Matter

On-Line Resources
go.hrw.com
Visit the HRW Web site for a variety of resources related to this chapter. Just type in the keyword HW0 Chapt1.

SCiLINKS SM
NSTA

National Science Teachers Association

On-Line Resources: www.scilinks.org
The following Scilinks Internet resources can be found in the student text for this chapter:

Page 5
TOPIC: Chemicals
KEYWORD: HW011

Page 9
TOPIC: Aspirin
KEYWORD: HW012

Page 12
TOPIC: SI units
KEYWORD: HW013

Page 24
TOPIC: Allotropes
KEYWORD: HW014

Page 25
TOPIC: Aluminum
KEYWORD: HW015

A WONDER DRUG

2000 years ago, the Greeks and Romans relied on a substance extracted from plants, particularly the bark of willow trees, to relieve pain and reduce fevers. Plant extracts were used to treat various ailments in other parts of the world, including North America, where Native Americans used a bark extract to treat fever and pain.

In the 1760s, Edward Stone, an English clergyman and naturalist, wrote that he used "twenty grains of powdered bark dissolved in water, administered every four hours" to treat 50 people suffering from acute shiver-provoking illnesses. The results, he reported, were excellent.

Following up on Stone's report, German chemists in the early 1800s isolated a tiny amount of what they believed to be the active ingredient in the willow bark extract and called it salicin, from *Salix,* the scientific name for willow trees. French chemists improved on the extraction process and discovered that salicin could be converted to a substance called salicylic acid, the active form of the pain reliever.

Once salicylic acid was identified as the active ingredient, a related substance, sodium salicylate, was made available for public use. Unfortunately, sodium salicylate was extremely irritating to the lining of the stomach. People who took it often suffered stomach irritation or nausea and occasionally developed ulcers.

In the late 1800s, Felix Hoffmann, a German chemist, began looking for ways to reduce some of the unpleasant side effects of sodium salicylate. Although his research focused on the chemistry of dyes, Hoffmann became interested in sodium salicylate because he wanted to help relieve the pain his father experienced from arthritis. Hoffmann was able to synthesize another derivative of salicylic acid, acetylsalicylic acid—the compound we know today as aspirin. Little did Hoffmann or Stone know that their treatments would someday become a common prescription—take two aspirin every four hours to relieve pain or reduce fever.

Chemistry has enabled tremendous changes to be made in the way we live. These changes can lead to new challenges that we all must face and, at times, to problems that we have yet to solve and questions that we have yet to answer. However, there are some questions that you should be able to answer after reading this chapter.

CHAPTER LINKS

What type of chemical substance is aspirin?

How is aspirin similar to other widely used pain relievers?

How does name-brand aspirin differ from generic brands of aspirin?

STORY BACKGROUND

Though salicylates could be obtained from natural plant sources (willow bark, the wintergreen plant, and the meadowsweet plant), they are expensive to isolate and produce from these sources. Fortunately, during the nineteenth century, German chemists had become expert in the development of synthetic forms of natural substances. German chemists were able to synthesize salicylic acid at one-tenth of the current market cost of producing the compound from natural sources. The point to emphasize in this chapter is that while natural products are held in high esteem, there are many instances where they are too costly for widespread consumption.

CNN Science in the News

PRESENTS **Feature story 1** *Chemical Industry Report* and **Feature story 2** *Chemicals Unknown and Untested.* See the Science in the News video guide for more details.

RESOURCE LINK

ChemFile Teaching Resources CD-ROM
Internet Activities
Assign Student Handouts 1–9 for background information on the World Wide Web.

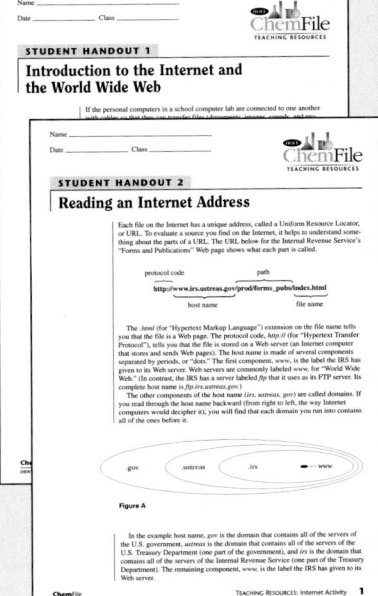

CONCEPT PREVIEW

Section 1-1

The study of matter
▶ Chemicals
▶ States of matter

Chemical reactions
▶ Reactants and products
▶ Exothermic and endothermic

Section 1-2

The nature of matter
▶ Volume, mass, weight

Measuring matter
▶ SI units
▶ Conversion factors

Properties of matter
▶ Physical properties
▶ Physical changes
▶ Chemical properties
▶ Chemical changes

Section 1-3

Composition of matter
▶ Atoms

▶ Molecules and allotropes

Section 1-4

Classifying compounds
▶ Molecular and ionic
▶ Acids and bases
▶ Organic and inorganic

Properties of mixtures
▶ Homogeneous
▶ Heterogeneous

SECTION 1-1

LESSON WARM-UP

Perceptions about Chemicals
Before students begin the chapter, ask them where they might find chemicals and what they think chemicals are. Try to elicit some of the commonplace ideas about chemicals—that they are poisonous, polluting to the environment, dangerous in food, smelly, toxic, and hazardous. Finally, point out that everything around them is made of chemicals.

TEACHING TIP

Learning the Language   In preparation for Sections 1-3 and 1-4, make a list of the 50 common elements and symbols that students are likely to encounter. Have students begin memorizing the list in groups of 15. Check their progress in periodic quizzes.

What is chemistry?

OBJECTIVES	▶ **Describe** the characteristics of the three most common physical states.	▶ **Identify** the reactants and products in a chemical reaction.
	▶ **Draw** models to represent solids, liquids, and gases.	▶ **Distinguish** between exothermic and endothermic reactions.
	▶ **Write** a word equation for a chemical reaction.	

Chemistry deals with the properties of matter

You probably think of chemistry as simply another subject that you study in high school. Or you may feel that chemistry is important only to people working in laboratories. But there is much more to chemistry than this. In fact, whether you are aware of it or not, chemistry is an important part of your daily life.

You depend on chemicals every day

Chemistry deals with the properties of chemicals. What is a chemical? A **chemical** is any substance with a definite composition. You will learn in this course that chemical reactions are taking place constantly all around you and that chemists are not the only people who work with chemicals. For example, the chef shown in **Figure 1-1** carefully controls

chemical
any substance with a definite composition

▶ **FIGURE 1-1**
The ingredients in your food are chemicals. A skilled chef understands how the chemicals interact in foods.

4   CHAPTER 1

RESOURCE LINK

ChemFile Lab D
Consumer Lab
Have students do Experiment D1: *How Sweet It Is!*

DEMONSTRATION 1

Changes in Matter

Approximate time: 10 minutes

1. Put 8 drops of phenolphthalein solution in a 600 mL beaker before class. Add 200 mL of 0.25 M NaOH solution to the beaker containing the dye.

2. Now add 1 M HCl to the beaker, and stir until the solution turns clear again.

3. Add more NaOH to the beaker until it turns pink again. Continue adding acid and base until the beaker is full.

4. Before class, gently mix 20 mL of dishwashing liquid with 100 mL of vinegar. Place 50 g of baking soda, $NaHCO_3$, into a 1000 mL graduated cylinder, and place the cylinder in a larger container that will be able to catch the resulting bubbles. Add the vinegar-soap mixture, and watch the bubbles appear. Ask students what different properties they observed in each demonstration.

the many chemical reactions necessary to produce a delicious meal. A photographer uses chemicals to develop exposed film and to stabilize the images on photographic paper. A boat owner applies a paint containing chemicals that will retard the growth of organisms on the hull. A consumer buying aspirin scans the label for chemicals that might cause an allergic reaction. Obviously, chemists are not the only people who benefit from a knowledge of chemistry. Because chemicals are an integral part of our everyday lives, everyone needs some understanding of chemistry. This text will give you that understanding and will also show you the variety of ways that chemistry plays a role in your daily life.

Some people think of chemicals mainly in negative terms—as the causes of pollution, cancer, and explosions. Many of these people believe that chemicals and chemical additives should be banned. But think for a moment what such a ban would mean—after all, everything around you is a chemical. Imagine going to the supermarket to buy fruits and vegetables grown without the use of any chemicals at all. The produce section would be completely empty! In fact, the entire supermarket would be empty because all foods are made of chemicals.

Without chemicals, you would have nothing to wear. Much of your clothing is made from synthetic fibers that are the products of chemical reactions. Even clothing made from natural fibers, such as cotton or wool, is the product of chemical reactions. As you can see from **Table 1-1,** the production of chemical compounds is a major industry. The top five chemical producers in the United States might be familiar to you, especially if you live in one of the top 10 chemical-producing states, shown in **Figure 1-2. Table 1-2,** on the next page, lists the top five chemicals produced in the United States.

internet connect

SCiLINKS
NSTA

TOPIC: Chemicals
GO TO: www.scilinks.org
KEYWORD: HW011

FIGURE 1-2 ▼

You can see that major chemical-producing states are clustered by region. Why do you think most chemical-producing states are located near the ocean or Great Lakes?

TABLE 1-1	Top Five Chemical Producers in the U.S.	

Rank	Name	Sales (in millions of dollars)
1	Dow Chemical	18 988
2	Du Pont	18 044
3	Exxon	11 430
4	Monsanto	7 267
5	Hoechst Celanese	6 906

Source: *Chemical and Engineering News,* May 1997

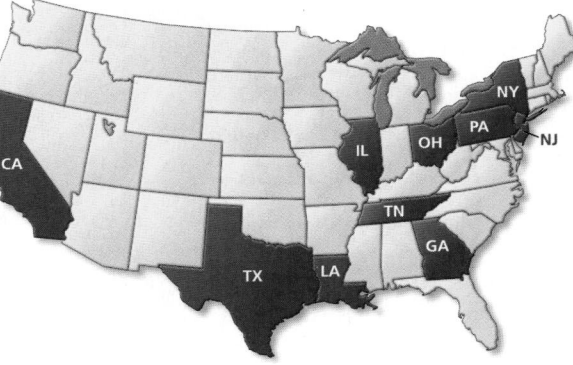

COMMON MISCONCEPTION

Many students think that chemicals differ from substances and materials in nature. Have students name their favorite foods and drinks. Point out that these foods are made up of carbohydrates, proteins, fats, water, and other components, all of which are chemicals.

TEACHING TIP

Point out that all matter is composed of chemicals. They are more often called *chemical substances* or just *substances.*

ADDITIONAL APPLICATION

Chemicals of one sort or another are produced in all states. Some students may be interested to find out where the nearest chemical production facility is, what it produces, and why it is located where it is. Caution them not to include operations that are only storage or warehousing facilities.

RESOURCE LINK

ChemFile Lab A
Skills Development
Have students do Experiment A1: *Laboratory Procedures.*

Safety
Wear safety goggles and a lab apron. Students should be at least 10 ft from the demonstration area.

Disposal
Neutralize the acid or base left over from each step, and pour it down the drain. Dissolve and flush any residue with plenty of water.

Sulfuric acid is such a widely used industrial chemical that a country's per capita production of sulfuric acid is considered an index of that country's economy.

About 54% of sulfuric acid is used in manufacturing fertilizer, particularly the phosphates found in fertilizers. It is a strong acid, but it is not volatile. It has a high affinity for water and can be used as a drying agent.

DISCUSSION STRATEGY

Before introducing the states of matter, invite students to discuss their own ideas about the properties of solids, liquids, and gases. For example, ask them what they would say to a person who wanted to know the differences in the states of matter. This activity will help reveal students' misconceptions about matter. Students should then read page 7 to see if their ideas match the descriptions found there.

VISUAL STRATEGY

Figure 1-3 Ask students how the models depicted in the circles help explain the different states of matter. If students express concern about the open appearance of the solid model, remind them that water is one of the few substances that expands when it freezes. In nearly any other substance, the particles would be as close together as they are in the liquid state.

CHEMISTRY INTERACTIVE TUTOR

Module 1: States of Matter
Topic: Defining the States and Classes of Matter
This engaging tutorial reviews the states and classes of matter through modeling and guided practice.

	Top Five Chemicals in the United States (production by weight)		
TABLE 1-2			
Rank	Name	Formula	Uses
1	sulfuric acid	H_2SO_4	production of fertilizer, metal processing, petroleum refining
2	nitrogen	N_2	packaging food, production of fertilizers
3	oxygen	O_2	rocket propellant, production of steel
4	ethene	C_2H_4	production of plastics
5	calcium oxide (lime)	CaO	production of glass and cement

Source: *Chemical and Engineering News*

Solids, liquids, and gases are physical states of matter

All matter is made of particles. The type and arrangement of the particles in a sample of matter determine its properties. A basic property of matter is its **physical state.** Most matter you observe is in one of three physical states: solid, liquid, or gas.

Figure 1-3 illustrates the solid, liquid, and gaseous states of water at the microscopic level. In this text *microscopic* refers to objects that are about the size of atoms. Contrast *microscopic* with *macroscopic,* which refers to objects large enough to be seen with the unaided eye.

physical state
the form matter takes as a result of the arrangement of its particles

▼ **FIGURE 1-3**

a Between 0°C and 100°C, water exists mostly as a liquid. In the liquid state, water particles are close together and can move about freely.

b At 0°C, water exists as ice. In the solid state, water molecules are in a rigid structure.

c At 100°C, water becomes a gas. Water molecules can move randomly over large distances.

DEMONSTRATION 2

Evidence of Chemical Change I

Approximate time: 10 minutes

This demonstration shows the reactivity of marble ($CaCO_3$, calcium carbonate) with acid.

1. Place a few small marble chips in a Petri dish on an overhead projector.

2. Add enough 5% vinegar to cover the chips.

3. Note the evidence of chemical change. What chemical property of marble is demonstrated?

Safety
Wear safety goggles and a lab apron. Students should stand back 10 ft.

Disposal
Wearing safety goggles and a lab apron, decant the mixture, rinse the residue with tap water, decant the rinse water, and repeat the rinse. Pour the rinse water down the drain.

Solids have fixed volume and shape. These properties result from the way solids are structured on the microscopic level. When matter is in the solid state, the particles that make up the matter are held tightly in a rigid structure. These particles are able to vibrate only slightly.

Liquids have fixed volume but variable shape. The particles in a liquid are not held together as rigidly as those in a solid. Like grains of sand, the particles of a liquid can slip past one another. Thus, a liquid as a whole is able to flow and take the shape of its container. But as with a solid, the particles of a liquid are held close to one another, and the adjacent particles are in contact most of the time. As a result, the overall volume of the liquid is constant.

Gases have neither fixed shape nor fixed volume, and they expand to fill any container they occupy. Even a few grams of a gas would become evenly distributed in a large room. This is because gas particles are not strongly attracted to one another. Instead, they are free to move about independently. The average distance between gas particles is always much greater than the average distance between particles in liquids or in solids.

Chemical reactions describe how matter behaves

You know from previous science courses that compounds, such as water, H_2O, and the sugar glucose, $C_6H_{12}O_6$, are made by **chemical reactions.** Acetylsalicylic acid, the active ingredient in aspirin, is also made by a chemical reaction. To produce acetylsalicylic acid in a laboratory, salicylic acid is mixed with a chemical called acetic anhydride and the mixture is heated. These two chemicals react to form acetylsalicylic acid in a reaction described by the following word equation.

salicylic acid + acetic anhydride $\longrightarrow$ acetylsalicylic acid + acetic acid

Salicylic acid and acetic anhydride, the starting materials in this reaction, are called **reactants.** Acetylsalicylic acid and acetic acid are called **products.** The arrow in the chemical equation separates the reactants from products and also indicates in which direction the reaction usually proceeds—from left to right. The equation above indicates that the two reactants form two new products.

Not all reactions involve reactants that combine. **Figure 1-4** shows a reaction that involves a single reactant breaking apart to form two or more products. This type of reaction is a decomposition. During the reaction, mercury(II) oxide decomposes to

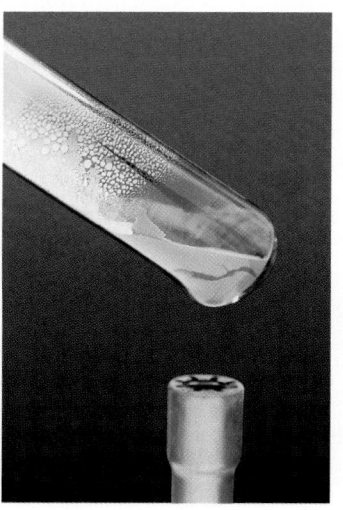

Nature of Reactions   Lead students to realize that chemical reactions are activities that take place everywhere, not just in glass containers in laboratories. Practically all life processes are chemical reactions.

Any reaction used to generate heat is exothermic. Light a burner or a candle, and ask students whether the reaction is exothermic or endothermic. Ask students where they think the energy comes from. (The energy comes from the breaking of chemical bonds, but students should not be expected to know that.) Accept any response that does not reflect a misconception. Most endothermic processes can be compared to cooking, where the continuous addition of heat cooks the food.

chemical reaction

the process by which elements and/or compounds interact with one another to form new substances

reactant

a chemical that is present at the beginning of a chemical reaction and that takes part in the reaction

product

a chemical produced as a result of a chemical reaction

FIGURE 1-4

The chemical reaction in which mercury(II) oxide decomposes to form mercury and oxygen requires energy. The energy is supplied by the burner.

THE SCIENCE OF CHEMISTRY   7

RESOURCE LINK

ChemFile Lab B
Microscale Lab
Have students do Experiment B1:
Laboratory Procedures.

Save the solid residue, wrap it in newspaper, and put it in the trash.

a The formation of silver chloride is an exothermic reaction because energy is released. The temperature of the matter in the beaker rises when the precipitate forms.

b The reaction of hydrated barium hydroxide and ammonium nitrate absorbs energy. The temperature of the matter in the flask drops as the product forms.

form mercury and oxygen gas. The word equation for this reaction is written as follows.

mercury(II) oxide → mercury + oxygen

Notice in Figure 1-4 that a burner is used to heat the mercury (II) oxide in the test tube. The burner supplies energy. Many reactions require some energy input for the reaction to begin. The energy needed to start a reaction is called *activation energy*. If there is insufficient energy present in the reactants as room temperature, heat, light, or some other source of energy must be used to supply activation energy.

There are two types of reactions, those that release energy overall and those that absorb energy overall. You can easily recognize a reaction that releases energy; light is given off or the temperature of the reaction system increases. If you add silver nitrate to hydrochloric acid, a precipitate like the one shown in **Figure 1-5a** forms. The beaker also feels warmer, indicating that the reaction releases energy. A reaction that releases energy is called an **exothermic reaction** (the prefix *exo-* means "outside").

Figure 1-5b shows what happens when you mix hydrated barium hydroxide with ammonium nitrate and shake the mixture. A reaction takes place because the two solids now form a liquid slush-like product. The reaction flask feels colder, indicating that this reaction absorbs energy. Reactions that absorb energy are called **endothermic reactions** (the prefix *endo-* means "within").

exothermic reaction

a reaction in which energy is released

endothermic reaction

a reaction in which energy is absorbed

8 CHAPTER 1

DEMONSTRATION 3

Evidence of Chemical Change II
Approximate time: 15 minutes

1. Sand and/or polish a large (30 cm × 30 cm) sheet of copper foil.

2. Hold the foil at a 45° angle over a Bunsen burner flame.

3. Have students note evidence of chemical change. What is the dark stain? *(copper(II) oxide)* What are the reactants in this reaction? *(copper and oxygen)*

Safety
Wear safety goggles and a lab apron.
Tie back loose hair and clothing.

Disposal
Save the foil for reuse at a later time. Sweep up any flakes of copper oxide, and put them in the trash.

CONSUMER FOCUS

ASPIRIN

The FDA and the safe use of aspirin

The FDA requires that every container of aspirin—the most widely used over-the-counter drug—have a warning label. This label warns not to give aspirin to children and adolescents with chickenpox or a severe case of flu. Some studies have shown that aspirin may cause liver malfunction and swelling of the brain, a condition known as Reye syndrome.

The label also warns that aspirin can cause side effects, such as nausea and vomiting, and can interfere with the clotting of blood. Aspirin should not be taken by pregnant women, hemophiliacs, or anyone who has recently had a tonsillectomy or oral surgery. Some people may also be allergic to aspirin.

internet connect

TOPIC: Aspirin
GO TO: www.scilinks.org
KEYWORD: HW012

Product warning labels

When you purchase a product, it is your responsibility as a consumer to check the warning label carefully for any warnings about the chemicals it contains.

WARNINGS: Children and teenagers should not use this medicine for chicken pox or flu symptoms before a doctor is consulted about Reye syndrome, a rare but serious illness reported to be associated with aspirin. As with any drug, if you are pregnant or nursing a baby, see the advice of a health professional before using this product. **IT IS ESPECIALLY IMPORTANT NOT TO USE ASPIRIN DURING THE LAST 3 MONTHS OF PREGNANCY UNLESS SPECIFICALLY DIRECTED TO DO SO BY A DOCTOR BECAUSE IT MAY CAUSE PROBLEMS IN THE UNBORN CHILD OR COMPLICATIONS DURING DELIVERY.** Keep this and all medicines out of the reach of children. In the case of accidental overdose, see professional assistance or contact a poison control center immediately.

SECTION REVIEW

Total recall

1. What are the common physical states of matter?

2. How do the particle models for the states of matter differ?

3. What is the difference between an endothermic reaction and an exothermic reaction?

4. In what ways do the three fundamental states of matter differ?

Critical thinking

5. During photosynthesis, light energy is captured by plants to make sugar from carbon dioxide and water. In the process, oxygen is also produced. Write the word equation for photosynthesis.

6. What observation indicates that a reaction is exothermic?

7. Draw a picture to show what happens to atoms when a piece of lead is heated until it melts (turns from a solid to a liquid).

ANSWERS

SECTION REVIEW

Total recall

1. The common physical states of matter are solid, liquid, and gas.

2. The particles of solids are closely-packed, and held rigidly in their positions. Liquid particles are close together, but free to move around each other. Gas particles are separated by empty space and move freely within their available volume.

3. An endothermic reaction absorbs energy. An exothermic reaction releases energy.

4. Solids have a fixed volume and shape. Liquids have a fixed volume but can flow and take the shape of the container. Gases have no fixed shape or volume. Gases flow and occupy all of the volume of any container they are in.

Critical thinking

5. carbon dioxide + water + energy ⟶ sugar + oxygen

6. The temperature of the reaction system increases when the reaction is exothermic.

7. Student drawings should show lead atoms in a regular geometrical pattern and very closely spaced to represent a solid. In the drawing of a liquid, particles should still be closely spaced but in a random, jumbled arrangement.

SECTION 1-2

What is matter?

OBJECTIVES	
▶ **Relate** mass, volume, and density.	▶ **Convert** measurements between SI units.
▶ **Distinguish** between qualitative and quantitative properties.	▶ **Distinguish** between physical and chemical properties.
▶ **Describe** the difference between a quantity and a unit.	▶ **List** four ways to determine if a chemical change has occurred.

LESSON WARM-UP

Write the following words on the board:

    peanut butter
    water
    fish
    light
    garbage
    time
    motion
    the human brain
    carbon dioxide
    air
    yourself
    an idea
    tree
    energy

Ask students to sort the words into three categories.

1. matter
2. not matter
3. not sure

Discuss responses. (Note that energy is not matter, although mass can be converted to energy.) Point out that all material things are matter. Finally, ask students why a clear definition of matter is important for studying chemistry.

CNN Science in the News
PRESENTS **Feature story 3**
Chemicals in the Home. See the Science in the News video guide for more details.

Matter has mass and volume

Matter, the stuff all things in the universe are composed of, exists in a dazzling variety of forms. Chemistry is an ongoing investigation into the nature of matter. **Matter** is anything that has mass and volume. Even the air you breathe is matter. Consider what happens when you blow up a balloon. When inflated, a balloon has more mass and greater volume than it does when it is deflated. The increase in the mass and volume of the balloon comes from the mass and volume of air that you blew into the balloon.

matter

anything that has mass and volume

volume

the space an object occupies

The space an object occupies is its volume

An object's **volume** is the space the object occupies. For example, this book has volume because it takes up space. Volume can be determined in several different ways, depending on the nature of the matter being examined. The *graduated cylinder* is commonly used to determine the volume of a liquid in the lab. The volume of a liquid must be read the same way every time, as shown in **Figure 1-6.** Can you see why? Volumes of solids are generally expressed in cubic units based on length, width, and height.

▼ **FIGURE 1-6**

To read the liquid level in a graduated cylinder correctly, read the level at the bottom of the meniscus. The volume shown is 50 mL.

RESOURCE LINK

IN-TEXT LAB

Skills Development
Have students do Exploration 1A, on page 702, to develop their skills using laboratory techniques.

Mass is not weight

The **mass** of an object is the quantity of matter in that object. Scientists measure mass using a balance. A type of electronic balance often used in industrial-chemistry laboratories is shown in **Figure 1-7**. This balance gives a quick, digital readout of mass.

Balances differ based on the *accuracy* of the mass reading you can obtain. The balance often found in a school chemistry laboratory is the triple-beam balance. This balance can be used for measurements of less than 300 g. If the smallest scale on the triple-beam balance is graduated in 0.1 g increments, you can obtain mass readings that are estimated to the hundredth place. You can get a reading to a greater number of decimal places by using a more accurate analytical balance than by using a simple triple-beam balance.

Mass is related but not identical to weight. Recall that mass reflects the amount of matter in an object. As long as an object remains intact, it will have the same mass—no matter where in the universe it is. Thus, the mass of an object is constant.

The weight of an object depends on where it is. This is because weight depends on gravity, while mass does not. **Weight** is defined as the force produced by gravity acting on mass. Scientists measure force in *newtons.* Because gravity can vary from one location to another, the weight of an object can vary. For example, an astronaut weighs about six times more on Earth than on the moon because the effect of gravity is less on the moon. The astronaut's mass, however, remains constant.

Keep in mind the difference between mass and weight as you conduct laboratory activities that call for the use of a balance. Determining the weight of an object is not the same as determining its mass. Although the term *weigh* is not literally equivalent to "determine the mass of," these expressions are often interchanged. In chemistry, when you read the word *weigh* in a laboratory procedure, you probably will be required to record the mass. Check with your teacher to be sure.

FIGURE 1-7

A balance is an instrument that measures mass.

mass
the quantity of matter in an object

weight
the force produced by gravity acting on mass

CONCEPT CHECK

1. What two properties are characteristic of matter?
2. What is the difference between mass and weight?
3. What units are used to express mass and weight?

THE SCIENCE OF CHEMISTRY **11**

💡 DID YOU KNOW?

In practice, most mechanical balances depend on the presence of a gravitational field because the force exerted by an object is compared with the force exerted by standard masses placed on another pan or moved to positions on a beam.

DISCUSSION STRATEGY

For students who don't grasp the distinction between mass and weight, try this thought problem. Suppose a bowling ball and a tennis ball hang from the ceiling on strings. Would you be willing to hit both with your fist at full force? Most students realize that you would probably fracture your hand by striking the bowling ball. Now suppose you take these two objects into Earth orbit, where both would appear weightless. Now would you hit both balls with your fist? Most students will sense that it would still be unsafe to hit the bowling ball. Even though the bowling ball appears weightless, they will sense that it is still "heavy" in some way. Inform students that they are sensing the ball's mass, not its weight.

ANSWERS

CONCEPT CHECK

1. Matter has mass and volume.

2. An object's mass is the amount of matter in the object. Its weight is the force exerted by that amount of matter in a gravitational field.

3. Mass is expressed in grams. Weight is expressed in units of force, such as newtons or pounds.

RESOURCE LINK

IN-TEXT LAB
Self-Directed Inquiry
Have students do Investigation 1A: *Conservation of Mass—Percentage of Water in Popcorn*, on page 706, to design an experiment for the concept of matter.

SI Unit Review Students' familiarity with SI units will depend on what they were taught in previous courses. You may want to check their understanding of the metric system before proceeding. Having a firm idea of the size of a gram, a meter, and a liter is probably more important here than an ability to manipulate quantities mathematically. A table comparing metric units with everyday objects is provided at the bottom of this page.

DISCUSSION STRATEGY

Ask students to list quantities with which they are familiar. Then ask what units would commonly be used to measure the quantities they list. Unless students are accustomed to metric measurement, they are likely to list some of the following:

length or distance: inches, feet, yards, miles
weight: pounds, ounces, tons
volume: gallons, cups, teaspoons, tablespoons, fluid ounces
time: days, years, hours, minutes, seconds
temperature: degrees Fahrenheit
electric current: amperes
potential difference: volts
heat: British thermal units (BTU)

▲ **FIGURE 1-8**

A measurement instrument like this graduated cylinder gives us quantitative descriptions of the volume of a liquid. The scale on the cylinder is an agreed upon standard.

quantity

something that has magnitude or size

unit

a standard used when measuring a quantity

internetconnect

SCiLINKS
NSTA
TOPIC: SI units
GO TO: www.scilinks.org
KEYWORD: HW013

Units of measurement

Terms such as *light, heavy, large,* and *small* are *qualitative* descriptions of matter. Some properties of matter, such as color and texture, are best described in qualitative terms.

Many properties of matter, including mass and volume, are best described in *quantitative* terms. Quantitative terms include numbers, which make descriptions more exact. But numbers alone are not sufficient because the significance of numbers alone is unclear. Standard units are needed along with numbers for more accurate descriptions. For example, 15 grams of sugar is a more accurate description than a spoonful of sugar. Measurement instruments, like the one shown in **Figure 1-8,** are used to quantify descriptions.

When working with quantitative terms, be sure to distinguish between a quantity and a unit. A **quantity** is something that has magnitude or size. Volume, mass, and distance are quantities. A **unit** is the standard used to measure a quantity. For example, you can measure the *quantity* mass with the *unit* kilogram. What quantity can be measured in meters?

Scientists express measurements in SI units

In 1960, the scientific community adopted a subset of the metric system as the standard system of measurement units. This is the Système Internationale d'Unités (SI); it features the seven base units listed in **Table 1-3.** The five you will use extensively in chemistry are meter, kilogram, second, kelvin, and mole.

SI base units can be modified with the prefixes listed in **Table 1-4** to match the scale of the object being measured. For example, the base unit for length, meter, is suitable for expressing a person's height, but distances between cities should be measured in *kilo*meters.

TABLE 1-3 SI Base Units

Quantity	Symbol	Unit	Abbreviation
Length	l	meter	m
Mass	m	kilogram	kg
Time	t	second	s
Thermodynamic temperature	T	kelvin	K
Amount of substance	n	mole	mol
Electric current	I	ampere	A
Luminous intensity	I_v	candela	cd

GRAPHIC ORGANIZER

Useful Metric Estimates

Measurement	Rough equivalent
1 m	a little more than a yard
1 cm	the diameter of a small shirt button
1 mm	slightly less than the thickness of a dime or penny (10 pennies ≈ 13 mm)
1 kg	a little more than the mass of a quart of water
1 g	the mass of 3 small shirt buttons
5 g	the mass of a nickel
5 mL	one teaspoonful
250 mL	one cupful

TABLE 1-4 SI Prefixes

Prefix	Unit abbreviation	Exponential multiplier	Meaning	Example using length
Giga-	G	10^9	1 000 000 000	1 gigameter (Gm) = 1×10^9 m
Mega-	M	10^6	1 000 000	1 megameter (Mm) = 1×10^6 m
Kilo-	k	10^3	1000	1 kilometer (km) = 1000 m
Hecto-	h	10^2	100	1 hectometer (hm) = 100 m
		10^0	1	**1 meter (m)**
Deci-	d	10^{-1}	1/10	1 decimeter (dm) = 0.1 m
Centi-	c	10^{-2}	1/100	1 centimeter (cm) = 0.01 m
Milli-	m	10^{-3}	1/1000	1 millimeter (mm) = 0.001 m
Micro-	μ	10^{-6}	1/1 000 000	1 micrometer (μm) = 1×10^{-6} m
Nano-	n	10^{-9}	1/1 000 000 000	1 nanometer (nm) = 1×10^{-9} m
Pico-	p	10^{-12}	1/1 000 000 000 000	1 picometer (pm) = 1×10^{-12} m
Femto-	f	10^{-15}	1/1 000 000 000 000 000	1 femtometer (fm) = 1×10^{-15} m

Conversion factors enable you to convert from one unit to another

Situations often arise in chemistry that require you to convert measurements from one unit to another. A **conversion factor** is a mathematical expression that relates two units that measure the same quantity. Conversion factors are based on statements of equality. For example, to convert a mass expressed in kilograms to grams, you need the equality that relates grams and kilograms.

$$1 \text{ kg} = 1000 \text{ g} \quad \text{or} \quad 1 \text{ g} = 0.001 \text{ kg}$$

These equalities can be written as the following conversion factors.

$$1 \text{ kg} = 1000 \text{ g} \text{ can be written as } \frac{1000 \text{ g}}{1 \text{ kg}} \quad \text{or} \quad \frac{1 \text{ kg}}{1000 \text{ g}}$$

$$1 \text{ g} = 0.001 \text{ kg} \text{ can be written as } \frac{1 \text{ g}}{0.001 \text{ kg}} \quad \text{or} \quad \frac{0.001 \text{ kg}}{1 \text{ g}}$$

How do you use conversion factors? Just multiply the original measurement by the appropriate conversion factor to convert the measurement to the desired unit. To convert 1.5 kg to grams, you need a factor that will allow you to cancel out kilograms, but will give grams in the final answer. The calculation looks like the following.

$$1.5 \text{ kg} \times \frac{1000 \text{ g}}{1 \text{ kg}} = 1500 \text{ g}$$

conversion factor

a mathematical expression that relates two units

DID YOU KNOW?

A light-year is about 10 000 000 Gm. The diameter of a hydrogen atom is about 100 pm. An average atomic nucleus is about 0.01 pm in diameter.

TEACHING TIP

Unit Cancellation and Conversions Use the equation at the bottom of this page to point out that an appropriate conversion factor will always have the unit being converted *to* on the top and the unit being converted *from* on the bottom of the fraction. That way, the units being converted *from* are sure to cancel out of the expression through division.

RESOURCE LINK

ChemFile Teaching Resources CD-ROM
Skills Review
Assign Basic Skills Worksheets 1 and 5: *Using Your Calculator* and *SI Conversions* to review or reteach these skills.

HOW TO

ADDITIONAL EXAMPLES

Using conversion factors

a. Convert 2500 mL to liters.

Ans. 2.5 L

b. A car travels 845 km. How many meters is this?

Ans. 845 000 m

c. Convert 0.0290 m to millimeters.

Ans. 29.0 mm

d. How many seconds pass in 3.11 h?

Ans. 11 200 s

TEACHING TIP

Designing a Model Construct a cubic meter framework from 12 meter-sticks or from 1 in. × 2 in. furring strips cut so that they can be assembled into a cube 1 m on a side. Students are likely to be surprised at its large size. A cubic meter of water has a mass of 1000 kg, more than 1 ton in weight.

RESOURCE LINK

ChemFile Mini-Guide to Problem Solving
Assign Chapter 1: *Conversions* for additional practice.

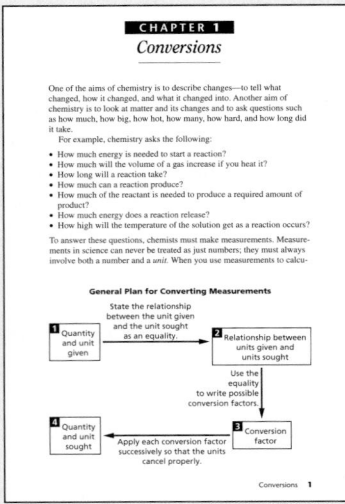

What is the mass, in kilograms, of a 22 000 g bag of fertilizer?

1 **Write the equality that relates the units given in the problem**

Use Table 1-5 for data. The equality for grams and kilograms is the following.

$$1000 \text{ g} = 1 \text{ kg}$$

2 **Write the conversion factor that is the bridge between the units you have and the units you want in the answer**

The conversion factor must have grams in the denominator to give an answer of kilograms.

$$\frac{1 \text{ kg}}{1000 \text{ g}}$$

3 **Set up the problem and solve**

Cancel units that divide out.

$$22\,000 \text{ g} \times \frac{1 \text{ kg}}{1000 \text{ g}} = 22 \text{ kg}$$

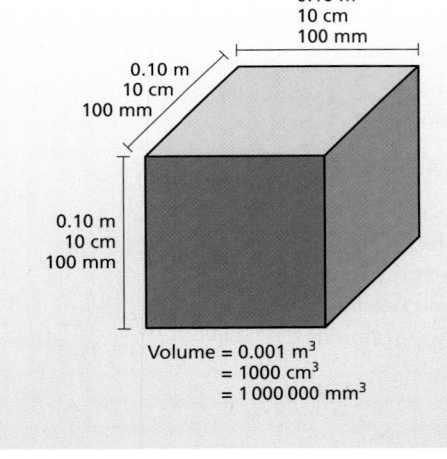

▼ FIGURE 1-9

Units for the volume of a cube are derived from three length measurements.

0.10 m
10 cm
100 mm

0.10 m
10 cm
100 mm

0.10 m
10 cm
100 mm

Volume = 0.001 m³
= 1000 cm³
= 1 000 000 mm³

Derived units can be obtained for any quantity

SI base units cannot be used to measure every observable quantity, so *derived units* must also be used. Derived units are created from combinations of the seven base units. One derived unit for volume, for example, is cubic meters, m^3. This derived unit can be obtained by multiplying the length, width, and height of an object, which are measurements expressed in meters.

$$\text{volume} = l \times w \times h$$
$$\text{m} \times \text{m} \times \text{m} = \text{m}^3$$

The cube shown in **Figure 1-9,** has a length, width, and height of 10 cm each. Each of these dimensions has equivalent values in meters and millimeters. The volume of the cube in cubic centimeters is calculated as follows.

$$10 \text{ cm} \times 10 \text{ cm} \times 10 \text{ cm} = 1000 \text{ cm}^3$$
$$\text{or } 0.001 \text{ m}^3 \text{ or } 1\,000\,000 \text{ mm}^3$$

This volume—1000 cm^3, or 0.001 m^3 or 1 000 000 mm^3—is 1 liter (1 L), which is a favorite unit of chemists. The liter and the milliliter, mL, are widely used in scientific work even though the cubic meter is the SI unit for volume. The prefix *milli-* tells you that there are 1000 mL in 1L.

ALTERNATIVE ASSESSMENT

Group Strategy

Have students use the library and the Internet to learn about the origin of the metric system in Napoleonic France. They should include information on accepted metric units and the original standards for those units. They should also report on ideas for other metric units that were never accepted, such as metric units of time.

CONCEPT CHECK

1. What are the five SI base units you will use in this chemistry course?

2. What is a conversion factor?

3. How does a quantity differ from a unit?

4. Write the equalities needed to make the following conversions:
   a. milliliters to liters
   c. kilometers to centimeters
   b. grams to micrograms
   d. milligrams to grams

5. Write conversion factors for each equality in item 4.

6. Convert the following:
   a. 50 mL to ? cm^3
   c. 25 mg to ? g
   b. 750 mL to ? L
   d. 3×10^5 cm to ? m

Properties of matter

The relationship between two properties can be represented by graphing. The masses and volumes of a set of aluminum blocks are listed in **Figure 1-10.** These values are plotted on the graph shown below. What do you notice about the line connecting these points?

The straight line rising from left to right indicates that mass increases at a constant rate as volume increases. As the volume of aluminum doubles, its mass doubles; as its volume triples, its mass triples; and so on. In other words, the mass of aluminum is directly proportional to its volume.

The slope of the line equals the ratio of mass, the value obtained from the vertical y-axis, divided by volume, the value obtained from the

FIGURE 1-10 ▼

The graph of mass versus volume shows a relationship of direct proportionality. Notice that the line has been extended to pass through the origin.

Mass and Volume Data for Samples of Aluminum

Block number	Mass (g)	Volume (cm³)
1	1.20	0.443
2	3.59	1.33
3	5.72	2.12
4	12.4	4.60
5	15.3	5.66
6	19.4	7.17
7	22.7	8.41
8	24.1	8.94
9	34.0	12.6
10	36.4	13.5

ANSWERS

CONCEPT CHECK

1. The five SI base units used in this course are meter, kilogram, second, kelvin, and mole.

2. A conversion factor is a factor that relates two different units used to measure the same quantity.

3. A quantity is a measurable property, such as length, mass, time, and temperature. A unit is a standard used to measure a quantity. Examples include meter, kilogram, second, and kelvin.

4. **a.** 1 L = 1000 mL
   b. $1 g = 10^6 \mu g$
   c. 1 km = 1000 m; 1 m = 100 cm; or 1 km = 100 000 cm
   d. 1 g = 1000 mg

5. **a.** for mL to L, $\dfrac{1 \text{ L}}{1000 \text{ mL}}$

   b. for g to μg, $\dfrac{10^6 \text{ μg}}{1 \text{ g}}$

   c. for km to cm, $\dfrac{1000 \text{ m}}{1 \text{ km}}$ and $\dfrac{100 \text{ cm}}{1 \text{ m}}$; or $\dfrac{100\,000 \text{ cm}}{1 \text{ km}}$

   d. for mg to g, $\dfrac{1 \text{ g}}{1000 \text{ mg}}$

6. **a.** 50 cm^3
   b. 0.75 L
   c. 0.025 g
   d. 3000 m

VISUAL STRATEGY

Figure 1-10 Assure students that this illustration is just a graph of the obvious. As you add quantities of a substance to the pan of a balance, thereby increasing the volume of the substance, the mass of the substance increases proportionally. The mass increases by a factor equal to the density of the substance.

DID YOU KNOW?

A football made of osmium would probably weigh over 200 lb. The density of osmium is 22.48 g/cm³. 1000 cm³ (1 L) of osmium would have a mass of 22.48 kg (about 50 lb). The same quantity of water has a mass of 1 kg, or 2.2 lb.

COMMON MISCONCEPTION

Students often imagine that differences in density among pure substances are due to intermolecular spacing. This happens because they can see that differences in density among common materials are often caused by the presence of air spaces or gas bubbles, such as in cork or plastic foam. For students to really understand the differences in density among pure substances, they must compare them in pure form and equal volumes, such as in cubes of solid lead, copper, iron, and aluminum. You can show students three identical 500 mL polyethylene bottles, one filled with hexane (density: 0.66 g/mL) or some other light-density, petroleum-based solvent; another filled with 95% ethanol (density: 0.81 g/mL); and the third filled with water (density: 1.00 g/mL). Students see three bottles of clear liquid, but when they lift the bottles, they can readily detect the density differences and see that those differences cannot be explained by air spaces. The bottles should have secure screw caps that are taped so that they cannot be opened.

horizontal x-axis. You may remember this as "rise over run" from math class. Slope is mathematically stated as follows.

$$\text{slope} = \frac{y_2 - y_1}{x_2 - x_1}$$

In this equation, x_1 and y_1 represent one ordered pair of values on the graph, and x_2 and y_2 represent another ordered pair.

Note that the slope of the graph shown in Figure 1-10 is constant. At any point on the line, if you divide the mass value by the corresponding volume value, you will get the value 2.70. This constant value showing the relationship between mass and volume has a special name—density. **Density** is the ratio of mass to volume.

density

the ratio of mass to volume

$$\text{density} = \frac{\text{mass}}{\text{volume}}, \quad \text{or} \quad D = \frac{m}{V}$$

Density is usually expressed in grams per cubic centimeter, g/cm³. **Table 1-5** lists the densities of various substances. As you saw in the previous example, the density of aluminum is 2.70 g/cm³. Osmium, a bluish white metal, is the densest substance on Earth. A piece of osmium the size of a football would be too heavy to lift.

Density can be used to identify substances

Because the density of a given substance is the same for all samples, density can be used to identify matter. For example, suppose you find

▼ **FIGURE 1-11**

Substances float in layers, and the order of the layers is determined by their densities. Dyes have been added to make the liquid layers more visible.

Cork
Ethanol
Paraffin
Oil
Water
Rubber
Glycerol

Increasing density

TABLE 1-5	Densities of Various Substances
Substance	**Density (g/cm³) at 25°C**
Hydrogen gas*	0.000 824
Carbon dioxide gas*	0.001 80
Ethanol (ethyl alcohol)	0.789
Water	0.997
Sucrose (table sugar)	1.587
Sodium chloride	2.164
Aluminum	2.699
Iron	7.86
Copper	8.94
Silver	10.5
Gold	19.3
Osmium	22.6

*at 1 atm

DEMONSTRATION 4

Mass, Volume, and Density

Approximate time: 15 minutes

This demonstration should motivate students to question their prior concepts of matter, mass, and volume.

1. Obtain several 100 g brass masses and several large pieces of Styrofoam that have been cut down to have a mass of 100 g.

2. Call students forward to compare each brass mass with a piece of Styrofoam.

Have students hold one in each hand. Ask them how the two objects compare in volume, how the objects compare in terms of mass, and what is apparent about the relative densities of the two materials.

3. Tell students to keep this demonstration in mind as they read pages 15–17.

a bracelet on the street that appears to be silver. To find out if it is pure silver, you can take the bracelet into the lab and measure its mass using a balance. Next you can measure its volume by measuring the volume of water the bracelet displaces. If the mass is 199.0 g and the volume is 20.5 cm^3, you can calculate the density of the bracelet.

$$D = \frac{m}{V}$$

$$= \frac{199.0 \text{ g}}{20.5 \text{ cm}^3} = 9.71 \text{ g/cm}^3$$

Because the density of silver is 10.5 g/cm^3, you can then deduce that the bracelet you found is not pure silver.

Density is a physical property of matter

To determine the density of the metal in a bracelet, you do not have to change any of the metal's characteristics or properties. Any property of matter that can be measured without changing its chemical nature is known as a **physical property.** You recognize your friends and family members by their physical properties, such as height, hair color, and the sound of a voice.

Quantities such as mass, volume, and density are physical properties of matter. Other physical properties of matter include color, texture, melting point, and boiling point. Keep in mind that matter can even be described in terms of the absence of a physical property. For example, a physical property of air is that it is colorless.

Matter can undergo **physical changes.** A physical change affects only physical properties of matter; chemical properties are not affected. For example, when you melt ice to get water, you still have the substance H_2O. When you boil water to get steam, it's still H_2O. Only the physical state of the substance has changed.

Physical changes can involve changes in energy. Melting and boiling are examples of endothermic changes because energy in the form of heat is transferred to the substance from its surroundings. Freezing and condensation are also physical changes. But in contrast to melting and boiling, freezing and condensation are examples of exothermic changes because heat energy is transferred from the substance to its surroundings.

physical property

any property of matter that can be measured without changing its chemical nature

physical change

a change that affects only physical properties

QUICKLAB

Thickness of Aluminum Foil

Using the density of aluminum, you can determine the thickness of a piece of aluminum foil. You will need to design a procedure that will give you the data you need to determine thickness.

Materials   aluminum foil, balances, metric ruler, calculator, scissors

Problem   There are two brands of aluminum foil in the front of the classroom. Your job is to use the known density of aluminum (see Table 1-5 on page 16) to calculate the thickness of a sample from each of these two different brands of aluminum foil.

Analysis   Your report should include your experimental procedure, a data table with all of your measurements and the thicknesses of each brand of aluminum foil.

Safety
No particular precautions are required.

Disposal
Save materials for reuse at a later time.

QUICKLAB

Students should cut a square or rectangle of aluminum foil so that it is easy to measure the area. They should fold or wad the aluminum before weighing it so that breezes do not affect the balance reading. Balances sensitive to 0.001 g will give good results. Less-sensitive balances will require larger sheets of foil. To calculate thickness, students employ the following two relationships:

$$D = m/V \text{ and } V = l \times w \times h$$

Substituting the expression for the volume of a rectangular solid yields the following:

$$D = \frac{m}{l \times w \times h}.$$

Solving for h (thickness) yields the following:

$$h = \frac{m}{D \times w \times h}.$$

Thickness will be near 0.0017 cm.

Analysis
Students should report two or three trials.

READING STRATEGY

Peer Teaching   Have each student read the remainder of this section on physical and chemical properties and physical and chemical changes. Divide the class into pairs. Each student should point to an object and ask their partner to describe some of its physical properties as well as some physical changes that might happen to the object. Next, each pair of students should take turns asking each other to point out or name three materials that undergo chemical changes. Finally, students should evaluate their choices together to see if they meet the criteria for physical and chemical changes.

COMMON MISCONCEPTION

Students may develop the idea that physical and chemical changes are mutually exclusive and that every observable change is easily classified as one or the other. In fact it is not always easy to separate and classify changes. Many chemical changes also involve physical changes. An example is the change of liquid water to a vapor because of the heat released in a chemical change. You can illustrate this problem by performing Demonstration 3 on a larger scale in a 400 mL beaker and pouring seltzer or sparkling water into an identical beaker alongside the demonstration beaker. The gases evolved are identical (CO_2), but one is the result of a chemical change, whereas the other results from a physical change—CO_2 coming out of water solution.

chemical property

a property of matter that can be observed only when substances interact with one another

chemical change

a change that produces one or more new substances

Matter also has chemical properties

Matter cannot be fully described by physical properties alone. Left out of the description is how matter will behave when it is in contact with other types of matter. To describe this type of behavior, **chemical properties** of matter must be considered. Chemical properties are often observed when matter reacts.

You learned earlier that a word equation can be used to describe this reaction. The reaction between hydrogen and oxygen results in a new substance—water. Whenever one or more substances are changed into new substances, a **chemical change** occurs.

The reaction on page 7 shows mercury(II) oxide decomposing. **Figure 1-12** shows the same reaction along with a comparison of the physical and chemical properties of the substances involved. As you look at this diagram, think about the definition of a chemical reaction. You can see from comparing the properties that the products of the chemical reaction have distinctly different chemical and physical properties from the reactants. Many of the physical and chemical properties of substances can be found in chemical reference handbooks.

All chemical changes are accompanied by changes in energy. Therefore, all chemical changes can be classified as either endothermic or exothermic processes. **Figure 1-13** shows some common types of chemical changes. Evidence that a chemical change has occurred is easily observed and generally fits one of the following categories.

1. **The evolution of a gas.** The production of a gas is often observed by bubbling, as shown in Figure 1-13a, or by the emission of an odor.
2. **The formation of a precipitate.** A precipitate is an insoluble solid formed from a solution, such as that shown in Figure 1-13b.
3. **The evolution or absorption of heat.** An increase in temperature of a reaction system signifies an exothermic chemical change. Similarly, a lower temperature indicates an endothermic reaction.

▼ **FIGURE 1-12**

The physical and chemical properties of the components of this reaction system are shown. Decomposition of mercury (II) oxide is a chemical change.

MERCURY
Physical properties: Silver-white, liquid metal; in the solid state, mercury is ductile and malleable and can be cut with a knife
Chemical properties: Combines readily with sulfur at normal temperatures; reacts with nitric acid and hot sulfuric acid; oxidizes to form mercury(II) oxide upon heating in air

OXYGEN
Physical properties: Colorless, odorless gas
Chemical properties: Supports combustion; soluble in water

MERCURY(II) OXIDE
Physical properties: Bright red or orange-red, odorless crystalline solid
Chemical properties: Decomposes when exposed to light or at 500°C to form mercury and oxygen gas; dissolves in dilute nitric acid or hydrochloric acid, but is almost insoluble in water

ALTERNATIVE ASSESSMENT

Group Strategy

Ask students to evaluate the following four examples and decide whether the process is primarily a physical change or a chemical change. Students may not be able to give definitive answers, but their responses should provide evidence that they are thinking about pertinent factors in each change.

▶ Baking soda gives up CO_2 and H_2O when heated strongly (*chemical*).

▶ Melting antimony and tin together produces pewter (*physical*).

▶ Rubbing alcohol cools your skin as it evaporates (*physical*).

▶ A piece of zinc is placed into a solution of hydrochloric acid, and bubbles begin to rise to the surface (*chemical*).

a When vinegar and baking soda are mixed, the solution bubbles as carbon dioxide forms.

b When solutions of sodium sulfide and cadmium nitrate are mixed, cadmium sulfide, a solid, forms.

c When aluminum reacts with iron oxide in the clay pot, heat and light are produced.

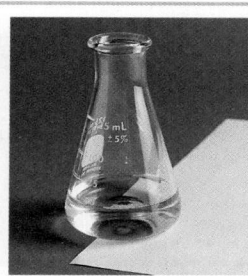

d When phenolphthalein is added to ammonia, a color change to pink occurs.

4. **The emission of light.** Some reactions will produce light, like that shown in Figure 1-13c.

5. **A color change in the reaction system.** The color change you noted during the decomposition of mercury(II) oxide is a clue that a reaction has occurred, producing new substances. Figure 1-13d shows the color change of an indicator in the presence of a base.

SECTION REVIEW

Total recall

1. What two physical properties characterize matter?

2. What SI unit is usually used to express the density of liquids?

3. How does mass differ from weight?

4. Why is density considered a physical property rather than a chemical property of matter?

Critical thinking

5. Classify the following as either a physical or a chemical property of matter: area, flammability, odor, temperature, oxygen changing into ozone.

6. When a piece of potassium metal is placed in water, a violent reaction occurs. But when a piece of copper metal is placed in water, nothing happens. Is this a physical or chemical property of the metal? Explain the reason for your choice.

7. **Interpreting Graphics** What evidence do you have that a chemical change has occurred in the reactions shown in Figure 1-5, on page 8?

Practice problems

8. **Interpreting Tables** Refer to Table 1-4. Perform the following conversions:
   a. milliliters in 21.59 L
   b. centimeters in 1.62 m
   c. nanometers in 0.064 mm
   d. kilograms in 2648 cg

SECTION 1-2

ANSWERS

SECTION REVIEW

Total recall

1. Two physical properties that characterize matter are mass and volume.

2. Density of liquids is usually expressed in grams per milliliter or cubic centimeter.

3. Weight is a measure of downward force due to gravitational attraction. Mass is the quantity of matter.

4. The density of a material may be observed and measured without any change in chemical nature.

Critical thinking

5. area, physical; flammability, chemical; odor, physical; temperature, physical; $O_2 \longrightarrow O_3$, chemical

6. Both are chemical properties. Just as the tendency to react is a chemical property, so is its lack of reactivity.

7. In part (a), a precipitate forms; in part (b), heat is absorbed. The evolution of ammonia gas would also be noted in part (b), but this is not apparent in the photograph.

Practice problems

8. **a.** 21 590 mL
   b. 162 cm
   c. 6.4×10^4 nm
   d. 0.02648 kg

SECTION 1-3

What is the nature of matter?

OBJECTIVES

▶ **Use** chemical tables to determine the names and symbols for various elements.

▶ **Distinguish** between atoms, elements, and molecules.

▶ **Describe** different forms of elements.

LESSON WARM-UP

Using the Periodic Table

Encourage students to use the periodic table as an information source for the names of elements and their symbols. If they become familiar with the table in this way, the ideas of periodicity and its relationship to electron configuration may be easier when students encounter these ideas in later chapters. Also, if students learn to use the table as a convenient source for atomic numbers and atomic masses, they will have an efficient source for chemical information.

VOCABULARY STRATEGY

Show students the derivation of the word *atom* from its Greek roots, and ask them what idea about matter is conveyed by that meaning.

a-: not   *tomos*: cutting

Literal meaning: *indivisible*. The idea, which also originated in ancient Greece, is that matter can be subdivided only as far as an elemental particle: the atom.

RESOURCE LINK

ChemFile Teaching Resources CD-ROM
Supplemental Reading Projects
Assign the guided reading worksheets for Roald Hoffmann's essay "What Are You" in *The Same and Not the Same* for cross-curricular connections to language arts.

Atoms and elements

atom

the basic unit of matter

element

one of the 111 simplest substances from which more complex substances are made

All matter is composed of **atoms.** Atoms are microscopic particles; it would take nearly 4 million of the largest atoms to form a line 1 mm long. Atoms come in over 110 basic types called **elements.** Each element has a unique set of chemical and physical properties that distinguish it from all other elements. Aluminum, copper, oxygen, and silicon are some elements that may be familiar to you. Each atom of an element has similar chemical properties to every other atom of that element.

Each element has a unique symbol that is internationally recognized. Symbols for the elements are shown on the periodic table in **Figure 1-14.** The symbol for an element consists of one to three letters. Three-letter symbols are used for newly discovered unnamed elements. The first letter of the symbol is always capitalized. You can find a complete listing of symbols with the names of the elements in **Table 1-6,** on page 22.

▼ **FIGURE 1-14**

This periodic table shows the symbols for all the known elements. The names are shown in alphabetical order in Table 1-6.

20   CHAPTER 1

DEMONSTRATION 5

Observing Elements

Approximate time: 10 minutes

The purpose of this demonstration is to give students an overview of actual elements. Place small quantities of the following elements in individual, covered Petri dishes: aluminum, magnesium, iron, iodine, gold leaf, silver foil, arsenic, red phosphorus, carbon, sulfur, zinc, copper, tin, lead, and any other element that you have on hand that can be handled safely. If you have alkali metals, exhibit small pieces submerged in oil, but do not allow students to handle the containers. Exhibit bromine in a closed bottle or glass-stoppered tube. Seal the dishes securely with tape, and label them.

Elements in Earth's Crust

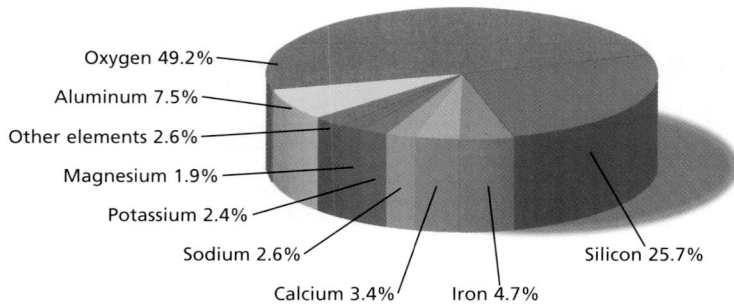

Oxygen 49.2%
Aluminum 7.5%
Other elements 2.6%
Magnesium 1.9%
Potassium 2.4%
Sodium 2.6%
Calcium 3.4%
Iron 4.7%
Silicon 25.7%

FIGURE 1-15 ◀

This pie chart shows the various elements in the Earth's crust and their abundances by mass.

It is easy to see how the symbols for hydrogen, H, helium, He, and silicon, Si, were chosen, but you may wonder about the symbols for tin, Sn, tungsten, W, and a few others. Both of these symbols come from languages other than English. Because Latin was the language of many early chemists, a number of symbols are based on the Latin names for the elements. For example, Sn is an abbreviation for *stannum,* the Latin word for "tin." The symbols for gold, silver, mercury, iron, and copper also come from the Latin names for these elements. Not all symbols come from English or Latin names—W stands for *Wolfram,* the German word for "tungsten."

Other elements have been named in honor of a person or after the place where the element was discovered. Curium, Cm, is a radioactive element named in honor of Marie and Pierre Curie, who first discovered radioactivity. Berkelium, Bk, was first synthesized in Berkeley, California. Where do you think francium, Fr, was discovered?

Every element has its own unique set of physical and chemical properties. Once it is purified, gold mined in Africa today is indistinguishable from gold panned in California during the gold rush or gold discovered by the Aztecs of Mexico centuries ago. Pure gold is the same substance regardless of where it is obtained, and it is made up of the same type of atoms.

A small number of elements make up most common substances

There are 111 known elements. However, the elements are not equally common. By far the most common element is hydrogen. More than 90% of the atoms in the known universe are hydrogen atoms. The elements oxygen and silicon make up more than 70% of the mass of the Earth's crust. **Figure 1-15** shows the other elements whose masses contribute substantially to the Earth's crust. Living things are composed primarily of four elements: carbon, hydrogen, oxygen, and nitrogen. These four elements combine to create thousands of different chemicals needed to sustain life.

SECTION 1-3

VISUAL STRATEGY

Figure 1-15 Students should note that the pie chart represents only the elements found in Earth's crust. If a pie chart were drawn for all of Earth, iron and nickel would dwarf all other elements. Emphasize that while there are many elements on the periodic table, only a few are present on Earth in large quantities. All the rest make up the wedge labeled 2.6% on the chart. Point out that aluminum is the most abundant *metallic* element in Earth's crust.

HISTORICAL CONNECTION

In 1750, only 16 elements were known. They are antimony, arsenic, bismuth, carbon, cobalt, copper, gold, iron, lead, mercury, phosphorus, platinum, silver, sulfur, tin, and zinc. The next element to be identified was nickel, in 1751. Notice that none of the common gaseous elements, such as hydrogen, oxygen, and nitrogen, nor any of the halogens had been identified. These elements had not been identified partly because scientists at that time were not clear about the nature of gases.

CNN. **Science in the News**
PRESENTS **Feature story 4**
Student Superconductors. See the Science in the News video guide for more details.

Safety
Wear safety goggles and a lab apron while preparing the display. Students should be warned not to open the Petri dishes.

Disposal
Save materials for reuse at a later time. Be sure to store the metals, carbon, sulfur, and phosphorus with the combustibles. Store the iodine and bromine with the oxidizers.

TABLE 1-6 Element Names and Symbols

Element	Symbol	Element	Symbol	Element	Symbol
Actinium	Ac	Hafnium	Hf	Promethium	Pm
Aluminum	Al	Hassium	Hs	Protactinium	Pa
Americium	Am	Helium	He	Radium	Ra
Antimony	Sb	Holmium	Ho	Radon	Rn
Argon	Ar	Hydrogen	H	Rhenium	Re
Arsenic	As	Indium	In	Rhodium	Rh
Astatine	At	Iodine	I	Rubidium	Rb
Barium	Ba	Iridium	Ir	Ruthenium	Ru
Berkelium	Bk	Iron	Fe	Rutherfordium	Rf
Beryllium	Be	Krypton	Kr	Samarium	Sm
Bismuth	Bi	Lanthanum	La	Scandium	Sc
Bohrium	Bh	Lawrencium	Lr	Seaborgium	Sg
Boron	B	Lead	Pb	Selenium	Se
Bromine	Br	Lithium	Li	Silicon	Si
Cadmium	Cd	Lutetium	Lu	Silver	Ag
Calcium	Ca	Magnesium	Mg	Sodium	Na
Californium	Cf	Manganese	Mn	Strontium	Sr
Carbon	C	Meitnerium	Mt	Sulfur	S
Cerium	Ce	Mendelevium	Md	Tantalum	Ta
Cesium	Cs	Mercury	Hg	Technetium	Tc
Chlorine	Cl	Molybdenum	Mo	Tellurium	Te
Chromium	Cr	Neodymium	Nd	Terbium	Tb
Cobalt	Co	Neon	Ne	Thallium	Tl
Copper	Cu	Neptunium	Np	Thorium	Th
Curium	Cm	Nickel	Ni	Thulium	Tm
Dubnium	Db	Niobium	Nb	Tin	Sn
Dysprosium	Dy	Nitrogen	N	Titanium	Ti
Einsteinium	Es	Nobelium	No	Tungsten	W
Erbium	Er	Osmium	Os	Ununnilium*	Uun
Europium	Eu	Oxygen	O	Unununium*	Uuu
Fermium	Fm	Palladium	Pd	Uranium	U
Fluorine	F	Phosphorus	P	Vanadium	V
Francium	Fr	Platinum	Pt	Xenon	Xe
Gadolinium	Gd	Plutonium	Pu	Ytterbium	Yb
Gallium	Ga	Polonium	Po	Yttrium	Y
Germanium	Ge	Potassium	K	Zinc	Zn
Gold	Au	Praseodymium	Pr	Zirconium	Zr

*Temporary names and symbols for elements greater than 109 will be used until the approval of trivial names by IUPAC.

FIGURE 1-16 ▼

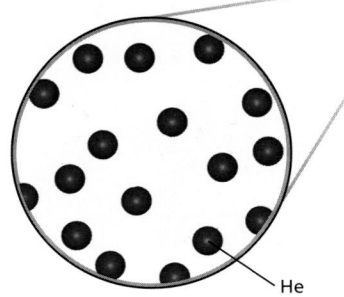

a The element helium, which is used to fill toy balloons, exists as individual atoms in the gaseous state. It is monatomic.

He

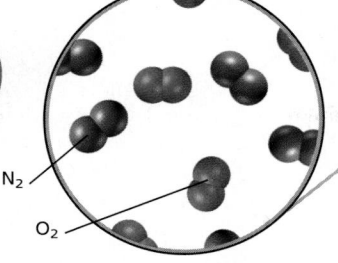

N₂

O₂

b A hot-air balloon contains a mixture of gases. Nitrogen, the most abundant gas, is diatomic. Each nitrogen molecule contains two nitrogen atoms.

Elements may exist as single atoms or as molecules

A **molecule** consists of two or more atoms combined in a definite ratio. The atoms in a molecule may be of the same element or of different elements. The nitrogen gas in the atmosphere is an example of a molecular element because it exists as two nitrogen atoms joined together. Acetylsalicylic acid, or aspirin, is made of molecules. Each molecule of acetylsalicylic acid consists of a set number of carbon, hydrogen, and oxygen atoms joined together.

Some elements exist as single atoms, others as molecules consisting of as few as two or as many as millions of atoms. For example, the helium gas in a balloon consists of individual atoms, as shown by the model in **Figure 1-16a**. Because it exists as individual atoms, helium gas is known as a *monatomic gas*. If an element consists of molecules, those molecules contain just one type of atom. For example, the element nitrogen, found in air, exists in the molecular state. Each nitrogen gas molecule consists of two nitrogen atoms joined together, as illustrated by the model in **Figure 1-16b**. Therefore, nitrogen is called a *diatomic gas*. Oxygen, another gas found in the air, is also diatomic.

Some elements have allotropic forms

A few elements, notably oxygen, phosphorus, sulfur, and carbon, are unusual because they exist as allotropes. An **allotrope** is one of a number of different molecular forms of an element. Oxygen has two allotropes, which are depicted in **Figure 1-17**. One is O_2, the diatomic oxygen gas you breathe. *Ozone,* O_3, is an oxygen allotrope that consists of three oxygen atoms.

The properties of allotropes can vary widely. Diatomic oxygen is a colorless, odorless gas essential to most forms of life. Ozone is a toxic, pale blue gas with a sharp odor. You can smell ozone after an intense

molecule

a neutral group of atoms held together by covalent bonds

allotrope

one of a number of different molecular or crystalline forms of an element

FIGURE 1-17 ▼

The allotropes of oxygen are oxygen gas and ozone.

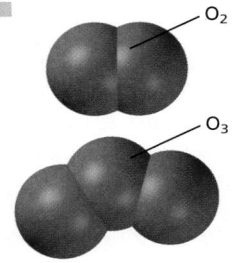

O₂

O₃

VISUAL STRATEGY

Figure 1-16 Remind students that hydrogen and oxygen exist as diatomic molecules. Use the periodic table to show students the locations and identities of the diatomic molecular elements. These are the halogens, hydrogen, oxygen, and nitrogen. Stress to students that they will need to know which elements are diatomic. One mnemonic device for learning these elements is "HON Family," referring to H_2, O_2, N_2, and the fluorine family.

TEACHING TIP

Molecular Elements Students should understand that a molecule may consist of two or more atoms of the same element or atoms of different elements. Besides diatomic elements, other molecular elements include sulfur, S_8, and phosphorus, P_4.

Definite Ratios If students do not understand what is meant by "combined in a definite ratio," illustrate this idea with substances whose formulas are already familiar to students. All water exists in a ratio represented by the formula H_2O, two atoms of hydrogen to every one atom of oxygen. It is a definite ratio because all water, regardless of its source, consists of these elements in the same ratio.

ADDITIONAL APPLICATION

Ozone is produced by any electric discharge through air. The odor of ozone is sometimes evident around dry-process copiers because the toner is attracted to an electrically charged drum before being transferred to paper. Students may recall the smell of ozone when separating clothes stuck together by "static cling." The crackling sound that occurs is a series of small sparks resulting from the transfer of charge between clothing items. Ozone is also used as a disinfectant. Some water treatment processes use ozone that is generated on site by electric discharge.

ANSWERS

SECTION REVIEW

Total recall

1. The atom is the fundamental particle of matter; a subunit of an element.

2. A molecule may consist of two or more atoms of the same element or different elements.

3. An allotrope is one of a number of molecular forms of an element.

Critical thinking

4. The symbols for newly discovered elements are based on the locations of their discovery as well as on the people who discover them.

5. **a.** C   **c.** H   **e.** Ne
   b. N   **d.** Au   **f.** At

6. **a.** helium   **d.** sulfur
   b. sodium   **e.** magnesium
   c. chlorine   **f.** antimony

RESOURCE LINK

ChemFile Teaching Resources CD-ROM

Internet Activities

Assign Internet Activity 9.

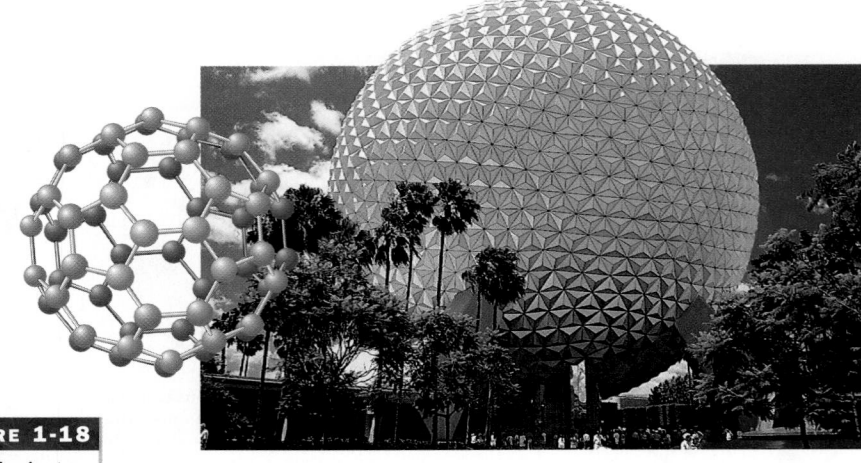

▲ **FIGURE 1-18**

The buckminster-fullerene molecule is known informally as a buckyball. It is a carbon allotrope consisting of 60 carbon atoms arranged like a geodesic dome.

internet connect

SCi LINKS
NSTA

TOPIC: Allotropes
GO TO: www.scilinks.org
KEYWORD: HW014

thunderstorm. Lightning provides the energy to convert diatomic oxygen to ozone in the lower atmosphere.

Carbon has several interesting allotropes in the solid state. One carbon allotrope is graphite, a soft gray solid with a slippery texture. Diamond, the hardest substance known, is another carbon allotrope. In the 1980s, a new carbon allotrope consisting of molecules with 60 carbon atoms was discovered. The atoms in this allotrope form a shape like the geodesic dome designed by the innovative American philosopher and engineer Buckminster Fuller. For this reason, the 60-carbon molecule, a model of which is shown in **Figure 1-18,** is called *buckminsterfullerene,* or, more informally, *buckyball*. Recently, another allotropic form of carbon, the *buckytube,* has been found. Combined with certain substances, fullerenes exhibit superconductivity, which is the ability to conduct electricity with no loss of energy.

SECTION REVIEW

Total recall

1. How does an atom differ from an element?

2. How is an atom related to a *molecule*?

3. What are allotropes?

Critical thinking

4. How do you think the symbols for newly discovered elements are determined?

5. **Interpreting Tables** List the symbols for the following elements.
   a. carbon   **c.** hydrogen   **e.** neon
   b. nitrogen   **d.** gold   **f.** astatine

6. **Interpreting Tables** Write the names of the elements with the following symbols.
   a. He   **c.** Cl   **e.** Mg
   b. Na   **d.** S   **f.** Sb

7. **Interpreting Tables** Why don't we use As as the symbol for astatine?

Aluminum's humble beginnings

In 1881, Charles Martin Hall was a 22-year-old student at Oberlin College, in Ohio. One day, Hall's chemistry professor mentioned in a lecture that anyone who could discover an inexpensive method for making aluminum metal would be rich. Working in a wooden shed and using a cast-iron frying pan, a blacksmith's forge, and homemade batteries, Hall discovered a practical technique for producing aluminum. Hall's process is the basis for the industrial production of aluminum today.

Industrial Uses

- Aluminum is the most abundant metal on Earth, but it is never found in nature as pure metal.
- The most important source of aluminum is the mineral bauxite. Bauxite consists mostly of hydrated aluminum oxide.
- In 1997, 3.6 million metric tons of aluminum was produced by the United States.
- Recycling aluminum by melting and reusing it is considerably cheaper than producing new aluminum.
- Aluminum is light, weather-resistant, and easily worked. These properties make aluminum ideal for use in aircraft, cars, cans, window frames, screens, gutters, wire, food packaging, hardware, and tools.

A1
13
Aluminum
26.981539
$[Ne]3s^2 3p^1$

Recycling just one aluminum can saves enough electricity to run a TV for four hours.

WHERE IS IT?

Earth's Crust
8% by mass

Sea Water
less than 0.1%

internetconnect

SC*LINKS*
NSTA
TOPIC: Aluminum
GO TO: www.scilinks.org
KEYWORD: HW015

Aluminum's resistance to corrosion makes it suitable for many outdoor uses.

ELEMENT SPOTLIGHT

Aluminum composes 7.5 % of the Earth's crust, making it the most abundant metal. Aluminum is found in many ores and minerals, such as granite, bauxite, and clay. Bauxite is by far the most important industrial source of pure aluminum, and large deposits of it are found all over the world.

Pure aluminum is a light, silvery-white metal that can be easily formed, that has a high thermal conductivity, and that has excellent corrosion resistance. Aluminum is commonly used in the production of kitchen utensils, and it has innumerable industrial applications. Pure aluminum is soft and relatively weak, but its alloys with copper, magnesium, and silicon are durable enough to be of great importance in the construction of airplanes and rockets.

One of the most important compounds of aluminum is alumina, or aluminum oxide. Alumina occurs naturally as ruby and sapphire, and it is used extensively in glassmaking and related fields. Synthetic ruby and sapphire are used in lasers to focus light.

The price of aluminum in 1852 was in excess of $540/lb. Just before Hall's discovery in 1886, the price was about $11/lb. Since he discovered the refining process named after him, the price of aluminum has been as low as 15 cents/lb.

A BRIEF HISTORY

1824: F. Wöhler isolates aluminum from aluminum chloride.

1886: Charles Martin Hall, of the United States, and Paul-Louis Héroult, of France, independently discover the process for extracting aluminum from aluminum oxide.

1700   1800   1900

1827: F. Wöhler describes some of the properties of aluminum.

1854: Henri Saint-Claire Deville, of France, and R. Bunsen, of Germany, independently accomplish the electrolysis of aluminum from sodium aluminum chloride.

THE SCIENCE OF CHEMISTRY 25

DID YOU KNOW?

Outside the United States, the spelling *aluminium* is generally used. Before the development of the Hall process, aluminum was so difficult to prepare from its ore that it was considered a precious metal. Aluminum was used in small quantities to decorate objects and to make novelty items, such as picture frames for the very wealthy.

How is matter classified?

OBJECTIVES
- ▶ *Distinguish* between pure substances and mixtures.
- ▶ *Interpret* chemical formulas.
- ▶ *Classify* mixtures as homogeneous or heterogeneous.
- ▶ *Classify* compounds as inorganic or organic.

LESSON WARM-UP

Using Graphic Organizers
Distribute a blank version of the Graphic Organizer at the bottom of this page. Leave enough room in each box for students to write notes and examples. Begin by instructing students to write the word *matter* in the top box. Have them add the characteristics of matter, mass, and volume. Then have them review Section 1-3 and skim Section 1-4 to decide what the two subdivisions of matter should be. Many students will say *elements* and *compounds*. Point to things that are obvious mixtures, such as a chunk of granite, a packet of powdered drink mix, some peppercorns, and a plant leaf. Challenge students to name the element or the compound that composes each item. Lead students to understand that matter can be divided into an even broader pair of categories—substances and mixtures.

Classifying matter

Notice how the objects have been classified in **Figure 1-19.** What would it be like to shop in a store where there was no order or organization for the items on display? Shopping would be time-consuming and confusing. To study matter, chemists start with an order. They use the properties of matter—both physical and chemical—to classify matter.

Compounds consist of bonded atoms

Pure substances composed of atoms from two or more different elements are classified as **compounds.** Two types of compounds are created in chemical reactions—covalent compounds and ionic compounds.

The smallest particle of a covalent compound that has the properties of the compound is a molecule. Water, sugar, and oxygen are *covalent compounds*. Compounds that consist of ions, such as table salt, are called *ionic compounds*. An **ion** is an atom or group of atoms with an electrical charge. You will learn more about the differences between covalent and ionic compounds in Chapters 5 and 6.

Because a compound is a pure substance, it has a unique set of chemical and physical properties. Acetic acid, shown in **Figure 1-20,** is a clear liquid with a very strong odor. The term **acid** in the name sig-

compound

the product that results when two or more different elements are chemically combined

ion

an atom or group of atoms with an electrical charge

acid

a class of compounds whose water solutions taste sour, turn blue litmus paper red, and react with bases to form salts

▶ **FIGURE 1-19**

Just as consumer products are classified and sorted by properties and uses, chemists classify matter by chemical and physical properties.

26   CHAPTER 1

GRAPHIC ORGANIZER

Matter
- Substances
  - Elements
    - Monatomic
    - Molecular
  - Compounds
    - Ionic
- Mixtures
  - Homogeneous (solutions)
  - Heterogeneous

FIGURE 1-20 ▼

a A strip of pH paper dipped in an acetic acid solution turns red, showing that the solution is acidic.

b A strip of pH paper dipped in a sodium hydroxide solution turns blue, showing that the solution is basic.

nifies that it belongs to a group of compounds that have certain chemical properties.

The degree to which an aqueous solution of compound shows the properties of an acid is expressed numerically as **pH.** In water, acids have pH values less than 7. For example, the pH of aspirin in water is 2.7. Compounds dissolved in water that have pH values greater than 7 are called **bases.** Bases have properties that are in some ways opposite those of acids, as shown in **Table 1-7.**

The pH of a solution is found by using a pH meter or by using special compounds called indicators. When the solution is tested by using an indicator, the color of the indicator often changes. Indicators are being used to test acidity in Figure 1-20.

Compounds can also be classified as organic or inorganic

Another way to classify matter depends on whether the element carbon is present in a compound. With some exceptions, compounds that contain the element carbon such as aspirin, with the formula $C_9H_8O_4$, are

pH

a numerical scale used to express acidity

base

a class of compounds that taste bitter, feel slippery in water solution, turn red litmus to blue, and react with acids to form salts

TEACHING TIP

Conductivity of Compounds
Inform students that a water solution containing significant amounts of ions will conduct an electric current. Dissolve some salt in one beaker of water and some sugar in a second beaker of water. Have a third beaker containing only distilled water. Use a conductivity apparatus to demonstrate that only the salt water will conduct a current. Use this opportunity to point out that pure water is evidently not ionic because it does not conduct.

Naming Acids Have students name all of the acids they know. Write formulas for them on the board so that students can start to associate words with symbolic representations. Students may think of some organic acids, such as citric, acetic, lactic, ascorbic, tartaric, and perhaps others, so you may want to have these formulas at hand.

TABLE 1-7   Some Properties of Acids and Bases

Water solutions of acids . . .	Water solutions of bases . . .
taste sour	taste bitter and feel slippery
turn blue pH paper red	turn red pH paper blue
have pH values less than 7	have pH values greater than 7
react with bases and certain metals to form salts	react with acids to form salts

THE SCIENCE OF CHEMISTRY   27

DEMONSTRATION 6

Litmus in Acid and Base

Approximate Time: 10 minutes

1. Place pieces of red and blue litmus paper in a beaker of vinegar.

2. Place pieces of red and blue litmus paper in a beaker of diluted household ammonia.

3. Crush an aspirin tablet using a mortar and pestle. Add a small amount of water and the powdered aspirin to a watch glass, and stir. Test with both red and blue

litmus paper, and use pH paper to determine the pH.

Disposal

Put the litmus paper and aspirin residue in the trash. Pour the liquid down the drain, and flush with water.

DID YOU KNOW?

Organic compounds generally include all carbon compounds except carbonates, carbides, and metal carbonyls. For simplicity's sake, inorganic compounds are sometimes defined as all compounds that are not organic.

CONTENT STRATEGY

Although high school chemistry courses typically focus on inorganic and physical chemistry, we have chosen to integrate organic chemistry where appropriate to be able to use more relevant examples and applications of basic concepts. This strategy puts the focus of organic chemistry on concepts and reaction behavior rather than on nomenclature. However, the classification of organic compounds by functional group is presented in Chapter 7.

$C_9H_8O_4$
Aspirin

$C_8H_9NO_2$
Acetaminophen

▲ FIGURE 1-21

Formulas and models are used by chemists to represent acetylsalicylic acid (aspirin), acetaminophen, and ibuprofen. Acetaminophen is commonly known by the brand name Tylenol®; ibuprofen is commonly known by the brand name Advil®.

$C_{13}H_{18}O_2$
Ibuprofen

organic compound

any covalently bonded compound containing carbon (except carbonates and oxides)

inorganic compound

any compound outside the organic family of compounds

classified as **organic compounds.** Generally, those that lack carbon are referred to as **inorganic compounds.** Because organic compounds play an important role in your daily life, you will study them throughout this text.

Compounds are represented by formulas

Four different ways of representing three compounds used as pain-relievers are shown in **Figure 1-21.** The *molecular formula,* such as $C_9H_8O_4$, shows the numbers of atoms of each element present in a molecule but not how the atoms are bonded. The *structural formula* shows the exact number of atoms present in a molecule and how these atoms are bonded to one another. The lines represent the bonds between atoms. The *ball-and-stick model* shows the geometric arrangement of atoms in a formula. The *space-fill model* also shows the geometric arrangment and most closely represents the actual shape of a molecule. What do all three structural formulas in Figure 1-21 have in common? What is unique about the structural formula of acetaminophen compared with the other formulas?

DEMONSTRATION 7

Separating a Compound into Elements

Approximate time: 15 minutes

1. Before class, prepare sufficient 1 M Na_2SO_4 solution to fill the electrolysis apparatus you will use.

2. Fill an electrolysis unit with the Na_2SO_4 solution. Extinguish any nearby flames.

3. At the beginning of class, apply a 9 to 12 V DC current to the leads. Let students observe for a little while to see what is happening.

4. When the gas-collecting tubes are sufficiently full, turn off the current. Have students note the relative volumes of hydrogen and oxygen formed, and remind them of water's formula.

5. Collect O_2 gas in an inverted test tube. Turn the tube upright, and immediately thrust a glowing splint into the tube. The

Mixtures can be classified as homogeneous or heterogeneous

A collection of two or more pure substances physically mixed together is classified as a **mixture.** The proportions of different substances in a mixture can vary. For instance, chicken soup is a mixture. Different batches of chicken soup may contain different relative quantities of celery, carrots, chicken, pepper, water, and other ingredients, depending on the recipe.

The properties of mixtures can vary because the proportions of the substances in them can vary. For example, gold is mixed with other metals in various proportions to obtain materials suitable for different purposes. The pure gold shown in **Figure 1-22a,** which is also called 24-karat gold, is too soft to keep its shape in jewelry, so it is often mixed with other metals to achieve necessary strength. The *alloy,* or solid mixture, of gold used in much jewelry is 18-karat gold; it contains 18 parts gold out of 24 parts, or 75% gold by mass. The remaining six parts are usually copper, silver, or nickel. For even greater hardness and strength, 14-karat gold, shown in **Figure 1-22b,** is used.

Mixtures can be classified as homogeneous or heterogeneous. A **homogeneous mixture** is one in which the components are uniformly distributed at the microscopic level. Gasoline, syrup, air, and 18-karat gold are homogeneous mixtures. All regions of a homogeneous mixture are identical in their composition and properties. The most common type of homogeneous mixture is the *solution*. Vinegar, tea, and salt water are examples of solutions.

A **heterogeneous mixture** contains substances that are not evenly distributed. Some regions of a heterogeneous mixture have different properties from other regions. Heterogeneous mixtures can take many forms. **Table 1-8,** on the next page, summarizes the differences between heterogeneous and homogeneous mixtures.

mixture
a collection of two or more pure substances physically mixed together

homogeneous mixture
a mixture containing substances that are uniformly distributed

heterogeneous mixture
a mixture containing substances that are not uniformly distributed

FIGURE 1-22 ▼

a The gold nugget is a pure substance—gold. Pure gold, also called 24 karat gold, is usually considered too soft for jewelry.

b 14-karat gold is 14/24, or 58.3%, gold. This homogeneous mixture is stronger than pure gold and is often used for jewelry.

THE SCIENCE OF CHEMISTRY   29

---

splint should flame up and burn brightly, indicating the presence of oxygen.

6. Collect H_2 in another tube, but leave the mouth of the tube pointed downward. Bring a burning splint near the mouth of the tube. The hydrogen should burn with a "bark" but may burn quietly if the contents of the tube are pure H_2.

7. Ask students to take note of what was required to separate a compound into its elements. (*An input of energy and a chemical change were required.*)

Safety
Wear safety goggles, a lab apron, and gloves when preparing the solution and performing the demonstration. If you use a power supply rather than a battery, make sure its output is DC, not AC. Have students stand back at least 10 ft.

Disposal
While wearing goggles and a lab apron, pour the liquid down the drain.

TABLE 1-8 Examples of Mixtures

Heterogeneous	Homogeneous
Orange juice or tomato juice (suspension) uneven distribution of components; settles out upon standing	**Iced tea** (solution) uniform distribution of components; components cannot be filtered out and will not settle out upon standing
Chocolate chip pecan cookie uneven distribution of components	**Stainless steel** (alloy) uniform distribution of components
Granite uneven distribution of components	**Carbonated beverage** (solution) uniform distribution of components
Salad uneven distribution of components; can be easily separated by physical means	**Maple syrup** (solution) uniform distribution of components; components cannot be filtered out and will not settle out upon standing

Mixtures can be distinguished from compounds

There are two principal differences between mixtures and compounds.

1. The properties of a mixture reflect the properties of the substances it contains, but the properties of a compound often bear no resemblance to the properties of the elements that compose it.

2. Compounds have a definite composition by mass of their combining elements, while the components of mixtures may be present in varying proportions.

For example, the compound acetylsalicylic acid has a definite composition—by mass. It is always 60.0% carbon, 35.5% oxygen, and 4.5% hydrogen. In contrast, substances in a mixture can have any mass ratio. The sand in a sand-and-gravel mixture may make up 99% or 1% of the overall mass.

Separating mixtures may require physical or chemical means

One major task a chemist often undertakes is the isolation and analysis of the components of a mixture. This task can be likened to sorting materials in a recycling bin. Recyclable items can be separated into different piles based on one or more physical properties. For example, soft-drink cans can be placed in the aluminum recycling bin, while glass and plastics are placed in other bins.

Although chemists can use physical properties to separate components, separating chemical mixtures is not always that easy. Often the only way to remove a substance from a mixture is to react the mixture to form a substance that can be easily removed by filtration. Techniques for separating mixtures will be described in Chapter 13.

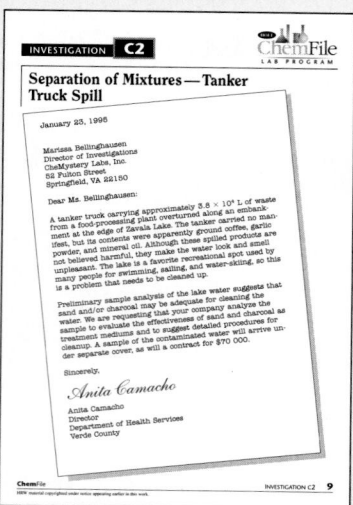
DEMONSTRATION 8

Separation by Distillation

Approximate time: 15 minutes

Show students that a water solution can be separated by removing the water in some way. Wear safety goggles and a lab apron

1. Dissolve 25 g of $CuSO_4 \cdot 5H_2O$ in 100 mL of water, and show the resulting blue solution to the class.

2. Pour the solution into a 250 mL Erlenmeyer flask that is clamped to a ring stand and

resting on an electric hot plate. Drop a boiling stone or marble chip into the flask.

3. Insert into the mouth of the flask a one-hole rubber stopper of the appropriate size fitted with a 10 cm piece of glass tubing.

4. Attach a 1 m piece of clear plastic or rubber tubing to the top of the glass tubing, and run the other end to another flask clamped

Stockroom chemicals may be mixtures

When is a substance pure? That's a difficult question to answer. When you drink water from the tap, you may think you are drinking pure water, but not likely. Even bottled water contains minerals that are impurities. Chemicals too contain impurities that can alter a reaction. For this reason, standards for chemical purity have been established so that chemists can control the effects of impurities in their work.

Figure 1-23 shows the label for a zinc compound that meets reagent-grade standards set by the Committee on Analytical Reagents of the American Chemical Society (ACS). *Primary-standard* grade chemicals are of higher purity than *reagent-grade* chemicals. You may be using *commercial* or *technical* grade chemicals in the lab because they are less expensive and because high-purity chemicals are not needed.

Figure 1-24, on the next page, summarizes the properties that characterize elements, compounds, and mixtures.

CONSUMER ACTIVITY

INQUIRYLAB

Using Physical Properties to Separate a Mixture

Observing physical properties, such as color, shape, texture, or mass, can be used to identify a substance. Chemists also use physical properties to separate the components of a mixture.

Materials — distilled water, filter funnel, filter paper, magnet, paper towels, clear plastic cups, plastic spoon, sample of mixture

Problem — Design an experiment using the given materials to separate the components of the sample mixture. Once you have separated the mixture, describe the components by their physical properties.

Analysis

1. What properties did you observe in each of the components of the mixture?
2. How did these properties help you to separate the mixture?
3. Did any of the components share similar properties?

FIGURE 1-23 ▼

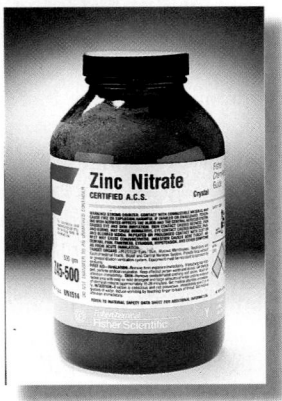

a This bottle of zinc nitrate would be considered a pure substance . . .

$Zn(NO_3)_2 \cdot 6H_2O$ F.W. 297.47

Certificate of Actual Lot Analysis

Acidity (as HNO₃)	0.008%
Alkalies and Earths	0.02%
Chloride (Cl)	0.005%
Insoluble Matter	0.001%
Iron (Fe)	0.0002%
Lead (Pb)	0.001%
Phosphate (PO₄)	0.0002%
Sulfate (SO₄)	0.002%

Store separately from and avoid contact with combustible materials. Keep container closed and in a cool, dry place. Avoid contact with skin, eyes and clothing.

LOT NO. 917356

FL-02-0588   CAS 10196-18-6

b . . . even though the label shows that it contains impurities.

THE SCIENCE OF CHEMISTRY   **31**

SECTION 1-4

TEACHING TIP

Designing a Model Some students may want to devise models to illustrate the differences between elements, compounds, homogeneous mixtures, and heterogeneous mixtures. One possibility is a relief model of each type of matter made by using painted craft balls (or half-balls) mounted on board. The models could be partially based on those in Figure 1-22. An element might be represented by balls of all one color in a regular arrangement. A compound could be repeating groupings of 2 or 3 balls somehow shown to be chemically bound to each other. A homogeneous mixture would be a random distribution of balls of two different colors. A heterogeneous mixture might have clumps of balls of all one color mixed with similar clumps of balls of a second color.

INQUIRYLAB

The mixture should contain 5 g samples of salt, sand, iron filings, and poppy seeds. Through their observations students should come up with a procedure that uses solubility, density, and magnetism to make their separation. Once they have devised their plans, you might want to give them another sample of the mixture without telling them the exact masses of each component. Students can run their procedures and determine the mass of each component.

Analysis

1. solubility, magnetism, low density

2. Salt is separated by solubility, poppy seeds by density, and iron filings by magnetism.

3. Sand, poppy seeds, and iron filings are insoluble.

 Science in the News

PRESENTS Feature story 6

Cleaner Gas. See the Science in the News video guide for more details.

---

so that it is submerged three-quarters of the way in a large beaker of cold water.

5. Gently heat the flask until boiling begins, and control the heat so that moderate boiling continues. The tubing acts as an air condenser, collecting distilled water in the cold flask.

6. After a few minutes, remove the tube from the cold flask and then turn off the heat.

7. Show the cold flask to the class, and compare it with the solution remaining in the boiling flask. Ask students to explain why the blue color does not appear in the condensate.

8. Pour some condensate and solution into separate Petri dishes and compare the residues after evaporation.

Disposal

Pour the colorless distillate down the drain. Let the blue solution evaporate, and save the crystals for reuse at a later time. Do not return them to the reagent bottle.

SECTION 1-4

ANSWERS

SECTION REVIEW

Total recall

1. Compounds are pure substances composed of two or more elements.

2. Acids have a sour taste, turn blue litmus paper red, have a pH lower than 7, and react with bases and some metals to form salts.

3. All organic compounds contain the element carbon.

4. The overall arrangement of the atoms in a molecule is shown in a structural formula.

5. In a heterogeneous mixture, substances are not evenly mixed. In a homogeneous mixture, the substances are uniformly mixed at the molecular level.

Critical thinking

6. An ionic compound is composed of ions, atoms, or groups of atoms with an electric charge. Molecular compounds are composed of uncharged molecules.

7. Aspirin has a sour taste. When in solution, it turns blue litmus paper red and has a pH lower than 7.

8. **a.** compound
   b. element
   c. homogeneous mixture
   d. compound
   e. homogeneous mixture
   f. compound

9. (a) and (f)

10. It is a mixture. The aspirin may be a compound, but the apple-sauce is a heterogeneous mixture. The aspirin-applesauce mixture is also heterogenous.

RESOURCE LINK

ChemFile Lab D
Consumer Lab
Have students do Experiment D2: *What's so Special about Bottled Drinking Water?*

▼ FIGURE 1-24

This figure summarizes the relationships between different classes of matter.

SECTION REVIEW

Total recall

1. Define the term *compound*.

2. What are some of the properties of an acid?

3. What element do all organic compounds contain?

4. What information is shown in a structural formula that is not shown in a molecular formula?

5. How is a homogeneous mixture different from a heterogeneous mixture?

Critical thinking

6. Compare and contrast molecular and ionic compounds.

7. Describe three properties of aspirin that classify it as an acid.

8. Identify each of the following as an element, compound, or mixture. If it is a mixture, classify it as homogeneous or heterogeneous.
   a. CH_4 **d.** distilled water
   b. S_8 **e.** salt water
   c. cup of coffee   **f.** CH_2O

9. Which of the compounds in item 8, if any, are organic?

10. **Story Clue** If you have ever had difficulty swallowing aspirin, you know it has an unpleasant taste. To help a child swallow aspirin, a parent may crush the tablet and add it to apple sauce. Is the aspirin-apple-sauce combination classified as a compound or a mixture? Is it homogeneous or heterogeneous? Explain the reasons for your choices.

ALTERNATIVE ASSESSMENT

Group Strategy

Chromatography is a technique widely used to separate mixtures. Students can find information on the Internet and in the library about chromatographic techniques and the circumstances in which each type is best applied. Students could include paper chromatography, column chromatography, thin-layer chromatography, gas chromatography, gas-liquid chromatography, high-pressure liquid chromatography, ion-exchange chromatography, and others.

You read at the beginning of the chapter that Felix Hoffmann produced acetylsalicylic acid by reacting two organic compounds, salicylic acid and acetic anhydride. Today, acetylsalicylic acid can be made from several other organic compounds. No matter what the starting reactant is, each process involves a number of chemical reactions in which the product of one step is the reactant in the next step.

Having finished this introduction to chemistry, you should now be able to answer the questions that were posed at the beginning of the chapter.

LOOKING BACK

What type of chemical substance is aspirin?

Aspirin is the common name for acetylsalicylic acid. You can see from the structure on the right that acetylsalicylic acid is an organic compound containing the elements carbon, hydrogen, and oxygen. Acetylsalicylic acid has both physical properties (for example, white color) and chemical proper-

ties (for example, a water solution of aspirin turns litmus indicator from blue to red).

How is aspirin similar to other widely used pain relievers?

Acetylsalicylic acid, ibuprofen, and acetaminophen are organic compounds that have been made by chemical reactions. All three have structural similarities, including a ring formed by six carbon atoms.

How does name-brand aspirin differ from generic brands?

Aspirin is a pure compound. Therefore, there is no difference between the effect of named brands and that of a generic aspirin product in the body. But different brands of aspirin can vary in terms of dosage, buffering systems that control acidity, and the time they take to act.

Ball-and-stick model

Space-fill model

RESOURCE LINK

ChemFile Teaching Resources CD-ROM
Supplemental Reading Projects
Assign the guided reading worksheets for Roald Hoffmann's essay "Chemistry and Industry" in *The Same and Not the Same* for cross-curricular connections to language arts.

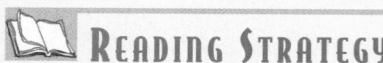

READING STRATEGY

Assimilating Knowledge

Have students return to their lists of things they want to know about the nature of matter, which they created at the beginning of the chapter. Have them place check marks next to the questions that they are now able to answer. Students should finish by making a list of what they have learned. Have students identify unanswered questions as well as new questions they may have. These questions could be used as the basis for a research project.

REVIEW & ASSESS ASSIGNMENT GUIDE

Term Review

Assign after Section 1-4.

Concept & Skills Review

Section 1-1
▸ Items 1–3

Section 1-2
▸ Items 4–16

Section 1-3
▸ Items 17–20

Section 1-4
▸ Items 21–25

Linking Chapters

Assign after Section 1-4.

Alternative Assessments

Assign after Section 1-4.

Test Prep

Assign prior to the chapter test.

KEY TERMS

1-1
chemical
chemical reaction
endothermic reaction
exothermic reaction
physical state
product
reactant

1-2
chemical change
chemical property
conversion factor
density
mass
matter
physical change
physical property

quantity
unit
volume
weight

1-3
allotrope
atom
element
molecule

1-4
acid
base
compound
heterogeneous mixture
homogeneous mixture
inorganic compound
ion
mixture
organic compound
pH

KEY CONCEPTS

1-1 What is chemistry?
▸ Chemistry is the study of chemicals, their properties, and the reactions in which they are involved.
▸ Matter can exist as a solid, liquid, or gas.
▸ The relative position and motion of particles in a substance determine whether the substance exists as a solid, liquid, or gas.
▸ A word equation can be used to describe a chemical reaction; an arrow separates the reactants on the left from the products on the right.

1-2 What is matter?
▸ Matter has both mass and volume; matter thus has density, which is the ratio of mass to volume.
▸ SI units are used in science to measure seven basic quantities: length, mass, time, electric current, thermodynamic temperature, amount of substance, and luminous intensity.
▸ Other quantities, including volume, are measured in derived units.
▸ Properties of matter may be either physical or chemical.

▸ Chemical properties are observed when one substance interacts with another or changes composition following an input of energy.

1-3 What is the nature of matter?
▸ All matter is made from atoms.
▸ All atoms of an element are the same.
▸ Elements may exist as single atoms or as molecules.
▸ Allotropes are different molecular or crystalline forms of an element.

1-4 How is matter classified?
▸ Matter can be classified as a pure substance or a mixture.
▸ Elements and compounds are pure substances; mixtures may be homogeneous or heterogeneous.
▸ Compounds can be classified as organic or inorganic.

KEY SKILLS

Review the following model before your exam. Be sure you can solve this type of problem.

How To Use conversion factors (p. 14)

TERM REVIEW

1. A change that produces one or more new substances is known as a ——.
(physical change, chemical change)

2. Examine the following word equation:

iron oxide + aluminum ⟶
iron + aluminum oxide

Aluminum is a —— in this reaction.
(reactant, product)

3. The simplest pure substance is a(n) ——.
(molecule, element)

4. A —— is used to measure a quantity.
(conversion factor, unit)

5. The ratio of mass to volume is defined as the —— of matter.
(weight, density)

6. A property of matter that can be measured without changing its chemical nature is known as a ——.
(chemical property, physical property)

7. Two or more different elements that are chemically combined are known as a(n) ——.
(compound, mixture, allotrope)

8. Matter that is composed of only one kind of atom or molecule is known as a(n) ——.
(organic compound, pure substance)

9. A(n) —— produces a solution with a pH value less than 7.
(acid, base)

10. Oil and water mixed for a salad dressing and left standing is an example of a ——.
(heterogeneous mixture, homogeneous mixture)

11. Cubic centimeter is a unit used to measure ——.
(mass, volume, weight)

12. Amount of substance is measured in ——.
(milliliters, grams, moles)

CONCEPT & SKILLS REVIEW

THE NATURE OF MATTER

1. Use particle-model descriptions to explain why liquids and gases take the shape of their containers.

2. Your friend mentions that she buys shirts made only of natural materials because she follows a chemical-free lifestyle. How would you respond?

3. Sodium salicylate is made by reacting sodium phenoxide with carbon dioxide in the presence of heat. Write a word equation for this reaction.

4. An astronaut plans to bring home a massive moon-rock collection. Mission control on Earth wants to know the weight of the collection in advance. What must the astronaut consider when sending the weight to mission control?

5. Pick an object you can see right now. List three physical properties of the object that you can observe. Can you also observe a chemical property of the object? Explain.

6. Compare the physical and chemical properties of salt and sugar. What properties do they share? Which properties could you use to distinguish between salt and sugar?

7. A student checks the volume, melting point, and shape of two unlabeled samples of matter and finds that the measurements are identical. From this he concludes that the samples have the same chemical composition. What is wrong with his thinking?

8. Describe how different substances can be distinguished by density.

9. For each pair below, indicate the substance with the greater density. Explain your answer.
a. rubber stopper and cork
b. ice cube and water

TERM REVIEW

1. chemical change
2. reactant
3. element
4. unit
5. density
6. physical property
7. compound
8. pure substance
9. acid
10. heterogeneous mixture
11. volume
12. moles

CONCEPT & SKILLS REVIEW

1. The molecules of liquids and gases are free to move around one another so those substances can flow. The molecules of a solid are rigidly held in geometric patterns.

2. You would tell here that all matter, including natural materials, consists of chemicals.

3. Sodium phenoxide + carbon dioxide + heat ⟶ sodium salicylate

4. A scale measures the gravitational attraction on an object, which would be only 1/6 of the attraction on Earth. The scale would give a weight that is 1/6 less than the value on Earth.

5. Answers will vary. Physical properties could include shape, texture, odor, state of matter, and taste. Chemical properties could not be observed unless a chemical change was taking place on the object.

6. Both salt and sugar are white, crystalline solids at room temperature. Both dissolve in water. The melting point of salt is very high compared with that of sugar. Their densities are different. Either melting point or density could be used to distinguish between them.

7. Two different substances may have similar melting points. Measuring volume is of no use unless mass is also measured to reveal density. The student should compare the densities of the two samples and perhaps compare their chemical properties.

8. Density of a substance is a characteristic physical property. To compare densities, the mass and volume of each sample of matter must be determined and density calculated.

9. a. The rubber stopper sinks in water and the cork floats, so the rubber stopper is more dense.
   b. Ice floats in liquid water, so the liquid water is more dense.
   c. Both the tire and the rubber stopper are made of vulcanized rubber, so the densities should be about the same. Tires, however, can contain both metal and cloth cord, so the densities may differ somewhat.

10. No. Despite their similar properties, they must be different. The same substance would always have the same density under the same conditions.

11. This is a physical change because the dyes have only been separated, not changed in composition.

12. a. Verbal descriptions may be interpreted in different ways by different people. Measurements usually conform to international standards and thus are understood by everyone in the same way.
   b. the numerical part and the unit

13. a. kilogram, mass; meter, length; second, time; mole, amount of substance; kelvin, temperature
   b. A derived unit can be expressed as a combination of base units. Examples include cubic meter, cubic centimeter, liter, and milliliter.

14. a. Possible answers include L/min and L/s.
   b. Possible answers include m/s, cm/s, km/h.
   c. Possible answers include m^3, yd^3, ft^3.

15. a. 10^{-9} m   e. 0.001 L
   b. 0.001 kg   f. 1000 mL
   c. 1000 g   g. 0.001 L
   d. 10^9 nm   h. 1000 cm^3

Continued on page 37.

---

10. Substances A and B are colorless, odorless liquids that are nonconductors and flammable. The density of substance A is 0.97 g/mL; the density of substance B is 0.89 g/mL. Are A and B the same substance? Explain.

11. A forgetful student leaves an uncapped watercolor marker on an open notebook. Later she discovers the leaking marker has produced a rainbow of colors on the top page. Is this an example of a physical change or a chemical change? Explain the reason for your choice.

12. a. Why are measurements often more useful than word descriptions?
    b. There are two parts to every measurement. What are they?

13. a. Name the five most common SI base units used in chemistry. What quantities are measured by each unit?
    b. Explain what derived units are. Give an example of one.

14. What derived unit is appropriate for expressing the following?
    a. rate of water flow
    b. speed
    c. volume of a room

15. Complete the following equalities
    a. 1 nm = ? m   e. 1 mL = ? L
    b. 1 g = ? kg   f. 1 L = ? mL
    c. 1 kg = ? g   g. 1 cm^3 = ? L
    d. 1 m = ? nm   h. 1 L = ? cm^3

16. Convert the following measurements to the units specified.
    a. 357 mL = ? L
    b. 25 kg = ? mg
    c. 650 nm = ? m
    d. 35 000 cm^3 = ? L
    e. 2.46 L = ? cm^3
    f. 250 µg = ? g
    g. 250 µg = ? kg
    h. 1.5 L = ? mL
    i. 10.5 mol = ? mmol

THE COMPONENTS OF MATTER

17. What is an element?

18. How are atoms and molecules related to one another?

---

19. Give one example of a monatomic gas and one example of a diatomic gas.

20. Both diamond and graphite are allotropic forms of carbon. Why do their physical properties differ?

CLASSIFYING MATTER

21. Compare and contrast the properties of homogeneous and heterogeneous mixtures.

22. Differentiate between pure substances and mixtures.

23. Differentiate between compounds and mixtures.

24. Steel is an alloy of the elements iron and carbon. In the steel used to make nails, iron makes up 99.8%, while carbon constitutes only 0.2%. Is this steel a homogeneous mixture or a heterogeneous mixture? Explain the reason for your choice.

25. Explain why steel is not considered a compound of iron and carbon.

ALTERNATIVE ASSESSMENTS

Performance assessment

1. Outline a study strategy for learning the important facts and understanding the concepts for this course. One effective strategy is to get a study partner. Another is to approach your study by pretending that you have to teach someone the material you are expected to learn. Discuss your plans with your teacher, and use your method throughout the course.

2. Your teacher will provide you with a sample of a metallic element. Determine its density. Check references that list the density of metals to identify the sample that you analyzed.

Portfolio projects

1. **Chemistry and you**
   Make a poster showing the types of product warning labels that are found on products in your home.

1. Magnesium dissolves in hydrochloric acid to produce magnesium chloride and hydrogen gas. Which of the following represents the reactants in this reaction?
   a. magnesium and magnesium chloride
   b. hydrochloric acid and hydrogen gas
   c. magnesium and hydrochloric acid
   d. magnesium chloride and hydrogen gas

2. Matter that has a definite shape and volume is a(n) _____ .
   a. acid
   b. base
   c. solid
   d. gas

3. Which of the following are equal?
   a. 1.63 kg and 163 g
   b. 0.0704 m and 7.04 mm
   c. 0.015 mL and 1.5 L
   d. 325 mg and 0.325 g

4. A chemical property of matter _____ .
   a. depends on how it reacts with other substances
   b. can be described when it undergoes a physical change
   c. cannot be quantitatively described
   d. cannot be qualitatively described

5. An SI base unit that is commonly used in chemistry is the _____ .
   a. degree Celsius
   b. gram
   c. liter
   d. mole

6. Matter can be defined as anything that _____ .
   a. has weight
   b. has mass and volume
   c. can be described in SI units
   d. exhibits both chemical and physical properties

7. Assume that you use time-lapse photography to film the rusting of a piece of iron. You then watch the film and observe the iron rust. What you see is both a _____ .
   a. chemical change and a qualitative observation
   b. physical change and a qualitative observation
   c. chemical change and a quantitative observation
   d. physical change and a quantitative observation

8. Which of the following is classified as a heterogeneous mixture?
   a. bean burrito
   b. blood
   c. hot chocolate
   d. plastic wrap

9. A compound differs from a mixture in that the former _____ .
   a. contains only one element
   b. varies in chemical composition depending on the sample size
   c. has a definite composition by mass of the elements it contains
   d. can be classified as either heterogeneous or homogeneous

10. Which of the following would be considered allotropes?
    a. CO and CO_2
    b. H_2O and H_2S
    c. C_2H_2 and C_6H_6
    d. S_6 and S_8

1. c   5. d   8. a
2. c   6. b   9. c
3. d   7. a   10. d
4. a

Continued from page 36.

16. a. 0.357 L
    b. 2.5×10^7 mg
    c. 6.5×10^{-7} m
    d. 35 L
    e. 2460 cm^3
    f. 2.5×10^{-4} g
    g. 2.5×10^{-7} kg
    h. 1500 mL
    i. 10 500 mmol

17. An element is one of the 111 simplest substances.

18. A molecule consists of two or more chemically combined atoms.

19. Monatomic gases include all of the noble gases. Diatomic gases include H_2, O_2, N_2, F_2, and Cl_2.

20. Although both diamond and graphite consist only of carbon atoms, their crystalline structure is different.

21. Both consist of two or more different substances and can vary in composition. Homogeneous mixtures are uniform in composition because the molecules of the substances are mixed completely. The substances in heterogeneous mixtures are not evenly mixed.

22. A pure substance is composed of only one type of particle (atom, ion pair, molecule), such as lead, water, or methane. A mixture is a physical combination of two or more substances.

23. A compound is composed of two or more elements combined in a specific ratio. A mixture is composed of two or more substances in no special ratio.

24. It is a homogeneous mixture because the carbon atoms are distributed evenly throughout the iron atoms.

25. It is not a compound because the steel may contain more or less carbon; there is no specific ratio.

Performance assessment

1. Students' strategies will vary. However, the importance of taking good notes in class, reviewing those notes, and working through assigned problems cannot be emphasized enough in reviewing strategies. Students must also be sure to keep current with the concepts and skills, or they will soon find themselves moving on to a new idea that they can't understand because they have not learned the prerequisite ideas.

2. Students will have to devise a way of determining the volume of the object if it does not have a regular shape.

Portfolio projects

1. Grade posters based on the variety of products shown, organization, labeling, spelling, and overall artistic quality.

Matter and Energy

CLASSROOM RESOURCES			
SECTIONS	**TEACHER'S DEMONSTRATIONS**	**PROBLEM SOLVING** ■ *Text* ◆ *ChemFile Mini-Guide*	**LABORATORIES** ■ *Text* ◆ *ChemFile Manuals: A, B, C, D*
2-1 **What is energy?** Section Review, p. 47			◆ **D4** Matter and Change: Pizza Mixture
2-2 **What is the process of science?** Section Review, p. 55	**Demo 1** Is Mass Conserved? p. 52		■ **InquiryLab** Applications of the Scientific Method, p. 49 ■ **QuickLab** Model of a Black Box, p. 53 ◆ **Exp. C1** Conservation of Mass ■ **Inv. 1A** Conservation of Mass—Percentage of Water in Popcorn, p. 706
2-3 **How do chemists measure quantities?** Section Review, p. 64		◆ **Chapter 2** Significant Figures ■ **How To** Determine the number of significant figures, p. 62 ◆ **Chapter 3** Scientific Notation	■ **Exp. 2A** Accuracy and Precision, p. 708 ◆ **A2** Accuracy and Precision in Measurement ◆ **B2** Accuracy and Precision: Calibrating a Pipet ■ **InquiryLab** U.S. Pennies Comparison, p. 61

SECTIONS	VIDEOS/VIDEODISC *Holt Chemistry Videodisc* CNN PRESENTS *Science in the NEWS*	CHEMFILE CD-ROMs ● *Teaching Resources* ◆ *Interactive Tutor*	OVERHEADS ● *Color Transparencies* ◆ *Transparency Masters*
2-1	Heat transfer from hot metal to water Heat and temperature: the microscopic view		
2-2	Activities of the Scientific Method CNN PRESENTS Segment 7 Science Controversy: Salt in the Diet	● Supplemental Reading: *The Same and Not the Same*, "Whirligigs" ● Supplemental Reading: *The Same and Not the Same*, "Thalidomide"	● **7** Scientific Method
2-3	Reporting measurements	● Math Skills: Operations with Scientific Notation	◆ **7A** Rules for Determining the Number of Significant Figures ◆ **8A** Rules for Making Calculations with Significant Figures *See also Transparency Masters 9A and 10A.*

ASSESSMENT RESOURCES

ALTERNATIVE ASSESSMENTS	CHAPTER TESTING	SCORING RUBRICS *Holt ChemFile Teaching Resources CD-ROM*
Student Text Performance assessments, p. 69 Portfolio projects 1–4, p. 70 **Teacher's Edition** Group Strategies, pp. 40, 44, 56 **Study Guide** Sections 2-1 to 2-3	**Student Text** Test Preparation, p. 71 **Holt Chemistry: Visualizing Matter Chapter 2 Test** (blackline masters) **Holt ChemFile Test Generator for Macintosh and Windows**	**Lab Work** Student-Designed Experiments Rubric Performance Tasks Scoring Rubric Assessment for Structured Inquiry Assessment for Open-Ended Inquiry **Portfolio Projects** Evaluating Concept Maps Assessing Portfolios Portfolio Assignment Student Evaluation Form

CHAPTER 2

Matter and Energy

READING STRATEGY

Assimilating Knowledge

Before students read this chapter, have them write a short, individual list of all the things they know about energy and energy transfer and about the process of scientific research, including the use of measurements in scientific calculations. Then have students list the things they might want to know about energy, scientific methods, and using measurements.

If students have trouble coming up with questions, here are some suggestions to get them on track.

- We eat food in order to have energy for life activities. So how is the energy stored in food?
- What are the major steps in scientific research?
- How do scientists record measurements in a way that reflects the precision of the measuring instrument?

ABOUT THE ILLUSTRATION

During the formation of a thunderstorm, a spinning effect results in the air of the lower atmosphere from changes in wind direction and air temperature. The tornadoes that form in these areas of strong rotation are powerful examples of the interaction between matter and energy.

internet connect

Holt Chemistry: Visualizing Matter
On-Line Resources
go.hrw.com
Visit the HRW Web site for a variety of resources related to this chapter. Just type in the keyword HW0 Chapt2.

SCILINKS
NSTA

National Science Teachers Association
On-Line Resources: www.scilinks.org
The following Scilinks Internet resources can be found in the student text for this chapter:

Page 40
TOPIC: Chemical energy
KEYWORD: HW021

Page 42
TOPIC: Physical/chemical change
KEYWORD: HW022

Page 65
TOPIC: Helium
KEYWORD: HW023

Page 70
TOPIC: Chance discoveries
KEYWORD: HW024

THE LAST VOYAGE
OF THE *GRANDCAMP*

On April 11, 1947, a cargo ship named the *Grandcamp* arrived in Texas City, a Texas port city of 50 000 people. The *Grandcamp* was carrying cargo destined for France—aid from the United States following World War II. Before departing for France, the *Grandcamp* had to be loaded with fertilizer.

Over the next few days, longshoremen loaded the ship with fertilizer, which consisted of a compound known as ammonium nitrate. Stored in 45 kg paper bags, 2300 metric tons of ammonium nitrate was loaded onto the ship. Also in the hold were 16 cases of ammunition, 380 bales of cotton, 9334 bags of shelled peanuts, 59 000 bales of twine, and some refrigeration and farm machinery. No one realized that with tons of ammonium nitrate on board the *Grandcamp* was a time bomb.

Soon after the last bags were loaded, one of the longshoremen noticed smoke coming from the ship's cargo hold. He alerted some co-workers, and they discovered flames coming from the bags of fertilizer. They tried to put out the fire, but it continued to spread and was soon burning out of control.

A little over an hour after the smoke was first detected, the *Grandcamp* exploded, causing a blast that was heard 240 km away. The blast created a 5 m wave of water that roared out of the harbor. Debris was tossed in every direction. An anchor from the ship flew 2.6 km through the air and created a 3 m wide hole in the ground where it landed. The blast triggered a series of explosions and fires throughout Texas City. When the catastrophe finally ended, 576 people were dead, 4000 were injured, and every building in the city was either destroyed or damaged. It was the worst industrial disaster in United States history.

The catastrophe on the *Grandcamp* was a direct result of a chemical process. As you will see, the explosion created by the ammonium nitrate was like all other processes in chemistry—it involved the interaction between matter and energy.

CHAPTER LINKS

Where did all the destructive energy that caused this catastrophe come from?

What happened in terms of energy when the Grandcamp exploded?

How much mass was converted to energy to produce the 350 gigajoules released by the explosion of the ammonium nitrate on the Grandcamp?

Ammonium nitrate is widely recognized as a potentially dangerous compound. But in the 1940s, few people were aware of its danger. Even though ammonium nitrate was used in the original formula for dynamite, the U.S. Department of Agriculture did not consider the compound dangerous when used as fertilizer. The only regulations concerning ammonium nitrate were to keep the fertilizer stored in paper bags or wooden crates and to keep it away from explosive materials, like the ammunition that was on the *Grandcamp*. This regulation was followed when the ship was loaded with its cargo, but a violent explosion occurred nonetheless.

CONCEPT PREVIEW

Section 2-1
The nature of chemical energy
▶ chemical bond
▶ kinetic energy
▶ potential energy
▶ conservation of energy
▶ energy transfer

Heat transfer
▶ temperature
▶ temperature scales
▶ specific heat capacity

Relationship between mass and energy

Section 2-2
The process of scientific research
▶ experiments
▶ accidental discoveries
▶ hypotheses
▶ theories
▶ models
▶ laws

Section 2-3
Measurements
▶ accuracy
▶ precision
▶ significant figures
▶ calculations involving measured quantities
▶ scientific notation

What is energy?

OBJECTIVES

▶ **Distinguish** between potential and kinetic energy.

▶ **Distinguish** between heat and temperature.

▶ **State** the law of conservation of energy.

▶ **Calculate** changes in heat energy.

▶ **Describe** the relationship between mass and energy.

LESSON WARM-UP

Sources of Energy Ask students where they would get the energy needed to perform the activities mentioned in the first paragraph. A common response is "from food." Then ask where the energy is stored in the food before it is released. Some students may already know that the energy involves chemical bonds. If so, ask how a chemical bond stores energy. Some students, recalling photosynthesis, may say that energy comes from the sun. Ask them to describe the flow of energy between the processes of photosynthesis in plants and metabolism in the body. Students may soon realize a need to learn more about the connection between energy and chemical substances.

VISUAL STRATEGY

Figure 2-1 Exhibit a ball-and-stick model of a water molecule similar to the one shown in this illustration, and manipulate it to show the ways the molecule as a whole can move and rotate. Then substitute springs for the O–H bonds and show the possible motions that can take place within the molecule.

Chemical energy

What comes to mind when you see or hear the word *energy*? Perhaps you think of a time when you were able to play an hour of basketball after taking two tests in school, wash the car when you got home, and then enjoy the school dance that night. Maybe the word *energy* brings to mind an image of a power plant. Or from what you have learned in previous science courses, you might associate *energy* with food or fuel.

Chemical energy involves chemical bonds

Chemical energy is the energy that matter possesses because of its chemical makeup. What does the chemical energy in an ordinary liquid compound like water involve? **Figure 2-1** shows the chemical structure of a water molecule. Notice that a water molecule consists of two hydrogen atoms that are connected to one oxygen atom. The electrons in each atom are moving, so they have energy. There is also energy associated with the force of attraction that holds hydrogen and oxygen atoms together. This force of attraction is known as a **chemical bond.** Water has chemical energy because of the atoms it contains and the bonds that hold them together.

internetconnect

SCILINKS
NSTA

TOPIC: Chemical energy
GO TO: www.scilinks.org
KEYWORD: HW021

chemical energy

the energy that matter possesses because of its chemical makeup

chemical bond

a mutual attraction between different atoms that binds the atoms together

▶ **FIGURE 2-1**

A water molecule consists of one oxygen atom attached to two hydrogen atoms. Chemical energy involves the chemical bonds holding the atoms together.

Oxygen atom

Chemical bond

Hydrogen atom

ALTERNATIVE ASSESSMENT

Group Strategy

Pose the following problems to assess students' understanding of potential energy, and take this opportunity to clear up any misunderstandings students may have.

You can lift a rock 2 m from the ground, increasing its gravitational potential energy, but suppose you leave the rock on the ground and dig a hole 2 m deep directly in front of it. Does the presence of the hole increase the potential energy of the rock? Explain your conclusion.

Suppose you take the same rock and hold it 2 m above the ground. Then you carry it to a canyon that is 500 m deep and hold the rock over the edge. Is its potential energy increased by being held over the canyon? Explain your conclusion.

The potential energy is increased in both cases, but not because work was done on the

Water molecules and the atoms that compose them have both kinetic and potential energy. **Kinetic energy** is the energy an object possesses due to its motion. Atoms and molecules are in constant motion, so they have kinetic energy. This is true even in ice. Although fixed somewhat in position in the ice crystal, as shown in **Figure 2-2,** the molecules vibrate back and forth. However, this vibrational energy is small compared with the energy of chemical bonds.

Potential energy is the energy an object has due to its position relative to other objects. To understand how the position of atoms is connected to energy, consider the reaction between the elements hydrogen and oxygen to form water. This reaction is shown symbolically in **Figure 2-3.** The process of forming water releases a large amount of heat. Why? The answer is that the relative positions of atoms have changed. Before the reaction, hydrogen atoms are bonded together and oxygen atoms are bonded together. The reaction changes the relative positions of the atoms, and therefore potential energy changes. Specifically, the potential energy of the atoms bonded in H_2O is lower than when the atoms bond in H_2 and O_2. The decrease in potential energy becomes heat energy. **Table 2-1,** on page 42, gives an overview of the energy changes that occur in the process of reacting hydrogen and oxygen to produce water. When chemical bonds are formed or broken, the energy changes are considered chemical energy.

All physical and chemical changes involve a change in energy

Think about any familiar chemical or physical change. What causes the change to occur? For a solid to melt, energy must be added to the solid. For a liquid to evaporate, the particles in the liquid must have enough energy to move away from the surface of the liquid. When you activate

FIGURE 2-2 ▲

Ice consists of water molecules held in a rigid, regular structure. Although the molecules in ice are not able to move freely, they are able to vibrate and therefore have kinetic energy.

kinetic energy

energy a moving object has because of its motion

potential energy

energy an object has because of its position

FIGURE 2-3 ▼

Hydrogen and oxygen react in a 2:1 ratio to produce water.

$2H_2$ $+$ O_2 $\longrightarrow$ $2H_2O$

TEACHING TIP

Potential Energy Select a fairly heavy object that cannot be damaged when it is dropped, and place it on the floor. Tell students that you will increase the object's potential energy. Then lift the object to shoulder height. Ask students to explain how the object's potential energy has increased. They should note the difference in the two positions of the object and the fact that the object has the potential to move back to its old position due to gravitational force. Drop the object, and point out the change from potential energy to kinetic energy as well as the dissipation of that energy (into heat and into the motion of other objects) when the object lands.

COMMON MISCONCEPTION

It is possible to increase the gravitational potential of an object by doing work on it. But students must avoid thinking of potential energy as a physical entity that is somehow stored somewhere. All potential energy involves matter and is simply the difference between the current condition and another possible condition of lower potential energy. In other words, the amount of potential energy an object possesses is relative to the state of lower energy that the object can assume.

rock. Potential energy is nothing more than the possible work that can be done by an object by virtue of its position. It should not be seen as stored energy. By extending this idea to chemistry, it is easy to see why a compound, such as glucose, has potential energy, considering that it is made by photosynthesis. But elements such as carbon or magnesium also have potential energy because they can react with other elements in ways that change the Mg or C atoms to a lower potential energy state.

42

DISCUSSION STRATEGY

Draw a roller coaster track on the board, and make the second peak higher than the first. Ask students to comment on whether such a design would work. *(It would not work.)* Ask them to analyze the motion of the car in terms of kinetic energy and potential energy and to explain why the roller coaster would not work as drawn. *(The gravitational potential energy of the car at the top of the first hill is relative to the dip between the hills. As the car accelerates down the hill, its potential energy is converted to kinetic energy, reaching a maximum at the bottom of the dip. As the car climbs the second hill, its kinetic energy is reconverted to potential energy. However, even if no energy is lost as friction, the car will have only enough energy to rise from the dip to the height of the first hill and thus will not make it over the second hill.)*

| TABLE 2-1 | Forms of Energy in a Water Molecule |

Forms of Energy in a Water Molecule

Energy change	Process	Symbolic picture
Energy in	Breaking bond between H atoms	
Energy in	Breaking bond between O atoms	
Energy out	Forming bonds between H and O atoms	

internet connect

SCLINKS
NSTA

TOPIC: Physical/chemical change
GO TO: www.scilinks.org
KEYWORD: HW022

energy
the capacity to do work

law of conservation of energy
in any chemical or physical process, energy is neither created nor destroyed

a light stick, such as the one in **Figure 2-4,** chemicals inside must react to give off light. When wood burns, it gives off heat. Energy from the sun drives some of the reactions of photosynthesis to produce food for the plant. All chemical or physical changes involve energy changes.

The term *energy* represents a broad concept. One definition of **energy** is the capacity to do some type of work, such as moving an object, forming a new compound, or producing light. In Chapter 1 you read that exothermic processes release energy, while endothermic processes absorb energy. The term *release* may give you the impression that energy can be created, while the term *absorb* may convey the idea that energy can be destroyed. However, the **law of conservation of energy** states that in any physical or chemical change, energy can change form, but the total amount of energy remains constant. Therefore, energy can be converted from kinetic energy to potential energy, but it cannot be created or destroyed.

► **FIGURE 2-4**

When you activate a light stick, chemical energy is converted to light energy.

FIGURE 2-5 ◄

A chemical reaction taking place inside the heat pack releases heat. The heat is transferred from the heat pack to its surroundings.

Energy can be transferred

Energy can be transferred from one object or substance to another. The most common energy transfers in chemistry are transfers of heat energy. **Heat** is the sum total of kinetic energy of the particles in a sample of matter. To keep track of energy transfers, chemists define the system being studied. A **system** consists of all the components that are being studied at a given time. Everything outside a system is referred to as the surroundings. A system can be quite complex and include a variety of substances and objects, or it can be very simple, like the heat pack shown in **Figure 2-5.**

One type of heat pack consists of a bag containing a metal disk and a compound called sodium acetate that is dissolved in water. The heat pack and its contents can be considered a system. Clicking the metal disk inside the pack causes the sodium acetate to crystallize, or come out of the solution. Energy is involved in the change when sodium acetate dissolves or crystallizes. All you need to recognize at this point is that these reactions involve a transfer of heat energy. The crystallization process for sodium acetate is exothermic. Although we say that heat is "released," it is more accurate to say that energy in the form of heat is transferred *from* the system *to* the surroundings. In this example, the surroundings may be your hands on a cold day.

Heat energy can also be transferred in the opposite direction—from the surroundings to a system. You can recharge the heat pack by placing it in boiling water so that energy can be transferred from the hot water (the surroundings) to the heat pack (the system). As heat energy is transferred, the sodium acetate dissolves. As the sodium acetate dissolves, its chemical energy increases. Energy transferred as heat into the heat pack is converted into the chemical energy of dissolved sodium acetate. Reactions in which energy is

heat

the sum total of kinetic energy of the particles in a sample of matter

system

a specific portion of matter in a given region of space that has been selected for study during an experiment or observation

STUDY SKILLS

TAKING AND REVIEWING NOTES

To achieve success in chemistry, it is important to take good class notes. This requires listening during the lecture and writing down only what seems important. It is a good idea to review your notes as soon as possible after each lecture, while the material is fresh in your mind. Write down questions, or attach adhesive notes to your notebook to identify the material that you don't understand. Ask your questions at the beginning of the next lecture.

TEACHING TIP

Identifying a System The concept of a system is better learned by example than by a verbal definition. To reinforce the idea, draw students' attention to (or have them identify) the system under consideration whenever they observe a demonstration or carry out an experiment.

ADDITIONAL APPLICATION

The crystallization of sodium acetate is an exothermic change. Some hot packs employ a chemical change in which fine iron filings are mixed with a solution containing a mild oxidizing agent. The iron is slowly oxidized, releasing heat in the process. Instant cold packs take advantage of spontaneous endothermic changes. One type contains ammonium nitrate and water in separate compartments. When the seal between the compartments is broken, the ammonium nitrate dissolves endothermically, absorbing heat from the surroundings. The disadvantage of these types of packs is that the processes cannot be reversed.

TEACHING TIP

Temperature Scales   Many properties of matter are mathematically dependent on the rate of particle motion; in other words, they are related to temperature. These properties are most easily described by using a temperature scale in which zero means no molecular motion, or stated another way, in which zero equals no temperature. You can illustrate the need for the Kelvin scale by having students imagine what mass measurements would be like if someone had decided to assign the value zero to the mass of 1 cm^3 (1 g) of water. Masses smaller than that would have negative values. As absurd as this may seem, it is analogous to the Celsius scale, in which zero is randomly assigned as a convenient reference point.

► **FIGURE 2-6**

Some of the heat that is transferred to the heat pack from its surroundings (the boiling water) is converted into chemical energy in the compounds inside the heat pack. Thus, the heat pack can be used over and over again.

transferred as heat from the surroundings into the system are endothermic processes. Thus energy is not really "absorbed" in an endothermic reaction—it is converted *into* chemical energy or some other form of energy. Once the energy transferred as heat is converted into chemical energy, the heat pack is ready to be used again. **Figure 2-6** shows the heat pack system after it has been recharged with heat energy.

CONCEPT CHECK

1. What is energy?
2. State the law of conservation of energy.

Energy transfer as heat

Temperature indicates how hot or cold something is. When energy is transferred to heat water, the temperature of the water increases. The more rapidly the water molecules move, the higher their average kinetic energy. As the average kinetic energy of the molecules increases, so does the temperature of the water. **Temperature** is a measure of the average kinetic energy of the random motion of particles in a substance.

temperature

a measure of the average kinetic energy of the particles in a sample of matter

Temperature is expressed using different scales

You know that a thermometer is a device used to measure temperature. The operation of most thermometers is based on the principle that matter expands as its temperature increases. Thermometers are usually marked with the Fahrenheit or Celsius temperature scales. However, the Fahrenheit scale is not used in chemistry. In Chapter 1 you learned that the SI unit for temperature is the kelvin, K. **Figure 2-7** shows a comparison of the Celsius and Kelvin temperature scales. The zero point on the Celsius scale is designated as the freezing point of water. The zero point on the Kelvin scale is designated as absolute zero, the lowest temperature theoretically possible. In chemistry, you will use both scales, and at times, you will have to convert between the two scales. Conversion between the Celsius and Kelvin scales simply requires an adjustment to account for their different zero points. The following equations show how to convert between these two temperature

ALTERNATIVE ASSESSMENT

Group Strategy

Pose the following question to students: Suppose you are working in a laboratory that has some thermometers graduated in kelvins and others graduated in degrees Celsius. You are assigned the task of trying to replicate the results of an experiment performed by another chemist in the lab. You have the chemist's laboratory notebook and are going over the details of the experiment. At one point you find the notation, "In the next

10 minutes, the temperature of the reaction rose 38." There is no unit indicated. Will you have to ask which type of thermometer the chemist was using? Explain your answer.

scales. The symbol t stands for temperature in degrees Celsius, and the symbol T stands for temperature in kelvins.

$$t(°C) = T(K) - 273.15\ K$$
$$T(K) = t(°C) + 273.15°C$$

Specific heat capacity— changing the temperature of a substance

If you have done much cooking, you know that metal pans transfer heat to food faster than glass or ceramic pans do. If you add the same heat energy to similar masses of different substances, they don't all show the same increase in temperature. This relationship between heat energy and temperature change, which is unique to each substance, is called the specific heat capacity. The **specific heat capacity** (c_p) of a substance is the amount of heat energy required to raise the temperature of 1 g of the substance by 1 K. The SI unit for energy is the *joule* (J). One joule is approximately equal to the amount of energy you expend bringing a cheeseburger to your mouth. Specific heat capacity is expressed in joules per gram kelvin (J/g•K). You will find the specific heat capacity of some elements listed in **Table 2-2.** Specific heat capacities are calculated from experimental data.

	Celsius	Kelvin
Boiling point of water	100	373
Body temperature	37	310
Freezing point of water	0	273
Absolute zero	−273	0

FIGURE 2-7

You will encounter two temperature scales in your study of chemistry. The Celsius scale is part of the metric system; the Kelvin scale is the SI temperature scale.

specific heat capacity

the amount of heat energy required to raise the temperature of 1 g of a substance by 1 K

TABLE 2-2 Specific Heat Capacities at Room Temperature of Some Elements

Substance	Specific heat capacity (J/g•K)	Substance	Specific heat capacity (J/g•K)
Aluminum	0.897	Lead	0.129
Cadmium	0.232	Neon	1.030
Calcium	0.647	Nickel	0.444
Carbon (graphite)	0.709	Platinum	0.133
Chromium	0.449	Silicon	0.705
Copper	0.385	Silver	0.235
Gold	0.129	Tin	0.228
Iron	0.449	Zinc	0.388

SECTION 2-1

TEACHING TIP

Temperature Conversions Let students know that there is no need to use the last two decimal places in the conversion factor 273.15 unless temperatures are expressed to one or two decimal places.

ADDITIONAL EXAMPLES

Have students work out the following temperature conversions in class:

a. 25°C to K

  Ans. 298 K

b. 300 K to °C

  Ans. 27°C

c. 37°C, normal body temperature, to K

  Ans. 310 K

d. 150 K to °C

  Ans. −123°C

VISUAL STRATEGY

Figure 2-7 Emphasize that a kelvin and a degree Celsius are the same size. In other words, they represent the same temperature interval. The only difference is the temperature at which the zero point occurs.

TEACHING TIP

Designing a Model Ask students to devise a way to demonstrate the differences in the specific heat capacity of several metals. If you wish, tell them that the rate of the temperature increase indicates the heat capacity of the metal. Be sure students' plans address the question of which factors must be kept constant. A satisfactory method is to place thermometers in blocks of the various metals. The blocks must have equal masses. All of the blocks are then simultaneously lowered into hot water. The specific heat capacity of each sample should be inversely proportional to the rate of the temperature increase.

COMMON MISCONCEPTION

If students look up heat capacities in a reference source, they are likely to find tables of *molar* heat capacities, which are more commonly used in thermodynamics. These have the units J/mol•K. These may be converted to specific (mass-based) heat capacities by dividing by the molar mass of the particular substance.

DID YOU KNOW?

The electric generators at Hoover Dam, on the Colorado River, produce energy at the rate of 1.3×10^6 kW (1.3×10^6 kJ/s). The energy available from the total conversion of 1 g of matter to energy is approximately equal to the energy produced in 19 hours by the generators at Hoover Dam.

CHAPTER CONNECTION

Students will apply Einstein's equation in Chapter 3 and again in Chapter 18.

Each value in Table 2-2 represents the amount of energy needed to raise the temperature of 1 g of the substance 1 K. It takes 0.897 J to raise the temperature of 1 g of aluminum by 1 K. It takes only 0.385 J of energy to raise the temperature of 1 g of copper by 1 K. Of course, it will take twice as much energy, 0.770 J, to raise the temperature of 2 g of copper by 1 K. For a single atom, however, the heat capacities of aluminum and copper are almost identical. In fact, all metal atoms have heat capacities close to 4.1×10^{-23} J/K.

Mass and energy are closely related

Toward the end of the nineteenth century, scientists believed that matter and energy were clearly distinct. Matter was perceived as something that consisted of particles. These particles had mass, and their exact location in space could be precisely pinpointed. In contrast, energy was perceived as something very different from matter. However, by the beginning of the twentieth century, scientists had come to realize that there was no clear-cut distinction between matter and energy.

In 1905, Albert Einstein proposed his special theory of relativity, a part of which implies that mass and energy are equivalent. From his theory, Einstein derived the following equation.

$$E = mc^2$$

E is the energy equivalent of an object, m is its mass, and c is the speed of light in a vacuum (2.998×10^8 m/s). Einstein's equation shows that energy has a mass equivalent. Conversely, mass has an energy equivalent. This relationship becomes clearer when the equation is rearranged.

$$m = \frac{E}{c^2}$$

Mass and energy are no longer considered completely different quantities. Each can be transformed into the other. In such transformations, a small amount of mass corresponds to a huge amount of energy. In nuclear power plants, an extremely small fraction of the mass of atoms is converted to heat energy, a part of which is then transformed to electric energy. Einstein's equation reveals how much energy can be obtained from a given amount of mass.

► **FIGURE 2-8**

Widely considered to have possessed one of the greatest scientific minds of all time, Albert Einstein gave the world theories that revolutionized how scientists look at the universe.

"Now that desk looks better. Everything's squared away, yessir, squaaaaaared away."

Assume that all the mass of a 1.000 g object could be converted to energy. Substituting the appropriate values into Einstein's equation reveals how much energy can theoretically be obtained from a 1.000 g object.

$$E = (1.000 \text{ g})(2.998 \times 10^8 \text{ m/s})^2 =$$

$$8.988 \times 10^{16} \text{ g} \cdot \text{m}^2/\text{s}^2 \times \frac{1 \text{ kg}}{1000 \text{ g}} = 8.988 \times 10^{13} \text{ kg} \cdot \text{m}^2/\text{s}^2$$

You learned that 1 kg m²/s² is 1 J. Thus, 8.998×10^{13} J of energy can be obtained from a 1.000 g object. Recall that 1 J is the energy you expend to bring a cheeseburger to your mouth. Thus, converting the mass of a 1.000 g object would give you enough energy to lift a cheeseburger to your mouth 90 trillion times! But converting mass to energy is not a simple task, as you will learn in Chapter 18.

SECTION REVIEW

Total recall

1. What is the difference between potential energy and kinetic energy?
2. What is the difference between heat and temperature?
3. Explain what the equation $E = mc^2$ signifies.
4. What energy changes are considered chemical energy?
5. What is a system?
6. Define *specific heat capacity*.

Critical thinking

7. What happens in terms of heat transfer when you hold a snowball in your hand?
8. **Interpreting Tables** Use Table 2-2 to determine the following.
   a. Which of the metals listed requires the most energy to raise its temperature by 1°C?
   b. If energy is added at the same rate to containers all of the same mass made of copper, chromium, and lead, which container will show the greatest rise in temperature after 10 minutes?

Practice problems

9. Convert the following Celsius temperatures to Kelvin temperatures.
   a. 100°C   c. 0°C
   b. 785°C   d. −37°C
10. Convert the following Kelvin temperatures to Celsius temperatures.
    a. 273 K   c. 0 K
    b. 1200 K   d. 100 K
11. **Story Clue** The formula for calculating kinetic energy is

$$KE = \frac{mv^2}{2}.$$

KE is the kinetic energy of an object, m is its mass, and v is its velocity. Recall that the explosion of the *Grandcamp* hurled the ship's anchor through the air. How much kinetic energy did the 1300 kg anchor have if it was traveling at a velocity of 50 m/s?

ANSWERS

SECTION REVIEW

Total recall

1. Both are the capacity to do work. Kinetic energy is the energy an object has due to its motion. Potential energy is the energy of an object that has the potential to move because of its position.
2. Heat is the total kinetic energy of the particles in a sample of matter. Temperature is a measure of the average kinetic energy of the particles in an object.
3. The equation represents the amount of energy available when a quantity of matter is changed completely into energy.
4. The potential energy changes that result from the destruction and formation of chemical bonds are considered chemical energy.
5. A system is all of the components that are being studied at a given time.
6. Specific heat capacity is the amount of heat required to raise 1 g of the substance by 1 K.

Critical thinking

7. Heat passes from your hand, which is at a higher temperature, to the snowball, which is at a lower temperature.
8. a. aluminum
   b. lead

Practice problems

9. a. 373 K
   b. 1058 K
   c. 273 K
   d. 236 K
10. a. 0°C
    b. 927°C
    c. −273°C
    d. −173°C

11. $KE = \dfrac{mv^2}{2}$

$$KE = \frac{(1300 \text{ kg})\left(50 \dfrac{\text{m}}{\text{s}}\right)^2}{2}$$

$$KE = 1\,625\,000 \text{ J}$$

What is the process of science?

OBJECTIVES

▶ *Describe* the process used by scientists to study matter and energy.

▶ *Explain* the purpose of controls in an experiment.

▶ *Describe* the role of models in chemistry.

▶ *Distinguish* between a hypothesis, a theory, and a law.

LESSON WARM-UP

The Scientific Method Introduce students to the scientific method by encouraging them to observe and question the following demonstration:

Secure a candle in a holder on the front desk. Light the candle, and ask students what part of the candle is burning *(the wax)*. Ask them what observations they would make to show that it is not the wick that is burning. *(Observe the flame closely for a time.)* Ask students what physical state the wax is in when it burns. Elicit a statement **(hypothesis)** similar to, "The wax is a liquid when it burns." Ask students what observations they would make **(experiment)** to verify this statement. *(Close observation of the flame will reveal that the flame begins at a small distance from the wick, strongly suggesting that the wax is gaseous when it burns.)* Have students formulate a statement **(theory)** that explains the observation that a lighted candle continues to burn. *(When the candle is lit, the wick burns for a short time until heat begins to melt and vaporize the wax. The wax vapor combines with oxygen in the air, producing heat, light, and a variety of combustion products. The heat from combustion continues to melt wax, which soaks the wick and replaces the wax that has burned.)*

CNN Science in the News

PRESENTS Feature Story 7 *Science Controversy: Salt in the Diet* See the Science in the News video guide for more details.

The scientific method

The first scientists placed great reliance on rational thought and logic. They rarely felt it was necessary to test their ideas or conclusions and were not inclined to experiment. Gradually, experiments became the crucial test for the acceptance of scientific knowledge. Today, experiments are an integral part of research in all sciences, including chemistry. Science is distinguished from other fields of study in that it provides precise guidelines and includes specific procedures for conducting research. Scientists constantly challenge the work of other scientists to ensure that their results and conclusions are correct.

Experiments are part of the scientific method

The way scientists carry out investigations is referred to as the *scientific method*. The scientific method is not a series of exact steps; rather, it is a strategy for drawing sound conclusions. A scientist chooses various scientific procedures to use in an investigation. **Figure 2-9** lists some of these procedures. Which ones have you used in investigations that you have performed in previous science courses?

A chemist selects procedures that best fit the nature of the particular investigation. For example, a chemist who has an idea for developing a

▼ **FIGURE 2-9**

The scientific method is not a stepwise procedure. Scientists may repeat steps many times before there is sufficient evidence to formulate a theory. You can see that each stage represents a number of different activities.

| **OBSERVING**
• collecting data
• measuring
• experimenting
• communicating | **FORMULATING HYPOTHESES**
• organizing and analyzing data
• classifying
• inferring
• predicting
• communicating | **TESTING**
• predicting
• experimenting
• communicating
• collecting data
• measuring | **THEORIZING**
• constructing models
• predicting
• communicating | **PUBLISHING RESULTS**
• communicating |

Data do not support hypothesis—revise or reject hypothesis.

Results confirmed by other scientists— validate theory.

better method to recycle plastics may research the literature, collect information, propose a method to separate the materials, and then test the method. This sequence of events forms the scientific method that will be used by this chemist.

In contrast, another chemist may be investigating the pollution caused by an incinerator. This investigation would follow a different procedure that might include collecting and analyzing samples, interviewing people, predicting the role the incinerator plays in producing the pollution, and conducting field studies to test that prediction. This approach would also constitute a scientific method.

Thus, the scientific method can be viewed as a logical approach to exploring a problem or question that has been raised through observation or mental reflection. No matter which procedures are selected, the scientific method used by a chemist consists of the fundamental activities outlined in Figure 2-9. Notice the last step in the figure. The research findings of any experiment or investigation must be reproducible by other scientists for those findings to be accepted as valid. Ultimately, the success of the scientific method depends on publishing what has been found so that others can repeat the procedures that were used and verify the results.

Scientific discoveries can come from unexpected observations

Not all discoveries and findings are the result of a carefully worked-out plan based on the scientific method. In fact, some important discoveries and developments have been made simply by accident. An example is the discovery of the chemical compound commonly known as Teflon®. You are probably familiar with Teflon as the nonstick coating used on pots and pans, but it has many more applications. Teflon is used

INQUIRYLAB

CONSUMER ACTIVITY

Applications of the Scientific Method

In this activity, you must design a successful experimental approach to solve four problems.

The first two problems involve studying the boiling point of a pure liquid. The boiling point of a substance can be defined as the temperature at which a liquid becomes a gas. The third and fourth problems involve observing how the addition of different substances affects the boiling point of the liquid.

Materials

beakers, graduated cylinders, sugar, thermometers, Bunsen burners, salt, ring stands, ring clamps

Problems

1. Design an experiment to determine what happens to the temperature of a liquid after it has started to boil.
2. Design an experiment to determine if the volume of a liquid has an effect on its boiling point.
3. Design an experiment to determine what happens to the boiling point of water when table salt is added.
4. Design an experiment to find out which chemical, salt or sugar, has a more dramatic effect on the boiling point of water.

Analysis

1. Consider two beakers of boiling water. The water in beaker A has been boiling for 5 minutes, and the water in beaker B has been boiling for 10 minutes. Which water sample is at a higher temperature?
2. Antifreeze is added to a car's radiator in the summertime. Explain how antifreeze affects the boiling point of the water in a radiator.

INQUIRYLAB

Thermometers should be supported by a clamp and should not be allowed to rest on the bottom of the beaker; the water may be superheated there, and temperature readings will not be accurate. Students should not expect to see increases in boiling points by dissolving only a little salt or sugar. One mole of particles (30 g of NaCl and 340 g of sucrose) per kilogram of water increases the boiling point only about 0.5°C. To see a 2°C increase in boiling point will require about 12 g of NaCl or 135 g of sucrose per 100 mL of water.

Analysis

1. Both samples of water will be at the same temperature because the water's temperature remains constant after it reaches the boiling point.
2. Antifreeze not only protects the radiator from freezing in the winter but also causes the solution to have a higher boiling point than that of water alone.

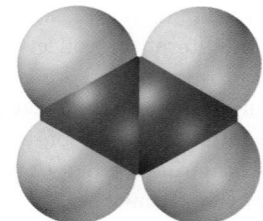

► **FIGURE 2-10**

Tetrafluoroethene is an example of a *fluorocarbon,* an organic compound composed of carbon and fluorine atoms. Teflon is prepared using tetrafluoroethene.

as thermal insulation in clothing, as a component in wall coverings and roofing materials, and as a protective coating on metals, glass, and plastics. Teflon's properties of low chemical reactivity and very low friction make it valuable in the construction of artificial joints for human limbs.

Teflon was discovered by chance

In 1938, Dr. Roy Plunkett, a chemist employed by DuPont, was working in his lab, trying to develop a new coolant gas to use as a refrigerant. At the time, a compound called dichlorotetrafluoroethene was the most widely used refrigerant. Plunkett's research had led him to believe that he could make a less expensive coolant by reacting a gas called tetrafluoroethene (TFE) with hydrochloric acid. A structural formula and model for TFE are shown in **Figure 2-10.** He cooled the canisters of TFE to liquefy the gas. Once everything was ready for the experiment, Plunkett placed a canister of TFE on a balance to record its mass. He then opened the valve to let the TFE flow into a container filled with hydrochloric acid. But no TFE came out of the metal canister.

Plunkett checked the valve to make sure it was open; it was. He then used a piece of wire to poke out anything that might be clogging the opening in the valve. Still nothing came out of the metal canister. Thinking that the TFE might have somehow leaked out of the canister, Plunkett noted its mass on the balance. Because the canister had the same mass as it did when it was filled with TFE, he knew that the TFE had not leaked out.

► **FIGURE 2-11**

The roof of the Hubert H. Humphrey Metrodome in Minneapolis, Minnesota, is made of Teflon, the polymer accidentally discovered by Roy Plunkett in 1938.

Puzzled, Plunkett removed the valve and shook the canister upside down. Only a few white flakes fell out. Curious about what had happened, Plunkett decided to analyze the white flakes. He discovered that he had accidentally created the proper conditions for TFE molecules to form a long chain known as a **polymer.** Further research revealed that the polymer he had made, called polytetrafluoroethene, was very slippery. In addition, the polymer was not affected by many of the chemicals that would normally break down a polymer. After 10 years of additional research and development, large-scale manufacture of the polymer, now known as Teflon, became practical.

The anticancer drug cisplatin was discovered accidentally

Another accidental discovery was made some 30 years later. In this case, Dr. Barnett Rosenberg had been using platinum probes to study the effects of electric fields on living cells. He and his colleagues observed that bacteria did not reproduce near the platinum probes. After conducting extensive experiments, they were able to show that a platinum compound formed near the probes in an electrochemical reaction. This compound, called cisplatin, has the chemical structure shown in **Figure 2-12.** After a long series of carefully planned experiments, researchers showed that cisplatin, and not the electric fields, caused the changes in cell reproduction.

Rosenberg reasoned that because cancer involves uncontrolled cell growth, perhaps cisplatin would be effective in treating cancer. The results of another series of experiments showed that Rosenberg's reasoning was correct. Rosenberg's initial work spawned further research of the anticancer properties of cisplatin. After years of testing by independent sources to verify the effectiveness of the drug, cisplatin was approved by the Food and Drug Administration in 1979 for treatment of certain types of cancer.

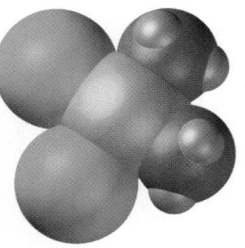

STUDY SKILLS

LEARNING TERMINOLOGY
Important terms and their definitions are listed in the margin of this book. Make sure you understand these definitions because you will be tested on them. Ask your teacher about any definitions that don't make sense to you. Review the terms frequently, and think up examples to help you remember them. One way to be sure you understand the definition of a term is to explain its meaning to a classmate.

polymer

a large organic molecule composed of smaller units bonded together

FIGURE 2-12 ◄

Cisplatin is a compound formed from platinum, chlorine, nitrogen, and hydrogen atoms.

DID YOU KNOW?
The substance cisplatin was identified in 1845, but no one recognized its therapeutic value until Dr. Rosenberg published his work. Cisplatin inhibits DNA synthesis by a process called *intercalation,* the insertion of a molecule between two adjacent base pairs in a DNA molecule.

TEACHING TIP
Anticancer Drugs Many anticancer drugs are toxic to all body cells, not just cancer cells. Ask students to speculate about why toxic drugs are effective in treating active cancer. (*Cancer cells have a high metabolic rate and reproduce rapidly, so the toxic properties of the drug affect these cells much more than they affect other body cells that do not reproduce or that reproduce at a slower rate.*)

RESOURCE LINK

ChemFile Teaching Resources CD-ROM
Supplemental Reading Projects Assign the guided reading worksheets for Roald Hoffmann's essay "Whirligigs" in *The Same and Not the Same* for cross-curricular connections to language arts.

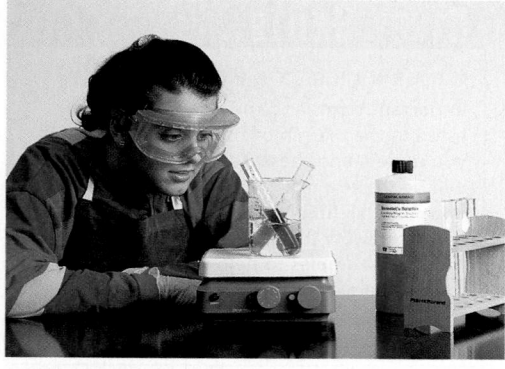

▲ **FIGURE 2-13**

This student is testing various food products claimed to be sugar-free for the presence of sugar. If the test reagent turns from blue to red after reacting with the samples, sugar is present in the product.

hypothesis
a reasonable and testable explanation of observations

A hypothesis is a testable explanation of an observation

Recognizing and defining a problem or question often stems from observing, as the student is doing in **Figure 2-13.** The discovery of cisplatin and its usefulness in treating cancer resulted from a simple observation—bacteria did not reproduce near the platinum probes. That observation led to further experiments and tests.

Once observations have been made, they must be analyzed. Scientists start by examining all the relevant information or data they have gathered. They look for patterns in the data that can suggest an explanation for their observations. This proposed explanation is called a hypothesis. A **hypothesis** is a reasonable and testable explanation for observations. Hypotheses are often written in an "if-then" format that describes a cause-and-effect relationship. A hypothesis for Rosenberg's work with cisplatin is as follows: *if* cisplatin can slow or stop cell reproduction, *then* it could be effective in treating cancer, which is caused by uncontrolled cell growth.

Experiments are used to test hypotheses

An *experiment* is a process carried out under controlled conditions, often to test the validity of a hypothesis, as shown in **Figure 2-14.** Rosenberg's work with cisplatin initially involved the question of what was inhibiting the growth of the cells. The most important part of his experimentation was documenting the effects of variables. A *variable* is any aspect of an experiment that can be changed to affect the outcome of the experiment. Before Rosenberg could come to the conclusion that cisplatin was indeed the reason that the growth of bacteria was slowed, he had to measure the effects of all other variables. How did he know the effect was not caused by a simple temperature change in the culture medium?

▶ **FIGURE 2-14**

These students are experimenting to determine how to get the largest volume of popped corn from the fewest kernels.

DEMONSTRATION 1

Is Mass Conserved?

Approximate time: 10 minutes

Present the following demonstration of an apparent contradiction to the law of conservation of mass.

1. Place a burner in the center of a metal tray or pan that is about 12 in. wide.

2. Take a small wad of medium steel wool, measure its mass on a balance, and record the mass on the board. A mechanical balance is best for the demonstration.

3. Ask students to think about things that burn and, have them formulate hypotheses on how the mass of the steel wool will change when it is burned. Some will think that it will decrease in mass or stay the same.

4. Pick up the steel wool with crucible tongs, and hold it in the burner flame. Try to regulate the burning so that very little of

How did he know the culture had not been contaminated? How did he know there weren't changes in the electric current? Because platinum is generally an unreactive element and the concentration of platinum compounds in the culture medium was very low, it initially seemed unlikely that platinum could be causing the cells to stop reproducing.

The researchers had to narrow the field of possible variables by keeping all of the variables constant except one, and that one was varied in each trial. Temperature, current, purity of the platinum, and the contents of the culture medium are some of the many variables that could change from experiment to experiment. When a variable is kept constant from one trial to the next, the procedure is called a *control experiment*. Control experiments allow researchers to isolate the key variable. It took many experiments over a two-year period for Rosenberg and his team to verify that the formation of cisplatin was the key factor that interfered with the growth of cells.

Data from experiments can lead to a theory

Any conclusion scientists make must come directly and solely from the data they obtain in their experiments. Many times, scientists discover that they are unable to arrive at a conclusion. In fact, they may discover that the data fail to support their hypothesis. In that case, they must re-examine the question and develop and test a new hypothesis.

Any hypothesis that withstands repeated testing may become part of a theory. A **theory** is a broad generalization that is based on observation, experimentation, and reasoning. Because theories are not facts, but rather explanations, they can never be completely proven. A theory is considered successful if it explains *most* of what is observed. When a theory is not successful, it may be modified or discarded as new information is discovered. An example of such a modification is the atomic theory, which you will learn about in Chapter 3. In the early 1800s, John Dalton collected data from experiments to support the idea that matter is made of atoms. Part of Dalton's atomic theory was that atoms are indivisible. This part of his theory had to be discarded after the discovery of subatomic particles. But much of Dalton's original theory is still valid.

Top Quark, Last Piece in Puzzle Of Matter, Appears to Be in Place

By WILLIAM J. BROAD

FIGURE 2-15 ▲

The discovery of the subatomic particles called quarks forced a revision of the theory of atomic structure.

theory

a well-tested explanation of observations

QUICKLAB

CONSUMER ACTIVITY

Model of a Black Box

In this activity, you will construct a model of objects in a sealed box by making inferences about them.

Materials
sealed box containing one or more objects

Problems
1. Carefully tilt, shake, or rotate the box.
2. Record all observations.
3. Use your observations to determine the number of objects in the box, their masses, general shapes, and sizes.
4. Compare observations and ideas about the objects in the box with others in your class. Make a hypothesis about the identity of each object.

Analysis
1. Provide a written description (model) of your objects. If you were able to infer the identity of the object, include its identity in your model.

TEACHING TIP

Identifying Theories Ask students to name any theories they have already learned. Possibilities include the theory of gravitation, of plate tectonics, of evolution by punctuated equilibrium, and of evolution by natural selection. Ask them to explain how these theories satisfy the scientific definition of a theory.

QUICKLAB

You may want to include objects with characteristic geometric shapes, such as a checker, a domino, a tennis ball, and the cardboard inside a roll of paper towels. Other objects could vary in density or in proportions. Place two or three objects in each box, and seal the boxes with packaging tape or duct tape. If students are going to compare results in step 5, each box should contain the same objects.

Analysis

1. Answers will vary but should include a summary of the observations that led the student to make conclusions about a particular object.

the material falls onto the tray. It is not important that all of the wool reacts.

5. After the steel wool has cooled sufficiently, place it back on the balance pan. Include material that fell on the tray. Measure and record the new mass. Students will notice that the mass has increased.

6. Ask the class to devise a hypothesis and an experiment that would determine whether or not the law of conservation of

mass was violated and explain the increase in mass.

Safety
Wear safety goggles and a laboratory apron. Avoid long, loose sleeves, and tie back long hair. Keep students at least 10 ft from the demonstration.

Disposal
Place cooled material in the trash.

People have known for centuries that when a hot object and a cool object are placed near each other, the cool object becomes warmer and the hot object becomes cooler. This observation led people to believe that heat was an invisible fluid, called caloric, that flowed from a warm object to a cool object. Materials that gave off a lot of heat when burned were thought to contain more caloric than materials that gave off only a little heat. We still have the word *calorie* today to remind us of the caloric theory of heat.

In the late eighteenth century an American-British scientist named Benjamin Thompson (1753–1814), also known as Count Rumford, was in Germany overseeing the manufacture of cannons. He noticed that a tremendous amount of heat was generated when the cannon barrels were bored. This observation led to research that replaced the caloric theory with the modern kinetic theory of heat.

FIGURE 2-16 ▼

a This blueprint is a two-dimensional model.

b The mouse is often used in research to model how humans might react to drugs and treatments.

c Computer-generated models, such as these of nitroglycerin and of ammonium nitrate, make it easy for chemists to compare the structures of different compounds.

Theories can be models

Models play a major role in science. A model is a simplified representation of an object, a system, a process, or an idea. Models can take many forms, from actual replicas to written descriptions. **Figure 2-16** shows several types of models. Models can be used in various ways. One of the models represents ammonium nitrate, the compound that caused the *Grandcamp* explosion. Compare the model of ammonium nitrate with the model of nitroglycerin in Figure 2-16. Nitroglycerin is the explosive used in dynamite. What do the structures of ammonium nitrate and nitroglycerin have in common?

It is important to remember that models are simplified representations. The atoms making up ammonium nitrate and nitroglycerin are not hard spheres, nor are they the sizes and colors shown. However, the model does show the geometrical arrangement of the atoms and their relative sizes. An effective model clearly depicts a particular set of characteristics of what is being modeled. Models, like theories, are refined as new information becomes available.

Scientific laws are based on facts

Certain facts in science hold true consistently. Such facts are known as scientific laws. A **scientific law** is a statement or mathematical expression that reliably describes the behavior of the natural world. Note that a scientific law *describes* events in the natural world but does not attempt to *explain* them. For example, the **law of conservation of mass**

scientific law
a description of the natural world that has proven reliable over time

law of conservation of mass
the products of a chemical reaction have the same mass as the reactants

states that the products of a chemical reaction have the same mass as the reactants. This law does not explain why matter in chemical reactions behaves this way; it simply describes this behavior.

In some cases, scientific laws are subject to reinterpretation based on the discovery of new information. For example, you learned in Section 2-1 that the law of conservation of energy states that energy can be neither created nor destroyed in any physical or chemical process. Similarly, the law of conservation of mass states that mass cannot be created or destroyed. Einstein's special theory of relativity connects these two laws. Through the equation $E = mc^2$, the theory of relativity explains that energy and mass are equivalent. Although neither can be created or destroyed, energy *can* be converted into mass, and vice versa. Einstein prompted a reevaluation of these two conservation laws by his assertion that energy and mass are interconvertible.

Because there are so few facts that are consistently reliable in describing the behavior of the natural world, there are a limited number of laws in science compared with the number of theories and hypotheses. Do not confuse a scientific law with either a hypothesis or a theory. A hypothesis *predicts* an event. A theory *explains* it. A law *describes* it.

SECTION REVIEW

Total recall

1. What activities are part of the scientific method?

2. How does a hypothesis differ from a theory?

3. State the law of conservation of mass.

4. What is a scientific law, and how does it differ from a theory?

5. Name two chemical compounds that were accidentally discovered, and describe what they are used for.

Critical thinking

6. Why does a scientist include a control in the design of an experiment?

7. Give two reasons why scientists publish the results of their experiments.

8. How do models help chemists acquire knowledge about matter and energy?

9. What variables would a chemist need to control when setting up an experiment to determine whether or not a low temperature is required for TFE to form a polymer?

10. Describe what is needed for a hypothesis to develop into a theory.

11. Why is there no single scientific method?

12. **Interpreting graphics** Refer to Figure 2-9 on page 48. Describe a sequence of actions that a chemist might take to develop a new drug to treat diabetics.

13. **Story Clue** What scientific processes listed in Figure 2-9 would you use to determine why the *Grandcamp* exploded?

ANSWERS

SECTION REVIEW

Total recall

1. The scientific method includes making observations and collecting data in order to formulate a question or hypothesis, testing the hypothesis by experimentation, interpreting the data and comparing the results with the hypothesis, revising the hypothesis if necessary, and communicating the results.

2. A hypothesis is a testable explanation for observations. A theory is also an explanation of observations, but it is the result of repeated testing and revision of hypotheses.

3. The total mass of the products of a reaction is the same as the total mass of the reactants.

4. A scientific law reliably describes the observed behavior of the natural world but does not explain it. A theory explains the observed behavior.

5. Answers include the compounds polytetrafluoroethylene, penicillin, saccharine, and cisplatin.

Critical thinking

6. A control is used to isolate the variable a scientist wants to study.

7. Research results are published so that researchers are credited for their work and so that other scientists can critique the results and attempt to replicate them.

8. Models can be used to make predictions about the behavior of matter and energy.

9. Accept all reasonable answers. Possibilities include the volume of the reaction vessel, the mass of reactants, the pressure of the reaction system, and the composition of the reaction mixture.

10. Usually, many experiments followed by revision and refinement of the hypothesis are required.

11. Scientists seldom follow a strict series of steps in their work.

12. Answers may vary. The following is one possible simplified scheme: Gather data on existing substances known to have effects on diabetes. Try to identify structural features common to molecules of effective substances. Then devise a way to synthesize a new substance that incorporates these structural or enhanced features. Test the resulting substances against diabetes in laboratory animals, and test them for possible toxicity. Conduct clinical trials on substances found to be effective and nontoxic.

13. Answers will vary but should include the collection of data from the explosion site and an analysis of residues. Propose a possible mechanism for the explosion.

LESSON WARM-UP

Group Strategy Before class, prepare several measuring sticks (one for each group of three students) of various lengths from old metersticks or paint stirrers. If possible, paint the sticks or use tape so that only the markings at certain intervals are left uncovered. Intervals could be visible at 1 cm, 5 cm, 10 cm, 20 cm, 50 cm, and 1 m.

Divide the class into groups of three. Pick a common object with a height and width that can be easily measured, such as a chalkboard or a desk. Ask each group to measure the object as accurately as possible with the measuring stick. Encourage each group to divide the intervals into tenths in order to estimate the last digit of the measurement. Have each group record its measurement on the board. Compare the results. Who has the correct answer? Which group is entitled to use the greatest number of digits in its measurement?

VISUAL STRATEGY

Figure 2-17 Ask students to identify the cylinder that is likely to give the most accurate volume measurement. Ask them to name two reasons why they would not use this cylinder for all volume measurements, even though it is the most accurate. *(Its capacity is too small to be practical for measuring large volumes, and a high degree of accuracy is not always needed in measuring large volumes.)*

How do chemists measure quantities?

OBJECTIVES

▶ *Distinguish* between accuracy and precision in measurements.

▶ *Determine* the number of significant figures in a measurement.

▶ *Perform* calculations using measurements, and round the results to the correct number of significant figures.

▶ *Write* very large and very small numbers in scientific notation.

Measuring and calculating

When you measure some quantitative property of matter or calculate a quantity of energy, how close to the "true" value are these measurements and calculations? No experimentally obtained value is exact because all measurements are subject to errors—human errors, method errors, and instrument errors.

Measurements must be made with standard procedures and the correct measuring instruments

Errors can arise depending on the instrument that is used to make the measurement. You must keep in mind the limitations of your measuring instruments when deciding which instrument to use in a particular situation. In Chapter 1, you read that there are a number of different types of balances available to the chemist for measuring mass. A chemist who needs 0.155 g of a substance cannot use a balance that is calibrated only to the nearest 1 g. Which graduated cylinder shown in **Figure 2-17** would you select for measuring 8.6 mL of a liquid?

▼ **FIGURE 2-17**

In order to obtain meaningful data, it is important to choose the correct instrument for your measurements. All of these graduated cylinders measure volume, but each is calibrated for different capacities.

50 mL   25 mL   10 mL

ALTERNATIVE ASSESSMENT

Group Strategy

Suppose you have three balances. You can weigh an object to the nearest 0.01 g on the most sensitive of the three. The second balance weighs to the nearest 0.1 g, and the third can be read to the nearest 1 g. Give an example of the mass of an object known to weigh a little less than 100 g as read from each balance. Examples of readings could be 96.56 g, 96.6 g, and 97 g. Ask students which balance will measure the mass with the largest number of significant figures? *(The mass read from the balance that measures to the nearest 0.01 g has the most significant figures.)* Suggest a way to check the accuracy and another way to check the precision of the three balances.

FIGURE 2-18 ▼

The difference between accuracy and precision

a Darts within large area
= Low precision

Area covered on bull's eye
= High accuracy
(on average)

b Darts within large area
= Low precision

Area far from bull's eye
= Low accuracy

c Darts within small area
= High precision

Area far from bull's eye
= Low accuracy

d Darts within small area
= High precision

Area centered around
bull's eye
= High accuracy

Accuracy differs from precision

There are two things to consider when making and reporting a measurement: accuracy and precision. The **accuracy** of a measurement is how exact it is—how close it is to the true value. Suppose you measure the volume of a solution as 35.8 mL and your lab partner measures the volume of the same solution as 37.2 mL. If the true volume of the solution is 36.0 mL, your measurement is more accurate than your lab partner's measurement because 35.8 mL is closer to the true value of 36.0 mL.

Precision refers to how closely several measurements of the same quantity made in the same way agree with one another. For example, suppose you measure the mass of a substance four times using the same balance, and you record the measurements 110 g, 109 g, 111 g, and 110 g. These measurements are close to one another, so you can say that your measurements are precise. The precision of a single measurement depends on how finely graduated the measuring scale is and how easily you can make the measurement. Keep in mind that precise measurements are not necessarily accurate measurements. For example, if the balance was not reset to zero before the measurements are made, the measurements may be close to one another, but they will not be very accurate. **Figure 2-18** illustrates a way to visualize the difference between accuracy and precision.

accuracy

the extent to which a measurement approaches the true value of a quantity

precision

the extent to which a series of measurements of the same quantity made in the same way agree with one another

CONCEPT CHECK

1. Define *accuracy*.
2. Explain how a series of measurements can be precise without being accurate.

TEACHING TIP

Accuracy and Precision Discuss the following hypothetical lab situation with the class:

Suppose you give students a mixture of metals and ask them to determine the percentage of copper in the mixture. They experiment to find a way to separate copper from the other metals. Then they take three samples of the mixture and carry out the procedure on each. They obtain the following results:

Sample A: % Cu = 23.53
Sample B: % Cu = 23.47
Sample C: % Cu = 23.55

Students report these results to you. You tell them that they have done good lab work, but the mixture actually contained 23.94% copper.

Why did you compliment their lab work? *(Their results are consistent, indicating good lab technique.)* Discuss the outcome of the analysis in terms of accuracy and precision. *(The results had good precision but were not very accurate.)* What should students look for to account for their results? *(They should check their measuring equipment for accuracy.)*

ANSWERS

CONCEPT CHECK

1. Accuracy is how close a measurement is to the true value.

2. Measurements of the same thing can be very close to one another but still differ significantly from the true value.

RESOURCE LINK

IN-TEXT LAB

Skills Development
Have students do Exploration 2A on page 708 to develop their skills in differentiating between accuracy and precision.

Significant figures

When making measurements or performing calculations, it is important to indicate how precise the values are. For example, if you report the mass of a sample as 10 g, it is not clear whether you mean that the mass of the sample is between 8 g and 12 g or that it is between 9.999 g and 10.001 g. In order to communicate the precision of their measurements and calculations, scientists report these values using significant figures. The **significant figures** of a measurement or calculation consist of all the digits known with certainty plus one estimated, or uncertain, digit. For example, a mass measurement of 10.7834 g is accurate to five places. The sixth place, 0.0004, is the estimated digit.

significant figure

any digit in a measurement that is known with certainty plus one final digit, which is somewhat uncertain or estimated

Measurements must be reported to the correct number of significant figures

It is necessary to report all measurements in an experiment to the correct number of significant figures in order to maintain the validity of the results. Suppose you are measuring temperature with a thermometer marked in intervals of 1°C. You can be certain of the temperature to the nearest degree. For example, the temperature may be slightly above 28°C, but it is definitely not less than 28°C nor greater than 29°C. However, by reading between the markings on the thermometer, you may be able to estimate the temperature to the nearest 0.2°C. For example, if the mercury in the thermometer appears to be slightly closer to 28°C than to 29°C, you may estimate the temperature as 28.4°C. Therefore, you can record the temperature to three significant figures—28.4°C. The first two digits you know with certainty; the third digit you estimated to the nearest 0.2°C. Therefore, the three significant figures in your recorded temperature of 28.4°C indicate that the actual temperature is between 28.2°C and 28.6°C.

Figure 2-19 shows two pieces of common laboratory equipment that you can use for measuring volumes. You are familiar with the first piece of equipment—a graduated cylinder. The other piece of equipment is known as a *buret*.

Suppose an experimental procedure requires 25.00 mL of water. A typical 100 mL graduated cylinder is calibrated to the nearest 1 mL; a typical buret is calibrated to the nearest 0.1 mL. Should you use the graduated cylinder or the buret to measure the water? If you use the graduated cylinder, your best measurement will be 25.0 mL with uncertainty in the tenths place. If you use the buret, your best measurement will be 25.00 mL with uncertainty in the hundredths place. Obviously, the buret is the best choice in this situation. Chemists often use a buret when precise volume measurements are essential.

Balances also allow for different degrees of precision. A microbalance can be used to determine mass to up to eight figures. A standard triple beam balance could provide precise readings to four figures.

▲ FIGURE 2-19

Both the graduated cylinder and the buret are used to measure volumes of liquids. When would you want to use the graduated cylinder? When would you want to use the buret?

TABLE 2-3	Rules for Determining Significant Zeros

Rule	Example
1. Zeros appearing between nonzero digits are significant.	a. 40.7 L has three significant figures. b. 87 009 km has five significant figures.
2. Zeros appearing in front of nonzero digits are not significant.	a. 0.0095 87 m has four significant figures. b. 0.0009 kg has one significant figure.
3. Zeros at the end of a number *and* to the right of a decimal point are significant.	a. 85.00 g has four significant figures. b. 9.070 000 000 has ten significant figures.
4. Zeros at the end of a number with no decimal point may or may not be significant. If such a zero has been measured or estimated, it is significant. If a zero has not been measured or estimated and is just a place holder, it is not significant. A decimal point placed after zeros indicates that they are all significant.	a. 2000 m may contain from one to four significant figures, depending on how many zeros are place holders. **In this text, if the value does not contain a decimal point, assume that none of the zeros at the end of a measurement are significant.** b. 2000. m has four significant figures, indicated by the decimal point.

Rules for determining significant figures

How can you tell the number of significant figures in a measurement? Why does 25.00 mL have four significant figures, 25 mL have two, and 20 mL have only one? Scientists have agreed on rules for determining the number of significant figures in a value. **The first rule is that nonzero digits are *always* significant.** Table 2-3 lists the rules for determining whether or not the zeros in a value are significant.

Calculations can exaggerate precision

You must pay special attention when calculating with significant figures to ensure that you get a meaningful result. The calculator in **Figure 2-20** was used to determine the density of isopropyl alcohol, commonly known as rubbing alcohol. The mass of a 32.4 mL sample of isopropyl alcohol was measured to be 25.42 g. In Chapter 1, you learned that mass and volume can be used to calculate density.

$$D = \frac{m}{V}$$

Notice that the calculator shown in Figure 2-20 reports the density of the liquid as 0.7845679 g/mL. The mass was measured to four significant figures, while the volume was measured to three significant figures. Yet the calculator displays a density that is calculated to seven significant figures. The

FIGURE 2-20 ▼

A calculator does not round the result to the correct number of significant digits. In this case, the answer should be rounded to three significant digits.

25.42/32.4
.7845679012

TEACHING TIP

Calculating with Measurements
Students have a tendency to trust pure numbers and their calculators. For this reason, they often have difficulty with the concept that measurements are different from numbers. They have difficulty understanding why they cannot use all of the digits that appear on the calculator's display. Pose the following problem:

Suppose you want to calculate the volume of air in a room measured to the nearest 0.01 m (the nearest centimeter) as 7.33 m × 5.27 m × 2.53 m. The calculator displays a value of 97.731 623 m^3. The last digit suggests that you have calculated the volume to the nearest 0.000 001 m^3. Ask students if they think that it is reasonable to claim such a degree of certainty about the volume of the room. Faced with this long number, most students will agree that the claim is unreasonable. At best, it can be said that the volume is 97.7 m^3.

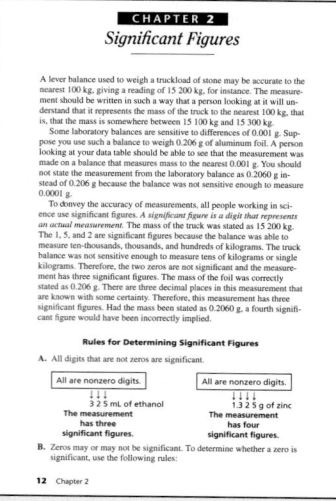

TABLE 2-4	Rules for Using Significant Figures in Calculations	
Operation	**Rule**	**Example**
Multiplication and division	The answer can have no more significant figures than there are in the measurement with the smallest number of significant figures.	12.257 × 1.162 ← four significant figures 14.2426234 —round off→ 14.24
Addition and subtraction	The answer can have no more digits to the right of the decimal point than there are in the measurement with the smallest number of digits to the right of the decimal point.	3.95 2.879 + 213.6 220.429 —round off→ 220.4

result provided by the calculator is misleading. It implies that we know the density of the isopropyl alcohol to a greater precision than we actually do.

To avoid exaggerating the precision of a calculated value, the result of the calculation must be rounded to the correct number of significant figures. The procedures for calculations involving multiplication and division are different from the procedures for calculations involving addition and subtraction. **Table 2-4** describes how to carry out each procedure.

Multiplication and division   Round the calculated result to the same number of significant figures as the measurement having the least number of significant figures. If a sequence of calculations is involved, do not round until the end. In the example for calculating the density of the isopropyl alcohol, the answer must have only three significant figures, the same number as in the volume of the alcohol (32.4 mL). Thus, the density is rounded to 0.785 g/mL.

Addition and subtraction   The answer can have no more digits to the right of the decimal point than there are in the measurement with the smallest number of digits to the right of the decimal point.

Consider the data shown in **Table 2-5**. The sum of the masses appears to be 14.592 g. However, to determine the correct number of significant figures, you must refer to the rule for calculations involving addition and subtraction. According to this rule, the result must be rounded to 14.6 g because 2.8 g has only one digit to the right of the decimal point. Note that 14.6 g has three significant figures even though 2.8 g has only two. When adding and subtracting, you are not concerned with the total number of significant digits; you are concerned only with the rightmost significant figure present in all values.

TABLE 2-5

Mass Measurements

Measurement	Mass (g)
1	4.73
2	5.375
3	2.8
4	1.687

Exact values have an infinite number of significant figures

Some of the values you will use in your calculations are *exact values.* Exact values have no uncertainty, so they have an unlimited number of significant figures. The exact values you will encounter most often in your study of chemistry fall into two categories. The first category is count values. A count value is a value that is determined by counting, not by measuring. For example, a water molecule contains *exactly* two hydrogen atoms and *exactly* one oxygen atom. There is no uncertainty in this value—the number of hydrogen and oxygen atoms is counted, not measured.

The second category of exact values is defined conversion factors. You read about conversion factors in Chapter 1. For example, if you want to convert millimeters to meters, you use the following conversion factor.

$$\frac{1 \text{ m}}{1000 \text{ mm}}$$

There is no uncertainty in the values that make up the conversion factor because a millimeter is defined as *exactly* one-thousandth of a meter.

$$1 \text{ mm} = 0.001 \text{ m}$$

Watch for any exact values that may occur in your calculations, and remember that exact values always have more significant figures than any other value in the calculation. Therefore, you never use exact values, either counted values or conversion factors, to determine the number of significant figures in your calculated results.

INQUIRYLAB

CONSUMER ACTIVITY

U.S. Pennies Comparison

Though materials may look the same, subtle differences in their properties can be used to tell them apart. In this activity, you will look at the differences in properties of pennies that were minted at different times.

Materials
two sets of pennies (pre-1982 and post-1983), 100 mL graduated cylinder, balance, graph paper, colored pencils, ruler

Problem
Design an experiment to determine the relationship between the masses and volumes of the two sets of pennies provided by your teacher. Compare the masses and volumes of pennies minted before 1982 with the masses and volumes of those minted after 1983. **Your masses and volumes must contain at least three significant figures.**

Analysis
1. Prepare a data table (or tables) to record your experimental masses and volumes.
2. Construct a best-fit line graph (mass versus volume) to illustrate the relationship between the masses and volumes for each set of pennies. Both graphs (pre-1982 and post-1983) can be placed on the same piece of graph paper. Use colored pencils to distinguish the lines.

3. Calculate the slopes of your best-fit lines for each type of penny.
4. Calculate the average density value for each type of penny.
5. Compare the slope values from item 3 with your calculated densities from item 4. Are they similar?
6. Compare your density values with the known density of copper. If pennies are made of copper, why is there a difference?

SECTION 2-3

INQUIRYLAB

Students will measure the volume of a sample of pennies by water displacement. They should use at least 15 pennies in each sample selected from a group of 50 pennies of one type and should then perform four more trials using progressively larger numbers of pennies. Pennies used in one trial may be dried and returned to the pile; then a new sample should be selected at random from the pile. Fifty-milliliter graduated cylinders may also be used.

Analysis

1. Students should record the mass and volume of at least three samples of each type of penny.

2. Graphs will vary. Students should draw the best-fit straight line that represents the points, not a connect-the-dots graph. If one point is far off the line, it can be regarded as an aberration, but students should attempt to get a better data point. If points are somewhat scattered, the line should represent the center of the trend.

3. The slope of a line is calculated by dividing the change in the y-axis values of two points in the set by the change in the x-axis values of the same two points.

4. Pennies dated pre-1982 should have densities that are about the same as copper: 8.96 g/cm^3. Pennies dated post-1983 should have densities that are about the same as zinc: 7.13 g/cm^3.

5. Slopes and densities should be similar.

6. Pennies are not composed of pure copper. They are mixtures of copper and zinc.

ADDITIONAL EXAMPLES

1. Determine the number of significant figures in each of the following quantities:

   a. 218 kPa

   Ans. 3

   b. 0.025 L

   Ans. 2

   c. 200. m^2

   Ans. 3

   d. 1.05 g

   Ans. 3

2. Round the following quantities to the number of significant figures indicated in parentheses:

   a. 32.068 km (3)

   Ans. 32.1 km

   b. 155.8 g (3)

   Ans. 156 g

   c. 0.02274 cm (2)

   Ans. 0.023 cm

   d. 12 000 kPa (3)

   Ans. 1.20×10^4 kPa

Unless students already know how to use scientific notation, they will find this example troublesome. Use it as a stepping-off point to show the need for scientific notation.

ANSWERS

CONCEPT CHECK

1. The number of significant figures indicates the degree of certainty to which a measurement is known.

2. Calculations exaggerate precision in results by producing more digits than are significant.

3. Digits that are always significant are nonzero digits, zeros between nonzero digits, zeros after a nonzero digit and before a decimal point, and zeros following a nonzero digit after a decimal point.

1 **Identify the limit of precision in each measurement given in the problem**

A measurement expressed to the appropriate number of significant figures includes all digits that are certain and one digit that is uncertain.

▸ *Nonzero digits are always significant*

673 kg has three	1.45×10^5 km has three
2.8 m has two	3567 mg has four

▸ *Using rule 1 in Table 2-3*

506 g has three	5060 mg has three
1.009 cm^2 has four	10 900 kg has three

▸ *Using rule 2 in Table 2-3*

0.984 kg has three	0.067 mL has two
0.6 mm has one	0.004 cm^3 has one

▸ *Using rule 3 in Table 2-3*

57.50 K has four	4.0 kg has two
2.90×10^3 km has three	61.00 m^2 has four

▸ *Using rule 4 in Table 2-3*

34 800. mL has five	8900 kg has two
70 K has one	10 900. cm has five

2 **Do not round any numbers in calculations until you reach a final answer**

Addition and subtraction

Round the answer so that it matches the number of digits to the right of the decimal point in the measurement with the fewest digits to the right of the decimal point.

2.89 m + 0.00043 m = 2.89043 m (round to 2 places after the decimal point)
= 2.89 m

Multiplication and division

Round the product or quotient to the same number of significant figures as in the measurement with the fewest significant figures.

3.5293 mol × 34.2 g/mol = 120.70206 g (round to 3 significant figures)
= 121 g

CONCEPT CHECK

1. Why are significant figures important when reporting measurements?

2. How can calculations such as addition and division skew experimental results?

3. What digits are always significant?

Scientific notation

At times, chemists make measurements and perform calculations with very large or very small numbers. In Chapter 3, for example, you will calculate how many copper atoms there are in one penny—29 640 000 000 000 000 000 000 copper atoms, a very large number. You will also calculate the mass that is converted to energy during a particular chemical reaction—0.000 000 000 000 003 322 kg, a very small number. Very large and very small numbers such as these are written in *scientific notation*.

Each value expressed in scientific notation has two parts. The first part consists of a number between 1 and 10, but it may have any number of digits after the decimal point. The second part consists of a power of 10. To write the first part, move the decimal point to the right or left so that there is only one nonzero digit to the left of it. The second part of the number—the exponent—is determined by counting the number of decimal places the decimal point must be moved. If the decimal point is moved to the left, the exponent is positive. If the decimal point is moved to the right, the exponent is negative.

$$29\,640\,000\,000\,000\,000\,000\,000 \text{ g becomes } 2.964 \times 10^{22} \text{ g}$$

$$0.000\,000\,000\,000\,003\,332 \text{ kg becomes } 3.322 \times 10^{-15} \text{ kg}$$

Scientific notation not only takes up less space but also eliminates the need to count zeros. For example, in which of the following quantities is it easier to see that there are four significant figures, in 3.322×10^{-15} kg or 0.000 000 000 000 003 332 kg? **Tables 2-6** and **2-7** provide guidelines for using scientific notation in calculations.

TABLE 2-6 Rules for Calculations with Numbers in Scientific Notation

Rule	Example
Addition and subtraction All values must have the same exponent before they can be added or subtracted. The result is the sum or difference of the first factors, all multiplied by the same exponent of 10.	$4.5 \times 10^6 - 2.3 \times 10^5 =$ $45 \times 10^5 - 2.3 \times 10^5 = 42.7 \times 10^5$ $\qquad\qquad\qquad\quad = 4.3 \times 10^6$
Multiplication The first factors of the numbers are multiplied, and the exponents of 10 are added.	$(3.1 \times 10^3)(5.01 \times 10^4) =$ $(3.1 \times 5.01) \times 10^{4+3} = 16 \times 10^7$ $\qquad\qquad\qquad\qquad = 1.6 \times 10^8$
Division The first factors of the number are divided, and the exponent of 10 in the denominator is subtracted from the exponent of 10 in the numerator.	$\dfrac{7.63 \times 10^3}{8.6203 \times 10^4} =$ $\dfrac{7.63 \times 10^{3-4}}{8.6203} = 0.885 \times 10^{-1}$ $\qquad\qquad\quad = 8.85 \times 10^{-2}$

RESOURCE LINK

Chem**File** Teaching Resources CD-ROM
Skills Review
Assign Math Skills Worksheet 4:
Operations with Scientific Notation to review or reteach this skill.

Chem**File** Mini-Guide to Problem Solving
Assign Chapter 3: *Scientific Notation* for additional practice.

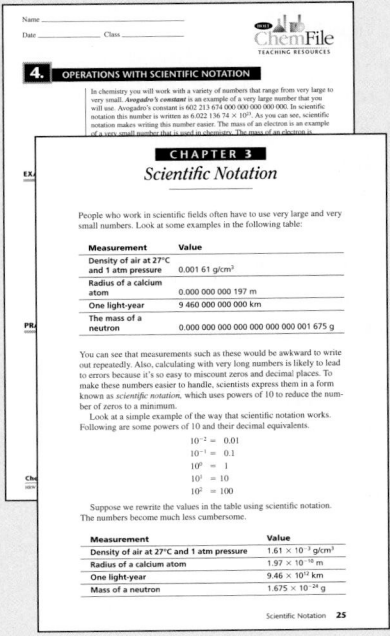

ANSWERS

SECTION REVIEW

Total recall

1. Accuracy indicates how close a measurement is to the true value. Precision indicates how close repeated measurements are to each other.

2. The significant figures in a measurement are an indication of the precision of the measurement.

3. Scientific notation makes it easier to write very large values and very small values.

4. Counts of items and conversion factors are exact values.
1000 mm = 1 m

Critical thinking

5. Calculators cannot make judgments about significant figures. Humans must do that. Therefore, calculator results must be rounded as needed.

6. Graduated cylinders can measure only to the nearest 0.1 mL. Most burets can measure to the nearest 0.01 mL.

7. The density value should have three significant figures because 9.03 mL has only three significant figures.

Practice problems

8. a. 3
   b. 3
   c. 6
   d. 4
   e. unlimited

9. a. 47.10 g
   b. 32.86 L
   c. 3.424×10^5 g
   d. 0.123 cm^2
   e. 28.62 mi/h

TABLE 2-7	Rules for Expressing Scientific Notation with Significant Figures

Rule	Example
Use scientific notation to eliminate all placeholding zeros.	$2400 \longrightarrow 2.4 \times 10^4$ (both zeros are not significant)
Convert the number to scientific notation and eliminate zeros before an unwritten decimal point that are not significant figures.	$600 \longrightarrow 6 \times 10^2$ (both zeros are not significant) $750\,000. \longrightarrow 7.50000 \times 10^5$ (all zeros are significant)

SECTION REVIEW

Total recall

1. How does accuracy differ from precision?

2. What do the significant figures in a measurement indicate?

3. Explain the advantage of using scientific notation.

4. What is an exact value? Give an example.

Critical thinking

5. Describe a problem that may arise when you use a calculator to compute an answer.

6. Why is a buret rather than a graduated cylinder used when precise volumes are required in a lab procedure?

7. If you measure the mass of a liquid as 11.50 g and its volume as 9.03 mL, how many significant figures should its density value have?

Practice problems

8. How many significant figures are there in these expressions?
   a. 470. km
   b. 0.0980 m
   c. 30.8900 g
   d. 0.09709 kg
   e. 1000 g/1 kg

9. Perform the following calculations, and express the answers in significant figures.
   a. 32.89 g + 14.21 g
   b. 34.09 L − 1.230 L
   c. 3.45×10^5 g − 2.6×10^3 g
   d. 1.8940 cm × 0.0651 cm
   e. 24.897 mi/0.8700 h

10. Express the following calculations in the proper number of significant figures. Use scientific notation where appropriate.
    a. 129g/ 29.2 mL =
    b. (1.551 mm)(3.260 mm)(4.9001 mm) =
    c. 35 000 kJ/0.250 s =
    d. 0.367 L + 2.51 L + 1.6004 L =

11. A chemical process produces 653 550 kJ of heat in 142.3 min. What is the rate of heat production in kJ/min?

12. Express the following quantities in scientific notation.
    a. 277 088 000 000 000 atoms
    b. 0.000 000 000 000 839 602 g
    c. 700 004 mm

13. **Story Clue** The *Grandcamp* was loaded with 2300 metric tons of ammonium nitrate. Convert this mass to grams of ammonium nitrate. Express your answer in scientific notation to the correct number of significant figures (1 metric ton = 1000 kg).

10. a. 4.42 g/mL
    b. 24.78 mm^3
    c. 1.4×10^5 kJ/s
    d. 4.48 L

11. 4593 kJ/min

12. a. $2.770\,88 \times 10^{14}$ atoms
    b. $8.396\,02 \times 10^{-13}$ g
    c. $7.000\,04 \times 10^5$ mm

13. 2300 metric tons $\times \dfrac{1000 \text{ kg}}{1 \text{ metric ton}} \times \dfrac{1000 \text{ g}}{1 \text{ kg}} = 2.3 \times 10^9$ g

He
2
Helium
4.002 60
1s²

Deep diving with helium

Divers who breathe air while at great undersea depths run the risk of suffering from a condition known as nitrogen narcosis. Nitrogen narcosis can cause a diver to become disoriented and exercise poor judgment, leading to dangerous behavior. To avoid nitrogen narcosis, professional divers who work at depths of more than 60 m breathe heliox, a mixture of helium and oxygen, instead of air.

The greatest advantage of heliox is that it does not cause nitrogen narcosis. A disadvantage of heliox is that it removes body heat faster than air does. This makes a diver breathing heliox feel chilled sooner than a diver breathing air.

Breathing heliox also affects the voice. Helium is much less dense than nitrogen, so vocal cords vibrate faster in a heliox atmosphere. This raises the pitch of the diver's voice and makes the diver sound like Donald Duck. Fortunately, this effect disappears when the diver surfaces and begins breathing air again.

In Florida, divers on the Wakulla Springs project team breathed heliox at depths in excess of 90 m.

Helium was discovered in the sun before it was found on Earth.

WHERE IS IT?

Universe
about 23% by mass

Earth's Crust
0.000001% by mass

Air
0.0005% by mass

internetconnect

SCLINKS
NSTA
TOPIC: Helium
GO TO: www.scilinks.org
KEYWORD: HW023

Industrial Uses

▶ Helium is used as a lifting gas in balloons and dirigibles.

▶ Helium is used as an inert atmosphere for welding very heavy sections and for high-speed machine welding of long seams.

▶ Helium liquefies at a temperature of −269°C. Liquid helium is used as a coolant in superconductor research.

▶ Helium is used as an inert atmosphere for growing high-purity silicon crystals for semiconducting devices.

A BRIEF HISTORY

1888: William Hillebrand discovers that an inert gas is produced when a uranium mineral is dissolved in sulfuric acid.

1908: Ernest Rutherford and Thomas Royds prove that alpha particles emitted during radioactive decay are helium nuclei.

1800   1850   1900

1868: Pierre Janssen, studies the spectra of a solar eclipse and finds evidence of a new element. Edward Frankland, an English chemist, and Joseph Lockyer, an English astronomer, suggest the name *helium*.

1894: Sir William Ramsay and Lord Rayleigh discover argon. They suspect that the gas Hildebrand found in 1888 was argon. They repeat his experiment and find that the gas is helium.

ELEMENT SPOTLIGHT

During the solar eclipse of 1868, Pierre Janssen (1824–1907) obtained the first evidence of the existence of helium when he detected a new line in the solar spectrum. Helium has since been detected spectroscopically in great abundance. It is the second most abundant element in the universe, and it is an important component in the processes by which stars get energy.

Although helium was probably present early in Earth's history, most of it drifted into space because of helium's low mass. All of the helium on Earth is the product of radioactive decay. It has collected in cavities, such as oil domes and gas domes, in Earth's crust. Commercial supplies of helium are extracted from natural gas, the bulk of which comes from Texas, Oklahoma, and Kansas.

Helium has the lowest melting point of any element. It is the only liquid that cannot be solidified by lowering the temperature. Near 0 K helium takes on a superfluid property, and it flows upward and covers all surfaces that it can reach. For this reason, helium has extensive applications in cryogenic research, and it is used as a coolant in superconductor research and in nuclear reactors.

Based on what you have learned about matter and energy, you should now be able to answer the questions posed at the beginning of this chapter.

LOOKING BACK

Where did all the destructive energy that caused this catastrophe come from?
In Section 2-1 you read that chemical compounds contain chemical energy. The chemical energy in the ammonium nitrate that was loaded on the *Grandcamp* was the source of all the destructive energy in the Texas City explosion. In fact, ammonium nitrate is an excellent source of chemical energy that can be used for destructive purposes. Recall in the discussion of chemical energy that the formation of water is an exothermic process. The reason that ammonium nitrate is an explosive is because its decomposition is an exothermic process. The decomposition of water is endothermic—thankfully, it cannot explode. In 1995, a small truck filled with a mixture of ammonium nitrate and fuel oil was used to blow up a federal office building in Oklahoma City, Oklahoma. That explosion killed 168 people.

What happened in terms of energy when the Grandcamp exploded?
Recall that energy can be transformed into various forms. When the ammonium nitrate was ignited, an exothermic chemical reaction took place. In this exothermic reaction, the chemical energy possessed by the ammonium nitrate was transformed into heat, light, sound, and mechanical energy.

Billowing black smoke filled the sky over Texas City in the aftermath of the *Grandcamp* explosion.

How much mass was converted to energy to produce the 350 gigajoules released by the explosion of the ammonium nitrate on the Grandcamp?
When 2300 metric tons of ammonium nitrate is ignited, about 3.5×10^{11} J of energy is released. Using the equation $m = \dfrac{E}{c^2}$, you can calculate the mass equivalent of this energy.

$$m = \frac{3.5 \times 10^{11} \text{ J}}{(3.00 \times 10^8 \text{ m/s})^2}$$

$$m = \frac{3.5 \times 10^{11} \text{ J}}{9.00 \times 10^{16} \text{ m}^2/\text{s}^2}$$

$$m = 3.9 \times 10^{-6} \text{ kg}$$

Thus, only 3.9 mg of matter was converted to energy in the Texas City explosion. A much greater fraction of matter is converted to energy in nuclear reactions, but the Einstein principle applies equally to both.

KEY TERMS

2-1
chemical bond
chemical energy
energy
heat
kinetic energy
law of conservation of
  energy

potential energy
specific heat capacity
system
temperature

2-2
hypothesis

law of conservation of
  mass
polymer
scientific law
theory

2-3
accuracy
precision
significant figure

KEY CONCEPTS

2-1 **What is energy?**
▶ Energy is the capacity to do some type of work.
▶ Potential energy depends on the position of an object; kinetic energy depends on its motion.
▶ Matter possesses chemical energy as a result of its chemical makeup.
▶ The law of conservation of energy states that the total amount of energy remains constant.
▶ Energy can be transferred between a system and its surroundings.
▶ The transfer of heat energy usually results in a change in temperature.
▶ The equation $E = mc^2$ shows that mass and energy are equivalent.

2-2 **What is the process of science?**
▶ The scientific method is a systematic approach to solving a problem or answering a question.
▶ Scientific discoveries are sometimes made accidentally.

▶ A hypothesis is a reasonable explanation of an observed phenomenon.
▶ A hypothesis that has been thoroughly tested can lead to a theory, which can take the form of a scientific model.
▶ A scientific law is a statement or mathematical expression that reliably describes the behavior of the natural world.
▶ The law of conservation of mass states that the total quantity of mass remains constant.

2-3 **How do chemists measure quantities?**
▶ The accuracy of a measurement reflects how close it is to the true or accepted value.
▶ The precision of a measurement reflects how closely several measurements of the same quantity agree.
▶ Measurements and the results of calculations must be reported to the correct number of significant figures.
▶ Scientific notation is used to write both very small and very large numbers.

KEY SKILLS

Review the following models before your exam. Be sure you know these rules.

Rules for Determining Significant Zeros (Table 2-3, p. 59)

Rules for Using Significant Figures in Calculations (Table 2-4, p. 60)

Rules for Calculations with Numbers in Scientific Notation (Table 2-6, p. 63)

Rules for Expressing Scientific Notation with Significant Figures (Table 2-7, p. 64)

How To Determine the number of significant figures (p. 62)

READING STRATEGY

Assimilating Knowledge
Have students return to their individual lists of things they want to know about energy and about the process of scientific research that they created on page 38. Have them place check marks next to the questions that they are now able to answer. Students should finish by making a list of what they have learned. Have students identify unanswered questions as well as any new questions they may have. These questions could be used as the basis for a research project.

REVIEW & ASSESS ASSIGNMENT GUIDE

Term Review
Assign after Section 2-3.

Concept & Skills Review
Section 2-1
▶ Items 1–10

Section 2-2
▶ Items 11–19

Section 2-3
▶ Items 20–28

Linking Chapters
Assign after Section 2-3.

Alternative Assessments
Assign after Section 2-3.

Test Prep
Assign prior to the chapter test.

REVIEW & ASSESS

TERM REVIEW

1. significant figures
2. kinetic energy
3. Temperature
4. control
5. system
6. theory
7. law
8. Precision

CONCEPT & SKILLS REVIEW

1. Kinetic energy is the energy of an object in motion. Examples include the energy of a falling rock, of a moving piston, of a moving car, and of moving molecules within a substance.

2. Potential energy is the energy of an object due to its position. Examples include a rock at the edge of a cliff, a suspended wrecking ball, a stretched spring or rubber band, and atoms in a chemical bond.

3. Many answers are possible. Any example of heat transfer is acceptable, but if the transfer must be visible, examples must involve changes in motion (acceleration and deceleration), such as a car starting from a stoplight or braking at a stop sign.

4. Mass can be converted to energy and vice versa according to Einstein's relationship $E = mc^2$, in which E is energy in joules, m is mass in kilograms, and c is the speed of light in meters per second.

5. Energy can undergo a chemical or a physical change, but the same amount of energy is present both before and after the change.

6. The skateboard contains potential chemical energy as chemical bonds and kinetic energy in the form of vibrating atoms and molecules, that is, heat. When the skateboard moves, it has additional kinetic energy.

TERM REVIEW

1. All the digits known with certainty plus one estimated digit indicate a measurement's _____.
   (scientific notation, significant figures)

2. The energy an object possesses because of its motion is known as _____.
   (kinetic energy, potential energy)

3. _____ is a measurement of the average kinetic energy of the particles in a substance.
   (Specific heat capacity, Temperature)

4. A _____ is often included in an experiment to identify the variable responsible for the results.
   (control, scientific process)

5. Heat energy is transferred between a _____ and its surroundings.
   (system, chemical bond)

6. A _____ is a reasonable explanation of an observation that can be tested.
   (theory, law)

7. A mathematical statement concerning some natural phenomenon is known as a scientific _____.
   (model, law)

8. _____ refers to how closely several measurements of the same quantity agree with one another.
   (Precision, Accuracy)

CONCEPT & SKILLS REVIEW

NATURE OF ENERGY

1. Define *kinetic energy*, and give an example.

2. Define *potential energy*, and give an example of an object that possesses it.

3. Give an example of energy transfer that you witnessed today.

4. What is the relationship between mass and energy?

5. State the law of conservation of energy.

6. Explain how a skateboard resting on the ground contains energy. If the skateboard were moving, would it have more energy than it did at rest? Explain.

7. Water evaporates from a puddle on a hot, sunny day faster than on a cold, cloudy day. Explain this phenomenon in terms of interactions between matter and energy.

8. Beaker A contains water at a temperature of 15°C. Beaker B contains water at a temperature of 37°C. Which beaker contains water molecules with greater average kinetic energy? Explain your answer.

INVESTIGATING MATTER AND ENERGY

9. Identify the requirements of a good hypothesis.

10. How does the phrase "cause and effect" relate to the formation of a good hypothesis?

11. Classify the following statements as observation, hypothesis, theory, or law:
    a. A system containing many particles will not go spontaneously from a disordered state to an ordered state.
    b. The substance is silvery white, is fairly hard, and is a good conductor of electricity.
    c. Bases taste bitter and feel slippery in water.
    d. If I pay attention in class, then I will succeed in this course.

12. What components are necessary for an experiment to be valid?

13. Explain the purpose of an experimental control.

14. Explain the relationship between models and theories.

15. Explain the statement, "No theory is written in stone."

16. a. The table below contains data from an experiment in which an air sample is sub-

jected to different pressures. Based on this set of observations, propose a hypothesis that could be tested.

b. What theories can be stated from the data in the table below?

c. Are the data sufficient for the establishment of a scientific law. Why or why not?

The Results of Compressing an Air Sample

Volume (cm^3)	Pressure (kPa)	Volume × pressure (cm^3 × kPa)
100.0	33.3	3330
50.0	66.7	3340
25.0	133.2	3330
12.5	266.4	3330

17. Is a hypothesis that is rejected through experimentation of any value to scientists? Defend your position.

MEASUREMENTS

18. Why it is important to keep track of significant figures?

19. a. If you add several numbers, how many significant figures can the sum have?

b. If you multiply several numbers, how many significant figures can the product have?

20. Perform the following calculations, and express the answers with the correct number of significant figures.

a. $(12.4 \times 7.943) + 0.0064$

b. $\left(\dfrac{246.83}{26.3}\right) - 1.349$

c. $0.1273 - 0.000008$

21. Why can a measured number never be exact?

22. Is it possible for a number to be too small or too large to be expressed adequately in the metric system? Explain your answer.

23. Around 1150, King David I of Scotland defined the inch as the width of a man's thumb at the base of the nail. Discuss the practical limitations of this early unit of measurement.

24. Which of the following are exact numbers?

a. There are 12 eggs in a dozen.

b. Some Major League Baseball pitchers can throw a ball over 140 km/h.

c. The accident injured 21 people.

d. The circumference of the Earth at the equator is 40 000 km.

e. The cost of filling the gas tank came to $17.85.

f. The tank was filled with 54 L of gas.

g. A nickel has a mass of 5 g.

25. Express 743 000 000 in scientific notation to the following number of significant figures:

a. one significant figure

b. two significant figures

c. four significant figures

d. seven significant figures

LINKING CHAPTERS

1. Scientific method
What might have constituted the scientific method Felix Hoffmann used in his study of aspirin that you read about in Chapter 1?

2. Scientific laws
Why are the conservation of energy and the conservation of mass considered laws and not theories?

3. Theme: Conservation
How does Einstein's equation $E = mc^2$ seem to contradict both the law of conservation of energy and the law of conservation of mass?

ALTERNATIVE ASSESSMENTS

Performance assessment

1. Your teacher will provide you with a passage to read. Identify the scientific processes that were used in this passage.

2. Find a solid object with an irregular shape, such as a pencil or a small stone. Determine its density, expressing your answer with the correct number of significant figures.

3. Design an experimental procedure for determining the specific heat capacity of a metal.

MATTER AND ENERGY **69**

7. On the hot sunny day, the water is warmer and the sun supplies a continuous source of light energy, some of which changes to heat when it strikes an object. As a result, the motion of the water molecules remains high and the water evaporates more rapidly than it would on a cold, overcast day.

8. Temperature is a measure of the average kinetic energy of the particles of an object. Therefore, the water molecules in the beaker at 37°C have higher average kinetic energy.

9. The hypothesis must explain an observation and must be testable.

10. Many hypotheses predict an effect from a cause. An example of a hypothesis of this sort is as follows: If sulfur and iron are placed together and heated, then iron(II) sulfide will form.

11. a. law
b. observation
c. observation
d. hypothesis

12. One factor is allowed to vary while others are kept constant. A control must be used for all variables under all reaction conditions.

13. A control assures that the experiment focuses on only one variable. It provides a baseline for comparison of the experimental results.

14. A theory can be interpreted in the form of a model, which can be a physical representation, a mathematical description, or a computer simulation.

15. As new discoveries are made, theories are revised or abandoned in favor of new theories that provide better explanations of phenomena.

16. a. Raising the pressure on a sample of air decreases its volume in a way that the product of the volume and the pressure is a constant value.

b. None. The volume-pressure phenomenon is observed, but the available data provide no explanation for the observation.

c. No. If this gas volume–pressure relationship is observed many times with differing gases and at varying pressures, then the description of this phenomenon is accepted as a law.

17. Yes, because it provides a record of what was tested and the conditions used. Others may be able to use that information to design new experiments or to develop new hypotheses.

18. The number of significant figures conveys the degree of certainty within a measurement.

19. a. The sum can have the number of significant figures in the value with the fewest decimal places.

b. The product can have the number of significant figures in the value with the least number of significant figures.

20. a. 98.5
b. 8.04
c. 0.1273

21. All measurements estimate the last figure. No measuring instrument can have an infinite number of divisions, which would be required to determine exact measurements.

22. No. As measuring technology advances and new magnitudes of measurement are possible, scientists add new prefixes to accommodate the new measurements.

23. Not every thumb was the same size.

24. a. exact
b. not exact
c. exact
d. not exact
e. exact
f. not exact
g. not exact

25. a. 7×10^8
b. 7.4×10^8
c. 7.430×10^8
d. $7.430\,000 \times 10^8$

Continued on page 71.

Portfolio projects

1. Chemistry and you

For one week, practice your observation skills by listing chemistry-related events around you. After your list is compiled, choose three events that are especially interesting or curious to you. Label three pocket portfolios, one for each event. As you progress through the chapters in this textbook, gather information that helps explain these events. Put pertinent notes, questions, figures, and charts in the folders. When you have enough information to explain each phenomenon, write a report and present it in class.

2. Research and communication

Make a poster of scientific laws that you have encountered in previous science courses. What facts were used to support each of these laws?

3. Chemistry and you

Energy can be transformed from one form to another. For example, light (solar) energy is transformed into chemical energy during photosynthesis. Prepare a list of several different forms of energy. Describe transformations of energy that you encounter on a daily basis. Try to include examples that involve more than one transformation, i.e., light → chemical → mechanical. Select one example, and demonstrate the actual transformation to the class.

4. internet**connect**

SC*i*LINKS
NSTA

TOPIC: Chance discoveries
GO TO: www.scilinks.org
KEYWORD: HW024

Research and communication

Check the Internet for information about a scientific discovery that was made accidentally. Prepare a report summarizing your findings. Be sure to include the scientific processes that were used in this discovery. Also include information about any technological impact this discovery has had.

1. The equation $E = mc^2$ shows that _____.
   a. chemical reactions are either exothermic or endothermic
   b. mass and energy are equivalent
   c. a hypothesis may develop into a theory
   d. the kinetic energy of an object relates to its motion

2. Which of the following measurements contains three significant figures?
   a. 200 mL
   b. 0.02 mL
   c. 20.2 mL
   d. 200.0 mL

3. A control in an experiment _____.
   a. is often not needed
   b. means that the scientist has everything under control
   c. is required only if the hypothesis leads to the development of a theory
   d. allows the scientist to identify the cause of the results in an experiment

4. A theory differs from a hypothesis in that the former _____.
   a. cannot be disproved
   b. always leads to the formation of a scientific law
   c. has been subjected to experimental testing
   d. represents an educated guess

5. All measurements in science _____.
   a. must be expressed in scientific notation
   b. have some degree of uncertainty
   c. are both accurate and precise
   d. must include only those digits that are known with certainty

6. If the temperature outside is 26°C, then the temperature would be _____ kelvins.
   a. 26
   b. 273
   c. 299
   d. –247

7. When numbers are multiplied or divided, the answer can have no more _____.
   a. significant figures than there are in the measurement with the smallest number of significant figures

   b. significant figures than there are in the measurement with the largest number of significant figures
   c. digits to the right of the decimal point than there are in the measurement with the smallest number of digits to the right of the decimal point
   d. digits to the right of the decimal point than there are in the measurement with the largest number of digits to the right of the decimal point

8. Which of the following is not part of the scientific method?
   a. making measurements
   b. introducing bias
   c. making an educated guess
   d. analyzing data

9. Chemical energy includes kinetic energy because _____.
   a. the atoms in a molecule remain in a fixed position
   b. all forms of energy include kinetic energy
   c. chemical bonds bend and stretch
   d. chemical compounds can release energy when they dissolve in solution

10. The accuracy of a measurement _____.
    a. is how close it is to the true value
    b. does not depend on the instrument being used to measure the object
    c. indicates that the measurement is also precise
    d. is something that scientists rarely achieve

11. A measurement of 23 465 mg converted to grams equals _____.
    a. 2.3465 g
    b. 23.465 g
    c. 234.65 g
    d. 0.23465 g

12. A metal sample has a mass of 45.65 g. The volume of the sample is 16.9 cm^3. The density of the sample is _____.
    a. 2.7 g/cm^3
    b. 2.70 g/cm^3
    c. 0.370 g/cm^3
    d. 0.37 g/cm^3

MATTER AND ENERGY 71

1. b	5. b	9. c
2. c	6. c	10. a
3. d	7. a	11. b
4. c	8. b	12. b

Continued from page 70.

LINKING CHAPTERS

1. Hoffman operated on the hypothesis that a compound that is structurally similar to salicylic acid will have the same medicinal properties.

2. These laws are observations that are found to be universally true in ordinary chemical and physical changes.

3. The equation indicates that mass and energy are interconvertible. However, the law is not demonstrated in ordinary chemical and physical changes.

ALTERNATIVE ASSESSMENTS

Performance assessment

1. Passages of the type required may be found in biographies of scientists or in books about the history of science and technology.

2. Students will probably have to measure volume by water displacement. Objects that float must be held underwater long enough for the new volume to be read.

3. Designs may vary but should generally involve heating the object and allowing its heat to warm a known mass of water. Then they can use the specific heat of water to calculate the heat absorbed by water.

Portfolio projects

1. Events that students choose should generally involve clear-cut chemical or physical changes involving specific substances. Collect the folders, and use them as a basis for assigning reports throughout the year by selecting one topic from each student's folder.

2. Student reports should also comment on the background of the person who made the discovery and how that background prepared the person to realize the discovery's importance.

3. Students should not overlook laws that they have learned in biology, especially genetics, or in Earth science, such as the law of uniformitarianism. The field of physics yields Newton's laws of motion, the law of gravitation, Ohm's law, Kepler's laws of planetary motion, Snell's law of light refraction, Hooke's law of springs, and others.

4. Many energy chains that students will think of involve devices that are powered by fuel, battery, or electric current. Consider having students trace energy back to its ultimate origin, usually the sun.

Atomic Structure and Electron Configuration

CLASSROOM RESOURCES

SECTIONS	TEACHER'S DEMONSTRATIONS	PROBLEM SOLVING ■ *Text* ◆ *ChemFile Mini-Guide*	LABORATORIES ■ *Text* ◆ *ChemFile Manuals: A, B, C, D*
3-1 **How do we know atoms exist?** Section Review, p. 81			◆ **EXP. C1** Conservation of Mass
3-2 **What is the internal structure of atoms?** Section Review, p. 90	**Demo 1** Magnets and Cathode Rays, p. 82		
3-3 **How are an atom's electrons configured?** Section Review, p. 101	**Demo 2** Emission Spectra, p. 94	■ **How To** Write an electron configuration, p. 101	■ **EXP. 3A** Flame Tests, p. 720 ■ **INV. 3A** Spectroscopy and Flame Tests—Identifying Materials, p. 724

TECHNOLOGY RESOURCES

See page 72 for a listing of Internet resources.

SECTIONS	VIDEOS/VIDEODISC *Holt Chemistry Videodisc* CNN PRESENTS *Science in the NEWS*	CHEMFILE CD-ROMs ● *Teaching Resources* ◆ *Interactive Tutor*	OVERHEADS ● *Color Transparencies* ◆ *Transparency Masters*
3-1	Law of Definite Composition Law of Conservation of Mass Law of Multiple Proportions	● Occupational Application: Recycling Engineer ● Supplemental Reading: *Linus Pauling: In His Own Words,* "What Is Chemistry?" ● Math Skills: Ratios	● **12** Law of Conservation of Mass ● **13** Law of Multiple Proportions
3-2	Cathode Rays Millikan's Oil-Drop Experiment Rutherford's Scattering Experiment CNN PRESENTS Segment 8 The Top Quark CNN PRESENTS Segment 9 Atom Lasers	● Math Skills: Averages ◆ **Module 2:** Models of the Atom **Topic:** Atomic structure	● **14** Gold-Foil Experiment ● **15** Gold-Foil Experiment on the Atomic Level ◆ **12A** Properties of Subatomic Particles
3-3	Ground and Excited States: Sodium Bohr Model of the Atom Quantum Atomic Models of Hydrogen and Oxygen Atomic Energy Level Model Orbitals of a Carbon Atom Electron Spin with Magnetic Field Lines Orbitals Writing Electron Configurations	◆ **Module 2:** Models of the Atom **Topic:** Electronic structure	● **17** Electromagnetic Spectrum ● **18** Wavelength and Frequency ● **19** Photoelectric Effect ● **20** Hydrogen's Line-Emission Spectrum ● **21** Photon Emission and Absorption ● **22** Shapes of s, p, and d Orbitals ● **23** Relative Energies of Orbitals ◆ *See also* **13A, 14A, 15A, 16A,** and **17A.**

ASSESSMENT RESOURCES

ALTERNATIVE ASSESSMENTS	CHAPTER TESTING	SCORING RUBRICS *Holt ChemFile Teaching Resources CD-ROM*
Student Text Performance assessments, p. 106 Portfolio projects 1–4, p. 106 **Teacher's Edition** Relating Dalton's Theory, p. 80 Gold Foil Experiment, p. 86 Group Strategies, pp. 88, 100, 101 Line Spectra and Electrons, p. 97 **Study Guide** Sections 3-1 to 3-3	**Student Text** Test Preparation, p. 107 **Holt Chemistry: Visualizing Matter Chapter 3 Test** (blackline masters) **Holt ChemFile Test Generator for Macintosh and Windows**	**Lab Work** Student-Designed Experiments Rubric Performance-Tasks Scoring Rubric Assessment for Structured Inquiry Assessment for Open-Ended Inquiry **Portfolio Projects** Evaluating Concept Maps Assessing Portfolios Portfolio Assignment Student Evaluation Form

Atomic Structure and Electron Configuration

 READING STRATEGY

Assimilating Knowledge

Before reading this chapter, have students write a short list of all the things they already know or think they know about the following:

▸ the particle composition of matter
▸ the structure of an atom
▸ the major subatomic particles—protons, neutrons, and electrons
▸ the characteristics, location, and arrangement of these particles

Ask students to make a drawing of what they think an atom looks like. When students finish their lists, ask them to contribute their entries to a group list on the board or on an overhead projector. Then have students list the things they might want to know about atoms and their structure. If students have trouble coming up with questions, the following is a suggestion to get them on track: Ask students to describe the structure of matter in common objects. If they could become very small, what would the inside of matter look like to them? How would an iron nail and a piece of sulfur differ?

ABOUT THE ILLUSTRATION

Fireworks are familiar and colorful examples of the transitions of electrons between energy levels. Refer to this example during the chapter to help students understand that the colors shown are not random or arbitrary, but specific to each substance and electron transition.

 internet connect

Holt Chemistry: Visualizing Matter

HRW On-Line Resources
go.hrw.com
Visit the HRW Web site for a variety of resources related to this chapter. Just type in the keyword HW0 Chapt3.

SC LINKS
NSTA

National Science Teachers Association
On-Line Resources: www.scilinks.org
The following Scilinks Internet resources can be found in the student text for this chapter:

Page 82
TOPIC: Subatomic particles
KEYWORD: HW031

Page 90
TOPIC: Radioisotopes
KEYWORD: HW032

Page 91
TOPIC: Essential elements
KEYWORD: HW033

Page 93
TOPIC: Electromagnetic spectrum
KEYWORD: HW034

Page 103
TOPIC: Beryllium
KEYWORD: HW035

Page 108
TOPIC: Element names
KEYWORD: HW036

EXCITED ATOMS AND THE FOURTH OF JULY

The national anthem blasts through loudspeakers, and the show is about to begin. It's the Fourth of July, and hundreds have come to watch the fireworks display. Crack! A rocket flares and red, white, and gold stars burst forth. Kaboom!

A dazzling, white chrysanthemum-shaped shower of light fills the sky. The show continues, but wait, something is missing. You've seen red and white fireworks, but what about blue?

The red, white, and gold stars are brilliant but any blue color is dull by comparison. The art of making fireworks is called pyrotechnics, and today's pyrotechnic technology can successfully create red, white, orange, green, gold, pink, and yellow displays but has not produced a bright blue. The search for bright blue keeps fireworks manufacturers scrambling.

Bill Page, the resident chemist at Astro Pyrotechnics fireworks manufacturing firm, is one of a number of chemists trying to produce a bright blue. Bill explains that a lit fuse supplies the energy to cause the fireworks to explode. When they explode, their chemical contents react to produce hot gases. The atoms and molecules in these gases absorb some of the energy released by the explosion. Almost as soon as this energy is absorbed, some of it is released in the form of light, producing spectacular displays of color.

Fireworks manufacturers control what colors are displayed by carefully mixing a variety of chemical compounds. Different elements, either in the elemental state or combined in compounds, produce different colors when heated to the right temperature. For example, compounds of strontium produce red light, aluminum compounds produce bright white light, barium compounds produce green light, and sodium compounds produce yellow light. A copper compound, copper(II) chloride, is the best producer of blue light to be identified so far. But copper(II) chloride is unstable at high temperatures.

A brilliant blue display may be achieved someday by Bill Page or some other pyrotechnic chemist, or maybe by someone who is studying chemistry today—maybe even by you.

CHAPTER LINKS

What is light, and how do various colors of light differ?

What is happening to atoms when fireworks produce colored light?

How does the instability of the copper(II) chloride molecule at high temperatures interfere with its ability to emit blue light?

STORY BACKGROUND

Pyrotechnics, the "science of fire," covers not only fireworks but also many similar devices, ranging from safety matches to hazard flares. Although fireworks may appear to involve burning in air, that is seldom the case. Fireworks utilize oxidation-reduction reactions between an oxygen source (oxidizer) and a fuel (reducing agent). The oxygen source and fuel are typically solid chemicals mixed together. When ignited, the reaction releases energy rapidly as all the fuel oxidizes almost at once.

The brilliant flashes of light produced by fireworks consist of electromagnetic radiation that ranges from the infrared to the ultraviolet, but the eye can detect light with wavelengths between 380 nm and 780 nm. Fireworks produce light through atomic emission and molecular emission. White light is produced when a reactive metal, such as magnesium, is used as a fuel. Solid metal oxide particles are created when the metal fuel is oxidized. The metal oxide particles glow white-hot in the intense heat generated in the reaction. The colors that we see in fireworks displays result from characteristic emission spectra of elements such as strontium and copper as excited electrons fall back to stable ground states.

CONCEPT PREVIEW

Section 3-1

Evidence for the atomic theory
- law of definite composition
- law of conservation of mass
- law of multiple proportions

Atomic theory
- Dalton's original theory
- modern changes in the theory

The mass of atoms
- atomic mass units

- the mole and Avogadro's constant

Section 3-2

The particles in atoms
- electrons and their discovery
- discovery of the nucleus
- protons and atomic number
- neutrons and atomic mass numbers
- nuclear forces
- isotopes

Section 3-3

Spectral evidence
- the relationship of light and electrons
- electromagnetic spectrum
- Bohr model of the atom

Modern atomic model
- the concept of orbitals
- quantum numbers and the Pauli exclusion principle
- using the Aufbau principle to write electron configurations

LESSON WARM-UP

Black Box Demonstration
Present students with a sealed shoe-box that has some type of noisy, rattling object inside. Pass the box around the room, and ask students to make inferences about the shape, dimensions, or any other properties of the object that they can detect. Ask students to suggest additional ways to learn about the identity of the object without opening the box. Relate the exercise to the way scientists began to learn about the atom—an object that was much too small to see.

VISUAL STRATEGY

Figure 3-1 Use this figure to emphasize that most of our knowledge of the component parts of an atom was gained in the twentieth century. The alchemists knew nothing of atoms and how their existence influenced the behavior of matter.

How do we know atoms exist?

OBJECTIVES

▶ *State* the three laws that support the existence of atoms.

▶ *List* the five principles of Dalton's atomic theory.

▶ *Calculate* the masses of atoms in amu and gram units.

▶ *Describe* how the atomic mass unit was chosen.

Atomic theory

You probably take the existence of atoms for granted. You have never seen an atom, yet you undoubtedly believe they exist. In fact, until recently even scientists had never seen an atom. Without actually seeing them, scientists *theorized* the existence of atoms based on their observations of the properties of matter.

Evidence for the existence of atoms

atomic theory

the theory that all matter is composed of indivisible particles called atoms

In Chapter 2 you learned that as early as 400 B.C. Greek philosophers proposed the **atomic theory,** which is the theory that all matter is composed of atoms. These ancient philosophers were great thinkers, but they did not place much emphasis on testing their hypotheses. Experimental results supporting the existence of atoms did not appear until more than 2000 years later, in eighteenth-century Europe. There, early investigators—the first true chemists—noticed certain characteristics shared by all chemical compounds. You read in Chapter 1 that a com-

▶ **FIGURE 3-1**

The history of chemistry dates back to the work of alchemists who searched for methods to change common metals to gold. Historical evidence indicates that alchemy was practiced throughout the world during the Middle Ages.

pound is a pure substance composed of atoms of two or more elements that are chemically combined. These observations about compounds, and the reactions they undergo, led to three important laws: the law of definite proportions, the law of conservation of mass, and the law of multiple proportions.

The law of definite proportions

The **law of definite proportions** states that a given compound contains the same elements in exactly the same proportions by mass, regardless of the size of the sample or the source of the compound. This means that every molecule of ethylene glycol shown in **Figure 3-2** contains the same number and types of atoms, regardless of how or where the antifreeze was produced. If a sample of ethylene glycol is found to have the formula $C_2H_6O_2$, then the law of definite proportions tells you that all other samples will have the same molecular formula.

Another example to illustrate this law is table salt, sodium chloride. No matter where it is mined or how it is prepared, any sample of pure sodium chloride always consists of the following proportions.

39.34% by mass of sodium and 60.66% by mass of chlorine

As chemists of the eighteenth century began to quantify their study of matter, it became apparent to John Dalton, an English schoolteacher, that there was a way to explain the patterns that emerged. Though the idea of atoms had been proposed well before his time, Dalton could finally use experimental data to support his hypothesis.

law of definite proportions

any sample of a compound always has the same composition

FIGURE 3-2 ▼

c Ethylene glycol contains exact proportions of these elements regardless of the size of the sample or its source.

Hydrogen: 9.74%   Oxygen: 51.56%

Carbon: 38.70%

Composition by Mass

a Ethylene glycol, the main component of automotive antifreeze, . . .

b . . . is composed of carbon, oxygen, and hydrogen.

Figure 3-3 Students will find writing and balancing chemical equations in Chapter 9 easier to grasp if they learn now that the law of conservation of mass means that all of the atoms involved in a reaction must be accounted for. You may want to write a few simple chemical equations illustrating the conservation law just to show students that they are a common way of communicating information in chemistry.

► **FIGURE 3-3**

For all practical purposes, the total mass of a system remains the same whether atoms are combined, separated, or rearranged. Mass is expressed here in atomic mass units, amu.

Combination of atoms

S   +   O₂   ⟶   SO₂

Sulfur atom
32.07 amu

Oxygen molecule
32.00 amu

Sulfur dioxide molecule
64.07 amu

C₃H₆   ⟶   C₃H₆

Cyclopropane molecule
42.08 amu

Propene molecule
42.08 amu

Separation of atoms

PCl₅   ⟶   PCl₃   +   Cl₂

1 Phosphorus
pentachloride molecule
208.22 amu

1 Phosphorus
trichloride molecule
137.32 amu

1 Chlorine molecule
70.9 amu

The law of conservation of mass

The law of conservation of mass states that the mass of the products of a reaction equals the mass of the reactants. This law applies when two or more elements combine to produce a compound, when a compound decomposes, or when the atoms in a compound are rearranged. Examples of these reactions are shown in **Figure 3-3.** Notice in Figure 3-3 that the masses of atoms and molecules are expressed in atomic mass units. You will learn more about atomic mass units later in this section.

From Einstein's equation $E = mc^2$, you know that mass and energy are equivalent. This relationship appears to contradict the law of conservation of mass. When 32.06 g of sulfur combines with 32.00 g of oxygen gas 296 800 J of energy is released in this exothermic reaction, usually as heat. Einstein's equation assures us that there must be a corresponding mass loss, which you can calculate as follows.

$$m = \frac{E}{c^2} = \frac{296\,800 \text{ kg} \cdot \text{m}^2/\text{s}^2}{(2.998 \times 10^8 \text{ m/s})^2} = 3.302 \times 10^{-12} \text{ kg}$$

The mass that is lost is so small compared with the masses of the reactants and products that scientists could never hope to detect any change in mass. In fact, the mass change in any chemical reaction is so small that it can be safely ignored. Thus, for all practical purposes, the law of conservation of mass is considered valid.

One gram of hydrogen combines with 7.94 g of oxygen in water

H_2O

H_2O_2

One gram of hydrogen combines with 15.87 g of oxygen in hydrogen peroxide

The ratio of the mass of oxygen in water to mass of oxygen in hydrogen peroxide is 7.94 g to 15.87 g, or 1:2

FIGURE 3-4 ▲

For water and hydrogen peroxide, the ratio of the masses of oxygen that combine with a fixed mass of hydrogen is 1:2.

The law of multiple proportions

The **law of multiple proportions** applies to different compounds formed from the same two elements. **Figure 3-4** and **Table 3-1** illustrate this important law. There are three different compounds made from the elements nitrogen and oxygen. All three compounds are gases, but each has its own physical and chemical properties. Table 3-1 shows the mass ratio of oxygen to nitrogen for each of these compounds. Notice that for a given mass of nitrogen, nitrogen dioxide contains twice as much oxygen as does nitrogen monoxide. In turn, nitrogen monoxide contains twice as much oxygen as does dinitrogen monoxide. The masses of oxygen that combine with a fixed mass of nitrogen are ratios of small whole numbers.

law of multiple proportions

the mass ratio for one of the elements in a compound that combines with a fixed mass of another element can be expressed in small whole numbers

TABLE 3-1 **Compounds of Nitrogen and Oxygen and the Law of Multiple Proportions**

Name of compound	Description	%O by mass	%N by mass	%O %N	Mass ratio	Formula
Nitrogen dioxide	poisonous brown gas in smog	69.56	30.44	2.285	4	NO_2
Nitrogen monoxide	colorless gas that reacts readily with oxygen	53.32	46.68	1.142	2	NO
Dinitrogen monoxide	anesthetic, "laughing gas"	36.35	63.65	0.571	1	N_2O

CONCEPT CHECK

1. What is the atomic theory?
2. State the laws of definite proportions, conservation of mass, and multiple proportions.

SECTION 3-1

VISUAL STRATEGY

Table 3-1 Point out that the %O/%N values are in the ratio 2:1:1/2. The formulas reflect this ratio for oxygen. In NO_2 there are 2 atoms O per 1 atom N; in NO, the ratio is 1:1; and in N_2O the ratio is the same as 1/2 O atom per 1 atom N. Emphasize that these three compounds differ greatly in properties even though they are composed of the same two elements.

ANSWERS

CONCEPT CHECK

1. the theory that all matter is composed of atoms

2. Law of definite proportions: A given compound always contains the same elements in the same proportion by mass, regardless of the size or source of the sample.
   Law of conservation of mass: Mass (matter) is neither created nor destroyed in a chemical reaction.
   Law of multiple proportions: When the same elements combine to form different compounds, they do so in mass ratios that can be expressed by small whole numbers.

RESOURCE LINK

ChemFile Teaching Resources CD-ROM
Career Extension
Assign Occupational Applications Worksheet 5.

HISTORICAL CONNECTION

Dalton based his 1803 atomic theory on the work of his contemporaries. Lavoisier's work with chemical reactions led him to describe the law of conservation of mass in 1782. In 1797, the French scientist Joseph Proust proposed the law of definite proportions. A law of multiple proportions had been put forth by another French chemist, Berthollet, in the 1790s, but it was not accepted by many scientists, especially Proust. But Dalton saw that it supported his idea of atoms and restated it along with his atomic theory. The Swedish chemist Berzelius, who was excited by the atomic theory, finally established the law several years later.

COMMON MISCONCEPTION

Dalton's atomic theory is a perfect example to use to clarify the nature of scientific laws and theories. Many (if not most) students and adults have the idea that all theories are just unproved notions because of the way the word is used in everyday speech. A theory explains a law and is supported by scientific evidence. Laws are simple statements of the behavior of nature. They can be demonstrated to be true at any time or place. Dalton was confident in proposing his atomic theory because his idea of indestructible, discrete atoms of elements accounted for the laws.

Module 2: Models of the Atom
Topic: Atomic Structure
This engaging tutorial reviews the discoveries that form the basis of our current atomic model.

Black powder used in some fireworks is a mixture of the three components shown. Sulfur and carbon are elements. Potassium nitrate is an ionic compound.

Potassium nitrate, KNO_3

Sulfur, S_8

Graphite, C

► **FIGURE 3-6**

Dalton's model explained the data chemists had collected about combinations of matter.

Dalton's atomic theory

John Dalton used the Greek concept of the atom and the laws of definite proportions, conservation of mass, and multiple proportions to give the atomic theory a scientific basis. Dalton believed that there were about a hundred different kinds of atoms from which all matter was formed. According to Dalton, elements were composed of only one kind of atom and compounds were built from two or more kinds of atoms. For example, the explosive in some fireworks is a mixture of carbon, sulfur, and potassium nitrate. Carbon and sulfur are elements and consist of only one kind of atom. Potassium nitrate is a compound and consists of three different types of atoms. **Figure 3-5** shows models of these structures.

Dalton proposed that the properties of elements differ from one another because their atoms differ. He also recognized that even though they may share the same atoms, compounds have properties that bear no relationship to those of the elements of which they are composed. For example, potassium nitrate, a white salt formed from atoms of potassium, nitrogen, and oxygen, is quite unlike the element potassium, a silvery metal, or the elements nitrogen and oxygen, which are colorless gases found in air.

Dalton recognized that the laws of definite composition, conservation of mass, and multiple proportions could be explained by the existence of tiny particles that combine with one another in small whole-number ratios. Based on this inference, Dalton proposed a theory of the atomic stucture of matter. Dalton's theory includes the five principles shown in **Figure 3-6.**

A Summary of Dalton's Atomic Theory

1. All matter is made of indivisible and indestructible atoms.

2. All atoms of a given element are identical in their physical and chemical properties.

3. Atoms of different elements differ in their physical and chemical properties.

4. Atoms of different elements combine in simple whole-number ratios to form compounds.

5. Chemical reactions consist of the combination, separation, or rearrangement of atoms.

Dalton's theory explained most of the chemical data of the day and was readily accepted by most of his fellow chemists. As you will learn later in this chapter, evidence gathered since Dalton's time has shown that the first two principles are not valid. A feature of atoms that Dalton overlooked is that most atoms will combine with others of their own kind. Oxygen, for example, is generally found as O_2, in which two oxygen atoms are combined. Sulfur is S_8. However, Dalton's theory has not been discarded, only modified and expanded as more was learned about the atom.

CONCEPT CHECK

1. According to Dalton, what is the difference between an element and a compound?
2. What are the five principles of Dalton's atomic theory?

Atomic mass

You would not expect something as small as an atom to have much mass, and indeed atoms have a very small mass. For example, a copper atom has a mass of only

1.0552×10^{-25} kg, or $0.000\ 000\ 000\ 000\ 000\ 000\ 000\ 000\ 105\ 52$ kg,

on average. That's pretty light! But isn't it remarkable that scientists have been able to measure such a small mass so precisely?

The mass of the copper atom given above, $(1.0552 \times 10^{-25}$ kg) is *an average* mass. Recall that Dalton thought all atoms of an element had the same mass. But now chemists know this is not true for copper and many other elements. 69.2% of copper atoms have a mass of 1.04497×10^{-25} kg, and 30.8% of copper atoms have a mass of 1.07815×10^{-25} kg. You'll see why the masses differ in Section 3-2.

Each penny shown in **Figure 3-7** has a mass of 3.1276×10^{-3} kg and is made mostly of copper. How many copper atoms are there in one penny? Assuming the penny is pure copper, you can find the number of atoms by dividing the mass of the penny by the average mass of a single copper atom, or by using the following conversion factor.

$$\frac{1 \text{ atom Cu}}{1.0552 \times 10^{-25} \text{ kg}}$$

The number of copper atoms in the penny is

$$3.1276 \times 10^{-3} \text{ kg} \times \frac{1 \text{ atom Cu}}{1.0552 \times 10^{-25} \text{ kg}} = 2.9640 \times 10^{22} \text{ atoms Cu}$$

This huge number serves to illustrate how small atoms are and that they are usually encountered in vast numbers.

FIGURE 3-7 ▲

These pennies each contain 2.9640×10^{22}, or about 29 640 000 000 000 000 000 000, copper atoms.

HISTORICAL CONNECTION

Dalton viewed atoms as hard, incompressible spheres surrounded by what he called an "atmosphere of heat." In his view, liquids possessed more of this heat than solids, and gases had the most.

ADDITIONAL APPLICATION

It is often said that the STM enables us to "see" atoms, but it is not sight as we normally think of seeing something. STM is more like the way a blind person "sees" with his or her fingers, using touch to visualize shapes, textures, sizes and arrangements.

ANSWERS

CONCEPT CHECK

1. An element is composed of atoms, all of which are alike in physical and chemical properties. A compound is a combination of two or more kinds of atoms, each of which has different properties, combined in a simple, whole-number ratio. The properties of the compound differ from those of the individual atoms.

2. The five points are:
   - All matter is made of indivisible and indestructible atoms.
   - All atoms of a given element are alike in their physical and chemical properties.
   - Atoms of different elements differ in their physical and chemical properties.
   - Atoms of different elements combine in simple whole-number ratios to form compounds.
   - Chemical reactions consist of the combination, separation, and rearrangement of atoms.

DEFINING STANDARDS

In this textbook, the word *amount* is used consistently to refer to moles of a substance. Also, because a mole is a count, amounts may also be expressed in numbers of atoms, molecules, or ions. It is important to make distinctions between quantities and units so students are not confused by the new terminology. Amount is a quantity; mole is a unit. Mass is a quantity; gram is a unit.

DISCUSSION STRATEGY

Ask students to study Figure 3-3 on page 76 and speculate why chemists may be interested in knowing the number of atoms, ions, or molecules in a sample of a substance. Substances react in simple ratios by number (or count) of particles. So, chemists need to be able to determine the number of particles present to measure reacting quantities. Ask also why it would be inconvenient for chemists to use atomic masses expressed in kilograms.

RESOURCE LINK

ChemFile Teaching Resources CD-ROM
Supplemental Reading Projects
Assign the guided reading worksheets for *Linus Pauling: In His Own Words,* Chapter 3 *"What Is Chemistry?"* for cross-curricular connections to language arts.

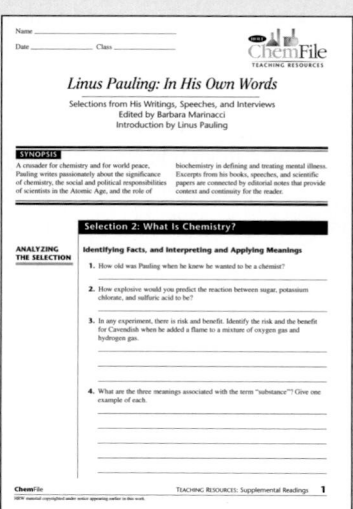

---

atomic mass
the mass of an atom in atomic mass units

Carbon atom
6 Protons   6 Neutrons

6 Electrons

$$^{12}_{6}\text{C}$$
Carbon

▲ **FIGURE 3-8**

Carbon-12 is the standard for the atomic mass scale. 1 amu = ½ the mass of carbon-12.

80   CHAPTER 3

Masses of atoms are measured in atomic mass units

Clearly, atoms are so light that the gram is not a very convenient unit for measuring their masses. Even the picogram (10^{-12} g) is unsuitable. A special mass unit is used to measure **atomic mass.** This unit has two names—the *atomic mass unit,* amu, and the *dalton,* Da. In this book, atomic mass unit will used. One atomic mass unit is equal to $1.6605402 \times 10^{-27}$ kg. The periodic table of the elements on the inside back cover of this book lists the atomic mass in atomic mass units. The mass of an atom in kilograms can be found by multiplying the atom's atomic mass in atomic mass units by the number of kilograms per atomic mass unit. For example, you can find the mass of a copper atom by performing the following calculation.

$$(63.546 \text{ amu})(1.6605402 \times 10^{-27} \text{ kg/amu}) = 1.0552 \times 10^{-25} \text{ kg}$$

This mass was reported on page 79 as the average mass of a copper atom. The periodic table lists the *average* mass of atoms for those elements that have atoms of different masses.

Chemists and physicists agree on the scale

You may wonder why 1 amu is equal to $1.6005402 \times 10^{-27}$ kg. After all, wouldn't it be more convenient if 1 amu were equal to 1.00×10^{-27} kg? Actually, the atomic mass unit has been defined in a number of different ways over the years. Originally atomic masses expressed the ratio of the mass of an atom to that of a hydrogen atom. Using hydrogen as the standard turned out to be inconvenient because hydrogen doesn't react with many elements. Early chemists determined atomic masses by comparing how much of one element reacted with another element. Because oxygen combines with almost all other elements, oxygen became the standard of comparison. The atomic mass of oxygen was defined as exactly 16, and the atomic masses of the other elements were based on this standard. But this choice also led to difficulties. Oxygen exists as three isotopes. Physicists based their atomic masses on assigning 16.0000 as the mass of the most common oxygen isotope. Chemists, on the other hand, decided that 16.0000 should be the average mass of all oxygen isotopes, weighted according to their abundances. Can you imagine the confusion that caused? To a physicist the atomic mass of fluorine was 19.0044, but to a chemist it was 18.9991. Finally, in 1962, a joint conference of chemists and physicists agreed on a scale based on an isotope of carbon, described in **Figure 3-8.** This scale, used by all scientists today, defines the atomic mass unit as exactly ½ the mass of one carbon-12 atom.

The SI unit for amount is the mole

So far we have discussed atoms in microscopic amounts, usually at the level of individual atoms. But most chemistry is done on the macroscopic level, and chemists often find it useful to work with a unit that represents a large collection of atoms. Such a unit serves as a bridge be-

---

ALTERNATIVE ASSESSMENT

Relating Dalton's Theory

The statements match the order of the points shown on page 78. Scramble the order, and ask students to determine which of Dalton's points explains each observation.

1. Matter can never really be thrown away. That is one reason that recycling is important.

2. There is no difference between copper found in an ancient Mayan necklace and copper wire freshly made from copper ore.

3. Zinc is a softer metal than iron, and it reacts more readily with acid than iron does.

4. The formula for ordinary ethanol is C_2H_6O, and the formula for acetic acid in vinegar is $C_2H_4O_2$.

5. When methane, CH_4, burns, it combines with oxygen, O_2, in the air to form molecules of water, H_2O, and carbon dioxide, CO_2.

tween the invisible world of atoms and the macroscopic world of materials and objects. This unit is called a **mole,** mol, and is the SI unit for amount of substance.

How big is a mole? A mole is a collection of $6.022\,1367 \times 10^{23}$ particles. In this text, the mole is usually rounded to 6.022×10^{23} particles. What is so special about this number? The answer is that 1 mol of atoms of any element has a mass in grams numerically equal to the atom's mass in atomic mass units. For example, the mass of a fluorine atom is 19.9984 amu, while the mass of one mole of fluorine atoms is

$$19.9984 \text{ amu} \times \frac{1.660\,5402 \times 10^{-27} \text{ kg}}{1 \text{ amu}} \times \frac{1000 \text{ g}}{1 \text{ kg}}$$

$$\times \frac{6.022\,1367 \times 10^{23}}{1 \text{ mol}} = 19.9984 \text{ g/mol}$$

In recognition of the value and importance of the number 6.022×10^{23}, scientists named it in honor of Amedeo Avogadro (1776–1856), shown in **Figure 3-9.** He was an Italian scientist whose ideas were crucial to the early development of chemistry. **Avogadro's constant** is the number of particles, $6.022\,137 \times 10^{23}$, in exactly 1 mol of a pure substance.

To appreciate how large Avogadro's constant is, imagine that all 6 billion people on Earth were to do nothing but count the atoms in 1 mol of an element. If each person counted at the rate of one atom per second, it would take over 3 million years to count all of the atoms in 1 mol!

FIGURE 3-9

Avogadro was a lawyer who later became a professor of physics and mathematics.

mole

the SI unit for measuring the amount of a substance

Avogadro's constant

the number of particles in 1 mol, $6.022\,1367 \times 10^{23}$/mol

SECTION REVIEW

Total recall

1. What laws provided evidence for the existence of atoms?

2. Which atom is used as the standard for the atomic mass scale?

3. State the law of definite proportions.

4. What is the SI unit for the amount of a substance?

Critical thinking

5. Which of Dalton's five principles still apply to the structure of an atom?

6. How does Einstein's equation $E = mc^2$ seem to contradict the law of conservation of mass?

7. What is the mass in grams of 1.00 mol of oxygen-16 atoms?

8. Three different compounds contain the elements sulfur (S) and fluorine (F). How do the following data support the law of multiple proportions?

   compound a: 1.188 g of F for every 1.000 g of S

   compound b: 2.375 g of F for every 1.000 g of S

   compound c: 3.563 g of F for every 1.000 g of S

9. Calculate the mass of a sulfur atom in kilograms using the atomic mass of sulfur.

ANSWERS

SECTION REVIEW

Total recall

1. the laws of conservation of mass, definite proportions, and multiple proportions

2. carbon-12

3. A given compound contains the same elements in the same proportion by mass regardless of the size of the sample or its source.

4. mole

Critical thinking

5. Principles 3, 4, and 5 still apply as stated. With the exception of accounting for the average mass of mixtures of isotopes, principle 2 is also still valid.

6. It indicates that mass can be changed to energy, and vice-versa.

7. 16.00 g

8. The masses of fluorine combined with 1 g sulfur in the three compounds are in a ratio of small whole numbers. The ratio is 1:2:3.

9. $(32.066)(1.6605402 \times 10^{-27} \text{ kg/amu}) = 5.3247 \times 10^{-26} \text{ kg}$

What is the internal structure of atoms?

Section 3-2

LESSON WARM-UP

Fascination with Cathode Rays
Scientists had experimented with cathode rays and speculated about their nature since the late 1850s. To enable students to understand why scientists were fascinated by cathode rays, ask them to examine Figure 3-10 carefully. Point out that current can flow only if there is a completed circuit. The inside of the tube was practically a vacuum. Yet when the voltage was high enough, current flowed between the widely spaced electrodes almost as if a wire connected them. The scientists deduced that electric current was flowing from the cathode to the anode by means of a type of ray.

HISTORICAL CONNECTION

J. J. Thomson originally was not very interested in theoretical science. He wanted to be a railroad engineer. But, he was offered a scholarship to study chemistry at Owen's College, in Manchester, England. The scholarship had just been established by the people of Manchester to honor John Dalton, who had lived there most of his life.

OBJECTIVES

▶ **Describe** the evidence for the existence of electrons and their presence in atoms.

▶ **Explain** how Rutherford's experiments led to the discovery of the nucleus.

▶ **Discuss** atoms of different elements in terms of the numbers of electrons, protons, and neutrons they contain.

▶ **Define** the terms *atomic number, mass number,* and *isotope.*

internetconnect

SCiLINKS
NSTA
TOPIC: Subatomic particles
GO TO: www.scilinks.org
KEYWORD: HW031

anode
an electrode through which electrons enter a metal

cathode
an electrode through which electrons leave a metal

Subatomic particles

Experiments by several scientists in the mid-1800s led to the first modification of Dalton's atomic theory. Atoms were found to be divisible after all. Scientists discovered that the atom was made of smaller particles, referred to as *subatomic particles*. While many types of subatomic particles have been discovered, only three are important to your study of chemistry. These particles are electrons, protons, and neutrons.

The first evidence that atoms consist of subatomic particles was obtained by researchers whose main interest was electricity, not atomic structure. One of these scientists was the English physicist J. J. Thomson. To study the flow of electric current, Thomson pumped most of the air out of a glass tube such as the one shown in **Figure 3-10**. He then applied a voltage to two metal plates placed at each end of the tube. These plates are called *electrodes*. One of these plates, called the **anode,** was attached to the positive terminal of the voltage source, so it had a positive charge. The other plate, called a **cathode,** carried a negative charge because it was attached to the negative terminal of the voltage source.

▶ **FIGURE 3-10**

Electric current flows through the cathode-ray tube when the electrodes are connected to a source of high voltage.

Gas at low pressure · Cathode ray · Cathode (metal disk) · Anode (metal disk) · To vacuum pump

DEMONSTRATION 1

Magnets and Cathode Rays

Approximate time: 5 minutes

If you do not have a demonstration cathode-ray tube like the one on the facing page, you can perform this simple demonstration with a television and a bar magnet. Do not use a computer monitor for this demonstration.

1. Use a freeze-frame function on a laser disc player or a VCR to get a picture with contrasting color boundaries on the screen.

2. Bring a bar magnet toward the screen. The colors will shift as the electron beams are deflected toward phosphors of different colors. Move the magnet around to see how it affects other parts of the picture.

3. Reverse the magnet, and bring the other pole near the screen. The colors should shift in the opposite direction.

Thomson observed that rays emerged from the cathode and struck the anode and the nearby glass walls of the tube. Because of their origin, these rays were called *cathode rays*. The apparatus shown in Figure 3-10 is called a cathode-ray tube (CRT). CRTs have become an important part of modern technology, being used in television sets, such as the one shown in **Figure 3-11,** computer monitors, oscilloscopes, and radar displays. For reasons that will soon be obvious, cathode rays are now usually called electron beams.

Cathode rays are composed of electrons

Thomson and other physicists observed that when a small paddle wheel was placed in the path of cathode rays, the wheel was set in motion. This observation suggested that the cathode rays consisted of tiny particles that were hitting the paddles of the wheel. The particles that made up the ray had mass. Because the rays originated at the negatively charged cathode, scientists reasoned that the particles, which they called **electrons,** were negatively charged. Thomson confirmed this prediction by observing the response of electrons to electric and magnetic fields, as illustrated in **Figure 3-12.** Subsequent experiments have shown that the mass of an electron is $5.485\,799 \times 10^{-4}$ amu, which is almost 2000 times smaller than the mass of the lightest atom. The charge of an electron was found to be $-1.602\,189 \times 10^{-19}$ C, where C stands for *coulombs,* the SI unit of electric charge.

Physicists soon found that the cathode rays were always identical, regardless of the metal used. Furthermore, the metal nor the gas was changed by the flow of current. The inescapable conclusion is that the cathode rays are electrons. It was later established that atoms of all elements contain electrons.

Electrons are negatively charged, but atoms are neutral. Therefore, atoms must contain positive charges that balance the negative charges of the electrons. Scientists could no longer view atoms as the simplest form of matter. The atom could be broken down into still smaller particles. Research continued to discover the nature of these particles. Dalton's theory that atoms were indivisible had to be abandoned.

electron

small, negatively charged particle found in atoms

FIGURE 3-12

A magnet near the cathode-ray tube causes the beam to be deflected as shown. The deflection of the beam toward the magnet indicates that the particles that compose the beam have a negative charge.

Labels in figure: Magnet, Deflected beam, Cathode

CONCEPT CHECK

1. What observations led scientists to propose the existence of subatomic particles?
2. What type of electrical charge does an electron carry?

SECTION 3-2

TEACHING TIP

Demonstrating Cathode Rays   If you have a cathode ray tube like the one pictured in Figure 3-12, use it to demonstrate the rays and their deflection by a magnet. You will need a high-voltage (~5000 V) power supply, such as a battery-powered induction coil or power supply for gas spectrum tubes. Follow the instructions that accompany the tube and the power supply. Keep students away from the apparatus and do not touch the terminals or the tube while the power supply is on. Keep magnets away from the ends of the tube. Demonstrate a Crooke's tube, which has a mica paddlewheel, and a Maltese cross tube if they are available.

VISUAL STRATEGY

Figure 3-12   If you do not have a CRT with a paddlewheel, show students a photograph of one. A good source is a lab equipment catalog. Make sure that students grasp the significance of the observation that cathode "rays" could exert a force and therefore move an object. This was strong evidence that the rays were unlike light, but rather were a stream of particles, i.e., matter. The only possible source of those particles was the atoms of the metal cathode.

ANSWERS

CONCEPT CHECK

1. the observation of cathode rays from a metal electrode and the fact that they could exert a force
2. a negative charge

4. Find a picture with thin straight horizontal or vertical lines, and repeat steps 2 and 3.

Caution: Do not hold the magnet near the screen for longer than is necessary to observe the effects because the metal grid just behind the screen can be magnetized and the colors will remain distorted. If this occurs, you can turn the set on and off several times to relieve the problem. Modern TVs have built-in demagnetizers.

▲ **FIGURE 3-13**

Thomson's model of an atom featured negatively charged electrons embedded in a ball of positive charge.

---

alpha particle

a positively charged particle produced by some nuclear disintegrations

---

nucleus

the central region of an atom made up of protons and neutrons

The nucleus

Thomson proposed that the electrons of an atom were embedded in a positively charged ball of matter. His picture of an atom, which is shown in **Figure 3-13,** was named the *plum-pudding model* because it resembled plum pudding, a dessert consisting of a ball of sweet cake with pieces of fruit embedded in it. One of Thomson's former students soon replaced the plum-pudding model of the atom.

Rutherford discovered the nucleus

It was the work of New Zealander Ernest Rutherford that made the plum-pudding model obsolete. His team of researchers carried out the experiment illustrated in **Figure 3-14.** A beam of small positively charged particles, called **alpha particles,** was directed at a thin gold foil. The team measured the angles at which the particles were deflected from their former straight-line paths as they emerged from the foil.

Rutherford found that most of the alpha particles shot at the foil passed straight through undeflected. But a very small number were deflected, some even backward, as illustrated in Figure 3-14. This greatly surprised the researchers—nothing like that was predicted by Thomson's plum-pudding model. As Ernest Rutherford expressed it, "It was almost as if you fired a 15-inch shell into a piece of tissue paper and it came back and hit you." He went on to reason that only a very concentrated positive charge, localized somewhere within the gold atom, could possibly repel the fast-moving, positively charged alpha particles sufficiently to reverse their direction of travel.

In addition, Rutherford hypothesized that this localized region, called the **nucleus,** must have a large mass compared with the alpha particle, or else the incoming particle would have knocked the positive

▼ **FIGURE 3-14**

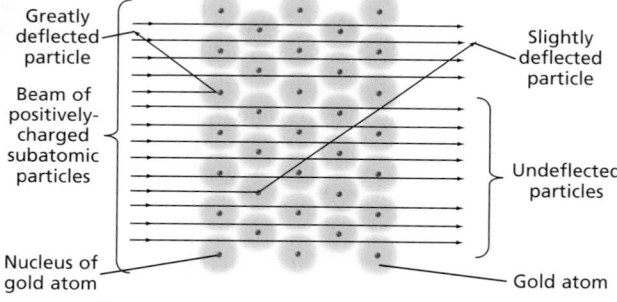

Gold Foil Micro View

a In the gold foil experiment, small positively charged particles were directed at a thin foil of gold atoms.

b The pattern of deflected alpha particles supported Rutherford's hypothesis that gold atoms were mostly empty space.

GRAPHIC ORGANIZER

Have students collect a summary of this section in a chart like the one below.

Major Subatomic Particles

FIGURE 3-15 ◄

If the nucleus of an atom were the size of one of the marbles shown, then the whole atom would be about the size of a football stadium.

HISTORICAL CONNECTION

Rutherford's gold-foil experiments were conducted mostly by Ernest Marsden, who was an undergraduate at the time. When Rutherford announced the results of his 1909 experiments in 1911, he only postulated the existence of an elementary, positively charged particle. He discovered the actual particle in 1914.

ANSWERS

CONCEPT CHECK

1. Most α-particles passed through the foil; only a few were deflected, and a few bounced back. He concluded that an atom must have a very small but very dense nucleus. In addition, the nucleus must have a positive charge in order to repel the positively charged α-particle.

2. that they are mostly empty space

READING STRATEGY

Organizing Concepts

Have students complete a table similar to the one below to summarize the development of the model of the nuclear atom. Two rows are completed as examples.

charge out of the way. The reason that most of the alpha particles were undeflected, Rutherford argued, was that most of the gold foil was almost empty space.

And so our modern picture of the nuclear atom emerged. The nucleus is the dense, central portion of the atom that contains all of the atom's positive charge and nearly all of its mass, but only a very small fraction of its volume. By measuring the fraction of alpha particles that were deflected and their angles of deflection, scientists calculated the radius of the nucleus to be less than $\frac{1}{10\,000}$ of the radius of the whole atom. **Figure 3-15** puts these relative sizes into perspective.

CONCEPT CHECK

1. How did the results of the gold foil experiment lead Rutherford to recognize the existence of atomic nuclei?
2. The fact the vast majority of alpha particles passed undeflected through the gold foil indicates what about atoms?

Protons and neutrons

The positive charges that repelled the alpha particles in the gold foil experiments were present on subatomic particles named **protons,** found in all nuclei. The charge of a proton was found to be exactly equal, but opposite in sign, to the charge of an electron. The mass of a proton was determined to be 1.0073 amu, almost 2000 times the mass of an electron.

Because protons and electrons have equal but opposite charges, a neutral atom must contain equal numbers of protons and electrons. However, the masses of all atoms except for hydrogen were known to be

proton

a particle with a positive charge found in atomic nuclei

GRAPHIC ORGANIZER

Question	Discovery	Inferences
Does the atom have a substructure?	Thomson: negatively charged particles can come from atoms	Atoms are not indivisible; they contain negatively charged electrons, thus positively charged particles must exist.
What is the arrangement of subatomic particles?	Rutherford: a small fraction of α-particles are reflected, repelled by gold atoms	The atom is mostly empty space; the nucleus is very small, but it is massive and positively charged.
How do we account for all of the atom's mass?		

| **TABLE 3-2** | **Properties of the Three Fundamental Subatomic Particles** |

Particle	Symbol	Charge (C)	Common charge notation	Mass (amu)	Where found
Electron	e, e^-, or $_{-1}^{0}e$	-1.602×10^{-19}	-1	0.000 549	outside nucleus
Proton	p, p^+, or $_{1}^{1}p^+$	$+1.602 \times 10^{-19}$	$+1$	1.007 276	inside nucleus
Neutron	n or $_{0}^{1}n$	0	0	1.008 665	inside nucleus

TEACHING TIP

Meaning of Atomic Numbers
Point out atomic numbers on the periodic table so students realize that these numbers are not just a sequencing of the elements, but rather the number of protons in an element's nucleus.

Designing a Model Have groups of students design models of the atom to show scientists' changing views over time. Include Thomson's plum pudding model, Rutherford's small-positive-nucleus model (no subparticles), the later model with protons and neutrons, Bohr's model with electrons in planetary orbits, and the modern model with electrons in clouds having different energy levels. Supply a small hard ball, such as a billiard ball or a steel pinball, to represent Dalton's model. For subsequent models, students could use clay of different colors, toothpicks, wires, construction paper, wooden craft sticks, and cotton or "angel hair" to represent electron clouds. Students may come up with even more imaginative ways to represent atoms. Student models should include a display of the evidence that led to that particular model.

Science in the News

PRESENTS Feature story 8

The Top Quark See the Science in the News video guide for more details.

greater than the combined masses of their protons and electrons. What could account for the rest of the mass? Hoping to find an answer, scientists began to search for a third subatomic particle.

About 30 years after the discovery of the electron, Irene Joliot-Curie (daughter of famous scientists Marie and Pierre Curie) discovered that when the element beryllium was bombarded with alpha particles, a beam of great penetrating power was produced. The British scientist James Chadwick found that this beam was made of particles that were not deflected by electric or magnetic fields. Logically, he concluded that the particles carried no electric charge. Further investigation showed that these neutral particles, which were named **neutrons,** have a mass of 1.0087 amu and are present in almost all atomic nuclei. **Table 3-2** summarizes the characteristics of the three fundamental subatomic particles.

neutron
a particle with no electric charge found in atomic nuclei

Atomic number is the number of protons in the nucleus

The number of protons an atom contains is known as its **atomic number.** Because all atoms are electrically neutral, the number of electrons must equal the number of protons. Thus, if you know the atomic number of an element, you immediately know the number of protons and the number of electrons found in one of its atoms. **Figure 3-16** shows the relationship between atomic number and atomic structure for oxygen.

atomic number
the number of protons in the nucleus of an atom

To date, scientists have identified a total of 111 elements, with atomic numbers from 1 to 111. Note that atomic numbers are always

 FIGURE 3-16

The atomic number shown on the periodic table for oxygen tells you that the oxygen atom has eight protons and eight electrons.

Oxygen atom

8
O
Oxygen
15.9994
$[\text{He}]2s^2 2p^4$

8 Protons

8 Neutrons

8 Electrons

ALTERNATIVE ASSESSMENT

Gold Foil Experiment

Present the following analogy to the gold-foil experiment. Have students imagine that 50 billiard balls are hung by strings at various heights throughout the front half of the room. A student is then blindfolded and given five tennis balls to throw toward the front of the room. Have students report what they think they would observe in this situation. Ask them what the billiard balls and the tennis balls symbolize. Some tennis balls would be deflected. The billiard balls represent gold nuclei, and the tennis balls represent the lighter alpha particles.

whole numbers—an atom can't have 2.5 protons! In addition, each atomic number is unique to a particular element. For example, all atoms with the atomic number 8 are oxygen atoms; conversely, all oxygen atoms have the atomic number 8.

Mass number is the total number of particles in the nucleus

In addition to atomic number, every atomic nucleus can be described by its **mass number.** The mass number is equal to the total number of particles in the nucleus, which is the total number of protons plus neutrons. For example, a particular atom of boron has a mass number of 11. Therefore, this atom has a total of 11 protons and neutrons in its nucleus. Recall that the atomic number for an atom of boron is 5 because it has 5 protons in its nucleus. You can calculate the number of neutrons the boron atom has by subtracting its atomic number (the number of protons) from its mass number (the number of protons and neutrons). In our example, the boron atom has 6 neutrons.

mass number

the total number of protons and neutrons in the nucleus of an atom

$$
\begin{aligned}
\text{number of protons and neutrons (mass number)} &= 11 \\
\underline{minus \text{ the number of protons (atomic number)}} &= -5 \\
\text{number of neutrons} &= 6
\end{aligned}
$$

How many protons, electrons, and neutrons are present in an atom of copper whose atomic number is 29 and whose mass number is 64?

Unlike the atomic number, which is the same for all atoms of an element, mass number can vary among atoms of a single element. In other words, all atoms of an element have the same number of protons, but they might have different numbers of neutrons. The atomic number of all oxygen atoms is 8, as shown in Figure 3-16, but oxygen atoms can have mass numbers of 16, 17, and 18. These atoms differ from one another in having 8, 9, and 10 neutrons, respectively.

Atomic structures can be represented by symbols

Each element has a name, and the same name is given to its atoms. For example, sulfur is composed of sulfur atoms, and tin consists of tin atoms. As you learned in Chapter 1, each element also has a symbol—S for sulfur, and Sn for tin—and the same symbol is used to represent one of its atoms. Thus, S represents a single atom of sulfur, 2S represents two sulfur atoms, and 8S represents eight sulfur atoms. However, chemists also write S_8 to indicate that the eight sulfur atoms are joined together as the molecule modeled in **Figure 3-17.**

Atomic number and mass number are sometimes written with an element's symbol. The atomic number always appears to the lower left of the symbol. For example, the symbols for the first five elements are written with atomic numbers as follows.

$_1$H $_2$He $_3$Li $_4$Be $_5$B

FIGURE 3-17 ▲

In nature, elemental sulfur exists as eight sulfur atoms joined to form a wreath-shaped molecule.

COMMON MISCONCEPTION

Students sometimes find it difficult to distinguish mass number from the average atomic masses given on the periodic table. Point out that mass number is not an actual atomic mass, but rather a way of stating the total number of particles in the nucleus. When you link mass numbers with isotopes, this distinction should be further reinforced in students' minds.

TEACHING TIP

Mass Number and Isotopes
Students can generally infer the mass number of the most abundant isotope of an element by rounding the average atomic mass given on the periodic table to the nearest integer. However, there are several notable exceptions, including zinc, 65.39, whose most abundant isotope is zinc-64 (48.6%), and gallium, 69.723, whose most abundant isotope is gallium-69 (60.1%). Two of the more striking examples are lead, as shown in Table 3-3, on page 90, and bromine, 79.904, whose stable isotopes are divided almost evenly between bromine-79 and bromine-81. The isotope bromine-80 does not occur in nature. Students should refer to the mass number of an atom or an isotope rather than the mass number of an element.

HISTORICAL CONNECTION

It was not until 1932 that Chadwick confirmed the existence of the neutron. The concept of atomic number was proposed by the British scientist Henry Moseley in 1915. At that time, there was still no explanation for the arrangement of the elements on the periodic table, and scientists continued to try to link periodicity to atomic mass. Moseley found that the progression of the elements in the table corresponded to an increase of one fundamental unit in the nucleus and that each element could be assigned an atomic number equal to the number of these units. Tragically, Moseley was killed in 1915 at the battle of Gallipoli in World War I. He was 27 years old. In 1920, Rutherford announced the existence of the proton, Moseley's fundamental unit.

CHAPTER CONNECTION

Symbols for atomic nuclei are used again in Chapter 18, Nuclear Chemistry. If students become familiar with this notation now, they will benefit in the later chapter.

Note that these subscript numbers add no new information; they are simply reminders of what the atomic number of a particular element is. On the other hand, mass numbers provide information that specifies particular atoms of an element. Mass numbers are written at the upper left of the symbol. The following are the symbols of stable atoms of the first five elements.

$$^1\text{H} \quad ^2\text{H} \quad ^3\text{He} \quad ^4\text{He} \quad ^6\text{Li} \quad ^7\text{Li} \quad ^9\text{Be} \quad ^{10}\text{B} \quad ^{11}\text{B}$$

Both numbers may be written with the symbol. For example, the most abundant isotope of each of the first five elements can be represented by one of the following symbols.

$$^1_1\text{H} \quad ^4_2\text{He} \quad ^7_3\text{Li} \quad ^9_4\text{Be} \quad ^{11}_5\text{B}$$

It is important to keep in mind that all atoms of an element have the same number of protons, and therefore the same atomic number, but may have different numbers of neutrons, and therefore different mass numbers. You will find out about the variability in the number of neutrons later in this section.

CONCEPT CHECK

1. What three subatomic particles are important to chemistry? What is the electric charge of each?

2. One particular atom of calcium can be represented as $^{44}_{20}\text{Ca}$. How many of each type of subatomic particle does this atom have?

Neutrons, protons, and Coulomb's law

Coulomb's law

the force between two charged particles is inversely proportional to the square of the distance between them

Coulomb's law states that the closer two charges come together, the greater the force between them. In fact, the force increases by a factor of four as the distance decreases by a factor of two, as illustrated in **Figure 3-18.** If the charges have different signs, they attract one another; if both charges have the same sign, they repel one another. As a consequence of their like charges, two or more free protons cannot come close enough together to form an atomic nucleus.

▼ FIGURE 3-18

a When two protons are 0.020 pm apart, they repel each other with a force of 0.58 N.

Force = 0.58 N
Distance = 0.020 pm

b The repulsive force quadruples to 2.32 N when the distance diminishes to 0.010 pm.

Force = 2.32 N
Distance = 0.010 pm

ALTERNATIVE ASSESSMENT

Group Strategy

Divide the class into groups of six, and supply each group with six 3 × 5 cards and a list of elements. Each group should get a different list. Students should place a nuclear symbol for an element on each card, leaving out one of the three parts of the symbol, such as in the following examples:

$$^?_{53}\text{I}, \quad ^{56}_?\text{Fe, and } \quad ^{32}_{16}?$$

The reverse side of the card should have the complete symbol. Once the cards are completed, have each group trade card sets with another group. The members of the group can quiz each other with the cards, challenging other members to complete each symbol. Have the groups continue trading until the cards are exhausted. Group members should change roles with each trade.

Keeping in mind Coulomb's law, it is easy to understand why—with the exception of some atoms of hydrogen—there are no atoms with nuclei containing only protons. All protons are positively charged, and at the close distances inside tiny nuclei, the forces of repulsion between particles of like charge are enormous.

Protons and neutrons can form a stable nucleus despite the repulsion between protons, due to the attraction of the *strong force*. This force is greater than the repulsive force at close distances. The simplest multi-proton atom, with a nucleus consisting of two protons and one neutron, is illustrated in **Figure 3-19.** This atom is called helium-3 because its mass number, the number of particles in its nucleus, is 3. Every atom of helium has 2 protons and therefore an atomic number of 2. But as you can see, not all helium atoms have a mass number of 3; in fact, 99.999% of helium atoms are helium-4.

Isotopes of an element have the same number of protons but different numbers of neutrons

All atoms of an element have the same atomic number and therefore the same number of protons. However, for many elements, the number of neutrons can vary. Atoms of the same element with different numbers of neutrons are called **isotopes.** The two atoms modeled in **Figure 3-19** are stable isotopes of helium.

The variation in the number of neutrons among isotopes is responsible for the average atomic masses of elements being far from whole numbers. A majority of the elements exist as mixtures of two or more isotopes. For example, the 82 protons in a lead nucleus are stable with 122, 124, 125, or 126 neutrons. When expressed in amu, the actual mass of each isotope is always very close to its mass number. **Table 3-3,** on the next page, lists lead's four stable isotopes, and all are present in natural lead. The abundance of lead isotopes varies a little depending on the source of the sample; chemists have therefore agreed on representative values. You can infer from the data in Table 3-3 that the average atomic mass for lead would be closer to 208 amu than to 204 amu.

isotope

one of two or more atoms of the same element with different numbers of neutrons

1 Neutron

2 Protons

Helium-3

2 Neutrons

2 Protons

Helium-4

FIGURE 3-19 ◄

The two stable isotopes of helium are helium-3 and helium-4. The nucleus of a helium-4 atom is known as an alpha particle.

COMMON MISCONCEPTION

Make it clear to students that the identity of an atom is determined entirely by the number of protons in its nucleus. Atoms of the same element (same number of protons) may have varying numbers of neutrons. When an atom forms an ion, it may have more or fewer electrons than protons. An atom in a plasma state may have no electrons at all.

Students may also have the idea that all isotopes are radioactive and therefore dangerous because of the way the word *isotope* is used in common speech. Point out that the water they drink every day contains two different isotopes of hydrogen (hydrogen-1 and hydrogen-2) and three isotopes of oxygen (oxygen-16, oxygen-17, and oxygen-18), none of which are either radioactive or dangerous.

RESOURCE LINK

ChemFile Teaching Resources CD-ROM
Skills Review
Assign Math Skills Worksheet 6:
Averages to review or reteach this skill.

TEACHING TIP

Vocabulary Strategy The word *isotope* was coined around 1910 and is derived from the Greek roots *iso*, which means "the same or equal" and *topos*, which means "place." *Isotope* was used to describe atoms of the same element (the *same place* on the periodic table) that had differing masses.

ANSWERS

SECTION REVIEW

Total recall

1. All isotopes of an element have the same number of protons in the nucleus and, when uncombined, the same number of electrons. Different isotopes have different numbers of neutrons.

2. An electron has a mass about 1/2000 that of protons and neutrons, which have masses of approximately 1 amu each. Protons have a 1+ charge, electrons have a 1– charge, and neutrons have no charge.

Critical thinking

3. **a.** $92p^+$, $92e^-$, $143n$

   b. $46p^+$, $46e^-$, $60n$

   c. $55p^+$, $55e^-$, $78n$

4. Thomson's interest in learning the nature of cathode rays resulted in the discovery of the electron, which was shown to have small mass and negative charge. This discovery showed that the atom was not indivisible and implied the existence of positively charged particles of much larger mass than the electron.

Name of atom	Number of neutrons	Symbol	Mass (amu)	Abundance (%)
Lead-204	122	^{204}Pb	203.973	1.4
Lead-206	124	^{206}Pb	205.974	24.1
Lead-207	125	^{207}Pb	206.976	22.1
Lead-208	126	^{208}Pb	207.977	52.4

TABLE 3-3 The Stable Isotopes of Lead—All Lead Atoms Have 82 Electrons and 82 Protons

Unlike lead, there are elements for which there is only one stable isotope. Beryllium is such an element. Outside nuclear laboratories, all the beryllium on Earth is ^9_4Be. Beryllium's four protons need five neutrons to form a stable nucleus. With four or six neutrons, or any number other than five, the beryllium atom is unstable, and sooner or later it will disintegrate in ways that are discussed in Chapter 18. Atoms having unstable nuclear configurations are called **radioisotopes** of an element.

Some elements have no stable isotopes. Technetium, element 43, is the lightest such element. There is no number of neutrons that will form a stable nucleus with its 43 protons. There are no known deposits of technetium on Earth. It was the first element to be artificially produced in a laboratory.

radioisotope
an unstable atom that undergoes radioactive decay

SECTION REVIEW

Total recall

1. How are isotopes of the same element alike? different?

2. Describe the major differences between electrons, protons, and neutrons in terms of size, mass, and location.

Critical thinking

3. Determine the number of electrons, protons, and neutrons for each of the following.

   a. $^{235}_{92}U$ **b.** $^{106}_{46}Pd$ **c.** $^{133}_{55}Cs$

4. How did a study of electricity contribute to an understanding of atomic structure?

5. Why did some of the alpha particles shot at the gold foil in Rutherford's experiment bounce backward?

6. What role does the strong force play in atomic structure?

7. **Story Clue** The element barium (Ba) is used in fireworks to produce a green color. All barium atoms contain 56 protons. One isotope of barium contains 74 neutrons, and another isotope contains 81 neutrons. Write the symbols for these two isotopes of barium.

5. They approached the gold nucleus head on and were repelled backward by coulombic force between the alpha particles and the positively charged nucleus.

6. The strong force is the attractive force between nuclear particles. It acts only at very close distances and holds a nucleus together.

7. $^{130}_{56}Ba$, $^{137}_{56}Ba$

CONSUMER FOCUS

ESSENTIAL ELEMENTS

Good health is elementary

Which of the 111 elements are needed for a healthful life? Four elements—hydrogen, oxygen, carbon, and nitrogen—account for more than 99% of all the atoms in the human body. These elements are the major components of the carbohydrate, lipid, and protein molecules that our bodies need for support, growth, and repair. Likewise, these four are the major elements in the food that you eat.

Another seven elements are used by our bodies in substantial quantities, more than 0.1 g per day. These are listed in the table below, together with the role that each plays in the body's struc-

internet**connect**

SC**LINKS**
NSTA

TOPIC: Essential elements
GO TO: www.scilinks.org
KEYWORD: HW033

ture and chemistry. These elements are known as *macronutrients* or, more commonly, as "minerals."

Some elements, known as **trace elements** or **micronutrients,** are necessary for healthy human life, but each only in very small amounts. In many cases, less than 15 ng per day is required for good health. Remember that *ng* stands for "nanograms" and *nano* means 10^{-9}, so you can easily show that you need less than 0.0004 g of each of these elements during your entire lifetime.

1 H																	2 He
3 Li	4 Be											5 B	6 C	7 N	8 O	9 F	10 Ne
11 Na	12 Mg											13 Al	14 Si	15 P	16 S	17 Cl	18 Ar
19 K	20 Ca	21 Sc	22 Ti	23 V	24 Cr	25 Mn	26 Fe	27 Co	28 Ni	29 Cu	30 Zn	31 Ga	32 Ge	33 As	34 Se	35 Br	36 Kr
37 Rb	38 Sr	39 Y	40 Zr	41 Nb	42 Mo	43 Tc	44 Ru	45 Rh	46 Pd	47 Ag	48 Cd	49 In	50 Sn	51 Sb	52 Te	53 I	54 Xe
55 Cs	56 Ba	57 La	72 Hf	73 Ta	74 W	75 Re	76 Os	77 Ir	78 Pt	79 Au	80 Hg	81 Tl	82 Pb	83 Bi	84 Po	85 At	86 Rn
87 Fr	88 Ra	89 Ac															

Elements in organic matter
Major minerals
Trace elements

Elements Other Than H, O, C, and N Needed to Sustain Human Life

Element	Symbol	Role in human body chemistry
Calcium	Ca	bones, teeth; essential for blood clotting and muscle contraction
Phosphorus	P	bones, teeth; component of nucleic acids, including DNA
Potassium	K	present as K^+ in all body fluids; essential for nerve action
Sulfur	S	component of many proteins; essential for blood clotting
Chlorine	Cl	present as Cl^- in all body fluids; important to maintaining salt balance
Sodium	Na	present as Na^+ in all body fluids; essential for nerve and muscle action
Magnesium	Mg	bones, teeth; essential for muscle action

LESSON WARM-UP

Familiar Waves To introduce the nature of light, ask students if they know how radio waves are produced. Perhaps a student who is interested in amateur radio can give a brief explanation. The students should conclude that electricity is involved. Some students have seen movies set in the early 1900s, such as *Titanic,* in which "wireless" telegraphy was used. They may remember the sparking sound that came from the telegraph. This sound occurred because the telegraph generated radio waves by allowing a spark to pass across a gap between two electrodes. The spark occurred every time a key was depressed.

VISUAL STRATEGY

Figure 3-20 Reinforce the idea that the visible spectrum is only a small part of a much wider electromagnetic spectrum. Point out that there is no qualitative difference between radio waves and visible light. Like a radio or TV antenna, the human eye contains antennae that respond to electromagnetic waves of wavelengths 10^{-8} times the wavelengths of radio waves.

HISTORICAL CONNECTION

The photoelectric effect was one of the first clues that light and atomic structure are somehow connected. Electric current flows across a space from one metal plate to another when light shines on the plates but not in the dark. In 1899, Thomson found that the particles passing across the space were the same as the particles in cathode rays—electrons. Thus, light energy was "knocking" electrons from atoms of the metal. From these observations, it was clear to scientists that light could interact with electrons. In 1905, Einstein explained the photoelectric effect in his theory that light behaves like a particle as well like a wave.

How are an atom's electrons configured?

OBJECTIVES

▶ ***Describe*** the nature of light and how it is produced.

▶ ***Explain*** how the wavelengths of light emitted by an atom provide information about electron energy levels.

▶ ***Compare*** the atomic models of Rutherford and Bohr.

▶ ***Describe*** the quantum mechanical interpretation of electrons in atoms.

▶ ***State*** Pauli's exclusion principle, the aufbau principle, and Hund's rule, and ***describe*** their roles in determining the electron configuration of atoms.

Electrons and light

▼ **FIGURE 3-20**

The electromagnetic spectrum is composed of radiation with a broad range of wavelengths. Our eyes can detect only the visible spectrum.

To a chemist, electrons are the most important parts of an atom. Though they are an insignificant part of an atom's mass, electrons occupy most of an atom's volume and determine virtually all of its chemistry. Much of our knowledge of electrons in atoms comes from studying the light they emit, so this section starts with a review of some properties of light. **Figure 3-20** shows the range of wavelengths for visible light and some other radiations.

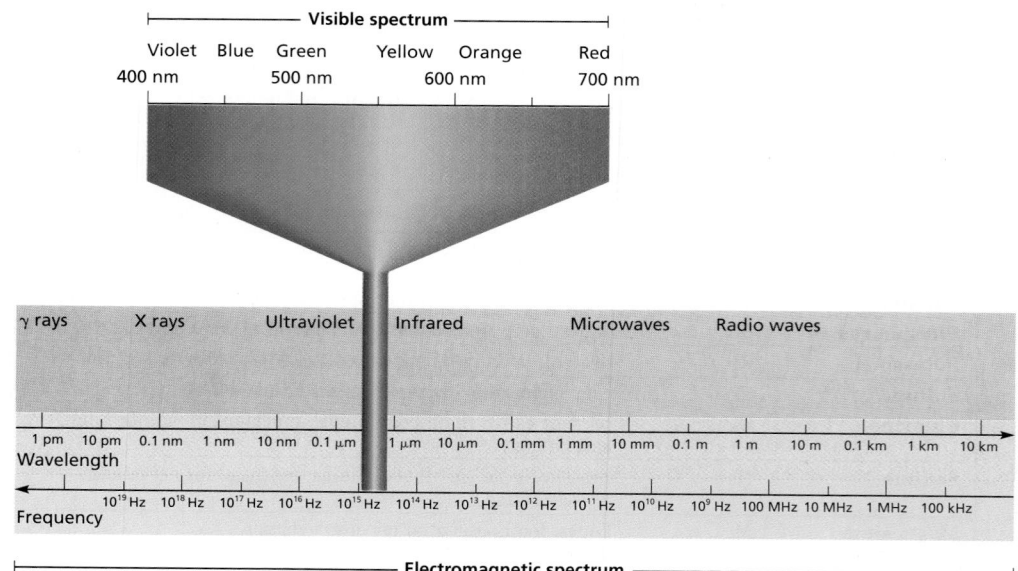

Light is an electromagnetic wave

Sunlight, when passed through a glass prism, produces the *visible spectrum*—all the colors of light that the human eye can perceive. You can see from Figure 3-20 that the visible spectrum is only a tiny portion of the **electromagnetic spectrum.** The electromagnetic spectrum also includes X rays, ultraviolet and infrared radiation, microwaves, and radio waves. The term *light* is often applied to regions of the spectrum that we cannot see, such as ultraviolet light.

Light, and all other electromagnetic radiation, can be thought of as moving waves. These waves, illustrated in **Figure 3-21,** can be described by three characteristics: speed, wavelength, and frequency. Though they move a little more slowly through matter, all electromagnetic waves travel at the same high speed in empty space. This is the so-called *speed of light,* which, as you saw in Chapter 2, is 2.998×10^8 m/s. Light travels so fast that it takes only 500 seconds to travel the 150 million kilometers between the sun and the Earth.

The distance between two consecutive peaks or troughs of a wave is its *wavelength,* and it is measured in meters. The wavelengths of electromagnetic radiation range from less than 10^{-13} m for gamma rays to more than 10^5 m for radio waves. Wavelength is closely related to frequency. The *frequency* of a wave is the number of waves that pass a stationary point in one second. One wave per second is called a *hertz,* Hz, the unit in which frequency is measured. One hertz is equal to one event per second. The frequencies of electromagnetic radiation range from less than 1000 Hz to more than 10^{22} Hz.

There is a very simple relationship between speed, wavelength, and frequency of electromagnetic waves, as shown in the following equation.

$$frequency \times wavelength = speed\ of\ light$$

With this equation, you can determine the wavelength of an electromagnetic wave given its frequency, or determine its frequency given its wavelength. For example, if you know that red light has a wavelength of 7.6×10^{-7} m, the following calculation provides its frequency.

$$frequency = \frac{speed}{wavelength} = \frac{2.998 \times 10^8 \text{ m/s}}{7.6 \times 10^{-7} \text{ m}} =$$
$$3.9 \times 10^{14}/s = 3.9 \times 10^{14} \text{ Hz}$$

The Rutherford model of the atom could not explain line-emission spectra

In the late nineteenth century, scientists observed that a characteristic lavender light was produced when a high-voltage electric current was passed through hydrogen gas. When the lavender light was sent through

---

Red light
Low frequency
Long wavelength

0 µm   0.5 µm   1.0 µm   1.5 µm   2.0 µm

Violet light
High frequency
Short wavelength

FIGURE 3-21 ▲

The frequency and wavelength of a wave are inversely related. As frequency increases, wavelength decreases. The higher the frequency of an electromagnetic wave, the shorter its wavelength.

electromagnetic spectrum

the total range of electromagnetic radiation, ranging from the longest radio waves to the shortest gamma waves

internetconnect

SCiLINKS.
NSTA
TOPIC: Electromagnetic spectrum
GO TO: www.scilinks.org
KEYWORD: HW034

TEACHING TIP
Demonstrating Wave Motion
Enlist the help of a student to demonstrate wave motion. Use a piece of rubber tubing about 3 m long. Have the student hold one end firmly while you shake the other end up and down at a steady rate, producing wave motion. Speed up the motion to produce an increase in frequency. You could have a second student use a meterstick or metric tape to measure the wavelength as you double the frequency of the wave. Students will notice that the wavelength is cut in half when the frequency doubles. Students can also see the tubing vibrate in two parts at one frequency, four parts at double the frequency, and eight parts at quadruple the frequency. Vary the energy of the vibration to demonstrate differences in amplitude. All involved in the demonstration should wear goggles.

COMMON MISCONCEPTION
The way units work out in the equation on this page may not be apparent to students. The frequency unit hertz also means *1/s* or s^{-1}. In fact, *1/s* really refers to waves, or "occurrences," per second. By substituting 7.6×10^{-7} m/wave for the wavelength 7.6×10^{-7} m in the equation, students will get answers in *waves/s.*

 Science in the News
PRESENTS Feature story 9
Atom Lasers See the Science in the News video guide for more details.

Teaching Tip

Heat and Light Ask students to think of examples of devices that emit visible light as a result of heat. Light bulbs and flames are obvious responses, as are electric range burners and hot or molten metal. If students know that there is a relationship between visible light and electrons, ask them to speculate about why heated materials can emit light.

Visual Strategy

Figure 3-22 Ask students to interpret the figure. The hydrogen gas is heated and excited by the high-voltage electric current passing through it. It gives off a pinkish violet glow. The prism breaks the light into a spectrum. Unlike plain white light, the spectrum consists of only a few very specific colors of light. For comparison, have students view a continuous spectrum through inexpensive diffraction gratings. A flashlight that uses a halogen bulb and that has strong batteries makes a good source of white light. After students study the Bohr model, return to this figure, and ask them to explain why the light consists of only a few different wavelengths.

► **FIGURE 3-22**

Excited hydrogen atoms emit a lavendar glow. When the visible portion of the emitted light is passed through a prism, it is separated into specific wavelengths that are part of hydrogen's line-emission spectrum.

Wavelength (nm)

410 nm
434 nm
486 nm   656 nm

Slits
Prism

Current passed through glass tube containing hydrogen at low pressure

line-emission spectrum

distinct lines of colored light that are produced when the light produced by excited atoms of an element is passed through a prism

a narrow slit, then through a prism, it separated into distinct lines of different colors. The spectrum shown in **Figure 3-22** is known as a **line-emission spectrum.** Experiments with other elements in the gas phase showed that each element emits characteristic colors of light that produce a distinctive line-emission spectrum for that element.

Scientists suspected that line-emission spectra provided information about the basic structure of atoms. But how could these distinctive spectra be explained by the arrangement of protons, neutrons, and electrons in atoms? The answer was provided by a young Danish physicist named Niels Bohr.

Excited electrons emit light

In 1913, Bohr showed that line-emission spectra could be explained by assuming that an electron in an atom is able to exist in any one of a number of energy states. An electron could move from a low energy state to a high energy state by absorbing energy. Conversely, an electron could move from a higher energy state to a lower energy state by releasing energy.

ground state

the lowest energy state of a quantized system

Normally, each electron in an atom is in a state of lowest possible energy, a **ground state.** If an electron acquires additional energy, then it is in an **excited state.** This unstable state is associated with a specific amount of energy that is greater than the ground state. The electron will quickly "fall" back to its ground state, and when it does, the excess energy is released as light. This light has a characteristic frequency (color) that reflects the energy released. It is the emission of characteristic frequencies of light that produces line-emission spectra.

excited state

the condition of an atom in a higher energy state than ground state

94 CHAPTER 3

Resource Link

In-Text Lab

Skills Development
Have students do Exploration 3A on page 720 to develop their skills using flame-test techniques.

DEMONSTRATION 2

Emission Spectra
Approximate time: 15 minutes

1. Obtain several gas spectrum tubes (Geissler tubes) to show students the emission spectra of excited atoms. Possibilities include H_2, He, O_2, Ne, Hg vapor, and CO_2.

2. Power the tubes with an induction coil or, preferably, a power supply made especially for these tubes. If you use an induction coil, mount the tube on a ring stand with a plastic-lined buret clamp. Do not turn on

the coil until after leads have been connected to the gas tube. Once the coil is on, do not touch the tube, clamp, or ring stand.

3. Supply students with spectroscopes or replica diffraction gratings in photographic slide mounts.

4. Before using the tubes, have students observe a continuous spectrum from a source of white light, such as a halogen-

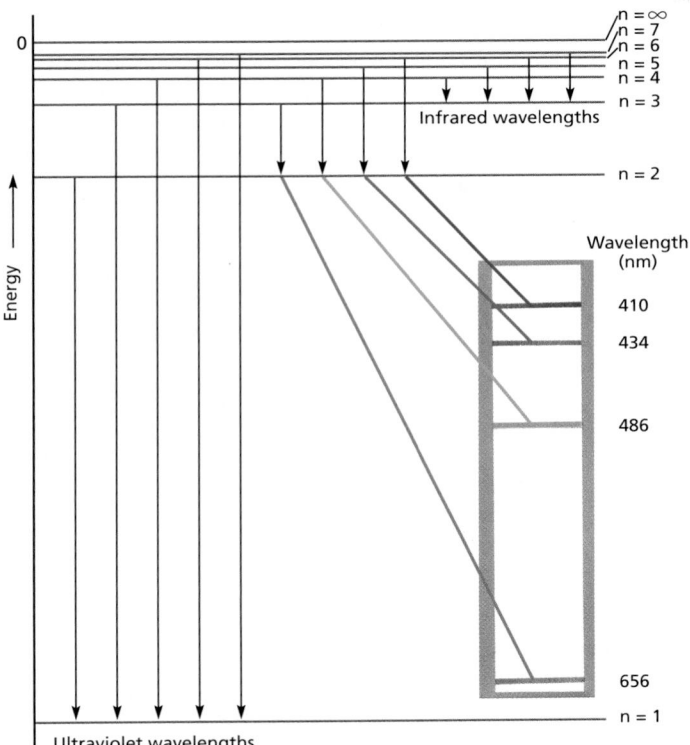

FIGURE 3-23 ◄

The seven lowest energy levels for the electron in the hydrogen atom are shown. When an electron in the $n = 3$ level falls to the $n = 2$ level, a flash of cherry red light, of wavelength 6.563×10^{-7} m, is emitted.

SECTION 3-3

According to Bohr, the only possible energies for the electron in the hydrogen atom are defined by the following equation.

$$\text{energy of electron} = \frac{-2.179 \times 10^{-18}\ \text{J}}{n^2}$$

In the equation, n can be any positive whole number, such as 1, 2, 3, 4, and so on. **Figure 3-23** shows several of these energy levels. A number such as n, which can take on only certain definite values, is called a **quantum number.** Bohr's formula matched the spectroscopic data so well that there was little doubt his hypothesis was correct.

When energies can only adopt certain values, the energy is said to be *quantized.* The effects of quantized energies are apparent only at the atomic level.

quantum number

a number with certain definite values

VISUAL STRATEGY

Figure 3-23 Students may wonder why there are many more energy transitions shown in this diagram than the number of lines they saw in the visible hydrogen spectrum. The most energetic transitions to the first energy level ($n = 1$) produce light in the ultraviolet region of the spectrum. The very small drops in energy produce light in the infrared region. The only transitions that produce visible light are those to the second energy level ($n = 2$) from higher levels.

COMMON MISCONCEPTION

Because students start with the electron configuration of the hydrogen atom, they sometimes come away with the mistaken idea that an atom in its ground state has all of its electrons in the first energy level.

HISTORICAL CONNECTION

Max Planck began to formulate the quantum theory in 1900. He theorized that energy is given off in fundamental amounts called *quanta.* Bohr based his atomic model on Planck's theory. This theory of quantization of energy paralleled Dalton's theory that matter was composed of discrete, fundamental units.

ANSWERS

CONCEPT CHECK

1. A line-emission spectrum is produced by the excited electrons of an atom as they fall back to lower energy states. The resulting light spreads into a spectrum when it passes through a prism.

2. Energy is quantized when it is emitted only in certain amounts, but not in intermediate amounts.

3. electromagnetic radiation of wavelengths between approximately 400 and 700 nm

CONCEPT CHECK

1. What is a line-emission spectrum?
2. What does it mean to say that energy is *quantized*?
3. Look at Figure 3-20. What wavelengths and what frequencies define light in the visible spectrum?

bulb flashlight. You may want to cover the flashlight lens with foil or black construction paper with a slit cut in it.

5. Start with the hydrogen tube to demonstrate the spectrum shown in Figure 3-22. Darken the room as much as possible. The dark blue lines are faint and hard to see with ambient light present. Students should concentrate on the spectral lines from the thin center section of the tube.

6. View the remaining tubes in order of increasing complexity of the atom. Neon tubes

show many distinct spectral lines and provide an impressive contrast with the hydrogen spectrum. Remind students that each line represents a possible electron transition from a higher energy state to a lower one. Also, some lines lie in the infrared and ultraviolet portions of the spectrum and are not visible.

7. If possible, keep the apparatus at hand and revisit the demonstration as needed for reinforcement.

CONTINUED ON PAGE 96

Orbitals replace orbits

The experiments of Rutherford's team led to the replacement of the plum-pudding model of the atom with a nuclear atom model. But Rutherford suggested that, like planets orbiting the sun, electrons revolve around the nucleus in circular or elliptical orbits. This was a very appealing explanation, and to this day, it is the model generally thought of by non-scientists. But Rutherford could not explain why the negatively charged electrons were not pulled into the positively charged nucleus as Coulomb's law would suggest. Thus, among scientists, the Rutherford model has been replaced by the Bohr atomic model, which describes electrons in terms of their energy states. Bohr postulated that electrons did not radiate energy while in orbit around the nucleus. But Bohr's model could not explain the spectra of larger atoms.

The present-day quantum model postulates that electrons have the properties of both particles and waves. According to quantum theory, each electron in an atom is assigned three quantum numbers, symbolized n, l, and m. Let's refer to an analogy again. If you have ever attended an event such as a concert, you know that your ticket specified your seat by a series of numbers and letters. For example, the ticket shown in **Figure 3-24** specifies seat number 20 in row U in section 3 of the south set of stands. These numbers are unique for this particular seat—no other seat shares this exact set of identifiers. Like section, row, and seat numbers, quantum numbers uniquely identify each electron in an atom.

orbital

a region of an atom in which there is a high probability of finding one or more electrons

In quantum theory, electrons are located in **orbitals,** regions of space in which you can expect to find electrons of specific energy. Despite the similar names, an orbital is very different from an orbit. An orbital is a region of high probability for finding a particular electron. It is as if the electron is smeared into a cloud, like the model in Figure 3-24b. The orbital is designated by a particular set of values of the quantum numbers n, l, and m in much the same way that a seat is identified by section, row, and seat numbers. Not every combination of the three quantum numbers is acceptable. Quantum theory provides rules for which combinations of n, l, and m are permitted.

▼ FIGURE 3-24

a A ticket for an event describes the location of a specific seat in much the same way a set of quantum numbers specifies where an electron is likely to be found.

Electron cloud composed of energy levels and orbitals

Nucleus containing protons and neutrons

b The current electron-cloud model of the atom describes orbitals as regions of high probability for electrons.

96   CHAPTER 3

DEMONSTRATION 2 *CONTINUED*

Safety
Wear safety goggles and a lab apron. If you do not have the special gas tube power supply in which all connections are enclosed, you will need to take the following precautions: Keep students at least 10 ft away; do not touch or allow anyone to touch any part of the apparatus while the power supply is on.

RESOURCE LINK

IN-TEXT LAB
Self-Directed Inquiry
Have students do Investigation 3A: *Spectroscopy and Flame Tests—Identifying Materials* on page 724 to design an experiment for the concept of spectroscopic identification.

TABLE 3-4 Quantum Numbers of the First 30 Atomic Orbitals

n	l	m	Orbital name	Number of such orbitals
1	0	0	$1s$	one
2	0	0	$2s$	one
2	1	−1, 0, 1	$2p$	three
3	0	0	$3s$	one
3	1	−1, 0, 1	$3p$	three
3	2	−2, −1, 0, 1, 2	$3d$	five
4	0	0	$4s$	one
4	1	−1, 0, 1	$4p$	three
4	2	−2, −1, 0, 1, 2	$4d$	five
4	3	−3, −2, −1, 0, 1, 2, 3	$4f$	seven

Rules for assigning quantum numbers

Refer to **Table 3-4** as you study the descriptions of quantum numbers. The *principal quantum number, n,* can take the values 1, 2, 3, 4, and so on. In practice, n values greater than 7 are not encountered. The larger n is, the farther the orbital is from the nucleus and the higher its energy is.

The l quantum number can take any whole-number value from 0 to $n - 1$. For example, if $n = 3$, l can take the values 0, 1, or 2. When discussing the l quantum number, chemists use a letter code. A quantum number $l = 0$ corresponds to an s orbital; $l = 1$ corresponds to a p orbital; $l = 2$ corresponds to a d orbital; $l = 3$ corresponds to an f orbital. For example, an orbital with $n = 3$ and $l = 1$ is called a $3p$ orbital, and an electron occupying that orbital is called a $3p$ electron.

The m quantum number may take whole-number values depending on the value of l. In Table 3-4 you see that if $l = 1$, m can take any of the three values −1, 0, or 1. An $l = 1$ orbital is a p orbital, and so there are three p orbitals for each principal quantum number.

The l and m quantum numbers designate the shapes and orientations of the orbitals. **Figure 3-25,** on the next page, illustrates the shapes that are encountered. You might ask, "Where exactly are the electrons in these orbitals?" But quantum theory doesn't provide an answer to that question. Quantum theory tells us the *exact* energy of the electron, but only the *probability* that the electron will be in a particular region. The models in Figure 3-25 show regions where an electron is most likely to be. Picture the electron as a cloud of electric charge that is dense in regions of high probability and less dense in regions of low probability.

SECTION 3-3

TEACHING TIP
Quantum Number Summary
Summarize quantum numbers and what they mean.

n: in which energy level the electron is located

l: in which sublevel within that energy level the electron is located

m: in which orbital within the sublevel the electron is located

spin: the identity of the particular electron of the two possible electrons in an orbital

Notice that n also indicates the number of energy sublevels that can exist within that energy level.

DID YOU KNOW?

The orbital letters *s, p, d,* and *f* are derived from the words *sharp, principal, diffuse,* and *fundamental.* These words were first used to describe the qualities of certain spectral lines. Later it was discovered that these qualities were related to the sublevel structure of the electron arrangement, so their letters were retained.

ALTERNATIVE ASSESSMENT

Line Spectra and Electrons

It is important that students have a sound mental model of the atom before proceeding further in chemistry. Understanding the link between line spectra and the arrangement of electrons in energy levels will help solidify that model. To help students reason through this connection in a stepwise fashion, assign the following questions.

▶ How did Bohr's model of the atom compare with Rutherford's model?

▶ Why were line-emission spectra important in forming a new atomic model?

▶ How did the new model account for the fact that emission spectra consisted only of light at very specific wavelengths?

▶ How did Bohr's model agree with the quantum theory?

▶ Why do atoms with more electrons have more complex line-emission spectra?

▼ **FIGURE 3-25**

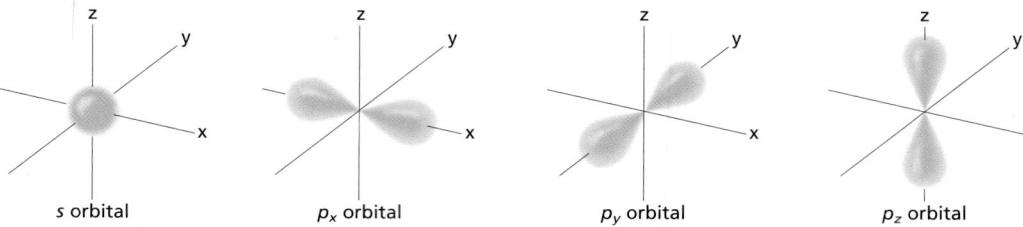

s orbital p_x orbital p_y orbital p_z orbital

a The s orbital is spherically shaped. There is one s orbital for each value $n = 1, 2, 3 \ldots$ of the principal quantum number.

b For each of the values $n = 2, n = 3, n = 4 \ldots$, there are three p orbitals. Each is dumbbell shaped, but they differ in orientation.

c For each of the values $n = 3, n = 4, n = 5, \ldots,$ there are five d orbitals. Four of the five have similar shapes, but differ in orientation.

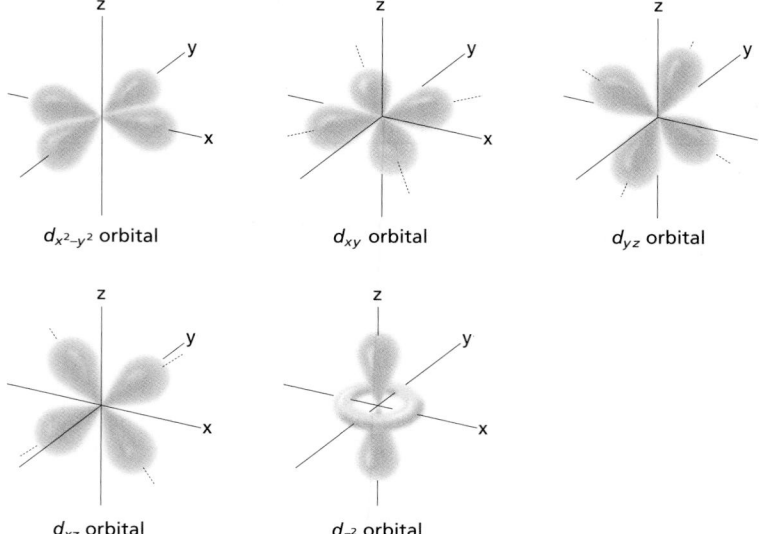

$d_{x^2-y^2}$ orbital d_{xy} orbital d_{yz} orbital

d_{xz} orbital d_{z^2} orbital

No more than two electrons occupy an orbital

German chemist Wolfgang Pauli determined that two, but no more than two, electrons can occupy a single orbital. This rule is known as the **Pauli exclusion principle.** Thus, the occupancy of an orbital is 0, 1, or 2 electrons. Chemists imagine that electrons spin, and they believe that if two electrons are in the same orbital, they must spin in opposite directions. Electrons are assigned a *spin quantum number, m_s,* to describe the direction of their spin. There are only two possible values for the spin quantum number, $m_s = -\frac{1}{2}$ and $m_s = +\frac{1}{2}$. The spinning electron is a tiny magnet. Two electrons in the same orbital spin in opposite directions.

Scientists have found out exactly which orbitals are occupied, and by how many electrons, in all of the 111 elements. This information describes the **electron configuration** of an atom.

Pauli exclusion principle

a maximum of two electrons can occupy each orbital, and these electrons must have different spin quantum numbers

electron configuration

a description of the occupied electron orbitals in an atom

Electrons occupy lower-energy orbitals first

In the ground state, you would expect electrons to fill those orbitals with the lowest available energy first. And that's exactly what happens. According to the **aufbau principle** (*aufbau* is the German word for "building up"), the electrons in an atom will occupy the lowest available orbitals.

Recall that the smaller the principal quantum number, the lower the energy. But also, for elements with many electrons, the smaller the l quantum number, the lower the energy. So the order in which the orbitals are filled matches the order of energies, which starts out as follows.

$$1s < 2s < 2p < 3s < 3p$$

After that, however, the picture is less straightforward. The energy levels of the $3d$ orbitals are slightly higher than those of the $4s$ orbitals.

$$1s < 2s < 2p < 3s < 3p < 4s \approx 3d$$

After the $4p$ orbital is filled, there is another irregularity because the $5s$ and $4d$ orbitals are close in energy.

$$1s < 2s < 2p < 3s < 3p < 4s \approx 3d < 4p < 5s \approx 4d$$

Still more irregularities occur with the higher-energy orbitals. **Figure 3-26** illustrates the overlap of some of the energy levels schematically.

For example, the electron configuration of sulfur, whose atomic number is 16, is written as follows.

$$S = 1s^2 2s^2 2p^6 3s^2 3p^4$$

This line of symbols tells us exactly how the 16 electrons of a sulfur atom are configured. There are two in the $1s$ orbital, two in the $2s$ orbital, six in the $2p$ orbitals (two in each of the 3 p orbitals), and so on. To save space, this configuration is sometimes written using the configuration of a noble gas.

$$S = [Ne] \, 3s^2 3p^4$$

The neon atom's configuration is $1s^2 2s^2 2p^6$. Similarly, the electron configuration of manganese is

$$Mn = [Ar] \, 3d^5 4s^2$$

There are some exceptions to the aufbau principle. Chromium is one such exception, its configuration shows both an unfilled $3d$ and $4s$.

$$Cr = [Ar] \, 3d^5 4s^1$$

You will find a listing of all the configurations on the inside back cover of this book. It should be emphasized that these are the *ground-state* configurations of the *isolated* atoms in the *gas* phase. In other circumstances, atoms may adopt configurations different from those listed on that periodic table.

FIGURE 3-26 ▼

This diagram illustrates how the energy levels of orbitals can overlap, creating exceptions to the aufbau principle.

READING STRATEGY

Peer Teaching

The material in this section will seem abstract to many students. Have students read the remainder of this section. Give students self-stick notes, and have them mark areas that are unclear with a question mark. Remind them to study the diagrams carefully because they help explain the text. When the students are finished, have them work with a partner to discuss what they did not understand. Assign an element to each pair, and have them build its electron configuration while they help each other understand the concepts of energy levels and the aufbau principle.

VISUAL STRATEGY

Figure 3-26 The orbital-filling diagram on the facing page reflects the increasing energy order of the sublevels as shown on this page. These diagrams represent ideal cases, however. The sequence works flawlessly through the elements in the first three periods. In the fourth period, there are two anomalies, chromium and copper, and even more occur in the remaining elements. By strictly following the orbital order, you arrive at the following electron configuration for chromium.

$$Cr: 1s^2 2s^2 2p^6 3s^2 3p^6 4s^2 3d^4$$

Experiments show that the configuration is something different. Anomalies occur because the $4s$ and $3d$ sublevels are so close in energy. In this case, an electron is "borrowed" from the $4s$ orbital in order to achieve a complete set of five half-filled $3d$ orbitals. The true configuration is the following.

$$Cr: 1s^2 2s^2 2p^6 3s^2 3p^6 4s^1 3d^5$$

This configuration confers greater stability on the atom than it would have with the configuration that follows the rules. Likewise, the copper atom has a configuration of $1s^2 2s^2 2p^6 3s^2 3p^6 4s^1 3d^{10}$ rather than $1s^2 2s^2 2p^6 3s^2 3p^6 4s^2 3d^9$ because the atom is more stable with a set of five full $3d$ orbitals. In the fifth period, Mo, Ru, Rh, Pd, and Ag have anomalous configurations.

Electron Configurations Divide the class into groups of three, and have them determine the electron configurations and the orbital notation for the following atoms: Sc, K, P, B, In, Ba, and Pr. You may want to supply paper with a 1/4 in. grid to facilitate writing the orbital notation.

Sc: $1s^2 2s^2 2p^6 3s^2 3p^6 4s^2 3d^1$

K: $1s^2 2s^2 2p^6 3s^2 3p^6 4s^1$

P: $1s^2 2s^2 2p^6 3s^2 3p^3$

B: $1s^2 2s^2 2p^1$

In: $1s^2 2s^2 2p^6 3s^2 3p^6 4s^2 3d^{10} 4p^6 5s^2 4d^{10} 5p^1$

Ba: $1s^2 2s^2 2p^6 3s^2 3p^6 4s^2 3d^{10} 4p^6 5s^2 4d^{10} 5p^6 6s^2$

Pr: $1s^2 2s^2 2p^6 3s^2 3p^6 4s^2 3d^{10} 4p^6 5s^2 4d^{10} 5p^6 6s^2 4f^3$

HOW TO

ADDITIONAL EXAMPLES

Have students write electron configurations for the following elements.

a. neon

Ans. $1s^2 2s^2 2p^6$

b. sulfur

Ans. $1s^2 2s^2 2p^6 3s^2 3p^4$

c. arsenic

Ans. $1s^2 2s^2 2p^6 3s^2 3p^6 4s^2 3d^{10} 4p^3$

Have students write abbreviated noble-gas electron configurations for the following elements.

a. calcium

Ans. $[Ar]4s^2$

b. bromine

Ans. $[Ar]4s^2 3d^{10} 4p^5$

c. tin

Ans. $[Kr]5s^2 4d^{10} 5p^2$

HOW TO   Write an electron configuration

Write the electron configuration for fluorine.

1 **Determine the number of electrons the atom has**

The element's atomic number tells you how many electrons it has. An atom of fluorine has an atomic number of 9 and therefore has 9 electrons.

9
F
Fluorine
18.9984032

2 **Fill orbitals in order of increasing energy, and use the figure at right as a guide**

▶ Each *s* orbital can hold 2 electrons.

▶ Each *p* orbital can hold 2 electrons. 3 available *p* orbitals can hold a total of 6 electrons.

▶ Each *d* orbital can hold 2 electrons. 5 available *d* orbitals can hold a total of 10 electrons.

▶ Each *f* orbital can hold 2 electrons. 7 available *f* orbitals can hold a total of 14 electrons.

The electron configuration for fluorine follows.

$$1s^2 2s^2 2p^5$$

Electrons usually fill orbitals in the order shown by the arrows.

3 **Make sure the total number of electrons in the electron configuration equals the atomic number**

The total number of electrons shown in the fluorine electron configuration is $2 + 2 + 5 = 9$.

Orbital diagrams are models of electron arrangements

Orbital diagrams are also used to show how electrons are distributed within sublevels. In an orbital diagram, each orbital is represented by a box, and each electron is represented by an arrow. The direction of spin is represented by the direction of the arrow.

Boron's electron configuration can be written as $1s^2 2s^2 2p^1$; therefore, its orbital diagram is written as follows.

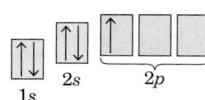

Following the aufbau strategy, let's think about constructing the boxed orbital diagram for carbon, the next element. A question arises: Does the next electron enter the first $2p$ orbital to pair with the single electron already there? Or does carbon have two electrons in two distinct $2p$ orbitals? According to Hund's rule, the second answer is correct. **Hund's rule** states that orbitals of the same n and l quantum numbers are each occupied by one electron, before any pairing occurs. For example, nitrogen has seven electrons. Its electron configuration is written as $1s^2 2s^2 2p^3$. This configuration is shown by the following orbital diagram.

Hund's rule

the most stable arrangement of electrons is that with the maximum number of unpaired electrons, all with the same spin quantum number

---

ALTERNATIVE ASSESSMENT

Group Strategy

Have students build a timeline for the major developments that led to our modern model of the atom. Have them begin with Dalton's atomic theory and build up through the discoveries about the nucleus and to our modern understanding of electrons arrayed in energy levels, sublevels, and orbitals. Students who are more enterprising should go outside the text to build a more complete chronology.

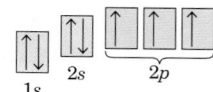

Recall that published configurations are for isolated atoms in the gas phase. But chemists seldom deal with monatomic gases. For example, the ground-state electron configuration of chromium is as follows.

$$[Cr] = 1s^2 2s^2 2p^6 3s^2 3p^6 3d^5 4s^1 = [Ar]3d^5 4s^1$$

Because the $4s$ and $3d$ levels are so close, it takes very little energy to excite a ground-state chromium atom by moving an electron to create the following configuration.

$$[Cr^*] = [Ar]3d^6 4s^0$$

Note that an asterisk is used to indicate an excited state. If it is to the energetic advantage of a chromium atom (to form stronger bonds, for example), the chromium atom can easily make the switch to the excited state. In such cases the gas-phase configuration is of little importance.

However, when dealing with electron levels that are energetically well separated, it is *very* important to know which orbitals are occupied by the electrons in the atom. Their configuration then affects both the properties and the reactions of the elements in question. This will be further explained in Chapter 4.

SECTION REVIEW

Total recall

1. How does Bohr's model of the atom differ from Rutherford's?

2. How does the quantum model of the atom differ from that suggested by Rutherford?

3. What happens when an electron returns to its ground state from its excited state?

4. What does n represent in the quantum theory of electrons in atoms?

Critical thinking

5. Use Pauli's exclusion principle or Hund's rule to explain why the following configurations are incorrect.

   a. $1s^2 2s^3 2p^6 3s^1$

   b.

   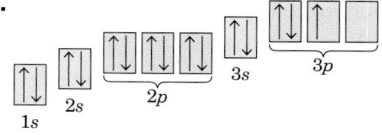

6. What information is provided by an electron configuration?

7. Calculate the maximum number of electrons that can occupy the fourth principal energy level.

8. **Story Clue** Write the electron configuration and draw the orbital diagram for an atom of aluminum, the element used in fireworks to produce a bright white light.

ANSWERS

SECTION REVIEW

Total recall

1. Bohr accounted for line-emission spectra by proposing that electrons were arranged in planetary orbits of particular energies.

2. This model suggests that electrons are not located in planetary orbits but rather in regions of space in which there is a high probability of finding an electron. These regions have specific three-dimensional shapes.

3. It emits a quantum of energy in the form of electromagnetic radiation.

4. a principal energy level

Critical thinking

5. **a.** The $2s$ orbital is shown with 3 electrons. An orbital can hold no more than two electrons.

   b. The third electron in the $3p$ sublevel must occupy the third available orbital. It cannot pair with an electron in another orbital.

6. the arrangement of electrons in energy levels, sublevels, and orbitals and their distribution within those orbitals

7. 32

8. $1s^2 2s^2 2p^6 3s^2 3p^1$
   $1s\updownarrow \quad 2s\updownarrow \quad 2p\updownarrow\updownarrow\updownarrow \quad 3s\updownarrow \quad 3p\uparrow$

ALTERNATIVE ASSESSMENT

Group Strategy

Give students the electron configuration for a few relatively simple atoms, such as lithium, boron, and oxygen. Have the students draw models of the atoms in any manner that fits their understanding. Be sure their drawings clearly indicate the energy differences between sublevels. Follow up by asking them to pick three more atoms, preferably from the third period of the periodic table, determine their electron configurations, and draw models as they did before.

Now that you have completed the chapter, you should be able to answer the questions about how fireworks and light are related to atomic structure.

LOOKING BACK

What is light, and how do various colors of light differ?

From Figure 3-20, you can see that visible light consists of electromagnetic radiation having wavelengths between 4×10^{-7} m and 7×10^{-7} m. The longest visible wavelengths are red, and the shortest visible wavelengths are at the violet end of the spectrum.

What is happening to atoms when fireworks produce colored light?

Energy is supplied to a fireworks system when a fuse ignites the chemicals. The high temperature of the fireworks' explosion vaporizes the atoms or molecules and the abundant energy moves electrons to an excited energy state. The colors are generated by atoms or molecules in an excited state. A line-emission spectrum is produced by excited atoms as energy-rich electrons quickly return to the ground state, shedding their extra energy as light of one or more specific wavelengths.

Sodium atoms, in particular, are potent light emitters. Heated to more than 1800°C by the violently exothermic chemistry of the fireworks, atoms of sodium give off mainly yellow light which has a wavelength of 5.89×10^{-7} m. The reaction of sodium that emits light can be represented by the following equation.

$$Na^* \longrightarrow Na + \text{light energy}$$

Na on the products side of the equation represents a ground-state sodium atom.

$$Na = 1s^2 2s^2 2p^6 3s^1$$

Na* on the reactants side of the equation represents an excited sodium atom. The atom differs from a ground-state sodium atom by having its 3s electron elevated into a normally unoccupied 3p orbital.

$$Na^* = 1s^2 2s^2 2p^6 3p^1$$

This light-emitting process is so efficient that it tends to overwhelm other atomic or molecular light emissions in a fireworks explosion.

How does the instability of copper(II) chloride at high temperature interfere with its ability to emit blue light?

Copper(II) chloride is unstable because it decomposes into copper and chlorine atoms at a temperature only slightly higher than that at which it emits light. Therefore, if the temperatures generated by the exploding shell and reacting chemicals are not precisely controlled, copper(II) chloride crystals will absorb so much energy that they decompose before electrons reach the excited state. The decomposition products cannot emit blue light.

4
Be
Beryllium
9.012 182
[He]2s^2

Beryllium has
only one naturally
occurring isotope,
beryllium-9.

WHERE IS IT?

Earth's Crust
0.005%

internet**connect**

SCI LINKS
NSTA
TOPIC: Beryllium
GO TO: www.scilinks.org
KEYWORD: HW035

A BRIEF HISTORY

Beryllium—An Uncommon Element

Although it is an uncommon element, beryllium has a number of properties that make it a very useful element. Beryllium has a relatively high melting point, 1278°C, and is an excellent conductor of heat and electricity. Beryllium transmits X rays extremely well and is therefore used to make "windows" for X-ray devices. All compounds of beryllium are toxic to humans. People who experience prolonged exposure to beryllium dust may contract berylliosis, a disease that can lead to severe lung damage and even death.

Industrial Uses

▶ The addition of 2% beryllium to copper forms an alloy that is six times stronger than copper. This alloy is used for nonsparking tools, critical moving parts in jet engines, and components in precision equipment.

▶ Emerald and aquamarine are precious forms of the mineral beryl, $Be_3Al_2(SiO_3)_6$.

▶ Beryllium is used in nuclear reactors as a neutron reflector and as an alloy with the fuel elements.

Crystals of pure beryllium look very different from the combined form of beryllium in an emerald.

1898: P. Lebeau discovers a method of extracting high-purity beryllium with an electrolytic process.

1828: F. Wöhler, of Germany, gives beryllium its name after he and W. Bussy, of France, simultaneously isolate the pure metal.

1942: A Ra-Be source provides the neutrons for Fermi's studies that lead to the construction of a nuclear reactor.

1700

1800

1900

1798: R. J. Haüy, a French mineralogist, observes that emeralds and beryl have the same optical properties and, therefore, the same chemical composition.

1926: M. G. Corson, of the United States, discovers that beryllium can be used to age-harden copper-nickel alloys.

READING STRATEGY

Assimilating Knowledge

Have students return to their lists of things they want to know about reaction rates and the factors that affect rates, which they created on page 72. Have them place check marks next to the questions that they are now able to answer. Students should finish by making a list of what they have learned. Have students identify unanswered questions as well as new questions they may have. These questions could be used as the basis for a research project.

REVIEW & ASSESS ASSIGNMENT GUIDE

Term Review

Assign after Section 3-3.

Concept and Skills Review

Section 3-1
▶ Items 1–7

Section 3-2
▶ Items 8–18

Section 3-3
▶ Items 19–31

Linking Chapters

Assign after Section 3-3.

Alternative Assessments

Assign after Section 3-3.

Test Prep

Assign prior to the chapter test.

KEY TERMS

3-1
atomic mass
atomic theory
Avogadro's constant
law of definite proportion
law of multiple proportions
mole

3-2
alpha particle
anode
atomic number
cathode
Coulomb's law
electron
isotope
mass number

neutron
nucleus
proton
radioisotope

3-3
electromagnetic
spectrum
electron configuration

excited state
ground state
Hund's rule
line-emission spectrum
orbital
Pauli exclusion principle
quantum number
aufbau principle

KEY CONCEPTS

3-1 How do chemists know atoms exist?

▶ Three laws support the existence of atoms: the laws of definite proportions, conservation of mass, and multiple proportions.

▶ Dalton's atomic theory contains five basic principles, some of which have been modified.

▶ The mass of atoms is measured in atomic mass units (amu); 1 amu is equal to 1.6605×10^{-27} kg.

▶ The mass of an atom of the carbon-12 isotope is defined as exactly 12 amu.

▶ The mole is the SI unit for amount of a substance.

▶ Avogadro's constant, 6.022×10^{23}/mol, is the number of particles in a mole.

3-2 What is the internal structure of atoms?

▶ Atoms consist of electrons, protons, and neutrons; protium is the only exception in that it consists solely of one electron and one proton.

▶ Protons, particles with a positive charge, and neutrons, particles with a neutral charge, make up the nucleus of an atom.

▶ Electrons, particles with a negative charge and very little mass, occupy the region around the nucleus.

▶ The atomic number of an atom is the number of protons it contains; its mass number is the number of protons plus neutrons.

▶ Isotopes are atoms that have the same atomic number but different mass numbers.

3-3 How are an atom's electrons configured?

▶ The electromagnetic spectrum spans a broad range of wavelengths of radiation, including those of visible light.

▶ Quantum theory places each electron in an atom into an orbital. The theory also describes the probability of locating an electron at any place.

▶ Each electron is assigned four quantum numbers that describe its orbital; no two electrons can have the same four quantum numbers.

▶ The electron configuration of an atom reveals which orbitals are occupied and how many electrons occupy each orbital.

KEY SKILLS

Review the following model before your exam. Be sure you can write electron configurations.

How To Write an electron configuration (p. 100)

1. Atoms of the same element that have different masses are known as ———.
   (radioisotopes, isotopes)

2. ——— are the particles in the nucleus that have mass but no charge.
   (Neutrons, Protons, Electrons)

3. The fact that no more than two electrons can occupy a single orbital is known as ———.
   (Hund's rule, the Pauli exclusion principle, Coulomb's law)

4. The electrode from which electrons leave a metal is the ———.
   (cathode, anode)

5. The total number of particles in the nucleus of an atom is its ———.
   (atomic number, mass number)

6. A(n) ——— is the positively charged particle emitted by a radioisotope.
   (alpha particle, proton)

7. Information about the electronic energy levels in an atom can be obtained from its ———.
   (line-emission spectrum, electromagnetic spectrum)

8. Light is emitted when an electron returns to its ———.
   (excited state, ground state)

9. The branch of science that explains the behavior of electrons in atoms is called ———.
   (atomic theory, quantum theory)

CONCEPT & SKILLS REVIEW

ATOMIC THEORY

1. What law is illustrated by the fact that ice, liquid water, and steam consist of 88.8% oxygen and 11.2% hydrogen by mass.

2. Identify the law that explains why the water molecules in a raindrop falling on Phoenix, Arizona, and the water flowing through the Nile Delta in Egypt both contain two hydrogen atoms for every oxygen atom.

3. Relate the law of definite proportions to the law of multiple proportions.

4. What is a mole? How is a mole related to Avogadro's constant?

5. How would you rewrite Dalton's fourth principle to account for such compounds as O_2, P_4, and S_8?

6. Calculate the mass of one atom of each of the following elements:
   a. gold
   b. neon
   c. uranium

7. Many elements exist as polyatomic molecules. Use atomic masses to calculate the molecular masses of the following:
   a. O_2 b. P_4 c. S_8

ATOMIC STRUCTURE

8. a. What flaws exist in Dalton's model of the atom?
   b. What flaws exist in Thomson's plum-pudding model of the atom?
   c. What flaws exist in Rutherford's model of the atom?
   d. What flaws exist in Bohr's model of the atom?

9. a. Which of Dalton's principles was contradicted by the work of J. J. Thomson?
   b. Which of Dalton's principles is contradicted by a doctor using radioactive isotopes to trace chemicals in the body?
   c. Do any of Dalton's principles still hold true today? If so, which ones hold true?

1. isotopes
2. neutrons
3. Pauli exclusion principle
4. anode
5. mass number
6. alpha particle
7. line-emission spectrum
8. ground state
9. quantum theory

CONCEPT & SKILLS REVIEW

1. the law of definite proportions

2. The law of definite proportions explains this.

3. Each different compound conforming to the law of multiple proportions has a definite composition.

4. The mole is the SI unit for the amount of a substance. Avogadro's constant is the number of particles in exactly 1 mol of a pure substance.

5. Answers will vary. It can be made more general by stating: Atoms of elements combine in simple, whole-number ratios.

6. a. 3.27×10^{-25} kg
   b. 3.35×10^{-26} kg
   c. 4.70×10^{-25} kg

7. a. 32.00 amu
   b. 123.9 amu
   c. 256.6 amu

8. a. The atom is not indivisible; it is composed of subatomic particles. Atoms of the same element can differ in mass. Atoms of an element sometimes combine with each other.
   b. Electrons surround a positive nucleus and are not a part of it.
   c. Electrons are in specific arrangements by energy. His model could not account for line emission spectra.
   d. Electrons do not orbit the nucleus in fixed paths.

9. a. Thomson contradicted Dalton's idea that atoms cannot be subdivided.

b. Radioactivity shows that atoms are not indivisible and that not all atoms of a given element are identical in their physical properties.

c. Yes. Atoms of different elements have different physical and chemical properties. Chemical reactions consist of the combination, separation, and rearrangement of atoms. With the exception of molecular elements, atoms combine in simple, whole-number ratios to form compounds.

10. a. Bohr   **c.** quantum
     b. Dalton   **d.** Thomson

11. a. Beams of charged particles are deflected by a magnet.

b. The existence of electron beams shows that negatively charged particles can originate from atoms.

12. Models of the atom were developed by observing the behavior of matter at the macroscopic level then developing explanations for these observations. Once atoms were assumed to exist, results of experiments such as those of Thomson and Rutherford led to inferences about the structure.

13. a. $^{234}_{92}\text{U}$ **b.** $^{235}_{92}\text{U}$ **c.** $^{238}_{92}\text{U}$

14. a. 8 protons, 8 electrons, and 8 neutrons

b. 8 protons, 8 electrons, and 9 neutrons

c. 8 protons, 8 electrons, and 10 neutrons

15. 6, 6, 6, 6
     6, 6, 6, 8
     3, 3, 3, 4
     11, 11, 11, 12

16. a. Chlorine would become argon gas.

b. Chlorine would form chloride ions.

c. The result would still be chlorine, but the atoms would have a mass number increased by 1—another isotope of chlorine.

---

10. Identify the scientists who proposed each of the models illustrated below.

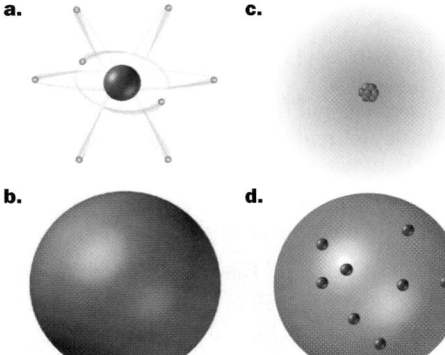

a. **c.**

b. **d.**

11. If a lightning bolt strikes your power lines while your color television is running, your screen may become magnetized, causing the color to become unbalanced. This problem can be fixed with a magnetic instrument known as a degausser.

a. Refer to the diagram below to explain how you know that the ray creating the picture on the screen is composed of charged particles.

b. How is this related to the development of the plum-pudding atomic model?

TELEVISION AND DEGAUSSER

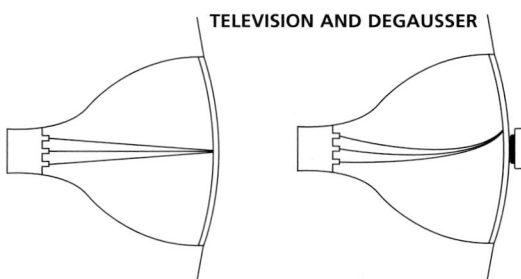

12. How were atomic models developed when no one had seen an atom?

---

13. Write nuclear symbols for isotopes of uranium with the following numbers of neutrons:

a. 142 neutrons

b. 143 neutrons

c. 146 neutrons

14. Three isotopes of oxygen are listed below. Identify how many protons, neutrons, and electrons are in each atom.

a. oxygen-16

b. oxygen-17

c. oxygen-18

15. Use the periodic table to complete the table below.

Isotope	Atomic number	Number of protons	Number of electrons	Number of neutrons
Carbon-12				
Carbon-14				
Lithium-7				
Sodium-23				

16. What would happen to poisonous chlorine gas if the following alterations were made?

a. A proton is added to each atom.

b. An electron is added to each atom.

c. A neutron is added to each atom.

17. In the diagram below, indicate which subatomic particles would be found in areas *a* and *b*.

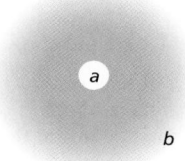

18. For hundreds of years, alchemists searched for ways to turn various metals into gold. How would the structure of an atom of $^{202}_{80}\text{Hg}$, have to be changed in order for it to become an atom of $^{197}_{79}\text{Au}$?

19. How are quantum numbers like an address?

20. Complete the following table involving quantum numbers.

Type	Symbol	Values	Description
Principal			
Orbital shape			
Magnetic			
Spin			

21. What do the electron configurations of neon, Ne; argon, Ar; krypton, Kr; xenon, Xe; and radon, Rn, have in common?

22. The element sulfur has an electron configuration of $1s^2 2s^2 2p^6 3s^2 3p^4$.
   a. What does the superscript *6* refer to?
   b. What does the letter *s* refer to?
   c. What does the coefficient *3* refer to?

23. Why does the Pauli exclusion principle include the word *exclusion*?

24. Write the electron configuration for calcium, a nutrient essential to healthy bone growth and development.

25. Write the electron configuration for copper, which is used in pennies.

26. Identify the atomic numbers of elements with the following electron configurations:
   a. $1s^2 2s^2 2p^2$
   b. $1s^2 2s^2 2p^6 3s^2 3p^1$
   c. $1s^2 2s^2 2p^6 3s^2 3p^6 4s^2 3d^{10} 4p^6 5s^1 4d^{10}$

27. Identify the element that has each of the following electron configurations:

   a.
   1s 2s

   b.
   1s 2s   2p

   c.
   1s 2s   2p   3s

   d.
   1s 2s   2p   3s   3p

28. Hydrogen's sole electron occupies the 1s orbital but can be excited to the 4p orbital. List all the orbitals this electron might occupy on its way back to its ground state.

29. The next element to be synthesized is element 112. What would be its electron configuration? Show both the complete configuration and the abbreviated form.

30. Answer the following regarding electron configurations of atoms in the fourth period of the periodic table.
   a. Which orbitals are filled by transition metals?
   b. Which orbitals are filled by nonmetals?
   c. How do the configurations of elements in the fourth period differ from those in the fifth period?

31. The magnetic properties of an element depend on the number of unpaired electrons it has. Explain why iron, Fe, is highly magnetic but neon, Ne, is not.

LINKING CHAPTERS

1. Theme: Conservation
   A Japanese company recently developed a signboard that uses no wiring and no power source. The characters are illuminated by absorbing surrounding light and then radiating different colors. Explain how this sign can emit light with no power source.

2. Theme: Micromodels
   Explain the different macroscopic observations that led to the following:
   a. the discovery of the nucleus
   b. the discovery of electrons

CHAPTER 3
Review Answers

17. a. protons and neutrons
   b. electrons

18. The mercury atom would need to lose one proton and four neutrons from the nucleus, as well as one electron from the electron cloud.

19. The quantum numbers of an electron describe the location of an electron in such a way that an address describes the location of a person's residence.

20. a. n; positive integers beginning with 1; energy level
   b. l; s, p, d, or f; type of orbital
   c. m_l; spatial orientation; designating spatial orientation of orbital
   c. ms; +1/2 or −1/2; direction of electron spin

21. Each electron configuration of these noble gases ends in a filled set of p orbitals.

22. a. the electrons in a sublevel
   b. the type of orbital
   c. the energy level

23. Electrons are excluded from an orbital that already contains an electron of the same spin.

24. $1s^2 2s^2 2p^6 3s^2 3p^6 4s^2$

25. $1s^2 2s^2 2p^6 3s^2 3p^6 4s^1 3d^{10}$

26. a. carbon
   b. aluminum
   c. silver

27. a. sodium   c. oxygen
   b. chlorine   d. lithium

28. 3d, 4s, 3p, 3s, 2p, 2s

29. $1s^2 2s^2 2p^6 3s^2 3p^6 4s^2 3d^{10} 4p^6 5s^2 4d^{10} 5p^6 6s^2 4f^{14} 5d^{10} 6p^6 7s^2 5f^{14} 6d^{10}$; [Rn] $7s^2 5f^{14} 6d^{10}$

30. a. s and p
   b. s
   c. The outermost electrons of elements in the fourth period are in the fourth energy level. The outermost electrons of elements in the fifth period are in the fifth energy level.

31. The electrons in neon are all paired. An iron atom has four unpaired electrons in 3d orbitals.

LINKING CHAPTERS

1. The light shining on the sign contains light of many wavelengths. The materials on the sign can absorb quanta of light of energies required to excite those electrons to higher available energy states. These absorbed wavelengths are re-emitted as the excited electrons drop back to the ground state.

2. a. When a beam of α-particles was directed at a sheet of thin gold foil, most particles passed straight through, but some were deflected or bounced backward. This indicated the presence of a small massive nucleus surrounded by a lot of empty space.

b. A current would pass from the cathode to the anode in an evacuated glass tube. This current was found to consist of particles of matter because they could exert force and turn a wheel. Experiments with magnets and electrostatically charged plates showed that these particles had a negative charge.

3. See the periodic table on the inside back cover of this book for configurations. All have a filled 1s sublevel. Each successive atom has one more electron in the second energy level. Two electrons complete an s sublevel as in the first energy level.

ALTERNATIVE ASSESSMENTS

Performance assessment

1. Point out the s, p, and d blocks on the periodic table and the fact that you can arrive at an electron configuration from looking at an element's position on the table.

2. Answers will vary according to the level assigned. You may want to extend this to have students write electron configurations with this box notation.

Continued on page 107.

3. Theme: Classification and trends
Prepare a table of elements with atomic numbers 3 through 10. List the names in order of increasing atomic number down one side of the table. Write the electron configuration for each element alongside its name. What do all these electron configurations have in common? What trend is evident as you proceed from one element to the next?

ALTERNATIVE ASSESSMENTS

Performance assessment

1. Your teacher will provide you with an index card that lists the name, atomic number, mass number, and an incorrect electron configuration of an element. Make the changes necessary to correct the electron configuration.

2. Your teacher will provide you with an index card listing a principal energy level and the number of electrons that are present in that level. Draw an orbital box diagram to show how the electrons are arranged in that energy level.

Portfolio projects

1. Research and communication
So-called "Neon" signs actually contain a variety. Research the different colors used for these signs. Determine the substances that are used. Design your own sign on paper, and identify which gases you would use to achieve the desired color scheme.

2. Cooperative activity
Build your own model of a particular isotope of an atom. Be sure to use a wide-open area for this project. Look up the radius of the atom, and build the atom with relative sizes. Discover how far away another atom would be if the atoms existed in the solid state.

3. Chemistry and you
Select one of the essential elements listed in the table on page 91. Check your school library or the Internet for details concerning the roles the element plays in the human body. Contact the Food and Drug Administration for any guidelines and recommendations they have regarding the element.

4. internet**connect**

SC*LINKS* NSTA
TOPIC: Element names
GO TO: www.scilinks.org
KEYWORD: HW036

Research and communication
Research several elements whose symbols are inconsistent with their English names. Some examples include silver, Ag; gold, Au; and mercury, Hg. Compare the origin for these names with the origin for their symbols.

1. Which of the following represents an electron configuration for a calcium atom, Ca?
   a. $1s^2 2s^2 2p^6 3s^2 3p^6 4s^2$
   b. $1s^2 2s^2 2p^6 3s^1 3p^6 4s^2 3d^1$
   c. $1s^2 2s^2 2p^6 3s^1 3p^6 4s^3$
   d. $1s^2 2s^2 2p^6 3s^2 3p^6 4s^2 3d^1$

2. Isotopes of an element differ in their _____.
   a. atomic numbers
   b. electron configurations
   c. number of protons
   d. masses

3. The ratio of protons to neutrons in the nucleus affects the atom's _____.
   a. stability
   b. ground state
   c. line-emission spectrum
   d. ability to travel through a cathode-ray tube

4. The law of multiple proportions states that elements _____.
   a. combine in mass ratios that can be expressed in small whole numbers
   b. combine in the same mass ratio in a compound regardless of the quantity of sample or its source
   c. have different physical and chemical properties
   d. cannot be created, destroyed, or subdivided when they participate in a chemical reaction

5. How many neutrons are present in an atom of tin that has the atomic number 50 and a mass number of 119?
   a. 50
   b. 69
   c. 119
   d. 169

6. As an electron in an excited state returns to its ground state, _____.
   a. light energy is emitted
   b. energy is absorbed by the atom
   c. the atom is likely to undergo spontaneous decay
   d. the electron configuration of the atom remains unchanged

7. Atomic masses for elements shown on the periodic table are not expressed as whole numbers because _____.
   a. the number of protons in an atom of an element varies
   b. atoms may gain or lose electrons during a chemical reaction
   c. they represent weighted averages of the isotopes of that atom
   d. scientists cannot measure the masses of atoms with great precision

8. The maximum number of electrons with quantum numbers $n = 2$ and $l = 1$ in one atom is _____.
   a. 2
   b. 12
   c. 8
   d. 6

9. According to quantum theory, an electron _____.
   a. remains in a fixed position
   b. can replace a proton in the nucleus
   c. occupies the space around the nucleus only in certain, well-defined orbitals
   d. has neither mass nor charge

10. Which of the following could represent a pair of isotopes?
    a. $^{20}_{8}X$ and $^{20}_{9}X$
    b. $^{44}_{23}X$ and $^{44}_{23}X$
    c. $^{32}_{15}X$ and $^{34}_{16}X$
    d. $^{40}_{19}X$ and $^{42}_{19}X$

11. Among the phenomena that enabled scientists to infer the existence of atoms was the _____.
    a. Pauli exclusion principle
    b. law of conservation of mass
    c. relationship between mass and energy shown by the equation $E = mc^2$
    d. observation that each element differed in the number of protons present in one of its atoms

12. The significance of Rutherford's work was to establish that _____.
    a. atoms have mass
    b. electrons have a negative charge
    c. gold is an element
    d. the atom is mostly empty space

1. b	4. a	7. c	10. d
2. d	5. b	8. d	11. b
3. a	6. a	9. c	12. d

Continued from page 106.

Portfolio projects

1. Answers and designs will vary. Sodium vapor produces yellow, mercury vapor produces blue-white, and hydrogen produces pink.

2. Students will discover that the large space is necessary in order to have a nucleus that is in proper scale and also visible. Students may want to construct a walk-through atom in a long hallway so that electrons can be as far as possible from the nucleus.

3. Students can research the functions of other trace elements, such as zinc, iron, copper, manganese, molybdenum, chromium, and selenium.

4. other possibilities are Na, K, W, Fe, Cu, Sb, Sn

The Periodic Table

CLASSROOM RESOURCES

SECTIONS	TEACHER'S DEMONSTRATIONS	PROBLEM SOLVING ■ *Text* ◆ *ChemFile Mini-Guide*	LABORATORIES ■ *Text* ◆ *ChemFile Manuals: A, B, C, D*
4-1 **What makes a group of elements?** Section Review, p. 123	**Demo 1** Families of the periodic table, p. 112 **Demo 2** Orange-yellow light of sodium, p. 118 **Demo 3** Reactivities of magnesium and calcium, p. 120		■ **EXP. 4A** The Mendeleev Lab of 1849, p. 726 ◆ **B3** Relative Solubility of Transition Elements ◆ **A3** Reactivity of Halide Ions ◆ **B5** Reactivity of Halide Ions
4-2 **What gives metals their distinctive properties?** Section Review, p. 131			◆ **D20** Measuring the Iron Content of Cereals
4-3 **What trends are found in the periodic table?** Section Review, p. 142	**Demo 4** Size of an oleic acid molecule, p. 134		◆ **B4** Periodicity of Properties of Oxides
4-4 **Where did the elements come from?** Section Review, p. 148	**Demo 5** Cloud chamber, p. 146		

TECHNOLOGY RESOURCES

See page 110 for a listing of Internet resources.

SECTIONS	VIDEOS/VIDEODISC *Holt Chemistry Videodisc* CNN PRESENTS *Science in the NEWS*	CHEMFILE CD-ROMs ● *Teaching Resources* ◆ *Interactive Tutor*	OVERHEADS ● *Color Transparencies* ◆ *Transparency Masters*
4-1	Main Block Elements Alkali Metals Alkali Earth Metals Transition Elements Actinides Lanthanides Noble Gases CNN PRESENTS Segment 10 Paint and Mercury	◆ **Module 3:** Periodic Properties	● **24** Periodicity of Atomic Numbers ● **25** Blocks of the Periodic Table ◆ **18A** Properties of Some Elements Predicted by Mendeleev ◆ **19A** Periodic Table of the Elements
4-2	CNN PRESENTS Segment 11 Superconductivity Segment 12 Alloy Technology		● **34** Sodium Metal Crystal ◆ See also **137A, 138A,** and **139A**
4-3	Atomic Radius of Chlorine Graph of Atomic Radii Trends in Ionization Energies Trends in Electronegativity		● **26** Atomic Radii ● **27** Ionization Energies ● **28** Electron Affinities ● **29** Electronegativity Values ◆ See also **25A**
4-4	CNN PRESENTS Segment 13 Atom Builders		● **136** Nuclear Fusion: Stellar Formation of Carbon-12

ASSESSMENT RESOURCES

ALTERNATIVE ASSESSMENTS	CHAPTER TESTING	SCORING RUBRICS *Holt ChemFile Teaching Resources CD-ROM*
Student Text Performance assessments, p. 154 Portfolio projects 1–4, p. 154 **Teacher's Edition** Group Strategies, p. 114, 122 **Study Guide** Sections 4-1 to 4-4	**Student Text** Test Preparation, p. 155 **Holt Chemistry: Visualizing Matter Chapter 4 Test** (blackline masters) **Holt ChemFile Test Generator for Macintosh and Windows**	**Lab Work** Student-Designed Experiments Rubric Performance-Tasks Scoring Rubric Assessment for Structured Inquiry Assessment for Open-Ended Inquiry **Portfolio Projects** Evaluating Concept Maps Assessing Portfolios Portfolio Assignment Student Evaluation Form

CHAPTER

4

Establishing Prior Knowledge

Make sure students understand the following concepts.
- Chapter 1: chemical and physical properties, composition of matter
- Chapter 3: nuclear structure, atomic number, electron configurations

 READING STRATEGY

Assimilating Knowledge

Before reading this chapter, have each student write a short list of all the things they know about the arrangement of elements on the periodic table, and have them write what that arrangement reveals about atomic structure. When students have finished their list, ask them to contribute their entries to a group list on the board. Then have students list the things they want to know about the periodic table and its arrangement. If students have trouble coming up with questions, offer the following suggestions to get them on track.

- What do the electron configurations of lithium and sodium have in common?
- What do the electron arrangements of fluorine and chlorine have in common?
- What metallic elements can you name? What nonmetallic elements can you name? Where are these elements located on the periodic table?

ABOUT THE ILLUSTRATION

The physical and chemical properties of the elements shown are periodic functions of their atomic numbers.

CHAPTER 4 The Periodic Table

 internetconnect

Holt Chemistry: Visualizing Matter
On-Line Resources
go.hrw.com
Visit the HRW Web site for a variety of resources related to this chapter. Just type in the keyword HW0 Chapt4.

 SCiLINKS NSTA

National Science Teachers Association
On-Line Resources: www.scilinks.org
The following Scilinks Internet resources can be found in the student text for this chapter:

Page 119
TOPIC: Alkali metals
KEYWORD: HW041

Page 120
TOPIC: Alkaline earth metals
KEYWORD: HW042

Page 121
TOPIC: Halogens
KEYWORD: HW043

Page 122
TOPIC: Noble gases
KEYWORD: HW044

Page 124
TOPIC: Oxygen
KEYWORD: HW045

Page 132
TOPIC: Superconductors
KEYWORD: HW046

Page 154
TOPIC: Synthetic elements
KEYWORD: HW047

PERIODIC TRENDS AND A MEDICAL MYSTERY

George Decker seemed to be in perfect health. He was 35 years old, did not smoke, and had no history of serious illness. But one day, after cooking something on his stove, Decker began to cough, wheeze, and gasp for air. A friend rushed him to the hospital for treatment.

Tests revealed that Decker had acute pneumonia in both lungs. Pneumonia is an inflammation of lung tissue that causes the air sacs to fill with white blood cells and cellular debris, which makes breathing difficult. Most pneumonias are caused by organisms such as bacteria, fungi, or viruses. But tissue samples taken from Decker's lungs showed no evidence of microorganisms or viruses. Extensive tests turned up nothing. The cause of Decker's pneumonia was a mystery. In the meantime, Decker's condition became worse. His health faded, and Decker was dead in three months.

A pathologist was called in to perform an autopsy. The autopsy confirmed that Decker had died of pneumonia, yet there was still no trace of pneumonia-causing microorganisms. Baffled, the pathologist scrutinized Decker's hospital records and discovered that Decker had been cooking something just before he began having breathing problems. What Decker had been cooking turned out to be the cause of the pneumonia.

Decker had worked in a metal shop. By talking to Decker's employer, the pathologist discovered that Decker collected old gold dental fillings. Gold dental fillings are actually mixtures of gold, palladium, platinum and silver with small amounts of zinc, iron, and copper. Decker would take the fillings home and heat them on his stove to extract the precious metals. Upon melting, the zinc, copper, and iron formed oxides; these oxides rose to the top, where they could be skimmed off. Decker sold the remaining precious metals for a sizable profit.

Decker thought he could apply the same process to extract silver from silver fillings. Silver dental fillings are composed of silver and mercury with copper or other metals. Unfortunately, Decker's ignorance about certain physical and chemical properties of metals proved fatal.

CHAPTER LINKS

Which metal melts first in gold fillings? in silver fillings?

Why did Decker's process work for gold fillings but prove fatal with silver fillings?

What element was most likely the cause of Decker's death?

STORY BACKGROUND

Mercury poisoning can occur not only from contact with the metal itself but also by breathing mercury vapors, which was the case for Decker in the story. Contact with both organic and inorganic mercury compounds can also result in mercury poisoning. Methyl mercury compounds caused a large outbreak of poisonings in Japan in the 1950s among people who ate fish and shellfish containing high levels of mercury compounds. This type of poisoning has also been a concern for people who consume fish from the Great Lakes region of the United States.

Absorbed mercury is concentrated in the kidneys and ultimately results in kidney dysfunction. Death occurs from the accumulation of toxic wastes in the blood. Chronic mercury poisoning is characterized by tremors, numbness, inflammation in the mouth, loss of appetite, and depression.

While mercury can appear to be fun to play with, it is a deadly poison and should not be touched or left uncovered. Mercury spills must be cleaned up quickly and completely to prevent the release of vapors.

RESOURCE LINK

ChemFile Teaching Resources CD-ROM *Supplemental Reading Projects* Guided reading worksheets for P. W. Atkins's *Periodic Kingdom* can be found on the Holt Teaching Resources CD-ROM.

CONCEPT PREVIEW

Section 4-1
Historical background
- grouping elements according to properties
- Mendeleev's table
- periodic law

Organization of the periodic table
- periods and groups
- metals, nonmetals, and semiconductors
- groups of elements

Section 4-2
Properties of metals
- electrical conduction
- heat conduction
- other metallic properties

Structure of metals
- crystal arrangements

Section 4-3
Patterns of properties
- atomic radii

- ionization energies
- electron affinities
- melting and boiling points

Section 4-4
Origins of elements
- naturally occurring elements
- synthetic elements

SECTION 4-1

LESSON WARM-UP

Interpreting the Periodic Table
Ask students to summarize what they have already learned about the periodic table in the first three chapters. They should know that it is an arrangement of elements in order of atomic number, which also means that the elements are in order of increasing numbers of protons in the nuclei. They should also know that the table gives the average atomic mass of an element, which is the weighted averages of the element's stable isotopes. Ask if students have learned anything that helps to account for the table's arrangement. Some students will have already noted the relationship between electron configurations and the arrangement of the elements.

VISUAL STRATEGY

Figure 4-1 Be sure students realize that the elements are in the top photo and the salts are arranged below them.

Science in the News

PRESENTS Feature story 10
Paint and Mercury Poisoning. See the Science in the News video guide for more details.

What makes a group of elements?

OBJECTIVES

▶ **Describe** the organization of the modern periodic table.

▶ **State** the periodic law.

▶ **Describe** characteristic properties of groups of elements.

▶ **Relate** the properties of the main-group elements to their electron configurations.

Elements are different yet similar

Some elements are gases, some are liquids, and still others are solids. Some are colored and some are colorless, as you can see in **Figure 4-1.** Yet there are similarities. For example, the elements lithium, sodium, potassium, rubidium, cesium, and francium can combine with chlorine in a 1:1 ratio to form the compounds LiCl, NaCl, KCl, RbCl, CsCl, and FrCl. All of these compounds are white solids, are soluble in water, and form solutions that are good conductors of electricity.

Similarly, fluorine, chlorine, bromine, iodine, and astatine combine with sodium to form white solids with the formulas NaF, NaCl, NaBr, NaI, and NaAt, respectively. All of these compounds are also white solids, are soluble in water, and form solutions that are good conductors of electricity. These examples highlight the similarities among the elements rather than differences.

Chlorine   Iodine   Bromine

Sodium chloride   Sodium bromide   Sodium iodide

▶ **FIGURE 4-1**

Though some elements may look dissimilar, they react similarly. Samples of the *elements* chlorine, bromine, and iodine show dissimilar physical characteristics. Samples of the *compounds* NaCl, NaBr, and NaI show similar physical characteristics.

112   CHAPTER 4

DEMONSTRATION 1

Families of the Periodic Table

Approximate time: 10 minutes

Obtain elements from the *s-, p-,* and *d*-block elements, and place them in well-sealed test tubes for display in the front of the room. Use the following elements: sodium (a very small piece covered with mineral oil containing no water); magnesium ribbon (polished with sandpaper); aluminum; carbon; phosphorus; sulfur; iodine crystals; Geissler (spec-trum) tubes with helium, neon, or argon; iron filings; tungsten; nickel; copper foil (polished with sandpaper); and a zinc sheet. Add any other available elements that can be safely displayed. Discuss with your students the different physical properties of the elements on display.

John Newlands notices a periodic pattern

Elements vary widely in their properties, but in an orderly way. In 1865, the English chemist John Newlands arranged the first 16 elements known at the time (excluding hydrogen) in order of increasing atomic mass. When Newlands placed the elements in two rows, as follows, he observed that the elements in each column had similar chemical and physical properties.

Li	Be	B	C	N	O	F
Na	Mg	Al	Si	P	S	Cl

Because the chemical and physical properties repeated with the eighth element, Newlands called this pattern the law of octaves.

Dmitri Mendeleev invented the modern periodic system

In 1870, the Russian chemist Dmitri Mendeleev made use of this scheme and other information to produce the first orderly arrangement of all 63 elements known at the time. Mendeleev wrote the symbol for each element on a card along with its physical and chemical properties and its relative atomic mass. He arranged and rearranged the cards in various configurations until he arrived at the pattern shown in **Figure 4-2,** which places the elements in order of increasing atomic mass. In Mendeleev's table, elements with similar properties fall in vertical columns.

There are two interesting things to notice about Mendeleev's table. First, the elements do not always fit neatly in the order of increasing atomic mass. For example, Mendeleev had to reverse the order of tellurium and iodine to keep similar elements in the same column. At first he thought that their atomic masses were in error. But careful research by others showed that the values were correct. He had no explanation for this discrepancy.

The second noteworthy point is that there were gaps in his table where elements with a particular atomic mass should occur. Mendeleev was able to predict the properties of these undiscovered elements, which he called ekaaluminum, ekaboron, and ekasilicon (the prefix *eka-* is derived from a Sanskrit word meaning "one beyond"). These elements were discovered shortly thereafter, and their properties were

ПЕРИОДИЧЕСКАЯ СИСТЕМА ЭЛЕМЕНТОВ

ГРУППЫ ЭЛЕМЕНТОВ

РЯДЫ	I	II	III	IV	V	VI	VII	VIII		
I	H 1									
II	Li 7	Be 9,4	B 11	C 12	N 14	O 16	F 19			
III	Na 23	Mg 24	Al 27,4	Si 28	P 31	S 32	Cl 35,5			
IV	K 39	Ca 40	? 45	Ti 50	V 51	Cr 52	Mn 55	Fe 56	Co 59	Ni 59
V	Cu 63,4	Zn 65,2	? 68	? 70	As 75	Se 79,4	Br 80			
VI	Rb 85,4	Sr 87,6	Yt ? 88	Zr 90	Nb 94	Mo 96	? 100	Ru 104,4	Rh 104,4	Pd 106,6
VII	Ag 108	Cd 112	In 113	Sn 118	Sb 122	Te 128?	J 127			
VIII	Cs 133	Ba 137	Di ? 138	Ce? 140						
IX										
X			Er ? 178	La? 180	Ta 182	W 186		Pt 197,4	Ir 198	Os 199
XI	Au 197?	Hg 200	Tl 204	Pb 207	Bi 210					
XII				Th 231		U 240				

FIGURE 4-2 ▲

Mendeleev's table grouped elements with similar properties into vertical columns called "groups" or "families." The elements highlighted in red in the table—fluorine, F, chlorine, Cl, bromine, Br, and iodine, I—constitute a group. Compare this periodic table with the modern periodic table on pages 114 and 115.

TEACHING TIP

Periodic Arrangement   Remind students that neither Newlands nor Mendeleev had knowledge of atomic numbers or electron structure. Because they knew that the elements had specific atomic masses, they logically based their tables on increasing atomic mass. The elements were arranged in families solely because of their observed properties, such as the ratios by which they combined with other elements, particularly oxygen. It is remarkable that an arrangement based primarily on chemical properties is now known also to represent an element's electron structure.

VISUAL STRATEGY

Figure 4-2   The illustration shows one representation of Mendeleev's original organization of the elements. Students should note the blocks that contain question marks and an approximate atomic mass. Because of his confidence in his "Periodic System of the Elements," Mendeleev predicted that elements with those masses would be discovered. When these predictions proved true, the attention of the scientific world was drawn to Mendeleev's table. Some names and symbols have changed over time. Also, Mendeleev used German symbols for elements, which resulted in *J* for iodine. Its name in German is *Jod,* pronounced "yote."

Safety
Wear safety goggles, gloves, and a lab apron while handling chemicals. Do not allow students to handle the test tubes or the Geissler tubes.

Disposal
Save materials for use at a later time.

RESOURCE LINK

IN-TEXT LAB

Self-Directed Inquiry
Have students do Investigation 4A: *The Mendeleev Lab of 1869,* on page 726, to design an experiment for the concept of periodicity.

VISUAL STRATEGY

Figure 4-3 Inform students of the information available in this table, including symbol, name, atomic number, average atomic mass, electron configuration, group number, period number, and whether the element is a metal, nonmetal, or semiconductor. Also point out that the lanthanide and actinide elements occur between Groups 3 and 4 in Periods 6 and 7 but are conventionally shown below the table so that the printed table is not too wide.

COMMON MISCONCEPTION

Students sometimes think that they will have to memorize the information in the table. Point out that the table exists as a scientific tool and that its purpose is to give information. The student's job is to learn to read and interpret the information on the table, not to memorize it.

Module 3: Periodic Properties
This engaging tutorial reviews trends found in atomic and ionic radii across a period and down a group.

▼ **FIGURE 4-3**

Key:

6	— Atomic number
C	— Symbol
Carbon	— Name
12.011	— Average atomic mass
[He]$2s^2 2p^2$	— Electron configuration

Period

Period 1

1
H
Hydrogen
1.00794
$1s^1$

Group 1

Group 2

Period 2
3
Li
Lithium
6.941
[He]$2s^1$

4
Be
Beryllium
9.012182
[He]$2s^2$

Period 3
11
Na
Sodium
22.989768
[Ne]$3s^1$

12
Mg
Magnesium
24.3050
[Ne]$3s^2$

Group 3 **Group 4** **Group 5** **Group 6** **Group 7** **Group 8** **Group 9**

Period 4
19
K
Potassium
39.0983
[Ar]$4s^1$

20
Ca
Calcium
40.078
[Ar]$4s^2$

21
Sc
Scandium
44.955910
[Ar]$3d^1 4s^2$

22
Ti
Titanium
47.88
[Ar]$3d^2 4s^2$

23
V
Vanadium
50.9415
[Ar]$3d^3 4s^2$

24
Cr
Chromium
51.9961
[Ar]$3d^5 4s^1$

25
Mn
Manganese
54.93805
[Ar]$3d^5 4s^2$

26
Fe
Iron
55.847
[Ar]$3d^6 4s^2$

27
Co
Cobalt
58.93320
[Ar]$3d^7 4s^2$

Period 5
37
Rb
Rubidium
85.4678
[Kr]$5s^1$

38
Sr
Strontium
87.62
[Kr]$5s^2$

39
Y
Yttrium
88.90585
[Kr]$4d^1 5s^2$

40
Zr
Zirconium
91.224
[Kr]$4d^2 5s^2$

41
Nb
Niobium
92.90638
[Kr]$4d^4 5s^1$

42
Mo
Molybdenum
95.94
[Kr]$4d^5 5s^1$

43
Tc
Technetium
(97.9072)
[Kr]$4d^6 5s^1$

44
Ru
Ruthenium
101.07
[Kr]$4d^7 5s^1$

45
Rh
Rhodium
102.906
[Kr]$4d^8 5s^1$

Period 6
55
Cs
Cesium
132.90543
[Xe]$6s^1$

56
Ba
Barium
137.327
[Xe]$6s^2$

57
La
Lanthanum
138.9055
[Xe]$5d^1 6s^2$

72
Hf
Hafnium
178.49
[Xe]$4f^{14} 5d^2 6s^2$

73
Ta
Tantalum
180.9479
[Xe]$4f^{14} 5d^3 6s^2$

74
W
Tungsten
183.84
[Xe]$4f^{14} 5d^4 6s^2$

75
Re
Rhenium
186.207
[Xe]$4f^{14} 5d^5 6s^2$

76
Os
Osmium
190.23
[Xe]$4f^{14} 5d^6 6s^2$

77
Ir
Iridium
192.22
[Xe]$4f^{14} 5d^7 6s^2$

Period 7
87
Fr
Francium
(223.0197)
[Rn]$7s^1$

88
Ra
Radium
(226.0254)
[Rn]$7s^2$

89
Ac
Actinium
(227.0278)
[Rn]$6d^1 7s^2$

104
Rf
Rutherfordium
(261.11)
[Rn]$5f^{14} 6d^2 7s^2$

105
Db
Dubnium
(262.114)
[Rn]$5f^{14} 6d^3 7s^2$

106
Sg
Seaborgium
(263.118)
[Rn]$5f^{14} 6d^4 7s^2$

107
Bh
Bohrium
(262.12)
[Rn]$5f^{14} 6d^5 7s^2$

108
Hs
Hassium
(265)†
[Rn]$5f^{14} 6d^6 7s^2$

109
Mt
Meitnerium
(266)†
[Rn]$5f^{14} 6d^7 7s^2$

† Estimated from currently available IUPAC data.

* The systematic names and symbols for elements greater than 109 will be used until the approval of trivial names by IUPAC.

58
Ce
Cerium
140.115
[Xe]$4f^1 5d^1 6s^2$

59
Pr
Praseodymium
140.908
[Xe]$4f^3 6s^2$

60
Nd
Neodymium
144.24
[Xe]$4f^4 6s^2$

61
Pm
Promethium
(144.9127)
[Xe]$4f^5 6s^2$

62
Sm
Samarium
150.36
[Xe]$4f^6 6s^2$

90
Th
Thorium
232.0381
[Rn]$6d^2 7s^2$

91
Pa
Protactinium
231.03588
[Rn]$5f^2 6d^1 7s^2$

92
U
Uranium
238.0289
[Rn]$5f^3 6d^1 7s^2$

93
Np
Neptunium
(237.0482)
[Rn]$5f^4 6d^1 7s^2$

94
Pu
Plutonium
244.0642
[Rn]$5f^6 7s^2$

ALTERNATIVE ASSESSMENT

Group Strategy

1. Number pieces of paper 1 through 36, and place them in a can.

2. Have each student draw a number. That number is the atomic number of the element they are to research.

3. Each student should write a descriptive paragraph about the element. The paragraph should contain hints that can be used to identify the element.

4. The next day, collect the paragraphs and distribute blank cards that have 25 boxes in a 5 × 5 in. square.

5. Have students fill the squares with any 25 of the 36 elements in any order.

6. Read the student-made clues, and allow students to mark an *X* through each element they identify. The first student to complete a vertical, horizontal, or diagonal row is the winner.

Metals
- ▨ Alkali metals
- ▨ Alkaline-earth metals
- ▨ Transition metals
- ▨ Other metals

Metalloids
- ▨ Semiconductors

Nonmetals
- ▨ Halogens
- ▨ Other nonmetals
- ▨ Noble gases

Group 18
2 **He** Helium 4.002602 $1s^2$

Group 13	Group 14	Group 15	Group 16	Group 17
5 **B** Boron 10.811 $[He]2s^22p^1$	6 **C** Carbon 12.011 $[He]2s^22p^2$	7 **N** Nitrogen 14.00674 $[He]2s^22p^3$	8 **O** Oxygen 15.9994 $[He]2s^22p^4$	9 **F** Fluorine 18.9984032 $[He]2s^22p^5$	10 **Ne** Neon 20.1797 $[He]2s^22p^6$
13 **Al** Aluminum 26.981539 $[Ne]3s^23p^1$	14 **Si** Silicon 28.0855 $[Ne]3s^23p^2$	15 **P** Phosphorus 30.9738 $[Ne]3s^23p^3$	16 **S** Sulfur 32.066 $[Ne]3s^23p^4$	17 **Cl** Chlorine 35.4527 $[Ne]3s^23p^5$	18 **Ar** Argon 39.948 $[Ne]3s^23p^6$

Group 10	Group 11	Group 12

			Group 13	Group 14	Group 15	Group 16	Group 17	
28 **Ni** Nickel 58.6934 $[Ar]3d^84s^2$	29 **Cu** Copper 63.546 $[Ar]3d^{10}4s^1$	30 **Zn** Zinc 65.39 $[Ar]3d^{10}4s^2$	31 **Ga** Gallium 69.723 $[Ar]3d^{10}4s^24p^1$	32 **Ge** Germanium 72.61 $[Ar]3d^{10}4s^24p^2$	33 **As** Arsenic 74.92159 $[Ar]3d^{10}4s^24p^3$	34 **Se** Selenium 78.96 $[Ar]3d^{10}4s^24p^4$	35 **Br** Bromine 79.904 $[Ar]3d^{10}4s^24p^5$	36 **Kr** Krypton 83.80 $[Ar]3d^{10}4s^24p^6$
46 **Pd** Palladium 106.42 $[Kr]4d^{10}5s^0$	47 **Ag** Silver 107.8682 $[Kr]4d^{10}5s^1$	48 **Cd** Cadmium 112.411 $[Kr]4d^{10}5s^2$	49 **In** Indium 114.818 $[Kr]4d^{10}5s^25p^1$	50 **Sn** Tin 118.710 $[Kr]4d^{10}5s^25p^2$	51 **Sb** Antimony 121.757 $[Kr]4d^{10}5s^25p^3$	52 **Te** Tellurium 127.60 $[Kr]4d^{10}5s^25p^4$	53 **I** Iodine 126.904 $[Kr]4d^{10}5s^25p^5$	54 **Xe** Xenon 131.29 $[Kr]4d^{10}5s^25p^6$
78 **Pt** Platinum 195.08 $[Xe]4f^{14}5d^96s^1$	79 **Au** Gold 196.96654 $[Xe]4f^{14}5d^{10}6s^1$	80 **Hg** Mercury 200.59 $[Xe]4f^{14}5d^{10}6s^2$	81 **Tl** Thallium 204.3833 $[Xe]4f^{14}5d^{10}6s^26p^1$	82 **Pb** Lead 207.2 $[Xe]4f^{14}5d^{10}6s^26p^2$	83 **Bi** Bismuth 208.98037 $[Xe]4f^{14}5d^{10}6s^26p^3$	84 **Po** Polonium (208.9824) $[Xe]4f^{14}5d^{10}6s^26p^4$	85 **At** Astatine (209.9871) $[Xe]4f^{14}5d^{10}6s^26p^5$	86 **Rn** Radon (222.0176) $[Xe]4f^{14}5d^{10}6s^26p^6$
110 **Uun*** Ununnilium (269)† $[Rn]5f^{14}6d^97s^1$	111 **Uuu*** Unununium (272)† $[Rn]5f^{14}6d^{10}7s^1$							

63 **Eu** Europium 151.966 $[Xe]4f^76s^2$	64 **Gd** Gadolinium 157.25 $[Xe]4f^75d^16s^2$	65 **Tb** Terbium 158.92534 $[Xe]4f^96s^2$	66 **Dy** Dysprosium 162.50 $[Xe]4f^{10}6s^2$	67 **Ho** Holmium 164.930 $[Xe]4f^{11}6s^2$	68 **Er** Erbium 167.26 $[Xe]4f^{12}6s^2$	69 **Tm** Thulium 168.93421 $[Xe]4f^{13}6s^2$	70 **Yb** Ytterbium 173.04 $[Xe]4f^{14}6s^2$	71 **Lu** Lutetium 174.967 $[Xe]4f^{14}5d^16s^2$
95 **Am** Americium (243.0614) $[Rn]5f^77s^2$	96 **Cm** Curium (247.0703) $[Rn]5f^76d^17s^2$	97 **Bk** Berkelium (247.0703) $[Rn]5f^97s^2$	98 **Cf** Californium (251.0796) $[Rn]5f^{10}7s^2$	99 **Es** Einsteinium (252.083) $[Rn]5f^{11}7s^2$	100 **Fm** Fermium (257.0951) $[Rn]5f^{12}7s^2$	101 **Md** Mendelevium (258.10) $[Rn]5f^{13}7s^2$	102 **No** Nobelium (259.1009) $[Rn]5f^{14}7s^2$	103 **Lr** Lawrencium (262.11) $[Rn]5f^{14}6d^17s^2$

The atomic masses listed in this table reflect the precision of current measurements. (Values listed in parentheses are those of the element's most stable or most common isotope.) In calculations throughout the text, however, atomic masses have been rounded to two places to the right of the decimal.

THE PERIODIC TABLE 115

VISUAL STRATEGY

Figure 4-3 If you have a large periodic table on display in your classroom, you may want to have students compare it with the one printed here, especially if the information on the two tables differs in some way. Even if the tables differ in appearance, assure students that the arrangement of elements is the same in both tables. Keep in mind that the answers to problems in this book depend on the atomic masses from the table shown here.

ADDITIONAL APPLICATION

Make students aware that jewelry is made from alloys of gold, silver, or platinum because the pure metals are soft. Sterling silver is an alloy containing 7.5% copper. Gold and platinum will not corrode in the air, but sterling silver will corrode slowly.

HISTORICAL CONNECTION

Iron played a very important role in the history of civilization. Bronze weapons were no match for the iron weapons in the Iron Age. The Dorians, a Greek tribe equipped with iron weapons, overcame the Mycenaean Greeks and penetrated all the way to Canaan. These Greeks became the well-known Philistines of Biblical times.

TEACHING TIP

Transition Elements Inform students that the outermost electrons of the transition elements are in both s and d orbitals, which leads to the variety of oxidation states that are characteristic of transition metals. The series of 10 elements per period forms a transition between the two divisions (s and p) of the main-group elements.

7. Check the declared winner's card for accuracy. If your class is small, assign two elements to each student. You may also have to limit the choices of elements to make sure there is a winner.

TABLE 4-1	Predicted versus actual properties for three elements

Properties	Ekaaluminum (gallium, 1875)		Ekaboron (scandium, 1877)		Ekasilicon (germanium, 1886)	
	Predicted	**Observed**	**Predicted**	**Observed**	**Predicted**	**Observed**
Density	6.0 g/cm^3	5.96 g/cm^3	3.5 g/cm^3	3.5 g/cm^3	5.5 g/cm^3	5.47 g/cm^3
Melting point	low	30°C	*	*	high	900°C
Oxide formula	Ea_2O_3	Ga_2O_3	Eb_2O_3	Sc_2O_3	EsO_2	GeO_2
Solubility of oxide	*	*	dissolves in acid	dissolves in acid	*	*
Density of oxide	*	*	*	*	4.7 g/cm^3	4.70 g/cm^3
Chloride formula	*	*	*	*	$EsCl_4$	$GeCl_4$
Color of metal	*	*	*	*	dark gray	grayish white

(Data listed in parentheses indicate current name of element and year of discovery.)

very close to Mendeleev's predictions, as illustrated in **Table 4-1.** Other scientists had created tables of the elements, but Mendeleev had the genius to perceive the periodic system and to predict the existence of elements unknown at the time.

About 40 years after Mendeleev published his table, a young English chemist named Henry Moseley established a physical basis for the periodic arrangement. Moseley studied the lines in the X-ray spectra of the elements. He found that with a few exceptions the wavelengths of the lines in the spectra decreased in a regular manner as atomic mass increased. With further work, Moseley realized that the spectral lines correlated not to atomic mass but to atomic number. When the elements in Mendeleev's table were arranged in order of increasing atomic number, the discrepancies disappeared.

The most common periodic table, recommended by IUPAC (the International Union of Pure and Applied Chemistry), is shown in **Figure 4-3,** on page 114 and 115. It is based on the **periodic law,** which states that the physical and chemical properties of the elements are periodic functions of their atomic numbers. This periodic table contains a wealth of information about individual elements. Examine the key to Figure 4-3 for the information it gives about carbon: atomic number, symbol, name, atomic mass, and electron configuration. Notice that a shorthand form is used to show electron configurations.

periodic law

the physical and chemical properties of elements are periodic functions of their atomic numbers

CONCEPT CHECK

1. Mendeleev arranged the elements in his periodic table according to what property?
2. What is the periodic law?

Overview of the modern periodic table

The rows of the periodic table are called **periods.** Elements in a period have similar electron configurations. For example, the first period has two elements, hydrogen and helium, and the electrons of these elements occupy the $1s$ orbital. Similarly, the outer electrons of second-period elements occupy the $2s$ and $2p$ orbitals, and the outer electrons of third-period elements occupy the $3s$ and $3p$ orbitals. Although there are exceptions, similar patterns are found in the electron configurations of elements in Periods 4 through 7.

The columns of the periodic table are called **groups.** The elements within a group have properties in common but with some gradation. For example, all Group 1 elements are solid at room temperature, are good conductors of electricity, and combine with chlorine in a 1:1 ratio. Although the elements in Group 14 exhibit a wide variety of properties, all of them combine with chlorine in a 1:4 ratio to form the chlorides CCl_4, $SiCl_4$, $GeCl_4$, $SnCl_4$, and $PbCl_4$.

It is convenient to divide the periodic table into two distinct regions, metals and nonmetals. The **metals** include all members of Groups 1 through 12 as well as some elements of Groups 13 through 16. As you can see, most of the known elements are metals. All metals are good conductors of electricity, and their conductivity increases as temperature decreases. Except for mercury, all are solid at room temperature. Elements in Groups 3 through 12, including the two long rows below the main table, are called the **transition metals.** As you move from left to right across the transition metals, you will see that electrons are usually added to d orbitals. For this reason the transition metals are sometimes referred to as the d-block elements. The transition metals are generally not as reactive as the elements in Groups 1 and 2, and they have varied properties.

The second region of the periodic table contains the **nonmetals.** Differences in the physical appearance of metals and nonmetals are shown in **Figure 4-4.** The nonmetals include all of Groups 17 and 18 as well as some members of Groups 14 through 16. The characteristic shared by all nonmetals is that they are poor conductors of electricity, but their

period

a series of elements that form a horizontal row in the periodic table

group

a series of elements that form a vertical column in the periodic table

metal

an element that is a good conductor of electricity

transition metals

elements in Groups 3 through 12

nonmetal

an element that is a poor conductor of electricity

FIGURE 4-4 ▼

Tin has the physical appearance typical of metals. Boron is a semiconductor. Sulfur is a nonmetal. Nonmetals vary widely in physical appearance.

Tin (metal)

Boron (semiconductor)

Sulfur (nonmetal)

READING STRATEGY

Organizing Concepts If possible, supply students with a large blank copy of the periodic table with columns for each group of elements. Students can use it to make notes about the divisions of the table and the groups they will study in this chapter. Encourage students to write only major facts and concepts to avoid filling all of the space with notes. Their first task should be to divide the table into metals, semiconductors, and nonmetals. Caution students to save space for general information and not to copy the data from Figure 4-3.

TEACHING TIP

Electron Configuration Point out to students that elements in a group have the same outer electron configuration.

RESOURCE LINK

ChemFile Lab B
Microscale Lab
Have students do Experiment B3:
Relative Solubility of Transition Elements.

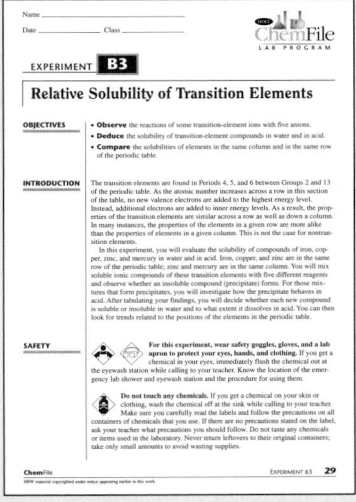

CONTENT STRATEGY

Chemistry texts generally apply one of three different words—*semimetal, metalloid,* or *semiconductor*—to the elements along the stairstep line. We have chosen to use the word *semiconductor* to characterize these elements because it describes the property for which they are best known.

COMMON MISCONCEPTION

The stairstep line passes above the element aluminum, but aluminum's properties best match those of metals. For example, aluminum is a good conductor of electric current and heat. Therefore, it is best classified as a metal even though it does exhibit some nonmetallic chemical properties.

💡 DID YOU KNOW?

Although mercury is the only liquid metal, three other metals—Rb, Cs, and Ga—have melting points not far above room temperature.

Nonmetals are usually nonconductors (insulators), but the graphite allotrope of carbon is a good conductor because electrons can move along the unbonded planes of carbon hexagons. Diamond, on the other hand, does not conduct electric current.

ANSWERS

CONCEPT CHECK

1. periods; groups

2. metals and nonmetals

TEACHING TIP

Main-Group Elements Inform students that the main-group elements are elements whose outer-level electrons are in *s* orbitals or in *s* and *p* orbitals.

---

semiconductor

a crystalline material with intermediate electrical conductivity

---

conductivity increases as temperature increases. In other respects, nonmetals exhibit a wide variety of properties. Nonmetals may be gases, liquids, or solids at room temperature.

Along the stair-step line separating metals from nonmetals are the elements known as **semiconductors,** or *metalloids*. As their name implies, these elements conduct electricity better than nonmetals but not as well as metals. The conductivity of semiconductors can be greatly enhanced by adding traces of selected substances. This makes semiconductors very useful in transistors and other electronic devices. Semiconductors are solid at room temperature.

CONCEPT CHECK

1. What are the horizontal rows of the modern periodic table called? What are the vertical columns called?
2. What are the two main regions of the periodic table?

The main-group elements

---

main-group elements

elements belonging to Groups 1, 2, and 13 through 18 in the periodic table and having very regular electron configurations

---

Groups 1, 2, and 13 through 18 are referred to as the **main-group elements.** The electron configuration of elements within each group is quite consistent. For example, all the elements in Group 14 have four electrons in the outermost shell. Their configuration can be written as ns^2np^2, where n is the period number. The regular electron configuration of the Group 14 elements explains the regular formulas for the chlorides CCl_4, $SiCl_4$, $GeCl_4$, $SnCl_4$, and $PbCl_4$ mentioned earlier.

The main-group elements are sometimes called *representative elements*. Look at **Figure 4-5** to see the elements in this block. Their electron configurations are regular and consistent. The main-group elements include gases (the noble gases, for example), liquids, solids, metals, and nonmetals. The main-group elements silicon and oxygen account for four of every five atoms found on or near the Earth's surface.

Four groups within the main-group elements have special names. These are the *alkali metals* (Group 1), the *alkaline-earth metals* (Group 2), the *halogens* (Group 17), and the *noble gases* (Group 18).

▶ **FIGURE 4-5**

Main-group elements have diverse properties and uses. They are highlighted in the long columns on the left and right sides of the periodic table.

Main-group elements

DEMONSTRATION 2

Orange-Yellow Light of Sodium

Approximate time: 10 minutes

1. Darken the room, and use a pair of crucible tongs to hold a piece of calcium sulfate in the burner flame. Calcium sulfate is gypsum, the mineral filler of drywall board. Note the low color production.

2. Next use the tongs to hold a piece of rock salt in the flame.

3. Have students note the bright orange-yellow flame typical of sodium.

4. (Optional) Place an opaque shield with a slit between the class and the burner, and pass out replica diffraction gratings to students.

5. Hold the salt in the flame again while students view sodium's emission spectrum through the gratings. Students should note the pair of strong yellow lines typical of sodium.

Group 1: the alkali metals

Group 1 elements are called **alkali metals** because they react with water to produce alkaline solutions and because they have metallic properties. The term *alkali* dates back to ancient times, when people discovered that wood ashes mixed with water produce a slippery solution that can remove grease. In the Middle Ages such solutions were named *alkaline,* after the Arabic word for wood ashes, *al-qili.* Chemists now know that wood ashes contain compounds of Group 1 elements, especially potassium hydroxide, KOH.

The alkali metals are so soft that they can be cut with a knife. The freshly cut surface of an alkali metal is shiny, but it dulls quickly as the metal reacts with oxygen and water in the air. In the laboratory, alkali metals are usually stored in oil or kerosene to isolate them from the air. Alkali metals react vigorously with cold water, forming hydrogen gas and a very alkaline solution.

The high reactivity of alkali metals is the result of their electron configuration—a single electron in the highest energy level. By losing this outer electron and becoming a cation an alkali metal can achieve the stable electron configuration of the noble gas.

The physical properties of the alkali metals are described in **Table 4-2.** All of the alkali metals are excellent conductors of electricity. In the gaseous state at high temperatures, alkali metals become plasmas. **Plasmas** are the fourth state of matter and consist of an electrically conductive mixture of cations, electrons, and neutral particles. As electricity flows through the gas, some electrons are transferred to higher-energy orbitals. When a sodium plasma goes through this process, its electrons emit yellow light as they return to the ground state. This yellow light is of higher intensity, but it uses less energy than the light emitted from a normal light bulb with a tungsten metal filament. Light of this wavelength penetrates fog better than white light. Sodium-vapor lamps are used as fog lights and for street lighting.

alkali metals

highly reactive metallic elements in Group 1 that react rapidly with water to form hydrogen and alkaline solutions and that burn in air

internet**connect**

SCi*LINKS*
NSTA

TOPIC: Alkali metals
GO TO: www.scilinks.org
KEYWORD: HW041

plasma

a gas composed of ions, electrons, and neutral particles

TEACHING TIP

Alkali Metals   If you have stock bottles containing Li, Na, and K, exhibit them to students and identify the oil that the metals are submerged in. The metals are too reactive to be exposed to air for any length of time. It is likely that the metal pieces have already become encrusted with oxidation products formed slowly over time.

DID YOU KNOW?

Because sodium is a lightweight electrical conductor, it has been incorporated into high-voltage power lines by encasing it completely with aluminum or another metal. Sodium's light density reduces the weight of the cables without impairing their conductivity. The light weight reduces sag and permits longer cable spans.

TABLE 4-2	Physical Properties of Alkali Metals

Element	Flame test	Hardness (Mohs' scale)	Melting point (°C)	Boiling point (°C)	Density (g/cm^3)	Atomic radius (pm)
Lithium	red	0.6	180.5	1342	0.53	134
Sodium	yellow	0.4	97.7	883	0.97	154
Potassium	violet	0.5	63.3	759	0.86	196
Rubidium	yellowish violet	0.3	39.3	688	1.53	(216)
Cesium	reddish violet	0.2	28.4	671	1.87	(233)
Francium	—	—	(27)	(677)	(3.0)	(250)

Values in parentheses are estimated.

Safety
Wear safety goggles and a lab apron. Students should be at least 30 m away from the demonstration because the rock salt could splatter.

Disposal
Put cooled specimens in the trash.

READING STRATEGY

Organizing Concepts Remind students to enter pertinent information about the alkali metals and the alkaline earth metals on their blank periodic tables. Point out that the outer electron configuration of all of the alkali metals (Group 1) is ns^1. They usually react by losing this electron to form +1 ions. The outer electron configuration of all alkaline earth (Group 2) metals is ns^2, and they normally lose these two electrons to form +2 ions.

DEFINING STANDARDS

Students should not be concerned if they find a slightly different table in another book. The table printed in this book is the form most commonly used. Chemists have disagreed over the proper way to show the lanthanides and actinides. If the energy order of sublevels were followed strictly, the lanthanum configuration would end in $6s^2\,4f^1$, and the actinium configuration would end in $7s^2\,5f^1$. For these reasons, some tables show lanthanum and actinium with the other lanthanide and actinide elements. However, the next electron after $6s^2$ is in a $5d$ orbital, and the next two electrons after $7s^2$ are in $6d$ orbitals. Accordingly, cerium is the first lanthanide to have f electrons, and protactinium is the first actinide to have f electrons. The f orbitals become full in Yb and No, so the elements Lu and Lr are sometimes placed in the main body of the table.

alkaline-earth metals

reactive metallic elements in Group 2 with two electrons in the outermost energy level

lanthanides

shiny, metallic transition metals with atomic numbers 58 through 71 in which electrons are added to $4f$ orbitals

internet**connect**

SC*LINKS*
NSTA
TOPIC: Alkaline-earth metals
GO TO: www.scilinks.org
KEYWORD: HW042

FIGURE 4-6

The alkaline-earth metals are the second column of elements in the periodic table.

FIGURE 4-7

Marble is used in sculptures. The polished forms have the formula $CaCO_3$.

Group 2: the alkaline-earth metals

The elements of Group 2, as shown in **Figure 4-6,** are called the **alkaline-earth metals.** Compared with the alkali metals, the alkaline-earth metals are harder, denser, stronger, and have higher melting points. The elements of this group are reactive, but less so than Group 1 elements. Beryllium is the least active of the alkaline-earth metals. In reactions with other elements, alkaline-earth metals often lose two electrons to become the M^{2+} cation and thus achieve the configuration of the preceding noble gas. Losing two electrons requires about twice as much energy as losing just one electron.

Consider the metal magnesium. If the surface of an object made from magnesium is exposed to air, the magnesium reacts with the oxygen in air to form the compound magnesium oxide, MgO. This reaction forms a protective coating of MgO that slows the corrosion of the magnesium metal underneath. Magnesium is lighter than other structural metals, yet it is still very strong, especially when alloyed with other metals. For all these reasons, magnesium metal has a wide variety of practical uses, especially in aircraft and aerospace applications, where materials must be strong but light.

Perhaps the best known alkaline-earth metal is calcium. Calcium compounds, such as those in limestone and marble, are common in the Earth's crust. Marble, shown in **Figure 4-7,** is almost pure calcium carbonate. Marble is hard and durable, but it is dissolved by acid rain.

The lanthanides and actinides

Part of the last two periods of transition elements are placed toward the bottom of the periodic table to keep the table conveniently narrow. The metals in these two rows, shown in **Figure 4-8,** on the next page, are referred to as the lanthanides and actinides. Moving left to right along these rows, electrons are added to the $4f$ orbitals in the lanthanides and to the $5f$ orbitals in the actinides. The **lanthanides** have atomic numbers from 58 to 71. The name of element 57 will give you a clue to how the lanthanides got their name. The lanthanides are shiny, reactive metals that have irregular electron configurations. Some have practical uses. For

mp = 1287°C bp = 2467°C density = 1.85 g/cm³	**4** **Be** Beryllium
mp = 649°C bp = 1090°C density = 1.74 g/cm³	**12** **Mg** Magnesium
mp = 839°C bp = 1484°C density = 1.54 g/cm³	**20** **Ca** Calcium
mp = 769°C bp = 1384°C density = 2.58g/cm³	**38** **Sr** Strontium
mp = 729°C bp = 1637°C density = 3.51 g/cm³	**56** **Ba** Barium
mp = 700°C bp = 1737°C density = 5.50 g/cm³	**88** **Ra** Radium

---

DEMONSTRATION 3

Reactivities of Magnesium and Calcium

Approximate time: 10 minutes

1. Place two Petri dishes half-full of room-temperature water on the overhead projector.

2. Add two drops of phenolphthalein indicator to each dish. Explain to students that phenolphthalein changes from clear to pink in the presence of a base.

3. Polish a 2 cm piece of magnesium ribbon with sandpaper, and immediately drop it into one of the dishes. Drop a pea-sized (or smaller) piece of calcium into the other dish. Be sure that both the Mg and Ca are submerged.

4. Students should observe bubbles and a pink color begin to form around the calcium. Inform students that calcium reacts with water, but much more slowly than an alkali

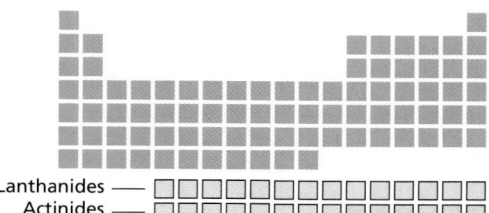

FIGURE 4-8 ◄

In order to keep the periodic table from becoming too wide, the lanthanides and actinides are placed below the rest of the table.

Lanthanides
Actinides

example, compounds of some lanthanide metals are used to make the phosphor dots in television tubes. When bombarded by a beam of electrons, the phosphors emit light of certain colors. The colors combine to create the brilliant images you see on a color television screen.

Elements 90 through 103 are the **actinides,** named for the first element in the series, actinium. Actinides are unique in that their nuclear structures are of more importance than their electron configurations. All actinides have an unstable arrangement of protons and neutrons in the nucleus, so actinides are *radioactive.* Perhaps the best-known actinide is uranium, which you will learn more about in Chapter 18. The nuclear disintegration of the uranium nucleus releases sufficient energy to run power plants, submarines, and aircraft carriers. Elements with atomic numbers 104 and above do not fall in the same category as the lanthanides or the actinides. These elements will be discussed further in Section 4-3.

Group 17: the halogens

The elements of Group 17, (fluorine, chlorine, bromine, iodine, and astatine) shown in **Figure 4-9,** are the **halogens.** The halogens combine with most metals to produce the compounds known as **salts.** The word *halogen* is derived from Greek and means "salt former." In common table salt, sodium chloride, the halogen chlorine has reacted with the alkali metal sodium to form sodium and chloride ions. You will learn more about salts in Chapter 5.

The halogens are the most reactive group of nonmetals and are members of the *p*-block elements. Electrons of elements in this group add to a *p* sublevel after the *s* sublevel in the same energy level is filled. Their electron configurations show why. Halogens have seven electrons in the outermost energy level,

actinides

shiny, metallic transition metals with atomic numbers 90 through 103 in which electrons are added to 5*f* orbitals

halogen

a nonmetallic element in Group 17 of the periodic table that has seven electrons in the outermost energy level and that combines with many metals to form salts

salt

a compound composed of positive and negative ions arranged in a regular three-dimensional pattern

mp = -219.62°C bp = -188.14°C density = 0.00153 g/cm³	**9** **F** Fluorine
mp = -100.98°C bp = -34.6°C density = 0.0029 g/cm³	**17** **Cl** Chlorine
mp = -7.2°C bp = 58.78°C density = 3.119 g/cm³	**35** **Br** Bromine
mp = 113.5°C bp = 184.35°C density = 4.93 g/cm³	**53** **I** Iodine
mp = 575.2°C bp = (610°C) density = no data	**85** **At** Astatine

internetconnect

SCLINKS
NSTA
TOPIC: Halogens
GO TO: www.scilinks.org
KEYWORD: HW043

FIGURE 4-9 ◄

The elements of Group 17 are called *halogens.* Halogens combine with metals to form salts.

DID YOU KNOW?

The lanthanide elements are increasingly being used in cutting-edge technology. In addition to their use in TV phosphors, lanthanides are being used in microwave technology, new high-strength permanent magnets, and in improved types of lasers.

TEACHING TIP

Halogen Elements Point out to students that the electron configurations of all halogen elements end in $ns^2\,np^5$. This configuration is one electron short of the complete octet found in the noble gas atoms. As a result, these elements react by gaining one electron to form –1 ions.

RESOURCE LINK

ChemFile Lab A
Skills Development
Have students do Experiment A3:
Reactivity of Halide Ions.

ChemFile Lab B
Microscale Lab
Have students do Experiment B5:
Reactivity of Halide Ions.

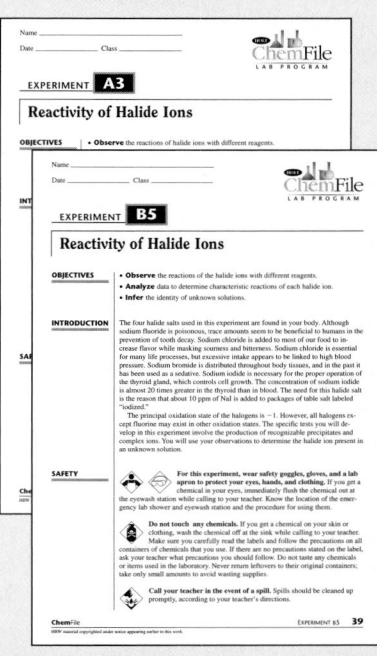

metal would. The products are hydrogen gas and calcium hydroxide, a base.

5. Students may or may not observe activity around the Mg sample. If nothing is observed, replace the room temperature water with boiling water. Add phenolphthalein. Magnesium should be about as reactive in hot water as calcium is in cold. Ask students why it is very unsafe to put water on a magnesium fire. *(The Mg reacts with the H_2O to produce hydrogen, which also burns.)*

Safety

Wear safety goggles and a lab apron while handling chemicals.

Disposal

Set out a disposal container for any used indicator solutions that are leftover at the end of the procedure. Unused indicators should be tightly covered and returned to the storage shelf. Save all metal strips for reuse next time, but if they are too corroded, put them in the trash. Put all other solids in the trash. Combine all liquids, and pour them down the drain.

HISTORICAL CONNECTION

Argon was the first noble gas to be identified. Its existence was proposed in 1785 because chemists could not account for all of the major constituents of air. Argon makes up about 1% of air. It was not until 1894 that British chemist William Ramsay identified it. Because of its chemical inertness, it was given the name argon from the Greek *argos,* which means "lazy" or "inactive."

TEACHING TIP

Noble Gases and Hydrogen Ask students to suggest reasons why the noble gases were not identified until almost the turn of the twentieth century, while most of their neighboring elements had been known since the late eighteenth and early nineteenth centuries. (Elements had been identified by their chemical properties. The noble gases do not normally undergo chemical reactions.)

Hydrogen's atomic structure explains the difficulty in classifying it. Like the halogens, it can gain one electron to have the electronic configuration of a noble gas, helium. When it does so, it forms H^-, called the hydride ion. Although hydrogen is routinely placed above the alkali metals, it is unlike them in that it cannot form a true +1 ion. Hydrogen atoms have only one electron, and to lose it would leave only the hydrogen nucleus, a proton. Needless to say, a bare proton is not stable in the presence of other matter. Although we sometimes say that acids form H^+ ions in water solution, what is really formed is a hydrated proton, usually written as H_3O^+, the hydronium ion.

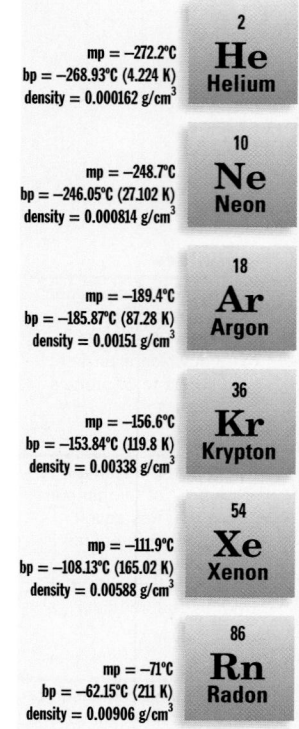

FIGURE 4-10

The noble gases family consists of gaseous elements with extrememly low reactivity.

noble gases

elements in Group 18 of the periodic table that are characterized by low reactivity

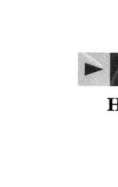

internet**connect**

SCI**LINKS**
NSTA

TOPIC: Noble gases
GO TO: www.scilinks.org
KEYWORD: HW044

122 CHAPTER 4

so the highest energy level of a halogen atom is just one electron short of a noble gas structure. When halogen atoms react chemically they often acquire one electron to achieve the stable outer electron configuration of their closest noble gas neighbor in the periodic table.

Group 18: the noble gases

The Group 18 elements, shown in **Figure 4-10** are called **noble gases.** They were formerly called inert gases because they were thought to be completely unreactive. But in 1962, the first noble gas compound, XeF_2, was prepared. No compounds of helium, neon, and argon have yet been prepared.

Except for helium atom, noble gas atoms are characterized by an octet of electrons, ns^2np^6, in the outermost energy level. From the low chemical reactivity observed in the noble gases, chemists infer that this *octet* of electrons makes these elements very stable. Although helium has only two electrons, the filled $1s$ shell of helium gives this gas the low reactivity characteristic of the other noble gases. Chemical reactions of the main-group elements show that these elements frequently achieve the stable outer electron configuration of the noble gases. For example, by losing an electron, lithium achieves the electron configuration of helium, $1s^2$, when forming compounds with most other elements.

A number of practical applications have been found for noble gases. Neon and argon, for example, are used in illuminated signs. The low reactivity of the noble gases leads to some special uses. Helium is the preferred gas in party balloons, blimps, and weather balloons because it is less dense than air but not flammable. Helium is also used to provide an inert atmosphere for welding.

Hydrogen is in a class by itself

Hydrogen is the most common element in the universe. It behaves unlike other elements because it has just one proton and one electron. This distinguishes hydrogen from all the other elements in the periodic table, as shown in **Figure 4-11.**

FIGURE 4-11

Hydrogen sits apart from all other elements in the periodic table.

Hydrogen can react with many elements, including oxygen. Hydrogen gas and oxygen gas react explosively to form water. Hydrogen is a component of all hydrocarbons as well as molecules that are essential to the chemistry of life, such as fats, proteins, and carbohydrates. The main industrial use of hydrogen is in the production of ammonia, NH_3. Large quantities of ammonia are used in the production of fertilizers. Elemental hydrogen is rare on the surface of Earth because free hydrogen is able to escape from Earth's atmosphere into space.

SECTION REVIEW

Total recall

1. State the periodic law.
2. What do elements in a period have in common? elements in a group?
3. What contribution did Moseley make to the development of the periodic table?
4. **Interpreting Tables** Write the atomic numbers and symbols for each of the following elements:
   a. silver   d. copper   g. palladium
   b. gold   e. zinc   h. radon
   c. mercury   f. platinum i. radium
5. **Interpreting Tables** Which element in item 4 has the greatest atomic mass? the least atomic mass?
6. **Interpreting Tables** Round the atomic masses for each element listed in item 4 to the hundredths place.
7. What is the name of the elements located between the metals and nonmetals in the periodic table?
8. Give the group number and period number for each of the elements listed in item 4.
9. Which elements are considered the most stable? Why?
10. What is produced when halogens combine with alkali metals?
11. Why do groups of main-block elements display similar chemical behaviors?
12. What do you expect the electron configuration of element 112 to be?
13. Explain what the transition metals have in common with respect to their electron configurations.
14. What features do the halogens have in common? the noble gases?
15. Why is hydrogen placed in a group by itself?

Critical thinking

16. What characteristic of Newland's periodic table did Mendeleev incorporate into his periodic table?
17. How do the alkali metals differ from the alkaline-earth metals?
18. What led Mendeleev to predict that some elements had not yet been discovered?
19. Why are the nuclear configurations of the actinides more important than their electron configurations?
20. **Story Clue** What are the melting points for silver, gold, mercury, and copper?
21. **Interpreting Graphics** Use Figure 4-2 to answer the following questions.
    a. What do the question marks represent on Mendeleev's table?
    b. What does the comma represent in the entries for rubidium and strontium?

14. The halogens are reactive and combine with metals to form salts. By gaining one electron, they achieve a stable octet and become −1 ions. Noble gases are unreactive and have stable octets of s and p electrons in the outer energy level.
15. Hydrogen has only one proton and one electron, and its behavior does not match that of any of the groups of elements.

Critical thinking

16. Newlands's law of octaves showed that the chemical and physical properties of elements repeated every eighth element.
17. The alkaline earth elements are less reactive than the neighboring alkali metals. Their electron configurations end in ns^2, whereas the configurations of alkali metals end in ns^1.

Answers continue on page 155A.

CHAPTER CONNECTION

Students will discover much more about hydrogen and its compounds when they study covalent bonding, organic compounds, solutions, and acids and bases in Chapters 6, 7, 13, and 15.

ANSWERS

SECTION REVIEW

Total recall

1. The periodic law states that the physical and chemical properties of the elements are periodic functions of their atomic numbers.
2. Elements in a period have the same core-electron configuration. Elements within a group have the same outer electron configuration, and they also share common properties.
3. Moseley realized that the X-ray spectra of the elements correlated with the atomic number of the elements and not the atomic mass. When the elements were arranged according to atomic number, the discrepancies in Mendeleev's periodic table disappeared.
4. *See page 155A.*
5. radium, copper
6. See table in item 4.
7. semiconductors
8. See table in item 4.
9. noble gases
   Each noble gas has a filled octet.
10. salt
11. All of the elements in a group have the same outer-level electron configuration.
12. $7s^2 5f^{14} 6d^{10}$
13. The outermost electrons in transition metals are in s orbitals and d orbitals, specifically, ns and $(n-1)d$ orbitals, which are close in energy. A few have no s electrons.

ELEMENT SPOTLIGHT

$\overset{8}{O}$
Oxygen
15.9994
[He]$2s^2 2p^4$

Learning to live with oxygen

Paleontologists believe that life evolved in an environment free of oxygen gas but rich in carbon dioxide. Some early organisms developed the ability to use the energy of sunlight to drive chemical reactions that would otherwise be nonspontaneous. This process is called photosynthesis.

At this early point in the development of Earth's atmosphere, oxygen was a pollutant. Photosynthetic organisms kept releasing oxygen into the atmosphere. At the time, there were many minerals around for the oxygen to react with, so the amount of oxygen in the atmosphere did not change much. But as these photosynthetic organisms thrived and evolved, they released more and more oxygen into the atmosphere. This eventually exhausted the oxidizable minerals, and the oxygen level in the air began to climb. Over millions of years, organisms adapted to the rising level of oxygen in their environment. Now, many organisms depend on atmospheric oxygen, a waste product of photosynthesis, to carry out their essential life functions.

Every oxygen molecule in the atmosphere is a product of a living organism.

WHERE IS IT?

Earth's Crust
49% by mass

Air
23% by mass

Water
89% by mass

Rocks
45% by mass

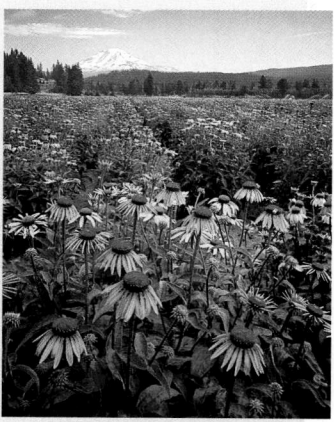
These photosynthetic plants release oxygen into the Earth's atmosphere.

internet connect

SCI LINKS
NSTA

TOPIC: Oxygen
GO TO: www.scilinks.org
KEYWORD: HW045

Industrial Uses

▶ Sixty-five to eighty-five percent of oxygen produced in many countries is used to speed up reactions in steel making.

▶ Environmental and biomedical uses of oxygen include sewage treatment, river revival, paper/pulp bleaching, and submarine work.

▶ Liquid oxygen is used as an oxidizer of rocket fuels, which are essential to space exploration.

A BRIEF HISTORY

1773–1774: C. W. Scheele and J. Priestley independently discover oxygen.

1840: Ozone is detected and named by C. F. Schönbein.

| 1400 | 1700 | 1800 | 1900 |

15th century: Leonardo da Vinci notes that a component of air supports combustion.

1781: H. Cavendish establishes oxygen as a large component of water.

1775–1777: A. L. Lavoisier determines that oxygen is an element. He is also responsible for its name.

1963: Liquid O_2 and liquid H_2 are used to successfully launch a rocket at Cape Kennedy.

What gives metals their distinctive properties?

OBJECTIVES

▸ **Identify** the defining property of metals.

▸ **Describe** the varied properties of metals.

▸ **Explain** why metals are good conductors of electricity and heat.

▸ **Describe** how the atoms in most metals pack.

Characteristics of metals

Metals make up most of the periodic table, as **Figure 4-12** shows. But what exactly are metals? Often you can recognize a metal by its shiny appearance, but some nonmetals, plastics, and mineral samples can appear metallic. Conversely, some unpolished metals can look black and dull. Metals are good conductors of electricity and heat, although the nonmetal carbon, in the form of diamond, is the best conductor of heat, especially if it is composed only of carbon-12.

Metals are good conductors of electricity

One property distinguishes metallic elements from nonmetals: They are excellent conductors of electricity. Even the least conductive metal conducts electricity 100 times better than the best nonmetallic conductor. Surprisingly, metallic nature is *not* an innate property of an element. Instead, metallic nature appears to depend on temperature. *At room temperature* the stair-step line in the periodic table roughly divides the metals from the nonmetals. However, tin changes spontaneously into a nonmetal if it is kept for a long time below 13.2°C. Most nonmetals have been changed into metallic form by being placed under high pressure, especially at low temperatures.

The high electrical conductivity of metals is one reason why they are of such great importance. Gold is used extensively in electronic equipment despite its relatively high cost, especially in applications where resistance to corrosion is important. The metal most widely used to conduct electricity is copper, as shown in **Figure 4-13.** Copper conducts almost as well as gold, yet it is relatively inexpensive. It is used for everything from the wires in your home to the chips in your computer. For a while, aluminum was used for electrical wiring in homes, but its tendency to corrode caused many problems.

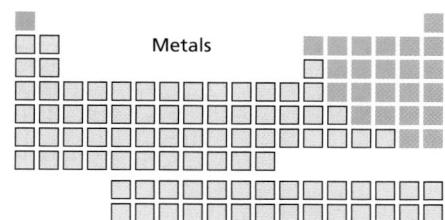

FIGURE 4-12 ▲

The majority of elements are metals, as this periodic table clearly indicates by its highlighted regions.

FIGURE 4-13 ▲

Copper, a transition metal, is used in wiring because it is an excellent conductor of electricity.

THE PERIODIC TABLE   **125**

LESSON WARM-UP

The Properties of Metals   As an overview of the properties of metals, exhibit objects that incorporate metals. Ask students to contribute to the collection. Try to include samples representing as many metals as possible. Include items such as jewelry, silver objects, brass musical instruments, pipes, foils, and structural materials, as well as electronic devices that have motors, magnets, or heating elements. Include electronic devices in order to show the use of metals in electronic circuitry. Include cards from a computer or another device that uses chips on a printed-circuit card. Also include a mirror. Most modern mirrors are coated with aluminum on the back.

Ask students to list the properties of metals that are exemplified by these objects.

COMMON MISCONCEPTION

Make sure students distinguish between the meaning of *metal* as applied to individual elements and as applied to metallic objects that we encounter every day, which are almost always alloys, homogeneous mixtures of metals with other metals and nonmetals.

ADDITIONAL APPLICATION

Although silver is the best conductor, gold is also a good conductor and has the advantage of not corroding or tarnishing under ordinary conditions. For this reason, gold is widely used on connectors in computers and other electronic devices.

 Science in the News

PRESENTS Feature story 11 *Superconductivity.* See the Science in the News video guide for more details.

ANSWERS

CONCEPT CHECK

1. Metals conduct electricity.

2. Metals that are good conductors of electricity are also good conductors of heat.

VISUAL STRATEGY

Figure 4-14 Have students note that all of the atoms in the silicon and diamond crystals are bonded to other atoms. The "rods" connecting atoms represent covalent bonds. This type of crystal is called a network crystal and can be considered as one continuous molecule. Network crystals tend to be very hard because of this internal bonding.

Metals that are good conductors of electricity are also good conductors of heat

In general, poor electrical conductors are poor heat conductors. What can you infer from that? Think about it. It indicates that the mechanism by which electricity is conducted must also be closely connected with the mechanism for conduction of heat.

You don't have to look far for the agent that causes conductivity in a metal. Ever since the discovery of electrons by J. J. Thomson and his colleagues, it has been known that electrons are responsible for the conduction of electricity by metals. Evidently, they are responsible for the conduction of heat as well. However, metals are the only elemental substances that are good conductors of electricity. It must be concluded that at least some of the electrons in metals must be in a different configuration than in nonmetals. These electrons are free to move through the metal in all directions.

CONCEPT CHECK

1. What is the single distinctive property of metals?

2. Explain the following statement: There is a relationship between high conductivity of electricity and high conductivity of heat.

Crystals and the conduction band

crystal

a substance in which the atoms or molecules are arranged in an orderly, geometric, repeating pattern

Consider the samples of carbon (diamond) and silicon shown in **Figure 4-14.** They are examples of matter in the form of crystals. A **crystal** is a substance in which atoms or molecules are arranged in an orderly, geometric repeating pattern in three dimensions.

▶ **FIGURE 4-14**

These samples of diamond and silicon are examples of matter in the form of crystals.

FIGURE 4-15 ▼

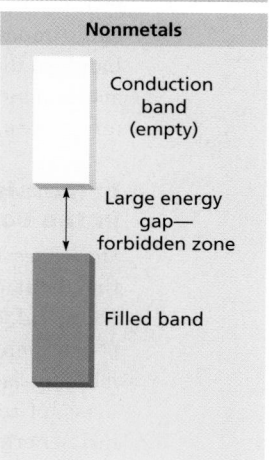

Metals

Conduction bands

Partially filled band | Overlapping bands

or

Semiconductors

Conduction band (empty)

Small energy gap

Filled band

Nonmetals

Conduction band (empty)

Large energy gap— forbidden zone

Filled band

a The forbidden gap is absent in many metals; very little energy is required to move electrons to the conduction band.

b The forbidden gap is smaller in semiconductors, so a few electrons are able to enter the conduction band.

c Electrons cannot occupy energy levels in the forbidden gap. This gap prevents practically all electrons from reaching the conduction band in insulators.

TEACHING TIP

Exciting Electrons   Remind students that the flow of current requires that a potential difference (voltage) exist between the two ends of a conductor. Attaching a battery or generator supplies the energy to excite the electrons and to force them through the conductor.

VOCABULARY STRATEGY

Another word for *nonconductor* is *insulator.* Most nonmetals are insulators, although they are seldom used in elemental form for that purpose. In effective insulators, the forbidden gap is so large that increasing the voltage eventually causes current to flow through air around the insulator rather than through it.

The outer electrons in the atoms of each element form the bonds that bind the atoms together in a crystal. In a crystal, each atom is bonded to all neighboring atoms. These electrons in the bonds exist in orbitals, just as electrons do in atoms. The electrons occupy the orbitals of lowest energy. However, just as in atoms, there are vacant orbitals of higher energy. Electrons in these higher orbitals are free to move about in three dimensions throughout the crystal, forming the **conduction band. Figure 4-15a** shows that in metals the orbitals of the conduction band actually overlap and are continuous with the bond orbitals in energy, so even at room temperature there are many electrons in the conduction band. Consequently, metals are very good conductors of electricity. On the other hand, the metal atoms are vibrating back and forth with thermal motion, interfering with the motion of electrons. The vibration increases as the temperature increases, so the conductivity of metals decreases as temperature increases.

In semiconductors, the energy of the higher (conducting) orbitals is not very high compared with the energy of the filled bonding orbitals, as shown in **Figure 4-15b.** It does not take much energy to excite electrons to these orbitals, so even at room temperature a semiconductor will carry a measurable current. At higher temperatures there are more electrons excited up to the conduction band, so the conductivity of semiconductors increases as the temperature increases.

conduction band

a band within which (or into which) electrons must move to allow electrical conduction

VOCABULARY STRATEGY

The word *ductile* is derived from the Latin verb *ducere*, which means "to lead." Thus, a ductile metal is one that can be led or pulled to a smaller diameter. The word *malleable* derives from the Latin noun *malleus,* meaning "hammer." A malleable metal can be hammered until it is thinner. Most metal today is not hammered but rather is rolled and pressed.

💡 DID YOU KNOW?

Most of the characteristic properties, including electrical conductivity, heat conductivity, ductility, malleability, and luster (reflectivity), are due ultimately to the fact that metals consist of atoms in a sea of loosely held electrons. Electrons in metals are said to be delocalized—not associated with particular atoms.

In typical nonmetals, such as carbon in the form of diamond, these orbitals have very high energy, as shown in **Figure 4-15c.** It is practically impossible to excite electrons to the orbitals of the conduction band, so diamond is a nonconductor. (There is no such thing as an absolute nonconductor. Extremely minute currents can be forced through any substance, but in practical terms they are nonconductors.)

In metals, heat is conducted by electrons in the conduction band

How does this apply to thermal conductivity? Recall from Chapter 2 that heat energy is the random motion of atom-sized particles. In a nonmetal, the conduction of heat is caused by the transfer of the energy of random vibrations from atom to atom. In metals the transfer medium is the conduction electrons. These electrons are of very low mass, of course, and they move very freely. Therefore, the transfer of heat energy is very efficient in metals. A high electrical conductivity will correspond to a high thermal conductivity.

It should be noted that high thermal conductivity does not always correspond to high electrical conductivity. For example, a diamond is the best known conductor of heat, yet it is a nonconductor of electricity. If electrons cannot move freely through a diamond crystal, how is heat conducted? The actual mechanism of heat conduction in diamond is complex, but it is related to the passage of vibration waves through the crystal, not to electrons.

The high thermal conductivity of metals explains why metals feel cold to the touch, even at room temperature. Your fingers are warmer than the metal, and when you touch the metal, it conducts heat away from your flesh, causing your fingers to sense cold. Which will feel colder to the touch, lead or aluminum?

Some other properties of metals

Aside from being good conductors of electricity and heat, metals exhibit a wide array of properties. Tungsten has the highest melting point, 3422°C, of any element. In contrast, mercury melts at –39°C. This low melting point, along with high density, makes mercury useful for barometers. Cesium is extremely reactive chemically, yet other metals, such as gold, are unreactive. This makes gold, along with copper and silver, invaluable in electronics and other sensitive applications. Many metals, such as iron, are very strong and durable. Aluminum and magnesium have a high strength-to-weight ratio, making them useful for many construction purposes where light weight is advantageous.

Some metals, such as manganese and bismuth, are very brittle, yet others, such as gold and iron, are ductile and

▼ **FIGURE 4-16**

Steel, a mixture of iron and carbon, is one of the most important industrial alloys. When heated, steel can be worked into many useful shapes.

128 CHAPTER 4

RESOURCE LINK

ChemFile Lab D
Have students do Experiment D20:
Measuring the Iron Content of Cereals

malleable. The capacity to be squeezed out into a wire is known as *ductility*. Gold can be drawn into wires only a few micrometers in diameter. The gold wires can then be spun into fine cloth. A *malleable* substance can be hammered or rolled into sheets. Gold can be hammered out into gold leaves only 25 nm thick. Iron becomes malleable when heated to red heat, as shown in **Figure 4-16** on page 128. It can also be rolled into thin sheets for cans.

Adding to the versatility of metals is the fact that two or more metallic elements can be mixed together to produce an alloy. An **alloy** is a solution of metallic, and sometimes nonmetallic, elements. Stainless steel, an alloy of iron and chromium, and either nickel or manganese, is extremely resistant to corrosion.

alloy

a solid or liquid solution of two or more metals

CONCEPT CHECK

1. What is a crystal?
2. What is the conduction band? How is the conduction band related to the conductivity of electricity and heat?

The structure of metallic crystals

The attraction between metal atoms and the electrons accounts for the metallic bonding in metals. Even a tiny piece of metal may contain millions of identical atoms. How are these atoms arranged in a sample of metal? Metallic atoms adopt regular arrangements in crystals. To a chemist, a crystal is a solid characterized by a regular, orderly arrangement of its constituent particles. Some examples are diamonds, table salt, sugar, and metals in the solid state. A crystal structure is an orderly array, like the display in a fruit store, as shown in **Figure 4-17.**

How can the atoms pack together in the densest fashion? One layer of atoms is shown in **Figure 4-18a.** Exactly six atoms fit around any one atom. The next layer, shown in **Figure 4-18b,** is an exact copy of the first but displaced slightly so that it fits into the depressions between atoms in the first layer. If you look down on these two layers, half the spaces between atoms show atoms in the first layer and

► **FIGURE 4-17**

The arrangement of oranges shows how spheres can be packed together to take up the least amount of space. You can think of the atoms in crystals as spheres that pack in the same pattern.

FIGURE 4-18 ▼

The arrangement of atoms in metals is similar to the packing of spheres. As the illustration shows, there are two ways spheres can pack as densely as possible.

a

b

c

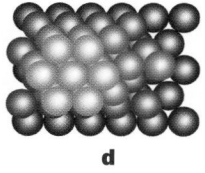

d

THE PERIODIC TABLE **129**

ANSWERS

CONCEPT CHECK

1. A crystal is a form of matter in which the molecules, ions, or atoms are arranged in an orderly geometric pattern that repeats in three dimensions.

2. The conduction band is a set of orbitals of higher energy than the ground-state orbitals through which electrons can travel when they have been excited into these orbitals.

TEACHING TIP

Constructing a Model No two-dimensional representation is as effective as a three-dimensional physical model in showing the packing arrangements in crystals. If you have models of the packing arrangements shown in Figure 4-17, display them now. If you do not have them, have students build models that can be taken apart into layers. Foam craft spheres and stiff wire connectors should suffice for materials.

CNN Science in the News

PRESENTS **Feature story 12**

Alloy Technology. See the Science in the News video guide for more details.

▼ **FIGURE 4-19**

 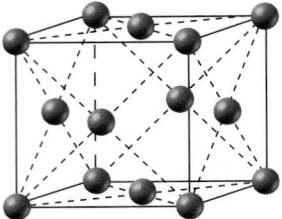

a The atoms in a lead crystal assume a cubic close-packed structure.

b This model shows that a cubic close-packed structure has an atom at each corner and at the center of each face of a cube.

half show spaces in the first layer. The third layer has two possible arrangements. It can fit directly above spaces in the first layer, as shown in **Figure 4-18c,** or directly above atoms in the first layer, as shown in **Figure 4-18d.**

If the atoms in the third layer are placed directly above spaces in the first layer and this process is repeated, the result is a *cubic close-packed* structure, also called *face-centered cubic.* This structure is shown in **Figure 4-19a.** Notice that the cube has an atom in each face. The unit structure is shown in **Figure 4-19b.** Repetition of this unit in three dimensions produces a macroscopic crystal of cubic shape.

If the atoms in the third layer are placed directly above the atoms in the first layer and this arrangement is repeated, the result is the *hexagonal close-packed* crystal structure, illustrated in **Figure 4-20a.** The unit structure is shown in **Figure 4-20b.** If this arrangement is repeated in three dimensions, the result is a macroscopic hexagonal crystal.

Most metals crystallize in one of these two structures, indicating that the atoms are essentially spherical in shape. The elements that do not crystallize in one of these two crystal forms have localized bonds between the atoms that force the crystal into some other shape.

▼ **FIGURE 4-20**

 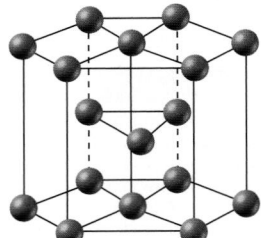

a The atoms in a magnesium crystal assume a hexagonal close-packed structure.

b This model shows the distinctive six-sided shape of a hexagonal close-packed structure.

Symbols for metallic elements

Some elements exist in nature as molecules. You read in Chapter 1 that hydrogen, nitrogen, and oxygen are diatomic gases. Therefore, we write the symbols of these elements as H_2, N_2, and O_2. The subscript on the symbol indicates the number of atoms in each molecule. However, metals as well as several nonmetallic elements, such as C and Si, form crystals of many atoms, all of which are bonded to one another. Thus a very small iron crystal might be $Fe_{1\,236\,459\,028}$. This indicates a lot of atoms in a very small crystal of iron. If you chop this crystal in half, you will have two crystals, each having the same properties of the original crystal but with half the number of atoms. This property applies to all solid metallic elements, but because there is no set number of atoms in the crystals of these elements, it is convenient to write their symbols as if they were monatomic: Fe, Hg, Pb, and so on. Keep in mind that the only truly monatomic elements at room temperature are the noble gases: He, Ne, Ar, Kr, Xe, and Rn.

SECTION REVIEW

Total recall

1. What is the difference between a metal and a nonmetal?

2. Why is copper used in electrical wiring? Would gold or aluminum be a better choice? Explain.

3. Define what is meant by malleability and ductility.

4. Identify the one property that all metals share.

5. How is an alloy made?

6. What are crystals?

7. Explain the difference in the conduction bands of metals, nonmetals, and semiconductors.

8. Which electrons form the bonds that bind atoms of an element together in a crystal?

Critical thinking

9. The conductivity of semiconductors increases with an increase in temperature, while the conductivity of metals decreases. Explain why this is so.

10. Why is the symbol for a piece of aluminum foil, which contains billions of aluminum atoms, written simply as Al?

11. Give two reasons why iron is such a useful metal.

12. What element has the highest melting point?

13. Suggest a reason why high pressure can change a nonmetal into metallic form.

14. An element is shiny, can be squeezed to form a wire, and can be hammered to form a sheet. Can this element be classified as a metal? Explain the reason for your answer.

15. Why are metals dense?

16. **Story Clue** Why are dental fillings classified as alloys?

Synthesis

10. All of the atoms are aluminum, so it is necessary to represent only one.

11. Iron is strong and relatively abundant; therefore, it is inexpensive.

12. tungsten

13. At high pressures, atoms of nonmetallic elements are squeezed close enough together that electrons become free to move among all the atoms. This freedom of electron movement confers metallic properties on an element.

14. Yes. Luster, ductility, and malleability are typical properties of metals.

15. Metals are dense because they contain millions of identical atoms.

16. Dental fillings are composed of a solution of metals in mercury.

ANSWERS

SECTION REVIEW

Total recall

1. A metal is a good conductor of electricity, while a nonmetal is not.

2. Copper is used in electrical wiring because it is an excellent conductor of electricity, resists corrosion, and is inexpensive.

3. Ductility is the capacity to be squeezed out into a wire. Malleability is the capacity to be hammered or pressed into sheets.

4. electrical conductivity

5. Alloys can be made by melting metals together. Sometimes nonmetals are included.

6. A crystal is a form of matter in which the molecules, ions, or atoms of a crystal are arranged in an orderly geometric pattern that repeats in three dimensions.

7. In metals, the conduction bands are low in energy, and electrons are easily excited into those bands. In semiconductors, the conduction bands are of higher energy, so more energy is required to excite electrons into those bands. Therefore, semiconductors are less conducive than metals. In nonmetals, the conduction bands are very high in energy, so it is very difficult to excite electrons into them. Therefore, nonmetals are poor conductors.

8. the outer electrons

9. As temperature increases in semiconductors electrons are excited up to the higher energy orbitals of the conduction band thereby increasing the conductance. An increase in temperature in metals causes the metal's atoms to vibrate back and forth. This vibration interferes with the motion of the electrons and lowers the conductance.

SCIENCE & TECHNOLOGY

SUPERCONDUCTORS

Saving Energy with Superconductors

When electric current passes along a wire, some of the energy of the flowing electrons is converted to heat as the electrons interact with the metal atoms in the wire. This effect, called *resistance,* is useful in a toaster, an electric heater, or a light bulb filament. In most cases, though, as in an electric motor, heat is an unwanted result of the resistance to flow of electrons and is wasted energy.

Superconductivity Discovered Since the nineteenth century scientists have known that a metal becomes a better conductor as its temperature is lowered. In 1911, a Dutch physicist was studying the decrease in resistance of mercury as its temperature decreased. When he used liquid helium to cool the metal to about 4 K, an unexpected thing happened—the mercury lost all electric resistance and became a *superconductor.*

Overhead power lines typically waste half the energy of the current that flows through them. If wires had no resistance at all, we could save a huge amount of energy.

Scientists were excited about this new discovery, but the use of superconductors was severely limited by the huge expense of cooling them to near absolute zero. Scientists began research to find a material that would superconduct at temperatures above 77 K, the boiling point of liquid nitrogen, which is cheap to produce.

High-Temperature Superconductors

Ceramic Conductors Finally, in 1987 scientists discovered materials that became superconductors when cooled to only 90 K. A surprise was that these "high-temperature" superconductors weren't metals at all. Rather, they were ceramics, usually copper oxides combined with elements such as yttrium or barium. These ceramic materials are brittle and difficult to form into wire-like strands. Since the discovery of ceramic superconductors, engineers have found ways to fabricate these materials into useful forms.

Electromagnets High-temperature superconductors are used in the construction of very powerful electromagnets that are not limited by resistance or heat buildup. These magnets can be used to build powerful particle accelerators as well as high-efficiency electric motors and generators. Electromagnets have already been used to levitate a passenger train above its guide rail so that it can move with minimum friction and thus save fuel. Engineers are now working to build a similar system that will use superconducting electromagnets.

Medical Tools Superconductors are being used to construct devices that can detect and measure the very faint magnetic fields of the heart and brain. The results allow physicians to diagnose and study heart disease and neurological disorders such as epilepsy. Similar devices can be used to detect flaws in the structure of an aircraft. This is a useful tool in the prevention of aircraft failure due to structural problems.

The strong magnetic field produced by these superconducting electromagnets can suspend this 8 cm disk. Such a disk could form a magnetically levitated bearing for a nearly frictionless electric motor or generator.

internet**connect**

SC*LINKS*
NSTA

TOPIC: Superconductors
GO TO: www.scilinks.org
KEYWORD: HW046

CAREER APPLICATION

What would it be like to . . .
- develop high-strength, ultralight ceramics for interplanetary travel?
- discover the first room-temperature superconductor?
- formulate a material that can replace human bones and tendons?

Science/Math Career Preparation	
High School	**College**
Biology	Physics
Chemistry	Chemistry
Physics	Mathematics
Mathematics	Biology

Materials Scientist

A materials scientist is interested in discovering materials that will withstand harsh conditions, have unusual properties, or perform unique functions. These materials might include the following: a lightweight plastic that conducts electricity; a ceramic that will superconduct; extremely light but strong materials to construct a space platform; a plastic that can replace iron and aluminum in building automobile engines; a new building material that expands and contracts very little, even when temperatures vary as much as 500 K; or a strong, flexible, but extremely tough material that can replace bone or connective tissue in surgery. Materials engineers develop such materials and discover ways to mold or shape them into usable forms. Many materials scientists work in the aerospace industry, developing new materials to reduce the mass of aircraft, rockets, and space vehicles.

SECTION 4-3

What trends are found in the periodic table?

OBJECTIVES ▸ *Describe* periodic trends in atomic radius, ionization energy, electron affinity, melting points, and boiling points.

▸ *Relate* trends in the periodic table to the atomic structures of the elements.

Periodic trends

You have read that elements are arranged in the periodic table in order of increasing atomic number. The elements are further organized into groups and periods. The arrangement of the periodic table reveals trends, or general tendencies, in the physical and chemical properties of elements. In this section you will look at some of these trends and learn how they can be explained in terms of electron configuration.

What is a trend? A trend is a predictable change in a particular direction. For example, as you move down Group 1, reactivity increases for each element. In other words, there is a trend toward greater reactivity among the alkali metals. This trend is illustrated in **Figure 4-21**. Knowing the various trends for elements in the periodic table enables you to make logical predictions about chemical behavior.

Periodic trends in atomic radii

The exact size of an atom is difficult to determine. It is determined by the volume occupied by the electrons surrounding the nucleus. The electrons in an atom are modeled as clouds, with no clear-cut boundary. The probability of encountering electrons decreases with distance from the nucleus, but the outer boundaries are fuzzy and actually depend on

▸ **FIGURE 4-21**

Chemical reactivity increases somewhat from top to bottom for Group 1 elements. Reactions of lithium, sodium, and potassium with water are shown.

Lithium   **Sodium**   **Potassium**

DEMONSTRATION 4

Size of an Oleic Acid Molecule

Approximate time: 30 minutes

This demonstration is based on the ability of an oleic acid solution to spread out, forming a film that is one molecule thick.

1. Clean a cafeteria tray with soap and water. Fill the tray with water to a depth of 1 cm.

2. Gently spread lycopodium powder or fine chalk dust over the surface of the water, and disperse it by blowing. (Too much dust will impede the oleic acid.)

3. Add one drop of 0.5% oleic acid solution (an oleic acid and alcohol solution) to the tray. When it stops spreading, measure the two largest diameters of the film. Record the measurement in centimeters.

4. The thickness of the film can be calculated by dividing the volume of oleic acid in the drop by the area of the film. Have a stu-

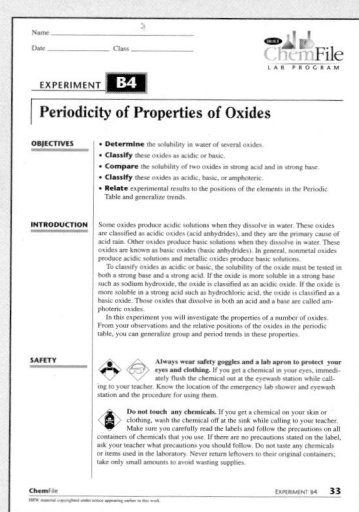

I₂ — I_2 ... Br₂ — Br_2

A

B

FIGURE 4-22

Lines A and B represent the distances between centers of like atoms that are in contact. Two ways of measuring atomic radii are shown: bond radius and van der Waals radius.

the physical and chemical condition of the atoms. Radii are usually determined for atoms that are chemically bonded or close together in the solid state, such as Br_2 and I_2. Half the distance between the nuclei of the atoms in each molecule is called the **bond radius.** Line segment A in **Figure 4-22** represents twice the bond radius of the halogen atom in question.

Line segment B represents the distance between the nuclei in adjacent nonbonded molecules, which is equal to twice the distance called the **van der Waals radius.** The van der Waals radius is sometimes used to state the size of atoms, but data are available for only a few of the main-group elements. Because of the "fuzziness" of atoms, van der Waals radii are generally not very precise. In this book, bond radius will be used to denote the size of atoms because there are more data available.

The bond radius is about two-thirds of the van der Waals radius and is known with great precision. The problem is that the bond types, even for the same atom, may be quite different. For example, the bonds between tin atoms in metallic tin are very different from the bonds between tin atoms and chlorine atoms in $SnCl_4$. Therefore, the bond radius of a tin atom in metallic tin is different from the bond radius of a tin atom in $SnCl_4$. Even with this limitation, measuring the bond radius is a useful way to compare the sizes of atoms.

Atomic radius increases as you move down a group

There is a general trend toward larger radii as you proceed down a group, as shown in **Figure 4-23** on page 136. This is caused by the addition of another principal energy level from one period to the next. The electrons in the inner energy levels are between the nucleus and the outermost electrons and therefore shield the outer electrons

bond radius

one-half the distance from center to center of two like atoms bonded together

van der Waals radius

half the distance between the nuclei in adjacent non-bonded molecules

STUDY SKILLS

ORGANIZING WHAT YOU'VE LEARNED

Organizing the information you have learned will help you both in understanding the information and in memorizing it. There are several strategies you can use to organize both your class notes and important ideas from the text. These strategies can also help you to develop and structure paragraphs for research papers and essay exams. Two of these are concept mapping and power notes, which are explained in detail in Appendix B.

THE PERIODIC TABLE 135

SECTION 4-3

VISUAL STRATEGY

Figure 4-22 Help students understand that the left and right atoms are bonded to each other but the top and bottom atoms are not bonded.

TEACHING TIP

The Structure of an Atom Ask students how atoms differ in structure from the top of a group toward the bottom. In addition to increased atomic mass and atomic number, the number of electrons also increases. Specifically, each lower atom has one more energy level of electrons than the one above it. Ask students if that pattern agrees with observed trends in atomic radius. *(It does.)*

HISTORICAL CONNECTION

The French physicist Jean Baptiste Perrin (1870–1942) published the first close estimate of the size of an atom in 1908. His calculations were based on an equation suggested by Albert Einstein in 1905.

RESOURCE LINK

ChemFile Lab B
Microscale Lab
Have students do Experiment B4: *Periodicity of Properties of Oxides.*

---

dent determine the number of drops of oleic acid that equal 5 mL.

(Note: To determine the volume of one drop, divide 5 mL by the number of drops. Then divide this volume by 200, which is the dilution factor of the oleic acid. This provides the volume of oleic acid one drop. Determine the area of the film by averaging the total diameter measurements and using the formula for the area of a circle, $A = \pi r^2$. Divide the volume of the drop by the area of the circle to get the thickness of the film.)

Safety

Wear safety goggles and a lab apron. Students must stand back at least 30 m. Ensure that there are no flames in the room. Do not use more than 10 mL of the oleic acid solution.

Disposal

Pour the water with the film down the drain. Save the oleic acid solution for reuse at a later time, or dilute it with 100 mL of water, and pour it down the drain. Clean the tray with soap and water.

Trends in atomic radii Before discussing the reasons for the decrease in atomic radii from left to right through a period, project a copy of Figure 4-24 from an overhead projector and ask students to study the trends illustrated. Ask them to describe the trend in radii from top to bottom in a group and to recall the reason for that trend. Next point out the decrease in radii across a period, and ask students to use their knowledge of atomic structure and electron configurations to propose reasons for this counterintuitive phenomenon.

Periodic Table of Atomic Radii (pm)

▲ **FIGURE 4-23**

Atomic radii decrease from left to right across a period and increase down a group.

electron shielding

the reduction of the attractive force between a positively charged nucleus and its outermost electrons due to the cancellation of some of the positive charge by the negative charge of the other electrons

from the full charge of the nucleus. This phenomenon is called **electron shielding.** Because the outermost electrons are not subject to the full charge of the nucleus, they are not held as close to the nucleus.

As you move down a group, the nuclear charge increases. At the same time, the screening of the inner electrons also increases. The net result is that the effective nuclear charge acting on the outer electrons is almost constant, regardless of the energy level in which the outer electrons are located. For example, the effective nuclear charge acting on the outermost electron in a cesium atom is about the same as it is in a sodium atom.

Atomic radius decreases as you move across a period

The trend to smaller atoms across a period is caused by the increasing positive charge of the nucleus. From left to right within a period, each atom has one more proton and one more electron than the element before it. However, the additional electrons are going into the same energy levels. Electrons in an outer energy level do not screen the other electrons in that energy level very effectively. Consequently, as the nuclear charge increases across a period, the effective nuclear charge also increases, pulling the electrons closer to the nucleus and reducing the size of the atom. The addition of electrons to d orbitals, as in the interval Ca to Ga, has little effect on atomic radius.

Atomic Radii of Main-Block Elements

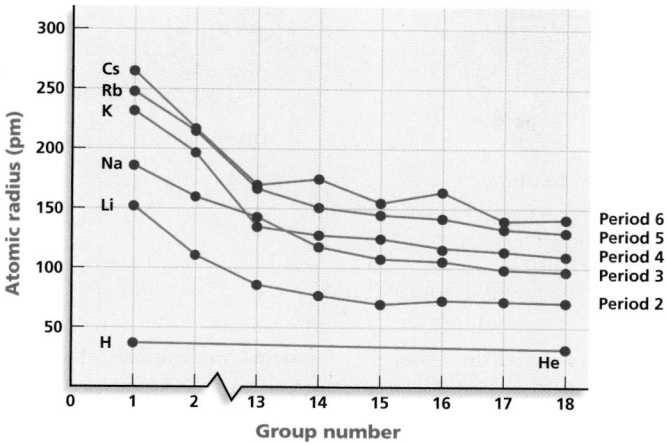

FIGURE 4-24 ◄

As you move across a period, the radii of atoms tend to decrease due to an increase in effective nuclear charge. As you move to the next highest period, the effective nuclear charge remains about the same, but there are more main energy levels, so the sizes of the atoms are greater.

ANSWERS

CONCEPT CHECK

1. A trend is a predictable change in a particular direction.

2. The reactivity of alkali metals increases from the top to the bottom of the group.

3. The atomic radii decrease across a period of elements and increase from the top to the bottom of a group.

4. Electron shielding is a masking of the nuclear charge by levels of electrons. Increased shielding in larger atoms tends to allow the outer electrons to be even farther from the nucleus.

As you can see in **Figure 4-24,** this trend is less pronounced in periods where there are many electrons between the nucleus and the outermost energy level. As you move from left to right in a period, one proton is added to the nucleus and one electron is added to the outer energy level. As you proceed from left to right in the period, the effective positive charge increases gradually, pulling the electrons closer to the nucleus. As the electrons are pulled closer to the nucleus, they get closer to one another and repulsions occur. Finally, the stage is reached when the electrons will not come much closer and the size of the atom tends to level off.

CONCEPT CHECK

1. What is a trend?
2. What trend is found in the reactivity of the alkali metals?
3. What trend is there among atomic radii as you move across a period? down a group?
4. What is electron shielding? How does it affect atomic radius?

COMMON MISCONCEPTION

Many students perceive numbers abstractly and not as representations of measurements or counts of real objects. They can solve problems such as $6 - (-2) = 8$ but fail to understand why losing an electron makes an atom more positive and why gaining an electron makes an atom more negative. List the numbers of protons and electrons for several atoms and their ions. Show how the charges of the ions arise from the gain or loss of electrons.

Ionization energy, electron affinity, and melting points

Recall that atoms are electrically neutral. However, if enough energy is added, an atom may lose an electron to become a positive ion. Imagine that you can reach into an atom and remove one of the outermost electrons, creating an ion. The energy you use to remove the electron is the **ionization energy** of the atom. **Figure 4-25,** on the next page, illustrates this process. The lithium ion is smaller than the lithium atom because the single electron has been removed from the outer energy level. The process of removing an electron can be expressed as an equation.

ionization energy

the amount of energy needed to remove an outer electron from a specific atom or ion in its ground state and in the gas phase

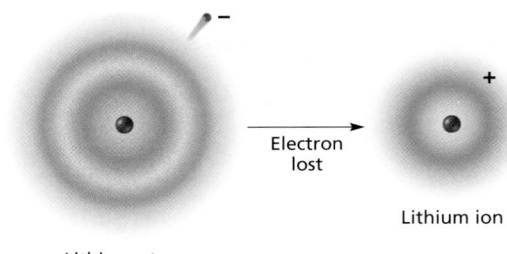

Lithium atom

Electron lost

Lithium ion

$$A + energy \longrightarrow A^+ + e^-$$
$$atom \qquad\qquad ion$$

Figure 4-26 shows ionization energies for some main-block elements. Examine Figure 4-26, and determine which group of elements has the lowest ionization energy.

Ionization energies increase across a period and decrease down a group

Periodic trends in ionization energies are opposite those for atomic size. Ionization energy tends to increase across a period and decrease down a group. As mentioned above, as more protons are added to the nucleus, the effective nuclear charge acting on the outermost electrons increases, holding the electrons more tightly to the nucleus. Hence ionization energy increases across a period.

Ionization Energies of Main-Block Elements

Ionization energy

Decreases ↓

Increases →

FIGURE 4-27 ◀

Ionization energy generally decreases from top to bottom and increases from left to right across the table.

Similarly, as you move down a group, the number of energy levels between the nucleus and the outermost electrons increases and the outermost electrons are farther from the nucleus. The effective nuclear charge is about the same, so the outer electrons are held less tightly to the nucleus, and less energy is required to remove one of them.

Moreover, as you move down a group, the outermost electrons are farther from the nucleus. According to Coulomb's law, which you read about in Chapter 3, the force between two charged particles decreases as the distance between the particles increases. Thus, as you move down a group, attractive forces between the nucleus and the outermost electrons decrease and the energy necessary to remove an electron from the atom decreases. The general trends are shown in **Figure 4-27**.

Periodic trends in electron affinity

The ability of an atom to attract and hold an electron is called **electron affinity.** You may wonder why a neutral atom would attract electrons in the first place. The answer is that the electrons in the orbitals generally do not shield the nuclear charge to a full 100%. An approaching electron therefore may experience a net pull because the effective nuclear charge is greater than zero. The electron enters a vacant orbital. This is illustrated in **Figure 4-28.**

When an atom gains an extra electron, it becomes a negative ion. In most cases energy is given off in the process. This process can be represented by the following equation.

$$A + e^- \longrightarrow A^- + \text{energy}$$
$$\text{atom} \longrightarrow \text{ion}$$

electron affinity

the energy emitted upon the addition of an electron to an atom or group of atoms in the gas phase

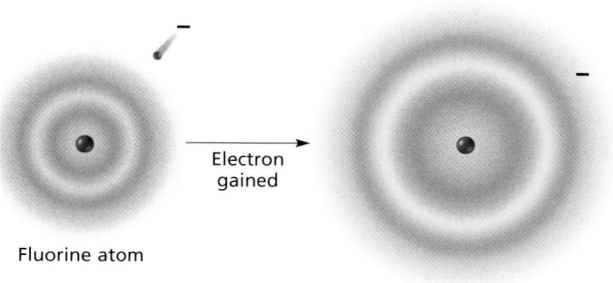

Electron gained

Fluorine atom

Fluoride ion

FIGURE 4-28 ◀

A fluorine atom gains an electron to become a negatively charged ion. Energy is emitted in the process, so the electron affinity of fluorine is assigned a negative value.

VISUAL STRATEGY

Figure 4-27 Have students compare Figure 4-27 with Figure 4-22 and describe the differences in the two processes with respect to energy, charge, and electron movement. Ask them to speculate about what might happen if the lithium atom in Figure 4-25 were in the presence of the fluorine atom in Figure 4-28. *(Lithium would lose an electron, which would be added to the fluorine.)*

CHAPTER CONNECTION

Electronegativity is another periodic property. It follows the same pattern as ionization energy, increasing from left to right across a period and decreasing from top to bottom in a group. Electronegativity is covered in Chapter 6, where it is relevant to bonding.

TEACHING TIP

Energy Changes Review with students the sign conventions used in chemistry (and other sciences) with respect to energy changes. All chemical and physical processes can be viewed as (1) the system undergoing change and (2) the surroundings. The movement of energy is always considered to be relative to the system. When energy is given off into the surroundings by a system, the change is considered negative because the system loses energy. Therefore, the energy change for all exothermic processes is negative. If a system acquires energy from the surroundings (endothermic), either spontaneously (melting ice in a 25°C room) or by being heated (melting glass in a furnace), the energy change is positive. When we observe processes, we are usually part of the surroundings, so we tend to sense that an output of energy should be positive, but that is not the case.

READING STRATEGY

Organizing Concepts Students should update the notes they have been keeping on blank periodic tables by adding the trends discussed in this section as well as short notes about the reasons for those trends.

TABLE 4-3   **Electron Affinities of the Main-Block Elements (in kJ/mol)**

1 H −72.77							2 He (7)
3 Li −59.6	4 Be (17)*	5 B −26.7	6 C −121.9	7 N −7	8 O −141.0	9 F −328.2	10 Ne (8)
11 Na −52.9	12 Mg (14)	13 Al −42.6	14 Si −133.6	15 P −72.0	16 S −200.4	17 Cl −348.6	18 Ar (9)
19 K −48.4	20 Ca (−4)	31 Ga −30	32 Ge −119.0	33 As −78	34 Se −195.0	35 Br −324.5	36 Kr (10)
37 Rb −46.9	38 Sr (−11)	49 In −29	50 Sn −107.3	51 Sb −103	52 Te −190.2	53 I −295.2	54 Xe (11)
55 Cs −45.5	56 Ba (−14)	81 Tl −20	82 Pb −35.1	83 Bi −91.3	84 Po (−180)	85 At (−270)	86 Rn (11)

*Numbers in parentheses were calculated.

In this text, a negative electron affinity indicates that energy is released when the atom gains an electron. A positive value indicates that energy is needed to add the electron to an atom.

Electron affinity is much more difficult to measure, or calculate, than ionization energy. This is especially true for the noble gas and alkaline-earth elements. Many previous texts gave these elements very large positive values. Only recently have values become available for many elements. Electron affinities for the main block elements are given in **Table 4-3.**

Electron affinity becomes more negative across a period

In a general way, electron affinity becomes more negative across a period and tends to decrease from top to bottom in a group. Think about the effects of electron shielding: across a period, shielding remains constant as nuclear charge increases. Therefore, the atom's attraction for extra electrons increases. Going down a group, both shielding and nuclear charge increase. However, the effect of shielding more than offsets the increase in nuclear charge. Therefore, the atom's attraction for extra electrons decreases.

Electron affinity trends within groups of elements are not as regular as trends for ionization energy. As you can see in Table 4-3, there are exceptions to this general trend. The alkaline-earth metals are one of these exceptions. An electron added to an alkaline-earth metal must go into a *p* orbital and is shielded to a greater extent by *s* electrons. The reason the effect is so large is not clear.

Periodic trends in melting and boiling points

Melting points and boiling points for elements in the sixth period are shown in **Figure 4-29.** At first, as the number of electrons increases, the melting and boiling points increase. This indicates stronger bonding. However, at about the stage where the *d* orbitals become half-filled, the melting and boiling points begin to decrease. This indicates that the added electrons become less involved in bonding. Finally, at the element mercury, a deep minimum is reached where the *d* orbitals are completely filled. The filled *d* orbitals result in low chemical bond strength and a low boiling point for mercury. For the same reason, zinc

Melting Points and Boiling Points of Period-6 Elements

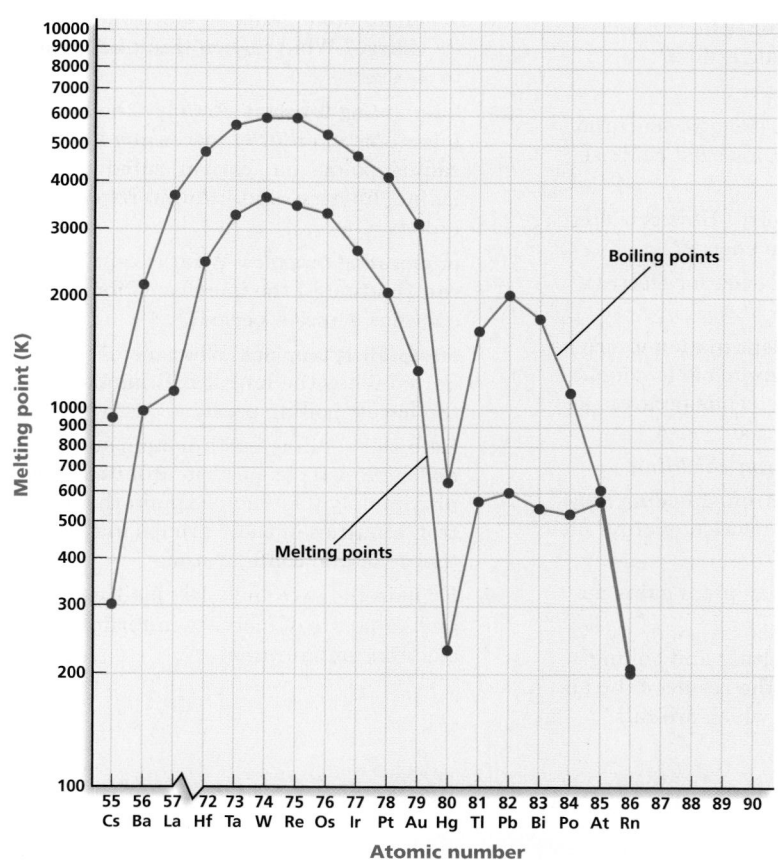

FIGURE 4-29 ◄

Melting points and boiling points of Period 6 elements in solid and liquid phases show a periodic trend.

SECTION REVIEW

Total recall

1. Atoms are very small, and there is no definite boundary to the electron cloud.

2. In this book, *atomic radius* means "bond radius," half the distance between the nuclei of bonded atoms.

3. Van der Waals's radius is half the distance between adjacent unbonded atoms.

4. Ionization energy is the amount of energy needed to remove an electron from an atom.

5. Ionization energy generally increases from left to right across a period and decreases from top to bottom in a group. Group 2 and Group 15 elements have higher ionization energies than the trend would indicate.

6. Electron affinity is the energy given off when an electron is added to an atom. Electron affinity involves adding an electron to an atom rather than taking one away.

7. Electron affinities generally increase (in negative value) across a period and decrease (in negative value) moving down through a group.

8. Atomic size increases, ionization energy decreases, and electron affinity decreases from top to bottom in a group. Atomic size decreases, ionization energy increases, and electron affinity increases from left to right across a period.

9. Electron shielding occurs when underlying levels of electrons reduce the attraction of the nucleus for the outermost electrons.

10. Electron shielding increases atomic size, decreases ionization energy, and decreases electron affinity.

---

and cadmium exhibit low melting and boiling points in their respective periods.

As *p* electrons are added, we see a similar rise and fall, with the maximum near the stage where the *p* orbitals are half filled. A minimum is reached when the *p* orbitals are filled and the atoms no longer bond. The noble gases are monatomic and have no chemical bonding forces between atoms. Therefore, their melting and boiling points are unusually low.

SECTION REVIEW

Total recall

1. Why is it difficult to measure the size of an atom?

2. What does the term *atomic radius* mean?

3. What is the difference between bond radius and van der Waals radius?

4. What is ionization energy?

5. What periodic trends exist for ionization energy? What exceptions exist in these trends?

6. What is electron affinity? How is it different from ionization energy?

7. What periodic trends exist for electron affinity?

8. What trends are evident in atomic size as you proceed down a group of elements? How do each of these trends progress as you move across a period?

9. Define the term *electron shielding*.

10. What effect does electron shielding have on atomic size? on ionization energy? on electron affinity?

11. What happens when an atom gains an extra electron?

12. The periodicity of melting and boiling points in Period 6 is the result of the addition of electrons to which orbitals?

Critical thinking

13. When an atom loses an electron, what is its charge? What do you think happens to the size of the atom?

14. When an atom gains an electron, what is its charge? What do you think happens to its size?

15. **Interpreting Graphics** Arrange the following atoms in order of increasing atomic radius: potassium, carbon, rubidium, iodine, fluorine, and lithium. Explain the order.

16. **Interpreting Graphics** What exceptions can you find in the increase of ionization energies across a period?

17. **Interpreting Graphics** What metal in Period 6 has the lowest melting point? the lowest boiling point?

18. Both the alkaline-earth metals and the noble gases have electron affinities of approximately 0 kJ/mol. Explain the electron affinities of these groups in terms of their electron configurations.

19. Explain the extremely low melting and boiling points of mercury in terms of electron configuration.

---

11. The atom becomes a negatively charged ion.

12. Electrons are added to 6*s*, 5*d*, and 6*p* orbitals.

Critical thinking

13. The ion formed has a +1 charge. The atom becomes smaller.

14. The ion formed has a –1 charge. The atom becomes larger.

15. The order is fluorine, carbon, iodine, lithium, potassium, rubidium. The alkali metals lithium, potassium, and rubidium are larger because they are at

the beginning of a period. Each metal has a new energy level with one electron and the minimum nuclear charge for that period. The halogens fluorine and iodine have the largest nuclear charge in their periods, with the exception of the noble gases, and therefore are small compared with alkali metals. Carbon is intermediate in its period but is still quite small.

16. Group 13 and Group 16

17. radon in both cases

Answers continue on page 155A.

Where did the elements come from?

OBJECTIVES

▶ **Distinguish** between naturally occurring and synthetic elements.

▶ **Describe** how the naturally occurring elements are formed.

▶ **Describe** how particle accelerators are used to create synthetic elements.

Natural and synthetic elements

Chemists have identified 93 naturally occurring elements. Three of these elements, technetium, promethium, and neptunium, are not found on Earth but have been detected in the spectra of stars. The nebula shown in **Figure 4-30** is a region in the galaxy where new stars are formed.

Chemists have created, or *synthesized,* more elements than the 93 that occur naturally. These are the *synthetic elements.* Most of the transuranium elements are synthetic. Those naturally occurring elements that are found on Earth in minute amounts, like francium and astatine, or not at all are usually categorized as synthetic elements.

Naturally occurring elements are created in the center of stars

According to current theory, some time between 12 billion and 16 billion years ago the entire universe could fit on a pinhead. Then with unbelievable violence the universe exploded, an event scientists named the big bang. Immediately after the big bang, temperatures were in the millions of kelvins, so high that matter could not exist, only energy. As the universe expanded, it cooled. When the universe cooled to a few thousand kelvins, some of its energy was converted to matter in the form of electrons, protons, and neutrons. As the universe continued to cool, these particles formed the first atoms, almost all hydrogen but also some helium.

Over time, huge clouds of hydrogen accumulated. Gravitational attraction pulled the clumps of hydrogen closer and closer together. As the clouds became denser, pressures and temperatures at the centers of the hydrogen clouds increased, and stars

FIGURE 4-30 ▼

Technetium, promethium, and neptunium have been detected in the spectra of stars.

THE PERIODIC TABLE **143**

LESSON WARM-UP

Remind students that one of the goals of the ancient alchemists was to turn lead and other "base" metals into gold. They attempted this feat by reacting different chemical substances with the metal. Today we realize that such a transmutation is not possible by chemical means. However, it is possible through nuclear reactions. Unfortunately, the cost of making gold in this way far exceeds the cost of obtaining it from ore. Although such reactions do not take place naturally on Earth, they occur constantly in stars.

COMMON MISCONCEPTION

The word *synthetic* as it is used here does not refer to synthesis by chemical means but rather by bombardment of nuclei with neutrons or other nuclei.

DID YOU KNOW?

Francium and astatine occur in nature as products of nuclear decay in uranium ores. Scientists have estimated that less than 25 g of each element exists in Earth's crust.

CNN Science in the News

PRESENTS Feature story 13 *Atom Builders.* See the Science in the News video guide for more details.

VISUAL STRATEGY

Figure 4-31 The reaction shown is simplified and is one of several possible fusion reactions believed to take place in the sun. Be sure that students note the composition of the alpha particle produced by fusion. It does not consist of the original four protons but instead has two protons and two neutrons. The neutrons have been formed from the protons by the emission of positrons.

DID YOU KNOW?

The sun is estimated to be 9.5 billion years old, with approximately 6 billion years left in its life span. The age of a star can be estimated from its color and the percentage of helium in its mass. Both can be determined by analyzing the light from the star with a spectrometer.

HISTORICAL CONNECTION

The first fusion reaction caused by humans occurred in 1952 with the detonation of the first fusion bomb (hydrogen bomb). The bomb is an example of uncontrolled fusion. Scientists have still not found a reliable way to control and maintain fusion reactions because of the extremely high temperatures required, more than 20 million degrees Celcius.

TEACHING TIP

Stable Nuclei Explain to students that iron and nickel nuclei are more stable than the nuclei of other elements. For this reason, these elements tended to accumulate and are abundant in the universe today.

CHAPTER CONNECTION

Students will learn more about fusion and the relative stability of nuclei in Chapter 18, "Nuclear Chemistry."

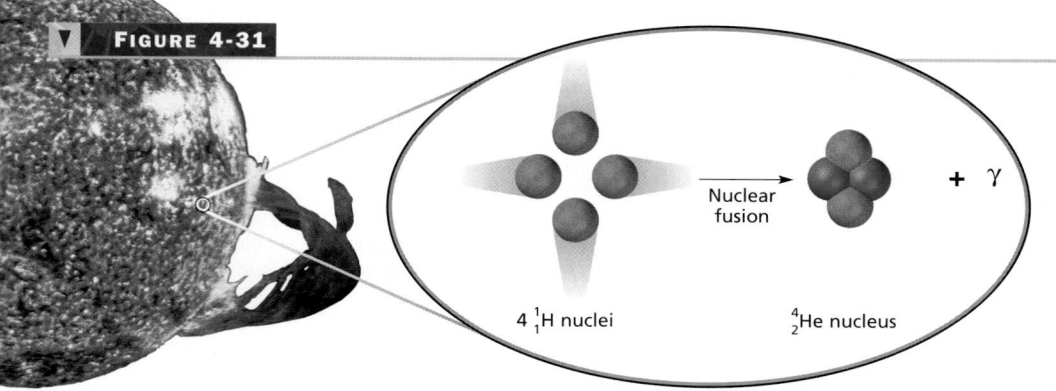

▼ FIGURE 4-31

4 $_1^1$H nuclei → (Nuclear fusion) → $_2^4$He nucleus + γ

a Nuclear fusion in the nearest star, our sun, has provided the Earth with energy for billions of years. Fusion reactions also create elements heavier than hydrogen.

b The single helium nucleus has less mass than the four hydrogen nuclei from which it is formed. The small amount of mass "lost" during fusion is converted to energy. The symbol γ, the Greek letter gamma, indicates that energy is released in the form of gamma radiation.

nuclear reaction

a reaction that involves a change in the composition of the nucleus of an atom

were born. In the high-temperature centers of stars, nuclear reactions took place. A **nuclear reaction** is a reaction involving protons and neutrons in the nuclei of atoms. In the nuclear reactions in the centers of the first stars, hydrogen nuclei fused with one another to form helium nuclei. This *nuclear fusion* reaction is modeled in **Figure 4-31.** Nuclear fusion reactions can take place only under conditions of extreme heat, such as the conditions found in stars. There the kinetic energy of the nuclei is great enough to overcome the repulsion between positively charged protons. For example, our sun converts about 3.6×10^{11} kg (4×10^8 tons) of hydrogen into helium every second.

Notice in Figure 4-31b the mass of a helium nucleus compared with the mass of the hydrogen nuclei that fuse to form it. The mass "lost" in a fusion reaction is actually converted to energy. Einstein's equation $E = mc^2$ describes this mass-to-energy conversion quantitatively. The constant, c, is the speed of light. The energy produced by fusion reactions is enough to maintain the extremely high temperatures in the centers of the stars. As the hydrogen is used up, the star shrinks and the temperature in the star's center increases. As the temperature increases, helium nuclei fuse with one another to form elements of higher atomic number. As the temperature continues to rise, elements of still higher atomic number are formed. **Figure 4-32** shows an example of this process. The most massive atoms formed by this process are iron and nickel. Geologists believe that the core of the Earth is composed of a mixture of iron and nickel.

When a star the size of the sun uses up all of the hydrogen and helium in its center, it collapses and then expands as a red giant. As this red giant forms, some atoms are torn apart, producing free protons and neutrons. These particles are absorbed by the nuclei of other atoms, creating elements with atomic numbers greater than that of iron and that

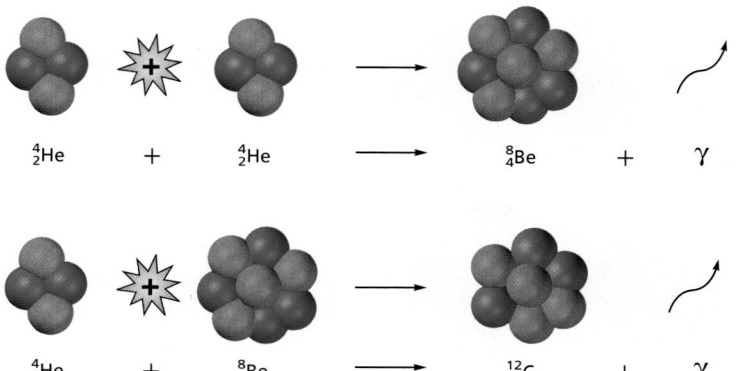

$$^4_2\text{He} + \,^4_2\text{He} \longrightarrow \,^8_4\text{Be} + \gamma$$

$$^4_2\text{He} + \,^8_4\text{Be} \longrightarrow \,^{12}_6\text{C} + \gamma$$

FIGURE 4-32 ◄

Carbon-12 is formed in stars through these nuclear reactions.

of nickel. The super-hot red giant expels some of its matter into space, including the elements it has produced. If the star is considerably larger than the sun, the star will eventually explode as a supernova and matter will spread across space for millions of kilometers. This matter includes, of course, all the elements previously formed in the star, including those with atomic numbers greater than iron and nickel.

Some of the matter from the supernova eventually condensed into new stars. Like earlier stars, these stars were mostly hydrogen, but they also contained heavier elements formed in the previous generation of stars. In turn, these new stars evolved, giving rise to a third generation, that was further enriched with heavy elements. The current theory indicates that the sun is a fourth- or fifth-generation star. When the sun first formed, it contained all the naturally occurring elements.

CONCEPT CHECK

1. Where were all the naturally occurring elements formed?
2. What is the most common element in the universe?

Artificial elements
Transmutations are a type of nuclear reaction

Many of the activities of the alchemists were directed toward changing, or *transmuting,* ordinary metals into gold. Although alchemists made many discoveries that contributed to the development of modern chemistry, their attempts to transmute metals were doomed from the start. What the alchemists didn't know was that a **transmutation** is a nuclear reaction that cannot be achieved by ordinary chemical means.

While studying the passage of high-speed alpha particles through water vapor in a cloud chamber, Ernest Rutherford noted some long, thin tracks. These tracks turned out to be caused by protons, the nuclei

transmutation

the process of changing one nucleus into another by radioactive disintegration or bombardment with other particles

VISUAL STRATEGY

Figure 4-32 Students should note the balance of these nuclear fusion equations. The total mass and total charge (protons) are equal on both sides of the equation. In these examples, no protons have converted to neutrons.

DID YOU KNOW?

The science of the origin and development of the universe is called *cosmology.*

TEACHING TIP

Heavy Elements Point out to students that all of the zinc, silver, gold, platinum, and mercury, as well as all of the bromine and iodine, came from explosions of red giant stars or from supernovae. Elements heavier than nickel also came from these sources.

ANSWERS
CONCEPT CHECK

1. All of the naturally occurring elements (other than hydrogen) were formed in stars.

2. hydrogen

ADDITIONAL APPLICATION

Students should contemplate the fact that all elements on Earth, including those that make up the molecules of the body, originated by fusion in stars somewhere in the universe.

Teaching Tip

Lead students to understand that the cyclotron accelerates particles to high velocities. Consequently, they have high kinetic energies. Cyclotrons accelerate particles by alternating electrostatic attraction and repulsion while a static magnetic field bends the path into a circle. Therefore, only charged particles can be used.

VISUAL STRATEGY

Figure 4-33 Inform students that physicists and chemists study particle-chamber tracks like this to find signs of small particles. As with other parts of atomic theory, we cannot view the particles themselves, but we can tell where the particles have been and how they behaved and interacted while moving.

▶ **FIGURE 4-33**

A cloud-chamber image provided the first evidence of transmutation. The arrow marks the spot where an alpha particle collided with the nucleus of a nitrogen atom. The left fork of the path was made by an oxygen atom, the right fork by a proton.

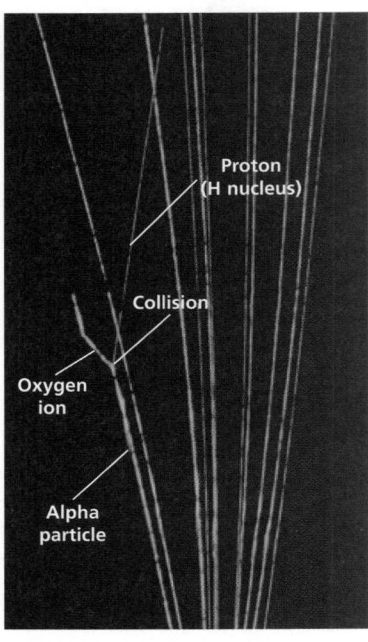

of hydrogen. While studying the passage of alpha particles through air, Rutherford noted the same long, thin tracks. Somehow protons were being produced. He guessed correctly that atomic nuclei in air were disintegrating upon being struck by helium nuclei into hydrogen nuclei (protons) plus the nuclei of some other atom.

The American W. D. Harkins and the Englishman P.M.S. Blackett studied this strange phenomenon further. Blackett took photos of 400,000 alpha particle tracks in the cloud chamber and found that eight of them forked to form a Y, as shown in **Figure 4-33.** Harkins and Blackett determined that the long, thin track was made by a proton. What produced the short, thick track? A transmutation had occurred—an isotope of oxygen was formed. In modern notation, the transmutation reaction is as follows.

$$\ce{^4_2He + ^{14}_7N \longrightarrow ^{17}_8O + ^1_1H}$$

This remarkable discovery started a flood of research. Before long, other transmutation reactions were discovered by bombarding various elements with alpha particles.

The cyclotron accelerates charged particles

It occurred to several scientists that charged particles, such as electrons or ions, could be accelerated by devices of the proper design. One of the best known of these devices is the *cyclotron,* invented in 1930 by the American E. O. Lawrence. In a cyclotron, charged particles are given successive pulses of energy, which accelerate the particles to very high energies. These extremely energetic ions are then made to collide with atomic nuclei. The accelerated ions fuse with the target nuclei to produce nuclei of much higher atomic number.

Using cyclotrons, scientists were able to prepare many new elements, including the transuranium elements.

The synchrotron is used to create superheavy elements

There is a limit to the energies that can be attained with the cyclotron. As the velocity of an accelerated particle increases, its kinetic energy

146   CHAPTER 4

DEMONSTRATION 5

Cloud Chamber

Approximate time: 15 minutes

1. To make a simplified Wilson cloud chamber, get a large glass jar with a lid, a piece of black velvet, a piece of blotter paper or felt, some alcohol, and a flat piece of dry ice.

2. Cut the velvet to fit inside the lid. Cut the blotter paper, and glue it to the bottom of the jar (or obtain a commercially produced cloud chamber).

3. Add rubbing alcohol to the blotter paper drop by drop until it is saturated but not dripping.

4. Place the jar lid on the dry ice. Place a packaged nuclear source (obtained from a scientific supply house) in the lid, and screw on the jar. (The jar should be sitting upside down on the dry ice.)

Synthetic Element Trivia

Rutherfordium
Discovered by Russian scientists at the Joint Institute for Nuclear Research at Dubna and by scientists at the University of California at Berkeley.

Meitnerium
Discovered August 29, 1982, by scientists at the Heavy Ion Research Laboratory, in Darmstadt, West Germany; named in honor of Lise Meitner, the Austrian physicist.

Mendelevium
Synthesized in 1955 by G. T. Seaborg, A. Ghiorso, B. Harvey, G. R. Choppin, and S. B. Thompson, at the University of California, Berkeley; named in honor of the inventor of the periodic system.

| 104 Rf Rutherfordium | 105 Db Dubnium | 106 Sg Seaborgium | 107 Bh Bohrium | 108 Hs Hassium | 109 Mt Meitnerium | 110 Uun Ununnilium | 111 Uuu Unununium |

| 93 Np Neptunium | 94 Pu Plutonium | 95 Am Amercium | 96 Cm Curium | 97 Bk Berkelium | 98 Cf Californium | 99 Es Einsteinium | 100 Fm Fermium | 101 Md Mendelevium | 102 No Nobelium | 103 Lr Lawrencium |

Curium
Synthesized in 1944 by G. T. Seaborg, R. A. James, and A. Ghiorso, at the University of California at Berkeley; named in honor of Marie and Pierre Curie.

Californium
Synthesized in 1950 by G. T. Seaborg, S. G. Thompson, A. Ghiorso, and K. Street, Jr, at the University of California, Berkeley; named in honor of the state of California.

Nobelium
Synthesized in 1958 by A. Ghiorso, G. T. Seaborg, T. Sikkeland, and J. R. Walton; named in honor of Alfred Nobel, discoverer of dynamite and founder of the Nobel Prize.

increases as well. As the particle reaches a velocity of about one-tenth the speed of light, the particle acquires enough energy that the equation $E = mc^2$ becomes a problem. According to $E = mc^2$, the increase in the particle's energy must be balanced by an increase in its mass. Due to its increased mass, the particle accelerates more slowly, causing it to arrive too late for the next pulse.

The solution to the delayed arrival of the particle is the *synchrotron,* which times the impulses to match the acceleration of the particles. A synchrotron can accelerate fewer types of particles than a cyclotron can, but enormous energies can be attained.

Once they have been accelerated in the synchrotron, the particles are made to collide head on with one another. See **Figure 4-34** for synthetic elements created with such collisions. The energy of collision is equal to the sum of the individual kinetic energies. These high energies of

FIGURE 4-34 ▲

All the highlighted elements are synthetic. Those shown in red were created by colliding moving particles with stationary targets. The elements shown in blue were created by colliding nuclei.

HISTORICAL CONNECTION

All transuranium elements (elements with atomic number greater than 92) have been discovered since 1940. Many were discovered under the leadership of the American physicist Glenn Theodore Seaborg. Element 106 was named seaborgium in his honor. Much of Seaborg's research was spurred by the defense needs of the Allies in World War II. Seaborg discovered that the isotope U-235 could undergo fission, and his laboratory produced the Pu-239 used in the first atomic bomb.

DID YOU KNOW?

Both cyclotrons and synchrotrons are types of particle accelerators. Both use magnetic and pulsed electric fields to accelerate particles.

TEACHING TIP

Research Strategy   Have students prepare short reports (about two or three paragraphs) on the naming of the other actinides and the super-heavy elements from berkelium to lawrencium. If the element is named for a person, the report should discuss that person's contribution to science, whether the person was awarded a Nobel Prize, and if so, the discoveries that led to the award. If the element is named for a place, students should report what happened at that location to make it important in atomic research.

5. The jar should become saturated with alcohol vapor. Shine the beam of a small projector or a bright halogen flashlight through the chamber. The emitted nuclear particles should leave white streaks that are visible against the black velvet.

ice. To break the dry ice, wrap it in a towel, place it on a firm surface, and strike it with a hammer. Ensure that there are no flames in the room. Have no more than 100 mL of alcohol in the room. Do not touch the radioactive source.

Safety
Wear safety goggles and a lab apron. Students must stand back at least 30 m. Use cloth or leather gloves when handling the dry

Disposal
Return leftover alcohol to the stock bottle. Allow the dry ice to sublime in a restricted location not accessible to students.

ANSWERS

SECTION REVIEW

Total recall

1. Naturally occurring elements are those that can be found in the universe. With few exceptions, the naturally occurring elements are found in the first six periods of the periodic table.

2. They are produced by fusion reactions in stars.

3. hydrogen

4. A synthetic element is made by the bombardment of another element with neutrons, protons, or other atomic nuclei.

5. A nuclear reaction changes to the protons and neutrons of an atom's nucleus. The nucleus usually transmutes to a different element.

6. The process by which one nucleus changes into another by radioactive disintegration or bombardment with other particles.

7. oxygen-17

8. The cyclotron accelerates charged particles such as electrons or ions to high energies. The particles are allowed to collide with existing nuclei, changing them to other nuclei.

9. an element with an atomic number greater than 106

10. Nuclei of atomic number 114 may be stable if they can be produced.

11. meitnerium

Critical thinking

12. Energy is given off in the fusion process. This energy comes from the conversion of mass to energy.

13. The atomic number of uranium is 92. The transuranium elements lie beyond uranium on the periodic table.

superheavy element
an element with an atomic number greater than 106

collision enable massive nuclei to interact. In this way, elements more massive than the actinides, **superheavy elements,** can be prepared. Because only an extremely small number of nuclei actually collide, the product of these collisions may be just a few new nuclei. Only three atoms of meitnerium were prepared in the first attempt, and these atoms existed for only 0.0034 seconds! As you can see, identification of the products is very difficult. Scientists in only a few nations have the resources to carry out such experiments. The United States, Germany, Russia, and Sweden are the locations of the largest research teams.

Today, scientists are attempting to create superheavy elements that may be more stable than those prepared so far. Some nuclear scientists predict an "island of stability" in the region of atomic number 114, and perhaps these elements, if they can be prepared, will be stable. But can element 114 be prepared? No one knows for sure. More experiments are needed to find out. The future promises to be exciting.

SECTION REVIEW

Total recall

1. Define the term *naturally occurring element*. Where are these elements located in the periodic table?

2. How and where were the naturally occurring elements created?

3. What element is the building block for all other natural elements?

4. What is a synthetic element?

5. What is a nuclear reaction?

6. What is transmutation?

7. In the first observed transmutation, nitrogen was bombarded with alpha particles to produce a hydrogen nucleus. The other product was an ion of which element?

8. How do scientists use cyclotrons to create synthetic elements?

9. How are superheavy elements prepared?

10. What do scientists mean by the term *island of stability* with respect to superheavy synthetic elements?

11. What synthetic element was discovered in 1982?

Critical thinking

12. Why is the mass of a helium atom slightly less than the mass of hydrogen atoms from which it was formed?

13. Why are the elements with atomic numbers greater than 92 referred to as transuranium elements?

14. Describe two processes that scientists use to create synthetic elements.

15. Which transuranium elements are not actinides?

16. Why is the following word equation not an example of a transmutation?
zinc + copper sulfate $\longrightarrow$
copper + zinc sulfate

17. **Story Clue** Where are the elements used in dental fillings created?

14. One method is to have accelerated particles collide with stationary nuclei. Another is to accelerate two nuclei and allow them to collide with each other and fuse into a larger nucleus.

15. Elements 104, rutherfordium, through 112, Uub, are not actinides.

16. The elements present in the products are the same as those in the reactants.

17. in stars

Now that you have completed the chapter, you should be able to answer the questions about the mysterious death of George Decker.

LOOKING BACK

Which metal melts first in gold fillings? in silver fillings?

Gold fillings contain gold, with added silver, platinum, and palladium, and trace amounts of zinc, iron, and copper. According to Figure 4-30, the metal in gold fillings with the lowest melting point is zinc, which has a melting point of 420°C. Silver fillings contain equal amounts of silver and mercury, with trace amounts of copper. The metal in silver fillings with the lowest melting point is mercury, which has a melting point of –39°C and a boiling point of 357°C.

Why did Decker's process work for gold fillings but prove fatal with silver fillings?

As the periodic trend in melting points predicts, all metals in gold fillings melt and boil at relatively high temperatures. To separate the metals, Decker heated the mixture until it melted. The liquid zinc, copper, and iron reacted with oxygen in the air and were easily skimmed off the top, leaving the gold and silver behind. Decker tried the same technique with silver fillings. However, the melting point of the silver-filling mixture is actually higher than the boiling point of mercury. When Decker melted silver fillings, the mercury evaporated before the copper and silver in the fillings could be separated. Decker produced toxic mercury vapors.

What element was most likely responsible for George Decker's death?

Mercury was the most likely cause of the tissue damage and inflammation that brought on Decker's pneumonia.

80
Hg
Mercury
200.59
$[Xe]4f^{14}5d^{10}6s^2$

Silver-white metal that is slightly volatile at room temperature. Poisonous! Readily absorbed through the respiratory tract, through the skin, and through the gastrointestinal tract. Spilled and heated elemental mercury is especially hazardous.

READING STRATEGY

Assimilating Knowledge

Have students return to the list of things they want to know about the periodic table, which they created on page 110. Have them place check marks next to the questions that they are now able to answer. Students should finish by making a list of what they've learned. Have students identify unanswered questions as well as new questions they may have. These questions could be used as the basis for a research project.

REVIEW & ASSESS ASSIGNMENT GUIDE

Term Review
Assign after Section 4-4.

Concept and Skills Review

Section 4-1
‣ Items 1–21

Section 4-2
‣ Items 22–31

Section 4-3
‣ Items 32–42

Section 4-4
‣ Items 43–51

Linking Chapters

Section 4-1
‣ Items 1–2

Section 4-2
‣ Item 4

Section 4-3
‣ Item 3

Alternative Assessments
Assign after Section 4-4.

Test Prep
Assign prior to the chapter test.

KEY TERMS

4-1
actinide
alkali metal
alkaline-earth metal
group
halogen
lanthanide
main-group element

metal
noble gas
nonmetal
period
periodic law
plasma
salt
semiconductor
transition metals

4-2
alloy
conduction band
crystal

4-3
bond radius
electron affinity

electron shielding
ionization energy
van der Waals radius

4-4
nuclear reaction
superheavy element
transmutation

KEY CONCEPTS

4-1 What makes a group of elements?

‣ According to the periodic law, properties of elements are periodic functions of their atomic numbers.

‣ In the periodic table, elements are ordered by increasing atomic number. Rows are called periods; columns are called groups.

‣ Two major families include the lanthanides and the actinides.

‣ Groups include the alkali metals, the alkaline-earth metals, the halogens, and the noble gases.

‣ Elements of the same group have similar characteristic properties even though their electron configurations may differ in some cases.

4-2 What gives metals their distinctive properties?

‣ Metals are excellent conductors of electricity and heat.

‣ In a solid metal the outer electrons bind a metal atom to its neighboring atoms to hold them together.

‣ In metals, very little or no energy is required to move electrons from their orbitals to the conduction band where they can conduct electricity.

‣ Some metals are ductile and malleable.

‣ The atoms in a metal assume an orderly arrangement to form a crystal.

4-3 What trends are found in the periodic table?

‣ Periodic trends are related to the atomic structure of the elements.

‣ The atomic radius of the elements usually decreases as you move left to right across a period and tends to increase down a periodic table group.

‣ Ionization energy and electron affinity generally increase as you move left to right across a period and decrease as you move down a group.

‣ Melting points and boiling points vary in a periodic way across a period.

4-4 Where did the elements come from?

‣ Naturally occurring elements (atomic numbers 1–92) were formed in the interior of stars. Synthetic elements (atomic numbers above 93) are made by research scientists.

‣ All elements larger than helium are formed by nuclear reactions in which nuclei are merged.

‣ Synthetic elements are made in particle accelerators, which launch particles with high enough kinetic energies to cause nuclear reactions.

KEY SKILLS

Examine the periodic table before your exam.

Be sure you understand the information it contains and how trends for atomic radius, ionization energy, electron affinity, and melting and boiling points progress across a period and down a group.

TERM REVIEW

1. The halogen elements represent a ———.
   (group, period)

2. Ca, Be, and Mg are ———.
   (alkali metals, alkaline-earth metals)

3. A mixture of two or more metals is known as a(n) ———.
   (alloy, superheavy element)

4. Half the distance between the nuclei in adjacent nonbonded molecules is known as the ——— radius.
   (bond, van der Waals)

5. The element californium is classified as a(n) ———.
   (actinide, lanthanide)

6. Every period on the table ends with a(n) ———.
   (main-group element, noble gas)

7. Electron shielding most affects ———.
   (ionization energy, electron affinity, radius)

8. Only a metal has a(n) ——— that is close to the energy levels of the electrons in their outermost orbitals.
   (conduction band, ionization energy)

9. The energy emitted when an atom gains an electron is known as ———.
   (ionization energy, electron affinity)

10. Most synthetic elements fall into the ——— group of the periodic table.
    (lanthanide, actinide, transition metal)

11. Nuclear reactions produce ———.
    (superheavy elements, salts)

CONCEPT & SKILLS REVIEW

ORGANIZATION OF THE PERIODIC TABLE

1. How do chemists use the periodic law to classify elements?

2. Yttrium, which follows strontium in the periodic table, has an atomic number one greater than strontium. Barium is 18 atomic numbers after strontium, but it falls directly beneath it in the periodic table. Does strontium share more properties with yttrium or barium? Explain your answer.

3. What determines the vertical arrangement of the periodic table?

4. What determines the horizontal arrangement of the periodic table?

5. All halogens are highly reactive. What causes this similarity among the halogens?

6. What property do the noble gases share? How does this property relate to the electron configuration of the noble gases?

7. Why is beryllium placed in Group 2?

8. Use the periodic table to describe the properties of the following elements.
   a. bromine, Br   e. rubidium, Rb
   b. barium, Ba   f. neptunium, Np
   c. xenon, Xe   g. promethium, Pm
   d. tungsten, W

9. Argon differs from both chlorine and potassium by one proton each. Compare the reactivity and electron configurations of these three elements.

10. How do the electron configurations of the transition metals differ from the electron configurations of the metals in Groups 1 and 2?

THE PERIODIC TABLE   **151**

TERM REVIEW

1. group
2. alkaline-earth metals
3. alloy
4. van der Waals
5. actinide
6. noble gas
7. ionization energy
8. conduction band
9. electron affinity
10. nonmetals
11. actinide
12. superheavy elements

CONCEPT & SKILLS REVIEW

1. According to the periodic law, the physical and chemical properties of the elements are periodic functions of their atomic numbers. Chemists use this law to classify elements into groups having similar properties.

2. Barium and strontium are in the same group, which means that they have similar arrangements of outer-level electrons. Therefore, they are likely to be chemically similar, yet both are chemically different from yttrium.

3. Repetition of outer-electron configuration determines the placement of elements in vertical columns.

4. The completion of a stable octet of electrons determines the points at which the elements begin new periods.

5. All halogens are one electron short of having a complete octet of electrons in the outer level.

6. Noble gases do not normally react with other elements. Except for helium, noble gas atoms have a completed octet of electrons in the outer energy level. Thus, they have little tendency to lose or gain electrons. Helium has a completed $1s$ sublevel, which renders it very stable.

7. Beryllium has two electrons in an outer *s* sublevel, as do all other elements in this group.

8. a. Br: nonmetal, reactive, halogen, reacts with metals to form salts

  b. Ba: metal, fairly reactive, alkaline earth metal, loses 2 electrons to form a +2 ion

  c. Xe: nonmetal, noble gas, unreactive

  d. W: transition metal, dense, weakly reactive (Tungsten is in the period with fairly unreactive jewelry metals.)

  e. Rb: alkali metal, more reactive than potassium, reacts by losing an electron to form +1 ions

  f. Np: actinide metal, dense, synthetic, radioactive

  g. Pm: lanthanide metal, moderately reactive, similar to other lanthanides

9. Chlorine and potassium are very reactive elements. Argon is unreactive because its electron configuration ends in $3s^2\, 3p^6$, a stable octet. Chlorine has one less electron than argon, $3s^2\, 3p^5$, so it tends to react by gaining one electron to form a -1 ion. Potassium has one more electron than argon, $3s^2\, 3p^6\, 4s^1$, and the last electron is in a higher energy level. Therefore, potassium reacts by losing this electron to form +1 ions.

10. The outer electrons of Groups 1 and 2 are in *s* orbitals. The transition metals have outer electrons in *d* orbitals in addition to *s* electrons.

11. The outer electrons include electrons in *f* orbitals.

12. Groups 1, 2, and 13 through 18

13. Because hydrogen consists of only one proton and one electron, it exhibits properties not shared by elements in any group, although it is nearest to Group 1 and Group 17 elements.

14. Mendeleev organized elements by atomic weight; the modern table is organized by atomic number. Mendeleev used some symbols that are different from modern symbols.

11. How do the electron configurations of the actinide and lanthanide series differ from the electron configurations of the other transition metals?

12. What groups make up the main-block elements?

13. Why is hydrogen in a family by itself?

14. Compare the modern periodic table to Mendeleev's periodic table in **Figure 4-2.** List the differences between Mendeleev's periodic table and the modern table.

15. Identify the discrepancies in Mendeleev's table that were rectified in Moseley's table.

16. While at an amusement park, you inhale helium from a balloon to make your voice higher pitched. A friend says this practice is dangerous because the helium will react with your blood and produce toxic compounds. Is your friend correct? Explain.

17. a. What is happening to the sodium atom shown in the diagram below?

  b. How will the electron configuration of the atom change when the atom becomes an ion?

  c. Could a potassium atom behave in a similar way? Explain.

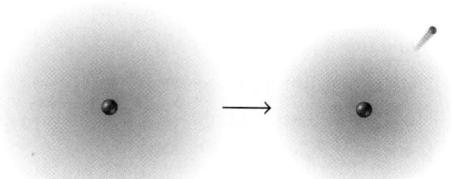

18. In Mendeleev's periodic table, he placed Be, Mg, Zn, and Cd in one group and Ca, Sr, Ba, and Pb in another group. Look at the electron configurations of these elements, and explain why he placed the elements in this order.

19. Why would you never expect a Ca^+ or Na^{2+} ion to exist?

20. Calcium ions, Ca^{2+}, play an important role in muscle relaxation. Potassium ion, K^+, is also found in your body. Why is there no danger of K^+ and Ca^{2+} reacting with each other?

21. You read a science fiction story about an alien race of silicon-based life-forms. Use information from the periodic table to hypothesize why the author chose silicon over other elements. **(Hint: Life on Earth is carbon-based.)**

PROPERTIES OF METALS

22. Explain why metals are good conductors of electricity.

23. Why is a nonmetal, carbon, added to iron to make nails?

24. Describe how atoms are arranged in a metal.

25. As more shells are added to atoms, the energies of the outer orbitals get closer and closer. Use this to explain why C is nonmetal, but Pb is a metal.

26. Use Figure 4-27 to explain why the reactivity of alkali metals increases down the group.

27. Compare the energy gaps between the conduction band and the outermost electrons in metals and nonmetals.

28. Why is metallic nature not considered an innate property of metals?

29. What evidence do we have that atoms are spherical in shape?

30. Describe the similarities and differences between a face-centered cubic metal crystal and a hexagonal close-packed metal crystal.

31. How will a room-temperature superconductor affect our lives?

PERIODIC TRENDS

32. Why don't scientists define atomic radius as the radius of a single electron cloud?

33. What periodic trends occur for atomic radius?

34. Use an analogy of a football team's offensive line protecting the quarterback to explain the shielding effect of electrons.

35. How does the periodic trend in atomic radius relate to the addition of electrons?

36. Define ionization energy and electron affinity.

37. a. What periodic trends exist for ionization energy?
b. How does this trend relate to different energy levels?

38. What happens to electron affinity values as you move left to right across a period? Explain why these values change as they do.

39. Identify which trends in the diagrams below describe atomic radius and ionization energy.

40. How do the trends in atomic radius compare with the trends in ionization energy?

41. Name three periodic trends you encounter in your life.

42. A scientist may measure the radius of an atom five different times and get five different results. His method is correct, and his instrumentation is working properly. Explain the results.

CREATING THE ELEMENTS

43. When two elements are involved in a nuclear reaction, a different element is created. How does this happen?

44. How does the nuclear fusion process create energy?

45. Cite two reasons why hydrogen is involved in the most common nuclear fusion reaction.

46. Compare the two charts below. Why are the most abundant elements in Earth's crust not the most abundant in the universe? Explain how the elements in stars formed the elements in Earth's crust.

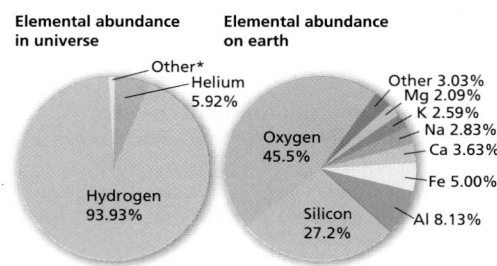

*Oxygen 0.075%, carbon 0.047%, nitrogen 0.0094%, neon 0.0087%, magnesium 0.0042%, silicon 0.0030%, other 0.0027%

47. Irene Joliot Curie created the first artificial radioactive isotope, phosphorus-30, in 1934 when she bombarded aluminum-27, a shiny metal with conductive properties, with helium nuclei. The resulting product was a nonmetal with completely different properties. What caused the change in properties?

48. Years ago, many people dreamed of transforming lead, an abundant metal, into gold, a rare and highly prized metal. Could gold be made from lead using the nuclear processes described in this chapter?

49. Why are technetium, promethium, and neptunium considered naturally occurring elements even though they are not found on Earth?

15. The elements potassium, nickel, protactinium, and iodine fall in different places in Mendeleev's table because their atomic weights are less than those of the preceding elements.

16. No, the friend is incorrect. Helium is a noble gas and reacts with no known substance.

17. a. The atom is losing an electron.
b. It will change from $1s^2 2s^2 2p^6 3s^1$ to $1s^2 2s^2 2p^6$.
c. A potassium atom would behave in the same way because its outer electron configuration is like sodium's.

18. After reviewing their electron configurations, Mendeleev placed elements Be, Mg, Zn, and Cd in one group because he found the outer electrons for each element occupied orbitals of the next energy level. The same held true for Ca, Sr, Ba, and Pb.

19. Calcium atoms have two electrons in an *s* orbital in the outer level. It is unlikely that calcium would lose only one electron because doing so does not achieve a noble gas configuration. Sodium achieves a noble gas configuration by losing one electron. Therefore, it is unlikely to lose two electrons.

20. Both ions have stable octets in the outer energy level and two cations will not react with each other.

21. Silicon is directly beneath carbon in the periodic table, so it is chemically similar to carbon. If life is based on carbon, it is plausible that another form of life could be based on silicon.

22. In order for conduction to occur, electrons must be excited into conduction bands. In metals, the energy of the conduction bands is very near the energy of the outer electrons of the atom.

23. Pure iron is too soft for the manufacture of nails. Adding carbon produces a harder alloy.

24. Atoms of metals are arranged in an orderly, repeating arrangement.

25. As the energies of the outer orbitals get closer and closer, electrons in the higher orbitals are free to move about and form the conduction band. Since lead has more shells, its outer orbitals are closer together. Carbon has fewer shells, so its outer orbitals are farther apart. The electrons in lead are free to move about which makes lead a good conductor. This property is distinctive to metals. Since carbon's shells are farther apart, the electrons cannot move as easily between orbitals. This makes carbon a nonconductor, a property distinctive of nonmetals.

26. The ionization energy from the alkali metals decrease down a group. This means it takes less energy to remove the outer electrons for this group of metals. When alkali metals lose their outer electron they achieve the stable electron configuration of the preceding noble gas which makes them reactive.

27. There is little or no energy difference between the outer orbitals of a metal atom and the conduction band. In nonmetals, there is a large difference in energy.

28. Metallic nature depends on temperature and pressure. Some nonmetals can be changed to a metallic form by lowering the temperature and applying pressure.

29. The symbols are written to represent a monatomic element.

30 In a face-centered cubic structure, the atoms in the third layer are opposite the spaces in the first layer. In a hexagonal close-packed metal crystal, the atoms in the third layer are directly opposite the atoms in the first layer.

31. Answers may vary. The use of electrical energy would become much more efficient. We could ride in trains or automobiles that are levitated by powerful magnets. Magnetic bearings would eliminate much energy loss due to friction.

Answers continue on page 155B.

50. Why must a synchrotron be used to create a superheavy element?

51. How could the transmutation of copper-65 to zinc-65 be performed?

LINKING CHAPTERS

1. Theme: Classification and trends
Explain the nature of the observations that Dmitri Mendeleev used to construct his periodic table.

2. Electron configuration and quantum numbers
   a. How does the electron configuration of alkali metals differ from that of the halogens?
   b. What quantum numbers are the same for the last electron in the alkaline-earth metals?
   c. What quantum numbers are the same for the last electron in all noble gases?

3. Theme: Classification and trends
   a. What trends were first used to classify the elements?
   b. What trends were discovered after the elements were classified in the periodic table?

4. Mixtures and compounds
How would you prove that an alloy is a mixture and not a compound?

ALTERNATIVE ASSESSMENTS

Performance assessment

1. Your teacher will give you an index card that identifies the ionization energy and electron affinity of an element. Identify the element by analyzing these periodic trends.

2. You are given a sample of an unknown element. Design a set of procedures that you could use to determine if the unknown is a metal, a nonmetal, or a metalloid. Organize your procedures in the form of a flow chart like the one for classifying matter that is found in Chapter 2.

3. Design an experiment to show that the conductivity of a metal increases as the temperature decreases and decreases as the temperature increases. Test various metals to compare their conductivities at different temperatures.

Portfolio projects

1. Cooperative group project
Construct your own periodic table, or obtain one of the posters available that show related objects in a periodic arrangement, like vegetables or fruits. Describe the organization of the table and the trends it exemplifies. Use this table to make predictions about your subject matter.

2. Chemistry and you
In many labeled foods, the mineral content is stated in terms of the mass of the element, in a stated quantity of food. Minerals are essential to your health. Examine the product labels of the foods you eat. Determine which elements are represented in your food and what function each element serves in the body. Make a poster of foods that are good sources of the minerals you need.

3. Chemistry and you
Select an alloy. You can choose one that has been mentioned in this chapter, or use the library or the Internet to find a different one. Obtain information on how the alloy is made. Is this process different from the one that was first used to make the alloy? What practical applications does the alloy have?

4.

internet**connect**
TOPIC: Synthetic elements
GO TO: www.scilinks.org
KEYWORD: HW047

Research and communication
The announcement of the creation of a new element is sometimes claimed by two groups of scientists working in different parts of the world. Research the history of one such element. What methods were used to create the element? How are disputes as to which group was actually the first to create the element settled in the scientific community?

1. As you move down the periodic table from carbon through lead, bond radii ——.
   a. generally increase
   b. generally decrease
   c. do not change
   d. vary unpredictably

2. The only element that has some of the properties of both alkali metals and halogens and is considered to be a chemical family by itself is ——.
   a. hydrogen
   b. carbon
   c. uranium
   d. helium

3. As electrons are added to the outer shells of atoms within a period, the atoms generally have ——.
   a. increasing radii, increasing ionization energies, and increasing electron affinity values
   b. decreasing radii, decreasing ionization energies, and decreasing electron affinity values
   c. decreasing radii, increasing ionization energies, and decreasing electron affinity values
   d. decreasing radii, increasing ionization energies, and increasing electron affinity values

4. The periodic law states that ——.
   a. no two electrons with the same spin can be found in the same place in an atom
   b. the physical and chemical properties of the elements are functions of their atomic number
   c. electrons exhibit properties of both particles and waves
   d. the chemical properties of elements can be grouped according to periodicity

5. In the modern periodic table, elements are ordered according to ——.
   a. decreasing atomic mass
   b. Mendeleev's original design
   c. increasing atomic number
   d. when they were discovered

6. The energy it takes to remove an electron from an atom —— as you move left to right across the period, from gold through bismuth.
   a. generally increases
   b. generally decreases
   c. does not change
   d. varies unpredictably

7. Group 17 elements, the halogens, are the most reactive of the nonmetals because they ——.
   a. are the farthest to the right of the periodic table
   b. require only one electron to form the stable configurations of the noble gases
   c. have the largest atomic radii
   d. have the greatest ionization energies

8. If oxygen is more abundant than carbon throughout the universe, then ——.
   a. carbon is more abundant than oxygen in the stars
   b. oxygen is more abundant than carbon in the stars
   c. carbon is not found in the stars
   d. oxygen is not found in the stars

9. Superconductivity of a metal refers to the ——.
   a. increase in electrical conductivity at higher temperatures
   b. decrease in the strength of bonds between metal atoms at lower temperatures
   c. increase in the energy level of the conduction band
   d. loss of all resistance to conductivity at low temperatures

10. —— is created in the center of stars.
    a. Curium
    b. Gold
    c. Einsteinium
    d. Americium

1. a
2. a
3. d
4. b
5. c
6. d
7. b
8. b
9. d
10. b

Answers from page 123

4.

	Symbol	Atomic number	Atomic mass (item 5)	Group and period number (item 7)
a.	Ag	47	107.87	11, 5
b.	Au	79	196.97	11, 6
c.	Hg	80	200.59	12, 6
d.	Cu	29	63.55	11, 4
e.	Zn	30	65.39	12, 4
f.	Pt	78	195.08	10, 6
g.	Pd	46	106.42	10, 5
h.	Rn	86	222.02	18, 6
i.	Ra	88	226.02	2, 7

18. Mendeleev left gaps in his periodic table in order to place elements in groups having similar properties. He predicted that these gaps would be filled by elements yet to be discovered.

19. All of the actinides are radioactive elements. The radioactivity is due to the structures of their nuclei.

20. Ag, 962°C; Au, 1064°C; Hg, –38.7°C; Cu, 1083°C

21. **a.** elements that had not been discovered

b. Commas are used as decimal points in some countries.

Answers from page 142

18. The outer electron configuration of the alkaline earth metals consists of a filled *s* orbital. Therefore, they have little tendency to add an electron, which would have to enter a *p* orbital. The noble gases have completed sets of both *s* and *p* orbitals in their outer levels and likewise have little tendency to add another electron.

19. Mercury's outermost electrons consist of filled *s* and filled *d* sublevels. Therefore, mercury atoms have a low attraction for electrons of neighboring mercury atoms, so the melting and boiling points are low.

Answers from page 154

32. An electron cloud has no definite boundary, so such a radius is impossible to measure.

33. Atomic radii decrease from left to right across a period and increase from top to bottom down a group.

34. The offensive line screens the quarterback from attack by the defensive players. In a similar way, underlying levels of electrons screen the outer electrons from the attractive force of the nucleus.

35. As electrons are added across a period, they are entering orbitals at about the same distance from the nucleus. The increasing nuclear charge pulls those electrons closer, making the atoms progressively smaller across a period.

36. Ionization energy is the energy input required to remove an electron from an atom. Electron affinity is the energy released when an electron is added to an atom.

37. a. Ionization energies increase from left to right across a period and decrease from top to bottom down a group.

b. Across a period, electrons are added to the same energy level while nuclear charge, and hence nuclear attraction, is increasing. Moving down a group, electrons are in successively higher energy levels. Underlying levels increasingly shield outer electrons, so outer electrons become easier to remove.

38. Electron affinity generally increases across a period because nuclear charge increases and attracts outside electrons more strongly. Because electrons are being added to the same energy level, shielding does not increase.

39. Diagram **b** describes the trends in atomic radius. Diagram **a** describes the trends in ionization energy.

40. An increase in atomic radius relates to a decrease in ionization energy because outer electrons become more loosely held.

41. Answers may vary but could include the pattern of seasons, the repeating school year, the arrival of weekends, or the pattern of daily meals.

42. One possibility is that the atom being measured is bonded to different atoms in each trial.

43. The number of protons in the nucleus either decreases or increases.

44. The mass of the fused nucleus is slightly less than the mass of the nuclei that created it. This mass is converted to energy during fusion. Energy cannot be created from nothing.

45. The most common fusion reaction takes place in stars and involves the fusion of hydrogen to form helium.

46. The Earth is made of matter that was rejected from stars as they cycled through generations. New stars are formed from hydrogen. Elements in stars undergo fusion to form successively heavier elements.

47. Phosphorus-30 was produced by reactions that add two protons to the aluminum nucleus. The atom also acquires two more electrons to balance the protons. The atom has the electron configuration of phosphorus, and electron configurations determine chemical and many physical properties.

48. Although the conversion of gold is possible, it is not possible by the processes discussed here, which involve increasing the atomic number of atoms. Gold has a smaller atomic number than lead.

49. Both elements can be detected elsewhere in the universe.

50. Only a synchrotron can accelerate nuclei to energies high enough to result in fusion.

51. One possibility is to cause one of the neutrons of copper-68 to change to a proton by the emission of an electron. This change does, in fact, occur naturally in the decay of copper-68, a radioactive isotope.

LINKING CHAPTERS

1. Mendeleev organized the elements based on observations of properties that repeated regularly within the elements.

2. a. All alkali metals have one s electron in the outer energy level. Halogens have two s electrons and five p electrons in the outer level.
   b. The last electron in all alkaline-earth metals has $l = s$ and the same m_L number because there is only one orbital in an s sublevel.
   c. The last electron in noble gas atoms has $l = p$, except for helium, in which $l = s$.

3. a. reactivity and weight
   b. electron configuration, atomic size, ionization energy, electron affinity, and other factors not covered in this chapter

4. You would find a way to separate it into its components.

ALTERNATIVE ASSESSMENTS

Performance assessment

1. Check students' work by having them write down the handbook data that they used to identify the elements.

2. Designs should include methods for determining electrical conductivity, density, and heat conduction.

3. Designs should include methods for varying and controlling the temperature of the conductor as well as measuring the current in amperes that is conducted at a constant voltage. An alternative method is to determine the change in voltage that will produce the same current in all trials.

Portfolio projects

1. Some of the superheavy elements fit this description, particularly those from atomic numbers 104 to 109. Students should also take note of the controversies over naming these elements.

2. Answers will vary. Students' explanations of their tables should reflect a periodic arrangement and discernible trends. Possible subjects are sports cards, music recordings, types of clothing, cars, and similar items.

3. Answers will vary. Students' work should demonstrate a comprehensive listing of the minerals found in foods and their functions.

4. There are a great number of alloys, especially of iron, aluminum, and magnesium. Some of the more interesting ones are used in aerospace applications. Even lithium is used in some lightweight, high-strength magnesium alloys. Students should discuss the applications for the alloys they choose.

Ionic Compounds

CLASSROOM RESOURCES

SECTIONS	TEACHER'S DEMONSTRATIONS	PROBLEM SOLVING ■ *Text* ◆ *ChemFile Mini-Guide*	LABORATORIES ■ *Text* ◆ *ChemFile Manuals: A, B, C, D*
5-1 **How are ions different from atoms?** Section Review, p.164	**Demo 1** Achieving a Stable Octet, p. 158	■ **How To** Write formulas for binary compounds, p. 164	◆ **B5** Reactivity of Halide Ions
5-2 **What holds a salt together?** Section Review, p. 175	**Demo 2** Electrical Conduction in Ionic Compounds, p. 174		■ **QuickLab** Can You Tell a Crystal by Its Shape?, p. 168 ◆ **B7** Conductivity as an Indicator of Bond Type
5-3 **What are polyatomic ions?** Section Review, p. 184	**Demo 3** Loss of Water from a Hydrate, p. 182	■ **How To** Write the name of a compound containing a polyatomic ion, p. 178 ■ **How To** Write the formula for a compound containing a polyatomic ion, p. 179 ■ **How To** Assign oxidation numbers to atoms in polyatomic ions, p. 181	■ **Exp. A5** Percentage Composition of a Hydrate, p. 730 ■ **Inv. A5** Hydrates—Gypsum and Plaster of Paris, p. 734 ◆ **B8** Tests for Iron(II) and Iron(III)

TECHNOLOGY RESOURCES

See page 156 for a listing of Internet resources.

SECTIONS	VIDEOS/VIDEODISC *Holt Chemistry Videodisc* CNN *Science* PRESENTS *in the NEWS*	CHEMFILE CD-ROMS ● *Teaching Resources* ◆ *Interactive Tutor*	OVERHEADS ● *Color Transparencies* ◆ *Transparency Masters*
5-1	Sodium Chloride Synthesis Cation Formation: Magnesium Anion Formation: Fluoride CNN Segment 14 PRESENTS Harvesting Salt	● Occupational Application: Water-Quality Manager ◆ **Module 4:** Chemical Bonding **Topic:** Ionic Bonding	
5-2	Crystal Lattice Formation: Sodium Chloride	◆ **Module 4:** Chemical Bonding **Topic:** Ionic Bonding	● **33** NaCl and CsCl Crystal Lattices
5-3	Ammonium Ion Rotation Phosphate Anion Rotation		

ASSESSMENT RESOURCES

ALTERNATIVE ASSESSMENTS	CHAPTER TESTING	SCORING RUBRICS *Holt ChemFile Teaching Resources CD-ROM*

Student Text
  Performance assessment, p. 190
  Portfolio projects 1–5, p. 190
 	
Teacher's Edition
  Group Strategies, pp. 160, 163, 172
  Lattice Structures and Formulas, p. 169
  Modeling Formulas, p. 177
 	
Study Guide
  Sections 5-1 to 5-3
	Student Text
	  Test Preparation, p. 191
	
	Holt Chemistry: Visualizing Matter Chapter 5 Test (blackline masters)
	
	Holt ChemFile Test Generator for Macintosh and Windows
		Lab Work
		  Performance-Tasks Scoring Rubric
		  Assessment for Structured Inquiry
		  Assessment for Open-Ended Inquiry
		
		Portfolio Projects
		  Evaluating Concept Maps
		  Assessing Portfolios
		  Portfolio Assignment Student Evaluation Form

CHAPTER
5

Establishing Prior Knowledge

Make sure students understand the following concepts.

▶ Chapter 3: atomic structure electron configurations
▶ Chapter 4: the relationship between electron configurations and groups on the periodic table

CHAPTER
5

Ionic Compounds

 READING STRATEGY

Assimilating Knowledge

Before students read this chapter, have them each write a short list of all the things they already know (or think they know) about ions, the formation of ions from atoms, and how ions might form compounds. When students have finished their list, work with them to form a group list on the board or on an overhead projector. Then have students list the things they might want to know about the formation, structure, and properties of ionic compounds. If students have trouble coming up with questions, offer the following suggestions to get them on track:

▶ How might positive and negative ions form?
▶ Why would atoms tend to become ions?
▶ If a compound is made of ions, what holds it together?
▶ Could a group of atoms form a single ion?

ABOUT THE ILLUSTRATION

The photograph shows the formation of sodium acetate crystals from a supersaturated solution. Sodium acetate is an *ionic compound* that includes a *polyatomic ion*. Both of these concepts are covered in this chapter.

 internet connect

Holt Chemistry: Visualizing Matter

 On-Line Resources
go.hrw.com
Visit the HRW Web site for a variety of resources related to this chapter. Just type in the keyword HW0 Chapt5.

SCI LINKS
NSTA

National Science Teachers Association
On-Line Resources: www.scilinks.org
The following Scilinks Internet resources can be found in the student text for this chapter:

Page 162
TOPIC: Salt formation
KEYWORD: HW051

Page 165
TOPIC: Sodium
KEYWORD: HW052

Page 173
TOPIC: Salt properties
KEYWORD: HW053

Page 174
TOPIC: Nonconductors
KEYWORD: HW054

Page 177
TOPIC: Compounds/ polyatomic ions
KEYWORD: HW055

Page 190
TOPIC: Salt substitutes
KEYWORD: HW056

IONS IN THE YEARBOOK

Click. The photography schedule is almost impossible: shooting 25 different clubs and teams in just two days. Students are everywhere, dressed in robes and uniforms. It's time for yearbook photos! One of the student photographers takes charge. She has assorted gadgets hanging from her neck and shoulder: a camera loaded with black-and-white film, a camera loaded with color film, light meters, and a bag of special lenses. "Move in just a little, please . . . that's better, thanks. You in the back, . . . yes, you in the cowboy hat . . . dark glasses off, please. Are you all ready?. . . smile." *Click.* "One more, just in case, please." *Click.* "That's good."

The student photographers capture the year on film, but film-processing technicians make those photos come alive. Film processing requires quite a bit of knowledge about chemistry.

Photographic film is a sheet of clear plastic coated with a very thin layer of *emulsion.* Spread throughout the emulsion are many tiny crystals of light-sensitive silver salts. Silver iodide, AgI, is more light sensitive than silver bromide, AgBr, which in turn is more sensitive than silver chloride, AgCl. Most photographic film contains AgBr and a small amount of AgI. These silver salts are ionic compounds consisting of silver ions, Ag^+, and a halogen ion, either I^-, Br^-, or Cl^-.

With the click of the shutter, light falls for a very brief instant of time on the photographic film. When this happens, the film is said to be *exposed.* The changes brought about by exposure are subtle indeed— because you can't see any change at all. However, some of the salt crystals now have silver atoms, Ag, on their edges. There are many such atom-edged crystals where the light was strongest. There are few where the light was dim, and there are none where no light fell. At this stage, the film has what is called a *latent image.*

The film is developed using several steps that all involve reactions with ions. Working in a room dimly lit by red light, film technicians add chemicals called *stoppers* and *fixers* to control the reactions started by light. In this chapter you will learn some of the basic concepts that underlie the photographic process and will find out how ions make their way into the yearbook.

CHAPTER LINKS

How do the properties of silver atoms differ from those of silver ions?

How can exposure to light change the chemical structure of a compound?

Although light falls on the entire salt crystal, why do silver atoms form only at the edges of the crystal?

STORY BACKGROUND

This story refers primarily to black-and-white photography. Light photons striking silver halide crystals excite electrons. When Ag^+ ions acquire these excited electrons and are reduced to silver metal atoms, chemists say that the silver halide crystal has become activated. When light striking the emulsion is brighter, more crystals are activated. Likewise, when the silver halide emulsion is exposed to light for a longer time, more crystals are activated. Thus, the photographer can control the exposure of the film in two ways—by adjusting the aperture to control the intensity of light striking the film, or by changing the shutter speed to control the length of exposure. The developer solution contains a reducing agent that changes these activated crystals to Ag metal. The resulting negative is darker where more silver has been produced. Note that the degree of darkness is related more to the number of crystals that were activated than to the degree of activation.

CONCEPT PREVIEW

Section 5-1

Atoms lose or gain electrons to become stable, simple ions
- cations and anions
- noble-gas configuration

Naming and writing formulas for binary ionic compounds
- use of subscripts in formulas

Section 5-2

Ions bond to form compounds
- characteristics of the ionic bond
- bond formation and energy

Nature of ionic crystals
- coulombic force
- crystal lattice
- unit cell
- lattice energy

Properties of ionic compounds
- melting and boiling points
- electrical conduction
- hardness and brittleness

Section 5-3

Polyatomic ions
- naming polyatomic ions
- writing and interpreting formulas containing polyatomic ions
- rules for assigning oxidation numbers
- silicates and hydrates
- anhydrous substances

SECTION 5-1

LESSON WARM-UP

Electron Transfers Have students review the properties and atomic structures of the noble gas (Group 18) elements. Ask them what the electron configurations of these elements have in common. Use magnets on the chalkboard to represent outer electrons and to demonstrate the electron transfers shown in Figures 5-1 and 5-2.

You can also model atoms, ions, and ionic compounds on an overhead projector. Use 10 cm disks cut from transparency film to represent the nuclei of atoms. Mark the center of each disk with the number of p^+ and n for each element you want to model. Using different colors to represent nuclei of different elements will help students identify the atom. Represent electrons with 6 mm disks marked with a horizontal line to represent negative charge. Arrange these disks to represent atoms and ions in the same way as those shown in Figure 5-1 and Figure 5-2.

How are ions different from atoms?

OBJECTIVES

▶ *Identify* ions that are isoelectronic with the noble gases.

▶ *Explain* why the properties of ions differ from the properties of their parent atoms.

▶ *Relate* an atom's tendency to form an ion to the element's position in the periodic table and to the octet rule.

▶ *Describe* the consequences of the electroneutrality principle.

▶ *Name* cations, anions, and salts.

▶ *Write* formulas for binary compounds.

Simple ions

ion
an atom or group of atoms that has an electric charge because it has lost or gained electrons

Think of an **ion** as an atom that has gained or lost one or more electrons. An ion is like an atom, but the number of electrons does not equal the number of protons, so it has a net electric charge. When a sodium atom loses its outermost electron, it becomes a positively charged ion that we call a *sodium ion*.

$$[Na] = 1s^2 2s^2 2p^6 3s^1$$
$$[Na^+] = 1s^2 2s^2 2p^6$$

The following equation shows the formation of a sodium ion from a sodium atom.

$$Na \longrightarrow Na^+ + e^-$$

▼ **FIGURE 5-1**

The sodium ion has a net +1 charge and is written as Na⁺.

Look at **Figure 5-1.** How does a sodium ion compare with a sodium atom? Are the properties the same? Even though the name of the element, sodium, is the same, a sodium atom behaves very differently from a

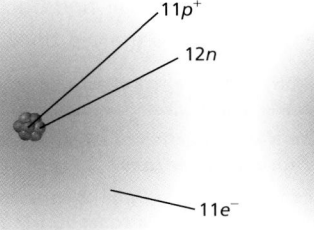

Sodium atom, Na

a The sodium ion has 10 electrons instead of 11.

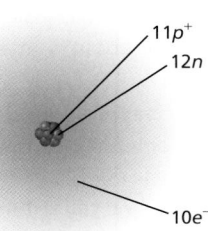

Sodium ion, Na⁺

b The electron configuration of the sodium ion is the same . . .

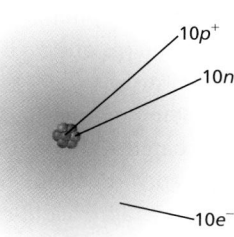

Neon atom, Ne

c . . . as that of a neon atom.

158   CHAPTER 5

DEMONSTRATION 1

Achieving a Stable Octet

Approximate time: 10 minutes

Place a Petri dish containing 10 mL of 1 M HCl solution on an overhead projector. Cut a 2 cm strip of magnesium ribbon and drop it into the acid solution. Point out that the vigorous reaction occurs as a result of magnesium atoms transferring their two outer-level electrons to achieve the electron configuration of neon. In this case, the electrons are transferred to H^+ ions existing as $H_3O^+(aq)$ to produce $H_2(g)$. Reinforce the idea of achieving stability by igniting a similar piece of Mg ribbon. Point out to students that the obvious energy release occurs as Mg gives up electrons to oxygen atoms from the air, and both achieve stable octets to form Mg^{2+} and O^{2-} ions.

sodium ion. Using the same name for both the atom and ion signifies that the nucleus is unchanged. The ion still has 11 protons and 12 neutrons, like the atom. But chemical properties depend on the number of electrons and their configuration. A sodium ion has only 10 electrons, and they are configured just like the electrons in a neon atom.

$$[Ne] = 1s^2 2s^2 2p^6$$

Does that mean that a sodium ion is a neon atom? Certainly not. Does it mean that the sodium ion has properties similar to those of the neon atom? Well, not quite; but the chemical properties of a sodium ion are certainly closer to those of a neon atom than they are to a sodium atom. The differences arise because the sodium ion has a positive charge.

Changes in electron arrangements change chemical properties

Recall that neon is one of the noble gases and, as such, is virtually inert. It is therefore not surprising that the sodium ion, Na^+, with the same electron structure is very stable and has no chemical properties other than those resulting from its positive charge and its ability to fill space.

Ions with a positive charge are known as **cations;** they have more protons than electrons. Negatively charged ions, such as the Cl^- ion, are called **anions,** and they have more electrons than protons, as shown in **Figure 5-2.** The Cl^- ion also has a noble-gas configuration. It matches that of the argon atom, but it carries a net negative charge acquired by the addition of a single electron to the chlorine atom.

$$[Cl^-] = 1s^2 2s^2 2p^6 3s^2 3p^6 = [Ar]$$
$$[Cl] = 1s^2 2s^2 2p^6 3s^2 3p^5$$

The following equation shows the formation of the chlorine ion from the chlorine atom.

$$Cl + e^- \longrightarrow Cl^-$$

Collections of cations are never found without a similar number of anions (or electrons) nearby to effectively neutralize the charges. The concept of having equal numbers of opposite charges is called **electroneutrality.**

cation
an ion that has a positive charge

anion
an ion that has a negative charge

electroneutrality
the condition of having equal numbers of positive and negative charges

FIGURE 5-2 ▼

Contrast this model for a chloride ion with the model for a sodium ion in Figure 5-1.

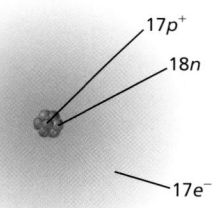

Chlorine atom, Cl

17p$^+$
18n
17e$^-$

a The chlorine atom forms a stable ion by gaining an electron.

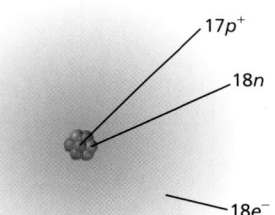

Chloride ion, Cl$^-$

17p$^+$
18n
18e$^-$

b The chloride ion, Cl$^-$, . . .

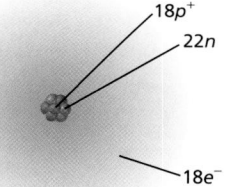

Argon atom, Ar

18p$^+$
22n
18e$^-$

c . . . has the same electron configuration as an argon atom.

IONIC COMPOUNDS 159

VISUAL STRATEGY

Figure 5-1 and Figure 5-2 Use these figures to help students understand how atoms can achieve noble gas structures by either losing or gaining electrons. Be sure students recognize that the atoms do not become noble gases, even though the electron configurations are the same. Ask students to account for the positive charge on one ion and the negative charge on the other.

TEACHING TIP

Vocabulary Strategy The terms *cation* and *anion* are derived from the names of the electrodes of an electrochemical cell, cathode and anode. The anode has a positive charge, and negative ions are attracted to it. Thus, they are called *anions.* The cathode has a negative charge and attracts ions of positive charge—*cations.*

COMMON MISCONCEPTION

Students are sometimes confused by how the sign of an ion's charge is related to the loss and gain of electrons. Remind them that the *gain* of an electron means the gain of a negative charge, producing a negatively charged ion. Conversely, the *loss* of an electron means the loss of a negative charge, leaving a positively charged ion behind.

CHEMISTRY INTERACTIVE TUTOR•

Module 4: Chemical Bonding
Topic: Ionic Bonding
This engaging tutorial reviews and reinforces ion formation and stability through modeling and guided practice.

Safety
Wear safety goggles, gloves, and a laboratory apron while handling chemicals. Caution students not to look directly at the burning magnesium ribbon. Immediately wipe up any spatters from the Petri dish.

Disposal
Neutralize the solution in the Petri dish with 1 M NaOH, and pour it down the drain. Place the dry residue from the burning of Mg into the trash.

Many simple ions have a noble-gas configuration

Sodium and chlorine are not the only atoms that form ions with an electron configuration identical to that of a noble gas. The sulfur atom can acquire two extra electrons and become an anion with the same configuration as an argon atom.

$$[S] = 1s^2 2s^2 2p^6 3s^2 3p^4 \quad (16e^-, 16p^+)$$
$$[S^{2-}] = 1s^2 2s^2 2p^6 3s^2 3p^6 \quad (18e^-, 16p^+)$$
$$[Ar] = 1s^2 2s^2 2p^6 3s^2 3p^6 \quad (18e^-, 18p^+)$$

In fact, most of the elements that are near the noble gases in the periodic table have atoms that gain electrons and thereby come to share the stable electron configuration of a noble gas. **Table 5-1** lists the electron configurations of some ions that match the configurations of noble gases. Atoms and ions with the same configuration are said to be **isoelectronic** with each other. The ions of elements in Groups 15–17 have configurations that are isoelectronic with noble gases in the same period. Ions of elements in Groups 1, 2, 3, and Al^{3+} have configurations that are isoelectronic with noble gases in the previous period. Like the

isoelectronic
having the same electron configuration as another atom

TABLE 5-1 Some Ions with Noble-Gas Configurations							Group 18 Noble Gases
							Helium **He** $1s^2$
Group 1	Group 2	Group 3	Group 13	Group 15	Group 16	Group 17	
Li$^+$ $1s^2$	**Be^{2+}** $1s^2$			**N^{3-}** [He]$2s^2 2p^6$	**O^{2-}** [He]$2s^2 2p^6$	**F$^-$** [He]$2s^2 2p^6$	Neon **Ne** [He]$2s^2 2p^6$
Na$^+$ [He]$2s^2 2p^6$	**Mg^{2+}** [He]$2s^2 2p^6$		**Al^{3+}** [He]$2s^2 2p^6$	**P^{3-}** [Ne]$3s^2 3p^6$	**S^{2-}** [Ne]$3s^2 3p^6$	**Cl$^-$** [Ne]$3s^2 3p^6$	Argon **Ar** [Ne]$3s^2 3p^6$
K$^+$ [Ne]$3s^2 3p^6$	**Ca^{2+}** [Ne]$3s^2 3p^6$	**Sc^{3+}** [Ne]$3s^2 3p^6$		**As^{3-}** [Ar]$3d^{10} 4s^2 4p^6$	**Se^{2-}** [Ar]$3d^{10} 4s^2 4p^6$	**Br$^-$** [Ar]$3d^{10} 4s^2 4p^6$	Krypton **Kr** [Ar]$3d^{10} 4s^2 4p^6$
Rb$^+$ [Ar]$3d^{10} 4s^2 4p^6$	**Sr^{2+}** [Ar]$3d^{10} 4s^2 4p^6$	**Y^{3+}** [Ar]$3d^{10} 4s^2 4p^6$			**Te^{2-}** [Kr]$4d^{10} 5s^2 5p^6$	**I$^-$** [Kr]$4d^{10} 5s^2 5p^6$	Xenon **Xe** [Kr]$4d^{10} 5s^2 5p^6$
Cs$^+$ [Kr]$4d^{10} 5s^2 5p^6$	**Ba^{2+}** [Kr]$4d^{10} 5s^2 5p^6$	**La^{3+}** [Kr]$4d^{10} 5s^2 5p^6$					

Ions that are isoelectronic with a noble gas are denoted by the same color. The small table at right shows the periodic table positions of the ions listed in Table 5-1.

ALTERNATIVE ASSESSMENT

Group Strategy

Write the electron configurations of the noble gases on the board as column headings. Divide the class into groups of three students each. Call out an element by name. Have the groups work out the electron configuration for the *ion* of that element and identify the noble gas with which the ion is isoelectronic. Pick a group, and have a student go to the board and write the symbol for the ion (including its charge) under the proper noble gas. Be sure to choose among only those elements listed in Table 5-1. Other elements are unlikely to have ions isoelectronic with noble gases because of the presence of *d* or *f* orbitals.

sodium ion, most of the ions in Table 5-1 are inert, and all of them are colorless.

Perhaps you have noticed that in Table 5-1 the elements that form simple cations are metals and the elements that form simple anions are nonmetals. This conclusion is a general rule that can be understood in terms of the principles discussed in Chapter 4. Atoms of nonmetals can achieve the stable noble-gas configuration by gaining electrons. Losing electrons enables the atoms of some metals to match the electron number of the noble gas in the previous period. The tendency of atoms to match the electron configuration of the s and p orbitals of a noble gas is called the **octet rule.** You will learn more about the octet rule in Chapter 6.

Transition metals form stable ions too

Not all simple ions are isoelectronic with noble-gas atoms. The ions listed in **Table 5-2** do not fit this pattern. They are mostly transition metals from Periods 4, 5, and 6. Notice that apart from Re^-, these ions are all cations. In addition, the lanthanide and actinide elements form cations, mostly with +3 charges, that are not isoelectronic with the noble gases. Notice that some elements form more than one cation.

octet rule

the tendency of atoms of elements to gain or lose electrons so that their outer s and p orbitals are full with eight electrons

COMMON MISCONCEPTION

Students sometimes make the mistake of thinking that all noble gases have "full" outer energy levels. Helium and neon have filled energy levels, but the remainder of the noble gases have unfilled d or f orbitals. For example, argon has a stable octet of $3s^2 3p^6$ in its outer level, and the third level still has ten d-orbitals available. These $3d$ orbitals fill with electrons in the transition elements in the fourth period.

VISUAL STRATEGY

Table 5-2 The octet rule is useful for predicting the ionic charges of only a few elements, mostly among the representative groups. Transition elements and a few others typically can have several different ionic charges because electrons in d orbitals are very close in energy to the s and p valence electrons. As a result, these d electrons sometimes participate in ion formation.

| TABLE 5-2 | Stable Ions Formed by the Transition Elements and Some Other Metals |

Group 4	Group 5	Group 6	Group 7	Group 8	Group 9	Group 10	Group 11	Group 12	Group 13	Group 14
Ti^{2+} Ti^{3+}	V^{2+} V^{3+}	Cr^{2+} Cr^{3+}	Mn^{2+} Mn^{3+}	Fe^{2+} Fe^{3+}	Co^{2+} Co^{3+}	Ni^{2+}	Cu^+ Cu^{2+}	Zn^{2+}	Ga^{2+} Ga^{3+}	Ge^{2+}
		Mo^{3+}	Tc^{2+}			Pd^{2+}	Ag^+ Ag^{2+}	Cd^{2+}	In^+ In^{2+} In^{3+}	Sn^{2+}
Hf^{4+}			Re^-			Pt^{2+} Pt^{4+}	Au^+ Au^{3+}	Hg_2^{2+} Hg^{2+}	Tl^+ Tl^{3+}	Pb^{2+}

The small table at left shows the periodic-table positions of the ions listed in Table 5-2.

ANSWERS

CONCEPT CHECK

1. by gaining electrons; by losing electrons

2. Ca: $1s^2\, 2s^2\, 2p^6\, 3s^2\, 3p^6\, 4s^2$;
Ca^{2+}: $1s^2\, 2s^2\, 2p^6\, 3s^2\, 3p^6$

When calcium forms an ion, it loses two outer 4s electrons to take on the electron configuration of the argon atom.

3. **a.** Kr
   b. Kr
   c. Kr
   d. Ne

4. **a.** Ne
   b. Xe
   c. Kr
   d. Rn

5. P^{3-}, S^{2-}, Cl$^-$, Ar, K$^+$, Ca^{2+}, Sc^{3+}

TEACHING TIP

Order in Formulas Write the following scrambled names on the board: Einstein Albert, Marie Madame Curie, Carver Washington George, and Mendeleev Dmitri. Have students put the names in the correct order. Discuss the importance of correct order and spelling to accurately denote the person. Extend the discussion to include the naming of ionic compounds. Cations and anions can be thought of as the first and last names, respectively, of ionic compounds. Point out that writing the name in the correct order and with correct spelling is important for accurately denoting an ionic compound.

internet connect

SCi LINKS
NSTA

TOPIC: Salt formation
GO TO: www.scilinks.org
KEYWORD: HW051

ionic compound

any chemical compound that is composed of oppositely charged ions

binary ionic compound

an ionic compound that consists of cations of one element and the anions of another element

CONCEPT CHECK

1. How does an atom form a negative ion? a positive ion?

2. Write the electron configuration of a calcium atom. Write the electron configuration of a calcium ion. How do the electron configurations of the calcium atom and the calcium ion differ?

3. **Interpreting Tables** Using Table 5-1, list the noble gas that is isoelectronic with each of the following ions:
   a. Br$^-$ **b.** Sr^{2+} **c.** Rb$^+$ **d.** Al^{3+}

4. **Critical Thinking** Use the periodic table to predict the noble gas that is isoelectronic with each of the following ions:
   a. Fr$^+$ **b.** La^{3+} **c.** Y^{3+} **d.** Ra^{2+}

5. **Interpreting Tables** From Table 5-1, list all of the atoms and ions that are represented by the following electron configuration:
$$1s^2 2s^2 2p^6 3s^2 3p^6$$

Names and formulas for ions and salts

Simple cations borrow their names from the names of the elements. K$^+$ is the potassium ion, and Zn^{2+} is the zinc ion. When an element forms two or more ions, the ions are distinguished by roman numerals to indicate charge. In the case of copper, Cu, the two ions are denoted as follows.

$$\text{Cu}^+ \text{ copper(I) ion} \qquad \text{Cu}^{2+} \text{ copper(II) ion}$$

When we speak about such ions, we say "copper one ion" or "copper two ion." **Figure 5-3** shows compounds formed between copper and chlorine.

Binary ionic compounds are easy to name

The name of a simple anion is also formed from the name of the element, but it ends in *-ide*. Thus, Cl$^-$ is the *chloride* ion, O^{2-} is the *oxide* ion, and P^{3-} is the *phosphide* ion.

The electroneutrality principle means that the total negative charge on the anions equals the total positive charge on the cations. The whole system has no net charge and is therefore neutral. Any chemical compound composed of oppositely charged ions is called an **ionic compound.**

An ionic compound composed of a simple cation and a simple anion is called a **binary ionic compound.** The adjective *binary* indicates that the compound is composed of two elements. Common table salt, NaCl, is composed of equal numbers of sodium ions, Na$^+$, and chloride ions, Cl$^-$.

Naming binary ionic compounds is simple. The name consists of two words: the name of the cation followed by the name of the anion.

NaCl sodium chloride	CuCl$_2$ copper(II) chloride
ZnS zinc sulfide	Mg$_3$N$_2$ magnesium nitride

FIGURE 5-3 ▼

Melting point	430°C	498°C
Density (at 25°C)	4.14 g/cm³	3.39 g/cm³
Percentage composition	64.19% Cu 35.81% Cl	47.26% Cu 52.74% Cl
Other physical properties	white crystalline powder; sparingly soluble in water, practically insoluble in alcohol and acetone	yellow to brown powder that readily absorbs moisture; soluble in water, alcohol, and acetone
Other chemical properties	turns green when exposed to moist air	forms a blue-green dihydrate, $CuCl_2 \cdot 2H_2O$, in moist air

Formulas must indicate the relative numbers of cations and anions. Because both ions carry a single charge, sodium chloride is composed of equal numbers of the ions Na^+ and Cl^-. The formula for sodium chloride is usually written as NaCl, which looks as if it is a molecule of bonded sodium and chlorine atoms. But, because it is composed of ions, a more appropriate formula would be

$$Na^+Cl^-$$

Remember, though, that the formula is not usually written this way. Rather the formula is written simply as NaCl.

The cation in zinc sulfide has a +2 charge and the anion has a –2 charge. Again there is a one-to-one ratio in the salt. Zinc sulfide has the formula ZnS.

Magnesium nitride is another story. The magnesium ion, Mg^{2+}, has two positive charges, and the nitride ion, N^{3-}, has three negative charges. We must combine cations and anions in such a way that there are as many negative charges as there are positive charges. Three Mg^{2+} cations are needed for every two N^{3-} anions to produce an electrically neutral compound. That way, there are six positive charges and six negative charges. **Subscripts** are used to denote the three magnesium ions and two nitride ions. Therefore, the formula for magnesium nitride is Mg_3N_2. The reason for the subscripts becomes clear by writing magnesium nitride as follows, though this is not the standard way of writing this salt's formula.

$$[Mg^{2+}]_3[N^{3-}]_2$$

subscript

a whole number written below and to the right of an element's symbol that is used to denote the number of atoms in a formula

IONIC COMPOUNDS 163

COMMON MISCONCEPTION

Students sometimes believe that the Roman numeral in the name of a compound represents the number of ions of that element present in the formula of that compound. Emphasize that Roman numerals represent the charge on the cation, whereas subscript Arabic numerals represent numbers of ions.

TEACHING TIP

Cation-anion Pairs Reinforce the idea of electroneutrality in the following drill. Make a vertical list of the symbols of six cations on the board, and make a parallel list of the symbols of six anions. The ions should have a variety of charges. Point to a cation-anion pair, and ask students to determine how many of each will produce electroneutrality. You may want to ask students to write or state the correct formula, but the main purpose of the exercise is to help students understand how to construct an electroneutral combination.

DEFINING STANDARDS

The outdated stock system for naming metal ions is not used in this text. Roman numerals are used to designate oxidation numbers for metals such as iron and copper.

ALTERNATIVE ASSESSMENT

Group Strategy

Have students make flashcards for each ion in Table 5-1 and Table 5-2. The name of the ion should be on one side of the card, while the symbol and charge for the ion are on the reverse side of the card. Divide the class into six groups. Have students practice associating the name of the ion with its symbol and charge by quizzing each other with the cards. Then hand each group a slip of paper on which you have written the names of three ionic compounds and the formulas of three others. Reproduce the names and formulas from the slips on the board. Ask a member from each group to write the group's response on the board next to the corresponding item.

HOW TO

ADDITIONAL EXAMPLES

What is the formula for

a. aluminum sulfide?

Ans. Al_2S_3

b. aluminum bromide?

Ans. $AlBr_3$

c. barium iodide?

Ans. BaI_2

d. barium oxide?

Ans. BaO

ANSWERS

SECTION REVIEW

Total recall

1. **a.** gain 1 electron
   b. lose 2 electrons
   c. gain 2 electrons
   d. no change

2. **a.** $CaCl_2$ **e.** CaS
   b. MgO **f.** K_3N
   c. NaI **g.** $CuBr$
   d. MgF_2 **h.** AlN

3. **a.** FeO **e.** $FeCl_3$
   b. Fe_2O_3 **f.** $NbCl_5$
   c. PbO_2 **g.** MnI_2
   d. SnO **h.** Ag_2S

4. **a.** rubidium oxide
   b. barium chloride
   c. iron(III) fluoride
   d. chromium(III) chloride

Critical thinking

5. The configuration of a K atom is $1s^2\,2s^2\,2p^6\,3s^2\,3p^6\,4s^1$. The config-uration of Br is $1s^2\,2s^2\,2p^6\,3s^2\,3p^6\,3d^{10}\,4s^2\,4p^5$. The K atom can acquire a stable octet by losing its one $4s$ electron, becoming a K^+ cation. Br can gain one electron to complete its $4p$ sublevel, which gives it a stable octet of $4s^2\,4p^6$. The resulting stable ion is Br^-. Therefore, the combination of one K^+ and one Br^- produces elec-troneutrality, so the formula of the resulting compound is KBr.

HOW TO   Write formulas for binary ionic compounds

What is the formula for aluminum oxide?

1 **Write the symbol and charges for the cation and anion**
Use Tables 5-1 and 5-2 as guides. Remember that the name of the anion has an *-ide* ending.

▶ symbol for aluminum cation: Al^{3+} ▶ symbol for oxide anion: O^{2-}

2 **Write the symbols for the ions side by side, beginning with the cation**

$$Al^{3+}O^{2-}$$

3 **Find the least common multiple of the ions' charges**

▶ The least common multiple of 3 and 2 is 6. To get a neutral compound, you would need a total of six positive charges and six negative charges.

▶ To get six positive charges, you need two Al^{3+} ions because

$$2 \times 3+ = 6+.$$

▶ To get six negative charges, you need three O^{2-} ions because

$$3 \times 2- = 6-.$$

Therefore, the ratio of Al^{3+} to O^{2-} is 2Al:3O, and the formula is

$$Al_2O_3$$

SECTION REVIEW

Total recall

1. How could each of the following atoms react to achieve a stable octet?
   a. iodine   **c.** sulfur
   b. barium   **d.** krypton

2. Write formulas for the following binary compounds:
   a. calcium chloride
   b. magnesium oxide
   c. sodium iodide
   d. magnesium fluoride
   e. calcium sulfide
   f. potassium nitride
   g. copper(I) bromide
   h. aluminum nitride

3. Write formulas for the following binary compounds:
   a. iron(II) oxide   **e.** iron(III) chloride
   b. iron(III) oxide   **f.** niobium(V) chloride
   c. lead(IV) oxide   **g.** manganese(II) iodide
   d. tin(II) oxide   **h.** silver(I) sulfide

4. Name the following binary ionic com-pounds. If the metal forms more than one cation, be sure to denote the charge.
   a. Rb_2O **c.** FeF_3
   b. $BaCl_2$ **d.** $CrCl_3$

Critical thinking

5. In terms of electron configurations, ex-plain why potassium bromide has the formula KBr instead of K_2Br or KBr_2.

ELEMENT SPOTLIGHT

Na
Sodium
11
22.989 77
[Ne]3s¹

For most people, the daily intake of sodium should not exceed 2400 mg.

WHERE IS IT?

Earth's Crust
2.36% by mass

Seventh most abundant element

Fifth most abundant metal

Sea Water
30.61% of all dissolved materials

1.03% by mass taking the water into account

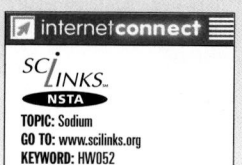

internetconnect

SCLINKS
NSTA

TOPIC: Sodium
GO TO: www.scilinks.org
KEYWORD: HW052

A Brief History

A major nutritional mineral

Sodium plays a major role in the regulation of fluid balance within the body. Most sodium in the diet comes from the use of table salt, NaCl, to season and preserve foods. Sodium is also supplied by a variety of compounds, including sodium carbonate and sodium hydrogen carbonate in baked goods. Sodium benzoate is a preservative in carbonated beverages. Sodium citrate and sodium glutamate are used in packaged foods as flavor additives.

In ancient Rome, salt was so scarce and highly prized that it was used as a form of payment. Today, however, salt is plentiful in the diet, and many people must limit their intake of sodium as a precaution against high blood pressure, heart attacks, and strokes.

Industrial Uses

▶ Common table salt is the most important commercial sodium compound. It is used in ceramic glazes, metallurgy, soap manufacture, home water softeners, highway de-icing, herbicides, fire extinguishers, and resins.

▶ The United States produces about 42.1 million metric tons of sodium chloride per year.

▶ Other important sodium compounds include sodium hydroxide, sodium carbonate, and sodium silicate.

▶ Sodium is used in sodium vapor lamps for lighting highways, stadiums, and industrial complexes.

▶ Liquid sodium is used as a coolant in liquid-metal fast-breeder nuclear reactors.

Nutrition Facts
Serving Size ¾ cup (30g)
Servings Per Container About 14

Amount Per Serving	Corn Crunch	with ½ cup skim milk
Calories	120	160
Calories from Fat	15	20

	% Daily Value**	
Total Fat 2g*	3%	3%
Saturated Fat 0g	0%	0%
Cholesterol 0mg	0%	1%
Sodium 160mg	7%	9%
Potassium 65mg	2%	6%
Total Carbohydrate 25g	8%	10%
Dietary Fiber 3g		
Sugars 3g		
Other Carbohydrate 11g		
Protein 2g		

*Amount in Cereal. A serving of cereal plus skim milk provides 2g fat, less 5mg cholesterol, 220mg sodium, 270mg potassium, 31g carbohydrate (19g sugars) and 6g protein.

**Percent Daily Values are based on a 2,000 calorie diet. Your daily values may be higher or lower depending on your calorie needs:

	Calories	2,000	2,500
Total Fat	Less than	65g	80g
Sat Fat	Less than	20g	25g
Cholesterol	Less than	300mg	300mg
Sodium	Less than	2,400mg	2,400mg
Potassium		3,500mg	3,500mg
Total Carbohydrate		300g	375g
Dietary Fiber		25g	30g

● **1807:** Sir Humphry Davy isolates sodium by the electrolysis of caustic soda (NaOH) and names the metal.

● **1940:** The Food and Nutrition Board of the National Research Council develops the first Recommended Dietary Allowances

1200	1800	1900	2000

● **1251:** The Wieliczka Salt Mine, located in Krakow, Poland, is started. The mine is still in use today.

● **1930:** Sodium vapor lamp is introduced for street lighting.

● **1990:** Nutrition Labeling and Education Act defines a Daily Reference Value for sodium to be listed in the Nutrition Facts portion of a food label.

SECTION 5-1

ELEMENT SPOTLIGHT

In the United States, 32% of salt is mined as rock salt from large underground deposits that were left when ancient seas dried up and were later covered by geological layers. Another 55% comes from the evaporation of brine. The brine is usually obtained by pumping water through underground salt deposits. Mined rock salt contains impurities and is used for purposes such as melting ice. Table salt is produced by dissolving the mined salt, purifying the solution, and recrystallizing the salt in a way that produces small crystals.

DID YOU KNOW?

Table salt as it is usually sold is not pure NaCl. It usually contains small amounts of finely divided insoluble substances such as silicates or complex salts of aluminum. Particles of these materials stick to the cubic NaCl crystals and keep them from clumping together in high humidity. In addition, much table salt is *iodized* and contains small amounts of KI, which provides dietary iodine for proper thyroid function. For these reasons, NaCl solutions made with table salt are cloudy and generally are not suitable for use in the chemistry laboratory.

IONIC COMPOUNDS   165

What holds a salt together?

OBJECTIVES

▸ **Describe** the nature of ionic bonding.

▸ **Explain** what is meant by a crystal structure, and distinguish between the structures of NaCl and CsCl.

▸ **Explain** the energy changes that occur in the formation of a salt.

▸ **Summarize** the properties of binary ionic compounds.

Ionic bonding

In the previous section it was explained that simple cations are atoms of metallic elements from which one or more electrons have been removed. Likewise, simple anions are formed by adding one or more electrons to the atoms of nonmetallic elements. You also learned that ionic compounds are cations and anions combined in small whole-number proportions to produce a state of electroneutrality. But why do elements lose or gain electrons and then come together to form a compound? Let's explore this process using a familiar example.

Sodium is a reactive Group 1 metal. Chlorine, a reactive Group 17 nonmetal, is a poisonous yellowish green gas that consists of molecules with two chlorine atoms bonded together. When the two elements are placed together, a violent exothermic reaction occurs, as shown in **Figure 5-4.** The white residue, a compound formed from two dangerous el-

▼ **FIGURE 5-4**

a When a small piece of sodium, a very reactive metal, is lowered into a flask filled with the poisonous gas chlorine, a violent reaction occurs, forming a white solid.

b The solid crystals that form are sodium chloride, NaCl, a common compound used as a flavor enhancer.

c Using a technique called X-ray diffraction, chemists have collected data that can be used to build a model of a sodium chloride crystal.

Cl^-

Na^+

ements, is something you probably eat every day—table salt. Chemists call it *sodium chloride* instead of salt because the word *salt* can be used to describe any one of thousands of different compounds. Yet all binary salts have something in common; they consist of ions and therefore share certain properties.

All ionic compounds are electrically neutral. They are made of cations and anions combined in a simple whole-number ratio. Sodium chloride consists of white cube-shaped crystals that are hard and brittle. Figure 5-4b is a photograph of sodium chloride taken with a high-powered microscope. Because the crystal is strong and rigid, sodium chloride must be heated to a high temperature of 801°C (1074 K) before it melts. Some force is holding the ions tightly together. Chemists use the word *bond* to describe a force that holds atoms or ions together. There are several kinds of bonds. You studied the metallic bond in Chapter 4 and will learn about the covalent bond in Chapter 6. The **ionic bond** holds salts and other ionic compounds together.

The crystal structures of salts depend on the sizes of the ions

All salts are held together by ionic bonds. The force of attraction between the +1 charge on a sodium ion and the −1 charge on a chloride ion creates the ionic bond in sodium chloride. The structure of salts shows that the attraction between ions extends beyond a single cation and a single anion. This attraction is so far-reaching that many sodium and chloride ions are pulled together into a tightly packed structure. The tight packing of the ions causes common salt to have a distinctive crystal arrangement—the one shown in **Figure 5-5.**

ionic bond

the coulombic force of attraction between ions of opposite charge

FIGURE 5-5 ▼

This diagram models the arrangement of ions in a sodium chloride crystal.

a The ions are actually in contact with each other, as in Figure 5-4; here they are shown separated so that you can see their relative positions.

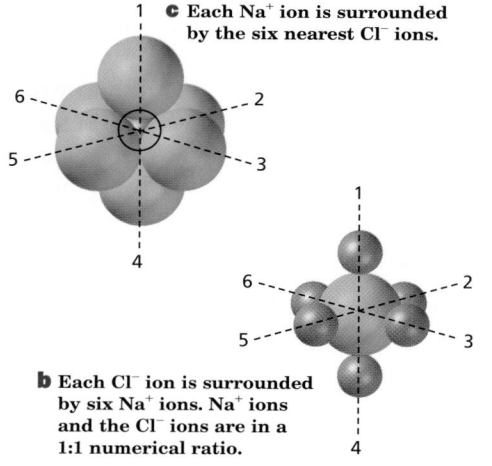

c Each Na$^+$ ion is surrounded by the six nearest Cl$^-$ ions.

b Each Cl$^-$ ion is surrounded by six Na$^+$ ions. Na$^+$ ions and the Cl$^-$ ions are in a 1:1 numerical ratio.

TEACHING TIP

Salt Formation Point out that binary ionic compounds form easily when an atom of fairly low ionization potential meets an atom of high electron affinity. (Such atoms also have a large electronegativity difference.) Then one or more electrons are transferred and ions are formed.

Point out that when atoms become ions, their properties are dramatically altered. In forming the white ionic compound NaCl, sodium changed from a silvery gray soft solid to colorless ions, and chlorine changed from a yellowish green gas to colorless ions.

Designing a Model Na$^+$ and Cl$^-$ ions have a size ratio of about 1 to 1.8 (5:9) when they are in a crystal of NaCl. If you can obtain spheres of this approximate size ratio, you can create a space-filling model of the lattice shown in **Figure 5-5.** Use the model to demonstrate that each ion is surrounded by six ions of opposite charge. Plastic-foam spheres from a craft shop can be used.

VISUAL STRATEGY

Figure 5-5 Be sure students realize that the open-crate model of NaCl shown in **Figure 5-5a** does not represent the way that the ions are really packed in the crystal and that the models shown in parts **b** and **c** are much closer to reality.

 Science in the News

PRESENTS Feature story 14

Harvesting Salt. See the Science in the News video guide for more details.

QUICKLAB

Use table sugar and table salt in this activity. If possible, have students use a stereoscopic dissection microscope of 10 or 15 power. Placing the crystals on a black surface and illuminating them from the side and top will best highlight the crystal shapes.

Analysis

1. One sample shows cubic crystals more consistently. The other sample shows some cubic crystals and some other geometric shapes.

2. Students may predict that the cubic crystals are table salt. Figure 5-5 shows that salt has a cubic crystal structure.

CHAPTER CONNECTION

Salts are formed in ways other than synthesis reactions. Salts are also formed during acid-base reactions, which are discussed in Chapter 15. In these reactions, the cation from a base forms a salt with the anion of an acid. Thousands of compounds belong to the category of salts.

QUICKLAB

CONSUMER ACTIVITY

Can You Tell a Crystal by Its Shape?

Materials   samples of two different white crystalline solids, microscope

Problem   No tasting is allowed. One of the solids is table salt. Use the microscope or magnifying lens to predict which substance is salt based on its crystal shape.

Analysis
1. Describe the geometric shape for the crystals in both samples.
2. Could you identify the salt?
3. Why do you think so?

coulombic force

the attraction or repulsion between two objects that have electric charges

halide

a salt that is composed of cations combined with anions of one of the halogen elements

crystal lattice

a repetitive geometric arrangement of points in space about which atoms, ions, or molecules are arranged to form a crystal structure

How many chloride anions surround each sodium cation? How does this number compare with the number of sodium cations that, in turn, surround each chloride anion? In the sodium chloride structure, notice that each ion is closest to six oppositely charged ions. The next closest are 12 similarly charged ions, then 8 more oppositely charged ions, and so on. The net effect is that the **coulombic force** of attraction of the oppositely charged ions is significantly greater than the coulombic force of repulsion from the ions of like charge. In fact, the net effect turns out to be 1.748 times as great as for just a pair of Na^+ and Cl^- ions. This attractive force is what holds clusters of ions together. Figure 5-5 could apply equally as well to any halide of sodium. The **halides** (the name is derived from *halogen*) comprise all the simple anions, namely F^-, Cl^-, Br^-, I^-, and At^-, formed from the Group 17 elements.

The smallest crystal of table salt that you could see would still contain more than a billion billion (10^{18} in scientific notation) Na^+ and Cl^- ions, all in one gigantic lattice. A particular packing arrangement of points in space is called a **crystal lattice.** Each sodium cation is surrounded by six anions, which in turn are surrounded by six cations— *except at the edges.* The ions are less uniformly arranged at the edges of a crystal, creating weak points. Disruptions start at these weak points. When a salt dissolves in water, the ions must be stripped off one layer at a time. Dissolving therefore can be a slow process.

Ionic compounds do not consist of molecules

A crystal of NaCl is composed of Na^+ ions and Cl^- ions held together by coulombic forces resulting from their opposite charges. There are no NaCl molecules. Therefore, the formula NaCl simply indicates that there is a 1:1 ratio of ions in the salt. In fact, the formulas of all ionic compounds represent the simplest numerical ratio between cations and anions. The simplest ratio of ions is called the formula unit for the compound. Because a formula is written as the simplest ratio or formula unit, we do not see formulas like $Na_{10}Cl_{10}$ or $Sr_{10}Cl_{20}$ for ionic salts.

You cannot be absolutely sure that something is made of ions or molecules just by looking at its formula. That determination must be made in the laboratory. But elements in Groups 1 and 2 and in Groups 16 and 17 will almost always form ionic compounds.

Salts have ordered packing arrangements

The ions in a salt form repeating patterns, with each ion held in place by an excess of attractive coulombic forces over repulsive coulombic forces. The way the ions are arranged is common to many different salts. For example, silver bromide, lead(II) sulfide, vanadium(III) nitride, and all the halides of lithium, potassium, and rubidium match the way the sodium halides are packed. Not all one-cation-to-one-anion salts, however, have the same crystal lattice as sodium chloride. The cesium chloride structure consists of one Cs^+ cation surrounded by *eight* Cl^- anions. Models for the NaCl and CsCl crystal structures are shown in **Figure 5-6**. Despite their differences, the crystals of both of these salts are made of simple repeating units that are cubic in shape. The smallest repeating unit in a crystal lattice is called a **unit cell**.

The sodium chloride and cesium chloride structures differ in the number of nearest neighbors that each ion possesses—six for the ions in NaCl, eight for those in CsCl. What determines the crystal pattern for a salt? Cesium ions are larger than sodium ions. The larger cesium ion can be surrounded by more chloride ions, causing cesium chloride to pack in an arrangement with eight, rather than six, nearest neighbors.

The structures shown in Figure 5-6 apply only to crystals containing an equal number of cations and anions. One structure that occurs in many salts with ions in a two-to-one ratio is shown in **Figure 5-7**. It is known as the calcium fluoride lattice because CaF_2 was the first one-cation-to-two-anion salt whose structure was discovered by X-ray crystallography. You can see that the lattice has twice as many anion sites as cation sites. Sodium sulfide, Na_2S, also crystallizes this lattice, but the sites are reversed to accommodate its two-cations-to-one-anion ratio.

NaCl crystal structure — Chloride ion, Cl⁻ — Sodium ion, Na⁺

CsCl crystal structure — Cesium ion, Cs⁺

unit cell

the simplest repeating unit of a crystal lattice

FIGURE 5-7 ▼

Calcium ion, Ca^{2+}

Flouride ion, F⁻

a The mineral *fluorite* contains calcium fluoride.

b Each calcium ion is surrounded by eight fluoride ions.

CONCEPT CHECK

1. What force holds ionic crystals together?
2. Crystals of the ionic compounds CaF_2 and $CaCl_2$ have different structures. Suggest a reason for this difference.

TEACHING TIP

Crystal Display   Display large crystals of various shapes. Include NaCl and quartz. Attractive crystals can be purchased at science museums and from science supply companies. Consider borrowing some samples from mineral collectors or amateur geologists.

HISTORICAL CONNECTION

In 1912, the German physicist Max von Laue discovered that X rays passed through a crystal are scattered, or diffracted, in a pattern that depends on the arrangement of atoms, ions, or molecules in the crystal. This technique, called X-ray crystallography, was used in the early 1950s by British scientist Rosalind Franklin to confirm the double-helix structure of DNA.

ANSWERS

CONCEPT CHECK

1. coulombic forces of attraction between ions of opposite charge
2. The F⁻ ion is much smaller than the Cl⁻ ion. Therefore, fewer Li⁺ ions can fit around a fluoride ion than can fit around the larger chloride ion.

ALTERNATIVE ASSESSMENT

Lattice Structures and Formulas

To make sure students do not confuse lattice structure with chemical formula, ask them to formulate an answer to the following question: If the crystal lattice of NaCl contains Na⁺ ions surrounded by six Cl⁻ ions, why isn't the formula of sodium chloride written as NaCl₆? Invite them to provide a structural explanation in addition to the fact that one Na⁺ and one Cl⁻ produce electroneutrality. The apparent 1:6 ratio describes only the packing arrangement of the ions. When you examine the overall arrangement of the crystal lattice, you see that ions occur in the ratio of 1:1.

Energy aspects of salt formation

As **Figure 5-8** illustrates, the elements sodium and chlorine spontaneously combine in a flash of yellow light when they are brought together. The reaction is evidently exothermic, but where does the energy come from?

Electron transfer between atoms is usually an endothermic process

Recall that ionization energy is the energy that must be supplied to remove the outermost electron from an atom. Atoms always resist having their electrons removed, so ionization energies are always positive. In the case of sodium, the energy needed to remove the outermost electron is 495 kJ/mol. The ionization process could be written as follows.

$$Na(g) + 495 \text{ kJ/mol} \longrightarrow Na^+(g) + e^-(g)$$

Notice that this equation describes the removal of an electron from a gaseous sodium atom.

Electron affinity is the energy needed to put an extra electron onto a neutral atom. Most electron affinities are negative, indicating that the recipient atom easily accepts another electron. Chlorine atoms are willing acceptors of extra electrons; they have an electron affinity that is equal to −349 kJ/mol. As an equation, this process can be expressed as follows.

$$Cl(g) + e^-(g) - 349 \text{ kJ/mol} \longrightarrow Cl^-(g)$$

or

$$Cl(g) + e^-(g) \longrightarrow Cl^-(g) + 349 \text{ kJ/mol}$$

By adding the above equation to the equation for the removal of an electron from an Na atom, we find that the electron transfer from a sodium atom to a chlorine atom is an endothermic reaction absorbing 146 kJ/mol overall. *Energy is needed for this reaction to occur.*

$$Na(g) + Cl(g) + 146 \text{ kJ/mol} \longrightarrow Na^+(g) + Cl^-(g)$$

The energy we just calculated was for transferring an electron between *isolated* atoms to create gaseous ions that are *separated* from each other. This is a very different situation from what happens in the flask shown in Figure 5-8.

The formation of ions is only one part of bonding

If adding an electron to a chlorine atom cannot supply enough energy to remove an electron from a sodium atom, why does an ionic bond form? The chemistry of the following salt-forming reaction can be thought of as five steps, which are shown in **Figure 5-9.** The steps do not represent the actual reactions for the formation of NaCl. Keep in mind that the starting materials are sodium metal and chlorine gas. Chlorine gas consists of pairs of bonded atoms. The final product is crystalline sodium chloride. From Figure 5-9, notice that the chief driving force for the reaction is the last step, in which the separated ions come together to form the crystal lattice.

▼ **FIGURE 5-8**

The reaction between sodium metal and chlorine gas is a spontaneous exothermic reaction.

GRAPHIC ORGANIZER

Energy changes in the formation of binary ionic compounds:

Some steps may or may not occur depending on the element.

3. No energy is required to convert chlorine into the gaseous state because it is already a gas. However, energy must be added to break up 0.5 mol of Cl_2 molecules to produce 1 mol of chlorine atoms.

$$\tfrac{1}{2}Cl_2(g) + energy \longrightarrow Cl(g)$$

Electron lost

2. More energy must be added to remove one electron from each sodium atom.

$$Na(g) + energy \longrightarrow Na^+(g) + e^-$$

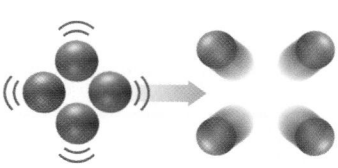

1. Energy must be added to convert 1 mol of sodium from a solid to a gas.

$$Na(s) + energy \longrightarrow Na(g)$$

At the Initial Energy State: The reactants, solid sodium and chlorine gas, start at an initial energy state that is assigned a value of zero at 25°C and 1 atm of pressure.

$$Na(s) \text{ and } Cl_2(g)$$

Scale (kJ/mol): 800, 600, 400, 200, 0 (Initial energy state), −200, −400

125 kJ/mol
495 kJ/mol
100 kJ/mol
778 kJ/mol

Electron gained

4. Some energy is given off when an electron is added to each chlorine atom to form a Cl^- ion. This is an exothermic process.

$$Cl(g) + e^- \longrightarrow Cl^-(g) + energy$$

349 kJ/mol

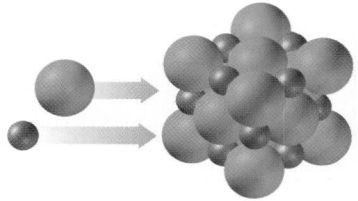

Lattice forms

5. Much more energy is given off when Na^+ and Cl^- ions come together to form an ionic crystal of NaCl.

$$Na^+(g) + Cl^-(g) \longrightarrow NaCl(s) + energy$$

Note that the energy state of crystalline NaCl is more than 400 kJ/mol below the initial energy state of the reactants, Na(s) and $Cl_2(g)$.

FIGURE 5-9 ▲

The reaction between Na(s) and $Cl_2(g)$ to form sodium chloride can be broken down into steps. More energy is released during the exothermic steps than is absorbed during the endothermic steps, so the overall reaction is exothermic.

VISUAL STRATEGY

Figure 5-9 Reinforce the concept of energy changes in the formation of an ionic compound by going through the steps in the diagram. Point out that in the case of a nonmetal that is not a gas, additional energy is required to bring it into the gaseous state. Examples include S_8, Br_2, and I_2. Emphasize that the potential energy of the crystalline product is far below that of the starting materials. Relate this to the chemical stability of ionic compounds.

Ask students how much energy would be given off if 0.500 mol of NaCl were formed (206 J).

CHAPTER CONNECTION

The formation of the NaCl crystal lattice from the elements involves potential energy, electron affinity, ionization potential, and endothermic and exothermic reactions. Have students review these topics, which were encountered in Chapter 2 and Chapter 4.

💡 DID YOU KNOW?

The idea of breaking down the formation of crystals of compounds into a series of discrete changes was devised in order to calculate lattice energies, which cannot be measured directly. This series, diagramed in Figure 5-9, is known as the Born-Haber cycle. It was devised by German physicist Max Born and German chemist Fritz Haber. This cycle is a specific application of Hess's law, which is discussed in Chapter 11.

CONCEPT CHECK

1. Considering that the lattice energy of NaBr is lower than that of LiBr, it is reasonable to assume that the lattice energy of CsCl is lower than that of KCl. As Na^+ is a larger ion than Li^+, Cs^+ is larger than K^+.

2. Endothermic: separation of Na from a solid to a gas; separation of Cl_2 molecules into Cl atoms; removal of electrons from sodium atoms

   Bond formation: formation of the crystal lattice from separated ions

3. Separation of sodium atoms and formation of the NaCl crystal are processes involving a change of state.

READING STRATEGY

Organizing Concepts

Have students copy the following categories of properties:

) Hardness
) Brittleness
) Melting point
) Boiling point
) Electrical conduction (solid)
) Electrical conduction (liquid)

Tell students that reading the lesson will give them information about the properties of binary ionic compounds in each of these categories. Students should also be prepared to explain why binary ionic compounds typically exhibit these properties.

Forming bonds in a lattice releases energy

The energy released in the fifth step in the sequence illustrated in Figure 5-9 is called the **lattice energy**. This is the energy released when the crystal structure is formed from well-separated ions. In the case of sodium chloride, the lattice energy is 778 kJ/mol, which is greater than the total energy input needed for steps 1, 2, and 3 of Figure 5-9. Without the lattice energy, there would not be enough energy from step 4 to make the overall process spontaneous. *Lattice energy is the key to ionic bond formation.*

Lattice energy is calculated by measuring the energy of all the subreactions as well as the energy released in the overall reaction. Lattice energies of some ionic compounds are given in **Table 5-3.** Generally those compounds with smaller ions, or greater charge, will have higher lattice energies. Notice in Table 5-3 that the lattice energy of lithium chloride is greater than that of lithium iodide. The chloride ion is much smaller than the iodide ion.

TABLE 5-3	Lattice Energies for Some Ionic Compounds	
Compound name	**Formula**	**kJ/mol**
Lithium chloride	LiCl	861
Lithium bromide	LiBr	818
Lithium iodide	LiI	759
Sodium chloride	NaCl	778
Sodium bromide	NaBr	751
Sodium iodide	NaI	700
Magnesium oxide	MgO	3760
Magnesium sulfide	MgS	3160
Calcium oxide	CaO	3385
Calcium sulfide	CaS	2775

lattice energy
the energy released when well separated atoms, ions, or molecules come together to form a crystal

CONCEPT CHECK

1. **Interpreting Tables** Using the trends in Table 5-3, predict whether the lattice energy of CsCl is larger or smaller than that of KCl.

2. **Interpreting Graphics** What steps in Figure 5-9 are endothermic processes? What step involves bond formation?

3. What steps in Figure 5-9 show change-of-state processes?

Properties of binary ionic compounds

A binary ionic compound consists of a simple cation paired with a simple anion in a combination that results in electroneutrality. All the salts that we have discussed so far in this chapter are binary ionic compounds. Metallic oxides (which are not classified as salts) are also binary ionic compounds.

Like most other binary ionic compounds, table salt is fairly hard and brittle. *Hard* means the crystal is able to resist a large force applied to it. *Brittle* means that when the applied force becomes too strong to resist, the crystal develops a widespread fracture rather than a localized dent. Both of these properties can be attributed to the regular planes of ionic charges that all crystal lattices possess.

The ions in a crystal are arranged in a repeating pattern, forming layers. As long as the layers stay in a fixed position relative to one an-

ALTERNATIVE ASSESSMENT

Group Strategy

This would be a good time to check students' understanding of the phase changes that occur in melting and boiling. Ask groups of four to write verbal descriptions of the structure of a solid, a liquid, and a gas in terms of particle spacing and arrangement. Beside these verbal descriptions, ask them to draw a model representing each state, using circles to represent particles.

Alternatively, you could provide each group with about 25 disks, such as poker chips, with which to construct flat physical models of a solid, liquid, and gas. Scan the models to find misconceptions.

Once correct descriptions and models have been established, ask each group to discuss misunderstandings among themselves in order to be sure all students have sound men-

FIGURE 5-10 ▼

a Sodium chloride is hard and brittle, yet it can be cut by applying force along any of its three cleavage planes.

Cl⁻

Na⁺

b The geometry of the cleavage planes matches the packing structure of the crystal.

other, the ionic compound will be hard and it will take a lot of energy to break all the bonds between the ions. However, if a force causes one layer to move slightly, ions of the same sign will be next to each other. When a force is large enough to reposition a layer of ions, the repulsive force between the layers will cause the layers to break apart. **Figure 5-10** shows cleavage planes for NaCl.

internet connect

SCLINKS.
NSTA

TOPIC: Salt properties
GO TO: www.scilinks.org
KEYWORD: HW053

Salts melt and boil at high temperatures

All ionic compounds share certain properties because of the strong attraction between their ions. Compare the boiling point of sodium chloride with that of water, a molecular compound—1413°C compared with 100°C. Similarly, most other binary ionic compounds have high melting and boiling points, as you can see in **Table 5-4**. Because each ion in these compounds forms strong bonds to neighboring ions, considerable energy is required to free them from their fixed locations, which must occur for the compound to melt. Still more energy is needed to move ions out of the liquid state and cause boiling.

TABLE 5-4   **Melting and Boiling Points of Compounds**

Compound name	Formula	Type of compound	Melting point °C	K	Boiling point °C	K
Calcium iodide	CaI_2	ionic	784	1057	1100	1373
Carbon tetrachloride	CCl_4	covalent	−23	250	77	350
Hydrogen fluoride	HF	covalent	−83	190	20	293
Hydrogen sulfide	H_2S	covalent	−86	188	−61	212
Iodine monochloride	ICl	covalent	27	300	97	370
Magnesium fluoride	MgF_2	ionic	1261	1534	2239	2512
Methane	CH_4	covalent	−182	91	−164	109
Sodium chloride	NaCl	ionic	801	1074	1413	1686

SECTION 5-2

DID YOU KNOW?

Many ionic compounds decompose or sublime before they reach a boiling point or, in some cases, a melting point. The high transition temperatures are still a sign of the strengths of ionic bonds. $MgSO_4$ decomposes at 1124°C without melting; KCl melts at 772°C and sublimes at 1500°C; NH_4Cl sublimes at 350°C without melting; and $CaCO_3$ decomposes at 825°C.

TEACHING TIP

Bond Strength   To reinforce the strength of ionic bonds, list the melting points of other ionic compounds, such as NaCl, 801°C; NaBr, 750°C; NaI, 662°C; K_2CO_3, 891°C; $CaCl_2$, 772°C; Na_2CO_3, 851°C; and $CaSO_4$, 1450°C.

CHAPTER CONNECTION

Call students' attention to the fact that certain covalently bonded substances have very high melting points. Table 5-4 shows only a limited range of covalent substances. For example, quartz, SiO_2, melts at 1610°C; silicon carbide, SiC, sublimes at 2700°C, titanium boride, TiB_2, melts at 2900°C, and tantalum carbide, TaC, melts at 3800°C. Point out that covalent compounds of this type are often very hard and can be used as abrasives. Ask students to speculate on why these substances are so different from the covalent compounds listed in Table 5-4. They form network crystals, which students will encounter in Chapter 6.

tal models. Students should realize that particles in a liquid are almost as close together as they are in solids, but in liquids there is a random arrangement and the particles are free to move past one another. Compare, for example, an ice cube standing in the bottom of a beaker with the liquid resulting from the melting of a cube. In a gas, the particles are widely separated compared with the particles' size.

Figure 5-11 You may wish to compare the sequence of diagrams in this figure with the results of Demonstration 2. Emphasize that the separation of ions when the salt melts and when it dissolves in water is the same process—breaking down of the crystal lattice. Both processes produce a mixture of freely moving ions. Be sure students recognize the differences in the two liquid systems. One contains water in the mixture of ions.

ADDITIONAL APPLICATION

Much of the salt that is mined is used in the commercial production of NaOH by electrolysis. Salt is dissolved in water to make a concentrated brine. A strong electric current is passed through the brine, and $H_2(g)$ is given off at one electrode while $Cl_2(g)$ comes off at the other electrode. Both of these gases are commercially valuable products. Na^+ and OH^- ions remain in solution and form NaOH crystals when the water is evaporated.

RESOURCE LINK

ChemFile Lab B
Microscale Lab
Have students do Experiment 7:
Conductivity as an Indicator of Bond Type.

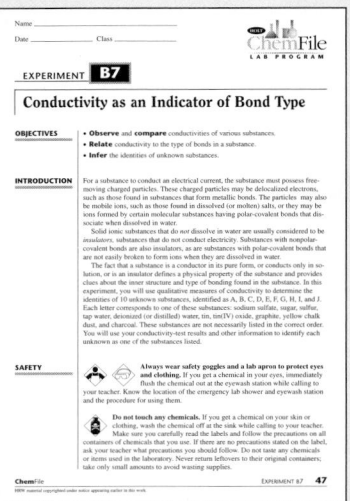

Ionic solids *generally* do not conduct electricity

To conduct an electric current, a substance must satisfy two conditions: it must contain charged particles, and those particles must be free to move. Ionic compounds certainly contain charged particles. So one might expect that ionic solids could be good conductors. Recall that particles in a solid have some vibrational motion; however, they remain in fixed locations, as shown by the model in **Figure 5-11a.** Thus, ionic solids, such as salts, generally are not conductors of electricity because the ions cannot move through the crystal.

However, when the ions can move about, salts are excellent electrical conductors. This situation occurs when a salt melts or dissolves. When a salt melts, the ions that make up the crystal can freely move past each other, as **Figure 5-11b** illustrates. Molten salts are good conductors of electricity, though they do not conduct as well as metals. Similarly, if a salt dissolves in water, its ions are no longer held tightly in the crystal; they are free to move, as shown by the model in **Figure 5-11c,** and the solution becomes an electrical conductor.

As often happens in chemistry, there are exceptions to the rule. There is a small class of compounds called *solid ionic conductors* that allow electricity to pass through their crystals. The lattices of these compounds have an unusually open structure, so certain ions can move past others, jumping from one lattice site to another. In the *mixed salt*

internetconnect

SC*LINKS*
NSTA

TOPIC: Nonconductors
GO TO: www.scilinks.org
KEYWORD: HW054

▼ FIGURE 5-11

a Charged particles in an ionic solid are rigidly held in fixed positions.

b When ionic solids melt, the ions are able to move about more freely.

c When ionic solids are dissolved in water, the ions are able to move about in a mixture with water molecules.

174   CHAPTER 5

DEMONSTRATION 2

Electrical Conduction in Ionic Compounds

Approximate time: 15 minutes

1. Construct the following assembly for use as a conductivity tester. Insert two straightened steel paper clips through a cork (not a rubber stopper) as shown. Spinning the paper clips will help drill them through the cork. Attach the battery, LED, resistor, and clips as shown.

TABLE 5-5 Some Characteristics of Ionic Compounds

- Are solids at room temperature
- Are hard and brittle
- Generally have high melting points and boiling points
- Generally do not conduct electricity when in solid form
- Are good conductors of electricity in the liquid state and when dissolved in water

silver rubidium iodide, $RbAg_4I_5$, the Ag^+ cations are mobile, even at room temperature. More compounds join the class of solid ionic conductors as the temperature rises.

Zirconium oxide, ZrO_2, does not conduct electricity at ordinary temperatures, but it does conduct at high temperatures. At temperatures well below its melting point, about 3000 K, the O^{2-} ions can move through the crystal lattice. This behavior is the basis of a device that controls emissions from the exhaust of automobiles. An electrochemical cell containing ZrO_2 as a separator measures the percentage of oxygen in the exhaust gases. The car's computer then adjusts the fuel-to-air ratio to obtain the best performance of the engine with the least emission of polluting gases.

SECTION REVIEW

Total recall

1. In the formation of most ionic crystals from free atoms, which step gives off the largest amount of energy, thereby driving the reaction?

2. Explain why the dissolution of a salt can be a slow process.

3. Explain why ionic compounds do not conduct electric current in the solid phase but do conduct in the liquid phase or when dissolved in water.

Critical thinking

4. **Interpreting Tables** Look at Table 5-3, on page 172. How is the size of an anion related to the lattice energy for compounds of Group 1 cations? Does this trend hold for compounds of Group 2 cations?

5. **Interpreting Tables** Table 5-4, on page 173, shows the melting and boiling points of ionic compounds and covalent compounds. What conclusions can you draw about the forces holding ionic crystals together as compared with the forces holding molecular crystals together?

6. **Interpreting Graphics** Use Figure 5-9, on page 171, to describe how the formation of $CaCl_2$ would differ from that of NaCl.

7. **Story Clue** What part of the silver halide crystal is most affected by light when film is exposed?

2. Half-fill a small uncracked porcelain crucible with crystalline lithium chloride, LiCl.

3. Insert the leads of the conductivity tester into the LiCl, and demonstrate that the LED does not light because the salt does not conduct electricity.

4. Remove the tester.

5. Support the crucible on a clay triangle resting on an iron ring on a ring stand. (See Figure 5-11.) Heat the crucible until the LiCl melts.

6. Insert the leads of the tester into the melted salt, and show that the LED lights because the melted salt now conducts. Remove heat, and let the crucible cool. Wash the leads of the tester with water to remove any LiCl.

7. Place 100 mL of distilled water into a clean 250 mL beaker. Place the clean leads into the water, and show that it does not conduct.

CONTINUED ON PAGE 176

SECTION 5-2

ANSWERS

SECTION REVIEW

Total recall

1. The step in which the ions come together to form a crystal is usually the most exothermic step.

2. Only the ions at the surface of the crystal can go into solution, so ions are stripped away one layer at a time.

3. Ions in the solid phase are locked into a crystal lattice, so the charged ions cannot move through the crystal. The ions in a melted or dissolved ionic compound are free to move, so they can conduct an electric current.

Critical thinking

4. As the anions in ionic compounds with Group 1 cations become larger, the lattice energy decreases. The same trend seems to hold true with Group 2 compounds when the anions are oxide and sulfide.

5. Ionic substances in the table have much higher melting points than the covalent compounds. Therefore, the forces holding ionic crystals together must be much greater than the forces that hold together crystals of covalently bonded compounds.

6. The process of formation of $CaCl_2$ would be the same as that of NaCl except that 2 mol of electrons would have to be removed from each mole of Ca and acquired by 2 mol of Cl atoms. Note that the separation of Cl_2 into separate Cl atoms must still take place.

7. Light is most likely to affect ions on the corners and edges of the crystals.

What are polyatomic ions?

OBJECTIVES

▸ **Explain** how polyatomic ions and their salts are named and how their formulas relate to their names.

▸ **Describe** the pattern used in naming oxyanions.

▸ **Assign** oxidation numbers to atoms in polyatomic ions and their compounds.

▸ **Discuss** differences between silicate minerals, hydrates, and conventional salts.

LESSON WARM-UP

Polyatomic Ions Emphasize the difference between monatomic (simple) ions and polyatomic ions by writing the names and formulas of a series of compounds containing monatomic ions and of a second series containing polyatomic ions. Include the compounds listed on the fertilizer bag shown in Figure 5-12. Lists could include the following:

Compounds with monatomic ions

calcium bromide	$CaBr_2$
sodium oxide	Na_2O
aluminum chloride	$AlCl_3$
iron(III) fluoride	FeF_3
barium iodide	BaI_2
copper(II) oxide	CuO

Compounds with polyatomic ions

sodium nitrate	Na_2SO_4
potassium carbonate	K_2CO_3
calcium chlorate	$Ca(ClO_3)_2$
ammonium nitrate	NH_4NO_3
calcium dihydrogen phosphate	$Ca(H_2PO_4)_2$
tin(II) acetate	$Sn(CH_3COO)_2$

Ask students to rewrite the formulas using square brackets in the same manner as the formula $[Mg^{2+}]_3[N^{3-}]_2$ on page 163. Stress that each poly-atomic ion is treated as a single unit and is kept together within a pair of brackets. Have students infer the charge of the anions from what they already know about the cations.

Many atoms can form one ion

In Section 5-1, the adjective *simple* was used to describe an ion formed from a single atom. A simple ion could also be called *monatomic*, meaning "one-atom." Just as the prefixes *mono-* and *mon-* mean "one," so *poly-* means "many." The term **polyatomic ion** means a charged group of two or more bonded atoms that functions as a single ion. Atoms in a polyatomic ion are covalently bonded, but the ion as a whole forms ionic bonds with other ions in the same way that simple ions do. The perox-ide ion, O_2^{2-}, the mercury(I) ion, Hg_2^{2+}, the azide ion, N_3^-, and the poly-sulfide ion, S_5^{2-}, each consists of atoms of a single element. Most polyatomic ions consist of atoms of several elements.

polyatomic ion

an electrically charged group of two or more chemically bonded atoms that functions as a single ion

Fertilizers contain compounds with polyatomic ions

The purpose of the fertilizers shown in **Figure 5-12** is to supply potas-sium, nitrogen, and phosphorus in a form that plants can readily use.

▶ **FIGURE 5-12**

Compounds containing polyatomic ions supply soil with nitrogen, phosphorus, and potassium in ratios to meet the needs of specific plants.

N-P-K
15-30-15

N-P-K
36-6-6

N-P-K
18-24-16

DEMONSTRATION 2 *CONTINUED*

8. While keeping the leads in the water, add about 5 g of LiCl and stir gently with a plastic or glass stirring rod. The LED should glow almost immediately and will reach maximum brightness in a few seconds.

Variations

You may substitute NaCl, NaBr, KCl, or KBr for the LiBr. Do not use nitrates.

Safety

Wear safety goggles and a laboratory apron. Keep students at least 10 ft away from the crucible once it is hot. Use only the battery-powered tester.

Disposal

Remove the battery from the tester, and put tape over the terminals. The tester circuit will be sturdier if all electrical connections are made using very small plastic wire nuts, available at any electronic supply store. Keep the crucible with its solidified LiCl to perform the same demonstration in the future.

Some potassium in fertilizers is in the form of K_2CO_3. The formulas for two compounds that can supply nitrogen are NH_4NO_3 and $(NH_4)_2SO_4$. The phosphorus often comes from $Ca(H_2PO_4)_2$. All these ionic compounds contain polyatomic ions. Most ionic compounds are called **salts,** whether their ions are simple or polyatomic (the exceptions are when oxide or hydroxide anions are present.) In K_2CO_3 or $Ca(H_2PO_4)_2$, the anion is polyatomic and the cation is a simple metal ion. In NH_4NO_3, both the anion and the cation are polyatomic.

The names of polyatomic ions can be complicated

You'll find that the nomenclature of polyatomic ions is not completely logical. Nevertheless there are rules you can count on to help you remember how to name some compounds.

Many polyatomic ions contain oxygen. The endings *-ite* and *-ate* show the presence of oxygen. Such ions are called **oxyanions.** If they are negatively charged, these oxyanion names do *not* specify exactly how many oxygen atoms are present. Sulf**ate** has four, nitr**ate** has three, acet**ate** has two. Often there are several oxyanions that differ only in the number of oxygen atoms present. For example, sulfur forms the SO_3^{2-} and SO_4^{2-} oxyanions. In such cases, the ion with more oxygen takes the *-ate* ending, sulfate in this case; the ion with less oxygen takes the *-ite* ending, sulfite. **Table 5-6** shows the names given to common oxyanions. Notice the pattern in the naming of these ions.

The presence of hydrogen in a polyatomic anion is often indicated by the ion's name starting with *hydrogen*. The prefixes *mono-* and *di-* are also used. Thus, HPO_4^{2-} and $H_2PO_4^{-}$ are monohydrogen phosphate and dihydrogen phosphate ions, respectively. The prefix *thio-* means "replace an oxygen by a sulfur" in the formula, as in potassium thiosulfate, $K_2S_2O_3$, compared with potassium sulfate, K_2SO_4. **Table 5-7,** on the next page, is a complete listing of the names and formulas for common polyatomic ions.

salt

an ionic compound that is composed of cations bonded to anions, other than oxide or hydroxide anions

oxyanion

a negative polyatomic ion containing oxygen

internet**connect**

SCILINKS™
NSTA

TOPIC: Compounds/Polyatomic ions
GO TO: www.scilinks.org
KEYWORD: HW055

TABLE 5-6	**Naming Conventions for Some Oxyanions**		

	Oxyanion formula	Number of oxygen atoms	Oxyanion name
With chlorine	ClO^-	1	*hypo*chlor*ite*
(other halogens	ClO_2^-	2	chlor*ite*
form similarly	ClO_3^-	3	chlor*ate*
named oxyanions)	ClO_4^-	4	*per*chlor*ate*
With sulfur	SO_3^{2-}	3	sulf*ite*
	SO_4^{2-}	4	sulf*ate*
With nitrogen	NO_2^-	2	nitr*ite*
	NO_3^-	3	nitr*ate*

IONIC COMPOUNDS 177

ALTERNATIVE ASSESSMENT

Modeling Formulas

Fill a sheet of paper with transfers of the following patterns.

a.

b.

c.

Divide the class into groups, and give each group a copy of the sheet and some tape. The blocks with tabs will represent anions; each tab indicates a −1 charge. The other blocks represent cations; each notch indicates a +1 charge.

Choose several anions from Table 5-7, and have students label the appropriate blocks with their name and formula. List common metal

CONTINUED ON PAGE 178

177

HOW TO

ADDITIONAL EXAMPLES

Write names for the following compounds:

a. $KHCO_3$

Ans. potassium hydrogen carbonate

b. $Fe(OH)_3$

Ans. iron(III) hydroxide

c. K_3PO_4

Ans. potassium phosphate

d. $Al_2(C_2O_4)_3$

Ans. aluminum oxalate

TEACHING TIP

Formula Writing   Check students' understanding of how to write formulas with polyatomic ions by asking students to determine the total number of atoms represented in formulas such as $Mg(HCO_3)_2$, $Sr(HSO_4)_2$, $(NH_4)_2SO_4$, and $Na_2HAl(PO_4)_2$.

Ans. 11, 13, 15, 14

COMMON MISCONCEPTION

Students may expect to find a single, systematic, numerical rule that allows them to write the formula of any oxyanion when given its name. The system of naming these ions is rooted in the nineteenth century and is related to the names of acids containing these oxyanions. Ions ending in *-ite* are derived from acids ending in *-ous.* Ions ending in *-ate* are derived from oxygen-containing acids ending in *-ic.* Aside from the progression of *hypo/ite,* . . . *ite,* . . . *ate,* and *per/ate,* students will have to memorize the number of oxygen atoms in the oxyanions of other nonmetal elements.

What is the name of the compound with the formula K_2CO_3?

1 Name the cation

You already know that K is potassium and that it forms a singly charged cation, K^+, of the same name. The subscript *2* indicates that there are two potassium ions, as shown below. Recall that salts are electrically neutral overall, so the two positive charges of the two potassium ions must be balanced by two negative charges associated with the carbonate anion, CO_3^{2-}.

2 Name the anion

The anion component of the salt is CO_3^{2-}. It helps to think of the formula as follows, though it is not written that way.

$$[K^+]_2[CO_3^{2-}]$$

If you consult **Table 5-7,** you will see that the CO_3^{2-} ion is called the *carbonate ion.*

K_2CO_3 is made of two potassium cations, each with one positive charge... K^+ K^+ K_2CO_3 CO_3^{2-} ...and a single doubly charged anion, a carbonate ion.

3 Name the salt

Remember that the name of a salt is just the names of its ions. K_2CO_3 is potassium carbonate.

TABLE 5-7   Some Polyatomic Ions

Ion name	Formula	Ion name	Formula	Ion name	Formula
Acetate	CH_3COO^-	Dihydrogen phosphate	$H_2PO_4^-$	Oxalate	$C_2O_4^{2-}$
Ammonium	NH_4^+	Dimercury(I) or mercury(I)	Hg_2^{2+}	Perchlorate	ClO_4^-
Arsenate	AsO_4^{3-}	Hydrogen carbonate (bicarbonate)	HCO_3^-	Permanganate	MnO_4^-
Azide	N_3^-			Peroxide	O_2^{2-}
Bromate	BrO_3^-	Hydrogen sulfate	HSO_4^-	Phosphate	PO_4^{3-}
Carbonate	CO_3^{2-}	Hydroxide	OH^-	Sulfate	SO_4^{2-}
Chlorate	ClO_3^-	Hypochlorite	ClO^-	Sulfite	SO_3^{2-}
Chlorite	ClO_2^-	Methylammonium	$CH_3NH_3^+$	Thiocyanate	SCN^-
Chromate	CrO_4^{2-}	Monohydrogen phosphate	HPO_4^{2-}	Thiosulfate	$S_2O_3^{2-}$
Cyanide	CN^-	Nitrate	NO_3^-	Uranyl	UO_2^{2+}
Dichromate	$Cr_2O_7^{2-}$	Nitrite	NO_2^-		

ALTERNATIVE ASSESSMENT   *CONTINUED*

cations on the board, and have students label the appropriate blocks with these.

Write pairs of cations and anions on the board, and have students construct a model of the resulting compounds. Include some compounds that pair an ion with a charge of 3 with an ion with a charge of 2.

HOW TO · Write the formula for a compound containing a polyatomic ion

A fertilizer shown in Figure 5-12 has calcium dihydrogen phosphate as an ingredient. What is the formula for this salt?

1 Use Table 5-7 to determine the formula and charge for the polyatomic ion

Dihydrogen phosphate is $H_2PO_4^-$. Notice that dihydrogen phosphate has seven atoms from three different elements, plus one extra electron.

2 Determine the formula and charge for the cation

Because the calcium ion is Ca^{2+}, we clearly need two dihydrogen phosphate anions for each calcium cation. The diagram below shows how we can assemble this information to create the formula $Ca(H_2PO_4)_2$.

Notice the use of parentheses to show that *everything* inside the parentheses is doubled by the subscript 2 outside. The formula written without the parentheses, CaH_2PO_{42}, would imply 42 oxygen atoms. Sometimes we need two sets of parentheses, such as in the case of mercury(I) phosphate, $(Hg_2)_3(PO_4)_2$.

For every calcium cation in calcium dihydrogen phosphate... Ca^{2+} $H_2PO_4^-$ $H_2PO_4^-$ ...there must be two dihydrogen phosphate anions.

$$Ca(H_2PO_4)_2$$

The two anions are shown in parentheses and designated by the subscript 2.

CONCEPT CHECK

1. In what ways are polyatomic ions like simple ions? In what ways are they different?
2. Identify and name the cations and anions that make up the following ionic compounds and indicate the charge on each ion:
   a. $NaClO_3$
   b. K_2SO_3
   c. $(NH_4)_2CrO_4$
   d. $Al_2(SO_4)_3$
3. Name the compounds represented by the following formulas:
   a. Na_3AsO_4
   b. NH_4ClO_4
   c. $Ca(NO_2)_2$
   d. $Fe(OH)_3$
4. Write formulas for the following compounds:
   a. mercury(II) sulfate
   b. calcium cyanide
   c. rubidium oxalate
   d. lithium thiosulfate
   e. potassium dichromate
   f. potassium chromate
   g. sodium azide
   h. methylammonium sulfide

ADDITIONAL EXAMPLES

Name the following compounds:
a. $Co(NO_3)_2$
   Ans. cobalt(II) nitrate

b. $Cu_3(PO_4)_2$
   Ans. copper(II) phosphate

c. CuC_2O_4
   Ans. copper(II) oxalate

d. $Na_2C_2O_4$
   Ans. sodium oxalate

COMMON MISCONCEPTION

Students learned in Section 5-2 that formulas for binary ionic compounds should represent the smallest possible ratio of ions. Some compounds of polyatomic ions may seem to violate this rule, especially compounds with mercury(I) ions, Hg_2^{2+}, or oxalate ions, $C_2O_4^{2-}$. Examples include Hg_2F_2 and $Ag_2C_2O_4$. Emphasize to students that these ions have particular structures that are reflected in their formulas and that their subscripts cannot be changed.

ANSWERS

CONCEPT CHECK

1. Both polyatomic and simple ions are electrically charged. Polyatomic ions contain two or more covalently bonded atoms, but simple ions are monatomic.

2. Cations are written first.
   a. Na^+; ClO_3^-
   b. K^+; SO_3^{2-}
   c. NH_4^+; CrO_4^{2-}
   d. Al^{3+}; SO_4^{2-}

3. a. sodium arsenate
   b. ammonium perchlorate
   c. calcium nitrite
   d. iron(III) hydroxide

4. a. $HgSO_4$
   b. $Ca(CN)_2$
   c. $Rb_2C_2O_4$
   d. $Li_2S_2O_3$
   e. $K_2Cr_2O_7$
   f. K_2CrO_4
   g. NaN_3
   h. $(CH_3NH_3)_2S$

Students will learn about the parallel processes of oxidation and reduction in Chapter 17. Oxidation occurs when an atom or ion loses electrons. As an atom loses electrons, its oxidation state or oxidation number increases. For example, when sodium reacts with chlorine, sodium's oxidation state increases from 0 to +1 as it loses an electron. The oxidation state of chlorine decreases from 0 to –1 as it accepts an electron. In the case of monatomic ions, the oxidation state is the same as the ionic charge. In a covalent bond, the higher oxidation state is assigned to the element with the lower electronegativity, because we think of it as "losing" electrons to the element with the higher electronegativity.

COMMON MISCONCEPTION

The text states clearly that the oxidation number of an atom in a polyatomic ion or a molecule does not represent an actual charge. Students, however, find it difficult not to believe that positive or negative numbers applied to atoms do not represent electrical charge.

RESOURCE LINK

ChemFile Lab B
Microscale Lab
Have students do Experiment 8: *Tests for Iron(II) and Iron(III).*

oxidation number

a number assigned to an atom in a polyatomic ion or molecular compound based on an assumption of complete transfer of electrons

► **FIGURE 5-13**

Use these guidelines when determining the oxidation state of any atom in a formula.

Oxidation numbers
Polyatomic ions and the oxidation number concept

The charges listed for ions are used to denote a transfer of electrons in the formation of an ionic bond. Atoms within polyatomic ions are bonded covalently. In the next chapter you will learn that in covalent bonds electrons are shared between atoms. Unlike transferred electrons in ionic bonds, shared electrons in covalent bonds are not considered part of either of the atoms that share them. For example, the bonds between sulfur and oxygen atoms in the sulfate ion, SO_4^{2-}, contain shared electrons. Neither sulfur nor oxygen is an ion in SO_4^{2-}. Chemists have devised a scheme for polyatomic ions and molecular compounds to describe the distribution of electrons among bonded atoms. This convention is called **oxidation number.** Unlike the charge on an ion, an oxidation number does not have a real physical meaning. Even though we assign a charge to an atom in a polyatomic ion or molecular compound, that atom is not an ion and does not possess a real charge. Because each oxygen atom is assigned an oxidation number of –2, the sulfur atom in SO_4^{2-} is assigned an oxidation number of +6. **Figure 5-13** is a list of guidelines that can be used in assigning oxidation numbers. The model on the next page takes you through the process of assigning oxidation numbers.

Some Guidelines for Assigning Oxidation Numbers

1. The oxidation number of any free (uncombined) element is zero.

2. The oxidation number of a monatomic ion is equal to the charge on the ion.

3. The more electronegative element in a binary compound is assigned the number equal to the charge it would have if it were an ion.

4. The oxidation number of each hydrogen atom is + 1 unless it is combined with a metal, then it has a state of – 1.

5. The oxidation number of fluorine is always – 1 because it is the most electronegative atom.

6. The oxidation number of each oxygen atom in most of its compounds is – 2. When combined with F, oxygen has a number of + 2. In peroxides, such as H_2O_2, oxygen has an oxidation number of – 1.

7. In compounds, the elements of Group 1 and Group 2, and aluminum have positive oxidation numbers of + 1, + 2, and + 3, respectively.

8. The algebraic sum of the oxidation numbers for all the atoms in a compound is zero.

9. The algebraic sum of the oxidation numbers for all the atoms in a polyatomic ion is equal to the charge on that ion.

Assign oxidation numbers to all atoms in $S_2O_7^{2-}$.

1 **If you know an element's oxidation number, start by placing those oxidation numbers above the elements**

▶ From rule 6, you know that oxygen has an oxidation number of –2.

$$\overset{-2}{S_2O_7^{2-}}$$

2 **If more than one atom of an element is present in the formula, calculate the total charge contributed by those atoms by multiplying the charge on the individual atom by its subscript in the formula**

▶ For oxygen the total charge is calculated as follows:

$$O: (-2)7 = -14$$

$$\underset{-14}{\overset{-2}{S_2O_7^{2-}}}$$

3 **Determine the charge needed to reach a net –2 for the ion**

$$2S + (-14) = -2$$

$$2S = +12$$

4 **Divide that charge by the number of atoms to determine the oxidation number for each atom**

$$S = \frac{12}{2}$$

$$S = +6$$

▶ In $S_2O_7^{2-}$ the oxidation state assigned to S is +6 and to O is –2.

CONCEPT CHECK

1. Determine the oxidation number assigned to Mn in MnO_4^-.
2. Determine the oxidation number assigned to each atom in NH_4^+.
3. Determine the oxidation number assigned to P in H_3PO_4.
4. Determine the oxidation number for each atom in BF_3.
5. Determine the oxidation number for each atom in the following compounds:
   a. $KMnO_4$
   b. $PbSO_4$
   c. iron(III) carbonate
   d. cobalt(II) nitrite

HOW TO

ADDITIONAL EXAMPLES

Assign oxidation numbers to each element in the following compounds or ions:

a. KOH

   Ans. K = +1; O = –2; H = +1

b. Na_3AsO_4

   Ans. Na = +1; As = +5; O = –2

c. NO_3^-

   Ans. N = +5; O = –2

d. NO_2^-

   Ans. N = +3; O = –2

e. $Ca(ClO_3)_2$

   Ans. Ca = +2; Cl = +5; O = –2

f. $NaClO_4$

   Ans. Na = +1; Cl = +7; O = –2

ANSWERS

CONCEPT CHECK

1. Mn = +7
2. N = –3; H = +1
3. P = +5
4. B = +3; F = –1
5. a. K = +1, Mn = +7, O = –2
   b. Pb = +2, S = +6, O = –2
   c. Fe = +3, C = +4, O = –2
   d. Co = +2, N = +3, O = –2

mineral

a naturally occurring inorganic substance that has a definite composition and ordered structure

silicate

any of the compounds containing silicon, oxygen, one or more metals, and possibly hydrogen

Silicates and hydrates
Even rocks consist of salts

All the rocks on Earth began as igneous rock, such as granite, which forms when molten magma solidifies. Weathering leads to sedimentary rock, such as sandstone. The action of heat and pressure converts other rocks into metamorphic rock, such as slate. Rocks contain inorganic crystalline materials called **minerals.** Some minerals are, in effect, salts of metal cations and oxyanions of silicon. They differ from the salts that you have studied so far in that some of them have large anions.

The **silicates** are one class of minerals whose anions are composed of long chains, sheets, or networks of alternating silicon and oxygen atoms with periodic negative charges. A simple example is the $Si_4O_{12}^{10-}$ anion shown in **Figure 5-14a.** The negative charges of these anions are balanced by the presence of metal cations such as Mg^{2+} in $Mg_3(Si_2O_6H)_2$. The silicate ions are arranged in layers in the mineral talc. This structure gives talc a slippery feel because the layers slide past each other.

Feldspars, the most abundant rocks in Earth's crust, are aluminosilicates that have some of the silicon atoms replaced by aluminum atoms. Feldspars can consist of large aluminosilicate anions with sodium, potassium, or calcium cations. As the rock slowly weathers, the cations are washed out and the rock eventually crumbles into clay. The semiprecious gem garnet, shown in **Figure 5-14b,** is an aluminosilicate that includes iron and has the formula $Fe_3Al_2(SiO_4)_3$.

▼ **FIGURE 5-14**

c Feldspars are the most abundant rocks on Earth. Half Dome, in Yosemite National Park, is composed of feldspars.

a Silicates are composed of long chains of anions arranged as shown in the model.

b Garnet is an aluminosilicate with an iron cation.

DEMONSTRATION 3

Loss of Water from a Hydrate

Approximate time: 20 minutes

1. Place a heat resistant test tube in a small beaker.

2. Add about 3 g of $Na_2CO_3 \cdot 10H_2O$ to the test tube. Place the beaker with the test tube on a balance, and record the total mass on the board.

3. Attach the test tube to a ring stand with a clamp. It should be mounted horizontally, with the mouth of the test tube pointed slightly downward.

4. Heat the crystals moderately for about 1 minute. During this time, students should observe water droplets condensing near the cooler mouth of the tube.

5. Heat strongly for 2 to 3 minutes until there is no more evidence of water vapor coming from the tube.

FIGURE 5-15 ▼

a Anhydrous copper(II) sulfate, CuSO$_4$, is a white powder . . .

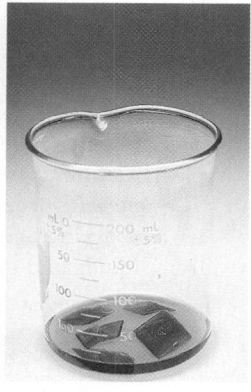

b . . . but when it is stirred in water, a blue solution forms.

c After the water evaporates, blue crystals form that are copper(II) sulfate pentahydrate, CuSO$_4$•5H$_2$O.

Some salts form hydrates

If you dissolve a soluble salt in water and then allow the water to evaporate, you don't always recover the same material you started with. **Figure 5-15** shows stages in such an experiment. When water is added to the white salt in the beaker, the salt dissolves, but the resulting solution becomes blue. If the water evaporates, blue crystals form. The white salt is copper(II) sulfate, CuSO$_4$. The blue salt that was recovered after the evaporation process is called copper(II) sulfate *pentahydrate*. The blue product still contains the Cu^{2+} cation and the SO$_4^{2-}$ anion in a one-to-one ratio, but in addition, it has five water molecules for each pair of ions. The formula for the blue salt is written as follows.

$$CuSO_4•5H_2O$$

Ionic compounds, like CuSO$_4$, with water molecules incorporated into their crystal lattices are called **hydrates.** The water molecules are referred as *water of hydration*. When a hydrated ionic compound is heated to drive off all the water, the remaining salt is **anhydrous,** which means "without water." The specific number of water molecules per formula unit of the ionic compound is indicated by the Greek prefixes *mono-, di-, tri-, tetra-, penta-,* and so on. **Table 5-8** shows examples of the use of prefixes in naming hydrates.

Not all hydrates have another color in their anhydrous form. Sodium carbonate, Na$_2$CO$_3$, forms the hydrate Na$_2$CO$_3$•10H$_2$O, which is called sodium

hydrate

an ionic compound that contains precise numbers of water molecules in its crystal lattice

anhydrous

without water

TABLE 5-8	**Names and Formulas for Some Common Hydrates**

Name	Formula
Barium chloride dihydrate	BaCl$_2$•2H$_2$O
Barium hydroxide octahydrate	Ba(OH)$_2$•8H$_2$O
Calcium nitrate tetrahydrate	Ca(NO$_3$)$_2$•4H$_2$O
Calcium sulfate dihydrate	CaSO$_4$•2H$_2$O
Calcium sulfate hemihydrate	CaSO$_4$•1/2H$_2$O
Cobalt(II) nitrate hexahydrate	Co(NO$_3$)$_2$•6H$_2$O
Cobalt(II) sulfate heptahydrate	CoSO$_4$•6H$_2$O
Iron(III) chloride hexahydrate	FeCl$_3$•6H$_2$O
Iron(III) nitrate nonahydrate	Fe(NO$_3$)$_3$•9H$_2$O
Magnesium sulfate heptahydrate	MgSO$_4$•7H$_2$O

IONIC COMPOUNDS **183**

TEACHING TIP

Counting Atoms Students should learn to count the number of atoms of each element in a compound by looking at the formula. This skill will be needed in Chapters 8, 9, and 10. Provide students with a list of the formulas of compounds that contain polyatomic ions. Several examples should include polyatomic ions in parentheses. Also include compounds that are hydrates. Possibilities include:

▸ Mg(NO$_3$)$_2$
▸ Zn(BrO$_3$)$_2$
▸ ZnSeO$_4$•5H$_2$O
▸ Sr(NO$_2$)$_2$•H$_2$O
▸ (NH$_4$)$_3$PO$_4$•3H$_2$O
▸ (NH$_4$)$_2$C$_2$O$_4$•H$_2$O
▸ Al$_2$(C$_2$O$_4$)$_3$•4H$_2$O
▸ Ba(C$_4$H$_7$O$_2$)$_2$ (barium benzoate)
▸ Be(NO$_3$)$_2$•3H$_2$O
▸ Bi$_2$(MoO$_4$)$_3$ (bismuth molybdate)
▸ Cr$_2$(SO$_4$)$_3$•18H$_2$O
▸ Cd(NH$_4$)$_2$(SO$_4$)$_2$•6H$_2$O (cadmium diammonium sulfate hexahydrate)

Make an additional list of compound names from which students must write formulas and then count atoms.

RESOURCE LINK

IN-TEXT LAB

Skills Development
Have students do Exploration 5A on page 730 to develop their skills using gravimetric techniques.

IN-TEXT LAB

Self-Directed Inquiry
Have students do Investigation 5A *Hydrates—Gypsum and Plaster of Paris* on page 734 to design an experiment for the concept of hydrates.

6. Allow the tube to cool for a few minutes. Ask students to speculate on how the mass of the tube may have changed and why.

7. Place the cooled tube in the beaker, and re-measure the mass. Record this new mass on the board, and compare it with the mass before heating.

Variation

Demonstrate the dehydration and rehydration of CuSO$_4$•5H$_2$O shown in Figure 5-15. Do not

overheat or the compound will decompose to black CuO.

Safety

Wear safety goggles and a lab apron. All forms of Na$_2$CO$_3$ are somewhat caustic. Avoid contact with skin or eyes. Wash with plenty of water if contact occurs.

Disposal

Collect the anhydrous Na$_2$CO$_3$ samples into a beaker. Dissolve the powder, and wash it down the drain with plenty of water.

carbonate *decahydrate*. *Deca-* is the prefix that denotes 10. This compound is also known as washing soda. Both the anhydrous salt and the hydrate are white, though they have different crystal lattices.

The ratio of water molecules in a hydrate is determined experimentally. You cannot predict the number of water molecules in the formula for a hydrate by looking at the formula for its anhydrous form. There are even hydrates called hemihydrates (meaning "half hydrate"). For example, potassium perborate hemihydrate has the formula $KBO_3 \cdot 1/2H_2O$.

Some anhydrous salts absorb moisture so readily that they can be used as drying agents to remove moisture from air or to remove water from liquids and gases other than those in air.

SECTION REVIEW

Total recall

1. How are minerals related to salts?

2. Describe the structure of a silicate.

3. Write formulas for the following compounds:
   a. ammonium monohydrogen phosphate
   b. zinc carbonate
   c. cobalt(II) acetate
   d. lead(II) azide
   e. copper(I) carbonate
   f. copper(II) chromate
   g. ammonium acetate
   h. ammonium dichromate
   i. calcium peroxide
   j. cobalt(II) phosphate

4. Write formulas for the following compounds:
   a. iron(II) bromide hexahydrate
   b. nickel(II) hydroxide dihydrate
   c. copper(II) phosphate trihydrate
   d. aluminum nitrate nonahydrate
   e. barium perchlorate tetrahydrate
   f. barium oxalate monohydrate

5. Name the following compounds:
   a. $CoSO_4$
   b. $Fe_2(C_2O_4)_3$
   c. $Mn(NO_3)_2$
   d. $NaClO$
   e. $CoSO_4 \cdot 7H_2O$
   f. $Fe_3(PO_4)_2 \cdot 8H_2O$
   g. $Mn(NO_3)_2 \cdot 6H_2O$
   h. $NaClO \cdot 5H_2O$

6. Describe a method that you could use to obtain $MgSO_4$ from $MgSO_4 \cdot 7H_2O$.

7. **Interpreting Tables** Using Table 5-8, write the prefixes used to denote 2, 4, 6, 7, and 9 water molecules in a hydrate formula.

8. **Story Clue** In photography, solid AgBr is dissolved in a solution of sodium thiosulfate. Write the formula for sodium thiosulfate.

9. Determine the oxidation number of bromine in the following polyatomic ions:
   a. bromate   c. hypobromite
   b. bromite   d. perbromate

10. Determine the oxidation number for each element in the following formulas:
   a. $HClO_4$ c. $Fe(NO_3)_3$
   b. $Al_2(SO_4)_3$ d. $(NH_4)_2Cr_2O_7$

Critical thinking

11. Suppose that a new nonmetal element is discovered and named *loftium*. How would the loftate and loftite ions compare in charge and composition? How would the hypoloftite and perloftate ions compare with the loftite and loftate ions?

12. How does oxidation number differ from the charge on an ion? In what case are the oxidation number and charge the same?

SECTION REVIEW

Total recall

1. Most minerals are salts, but they often have large or complex anions.

2. Silicate anions are long chains or sheets of silicon and oxygen atoms.

3. a. $(NH_4)_2HPO_4$
   b. $ZnCO_3$
   c. $Co(CH_3COO)_2$
   d. $Pb(N_3)_2$
   e. $CuCO_3$
   f. $CuCrO_4$
   g. NH_4CH_3COO
   h. $(NH_4)_2Cr_2O_7$
   i. CaO_2
   j. $Co_3(PO_4)_2$

4. a. $FeBr_2 \cdot 6H_2O$
   b. $Ni(OH)_2 \cdot 2H_2O$
   c. $Cu_3(PO_4)_2 \cdot 3H_2O$
   d. $Al(NO_3)_3 \cdot 9H_2O$
   e. $Ba(ClO_4)_2 \cdot 4H_2O$
   f. $BaC_2O_4 \cdot H_2O$

5. a. cobalt(II) sulfate
   b. iron(III) oxalate
   c. manganese(II) nitrate
   d. sodium hypochlorite
   e. cobalt(II) sulfate heptahydrate
   f. iron(II) phosphate octahydrate
   g. manganese(II) nitrate hexahydrate
   h. sodium hypochlorite pentahydrate

6. Heat $MgSO_4 \cdot 7H_2O$ strongly until all the water of hydration is driven off, leaving anhydrous $MgSO_4$.

7. di-, tetra-, hexa-, hepta-, nona-

8. $Na_2S_2O_3$

9. a. BrO_3^-; $Br = +5$
   b. BrO_2^-; $Br = +3$
   c. BrO^-; $Br = +1$
   d. BrO_4^-; $Br = +7$

10. a. $H = +1$, $Cl = +7$, $O = -2$
   b. $Al = +3$, $S = +6$, $O = -2$
   c. $Fe = +3$, $N = +5$, $O = -2$
   d. $N = -3$, $H = +1$, $Cr = +6$, $O = -2$

Critical thinking

11. Loftate ions would have one more oxygen atom than loftite ions. Perloftate would have one more oxygen atom than loftate. Hypoloftite would have one less oxygen atom than loftite. All four ions would have the same charge, probably 1–, because loftium has a different oxidation number in each type of ion.

12. Oxidation number is a convention for assigning electrons to an atom, even though the electrons are actually shared by two atoms. It does not represent a true charge on an atom. When oxidation numbers are assigned to the elements in an ionic compound, the number represents the true charge on an atom of that element.

The technician *develops* the film by placing it in a special developer solution that is mildly alkaline. The developer must be at just the right temperature and concentration and must remain in contact with the film for just the right length of time if the photograph is to be picture perfect. During the development stage, silver halide crystals that have silver atoms around their edges are converted to silver metal.

To stop further development, a *stopper* is added, followed by a *fixer,* which removes all the remaining silver halide crystals. When the film has been through these two solutions (they are sometimes combined) and has been thoroughly washed with pure water, it is safe to bring the film out of the darkroom. After it dries, the film has islands of silver metal distributed throughout the emulsion. There is a lot of silver where the light fell the strongest, and none where no light fell. At this stage, the film is called a *negative.* The negative is dark where the scene was lightest and light where the scene was darkest.

Next comes the printing process. Using an enlarger, the technician projects light through the negative and onto a sheet of photographic paper. The paper contains silver chloride, AgCl. The entire photographic process—exposure, development, stopping, fixing, washing, and drying—is carried out again on the print. This process causes a second reversal, so that ultimately the dark areas on the print correspond to the dark areas on the original scene to form a positive image.

Color-film processing is similar to the black-and-white process just described. However, color-film emulsions consist of three distinct silver halide-impregnated layers, each incorporating a different-colored dye to make the final three-color print.

LOOKING BACK

How do the properties of silver atoms differ from those of silver ions?

A silver ion contains one less electron than a silver atom, which gives the ion an overall 1+ charge.

How can exposure to light change the chemical structure of a compound?

Light provides the energy needed to drive the reaction that changes silver ions to silver atoms.

Although light falls on the entire salt crystal, why do silver atoms form only at the edges of the crystal?

Recall that the silver bromide and silver iodide crystals are distributed throughout a gelatin matrix and exposed to light. The energy of the light is sufficient to knock one electron off a bromide ion, leaving an unstable bromine atom in the salt lattice.

$$Br^-(s) + \textit{light energy} \longrightarrow e^- + Br(s)$$

Attracted to the positive charges of the Ag^+ ions, the free electron moves through the lattice. The Ag^+ ions at the crystal's edge are not surrounded by six bromide ions, and they *are* susceptible to a reaction with the wandering electron.

$$Ag^+(edge) + e^- \longrightarrow Ag(edge)$$

So it is the instability of ions at the surface of the ionic crystal that leads to the formation of latent images.

HIGHLIGHTS

CHAPTER 5

READING STRATEGY

Assimilating Knowledge

Have students return to the list of things they want to know about ions and ionic compounds that they created on page 156. Have them place a check mark next to each question that they are now able to answer. Students should finish by making a list of what they have learned. Have students identify unanswered questions as well as new questions they may have. These questions could be used as the basis for a research project.

REVIEW & ASSESS ASSIGNMENT GUIDE

Term Review

Assign after Section 5-3.

Concept & Skills Review

Section 5-1
▶ Items 1–14

Section 5-2
▶ Items 15–22

Section 5-3
▶ Items 23–35

Linking Chapters

Section 5-1
▶ Item 1

Section 5-2
▶ Item 2

Alternative Assessments

Assign after Section 5-3.

Test Prep

Assign prior to the chapter test.

KEY TERMS

5-1
anion
binary ionic compound
cation
electroneutrality
ion
ionic compound

isoelectronic
octet rule
subscript

5-2
coulombic force
crystal lattice
halide

ionic bond
lattice energy
unit cell

5-3
anhydrous
hydrate
mineral

oxidation number
oxyanion
polyatomic ion
salt
silicate

KEY CONCEPTS

5-1 How are ions different from atoms?
▶ Some atoms may gain or lose electrons to achieve electron configurations that are isoelectronic with a noble gas.
▶ Ions are electrically charged particles that have different chemical properties than their parent atoms.
▶ Metals tend to form cations, while nonmetals tend to form anions.
▶ Ionic compounds are named by joining the cation and anion names.
▶ The subscripts in the formula for an ionic compound indicate the lowest electrically neutral whole-number ratio of cations to anions.

5-2 What holds a salt together?
▶ The opposite charges of anions and cations attract, forming a tightly packed substance of bonded ions called a crystal structure.
▶ Salts have high melting and boiling points and usually do not conduct electricity in the solid state.

▶ Salts conduct electricity when melted or dissolved in water.
▶ An input of energy is needed to break chemical bonds between atoms. Energy is released when bonds form between atoms.
▶ An ionic compound will form if the energy released to create anions and form the crystal structure is greater than the energy absorbed to create cations.

5-3 What are polyatomic ions?
▶ A polyatomic ion is a group of two or more atoms bonded together that functions as a single unit.
▶ Parentheses are used to group polyatomic ions in a chemical formula with a subscript.
▶ Oxidation numbers are a convention for assigning a relative charge to atoms that share electrons.
▶ Polyatomic ions are found in silicates.
▶ Hydrates are compounds that contain water molecules within the crystal lattice.

KEY SKILLS

Review the following models before your exam. Be sure you can write formulas and name compounds.

How To Write formulas for binary ionic compounds (p. 164)

How To Write the name of a compound containing a polyatomic ion (p. 178)

How To Write the formula for a compound containing a polyatomic ion (p. 179)

How To Assign oxidation numbers to atoms in a polyatomic ion (p. 181)

TERM REVIEW

1. By losing an electron, a metal atom becomes a(n) ———.
   (cation, anion)

2. CaO is an example of a ———.
   (binary compound, cation)

3. The driving force in the formation of a salt is the ———.
   (lattice energy, nuclear force)

4. The simplest repeating unit that makes up a crystal is the ———.
   (unit cell, crystal lattice)

5. A(n) ——— is a negatively charged polyatomic ion containing oxygen.
   (oxyanion, oxycation)

CONCEPT & SKILLS REVIEW

FORMATION OF IONS

1. Propose a reason why magnesium forms Mg^{2+} ions and not Mg^{6-} ions.

2. Complete the table below.

Atom	Ion	Noble-gas configuration of ion
S		
Be		
I		
Rb		
O		
Sr		
F		

3. Why are most metals found in nature as ores and not as pure metals?

4. A classmate insists that sodium gains a positive charge when it becomes an ion because it gains a proton. Explain this student's error.

5. Which of the following diagrams illustrates the electron diagram for a potassium ion found in the nerve cells of your body? (Hint: potassium's atomic number is 19.)

6. Write a chemical symbol for each of the following particles. If the particle is an ion, indicate its charge and identify it as a cation or an anion.

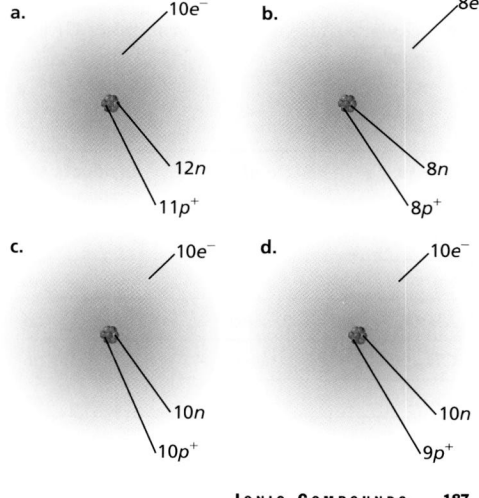

TERM REVIEW

1. cation

2. binary compound

3. lattice energy

4. unit cell

5. oxyanion

CONCEPT & SKILLS REVIEW

1. Mg atoms have two outer-level electrons. Losing those two electrons forms the Mg^{2+} ion, which has the stable noble-gas configuration of neon.

2. S; S^{2-};   Ar
   Be; Be^{2+};   He
   I; I^-;   Xe
   Rb; Rb^+;   Kr
   O; O^{2-};   Ne
   Sr; Sr^{2+};   Kr
   F; F^-;   Ne

3. Most metals are active elements that lose electrons easily to form ions with stable octets. Thus, metals are usually found as salts or oxides.

4. The nucleus of an atom cannot undergo change in a normal chemical reaction. Therefore, the only way an atom can become a positive ion is by losing a negative charge—an electron.

5. b

6. a. Na^+ c. Ne
   b. O   d. F^-

7. Li^+: $1s^2$; I^-: $1s^2\,2s^2\,2p^6\,3s^2\,3p^6\,4s^2\,3d^{10}\,4p^6\,5s^2\,4d^{10}\,5p^6$

8. barium, Cl^-, chromium(III), fluoride, Mn^{2+}, O^{2-}
   a. $MnCl_2$ b. CrF_3 c. BaO

9. Elements in this group do not ordinarily form ions. They all have stable outer energy levels.

10. a. AlF_3 c. CaS
    b. MgO   d. $SrBr_2$

11. a. $CdBr_2$ c. V_2O_5
    b. $PdCl_2$ d. CoS

12. a. $FeCl_2$, $FeCl_3$ d. $HgCl_2$, Hg_2Cl_2
    b. Cu_2O, CuO   e. MnO, Mn_2O_3
    c. SnF_2, SnF_4 f. $CrCl_2$, $CrCl_3$

13. a. Rubidium forms 1+ ions, RbCl
    b. The formula does not represent the simplest ratio of elements. GeS_2
    c. Both Na and Cs normally form only 1+ ions and would not form such a compound.
    d. Neon is a noble gas with a stable octet, so it would not combine with sodium.

14. a. Barium usually forms only Ba^{2+} ions. This formula shows the subscript next to the wrong element symbol.
    b. This formula implies that the barium ion has a +3 charge.
    c. The formula does not represent the simplest ratio.

15. KI is ionic. It has a high melting point and is a conductor.

    Fe is nonionic. It is a metal.

    $AlPO_4$ is ionic. It has a high melting point and is a conductor.

    CH_4 is nonionic. It has a low melting point and is not a conductor.

    NaBr is ionic. It has a high melting point and is a conductor.

    $C_6H_{12}O_6$ is nonionic. It has a low melting point and is not a conductor.

16. a. $1Sr^{2+}:2Cl^-$ d. $1Ba^{2+}:1O^{2-}$
    b. $1Rb^+:1Cl^-$ e. $2Al^{3+}:3O^{2-}$
    c. $1Al^{3+}:3Cl^-$ f. $1Al^{3+}:1N^{3-}$

17. The coulombic attraction between cations and anions in the crystal lattice is strong. Therefore, a high temperature is required to break down the lattice and change the ionic compound to a liquid. In the liquid phase, ions still have strong coulombic attractions. Therefore, an even higher temperature is required to separate the ions into a gas.

18. Ionic substances will conduct in the molten state or when dissolved in water. Under these conditions, ions are free to move. The ionic compound would be a solid on the circuit board, so it would not conduct.

7. The electron configuration for a lithium atom is $1s^2 2s^1$. The configuration for an iodine atom is $1s^2 2s^2 2p^6 3s^2 3p^6 4s^2 3d^{10} 4p^6 5s^2 4d^{10} 5p^5$. Write the electron configurations for the ions that form lithium iodide, a salt used in photography.

BINARY COMPOUNDS AND NOMENCLATURE

8. Complete the table below, and then use it to answer the questions that follow.

Element	Ion	Name of ion
Barium	Ba^{2+}	
Chlorine		chloride
Chromium	Cr^{3+}	
Fluorine	F^-	
Manganese		manganese(II)
Oxygen		oxide

   a. Write the formula for a salt found in electrical batteries containing manganese and chlorine.
   b. Write the formula for a compound containing chromium and fluorine used to treat silk.
   c. Write the formula for a compound containing barium and oxygen used to manufacture lubricating-oil detergents.

9. Why are there no rules for naming Group 18 ions?

10. Write formulas for the following compounds.
    a. aluminum fluoride, used in ceramics
    b. magnesium oxide, an antacid
    c. calcium sulfide, used in luminous paints
    d. strontium bromide, an anticonvulsant

11. Write formulas for the following compounds.
    a. cadmium(II) bromide, used in process engraving
    b. palladium(II) chloride, used in some photographic toning solutions
    c. vanadium(V) oxide, an ingredient in yellow glass
    d. cobalt(II) sulfide, used as a catalyst

12. Use **Table 5-2** to write all possible formulas for the ionic compounds listed.
    a. iron chloride
    b. copper oxide
    c. tin fluoride
    d. mercury chloride
    e. manganese oxide
    f. chromium chloride

13. Explain what is wrong with each of the following chemical formulas:
    a. $RbCl_2$ c. NaCs
    b. $Ge_{12}S_{24}$ d. NaNe

14. Explain the error contained in each of the following formulas for barium chloride:
    a. Ba_2Cl c. Ba_2Cl_4
    b. $BaCl_3$

IONIC COMPOUNDS

15. Use the table below to identify the chemicals listed as ionic or molecular. State reasons for your answers.

Substance	State at room temperature	Conducts electricity at room temperature	Melting point (°C)	Conducts electricity as a liquid
KI	solid	no	680	yes
Fe	solid	yes	1535	yes
$AlPO_4$	solid	no	1460	yes
CH_4	gas	no	−182.6	no
NaBr	solid	no	755	yes
$C_6H_{12}O_6$	solid	no	150	no

16. Determine the ratio of cations to anions for the following compounds:
    a. strontium chloride, an ingredient in fireworks
    b. rubidium chloride, an ingredient in drugs
    c. aluminum chloride, an ingredient in wood preservatives
    d. barium oxide, a substance used in making detergents for lubricating oils
    e. aluminum oxide, an ingredient in some dental cements
    f. aluminum nitride, a substance used in making semiconductors

17. Why do most ionic compounds have such high melting and boiling points?

18. Under the right conditions, ionic substances can conduct electricity very well. Describe these conditions, and explain why an ionic substance would be a poor choice as a conductor for a computer circuit board.

19. Does a cube of salt have a different unit cell than powdered salt has? Explain your answer.

20. Label the drawings below as representing a solid, a liquid, or a solution. State whether the substance pictured will or will not conduct electricity.

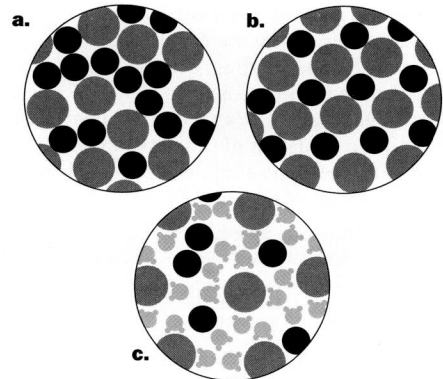

21. Sodium chloride can be prepared by reacting sodium metal with chlorine gas. Another way to prepare it is to combine sodium hydroxide and hydrochloric acid and allow any water present to evaporate. Will the method of preparation affect the type of unit cell and crystalline structure of NaCl? Explain.

22. The equations below show the energy changes that are necessary for calcium bromide, $CaBr_2$, to form from the elements calcium and bromine. Is formation of $CaBr_2$, from its elements, an exothermic or an endothermic process? Explain.

$$Ca(s) + 8.5 \text{ kJ} \longrightarrow Ca(g)$$
$$Ca(g) + 1735 \text{ kJ} \longrightarrow Ca^{2+}(g) + 2e^-$$
$$Br_2(g) + 193 \text{ kJ} \longrightarrow 2Br(g)$$
$$2Br(g) + 2e^- \longrightarrow 2Br^-(g) + 650 \text{ kJ}$$
$$Ca^{2+}(g) + 2Br^-(g) \longrightarrow CaBr_2(s) + 2176 \text{ kJ}$$

POLYATOMIC IONS

23. Why is the strontium nitrate found in roadside emergency flares represented as $Sr(NO_3)_2$ rather than SrN_2O_6?

24. What is the difference between the chlorite ion and the chlorate ion? **(Hint: Refer to Table 5-7.)**

25. Write the symbol and charge for each ion found in the following compounds:
    a. NaClO   e. FeC_2O_4
    b. $(NH_4)_2CO_3$ f. $Mn(CH_3COO)_2$
    c. K_2HPO_4 g. Hg_2SO_4
    d. CuCN

26. Write formulas for the following compounds:
    a. potassium hydrogen phosphate, an ingredient in nondairy creamers
    b. strontium nitrate, an ingredient in red safety flares
    c. lithium sulfate, an antidepressant
    d. magnesium dihydrogen phosphate, used to make wood fireproof.

27. Write formulas for the following compounds:
    a. ammonium acetate, a meat preservative
    b. mercury(I) nitrate, used to blacken brass
    c. titanium(III) sulfate, used as a stain remover
    d. chromium(III) phosphate, a green pigment

28. Determine the subscripts that are most likely in the formulas for ionic substances of the following elements:
    a. an alkali metal and a halogen
    b. an alkaline-earth metal and a halogen
    c. an alkali metal and a member of Group 16
    d. an alkaline-earth metal and a member of Group 16

19. No. Salt has the same unit cell in the solid state no matter what size the crystal is or whether the crystal has been ground into small particles.

20. a. liquid; conducts
    b. solid; does not conduct
    c. solution; conducts

21. No. NaCl(s) forms with a specific unit cell.

22. The process is exothermic. Total energy input is 1936 kJ. Total energy output is 2826 kJ. Therefore, the net reaction is exothermic, giving off 890 kJ/mol.

23. The nitrate ion has a specific structure and charge that is represented by NO_3^-. The only way of representing two of these ions is by writing $(NO_3)_2$.

24. The chlorate ion contains three oxygen atoms, ClO_3^-; the chlorite ion contains two oxygen atoms, ClO_2^-.

25. a. Na^+, Cl^+, O^{2-} e. Fe^{2+}, $C_2O_4^{2-}$
    b. NH_4^+, CO_3^{2-} f. Mn^{2+},
    c. K^+, HPO_4^{2-} CH_3COO^-
    d. Cu^+, CN^- g. Hg_2^{2+}, SO_4^{2-}

26. a. K_2HPO_4 c. Li_2SO_4
    b. $Sr(NO_3)_2$ d. $Mg(H_2PO_4)_2$

27. a. NH_4CH_3COO c. $Ti_2(SO_4)_3$
    b. $Hg_2(NO_3)_2$ d. $CrPO_4$

28. Subscripts given as 1 are, of course, not written.
    a. alkali metal: 1; halogen: 1
    b. alkaline-earth metal: 1; halogen: 2
    c. alkali metal: 2; Group 16 element: 1
    d. alkaline-earth metal: 1; Group 16 element: 1

29. 1Fe, 3C, 5H, 7O

30. Cl = +5; O = −2

31. H = +1; C = +4; O = −2

32. $AuCl_4^-$, Au = +3, Cl = −1

$Zn(OH)_4^{2-}$, Zn = +2, O = −2, H = +1

VO_2^+, V = +5, O = −2

$S_2O_3^{2-}$, S = +2, O = −2

$H_2BO_3^-$, H = +1, B = +3, O = −2

BH_4^-, B = +3, H = −1

33. Pb = +2, Cl = −1

34. Mg = +2, O = −2, H = +1

35. PbS   Pb = +2; S = −2

MnO_2 Mn = +4; O = −2

$LiAlH_4$ Li = +1; Al = +3; H = −1 (in the hydride ion)

Na_2O_2 Na = +1; O = −1 (in the peroxide ion)

HgO   Hg = 2+; O = −2

NiO(OH)   Ni = +3; O = −2 (in both cases); H = +1

$PbSO_4$ Pb = +2; S = +6; O = −2

LINKING CHAPTERS

1. a. helium: $1s^2$

neon: $1s^2\,2s^2\,2p^6$

argon: $1s^2\,2s^2\,2p^6\,3s^2\,3p^6$

krypton: $1s^2\,2s^2\,2p^6\,3s^2\,3p^6\,4s^2$
$3d^{10}\,4p^6$

xenon: $1s^2\,2s^2\,2p^6\,3s^2\,3p^6\,4s^2$
$3d^{10}\,4p^6\,5s^2\,4d^{10}\,5p^6$

The outermost electrons of krypton and xenon are farther from the nucleus than those in neon or argon and therefore are more loosely held. Therefore, an element with a very strong attraction for electrons can pull krypton's or xenon's outer electrons into a bond.

b. Because radon is even larger than xenon, radon's attraction for the outermost electrons is weaker than that of xenon. Thus, radon is likely to form a compound with fluorine.

2. Metals conduct an electric current in the solid state. Salts do not conduct in the solid state. In addition, they are brittle, hard, and break easily, unlike metals, which bend and stretch and therefore can be formed into wires easily.

Continued on page 191.

---

29. How many atoms of each element are contained in a single formula unit of iron(III) formate, $Fe(HCOO)_3 \cdot H_2O$, a compound used as a preservative?

OXIDATION NUMBERS

30. Assign oxidation numbers to the atoms in the chlorate ion, ClO_3^-, which is used in explosives.

31. Assign oxidation numbers to the atoms in a bicarbonate ion, HCO_3^-.

32. Assign oxidation numbers to the atoms in the following ions: $AuCl_4^-$, $Zn(OH)_4^{2-}$, VO_2^+, $S_2O_3^{2-}$, $H_2BO_3^-$, BH_4^-.

33. Assign oxidation numbers to the atoms in lead chloride, $PbCl_2$.

34. Assign oxidation numbers to the atoms in magnesium hydroxide, $Mg(OH)_2$, an antacid.

35. Assign oxidation numbers to the atoms in the following compounds: PbS, MnO_2, $LiAlH_4$, Na_2O_2, HgO, NiO(OH), $PbSO_4$.

LINKING CHAPTERS

1. Electron configurations

Scientists have been able to create fluoride compounds with krypton and xenon. However, fluorine will not form compounds with helium or neon. Use the different electron configurations of the noble gases to explain why fluorine can form compounds with certain noble gases.

2. Metals

Although metals and salts have similar lattice structures, metals are used for electrical wiring. Why aren't salts used?

ALTERNATIVE ASSESSMENTS

Performance assessment

1. Devise a set of criteria that will allow you to classify the following substances as ionic or nonionic: $CaCO_3$, Cu, H_2O, NaBr, and C (graphite). Show your criteria to your instruc-

---

tor, and obtain some of the substances. Are these substances ionic or nonionic?

Portfolio projects

1. Research and communication

Use an analogy, a picture, a mechanical model, or a computer program to create your own model of an ionic bond. Present your model to the class, and explain the ways your model does or does not match experimental observations.

2. Chemistry and you

Ions play an important physiological role in your body. Select one such ion, and write a report detailing its function. Be sure to include recent medical information.

3. Cooperative activity/Group project

Keep the ingredients labels from all of the food products you eat in one day. Make a list of all the salts contained in each product. As a class, compile a master list identifying which salts were eaten by the most people. Research the properties and uses of the salts that were most frequently eaten; then, as a class, create an information poster describing the functions of these compounds.

4. Research and communication

Free radicals are atoms with electrons that are not in pairs; thus, they do not have an octet. Some people believe that free radicals are responsible for cancer, the effects of aging, and the depletion of the ozone layer. Find out what would cause free radicals to be so environmentally dangerous.

5. internetconnect

SCi LINKS
NSTA

TOPIC: Salt subtitutes
GO TO: www.scilinks.org
KEYWORD: HW056

Research and communication

Many people follow low-sodium diets. However, they still desire a flavor enhancer like common table salt. Research the different types of salt substitutes and the physiological effects of each. Determine which is the safest salt substitute, and organize your information in a report.

1. The correct formula for a copper atom that has lost two electrons is ____.
   a. Co^+
   b. Co^{2+}
   c. Cu^{2-}
   d. Cu^{2+}

2. The electroneutrality principle ____.
   a. states that the number of cations equals the number of anions
   b. is demonstrated in any polyatomic ion
   c. states that the net charge on a binary ionic compound is zero
   d. All of the above

3. Which of the following atoms can become isoelectronic with a noble gas when the atom forms an ion?
   a. argon
   b. potassium
   c. nickel
   d. iron

4. In forming NaCl, energy is required to ____.
   a. change chlorine to a gas
   b. add an electron to a chlorine atom
   c. remove an electron from a sodium atom
   d. bring together the sodium ions and chloride ions

5. Which of the following is not a characteristic of a salt?
   a. hardness
   b. a high melting point
   c. an ability to conduct electricity in the molten state
   d. an ability to conduct electricity in the solid state

6. Which elements on the periodic table are most likely to form two or more ions?
   a. halides
   b. alkali metals
   c. transition metals
   d. noble gases

7. The factor that changes the unit cell structure for NaCl from that of CsCl is ____.
   a. lattice energy
   b. ion size
   c. crystal structure
   d. ion charge

8. Which of the following compounds does not contain a polyatomic ion?
   a. sodium azide
   b. sodium sulfate
   c. sodium sulfite
   d. sodium sulfide

9. The correct formula for ammonium azide is ____.
   a. NH_4N_3
   b. $(NH_4)_2NH_3$
   c. N_4H_4
   d. $NH_4(N_3)_2$

10. When writing the formula for a compound that contains a polyatomic ion, ____.
    a. the anion's formula is written first
    b. superscripts are used to show the number of polyatomic ions present
    c. parentheses must be used if the number of polyatomic ions is greater than 1.
    d. the polyatomic ion must always be placed in parentheses

11. The concept of electroneutrality involves equal numbers of ____.
    a. anions and cations
    b. positive and negative charges
    c. molecules
    d. ionic bonds

12. The prefix used to denote six water molecules in a hydrate formula is ____.
    a. *hemi-*
    b. *penta-*
    c. *hepta-*
    d. *hexa-*

13. The correct name for NH_4CH_3COO is ____.
    a. ammonium carbonate
    b. ammonium hydroxide
    c. ammonium acetate
    d. ammonium nitrate

14. Which of the following is the correct formula for iron(III) sulfate?
    a. Fe_3SO_4
    b. $Fe_3(SO_4)_2$
    c. $Fe_2(SO_4)_3$
    d. $3FeSO_4$

15. The oxidation number of N in NO_3^- is ____.
    a. +5
    b. −5
    c. −2
    d. +2

1. d	6. c	11. b
2. c	7. b	12. d
3. b	8. d	13. c
4. c	9. a	14. c
5. d	10. c	15. a

Continued from page 190.

ALTERNATIVE ASSESSMENTS

Performance assessment

1. Student answers will vary. Testing criteria should include electrical conductivity (with a battery-powered tester), hardness, and crystalline structure. When possible, students should use simpler observations instead of melting or boiling points.

Portfolio projects

1. Student models will vary. Models should in some way indicate the force of attraction between ions of opposite charge.

2. Responses will vary. Good choices include Na^+, K^+, Ca^{2+}, and HCO_3^-.

3. Answers will vary.

4. These free radicals are very reactive and combine with almost any nearby atoms or molecules to complete their octet of electrons.

5. Answers will vary. Many salt substitutes contain KCl. Students who choose to discuss this substance should research the critical Na^+/K^+ balance in the body to learn why excess use of KCl can be dangerous. MSG is not strictly a salt substitute because it, too, contributes sodium ions to the diet.

Covalent Bonds and Molecular Forces

CLASSROOM RESOURCES

SECTIONS	TEACHER'S DEMONSTRATIONS	PROBLEM SOLVING ■ *Text* ◆ *ChemFile Mini-Guide*	LABORATORIES ■ *Text* ◆ *ChemFile Manuals: A, B, C, D*
6-1 **Why do some atoms form covalent bonds?** Section Review, p. 201	**Demo 1** Paper Chromatography, p. 200		◆ **Inv. C3** Covalent and Ionic Bonding— Ceramics Fixative ◆ **B6** Chemical Bonds
6-2 **How are molecules depicted?** Section Review, p. 213		■ **How To** Draw Lewis structures, p. 204 ■ **How To** Draw Lewis structures with multiple bonds, p. 207 ■ **How To** Draw Lewis structures of polyatomic ions, p. 210	
6-3 **How are molecular shapes determined?** Section Review, p. 218	**Demo 2** Like Charges Repel, p. 214	■ **Sample Problem 6A** Predicting molecular shapes, p. 217	
6-4 **What forces exist between molecules?** Section Review, p. 224	**Demo 3** Properties—Polar Versus Nonpolar, p. 220		■ **QuickLab** Watery Attraction, p. 220 ◆ **D6** Cloth of Many Colors

SECTIONS	VIDEOS/VIDEODISC *Holt Chemistry Videodisc* CNN PRESENTS *Science in the NEWS*	CHEMFILE CD-ROMs ● *Teaching Resources* ◆ *Interactive Tutor*	OVERHEADS ● *Color Transparencies* ◆ *Transparency Masters*
6-1	Bond Energy Bond Energy for Ethane Bond Length	● Supplemental Reading: *Linus Pauling: In His Own Words,* "Mind and Molecules" ● Supplemental Reading: *Consumer's Good Chemical Guide,* "Sweetness and Light" ◆ **Module 4:** Chemical Bonding **Topic:** Covalent Bonding	● **29** Electronegativity Values ● **30** Ionic vs. Covalent Bonding ● **31** Predicting Bonding Type from Electronegativity Differences ● **32** Bond Length and Stability ◆ **24A** Trends in Electronegativity ◆ **42A** Elements that Normally Exist as Diatomic Molecules
6-2	Ethene Molecular Rotation	● Occupational Application: Air-Quality Specialist	◆ **26A** Electron-Dot Notation
6-3	Sulfur Trioxide Molecular Rotation VSEPR Models VSEPR: Linear Electron Clouds VSEPR: Trigonal Electron Clouds VSEPR: Tetrahedral Electron Clouds	◆ **Module 4:** Chemical Bonding **Topic:** Molecular Geometry	● **35** VSEPR Models of Ammonia and Water ● **37** Predicting Polarity ◆ **27A** VSEPR and Molecular Geometry
6-4	Induced Dipole in an Oxygen Molecule London Dispersion Forces CNN PRESENTS Segment 15 Coal-Oil Technology		● **38** Hydrogen Bonding Between Water Molecules

ASSESSMENT RESOURCES

ALTERNATIVE ASSESSMENTS	CHAPTER TESTING	SCORING RUBRICS *Holt ChemFile Teaching Resources CD-ROM*
Student Text Performance assessment, p. 230 Portfolio projects 1–3, p. 230 **Teacher's Edition** Designing a Model, p. 194, p. 206 Conceptual Connections, p. 198 Group Strategy, p. 218 **Study Guide** Sections 6-1 to 6-4	**Student Text** Test Preparation, p. 231 **Holt Chemistry: Visualizing Matter Chapter 6 Test** (blackline masters) **Holt ChemFile Test Generator for Macintosh and Windows**	**Lab Work** Student-Designed Experiments Rubric Performance-Tasks Scoring Rubric Assessment for Structured Inquiry Assessment for Open-Ended Inquiry **Portfolio Projects** Evaluating Concept Maps Assessing Portfolios Portfolio Assignment Student Evaluation Form

CHAPTER 6

Covalent Bonds and Molecular Forces

Establishing Prior Knowledge

Make certain students understand the following concepts.

- Chapter 3: atomic structure, electron configurations
- Chapter 4: periodic table, periodic trends
- Chapter 5: ionic bonds, polyatomic ions

READING STRATEGY

Assimilating Knowledge

Before students read this chapter, have them write short, individual lists of all the things they already know or think they know about molecules. When students finish their lists, ask them to contribute their entries to a group list on the board or on an overhead projector. Then have students list the things they might want to know about molecules.

If students are having trouble coming up with questions, offer the following suggestions to get them on track:

- What is a molecule?
- Do all substances exist as molecules?
- What type of bonding is present in a molecule?
- How do you know the shape of a molecule?

Have students save their lists for later use in the Reading Strategy on page 226.

ABOUT THE ILLUSTRATION

Deoxyribonucleic acid, or DNA, is made up of two strands of covalently bonded molecules. The two strands are held together by hydrogen bonds to form a double helix structure.

 internet**connect**

Holt Chemistry: Visualizing Matter

 On-Line Resources
go.hrw.com
Visit the HRW Web site for a variety of resources related to this chapter. Just type in the keyword HW0 Chapt6.

SCLINKS NSTA

National Science Teachers Association

On-Line Resources: www.scilinks.org
The following Scilinks Internet resources can be found in the student text for this chapter:

Page 194
TOPIC: Covalent bonds
KEYWORD: HW061

Page 215
TOPIC: Molecular shapes
KEYWORD: HW062

Page 222
TOPIC: Hydrogen bonding
KEYWORD: HW063

Page 230
TOPIC: Silicon
KEYWORD: HW064

LIFE, WATER, AND MARS

On December 19, 1997, four people set a record for the longest stay in a closed chamber in the United States. The crew spent 91 days in a two-chamber complex as part of the Lunar-Mars Life Support Test Project sponsored by the National Aeronautics and Space Administration (NASA).

Plans are under way for four crew members to spend 425 days in a five-chamber complex starting in the year 2006. This project is a major component in NASA's plans to send a manned mission to Mars.

Interest in Mars has recently been rekindled by evidence that life may have once existed there. In 1996, chemical examination of a meteorite from Mars revealed the presence of organic molecules. In July 1997, photographs taken by the *Pathfinder* spacecraft revealed crusty soil and numerous rocks with smooth, rounded surfaces. Photographs taken by the *Mars Global Surveyor* spacecraft in January 1998 revealed a canyon about 2.5 km wide.

The smooth rocks, crusty soil, and canyons suggest to scientists that water was once abundant on Mars, perhaps as much as 4 billion years ago. Today, Mars is bone dry.

But the presence of water on Mars in the past means that life could have once existed on the planet.

Life as we know it is not possible without water. Living organisms are 70% to 90% water by mass. Most of the chemical reactions required for life take place in water. Water also has many interesting physical properties that help make it a very important compound. Mars may not be the only celestial body that once supported life. In 1979, the *Voyager* spacecraft sent back to Earth images of a lunar surface that appeared to be covered by a shell of ice. Europa, one of Jupiter's moons, appears to be nearly covered with ice. Some scientists believe that beneath that ice may be an ocean and thus water that might harbor life.

In this chapter you will explore covalent compounds. Based on your study of these compounds, you should be able to answer the following questions about water.

CHAPTER LINKS

Why don't the two hydrogen atoms in water give up their sole electrons to the oxygen atom to form an ionic bond?

Based on its composition, what is the actual chemical name for water?

What is the three-dimensional structure of water?

STORY BACKGROUND

Evidence of water on Mars is similar to evidence of water on Earth. Students are familiar with rocks in a stream bed that are worn smooth by the flow of water. After a hard rain, students have seen channels cut in the soil by running water and have observed the hard crust left on soil as it dries. They can further explore the evidence of water on Mars by accessing the NASA Web site.

Some of the specific reactions necessary to life that involve water include photosynthesis and respiration. Photosynthesis uses water and carbon dioxide to produce sugar and oxygen. In cellular respiration, sugar reacts with oxygen to produce carbon dioxide, water, and energy. This energy is used for cellular activity.

RESOURCE LINK

ChemFile Teaching Resources CD-ROM
Supplemental Reading Projects
Assign the guided reading worksheets for Barbara Marinacci's *Linus Pauling: In His Own Words*, Selection 10, "Mind and Molecules," and John Emsley's *Consumer's Good Chemical Guide*, Chapter 2, "Sweetness and Light," for cross-curricular connections to language arts.

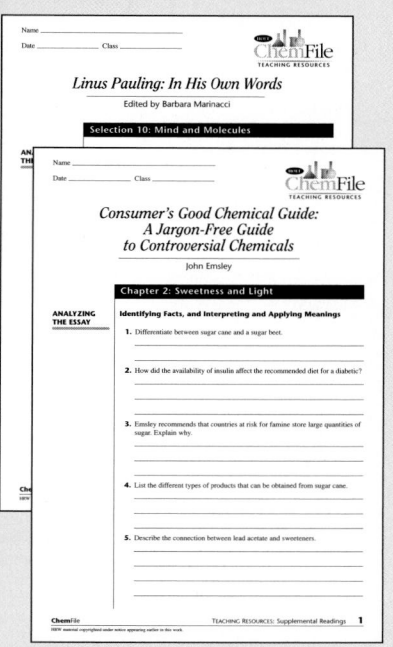

CONCEPT PREVIEW

Section 6-1
Covalent bonds
▶ How covalent bonds form
▶ Comparison of nonpolar covalent and polar covalent bonds

Section 6-2
Lewis molecular structures
▶ Representing valence electrons

▶ Resonance
▶ Naming molecular compounds

Section 6-3
Molecular shapes
▶ VSEPR theory
▶ Possible shapes

Section 6-4
Forces between molecules
▶ Dipole forces
▶ Hydrogen bonds
▶ London forces

LESSON WARM-UP

Discussion Strategy Ask students to provide a possible solution to the following problem. Two entrepreneurs want to start a restaurant. One wants to serve Italian food, and the other wants to serve Chinese food. One owns a suitable, large building. The other owns an abundance of cooking equipment. How can these two people improve their situations? Student solutions should include the idea of the two sharing the building and equipment that they both need while maintaining their separate restaurants. Tell students that Section 6-1 describes a similar situation involving certain atoms.

Why do some atoms form covalent bonds?

OBJECTIVES

▶ *Explain* how a covalent bond forms between two atoms.

▶ *Describe* the change in energy and stability as a covalent bond forms.

▶ *Describe* the differences between covalent and ionic

bonds and between polar and nonpolar covalent bonds.

▶ *Describe* the influence of electronegativity difference on bonding.

▶ *Classify* the types of bonds between atoms using electronegativity values.

Sharing electrons

Chemical reactions involve changes in the distribution of electrons as the reactants combine to form products. In one kind of chemical change, the type discussed in the previous chapter, electrons transfer from one atom to another to form ions. Sodium metal reacting with chlorine gas to form the ionic compound sodium chloride, NaCl, is an example of this type of reaction. The reaction of hydrogen and oxygen to form water involves another kind of rearrangement—the sharing of electrons between atoms. When hydrogen and oxygen are combined, electrons rearrange to produce a new, more stable compound—water—and energy is released as heat and light. The hot flame shown in **Figure 6-1** was produced by this reaction.

internet**connect**

SC*LINKS*
NSTA

TOPIC: Covalent bonds
GO TO: www.scilinks.org
KEYWORD: HW061

O_2 + $2H_2$ → $2H_2O$

▶ **FIGURE 6-1**

This diver is using an oxyhydrogen torch to cut metal. It works even underwater because of the intense heat given off by the reaction between hydrogen and oxygen.

ALTERNATIVE ASSESSMENT

Designing a Model

Have students use Legos® or similar building blocks to demonstrate the difference between ionic and covalent bonding. They should assemble a number of blocks so that all sides of the object created are flush. This is a model of a molecule—the atoms are bonded to create an individual unit capable of existing on its own.

Have them assemble a number of blocks so that pieces of the various blocks jut out of

the sides of the object. This represents a small portion of the ionic arrangement within an ionic compound. The pieces of blocks jutting out represent cations and anions, which attract more ions (more blocks) to create a large array of packed ions. The result is a huge aggregate of ions that have minimized their potential energy through electrical attraction (as opposed to electron sharing).

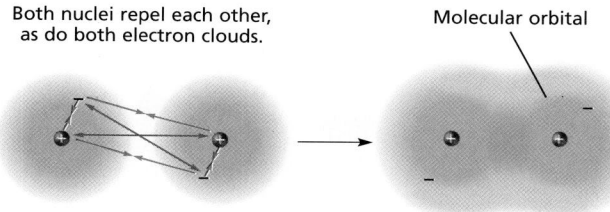

Both nuclei repel each other, as do both electron clouds.

Molecular orbital

The nucleus of each atom attracts both electron clouds.

FIGURE 6-2 ◄

When the forces of attraction and repulsion between atoms balance, a covalent bond is formed, and the two electrons move about the nuclei in a single molecular orbital.

Molecular orbitals are formed from overlapping atomic orbitals

The simplest example of sharing electrons occurs in diatomic molecules, such as hydrogen, H_2, and oxygen, O_2. When two hydrogen atoms approach each other, the positive nucleus of each atom attracts its own electron and the electron of the other atom. At the same time, the positive nuclei of the two atoms repel each other. Likewise, the electron clouds of the atoms repel. Because the two atoms are of the same element, neither has enough attraction to take an electron from the other. Instead of forming ions, the two hydrogen atoms *share* electrons. The two shared electrons form a single electron cloud around both hydrogen nuclei. The result is a diatomic molecule that is more stable than either hydrogen atom alone. **Figure 6-2** illustrates the balancing of forces to form an H_2 molecule.

The H_2 molecule is stable because each hydrogen atom now has a *shared pair* of electrons. This gives both atoms a stability similar to that of a helium configuration. This bond in which electrons are shared between two atoms is a **covalent bond.**

A bond in which two atoms share one pair of electrons between them is called a *single bond.* A single bond can be represented by a single line, so H_2 can also be written as H—H. The shared electrons moving about in the space surrounding the two nuclei are in a **molecular orbital.** A molecular orbital results from the overlap of two atomic orbitals.

covalent bond

a bond formed when two or more valence electrons are attracted by the positively charged nuclei of two atoms and are thus shared between both atoms

molecular orbital

a region where an electron pair is most likely to exist as it travels in the three-dimensional space around two nuclei

FIGURE 6-3 ◄

The sugar (sucrose, $C_{12}H_{22}O_{11}$) and water in this cup of tea are examples of covalent, or molecular, compounds.

VISUAL STRATEGY

Figure 6-2 The electrons of an isolated atom exist at a predictable radius around the nucleus. Have students describe how the location of the electrons differs in a diatomic molecule.

CHEMISTRY INTERACTIVE TUTOR

Module 4: Chemical Bonding Topic: Covalent Bonding
This engaging tutorial reviews and reinforces the concept of covalent bonding through modeling and guided practice.

TEACHING TIP

Designing a Model Have students use two small, soft rubber balls and a rubber band to model Figure 6-5. Have them place the rubber band around the balls. This model represents the position of least potential energy. Have a student push the balls together, then stop pushing. During the compression, the balls represent the molecule to the left of the stable position in the figure. The balls will return to the stable state when the student releases them. If the student pulls the balls apart, then the balls represent the atoms to the right of the stable position in the figure. When the balls are released, they return to the stable position.

► **FIGURE 6-4**

As a covalent bond forms between two atoms, they reach a distance from each other at which attractive and repulsive forces are balanced and the energy is at a minimum.

Potential Energy Curve for H_2

Covalent bonds occur at a potential energy minimum

The energy change that takes place as two atoms approach each other is depicted in **Figure 6-4**. Moving from right to left along the curve, you see the two H atoms approaching each other. As they come nearer, the potential energy of the combination becomes lower and lower until it reaches the minimum value of −436 kJ/mol at a distance of 75 pm. At the lowest energy, the H−H combination is most stable because lower energy means greater stability. At the distance of 75 pm, the repulsion between the like charges equals the attraction of the opposite charges. This is considered the length of the H−H bond. If the atoms come closer than 75 pm, the two nuclei and the electrons repel strongly, and the energy rises sharply.

Bonded atoms vibrate, and bonds vary in strength

bond length

the distance between two bonded atoms at their minimum potential energy; the average distance between two bonded atoms

Although models often show bonds as rigid "sticks," the nuclei are not at a fixed distance from each other. Instead, the two nuclei vibrate back and forth like a spring, coming closer and then stretching farther apart, as shown in **Figure 6-5**. The distance of minimum energy is the average distance between the nuclei. This is known as the **bond length.**

► **FIGURE 6-5**

The two atoms involved in a covalent bond vibrate back and forth about an average distance.

The Bond/Spring Analogy

TABLE 6-1 Bond Energies and Bond Lengths for Bonds in Diatomic Molecules

	Bond energy (kJ/mol)	Bond length (pm)
H—F	570	92
C—F	552	138
O—O	498	121
H—H	436	75
H—Cl	432	127
C—Cl	397	177
H—Br	366	141
H—I	299	161
C—Br	280	194
Cl—Cl	243	199
C—I	209	214
Br—Br	193	229
F—F	159	142
I—I	151	266

VISUAL STRATEGY

Table 6-1 Be sure students understand that bond length is generally inversely related to bond strength. Bond strength is reflected by the amount of energy needed to break a bond, also known as bond energy.

ANSWERS

CONCEPT CHECK

1. Each hydrogen atom now has a shared pair of electrons. A duet is a more stable configuration than an unpaired electron.
2. a molecular orbital
3. The potential energy decreases.
4. the bond length
5. Student answers will vary but can include H_2, HF, HCl, HBr, HI, H_2O, and sugar.

Because the potential energy minimum of the H—H bond is −436 kJ/mol, 436 kJ/mol of energy must be supplied to a hydrogen molecule in order to break the bond and separate the two hydrogen atoms. The energy required to break a bond between two atoms and separate them is the **bond energy.**

Table 6-1 lists the energies and lengths of some common bonds. Note that the bonds with the highest bond energy (those with the "strongest" bonds) usually involve the elements H or F. Note also that, with a few exceptions, there is a general trend for stronger bonds to have shorter bond lengths.

bond energy

the energy required to break a chemical bond between two atoms and separate them

CONCEPT CHECK

1. Why is the hydrogen molecule, H_2, more stable than the individual hydrogen atoms that bond to form it?
2. What is created when two atomic orbitals overlap?
3. What happens to the potential energy as two atoms approach each other to form a covalent bond?
4. What is the distance of minimum potential energy between two atoms in a covalent bond?
5. List four examples of covalent compounds.

electronegativity

the tendency of an atom to attract bonding electrons to itself when it bonds with another atom

nonpolar covalent bond

an attraction between two atoms in which bonding electrons are shared equally between the atoms

▼ **FIGURE 6-6**

Electronegativity tends to decrease down a group and increase across a period.

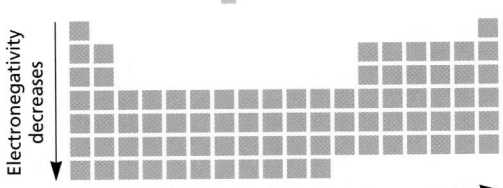

Electronegativity decreases

Electronegativity increases

Electronegativity and bonding

You learned in Chapter 5 that when sodium and chlorine combine, an electron is removed from sodium and transferred to chlorine to form Na^+ and Cl^- ions. However, when H_2 and O_2 react, they bond by sharing electrons to form water. What factors cause some combinations of atoms to form ions and other combinations of atoms to form covalent bonds?

Atoms share electrons equally or unequally

To help explain why some combinations of atoms form ionic bonds and some form covalent bonds, the concept of **electronegativity** was developed. Linus Pauling, a Nobel Prize–winning chemist, assigned electronegativity values to the elements. He assigned fluorine—the element most likely to form ionic bonds—an electronegativity of 4.0. **Table 6-2** gives the electronegativity for each element. You can see in **Figure 6-6** that electronegativity values generally increase as you go from left to right across a period. In going down a group, electronegativity values generally decrease.

In a molecule such as H_2, the atoms are identical, so they pull on the bonding electrons with the same force. The electrons are shared equally. Such a covalent bond, in which the bonding electrons are shared equally, is called a **nonpolar covalent bond,** or a *pure covalent bond.*

If the electronegativities of two atoms are equal, they form a nonpolar covalent bond. If

TABLE 6-2	**Electronegativities**																
H 2.2																	
Li 1.0	**Be** 1.6												**B** 2.0	**C** 2.6	**N** 3.0	**O** 3.4	**F** 4.0
Na 0.9	**Mg** 1.3												**Al** 1.6	**Si** 1.9	**P** 2.2	**S** 2.6	**Cl** 3.2
K 0.8	**Ca** 1.0	**Sc** 1.4	**Ti** 1.5	**V** 1.6	**Cr** 1.7	**Mn** 1.6	**Fe** 1.9	**Co** 1.9	**Ni** 1.9	**Cu** 2.0	**Zn** 1.7	**Ga** 1.8	**Ge** 2.0	**As** 2.2	**Se** 2.5	**Br** 3.0
Rb 0.8	**Sr** 1.0	**Y** 1.2	**Zr** 1.3	**Nb** 1.6	**Mo** 2.2	**Tc** 1.9	**Ru** 2.2	**Rh** 2.3	**Pd** 2.2	**Ag** 1.9	**Cd** 1.7	**In** 1.8	**Sn** 1.9	**Sb** 2.0	**Te** 2.1	**I** 2.7
Cs 0.8	**Ba** 0.9	**La** 1.1	**Hf** 1.3	**Ta** 1.5	**W** 2.4	**Re** 1.9	**Os** 2.2	**Ir** 2.2	**Pt** 2.3	**Au** 2.5	**Hg** 2.0	**Tl** 1.8	**Pb** 2.1	**Bi** 2.0	**Po** 2.0	**At** 2.2
Fr 0.7	**Ra** 0.9	**Ac** 1.1															

ALTERNATIVE ASSESSMENT

Conceptual Connections

Ionization energy is another concept that shows the same periodic trends as electronegativity. Have students write a short paragraph comparing and contrasting these two concepts. Have students think of reasons why ionization energy and electronegativity might show the same periodic trends.

Figure 6-7 labels

Even electron distribution

Atom with partial negative charge, δ⁻

Atom with partial positive charge, δ⁺

Positively charged ion

Negatively charged ion

+   −

Electronegativity difference

Nonpolar covalent	Polar covalent	Ionic

0   0.5   0.8   1.8   2.1   3.1   3.3

H₂   CO   HF   NaF

FIGURE 6-7 ▲

Electronegativity differences can be used to predict the properties of a bond. Keep in mind that a whole range of bond polarity is possible and that there are no strict lines dividing bond types.

COMMON MISCONCEPTION

Electronegativity difference is only a general guide for determining bonding type. For example, the electronegativity difference between gallium and fluorine is 2.2. Yet scientists know through experimentation that gallium fluoride is a covalently bonded compound.

the electronegativities are greatly different, an ionic bond is formed. Between these two extremes is a range of bonding in which electrons are shared, but not equally. These bonds are called **polar covalent bonds.** A polar covalent bond occurs when two atoms form a covalent bond but one atom attracts electrons more strongly than the other atom. The attraction is not strong enough to transfer an electron from one atom to the other. The more electronegative atom, which attracts electrons more strongly, has a higher *electron density* than the less electronegative atom. **Figure 6-7** shows a model of the molecular orbital around a polar covalent molecule. Note that electrons are much more likely to be found around the more electronegative atom.

Bonds are more appropriately classified by bond character

The actual electronegativity value of an atom is not as important as electronegativity differences between bonding atoms. For any bond between two atoms, the electronegativity difference can be easily calculated. The larger this value is, the more polar the bond is. Bonds between atoms with very large electronegativity differences are considered to have more ionic character than covalent character. Eventually, the electronegativity difference is so great that one of the atoms has essentially removed an electron permanently from the other atom. At an electronegativity difference larger than 2.1, the bond is usually ionic.

There is a general rule that can be used to predict the type of bond that forms between two atoms. If the *difference* in electronegativity is between zero and 0.5, the bond is nonpolar covalent. If the difference in electronegativity is between 0.5 to 2.1, the bond is polar covalent. If the difference is larger than 2.1, the bond is usually ionic.

polar covalent bond

an attraction between two atoms in which bonding electrons are localized on the more electronegative atom

RESOURCE LINK

ChemFile Lab C
Self-Directed Inquiry
Have students do Investigation 3:
Covalent and Ionic Bonding—Ceramics Fixative.

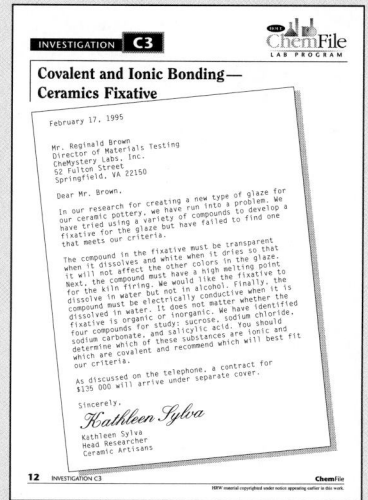

INVESTIGATION C3   ChemFile LAB PROGRAM

Covalent and Ionic Bonding—Ceramics Fixative

200

DISCUSSION STRATEGY

Have students compare and contrast full charges as they occur in electrons and protons and partial charges as they occur in polar molecules. Be certain students acknowledge that full charges are a set amount of charge and that a partial charge is any amount less than that. The partial charge depends on electronegativity differences and will vary, depending on the elements involved.

ADDITIONAL APPLICATION

A process called chromatography can be used to separate mixtures of covalent compounds. One type of chromatography, called paper chromatography, separates molecules based on their polarity. Water or some other liquid solvent carries the components of the mixture through a porous paper. The more polar the compound, the more it is attracted to the paper. Thus, the more polar the component, the less distance the component will travel in the paper.

▼ **FIGURE 6-8**

a Both H_2 and F_2 have nonpolar bonds. The bonding electrons are shared equally between the two atoms.

b When H and F combine, they form a highly polarized bond in which electrons are pulled more toward the F atom. As a result, the molecule has a somewhat negative end and a somewhat positive end.

dipole
a molecule in which one end has a partial positive charge and the other end has a partial negative charge

▼ **FIGURE 6-9**
HF(*aq*), or hydrofluoric acid, is used to etch glass.

For example, the compound AlF_3 is predicted to be ionic because the electronegativity difference between Al and F is 2.4. All three of the Al—F bonds are predicted to be ionic. On the other hand, the compound $AlCl_3$ is predicted to be polar covalent because the electronegativity difference between Al and Cl is 1.6. So each of the three Al—Cl bonds is polar covalent. Physical properties differ significantly between nonpolar covalent compounds, polar covalent compounds, and ionic compounds.

Polar molecules have positive and negative ends

The word *polar* suggests that these bonds have ends that are somehow opposite one another, like the two poles of a magnet or a battery. Hydrogen fluoride, H—F, is an example of a molecule with a polar bond. The electronegativity of fluorine is much higher than the electronegativity of hydrogen. Therefore, the fluorine atom attracts electrons much more strongly than the hydrogen atom does. With a greater electron density, the fluorine atom in the HF molecule has a partial negative charge. The hydrogen atom, having its electron pulled away, has a partial positive charge, as you can see in **Figure 6-8.** Note that this is not an ionic bond; the electron is not completely transferred from hydrogen to fluorine. A molecule in which one end has a partial positive charge and the other end has a partial negative charge is called a **dipole.**

To emphasize the dipole nature of the HF molecule, the formula can be written as $H^{\delta+}—F^{\delta-}$. The symbol δ is a lowercase Greek *delta,* which is used in science and mathematics to indicate *partial.* In the case of $H^{\delta+}—F^{\delta-}$ and other polar molecules, it is used to indicate a partial positive charge, δ^+, on one end of a bond and a partial negative charge, δ^-, on the other end. A molecule may have polar bonds but not be a dipole, as you will see later. This occurs when a molecule contains more than one polar bond, and the polar bonds cancel each other out.

DEMONSTRATION 1

Paper Chromatography
Approximate time: 20 minutes

1. Cut a strip about 4 cm wide from a coffee filter.

2. Lay a pencil across a transparent plastic cup.

3. Tape the paper to the middle of the pencil so that the unattached end of the paper falls just above the bottom of the cup. Cut off any excess paper from the bottom.

4. Remove the pencil and paper from the cup.

5. Using another pencil, draw a line across the paper 1 cm above the unattached end. This line will serve as a reference point. Use a water-soluble black marker to make a dot in the middle of the line.

TABLE 6-3 Dipole Moment and Bond Energy for Hydrogen Halides

Molecule	Dipole moment	Bond energy
H−F	1.8	570 kJ/mol
H−Cl	1.0	432 kJ/mol
H−Br	0.8	366 kJ/mol
H−I	0.5	298 kJ/mol

Electronegativity is related to the dipole moment

While Pauling was assigning electronegativities, he noted a connection between the polarity of a bond and the strength of that bond. The polarity of a molecule is measured by the *dipole moment*. A larger dipole moment indicates a higher degree of polarity.

Of the compounds in **Table 6-3,** hydrogen fluoride has the greatest polarity, as indicated by its largest dipole moment. It also has the strongest bond. Hydrogen iodide has the least polarity. Consequently, it has the weakest bond. As the polarity of the molecule increases, its bond strength increases.

SECTION REVIEW

Total recall

1. Describe the attractive forces and repulsive forces that occur as two atoms move closer together.
2. Compare the motion of a bond between two atoms to that of a spring.

Critical thinking

3. What is bond energy? How does bond energy (or the strength of a bond) relate to the length of a covalent bond?
4. How does an element's electronegativity relate to its position on the periodic table.
5. Compare the degree of polarity in HF, HCl, HBr, and HI.

Practice problems

6. Use Figure 6-7 and Table 6-2 to classify the bond between the following as nonpolar covalent, polar covalent, or ionic.
   a. Cs and Br
   b. H and S
   c. Ca and O
   d. Si and Cl
   e. As and P
   f. Se and Br
7. In the previous question, which atom in each pair has the higher electron density?
8. **Story Clue** Is the covalent bond between hydrogen and oxygen in water polar or nonpolar? Explain your choice.

ANSWERS

SECTION REVIEW

Total recall

1. The positive nucleus of each atom attracts its own electrons and the electrons of the other atom. At the same time, the nuclei repel each other, as do the electron clouds. When the attractive and repulsive forces balance, a bond forms.
2. The two nuclei vibrate back and forth like a spring, coming closer and then stretching farther apart.

Critical thinking

3. Bond energy is the energy needed to break a chemical bond between two atoms and separate them. Generally, the higher the bond energy, the shorter the bond.
4. In general, electronegativity increases from the bottom to the top of a group in the periodic table and from left to right across a period.
5. HF is the most polar, followed by HCl, then HBr, and finally HI.

Practice problems

6. a. ionic
   b. nonpolar covalent
   c. ionic
   d. polar covalent
   e. nonpolar covalent
   f. polar covalent

7. a. Br
   b. S
   c. O
   d. Cl
   e. neither
   f. Br

8. The bond is polar covalent as indicated by an electronegativity difference of 1.2.

6. Add water to the cup to a depth of 1 cm.
7. Return the pencil and paper to the cup. The dot should be just above the water level.
8. Have students observe the results at the end of class. Remove the paper, and let it dry.
9. Have students look at the paper, and discuss the results in terms of polarity.

10. Variations to the demonstration can include using food dyes and other colors of markers. Some will produce separation, and some will not.

Disposal

Throw the paper in the trash. Clean and save the pencil and cup. Pour the water down the drain.

SECTION 6-2

How are molecules depicted?

▶ **Draw** Lewis structures to show the arrangement of valence electrons among atoms in molecules and polyatomic ions.

▶ **Explain** the differences between single, double, and triple covalent bonds.

▶ **Draw** resonance structures for simple molecules and polyatomic ions, and recognize when resonance structures are required.

▶ **Name** binary inorganic compounds using prefixes, roots, and suffixes.

LESSON WARM-UP

Valence Electrons Using the chalkboard or an overhead projector, draw the electron configurations of a few elements. Have the students decide which of the electrons shown are inner-shell electrons and which are valence electrons. Point out to the students that inner-shell electrons are often represented by the symbol for the noble gas in the electron configuration. For example, the electron configuration for chlorine can either be written as $1s^2 2s^2 2p^6 3s^2 3p^5$ or as [Ne] $3s^2 3p^5$. The second configuration represents the inner-shell electrons with the symbol [Ne] and lists the valence electrons.

HISTORICAL CONNECTION

Gilbert Newton Lewis (1875–1946) and Irving Langmuir (1881–1957) independently developed the idea of two chlorine atoms sharing an electron to stabilize each other's orbits. Both were versatile and productive scientists. Lewis also studied thermodynamics, developed an acid-base theory, and co-discovered deuterium oxide, D_2O, or heavy water. Langmuir's work in the field of surface chemistry earned him a Nobel Prize in 1932.

Lewis electron-dot structures

valence electron

an electron in the outermost energy level of an atom, where it can participate in bonding

As you know, the electrons in the outermost energy level of an atom are involved in bonding, both ionic and covalent. These outer-level electrons are referred to as **valence electrons.** G. N. Lewis, the American chemist, is responsible for important theories of bonding and valency. In 1920 Lewis developed a system to represent bonding in compounds. This system uses electron-dot diagrams in which dots represent valence electrons.

While Lewis dot structures are valuable tools for understanding bonding, they are merely diagrams and in no way represent the actual location of the valence electrons. In an atom, valence electrons are in atomic orbitals of specific shape and orientation. Once valence electrons become part of a bond, they are in molecular orbitals surrounding the two nuclei involved in the bond. The exact location of an electron at any particular time is impossible to determine.

▶ **FIGURE 6-10**

G. N. Lewis (1875–1946) not only developed important theories of bonding, but also gave a new definition to acids and bases.

TABLE 6-4	Lewis Dot Structures of the Second Period Elements

Element	Electron configuration	Lewis dot structure
Li	$1s^2 2s^1$	Li·
Be	$1s^2 2s^2$	Be·
B	$1s^2 2s^2 2p^1$	·Ḃ·
C	$1s^2 2s^2 2p^2$	·Ċ·
N	$1s^2 2s^2 2p^3$	:Ṅ·
O	$1s^2 2s^2 2p^4$	:Ö·
F	$1s^2 2s^2 2p^5$	:F̈·
Ne	$1s^2 2s^2 2p^6$	:N̈e:

Covalent bonds can be modeled with Lewis structures

A **Lewis structure** represents the valence electrons in a molecule. The nuclei and the electrons of the inner energy levels, the inner shells, are represented by the symbol of the element. A hydrogen atom has the electron configuration $1s^1$; it has only one valence electron. When drawing its Lewis structure, hydrogen's nucleus and lone valence electron are represented by the hydrogen symbol with a dot, H·.

When two hydrogen atoms form a covalent bond, they share two electrons, which are represented by a pair of dots written between the symbols. Hydrogen can never share more than two electrons, so this represents a stable hydrogen molecule in which both atoms share a pair of electrons.

$$H:H$$

Next consider a chlorine atom, which has the electron configuration $1s^2 2s^2 2p^6 3s^2 3p^5$. Only the electrons in the outermost energy level are involved in bonding, so in the Lewis structure only the seven valence electrons of chlorine, $3s^2 3p^5$, are represented by dots. As you know, electrons usually occur in pairs with opposite spins, so you write three pairs and one unpaired electron around the chlorine symbol as follows.

$$·C̈l:$$

Recall that noble gases, with eight valence electrons, are the most stable elements. An octet of electrons is a stable configuration. So when two chlorine atoms bond, they each share one electron, giving both atoms a stable octet and forming a covalent bond.

$$:C̈l:C̈l:$$

Each chlorine atom in Cl_2 has three pairs of electrons that are not involved in the bond. These are called the **unshared pairs,** or lone pairs. Notice that each atom is surrounded by four pairs of electrons, showing that each atom has a stable octet of electrons.

Lewis structure

a structure in which atomic symbols represent nuclei and inner-shell electrons, and dots are used to represent valence electrons

FIGURE 6-11 ▲

To write an element's Lewis structure, determine the number of valence electrons for the atom. Then place a corresponding number of dots around the element's symbol, as shown.

unshared pair

a pair of valence electrons not involved in bonding to another atom

COVALENT BONDS AND MOLECULAR FORCES 203

GRAPHIC ORGANIZER

Valence Electrons and the Periodic Table

Group in the periodic table	1	2	13	14	15	16	17	18
Number of valence electrons	1	2	3	4	5	6	7	8

HOW TO

ADDITIONAL EXAMPLES

Determine the Lewis structure for each of the following:

1. SCl_2

Ans. $:\ddot{C}l\,.\overset{..}{\underset{..}{S}}.\,\ddot{C}l:$

2. AsF_3

Ans. $:\ddot{F}-\ddot{A}s-\ddot{F}:$
$\qquad\quad:\ddot{F}:$

3. SiH_4

Ans.
$$\begin{array}{c} H \\ | \\ H-Si-H \\ | \\ H \end{array}$$

Rules for Drawing Lewis Structures with Many Atoms

When drawing Lewis structures for a molecule with more than two atoms, a little more planning is needed. Following are some general rules:

1. Hydrogen and halogen atoms often bind to only one other atom and are usually on the outside or the end of the molecule.

2. The atom with the lowest electronegativity is often the central atom. These atoms often have fewer than seven electrons and may form more than one bond.

3. When placing valence electrons around an atom, place one electron on each side before pairing any electrons.

---

single bond

a covalent bond in which one pair of electrons is shared between two atoms

When drawing electron-dot diagrams, the pair of dots representing a shared pair, or a **single bond**, can also be shown by a long dash.

$$H:H \quad or \quad H-H$$

$$:\ddot{C}l:\ddot{C}l: \quad or \quad :\ddot{C}l-\ddot{C}l:$$

When deciding how to arrange the valence electrons around the symbol, keep in mind that all locations must contain an unpaired electron before any location can contain a pair of electrons. The Lewis structure for carbon, with four valence electrons, is as follows.

$$\cdot\overset{.}{\underset{.}{C}}\cdot$$

Pairing the electrons can be done in any order, but it is often done so that any unpaired electrons are oriented conveniently for bonding. Examine the following model of a chemical reaction; the unpaired electrons on the hydrogen and chlorine atoms are oriented toward each other.

$$H\cdot + \cdot\ddot{C}l: \longrightarrow H-\ddot{C}l:$$

HOW TO   Draw Lewis structures

Until now, you have examined only very simple Lewis structures. But how do you represent the Lewis structures of more-complicated molecules, such as CH_3I?

1 Determine the total number of valence electrons in the compound

▸ First draw the Lewis structures of the separate atoms. Carbon has four valence electrons. Hydrogen has only one electron. Iodine has seven valence electrons. Remember that each side of the element's symbol should be given one electron before any electrons are paired.

$$\cdot\overset{.}{\underset{.}{C}}\cdot \quad H\cdot \quad H\cdot \quad H\cdot \quad \cdot\ddot{\underset{..}{I}}:$$

Now add the valence electrons of each atom.

$$1 \text{ C atom with 4 electrons} = 1 \times 4 = 4$$
$$3 \text{ H atoms with 1 electron} = 3 \times 1 = 3$$
$$\underline{1 \text{ I atom with 7 electrons} = 1 \times 7 = 7}$$
$$\text{Total number of valence electrons} = 14$$

2 **Arrange the atoms' symbols to show how the atoms bond**

▸ Be sure to distribute the paired dots so that there are eight electrons around each atom (so that the octet rule is followed). Hydrogen is an exception; it is stable with only a duet of electrons. Hydrogen and iodine, lacking one electron each, will form only one bond.

$$\text{H} : \overset{\text{H}}{\underset{\text{H}}{\text{C}}} : \ddot{\text{I}} :$$

3 **Compare the number of valence electrons used in the structure with the number available from step 1**

▸ There are two electrons in each covalent bond and three unshared pairs around the iodine atom.

$$4 \text{ covalent bonds with 2 electrons each} = 4 \times 2 = 8$$
$$\underline{3 \text{ lone pairs of electrons around I} = 3 \times 2 = 6}$$
$$\text{Total number of electrons shown} = 14$$

4 **Change each pair of dots that represents a shared pair of electrons to a single dash**

$$\text{H} - \overset{\text{H}}{\underset{\text{H}}{\text{C}}} - \ddot{\text{I}} :$$

5 **Be sure that all atoms, with the exception of hydrogen, follow the octet rule**

Both carbon and iodine have stable octets. Each hydrogen atom has a duet. Note that H forms only one bond. It will always be "outside" on Lewis structures.

ANSWERS

CONCEPT CHECK

1. $: \ddot{\text{I}} - \ddot{\text{Cl}} :$, $\text{H} - \ddot{\text{Br}} :$

2.
$$:\ddot{\text{Cl}} - \overset{\text{H}}{\underset{\text{H}}{\text{C}}} - \ddot{\text{Cl}} :$$

3.
$$\text{H} - \overset{\text{H}}{\underset{\text{H}}{\text{C}}} - \ddot{\text{O}} - \text{H}$$

4.
$$\text{H} - \overset{\text{H}}{\underset{\text{H}}{\text{C}}} - \overset{\text{H}}{\underset{\text{H}}{\text{C}}} - \text{H}$$

CONCEPT CHECK

1. Draw Lewis structures for iodine monochloride, ICl, and hydrogen bromide, HBr.
2. Using iodomethane, CH_3I, as a model, draw the Lewis structure for dichloromethane, CH_2Cl_2.
3. Draw the Lewis structure for methanol, CH_3OH. Draw the CH_3 part first, then add O and H.
4. Draw the Lewis structure for ethane, C_2H_6.

Multiple bonds
Atoms can share more than one pair of electrons in a bond

Consider the bond between two oxygen atoms forming an O_2 molecule. Oxygen is in Group 16. Therefore, it has six valence electrons.

$$:\ddot{O}\cdot \quad \cdot\ddot{O}:$$

In order to achieve an octet, each atom needs two more electrons. Therefore, each atom shares two electrons with the other atom. The covalent bond formed by the sharing of two pairs of electrons is a double bond, represented as follows.

$$:\ddot{O}::\ddot{O}: \quad \text{or} \quad :\ddot{O}=\ddot{O}:$$

Oxygen can form double bonds, as in O_2 above, or it can form single bonds with two other atoms, as in methanol, CH_3OH.

Another example of a molecule containing a double bond is the plant pheromone ethene, C_2H_4, also called ethylene, shown in **Figure 6-12.** The four hydrogen atoms each form a single bond with carbon.

$$\begin{array}{cc} H & H \\ H:\ddot{C}\cdot & \cdot\ddot{C}:H \end{array}$$

Each carbon atom has two nonbonded electrons and needs two more electrons to complete an octet. The only possibility is that they bond to each other with a double bond, as oxygen does in the oxygen molecule.

$$\begin{array}{cc} H\ H & H\ H \\ H:\ddot{C}::\ddot{C}:H \quad \text{or} \quad H-C=C-H \end{array}$$

The elements carbon, nitrogen, and oxygen commonly form double bonds. Hydrogen and the halogens usually share one pair of electrons, so they do not form multiple bonds. Sulfur rarely forms a true double bond; the only common example of a double-bonded sulfur compound is carbon disulfide, CS_2.

Nitrogen and carbon atoms can share three pairs of electrons to form a triple bond. Consider the molecule N_2. Each nitrogen atom has five valence electrons, and each needs three more for a stable octet. Each nitrogen atom contributes three electrons to form a triple bond. Six electrons constitute three electron-pair bonds.

$$:N::N: \quad \text{or} \quad :N\equiv N:$$

▶ **FIGURE 6-12**

Ethene, C_2H_4, is a pheromone found in most plants. Tomatoes release ethene as they ripen.

The compound ethyne, C_2H_2, commonly called acetylene, also contains a triple bond.

$$H:C::C:H \quad \text{or} \quad H-C\equiv C-H$$

Nitrogen can form three single bonds, a combination of a double and single bond, or one triple bond. Carbon can form four single bonds or a combination of single, double, and triple bonds. Carbon almost always forms a total of four bonds.

HOW TO   Draw Lewis structures with multiple bonds

If no arrangement of single bonds provides an appropriate Lewis structure, the molecule could contain multiple bonds. Keep this in mind as you draw the Lewis structure for formaldehyde, CH_2O.

1 **Determine the total number of valence electrons**
- Draw the Lewis structures of the separate atoms.

$$\cdot\overset{\cdot}{C}\cdot \quad H\cdot \quad H\cdot \quad :\overset{\cdot\cdot}{O}\cdot$$

1 C atom with 4 electrons = $1 \times 4 = 4$
2 H atoms with 1 electron = $2 \times 1 = 2$
1 O atom with 6 electrons = $1 \times 6 = 6$
Total number of valence electrons = 12 valence electrons

2 **Arrange the atoms' symbols to show how the atoms are bonded**
- The carbon atom is in the center. Carbon forms four bonds; two hydrogen atoms and one oxygen atom form a total of four bonds. Therefore, these atoms must be bonded directly to carbon.

$$\begin{array}{c} :O: \\ :: \\ H:C:H \end{array}$$

3 **Compare the number of valence electrons used in the structure with the number available from step 1**
- All 12 valence electrons are accounted for.

4 covalent bonds with 2 electrons each = $4 \times 2 = 8$
2 lone pairs of electrons around O = $2 \times 2 = 4$
Total number of electrons shown = 12

4 **Change each pair of dots that represent shared pairs of electrons to a single dash**

$$\begin{array}{c} :O: \\ \| \\ H-C-H \end{array}$$

5 **Be sure that all atoms, with the exception of hydrogen, follow the octet rule**
- Both carbon and oxygen atoms have stable octets.

COMMON MISCONCEPTION

Triple bonds are sometimes represented horizontally, $H:C:::C:H$. This representation may lead students to think that three electrons are involved in each of two bonds. Triple bonds are more accurately represented as stacked electron pairs, $H:\overset{\cdot\cdot}{C}:C:H$.

HOW TO

ADDITIONAL EXAMPLES

Draw Lewis structures for the following molecules:

1. C_3H_6O

Ans.

$$\begin{array}{c} H \ \ \overset{\cdot\cdot}{O} \ \ H \\ | \ \ | \ \ | \\ H-C-C-C-H \\ | \ \ \ \ \ \ | \\ H \ \ \ \ \ H \end{array} \quad \text{or} \quad \begin{array}{c} H \ \ H \ \ \overset{\cdot\cdot}{O} \\ | \ \ | \ \ \| \\ H-C-C-C-H \\ | \ \ | \\ H \ \ H \end{array}$$

2. CO

Ans. $:C\equiv O:$

3. O_2

Ans. $:\overset{\cdot\cdot}{O}=\overset{\cdot\cdot}{O}:$

4. N_2F_2

Ans. $:\overset{\cdot\cdot}{F}-\overset{\cdot\cdot}{N}=\overset{\cdot\cdot}{N}-\overset{\cdot\cdot}{F}:$

5. $B_3N_3H_6$

Ans.

$$\begin{array}{c} H \\ | \\ B \\ H-N \quad N-H \\ | \quad\quad | \\ B \quad B \\ H-\ \ N\ \ -H \\ | \\ H \end{array}$$

Figure 6-13 Sulfur dioxide dissolves in atmospheric water to produce sulfurous acid, H_2SO_3.

$$H_2O(l) + SO_2(g) \longrightarrow H_2SO_3(aq)$$

This acid solution falls to the ground in the form of rain and snow.

CHAPTER CONNECTION

Acid rain will be discussed in more detail in Chapter 15.

resonance structure

a possible Lewis dot structure of a molecule for which more than one Lewis structure can be written

Some molecules are represented by more than one Lewis structure

If you wanted to draw the structure for sulfur dioxide, SO_2, you would start with the sulfur atom in the middle. Sulfur and oxygen have six electrons each, so you might expect a double bond between sulfur and one of the oxygen atoms.

If the second oxygen atom is placed so that it uses one of the sulfur atom's unshared pairs of electrons to complete its octet, the following Lewis structure results. In this structure, each atom has an octet of electrons, although one shared pair of electrons comes entirely from the sulfur atom. When a shared pair of electrons originates from one atom, the bond is called a *coordinate-covalent bond*.

$$\ddot{O}=\ddot{S}-\ddot{O}: \quad \text{or} \quad \ddot{O}::\ddot{S}:\ddot{O}:$$

Experimental evidence shows that this structure is not correct. Data show that both of the S—O bonds in SO_2 are the same length—shorter than a single S—O bond, but longer than a double S—O bond. In addition, SO_2 is chemically more stable than it would be if it contained a single bond on one end and a double bond on the other.

You can draw two possible Lewis structures for SO_2. These two structures are called **resonance structures.**

$$\ddot{O}=\ddot{S}-\ddot{O}: \longleftrightarrow :\ddot{O}-\ddot{S}=\ddot{O}$$

Experimental evidence indicates that the actual structure is a sort of average or *resonance hybrid,* of the two possible structures drawn. This structure is sometimes represented as follows.

$$:\ddot{O}\text{-}\!\!\text{-}\ddot{S}\text{-}\!\!\text{-}\ddot{O}:$$

The dotted lines represent two bonding pairs of electrons that are shared by all three atoms at the same time. When electrons are shared between more than two atoms at the same time, the electrons are said to be *delocalized*.

▶ **FIGURE 6-13**

Sulfur dioxide, SO_2, is a byproduct of coal-burning power plants. It is one of the leading contributors to acid rain.

FIGURE 6-14

Brown nitrogen dioxide gas is extremely poisonous and is produced in the series of reactions leading to smog.

COMMON MISCONCEPTION

Students may think that a compound contains only one type of bonding. Emphasize that polyatomic ions are ionically bonded to other oppositely charged ions but that the bonding within the ion is covalent.

The resonance model explains why the bonds between S and O are identical in both length and strength. It also shows that the molecule is more stable than either of the Lewis structures indicates. Resonance can explain the existence of molecules that have odd numbers of electrons and do not follow the octet rule, such as NO_2. The resonance structures of NO_2 are illustrated below. The presence of the odd number of electrons indicates that NO_2 will readily react with other substances.

$$:\ddot{O}-N=\ddot{O} \longleftrightarrow \ddot{O}=N-\ddot{O}:$$

Although it may seem easy to draw a Lewis structure for nitrogen dioxide, no single structure satisfies the octet rule. Nitrogen dioxide is a resonance hybrid of the structures shown.

Lewis structures can represent bonding in polyatomic ions

The ammonium ion, NH_4^+, is a common polyatomic ion. It is found in items such as the smelling salts shown in **Figure 6-15.** To draw the Lewis structure of the ammonium ion, first consider the structure of the ammonia molecule, NH_3, from which the ammonium ion is derived. Nitrogen is a Group 15 element. That tells you that nitrogen has five valence electrons. Therefore, nitrogen can achieve a stable octet by forming three covalent bonds, one with each hydrogen atom.

$$\begin{array}{c} H \\ H:\ddot{N}: \\ \ddot{H} \end{array}$$

FIGURE 6-15

An ammonium cation forms when a hydrogen ion combines with an ammonia molecule. Smelling salts often contain an unstable ionic compound composed of ammonium ions, NH_4^+, and carbonate ions, CO_3^{2-}.

$$\left[\begin{array}{c} H \\ H:\ddot{N}:H \\ \ddot{H} \end{array}\right]^+$$
Ammonium ion

COVALENT BONDS AND MOLECULAR FORCES 209

RESOURCE LINK

Chem**File** Teaching Resources CD-ROM
Career Extension
Assign Occupational Applications Worksheet 9: *Air-Quality Specialist* to emphasize relevant applications of text concepts.

Ammonium ions form when ammonia is combined with a substance that easily gives up hydrogen ions, H^+. Hydrogen chloride, HCl, is one such substance. A hydrogen ion is simply the nucleus of the hydrogen atom, a proton. It has no electrons to share. The formation of an ammonium ion from ammonia and a proton is as follows.

$$\begin{array}{ccc} \overset{\displaystyle H}{\underset{\displaystyle H}{H:\ddot{N}:}} & + & H^+ \\ \text{Ammonia molecule} & & \text{Proton} \end{array} \longrightarrow \left[\overset{\displaystyle H}{\underset{\displaystyle H}{H:\ddot{N}:H}}\right]^+$$

Ammonium ion

Notice that the nitrogen atom in ammonia has an unshared pair of electrons. The hydrogen ion can bond to nitrogen's unshared pair of electrons, forming a coordinate-covalent bond. The nitrogen atom retains its stable octet, and all four hydrogen atoms have a stable duet of electrons. After the hydrogen ion has bonded to nitrogen, all four hydrogen atoms are equivalent. The structure is enclosed in brackets to indicate that the positive charge is distributed over the entire ammonium ion.

HOW TO   Draw Lewis structures of polyatomic ions

When drawing a Lewis structure of a polyatomic ion, take the ionic charge into account and add or subtract electrons when determining the total number of valence electrons. How would you draw the Lewis structure of the NH_4^+ ion if you did not know how it formed?

1 **Determine the total number of valence electrons in the ion**

▸ First draw the Lewis structures of the separate atoms. Nitrogen has five valence electrons. Hydrogen has one valence electron.

$$:\dot{\ddot{N}}\cdot \quad H\cdot \quad H\cdot \quad H\cdot \quad H\cdot$$

▸ Now add the valence electrons of each atom. The polyatomic ion has a charge of 1+, meaning that it has one less electron than it would have if it were a neutral molecule. Subtract one electron for the positive charge on the ion.

1 N atom with 5 valence electrons $= 1 \times 5 =$	5
4 H atoms with 1 valence electron $= 4 \times 1 =$	4
charge on ammonium ion $+1$	-1
Total number of valence electrons $=$	8

2 **Arrange the atoms' symbols to show how the atoms are bonded**

$$\overset{\displaystyle H}{\underset{\displaystyle H}{H:\ddot{N}:H}}$$

HOW TO

ADDITIONAL EXAMPLES

Draw Lewis structures of the following polyatomic ions:

1. ClO_3^-

Ans. $$\left[\begin{array}{c} :\ddot{O}: \\ | \\ :\ddot{O}-\ddot{Cl}-\ddot{O}: \end{array}\right]^-$$

2. SO_4^{2-}

Ans. $$\left[\begin{array}{c} :\ddot{O}: \\ | \\ :\ddot{O}-S-\ddot{O}: \\ | \\ :\ddot{O}: \end{array}\right]^{2-}$$

3. CO_3^{2-} (This ion has resonance structures.)

Ans. $$\left[\begin{array}{c} :\ddot{O}: \\ \| \\ C \\ :\ddot{O}: \quad :\ddot{O}: \end{array}\right]^{2-} \longleftrightarrow \left[\begin{array}{c} :\ddot{O}: \\ C \\ :\ddot{O}: \quad :\ddot{O}: \end{array}\right]^{2-} \longleftrightarrow \left[\begin{array}{c} :\ddot{O}: \\ C \\ :\ddot{O}: \quad :\ddot{O}: \end{array}\right]^{2-}$$

3 Compare the number of valence electrons used in the structure with the number available from step 1

- There are two electrons in each covalent bond.

$$\text{4 covalent bonds with 2 electrons each} = 4 \times 2 = 8$$
$$\overline{\text{Total number of electrons shown} = 8}$$

- This matches the number of electrons determined in step 1.

4 Change each pair of dots that represents a shared pair of electrons to a single dash

- There are four pairs of bonding electrons in the ammonium ion. Therefore, there are four single covalent bonds in the Lewis structure.

$$\begin{array}{c} \text{H} \\ | \\ \text{H}-\text{N}-\text{H} \\ | \\ \text{H} \end{array}$$

5 Indicate the delocalized charge

- Place brackets around the ion, and place a 1+ charge outside the bracket to indicate that the charge is spread over the entire ion.

$$\left[\begin{array}{c} \text{H} \\ | \\ \text{H}-\text{N}-\text{H} \\ | \\ \text{H} \end{array} \right]^{+}$$

6 Be sure that all atoms, with the exception of hydrogen, follow the octet rule

- The N atom has a stable octet. Each H atom has a stable duet.

CONCEPT CHECK

1. Draw resonance structures for the NO_2 molecule and the SO_3 molecule.
2. Draw a Lewis dot structure for the methylammonium ion, $CH_3NH_3^+$. (Hint: Carbon and nitrogen are bonded together by a single covalent bond.)
3. Draw Lewis structures for the NO_3^- ion and the SO_3^{2-} ion. Remember that resonance structures may be necessary to adequately describe an ion.
4. Draw Lewis structures for the following molecules.
   a. carbon dioxide, CO_2
   b. hypochlorous acid, HOCl
   c. chloroethene, C_2H_3Cl, also called vinyl chloride
   d. hydrogen cyanide, HCN
5. A benzene molecule, C_6H_6, is a ring of six carbon atoms. Each carbon atom is bonded to two other carbon atoms as well as to one hydrogen atom. Draw the two resonance structures of benzene.

COVALENT BONDS AND MOLECULAR FORCES   211

ANSWERS

CONCEPT CHECK

1. *See below.*
2. $$\left[\begin{array}{c} \text{H} \quad \text{H} \\ | \quad\quad | \\ \text{H}-\text{C}-\text{N}-\text{H} \\ | \quad\quad | \\ \text{H} \quad \text{H} \end{array} \right]^{+}$$
3. *See below.*
4. a. $\ddot{\text{O}}=\text{C}=\ddot{\text{O}}$
   b. $\text{H}-\ddot{\text{O}}-\ddot{\text{C}}\text{l}:$
   c.
$$\begin{array}{ccc} \text{H} & & :\ddot{\text{C}}\text{l}: \\ & \text{C}=\text{C} & \\ \text{H} & & \text{H} \end{array}$$
   d. $\text{H}-\text{C}\equiv\text{N}:$
5.
$$\begin{array}{c} \text{H} \\ \text{H} \quad \text{C} \quad \text{H} \\ \text{C} \quad\quad \text{C} \\ | \quad\quad\quad | \\ \text{C} \quad\quad \text{C} \\ \text{H} \quad \text{C} \quad \text{H} \\ \text{H} \end{array} \quad\longleftrightarrow\quad \begin{array}{c} \text{H} \\ \text{H} \quad \text{C} \quad \text{H} \\ \text{C} \quad\quad \text{C} \\ | \quad\quad\quad | \\ \text{C} \quad\quad \text{C} \\ \text{H} \quad \text{C} \quad \text{H} \\ \text{H} \end{array}$$

1. $:\ddot{\text{O}}-\text{N}=\ddot{\text{O}} \longleftrightarrow \ddot{\text{O}}=\text{N}-\ddot{\text{O}}:$

$$\begin{array}{ccc} :\ddot{\text{O}}: & & \ddot{\text{O}} & & :\ddot{\text{O}}: \\ | & & \| & & | \\ \ddot{\text{O}}=\text{S}-\ddot{\text{O}}: \longleftrightarrow :\ddot{\text{O}}-\text{S}-\ddot{\text{O}}: \longleftrightarrow :\ddot{\text{O}}-\text{S}=\ddot{\text{O}} \end{array}$$

3.
$$\left[\begin{array}{c} :\ddot{\text{O}}: \\ | \\ \text{N} \\ :\ddot{\text{O}} \quad \ddot{\text{O}}: \end{array} \right]^{-} \longleftrightarrow \left[\begin{array}{c} \ddot{\text{O}} \\ \| \\ \text{N} \\ :\ddot{\text{O}} \quad \ddot{\text{O}}: \end{array} \right]^{-} \longleftrightarrow \left[\begin{array}{c} :\ddot{\text{O}}: \\ \| \\ \text{N} \\ :\ddot{\text{O}} \quad \ddot{\text{O}}: \end{array} \right]^{-}$$

$$\left[\begin{array}{c} :\ddot{\text{O}}: \\ | \\ :\ddot{\text{O}}-\text{S}-\ddot{\text{O}}: \end{array} \right]^{2-}$$

DISCUSSION STRATEGY

Elicit from students examples of words containing prefixes that denote a number. Examples might include *bicycle, tricycle, octopus,* or *decade.* Other examples might include terms from mathematics, such as *triangle, pentagon, quadrilateral,* or *hexagon.* Tell students that such prefixes are also used to name molecular compounds.

DEFINING STANDARDS

It is common practice to omit the prefix *mono-* when naming the second element of a binary molecular compound. For example, nitrogen monoxide, NO, is frequently referred to as nitrogen oxide. One exception to this practice is carbon monoxide; in this case, the prefix is never omitted.

COMMON MISCONCEPTION

Students often think that, like an ionic formula, a correctly written molecular formula should show the simplest ratio of atoms in the compound. However, a molecular formula represents the actual numbers of individual atoms in a molecule. Thus, the subscripts in such formulas are not always reduced to the smallest possible ratio. For example, the molecular formulas for acetylene and benzene are C_2H_2 and C_6H_6, respectively. Reducing the subscripts to the smallest possible ratios would produce CH in both cases, although the compounds are completely different.

Naming covalent compounds

Naming conventions for most covalent, or molecular, compounds are relatively straightforward, especially for binary compounds that are inorganic. Organic compounds have their own special naming scheme, as you will see in Chapter 7. As shown below, inorganic molecular compounds are generally named in a way similar to the methods used to name the salts that were described in Chapter 5. Chemists distinguish two compounds composed of the same elements by specifying the number of each type of atom in the compound's name.

$$P_4O_6 \qquad\qquad P_4O_{10}$$
tetraphosphorus hexoxide   tetraphosphorus decoxide

The most common naming system uses prefixes, roots, and suffixes

The system of prefixes shown in **Table 6-5** is used in naming most inorganic binary compounds. Prefixes and suffixes are usually attached to root words. In the case of a binary molecular compound, the root word is the name of the element. The first element named is usually the one first written in the formula—the least electronegative element. If the molecule contains only one atom of the first element given in the formula, the prefix *mono-* is omitted in the name of the compound. For example, to distinguish between the two oxides of carbon, the prefixes *mono-* and *di-* are used.

$$CO \qquad\qquad CO_2$$
carbon monoxide   carbon dioxide

Each compound contains only one carbon atom, so no prefix for carbon is used in naming either compound.

TABLE 6-5   **Prefixes for Naming Covalent Compounds**

Prefix	Number of Atoms	Example	Name
mono-	1	NO	nitrogen monoxide
di-	2	SiO_2	silicon dioxide
tri-	3	SO_3	sulfur trioxide
tetra-	4	SCl_4	sulfur tetrachloride
penta-	5	$SbCl_5$	antimony pentachloride
hexa-	6	CeB_6	cerium hexaboride
hepta-	7	IF_7	iodine heptafluoride
octa-	8	Np_3O_8	trineptunium octoxide
nona-	9	I_4O_9	tetraiodine nonoxide
deca-	10	S_2F_{10}	disulfur decafluoride

The element with the higher electronegativity value is usually written last and has the ending *-ide,* just as anions in an ionic compound do. The compound CO has one oxygen atom and is named carbon *mon*oxide. The compound CO_2 has two oxygen atoms, and so it is named carbon *di*oxide. Notice that the vowels *o* and *a* are dropped from a prefix before a root that begins with a vowel. For example, you have sulfur hexafluoride, SF_6, but dinitrogen tetroxide, N_2O_4. Several compounds have common names that are widely used in place of the technical name. For example, H_2O is always called *water,* not *dihydrogen monoxide.*

SECTION REVIEW

Total recall

1. Which electrons in an atom are involved in bonding?

2. List three rules for drawing Lewis structures with many atoms.

3. What do you call electrons that are shared among several atoms at the same time?

Critical thinking

4. Use the electronic structure of a noble gas to explain why atoms are most stable when they have an octet of valence electrons.

5. Why does the five-atom grouping NH_4^+ exist only as a cation?

6. Draw a Lewis structure to show where the unshared pairs of electrons exist in carbon dioxide, CO_2.

Practice problems

7. Write the number of valence electrons for atoms with each of the following electron configurations.
   a. $1s^2 2s^2$
   b. $1s^2 2s^2 2p^3$
   c. $1s^2 2s^2 2p^6 3s^2 3p^2$
   d. $1s^2 2s^2 2p^6 3s^2 3p^6 4s^1$

8. Identify each element in item 7, and write its Lewis dot structure.

9. Draw Lewis structures for each of the following molecules and ions.
   a. bromine, Br_2
   b. trimethyl amine, $N(CH_3)_3$
   c. ozone, O_3 (Hint: form O_2 first)
   d. hydronium ion, H_3O^+
   e. bromine monofluoride, BrF
   f. hydrazine, N_2H_4
   g. nitrite ion, NO_2^-

10. **Interpreting Tables** Use the system of prefixes and suffixes in Table 6-5 to name the following compounds.
    a. SiO_2 **c.** SnI_4
    b. PBr_3 **d.** N_2O_3

11. Write the formula of each of the following compounds.
    a. phosphorus pentabromide
    b. pentaboron nonahydride
    c. diphosphorus trioxide
    d. dinitrogen tetroxide

12. **Story Clue** Draw the Lewis structure for water.

ANSWERS

SECTION REVIEW

Total recall

1. the outer, or valence, electrons

2. Hydrogen and halogen atoms bind to only one other atom and are usually on the outside or end of the molecule. The atom with the lowest electronegativity is often the central atom. When placing valence electrons around an atom, place one electron on each side before pairing any electrons.

3. delocalized electrons

Critical thinking

4. Noble gases have an octet of valence electrons. The *s* and *p* sublevels are filled, making a stable configuration. Therefore, any atom with an octet of valence electrons should be stable.

5. For the nitrogen atom to have an octet and each of the hydrogen atoms to have a duet after bonding, eight valence electrons must be used. Nitrogen has five, and each hydrogen atom has one, giving a total of nine. Therefore, one electron must be lost to provide an octet, resulting in an overall positive charge.

6. $\ddot{O}=C=\ddot{O}$

Practice problems

7. **a.** 2
   b. 5
   c. 4
   d. 1

8. **a.** Be, Be·
   b. N, ·N·
   c. Si, ·Si·
   d. K, K·

9. **a.** $:\!\ddot{Br}\!-\!\ddot{Br}\!:$

b.
$$H-\underset{\underset{H}{|}}{\overset{\overset{H}{|}}{C}}-\underset{\underset{H}{|}}{\overset{\overset{H\ H-C-H\ H}{|}}{N}}-\underset{\underset{H}{|}}{\overset{\overset{H}{|}}{C}}-H$$

c. $\ddot{O}=\ddot{O}-\ddot{O}: \longleftrightarrow :\ddot{O}-\ddot{O}=\ddot{O}$

d. $\left[H-\underset{\underset{\ddot{}}{|}}{\overset{\overset{H}{|}}{O}}-H \right]^+$

e. $:\!\ddot{Br}\!-\!\ddot{F}\!:$

f.
$$\underset{\underset{H}{|}}{\overset{\overset{H}{|}}{:N}}-\underset{\underset{H}{|}}{\overset{\overset{H}{|}}{N:}}$$

g. $\left[\ddot{O}=\ddot{N}-\ddot{O}: \right]^- \longleftrightarrow \left[:\ddot{O}-\ddot{N}=\ddot{O} \right]^-$

10. **a.** silicon dioxide   **c.** tin tetraiodide
    b. phosphorus tribromide **d.** dinitrogen trioxide

11. **a.** PBr_5 **c.** P_2O_3
    b. B_5H_9 **d.** N_2O_4

12.
$$\overset{\overset{\ddot{O}\cdot}{}}{\underset{H\quad H}{}}$$

How are molecular shapes determined?

OBJECTIVES ▸ ***Predict*** the shape of a molecule from its Lewis structure using VSEPR theory.

▸ ***Associate*** the polarity of molecules with their shapes.

▸ ***Relate*** the boiling point of a molecular substance to the shape and polarity of its molecules.

Molecular shapes

The three-dimensional shape of a molecule is an important factor in determining its physical and chemical properties. For example, the protein hemoglobin transports oxygen through your bloodstream to all parts of your body. Its structure is shown in **Figure 6-16.** One type of genetic mutation causes the shape of hemoglobin to change, resulting in a life-threatening condition called sickle cell anemia.

▼ **FIGURE 6-16**

a The round, doughnut shape of healthy red blood cells is determined by the hemoglobin molecules in the cell.

b Hemoglobin consists of four polypeptide chains; a fragment of one chain is shown in green.

c Each of the chains is a polymer of 141–146 amino acid subunits, such as the glutamic acid monomer shown here.

d Because of their shape, sickle cells clog small blood vessels.

e A genetic mutation causes glutamic acid to be replaced by valine, shown in red.

f The sickle shape results from the valine substitution.

DEMONSTRATION 2

Like Charges Repel

Approximate time: 10 minutes

1. Inflate two round balloons. Tie a string about 50 cm long to each balloon.

2. Keep the balloons separated. Rub each one with some wool cloth. Avoid handling the balloons directly after they have been charged by the cloth.

3. Bring the ends of the strings together, and have students observe what happens to

the balloons. Because they have like charges, they will repel each other.

Safety

Because balloons could burst, have students remain at least 3 m from the demonstration and wear safety goggles.

A Lewis structure can help you predict the shape of a molecule

A molecule with a relatively simple molecular formula also has a simple shape. In a molecule of only two atoms, such as HF, shown in **Figure 6-17,** or H_2, only a linear shape is possible. But for molecules of more than two atoms, molecular shapes become more complicated.

There is frequently no obvious relationship between the molecular formula of a compound and its shape. Look at the models of carbon dioxide, CO_2, and sulfur dioxide, SO_2, shown in **Figure 6-18.** Their formulas are similar, so why is CO_2 linear, while SO_2 is bent?

There is a simple model that can be used to determine the three-dimensional arrangement of the atoms in a molecule. This model is based on the **valence shell electron pair repulsion (VSEPR) theory.** According to this theory, you can predict the shape of a molecule by knowing the number of electron pairs around a central atom. The pairs can be bonding or nonbonding. Because like-charges repel each other, the electron pairs position themselves as far apart as possible.

Determine molecular geometry based on the number of electron pairs

The first step in determining the geometry of a molecule or polyatomic ion is to count the number of electron clouds surrounding the central atom. Each single or multiple bond counts as one electron group. Each nonbonding electron pair counts. Look at the Lewis structure for carbon dioxide below.

$$\ddot{O}=C=\ddot{O}$$

There are two double bonds around the central carbon atom. Therefore, there are two electron groups around this atom.

Electron clouds have a negative charge, and like charges repel each other. That means that the electron groups around an atom will repel one another and will remain as far apart as possible. If a central atom has only two electron groups, the molecule will be linear. These two electron groups are as far apart as they can get when they are on opposite sides of the carbon atom.

FIGURE 6-17 ▲

Molecules with only two atoms, such as HF, have a linear shape.

VSEPR (valence shell electron pair repulsion) theory

a simple model that predicts the general shape of a molecule based on the repulsion between both bonding and nonbonding electron clouds

internet**connect**

SCI**LINKS**
NSTA
TOPIC: Molecular shapes
GO TO: www.scilinks.org
KEYWORD: HW062

TEACHING TIP

Designing a Model To help students determine molecular shapes, have available round, well-inflated balloons with strings tied to the ends. Students can use the balloons to represent electron pairs and thus model molecular shapes. For example, if you hold four balloons with the ends close together, they will be arranged in a tetrahedron. Be sure students wear safety goggles while they use the balloons in case the balloons burst.

CHEMISTRY INTERACTIVE TUTOR

Module 4: Chemical Bonding Topic: Molecular Geometry
This engaging tutorial reviews and reinforces how to determine molecular geometry.

FIGURE 6-18 ▼

Even though carbon dioxide and sulfur dioxide have the same number of atoms, they have different shapes.

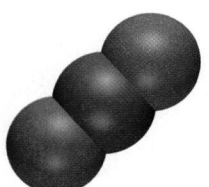

Sulfur dioxide   Carbon dioxide

► **FIGURE 6-19**

When a molecule consists of a central atom bonded to three other atoms, its shape will be trigonal planar as long as there are only three electron groups determining its geometry.

 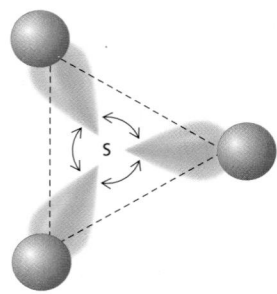

What happens if there are three electron groups? Look at the resonance structures for sulfur trioxide, SO_3.

$$\ddot{O}=S-\ddot{O}: \longleftrightarrow :\ddot{O}-S-\ddot{O}: \longleftrightarrow :\ddot{O}-S=\ddot{O}$$

Because of resonance, the three electron clouds surrounding the sulfur atom in SO_3 are identical, as shown in **Figure 6-19.** In order to be as far apart as possible, the groups arrange like three spokes of a wheel, extending out from the sulfur atom. This geometry of electron clouds is called *trigonal planar.* Because the atoms and bonds are equivalent, the angle between the bonds is 120°.

What happens if one of the electron pairs is a lone pair? This was the case with sulfur dioxide, shown in Figure 6-18. The nonbonding electrons repel the bonding electrons, causing the three electron pairs to orient in a trigonal planar geometry, but the shape of the triatomic molecule is angular, or bent.

Examine **Figure 6-20.** Four electron pairs are farthest apart when they orient themselves toward the corners of a tetrahedron, as shown in the methane, CH_4, molecule. This geometry is more difficult to view on a page because the atoms are now spread in three dimensions. If the pairs are all equivalent (if there are four identical bonds on the central atom), all four of the angles between the bonds are 109.5°.

FIGURE 6-20 ▼

a A tetrahedral shape cannot be shown accurately with a flat structural formula.

b The true shape can be shown only by a three-dimensional model or . . .

c . . . with wedge-shaped bonds that seem to recede or protrude from the plane of the page.

d Another way to portray the tetrahedral shape is to show the location of the atoms' bonding orbitals within the molecule.

GRAPHIC ORGANIZER

VSEPR and Molecular Geometry

Molecular shape		Atoms	Lone pairs	Example	Lewis structure
Linear		2	0	BeF_2	$:\ddot{F}-Be-\ddot{F}:$
Bent		2	1	$SnCl_2$	$:\ddot{Cl} \quad \overset{\ddot{S}n}{\quad} \quad \ddot{Cl}:$
Trigonal planar		3	0	BF_3	$:\ddot{F} \quad \ddot{F}: \\ B \\ :\ddot{F}:$

SAMPLE PROBLEM 6A Predicting molecular shapes

Determine the shapes of NH₃ and H₂O molecules.

1 Draw Lewis structures

2 Count the electron clouds around the central atoms

▶ NH₃ has three bonds to H atoms and one nonbonding pair: four electron clouds.

▶ H₂O has two bonds to H atoms and two nonbonding pairs: four electron clouds.

3 Apply the proper VSEPR geometry

▶ Both atoms have a tetrahedral arrangement of electron clouds.

4 Account for unbonded pairs

▶ If the unshared electron pair on nitrogen is placed in one of the positions of the tetrahedron, the shape of the molecule is actually trigonal pyramidal.

Ammonia, NH₃

▶ The water molecule will have an angular, or bent, shape.

Water, H₂O

PRACTICE PROBLEMS

1. Draw a Lewis structure for each of the following molecules, and then use the VSEPR theory to predict the shape of each.
   a. NH₂Cl   **b.** ONCl
2. Draw Lewis structures and then use the VSEPR theory to determine the shape of each of the following polyatomic ions.
   a. NO₃⁻   **b.** NH₄⁺

ANSWERS

PRACTICE PROBLEM 6A

1. a. trigonal pyramidal

$$H-\ddot{N}-H$$

b. bent

2. a. trigonal planar

b. tetrahedral

$$\left[\begin{array}{c} H \\ H-N-H \\ H \end{array}\right]^{+}$$

ADDITIONAL EXAMPLES

SAMPLE PROBLEM 6A

Use VSEPR theory to predict the molecular geometry of the following molecules:

a. CCl₄
   Ans. tetrahedral

b. HCN
   Ans. linear

c. SiBr₄
   Ans. tetrahedral

Molecular shape		Atoms	Lone pairs	Example	Lewis structure
Tetrahedral		4	0	CH₄	H—C—H (with H above and below)
Trigonal pyramidal		3	1	NH₃	N with H H H
Bent		2	2	H₂O	Ö with H H

ANSWERS

SECTION REVIEW

Total recall

1. the number of electron groups around it and how many of those groups represent bonds

Critical thinking

2. In general, the greater the polarity is, the higher the boiling point is, and the lower the polarity, the lower the boiling point. Positive ends of polar molecules attract negative ends of other molecules, so more energy is needed to overcome this attraction when trying to separate the molecules.

3. The unshared electrons repel the other electrons, taking the place of an atom at a corner of a tetrahedron. However, because there is no atom actually there, the fourth corner doesn't show as part of the molecule, and the overall shape is trigonal pyramidal.

4. The molecule would not be polar, so it would have lower boiling and melting points and would probably exist as a gas at room temperature.

Practice problems

5. Both are linear. Br_2 is nonpolar. H−Br is a polar bond, so the molecule is polar.

6. SCl_2 is bent. PF_3 is trigonal pyramidal, as is NCl_3. PF_3 will be the most polar. The electronegativity difference is greatest between P and F, and the bond angles of all three molecules are similar, so PF_3 is the most polar.

▼ **FIGURE 6-21**

The bond polarities in a water molecule add together, causing a molecular dipole. In carbon dioxide, bond polarities extend in opposite directions, canceling each other.

Water

Carbon dioxide, CO_2
(no molecular dipole)

How does shape affect properties?

Earlier you learned that the shape of a molecule such as hemoglobin affects its physical and chemical properties. Many of these properties depend on the polarity of the molecule. For molecules containing more than two atoms, molecular polarity depends on both the polarity of each bond and its orientation. For example, contrast CO_2, whose two electron clouds give it a linear shape, with H_2O, whose four electron clouds give it a bent shape.

The double bonds between C and O in CO_2 are polar because oxygen attracts electrons more strongly than does carbon. However, the linear shape of the molecule causes the two bond dipoles to act in opposite directions, canceling each other and causing the molecular polarity to be zero. In the water molecule, the polar H−O bonds are oriented at a 105° angle to each other, which creates a dipole for the molecule. The symbol ↔ is used to indicate a dipole. The arrow points to the region of greater electron density. **Figure 6-21** illustrates this concept for H_2O and CO_2.

Positive ends of polar molecules attract negative ends of other molecules. So more energy is required to separate these polar molecules than nonpolar molecules. Section 6-4 will further explain this phenomena by examining the boiling points of many polar molecules compared with nonpolar molecules.

SECTION REVIEW

Total recall

1. In VSEPR theory, what information about a central atom do you need in order to predict the shape of a molecule?

Critical thinking

2. What is the general relationship between the polarity of the molecules of different substances and the boiling points of those substances? Explain why this relationship exists.

3. Why does the presence of an unshared pair of electrons in the NH_3 molecule cause the molecule to have a trigonal pyramidal shape rather than a trigonal planar shape?

4. **Story Clue** Assume that the water molecule is linear like CO_2. How would water's physical properties be different, if at all, from the properties it has as a bent molecule?

Practice problems

5. Determine the shape of Br_2 and HBr molecules. Which is more polar and why?

6. Use VSEPR to determine the shapes of SCl_2, PF_3, and NCl_3 molecules. Which of these will be the most polar? Consider both shape and electronegativity differences.

ALTERNATIVE ASSESSMENT

Group Strategy

Have pairs of students use toothpicks and modeling clay or gumdrops to model tetrahedrons, trigonal pyramids, bent structures, and trigonal planar structures. Have them try to determine the shape of a molecule with six electron groups around the central atom such as SF_6.

What forces exist between molecules?

OBJECTIVES

▶ **Contrast** ionic solids and covalent solids.

▶ **Describe** the types of forces that exist between molecules.

▶ **Explain** how a hydrogen bond differs from other polar-polar forces.

LESSON WARM-UP

Visual Strategy Have students study Table 6-6. The substances in this table include both ionic and covalently bonded materials. The covalent compounds in this table are difficult to compare to determine trends in polarity and melting point. Draw a graph similar to the graphic organizer below on the chalkboard or overhead projector. Have the students use the graph to determine the relationship between polarity and melting point.

Physical characteristics of covalent compounds

Most covalent compounds melt at lower temperatures than ionic compounds do. You can see in **Table 6-6** that ionic substances tend to be solids with high melting points, and molecular substances are more likely to be gases, liquids, or solids with low melting points.

These differences between ionic and covalent substances result from differences in attractions between particles. Recall that ionic substances consist of separate ions, each of which is attracted to all ions of opposite charge. These attractions tend to hold the ions tightly in a crystal lattice that can be disrupted only by heating to very high temperatures.

TABLE 6-6 **Comparing Ionic and Molecular Substances**

Type of substance	Common use	State at room temperature	Melting point (°C)	Boiling point (°C)
Ionic substances				
Potassium chloride, KCl	salt substitute	solid	770	sublimes at 1500
Sodium chloride, NaCl	table salt	solid	801	1413
Calcium fluoride, CaF_2	fluoridation of water	solid	1423	2500
Covalent molecular substances				
Oxygen, O_2	respiration	gas	−218	−183
Methane, CH_4	natural gas	gas	−182	−164
Ethyl acetate, $CH_3CH_2OOCCH_3$	fingernail polish	liquid	−84	77
Water, H_2O	many	liquid	0	100
Naphthalene, $C_{10}H_8$	mothballs	solid	80	218

COVALENT BONDS AND MOLECULAR FORCES 219

GRAPHIC ORGANIZER

Relationship Between Melting Point and Electronegativity Difference for the Sodium Halides

QUICKLAB

Clean, fine, long hair works best for charging the comb. Cool temperatures and low humidity also result in a better charge.

Analysis

1. The closer the comb and the water are, the greater the effect.

2. The effect was less.

3. A larger stream bends less.

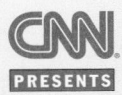 **Science in the News**

PRESENTS **Feature Story 15**
Coal-Oil Technology See the Science in the News video guide for more details.

Intermolecular forces hold molecules together

Covalent substances consist of molecules. If there are no attractive forces between molecules, the substance will exist as a gas because an attractive force is required to hold molecules together as liquids and solids. Because covalent solids have lower melting points than ionic solids have, the forces between molecules must be weaker than attractive forces between ions of opposite charge. Forces that exist between molecules are called **intermolecular forces.**

intermolecular force

an attraction that exists between molecules

You can see how the strength of intermolecular forces varies by comparing the molecular compounds listed in Table 6-6. Oxygen must have very weak intermolecular forces because oxygen must be cooled to a very low temperature to form liquid oxygen. In contrast, naphthalene must have much stronger intermolecular forces because it is a solid at room temperature. Why do we see such differences?

Dipole forces affect melting points and boiling points

Recall that one end of a polar molecule has a partial positive charge and the opposite end has a partial negative charge. Because opposite charges attract, the positive end of one molecule can attract the negative end of another molecule, holding the two molecules together. The force that exists between the positive and negative ends of polar molecules is called a *dipole force*. Dipole forces allow molecular substances to exist as solids and liquids.

The more polar the molecules are, the stronger the dipole force between molecules. Look again at the molecular compounds listed in Table 6-6. Oxygen and methane are nonpolar molecules, but molecules of ethyl acetate and water are polar. Because of dipole forces attracting the molecules to each other, ethyl acetate and water melt and boil at much higher temperatures than oxygen and methane, which have no dipole forces.

QUICKLAB

CONSUMER ACTIVITY

Watery Attraction

When hair and a nylon comb are rubbed together, electrons are transferred to the comb, which acquires a negative charge. When the charged comb comes close a stream of water, the positive end of the water dipoles are attracted to the negatively charged comb, causing the stream to move toward the comb.

Materials nylon hair comb, faucet with cold running water

Problem Turn on a cold water faucet. Adjust the stream to a width of 1.5 mm. Make sure the stream is a steady flow. Pull a comb through your hair several times. Holding the comb about 10 cm below the faucet, slowly bring the teeth of the comb closer to the water. Observe what happens. Repeat these steps. Note any changes in your initial observations. Adjust the faucet to produce a larger stream of water, and repeat the experiment.

Analysis
1. How does distance between the comb and the water stream affect your observations?
2. How does a second "charging" of the comb affect the bending of the water stream?
3. When the size of the water stream is increased, does it bend more or less than it originally bent?

DEMONSTRATION 3

Properties—Polar Versus Nonpolar

Approximate time: 15 minutes

1. Show students a candle, and tell them that it is made up of compounds composed of carbon, oxygen, and hydrogen. Tell them that completely burning such compounds yields the products carbon dioxide and water.

2. Light the candle.

3. Turn a 400 mL beaker upside down, and place ice on top of it.

4. Use beaker tongs to pick up the inverted beaker and hold it over the burning candle.

5. After a few minutes, move the beaker from the flame, and remove the ice. Extinguish the flame.

6. Hold the beaker upright, and observe the inside of the beaker. Students should observe drops of a liquid there.

TABLE 6-7 Boiling Points of the Hydrogen Halides

Substance	HF	HCl	HBr	HI
Boiling point (°C)	20	−85	−67	−35
Electronegativity difference	1.8	1.0	0.8	0.5

Hydrogen bonds are stronger dipole forces

Figure 6-8, on page 200, shows a model of a dipole in which a hydrogen atom is bonded to an atom that is much more electronegative. Some compounds that fit this model are listed in **Table 6-7.** Compare the boiling points and electronegativity differences of these hydrogen halides.

The boiling points increase moderately from HCl to HBr to HI, but notice the jump in the boiling point of HF. One reason the boiling point of HF is so high is that strong dipole forces exist between HF molecules due to the large electronegativity difference between H and F.

Another factor pertains to the nature of the hydrogen atom, which is small and has only one electron. When that electron is pulled away strongly by a highly electronegative atom, there are no underlying electrons as there would be in all elements other than helium. The attraction leaves the single proton of the hydrogen nucleus partially exposed. As a result, hydrogen's proton is strongly attracted to the electron-rich fluorine end of another HF molecule. This especially strong form of dipole attraction is called a **hydrogen bond.** It can be a rather strong intermolecular force, but it is not as strong as a full covalent bond.

Hydrogen bonds form with highly electronegative atoms

Strong hydrogen bonds usually form between molecules in which hydrogen is bonded to a small atom with a high electronegativity, particularly fluorine, oxygen, or nitrogen. The HCl, HBr, and HI molecules are somewhat polar, but they are much larger than HF, so the distance between molecules is greater. Consequently, the hydrogen bonds are much weaker in these substances. **Figure 6-22** shows an example of hydrogen bonding with oxygen.

Water is one of the more unusual covalent compounds because of the great extent to which it can participate

hydrogen bond

a form of dipole attraction in which a hydrogen atom bonded to a strongly electronegative atom is attracted to another electron-rich atom

FIGURE 6-22 ◄

Many of water's unique properties are a result of hydrogen bonding in three dimensions. This bonding causes water molecules to stick together.

COVALENT BONDS AND MOLECULAR FORCES 221

HISTORICAL CONNECTION

Because of its strong hydrogen bonding, water can absorb great amounts of energy before it boils. It often absorbs this energy from objects that come into contact with it. Native Americans made food containers from birch bark. If these containers were filled with water, they could be placed on a fire. As long as the flames did not rise past the water level, the water absorbed energy from the bark, and the bark did not burn.

CHAPTER CONNECTION

As students learn about solutions in Chapter 13, they will understand the importance of bond type and intermolecular forces in the dissolving process. They will investigate the behavior of both ionic and covalent compounds as the compounds become solutes, and they will understand the importance of considering polarity when choosing solvents.

---

7. Test any liquid with cobalt chloride test paper to determine whether it is water or not.

8. Ask students to explain the results in terms of the boiling points and the intermolecular forces between molecules of water and carbon dioxide.

Safety

Use caution around the flame and while handling hot glassware. Be careful to avoid dripping hot wax when extinguishing the candle.

Disposal

Keep the candle for later use. Throw the cobalt chloride test paper in the trash can.

1. In ionic substances, the ions are held together in a crystal lattice and are attracted to several ions of opposite charge. These forces are much stronger than intermolecular forces between covalent molecules, so it takes more energy to cause the ionically bonded particles to separate.

2. the gas phase

3. Hydrogen bonds form between hydrogen and highly electronegative elements, such as the halogens, nitrogen, or oxygen.

4. Fluorine is a small atom compared with the other halogens, and fluorine is extremely electronegative. Thus, the fluorine atom strongly attracts the electrons in an HF molecule. The resulting molecule is more polar than any of the other hydrogen-halide molecules. The hydrogen part of the HF molecule forms strong hydrogen bonds with nearby fluorine parts of other HF molecules.

in strong hydrogen bonding. In water, two hydrogen atoms are bonded to oxygen by polar covalent bonds. With its angular shape, each molecule can form two hydrogen bonds with neighboring molecules. As a result, the intermolecular forces in water are strong.

Hydrogen bonding explains water's unique properties

Because molecules of water are held together by hydrogen bonds, water's boiling point is higher than nearly all other covalent compounds of similar molecular size and mass. Compare the boiling points of water, 100°C, and hydrogen sulfide, −60.3°C. Water is more polar than hydrogen sulfide because oxygen is much more electronegative than sulfur. The electronegativity difference in the H−S bond is only 0.4, which means that the bond is essentially nonpolar. However, the electronegativity difference in the H−O bond is 1.2, so the bond is polar. As a result, H_2O molecules hydrogen-bond strongly but H_2S molecules do not. Water has a much higher boiling point than hydrogen sulfide because of this difference in intermolecular forces. Hydrogen bonding is an important factor in many of the chemical reactions that make life possible. DNA strands in your cells are held together by hydrogen bonds. Hydrogen bonding also attracts enzymes to the molecules they cause to react to build essential materials and release energy in your body.

> **internetconnect**
>
> SCI *LINKS*
> **NSTA**
>
> **TOPIC:** Hydrogen bonding
> **GO TO:** www.scilinks.org
> **KEYWORD:** HW063

CONCEPT CHECK

1. What causes the differences in melting points and boiling points between ionic and molecular substances?
2. In which phase will a substance with no intermolecular forces most likely be found?
3. Hydrogen bonds form between what atoms?
4. Explain why the hydrogen bonds between HF molecules are much stronger than those between HBr, HI, and HCl molecules.

► **FIGURE 6-23**

Dry ice is used to keep food products cold during shipping.

Other intermolecular forces

If dipole forces were the only attractions between molecules, all nonpolar substances would be gases at room temperature. However, most of the components of liquid gasoline are nonpolar molecules. Carbon dioxide is nonpolar, but it can be compressed and cooled to produce the dry ice shown in **Figure 6-23.** Iodine, I_2, is nonpolar, and it exists as a solid at room temperature.

Intermolecular forces exist between nonpolar molecules

As the temperature of a liquid is raised, the random motion of molecules increases. Eventually, the kinetic energy is high enough that molecules overcome the intermolecular forces and separate from each other. This is the point at which the liquid boils. Therefore, the boiling temperature of a substance is a good measure of the force of attraction between molecules or between atoms. Consider the fact that the boiling points of the noble gases He, Ar, and Rn are −269°C, −186°C, and −62°C, respectively.

Higher boiling points of the noble gases indicate increased forces of attraction between the atoms. This was explained by the German physicist Fritz W. London in 1930. He found that boiling point increases roughly as the number of electrons in the molecule or atom increases. These forces of attraction are called **London forces**, or *dispersion forces*. They exist between all molecules but are usually overshadowed by dipole forces in polar substances.

London forces result from temporary dipoles

London forces of attraction exist because any atom or molecule becomes a dipole at any instant when its electrons are unequally distributed around the nucleus or nuclei. This *instantaneous dipole* polarizes a nearby molecule, causing that molecule to also become an instantaneous dipole. The momentary dipoles attract each other momentarily. This attraction brings the molecules together until the repulsion of the outer electrons equals the London force of attraction. This balance of forces determines the spacing of the molecules in the liquid or solid state. **Figure 6-24** illustrates how London forces arise. The attractive force increases as the number of electrons in the molecules increases.

London force

an attraction between atoms and molecules caused by the formation of instantaneous dipoles in the atoms and molecules

SECTION 6-4

TEACHING TIP

Vocabulary Strategy London forces are also known as *dispersion forces*. Have students investigate the meaning of the term *dispersion* and use this definition to explain why the term applies to molecules that are instantaneous dipoles. *Disperse* means to spread out to other areas. In molecules experiencing temporary dipoles, electrons are dispersed to areas of the molecule where they otherwise would not be.

VISUAL STRATEGY

Figure 6-24 Assemble several small iron objects, such as paper clips. Try to pick them up by touching them with an iron nail. Elicit from students that the nail won't pick up the objects because the nail is not a magnet. Then rub the nail with a magnet. Again try to pick up the objects with the nail. Point out that the magnet has made the nail magnetic just as an instantaneous dipole can cause a dipole in another molecule.

FIGURE 6-24 ▼

a Nonpolar molecules can collide . . .

b . . . to become temporary dipoles. They can then collide with more molecules, . . .

c . . . causing the formation of dipoles in adjacent molecules. These instantaneous dipoles attract each other.

COVALENT BONDS AND MOLECULAR FORCES   **223**

RESOURCE LINK

ChemFile Lab D
Consumer Lab
Have students do Experiment 6: *Cloth of Many Colors.*

SECTION REVIEW

Total recall

1. a gas

2. The greater the difference in electronegativity that exists between hydrogen and the element bonded to it, the stronger the hydrogen bonds that are formed between molecules of that compound.

3. hydrogen bonds

4. Nonpolar molecules collide to form a temporary dipole. This dipole induces the formation of dipoles in adjacent molecules. These instantaneous dipoles attract each other.

Critical thinking

5. Intermolecular forces are much weaker than the strong electrical forces that hold ions together in an ionic solid. Because more energy must be put into an ionic solid to separate the parts, the boiling points and melting points of ionic solids are higher than those of molecular substances.

6. Hydrogen bonds are stronger and only form between hydrogen and a highly electronegative element such as N, O, or F.

7. Ordinary dipole attractions occur between polar molecules. London forces result from temporary dipoles being induced in nonpolar molecules and are weaker than ordinary dipole attractions.

▼ **FIGURE 6-25**

 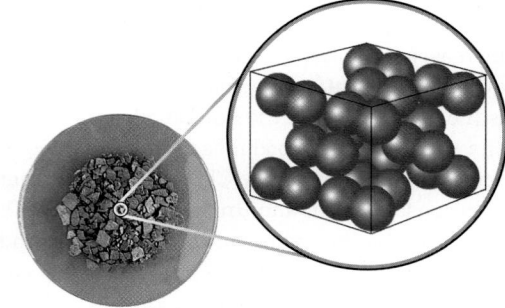

a In the sodium chloride crystal, each ion is strongly attracted to six oppositely charged ions. NaCl has a melting point of 801°C . . .

b . . . but in iodine crystals, the particles are neutral molecules that are not as strongly attracted to each other. I_2 has a melting point of 114°C.

London and dipole forces between molecules are usually much weaker than ionic forces in crystals. The very strong forces of ionic bonds lead to much higher melting points and boiling points for ionic compounds than for molecular compounds. Compare the properties of an ionic compound with those of a molecular compound in **Figure 6-25**.

SECTION REVIEW

Total recall

1. If there are no attractive forces between molecules in a substance, should the substance exist as a gas, a liquid, or a solid?

2. Describe the relationship between electronegativity and hydrogen bonding.

3. What type of intermolecular force holds together the DNA strands in your body?

4. How are London forces between molecules produced?

Critical thinking

5. Compare the melting and boiling points of molecular and ionic substances. How do these differences relate to bond types?

6. How does a hydrogen bond differ from ordinary dipole attraction?

7. Compare and contrast ordinary dipole attraction and London forces.

8. The molecular mass of methane, CH_4, is 16.05 g/mol, and its boiling point is −164°C. The molecular mass of water, H_2O, is 18.02 g/mol, only slightly more than that of methane. However, water's boiling point is 100°C, which is 264°C higher than that of methane. How can you account for this large difference?

9. Explain how the formation of instantaneous dipoles causes attractive forces between nonpolar molecules.

8. The electronegativity difference between carbon and hydrogen is small, so the CH_4 molecule is nonpolar. Thus, the CH_4 molecule is not strongly attracted to other methane molecules. Water is polar because of its geometry and the difference in electronegativity between hydrogen and oxygen atoms, and it forms hydrogen bonds between water molecules. Because of the difference in attraction, it takes more energy to separate water molecules than to separate methane molecules.

9. As one nonpolar molecule instantaneously becomes a dipole, the negative end of the molecule repels the electrons in other molecules around it, and the positive end of the dipole attracts electrons in other molecules around it, making them temporary dipoles.

Now that you have finished your study of covalent bonds, you should be able to answer the questions that were posed in the opening story.

LOOKING BACK

Why don't the two hydrogen atoms in water give up their sole electrons to the oxygen atom to form an ionic bond?

With its six valence electrons, an oxygen atom needs two more electrons to achieve a stable octet. The two hydrogen atoms, each with one electron, seem to be perfect candidates to give up their two electrons and form two ionic bonds. But the electronegativity difference is small, and oxygen cannot "steal" hydrogen's electrons. Consequently, they share electrons. By sharing electrons and forming a covalent bond, the oxygen atom in a water molecule can have a stable octet and each hydrogen atom can have a stable duet of electrons.

The electronegativity of oxygen is 3.4, and the electronegativity of hydrogen is 2.2. Therefore, a bond between hydrogen and

This Mars rock, named Yogi, has a smooth, rounded surface. This surface indicates that the rock may have been worn down by water.

One of Jupiter's moons, Europa, appears to be nearly covered by ice. Scientists speculate that life could exist in oceans below this ice shell.

oxygen has an electronegativity difference of 1.2, making the bond a polar covalent bond.

Based on its composition, what is the actual chemical name for water?

The full chemical name for water is dihydrogen monoxide, reflecting that a water molecule contains two hydrogen atoms and one oxygen atom.

What is the three-dimensional structure of water?

The Lewis structure for water is as follows.

H_2O has two bonds to H atoms and two nonbonding pairs for a total of four electron clouds. A water molecule thus has the geometry of a tetrahedron, with two hydrogen atoms occupying two legs and two nonbonding pairs occupying the other two legs. As a result, a water molecule has a bent shape. This bent shape means that water is a polar molecule, a physical feature that has important chemical applications. You will learn more about the special properties of water in Chapter 13.

Water has also been called the universal solvent; not all substances are soluble in water, but many are. Because of this property of water, it dissolves and carries many substances throughout the body.

CHAPTER 6
Highlights

READING STRATEGY

Assimilating Knowledge

Have students return to their lists that they created on page 192 of things they wanted to know about molecules. Have them place check marks next to the questions that they are now able to answer. Students should finish by making a list of what they've learned. Have students identify unanswered questions as well as new questions they may have. These questions could be used as the basis for a research project.

REVIEW & ASSESS ASSIGNMENT GUIDE

Term Review
Assign after Section 6-4.

Concepts & Skills Review

Section 6-1
▶ Items 1–11

Section 6-2
▶ Items 12–29

Section 6-3
▶ Items 30–35

Section 6-4
▶ Items 36–48

Linking Chapters

Section 6-1
▶ Item 1

Section 6-2
▶ Item 3

Section 6-4
▶ Item 2

Alternative Assessments
Assign after Section 6-4.

Test Prep
Assign prior to the chapter test.

KEY TERMS

6-1
bond energy
bond length
covalent bond
dipole
electronegativity
molecular orbital
nonpolar covalent bond
polar covalent bond

6-2
Lewis structure
resonance structure
single bond
unshared pair
valence electron

6-3
VSEPR (valence shell electron pair repulsion) theory

6-4
hydrogen bond
intermolecular force
London force

KEY CONCEPTS

6-1 Why do some atoms form covalent bonds?
▶ Covalent bonds form when atoms share pairs of electrons.
▶ The greater the electronegativity difference is, the more polar the bond is.

6-2 How are molecules depicted?
▶ A Lewis structure represents an atom's nucleus and inner-shell electrons with the element's symbol and its valence electrons with dots.
▶ Some molecules have more than one valid Lewis structure. This is called resonance, and it makes the molecules more stable and affects geometry.
▶ Molecular compounds are named using the elements' names and a system of prefixes and suffixes.

6-3 How are molecular shapes determined?
▶ VSEPR theory states that electron pairs in the valence shell stay as far apart as possible.
▶ This model can be used to qualitatively predict the shapes of molecules, including linear, planar, trigonal pyramidal, and tetrahedral.

6-4 What forces exist between molecules?
▶ Ionic substances have much stronger forces of attraction between particles than do covalent substances.
▶ If the molecules are polar, then added electrical attractions exists between the dipoles.
▶ If one of the atoms in a strong dipole is a hydrogen atom, the polar-polar force is stronger. This force is called a hydrogen bond.
▶ Intermolecular forces of attraction, such as London forces, dipole forces, and hydrogen bonds, pull molecules together.

KEY SKILLS

Review the following models before your exam. Be sure you can solve these types of problems.

How To Draw Lewis structures (p. 204)

How To Draw Lewis structures with multiple bonds (p. 207)

How To Draw Lewis structures of polyatomic ions (p. 210)

Sample Problem 6A: Predicting molecular shapes (p. 217)

TERM REVIEW

1. Two atoms of differing electronegativity form a(n) _____.
(London force, intermolecular force, polar covalent bond)

2. In a _____, atomic symbols represent nuclei and inner-shell electrons.
(London force, Lewis electron dot structure, double bond)

3. A molecule with a positive end and a negative end is called a _____.
(dipole, molecular compound, covalent bond)

4. Pulling two bonded atoms apart requires putting in energy equal to the _____.
(covalent bond, bond energy, intermolecular force)

5. _____ helps explain molecular shape.
(bond energy, VSEPR theory, electronegativity)

6. The force between a hydrogen atom bonded to a highly electronegative atom and another electron-rich atom is called a _____.
(hydrogen bond, polar covalent bond, London force)

7. Some molecules are represented by two or more Lewis structures called _____.
(resonance hybrids, resonance structures, molecular orbitals)

8. A _____ is the region where an electron is most likely to exist as it travels around two nuclei in a covalent bond.
(atomic orbital, molecular orbital, resonance structure)

9. Atoms share electrons equally in a(n) _____.
(nonpolar covalent bond, ionic bond, polar covalent bond)

10. Molecules are attracted to each other by _____.
(electronegativity, bond energy, intermolecular forces)

CONCEPT & SKILLS REVIEW

CHEMICAL BONDS

1. a. How does a covalent bond differ from an ionic bond?
   b. How do molecular compounds differ from ionic compounds?

2. What is the general trend relating bond energy and bond length?

3. a. Draw and label the forces that affect atoms in a covalent bond.
   b. Explain why bonding electrons are able to come relatively close to each other.
   c. Why is a spring a better model than a stick for a covalent bond?

4. Contrast the distribution of electrons in a covalent bond and an ionic bond.

5. What is the periodic trend in electronegativity?

6. What determines the electron distribution of a bond?

7. Describe the energy changes involved when two atoms come together and form a covalent bond.

8. Do atoms actually remain at the distance stated as the bond length?

9. Describe the electron distribution in a polar covalent bond, and compare it with the electron distribution in a nonpolar covalent bond.

10. Use Table 6-2 and electronegativity differences to predict whether the bonds between the following pairs of elements are ionic, polar covalent, or nonpolar covalent.
   a. Na–F
   b. K–Cl
   c. N–O
   d. H–I
   e. Al–O
   f. S–O
   g. Cl–Br

TERM REVIEW

1. polar covalent bond
2. Lewis electron dot structure
3. dipole
4. bond energy
5. VSEPR theory
6. hydrogen bond
7. resonance structures
8. molecular orbital
9. nonpolar covalent bond
10. intermolecular forces

CONCEPT & SKILLS REVIEW

1. a. An ionic bond results from attraction between positive and negative ions. A covalent bond results from atoms' sharing electrons.
   b. Molecular compounds have covalent bonds and usually contain individual molecules. Ionic compounds have ionic bonds and contain ions bonded within a crystal lattice structure.

2. As bond energy increases, bond length generally decreases.

3. a. Student drawings should show that the nuclei repel each other, as do the electron clouds, and that the nuclei and the electron clouds attract each other.
   b. The force of attraction between nuclei and electrons is stronger than the repulsion between electrons.
   c. The spring better represents the bond's flexibility. Like a spring, a bond can stretch or compress.

4. In a covalent bond, two atoms share electrons. The sharing is not always equal, but the shared electrons spend some time around each atom. In an ionic bond, at least one electron has been completely transferred from one atom to another and spends no time at all in the electron cloud of the source atom.

5. Electronegativity increases from left to right across a period and decreases down a group.

CHAPTER 6
Review Answers

6. The electronegativity differences between the atoms involved determine the bond's electron distribution; the more electronegative element holds electrons more closely than the less electronegative element.

7. As two atoms come together to form a bond, their potential energy decreases until they are at a distance known as the bond length. If the two atoms get any closer to one another, their energy increases sharply.

8. No; because atoms vibrate, stretch, and pull along the bond, the bond length is not an absolute value. It is an average length.

9. In a nonpolar covalent bond, the electrons are distributed evenly throughout the molecular orbital surrounding the two atoms. In a polar covalent bond, there is a region of greater electron density around one atom.

10. a. $4.0 - 0.9 = 3.1$; ionic

b. $3.2 - 0.8 = 2.4$; ionic

c. $3.4 - 3.0 = 0.4$; nonpolar covalent

d. $2.7 - 2.2 = 0.5$; polar covalent

e. $3.4 - 1.6 = 1.8$; polar covalent

f. $3.4 - 2.6 = 0.8$; polar covalent

g. $3.2 - 3.0 = 0.2$; nonpolar covalent

11. from least to most polar: $I-Cl$, $H-Br$, $H-F$

12. the nucleus and inner-shell electrons

13. a double bond; a triple bond

14. 3, $\cdot\dot{B}\cdot$; 5, $:\dot{N}\cdot$; 7, $:\ddot{\underset{..}{F}}:$

15. a. resonance
b. It is more stable.

16. a. Hydrogen is never a central atom. The second hydrogen atom contains two single bonds and can contain only one single bond. The total number of valence electrons is wrong.

11. Arrange the following diatomic molecules in order of increasing bond polarity. You may need to refer to Table 6-2 and Figure 6-7.
a. $I-Cl$
b. $H-F$
c. $H-Br$

LEWIS STRUCTURES

12. In a Lewis structure, what does a chemical symbol, such as C, represent?

13. What kind of bond is formed between two atoms that share two electron pairs? three electron pairs?

14. Determine the number of valence electrons in boron, nitrogen, and fluorine. Draw the electron-dot diagram for each.

15. a. What term is used when molecules have more than one valid Lewis structure?
b. How does this affect the stability of a molecule?

16. Explain what is wrong with the following structures, then correct each one.
a. $H-H-\ddot{\underset{..}{S}}:$

b.

c.

17. Unlike other elements, noble gases are relatively inert. When they do react, they sometimes do not follow the octet rule. Examine the following Lewis structure for the molecule XeO_2F_2.

a. Do the valence electrons of the Xe atom follow the octet rule? Explain.
b. How many unshared pairs of electrons are present in this molecule?
c. Can this molecule form a hydrogen bond? Explain.

18. Boron trifluoride, BF_3, reacts violently with various compounds, including water and ammonia.
a. Draw the Lewis structure for BF_3, showing a single covalent bond between the central B atom and each F atom.
b. Draw the Lewis structures for water and ammonia. Explain why they react so readily with BF_3.
Hint: what might their unshared pairs do?

Practice Problems

19. Draw Lewis structures for the following molecules. (Remember, hydrogen can form only one covalent bond.)
a. NF_3 c. CH_3OH
b. $SiCl_4$

20. Draw Lewis structures for the following molecules:
a. ClF c. $HOCl$
b. CCl_2F_2

21. Draw Lewis structures for the following molecules:
a. O_2 c. HCN
b. CS_2

22. Draw Lewis structures for the following molecules exhibiting resonance:
a. SO_2 c. O_3
b. N_2O (Hint: the order of the atoms is NNO.)

23. Draw Lewis structures for the following molecules:
a. a refrigerant with one C atom, one H atom, and three F atoms
b. a natural-gas ingredient with two C atoms and six H atoms

24. Draw Lewis structures for the following polyatomic ions.
a. OH^- c. NO^{2+}
b. NO^{2-}

25. NO_3^- has three resonance structures. Draw two of them.

NAMES AND FORMULAS FOR MOLECULAR COMPOUNDS

26. Using the system of prefixes and suffixes, name the following compounds:
  a. SF_4 **d.** N_2O_5
  b. BCl_3 **e.** S_2Cl_2
  c. PBr_5 **f.** SO_3

27. Give formulas for the following compounds:
  a. carbon disulfide
  b sulfur hexafluoride
  c. dinitrogen tetroxide
  d. chlorine trifluoride

Practice Problems

28. Name the following compounds whose Lewis structures are shown:

  a.
    :F:
    :F−C−F:
    :F:

  c. H−Ö−Ö−H

  b.
    :Ö:
    :Ö−Xe−Ö:

29. Draw the Lewis structure for each of the following compounds:
  a. carbon tetrachloride
  b nitrogen tribromide
  c. dichlorine oxide

MOLECULAR SHAPES

30. Why do the electron clouds around a central atom stay as far apart as possible?

31. Name the following molecular shapes:

  a.   **b.**   **c.**

Practice Problems

32. Determine the shape of the following compounds:
  a. ClF   **d.** CF_4
  b. OF_2 **e.** BF_3
  c. NF_3

33. Draw the shapes of the following ions:
  a. NH_4^+ **c.** CO_3^{2-}
  b. OCl^-

34. Use these Lewis structures to deduce the shape of the molecules.
  a. H−C≡C−H   **c.** :Br−P−Br:
  b. :Cl−Ö−Cl: :Br:

35. Draw the Lewis structures of BF_3 and NF_3, and determine their shapes.

FORCES BETWEEN MOLECULES

36. List two intermolecular forces of attraction.

37. What is a hydrogen bond?

38. Why do compounds exhibiting hydrogen bonds boil at a higher temperature than similar polar compounds without hydrogen bonds?

39. Describe London forces and compare them to dipole forces.

40. How does size affect the force of attraction between noble gas atoms?

41. a. What affects the strength of London forces in molecular compounds?
  b. Why are the London forces between H_2 molecules very weak?

42. Describe dipole forces, London forces, and hydrogen bonds in terms of water molecules.

43. a. Describe what attractive force(s) must be overcome to melt ice.
  b. Describe what attractive force(s) must be overcome to produce hydrogen gas and oxygen gas from the water that forms from the melted ice.

44. Explain why CH_3OH can form a hydrogen bond with water but CH_4 cannot. (Hint: Draw the Lewis structure for both compounds.)

45. Why does SO_2 have a higher boiling point than CO_2? (Hint: Determine the shape of each molecule, and then compare the intermolecular force that would be present between their respective molecules.)

46. Explain why melting and boiling points of molecular compounds are usually lower than those of ionic compounds.

  b. The octet rule is not followed for the carbon atom.

    :Ö:
    H−C−Ö−H

  c. The top chlorine atom contains too many electrons.

    :Cl:
    :Cl−N−Cl:

17. a. No, the xenon atom has 10 valence electrons in this compound.
  b. 13
  c. If only XeO_2F_2 is present, no hydrogen bonds form because no hydrogen atoms are present. However, fluorine and oxygen are both highly electronegative. Xenon is not. The fluorine and oxygen could form a hydrogen bond with a polar hydrogen-containing molecule, such as water.

18. a.

  b. Both water and ammonia contain unshared pairs of electrons that could complete an octet for boron, forming a coordinate-covalent bond.

    :Ö: H
    H H ; H−N−H

19. a. :F−N−F:
         :F:

  b.
      :Cl:
    :Cl−Si−Cl:
      :Cl:

  c.
      H
    H−C−Ö−H
      H

20. a. :Cl−F:

  b.
      :Cl:
    :F−C−F:
      :Cl:

  c. H−Ö−Cl:

21. a. $\ddot{O}=\ddot{O}$

b. $\ddot{S}=C=\ddot{S}$

c. $H-C\equiv N:$

22. a. $\ddot{O}=\ddot{S}-\ddot{O}: \longleftrightarrow :\ddot{O}-\ddot{S}=\ddot{O}$

b. $\ddot{O}=N=\ddot{N} \longleftrightarrow :\ddot{O}-N\equiv N:$

c. $\ddot{O}=\ddot{O}-\ddot{O}: \longleftrightarrow :\ddot{O}-\ddot{O}=\ddot{O}$

23. a.

$$\ddot{F}-\underset{\underset{:\ddot{F}:}{|}}{\overset{\overset{H}{|}}{C}}-\ddot{F}:$$

b.

$$H-\underset{\underset{H}{|}}{\overset{\overset{H}{|}}{C}}-\underset{\underset{H}{|}}{\overset{\overset{H}{|}}{C}}-H$$

24. a. $\left[:\ddot{O}-H\right]^{-}$

b. $\left[\cdot\ddot{N}-\ddot{O}:\right]^{2-}$

c. $\left[\cdot N=\ddot{O}:\right]^{2+}$

25. *See page 231A.*

26. a. sulfur tetrafluoride
b. boron trichloride
c. phosphorus pentabromide
d. dinitrogen pentoxide
e. disulfur dichloride
f. sulfur trioxide

27. a. CS_2
b. SF_6
c. N_2O_4
d. ClF_3

28. a. carbon tetrafluoride
b. xenon trioxide
c. dihydrogen dioxide

Answers continue on page 231A.

47. Which compound in each pair has the higher boiling point? Explain.
a. NaF and F_2 **c.** CO_2 and SO_2
b. Cl_2 and F_2 **d.** H_2O and H_2S

48. Arrange the following pairs according to the strength of the intermolecular force that exists between the two molecules or ions in the pair:
a. polar molecule and polar molecule
b. nonpolar molecule and nonpolar molecule
c. ion and ion

LINKING CHAPTERS

	Carbon and carbon	Oxygen and oxygen	Carbon and nitrogen
Single	376 kJ/mol	214 kJ/mol	331 kJ/mol
Double	720 kJ/mol	498 kJ/mol	644 kJ/mol
Triple	962 kJ/mol	N/A	937 kJ/mol

1. Theme: Classification and trends
The table above shows different bond energies for single, double, and triple bonds.
a. Which is the shortest type of bond?
b. Predict how the N—O bond would compare to the N=O bond in terms of bond energy.

2. Ionic compounds
a. What kind of attractive force is responsible for the binding of water in hydrated salts such as $CuSO_4 \cdot 5H_2O$?
b. Describe the attractive forces involved in the dissolving of NaCl in water.

3. Molar mass
Find the molar mass of each of the following polyatomic ions:

a. $\left[\begin{array}{c} :\ddot{O}: \\ :\ddot{O}-S-\ddot{O}: \\ :\ddot{O}: \end{array}\right]^{2-}$ **c.** $\left[\begin{array}{c} :\ddot{O}: \\ :\ddot{O}-Cl-\ddot{O}: \\ :\ddot{O}: \end{array}\right]^{-}$

b. $\left[\begin{array}{c} :O: \\ :\ddot{O}-N-\ddot{O}: \end{array}\right]^{-}$ **d.** $[:C\equiv N:]^{-}$

ALTERNATIVE ASSESSMENTS

Performance assessment

1. Molecular structure plays a large part in function. Design an experiment that demonstrates this relationship between molecular structure and function. If your plan gets your teacher's approval, test your design.

Portfolio projects

1. Chemistry and you
Searching for the perfect artificial sweetener—great taste with no calories—has been the focus of chemical research for some time. Molecules such as aspartame and saccharin owe their sweetness to their size and shape. One theory holds that any sweetener must have three sites that fit into the proper taste buds on the tongue. This theory is appropriately known as the "triangle theory." Research artificial sweeteners to develop a model to show how the triangle theory operates.

2. Cooperative activity
Some central atoms achieve an expanded valence when they form a covalent bond. This means that the atom has more than an octet of valence electrons. One example is phosphorus pentachloride, PCl_5. Draw the Lewis structure for this compound. Each group should find as many examples as possible of molecules that contain an atom with an expanded valence. Draw their Lewis structures. If possible, determine the shape of each of these molecules.

3.

SCI LINKS
NSTA

TOPIC: Silicon
GO TO: www.scilinks.org
KEYWORD: HW064

Research and communication
Covalently bonded solids, such as silicon, used in computer components, are harder than pure metals. Research theories that explain the hardness of covalently bonded solids and their usefulness in the computer industry. Present your findings to the class.

1. A chemical bond results from the mutual attraction of the nuclei for _____.
   a. electrons
   b. neutrons
   c. protons
   d. dipoles

2. A nonpolar covalent bond is unlikely to form between two atoms that differ in _____.
   a. electronegativity
   b. state of matter
   c. density
   d. polarity

3. To draw a Lewis structure, it is not necessary to know _____.
   a. bond energies
   b. the number of valence electrons for each atom
   c. the types of atoms in the molecule
   d. the number of atoms in the molecule

4. Multiple covalent bonds may occur in atoms that contain carbon, nitrogen, or _____.
   a. chlorine
   b. oxygen
   c. hydrogen
   d. helium

5. The Lewis structure of methane, CH_4, contains _____ covalent bonds.
   a. 3
   b. 5
   c. 4
   d. 8

6. VSEPR states that the electrostatic repulsion between electron pairs surrounding an atom causes _____.
   a. an electron sea to form
   b. these pairs to be oriented as far apart as possible
   c. positive ions to form
   d. a bond to break

7. In a polar covalent bond, the electronegativity of the two atoms is _____.
   a. approximately the same
   b. so different that one atom takes an electron away from the other atom
   c. different, but the electrons are still shared by both atoms
   d. zero

8. According to VSEPR theory, the shape of an AB_4 molecule with no unshared electrons would be _____.
   a. linear
   b. bent
   c. octahedral
   d. tetrahedral

9. Compared with covalent bonds, the strength of intermolecular forces is generally _____.
   a. weaker
   b. about the same
   c. stronger
   d. too variable to compare

10. In writing a Lewis structure for a polyatomic ion, one electron must be added for each unit of _____.
    a. moles
    b. positive charge
    c. mass
    d. negative charge

11. In Lewis electron-dot structures, the atomic symbol represents _____.
    a. valence electrons
    b. the nucleus and inner-shell electrons
    c. atomic number
    d. a stable octet of electrons

12. Due to the presence of an unshared pair of electrons, the shape of ammonia, NH_3, is _____.
    a. tetrahedral
    b. linear
    c. trigonal pyramidal
    d. octahedral

13. The energy released in the formation of a covalent bond is the difference between zero and the _____.
    a. maximum potential energy
    b. kinetic energy of the atom
    c. minimum potential energy
    d. bond length expressed in picometers

1. a
2. a
3. a
4. b
5. c
6. b
7. c
8. d
9. a
10. d
11. b
12. c
13. c

Answers from page 228

25. Any two of the following:

Answers from page 229

29. a.
:Cl:
|
:Cl—C—Cl:
|
:Cl:

b.
:Br:
|
:Br—N—Br:

c.
:O:
:Cl.   .Cl:

30. The electron clouds are negatively charged, and like charges repel. They arrange themselves so that the repulsion is minimized.

31. a. tetrahedral
b. linear
c. trigonal planar

32. a. linear
b. bent
c. trigonal pyramidal
d. tetrahedral
e. trigonal planar

33. a.

b. [●—●]⁻

c.

34. a. linear
b. bent
c. trigonal pyramidal

35.
:F: :F:
| |
B   :F—N—F:
:F.   .F:

trigonal   trigonal
planar   pyramidal

36. Students should list two of the following: London forces, hydrogen bonds, and dipole forces.

37. the attraction occurring when a hydrogen atom bonded to a strongly electronegative atom is also attracted to another electronegative atom of a different molecule

38. Hydrogen bonds are stronger than other intermolecular forces, such as other dipole forces and London forces, so hydrogen-bonded compounds have higher boiling points than other polar compounds.

39. London forces are weak dipole forces. They result from temporary induced dipoles.

40. Large noble-gas atoms have more levels of electrons that shield the pull of the nucleus. Smaller atoms have fewer levels of electrons, and the pull of the nucleus is greater. Thus, smaller atoms are held more closely together because the force of attraction is greater.

41. a. how many electrons are free to move and how easily they can move from one part of a molecule to another
b. Only two electrons are present in each molecule.

42. London forces exist in normally nonpolar molecules, so they don't apply to water molecules. Water molecules do exhibit dipole forces because oxygen is more electronegative than hydrogen, so the H–O bonds in water are polar. Hydrogen bonds form between hydrogen atoms in water molecules and oxygen atoms in other water molecules.

43. a. In ice, the polar water molecules are arranged in a crystal lattice. The dipole attraction between molecules must be overcome enough that the molecules can move away from each other.
b. More energy must be added to water to produce hydrogen gas and oxygen gas because the covalent bonds in the molecules must be broken.

44. CH_4 is nonpolar because the molecule is symmetrical and there is little electronegativity difference between carbon and hydrogen. In CH_3OH, the oxygen atom and the hydrogen atom differ in electronegativity. Therefore, the —OH part of the molecule is a dipole, and that hydrogen atom can form a hydrogen bond with an oxygen atom in a water molecule.

45. SO_2 is bent, and CO_2 is linear, so SO_2 is polar. Because SO_2 is polar, dipole forces exist between its molecules. Because more energy must be added to separate the molecules, it has a higher boiling point.

46. Intermolecular forces are much weaker than the strong electrical forces that hold ions together in an ionic solid. Because more energy must be put into an ionic solid to separate the parts, the boiling points and melting points of ionic solids are higher.

Answers from page 230

47. a. NaF, because it is ionic; strong forces attract each ion to other, oppositely charged ions around it. F_2 molecules are attracted only by weak London forces.
b. Cl_2; it is more massive.
c. SO_2, because its molecules are bent and are polar. As a result, dipole forces attract them. CO_2 is linear and not subject to dipole forces.
d. H_2O, because oxygen is more electronegative than is sulfur. This difference in electronegativity makes water more polar, and it forms strong hydrogen bonds with other water molecules.

48. from strongest to weakest: c, a, b

LINKING CHAPTERS

1. a. Triple bonds are shortest.
b. The double bond is shorter and requires more energy to break than does the single bond.

2. a. Hydrates contain water trapped within their crystal structures. The attractions holding the water there must be dipole forces, and may include hydrogen bonds.

b. The oxygen atom in the water molecule with a partial negative charge is attracted to a positive sodium ion on the surface of the crystal, pulling the cation away from the solid. The same thing happens between the hydrogen atoms in a water molecule with partial positive charges and negative chloride ions on the surface of the crystal.

3. a. 96.07 g/mol
b. 62.01 g/mol
c. 99.45 g/mol
d. 26.02 g/mol

ALTERNATIVE ASSESSMENTS

Performance assessment

1. Encourage students to choose examples other than water. Water has a strong structure-function relationship, but it has been thoroughly discussed in the chapter. Student examples might include ammonia. The molecule's unshared electrons on the nitrogen atom make the molecule somewhat reactive, which aids in its effectiveness as a cleaning agent.

Portfolio projects

1. Answers will vary.

2.

trigonal
bipyramidal

3. Answers will vary. Verify that the theories explain hardness only of substances with covalent bonds. Students might also discuss some properties of semiconductors.

CHAPTER 7 PLANNING GUIDE

Carbon and Organic Compounds

CLASSROOM RESOURCES

SECTIONS	TEACHER'S DEMONSTRATIONS	PROBLEM SOLVING ■ *Text* ◆ *ChemFile Mini-Guide*	LABORATORIES ■ *Text* ◆ *ChemFile Manuals: A, B, C, D*
7-1 **What kinds of covalent compounds can carbon form?** Section Review, p. 243	**Demo 1** Isomers and Properties, p. 237		◆ **A23** Carbon ◆ **A24** Oil-Degrading Microbes
7-2 **How are carbon compounds named and drawn?** Section Review, p. 252	**Demo 2** Unsaturated Fats, p. 250	■ **How To** Name branched hydrocarbons, p. 247 ■ **How To** Decipher skeletal structures, p. 251	◆ **D7** All Fats Are Not Equal!
7-3 **What is a polymer?** Section Review, p. 263	**Demo 3** Polyethylene, p. 256 **Demo 4** What Type of Fiber Is It?, p. 260		■ **QuickLab** Properties of Polymers, p. 257 ■ **Exp. 7A** Polymers and Toy Balls, p. 736 ◆ **A25** Polymers ◆ **D8** Polymers as Straws ◆ **D9** The Slime Challenge

232A

TECHNOLOGY RESOURCES

See page 232 for a listing of Internet resources.

SECTIONS	VIDEOS/VIDEODISC *Holt Chemistry Videodisc* CNN PRESENTS *Science in the NEWS*	CHEMFILE CD-ROMs ● *Teaching Resources* ◆ *Interactive Tutor*	OVERHEADS ● *Color Transparencies* ◆ *Transparency Masters*
7-1	Carbon: graphite Carbon: diamond Carbon: C_{60} (buckyball) Diamond, silicon, and silicon carbide Butane molecular rotation Ethene molecular rotation Benzene molecular rotation CNN PRESENTS Segment 16 Carbon Nitride Segment 17 Advances in Fuel Technology	● Supplemental Reading: *The Same and Not the Same,* "Handshakes in the Dark" ● Supplemental Reading: *The Same and Not the Same,* "Representation and Reality" ● Occupational Application: Perfumer	● **114** Representations of Methane: The Tetrahedron ● **115** Bonding in Ethene ● **116** Comparing the Structures of Diamond and Graphite ● **117** Alkanes ● **118** Alkenes ● **119** Resonance Structures of Benzene ● *See also* **120–125.** ◆ *See also* **114A, 118A, 120A, 121A,** and **123A.**
7-2	2-propanol molecular rotation Palmitic acid molecular rotation Oleic acid molecular rotation Linoleic acid molecular rotation	● Supplemental Reading: *Consumer's Good Chemical Guide,* "Cholesterol, Fat, and Fibre" ● Supplemental Reading: *The Same and Not the Same,* "Molecular Mimicry"	● **127** Hydrogenation of Fatty Acid ● **128** Fatty Acid Composition of Dietary Fats ◆ *See also* **115A–117A, 119A,** and **122A.**
7-3	Polymerization by addition Polymerization: nylon CNN PRESENTS Segment 18 Chemical Separation Techniques for Plastics	● Occupational Application: Recycling Engineer ● Occupational Application: Organic Composter	● **129** Forms of Polyethylene ◆ **124A** Addition Polymers

ASSESSMENT RESOURCES

ALTERNATIVE ASSESSMENTS	CHAPTER TESTING	SCORING RUBRICS *Holt ChemFile Teaching Resources CD-ROM*
Student Text Performance assessment, p. 270 Portfolio projects 1–3, p. 270 **Teacher's Edition** Finding Patterns, p. 238 Prefixes, p. 244 Nomenclature, p. 248 Group Strategy, p. 262 **Study Guide** Sections 7-1 to 7-3	**Student Text** Test Preparation, p. 271 **Holt Chemistry: Visualizing Matter Chapter 7 Test** (blackline masters) **Holt ChemFile Test Generator for Macintosh and Windows**	**Lab Work** Student-Designed Experiments Rubric Performance-Tasks Scoring Rubric Assessment for Structured Inquiry Assessment for Open-Ended Inquiry **Portfolio Projects** Evaluating Concept Maps Assessing Portfolios Portfolio Assignment Student Evaluation Form

CHAPTER 1

Carbon and Organic Compounds

Establishing Prior Knowledge

Make certain students understand the following concepts.

▶ Chapter 3: electron configurations
▶ Chapter 6: covalent and hydrogen bonds, Lewis structures

 READING STRATEGY

Assimilating Knowledge

Before students read this chapter, have them write a short list of all the things they already know or think they know about carbon and organic compounds. When students finish their lists, ask them to contribute their entries to a group list on the board or on an overhead projector. Then have students list the things they might want to know about carbon and organic compounds.

If students are having trouble coming up with questions, offer the following suggestions to get them on track:

▶ What makes organic compounds different from other compounds?
▶ Are all carbon compounds organic compounds?
▶ What type of bonding is present in organic compounds?
▶ What are some common organic compounds, and what are their uses?

Have students save their list for later use in the Reading Strategy on page 266.

ABOUT THE ILLUSTRATION

Living organisms are made up of organic compounds. Rain forests, exhibit a great diversity of life, which in turn exhibits great molecular diversity. From the chlorophyll molecules that allow plants to use solar energy to the pigments that give flowers their bright colors, carbon compounds are involved in all aspects of life.

 internetconnect

Holt Chemistry: Visualizing Matter
On-Line Resources
HRW go.hrw.com
Visit the HRW Web site for a variety of resources related to this chapter. Just type in the keyword HW0 Chapt7.

SCiLINKS
NSTA

National Science Teachers Association
On-Line Resources: www.scilinks.org
The following Scilinks Internet resources can be found in the student text for this chapter:

Page 235
TOPIC: Diamond/Graphite
KEYWORD: HW071

Page 236
TOPIC: Organic compounds
KEYWORD: HW072

Page 239
TOPIC: Aromatic compounds
KEYWORD: HW073

Page 249
TOPIC: Fats
KEYWORD: HW074

Page 253
TOPIC: Polymers
KEYWORD: HW075

Page 263
TOPIC: Recycling codes
KEYWORD: HW076

Page 270
TOPIC: Recycling plans
KEYWORD: HW077

COVALENT BONDING AND TRASH BAGS

What is the largest structure ever made by humans? It's not the Great Wall of China that extends across northern China for 6300 km. It is the Fresh Kills landfill on Staten Island, New York. If the amount of trash the landfill holds were spread over 1000 football fields, the mound would be as tall as a 21-story building. Begun in 1948 atop a swamp, the Fresh Kills landfill currently receives up to 18 000 metric tons of garbage every day, but plans have been made to close the landfill by 2002.

The average person in the United States produces 1.8 kg (4 lb) of trash each day, about 55% of which will end up in a landfill. With landfills such as Fresh Kills filling up or closing, the challenge of getting rid of so much trash is overwhelming.

The best solution is to reduce the amount of trash produced. In addition, trash should be separated into biodegradable and non-biodegradable material. Bacteria in the soil can readily decompose biodegradable material. Because biodegradable waste makes up a large part of total household waste, we can drastically reduce the amount of garbage going into landfills by sending this material to a compost facility. At a compost facility, materials such as food and yard trimmings are converted into fertile soil. A few communities have already set up composting programs.

Trash bags have been a target in the search for biodegradable materials because people often put biodegradable material into nonbiodegradable trash bags. The trash bag acts as a barrier, preventing bacteria in the soil from breaking down the material inside the bag. Most plastic trash bags are made of polyethylene, a nonbiodegradable plastic. In the 1980s, corn starch was combined with polyethylene to create trash bags that were considered to be biodegradable. While the cornstarch did degrade, plastics were left in the soil. Since then, bags have been developed that are nearly 100% biodegradable. Because truly biodegradable products are more expensive, the market for them remains small.

Carbon is the major element in a wide range of biodegradable and nonbiodegradable compounds, from a banana peel to a polyethylene trash bag. In this chapter, you will learn about the nature of carbon and its many compounds.

CHAPTER LINKS

What determines whether something is biodegradable?

What is the structure of polyethylene?

Why is polyethylene so stable?

Most trash bags are made from low-density polyethylene, or LDPE. LDPE is formed when ethylene polymerizes in the presence of a catalyst at 200°C and 2000 atm of pressure. The catalyst removes an electron from the double bond, creating a free radical. This end of the molecule traps ethylene units, and the electron is transferred down the chain. In this way, the chain grows.

$$\underset{\underset{H}{|}}{\overset{\overset{H}{|}}{C}} - \underset{\underset{H}{|}}{\overset{\overset{H}{|}}{C}} \cdot \; + \; \underset{\underset{H}{|}}{\overset{\overset{H}{|}}{C}} = \underset{\underset{H}{|}}{\overset{\overset{H}{|}}{C}} \longrightarrow H - \underset{\underset{H}{|}}{\overset{\overset{H}{|}}{C}} - \underset{\underset{H}{|}}{\overset{\overset{H}{|}}{C}} - \underset{\underset{H}{|}}{\overset{\overset{H}{|}}{C}} - \underset{\underset{H}{|}}{\overset{\overset{H}{|}}{C}} \cdot$$

If the polymerization occurs without heating or pressurizing the ethylene gas, the occurrence of side chains decreases. Side chains affect the polymer's density. Polyethylene formed under low pressure is called high-density polyethylene, or HDPE.

RESOURCE LINK

ChemFile Teaching Resources CD-ROM *Supplemental Reading Projects* Assign the guided reading worksheets for Roald Hoffmann's *The Same and Not the Same;* Essay 9, "Handshakes in the Dark," and Essay 16, "Representation and Reality," for cross-curricular connections to language arts.

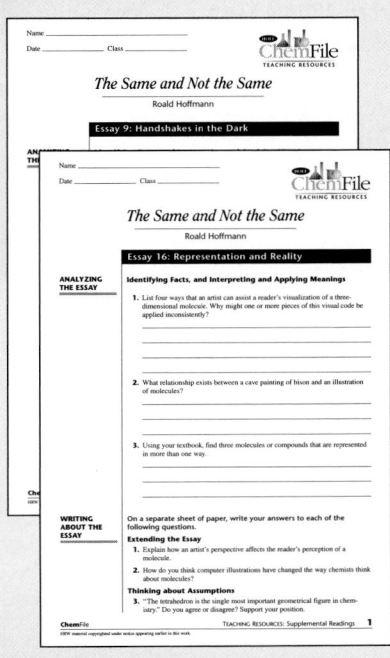

CONCEPT PREVIEW

Section 7-1
Carbon compounds
▶ how carbon bonds
▶ hydrocarbons
▶ functional groups
▶ classes of organic compounds

Section 7-2
Names and structures of carbon compounds
▶ basic nomenclature
▶ numbering carbon atoms
▶ saturated and unsaturated compounds
▶ representations of molecules

Section 7-3
Polymers
▶ macromolecules
▶ combining monomers
▶ addition and condensation polymers
▶ elastomers, fibers, and plastics

What kinds of covalent compounds can carbon form?

OBJECTIVES

▶ **Differentiate** between two allotropes of carbon.

▶ **Relate** the structures of diamond and graphite to their properties.

▶ **Describe** the bonding in alkanes, alkenes, and alkynes.

▶ **Classify** organic molecules by their functional groups.

Carbon and the covalent bond

Carbon is unique among the elements in that it forms long-chain and ring compounds by forming strong bonds with other carbon atoms. Also, carbon compounds have low chemical reactivity compared with compounds of other nonmetals. As a result, an enormous variety of stable carbon compounds with very diverse properties exist.

There must be something special about the bonding properties of carbon that makes so many compounds possible. Carbon nearly always forms covalent bonds. Three factors make the bonding of carbon unique. The first factor is the strong bonds between carbon atoms. This property is in contrast to other second-period nonmetals. Oxygen-oxygen single bonds, as in HO—OH, hydrogen peroxide, are so weak that this compound decomposes at room temperature.

The second factor is the low reactivity of carbon compounds compared with compounds of other elements. Butane, C_4H_{10}, is stable in air and catches fire only when a spark hits it. In contrast, the corresponding silicon compound, tetrasilane, Si_4H_{10}, catches fire spontaneously in air. Carbon tetrachloride, CCl_4, does not react with water at room temperature, whereas silicon tetrachloride, $SiCl_4$, reacts very rapidly.

The third factor is the geometry of carbon compounds. With four outer electrons, carbon can form four single covalent bonds. The most stable arrangement of these bonds has them pointing to the corners of a tetrahedron with angles near 109°.

▼ **FIGURE 7-1**

The great strength of carbon-carbon bonds makes long-chain molecules, such as the polyethylene used to make milk jugs, possible.

FIGURE 7-2 ▼

109.5°

a Because the tetrahedral network of carbon atoms is very strong, diamond is the hardest substance known.

b Electrons can pass freely along the planes, so graphite is a conductor of electricity even though carbon is a nonmetal.

TEACHING TIP

Designing a Model Have groups of students use toothpicks and gumdrops to model the structures of diamond and graphite. You may want to model one tetrahedron and one hexagon as a demonstration. After students have at least a dozen "atoms" in their diamond structure and two layers of graphite structures, have them demonstrate the strength of the tetrahedral structure and show how the layers of hexagons can slip past each other. Caution students against eating anything in a laboratory setting.

Diamond and graphite are covalent network solids

The crystal structure of diamond, an **allotrope** of carbon, involves many carbon atoms, each bonded at an angle of 109.5°. Diamond is a **covalent network solid.** Any crystal of a covalent network solid is an enormous single molecule containing trillions of atoms. The structure of diamond can be seen in **Figure 7-2a.** Gemstones are not the only use for diamond. The hardness of this solid makes it suitable for many industrial uses, such as grinding and polishing tools like dental drills.

Graphite is another allotrope of carbon. The carbon atoms in graphite are bonded in a hexagonal pattern and lie in planes. The bonds within each plane are very strong, and each plane can be considered a giant molecule, as shown in **Figure 7-2b.** Weaker London forces hold the planes together so that the planes can slip past each other. This makes graphite a good lubricant. The sliding layers also allow graphite to be used in the application with which you are probably most familiar, pencil lead. You can write with a pencil because the graphite layers that make up the pencil point slide apart, leaving a trail of graphite on the paper.

allotropes

forms of an element differing in either bonding or structure

covalent network solid

solid composed of atoms covalently bonded in a network in two or three dimensions

ANSWERS

CONCEPT CHECK

1. the strong bonds between carbon atoms, the low reactivity of carbon compounds compared with compounds of other elements, and the tetrahedral geometry of carbon compounds

2. forms of an element that differ either in bonding or in structure

3.
$$H:\overset{..}{\underset{..}{C}}:\overset{..}{\underset{..}{C}}:H \quad \text{or} \quad H-\overset{|}{\underset{|}{C}}-\overset{|}{\underset{|}{C}}-H$$

CONCEPT CHECK

1. List the three special factors involved in the bonding of carbon atoms.
2. What are allotropes?
3. Draw a Lewis dot structure of C_2H_6 to show how each carbon forms four covalent bonds.

internetconnect

SC*LINKS*
NSTA

TOPIC: Diamond/Graphite
GO TO: www.scilinks.org
KEYWORD: HW071

RESOURCE LINK

Chem**File** Lab A
Skills Development
Have students do Experiment 23: *Carbon.*

internet connect

SC LINKS.
NSTA
TOPIC: Organic compounds
GO TO: www.scilinks.org
KEYWORD: HW072

hydrocarbon

the simplest class of organic compounds, consisting of only hydrogen and carbon atoms

alkane

a hydrocarbon that contains only single bonds

Organic compounds

Most compounds of carbon are referred to as organic compounds. Organic compounds contain carbon, of course, and most also contain hydrogen. In addition, many other elements, including oxygen, nitrogen, sulfur, phosphorus, and the halogens, can bond to the carbon atoms. Organic compounds include proteins, carbohydrates, nucleic acids, lipids (fats), and plastics. A few of the organic compounds around you can be seen in **Figure 7-3.** More than 12 000 000 organic compounds are known, and thousands of new ones are discovered or synthesized each year. There are more known compounds of carbon than compounds of all the other 111 elements combined.

Hydrocarbons are the simplest organic molecular compounds

Just as the name suggests, **hydrocarbons** are compounds that consist only of hydrogen and carbon atoms. Hydrocarbons are grouped into three categories based on the type of bonding that exists between the carbon atoms. The simplest hydrocarbons are called **alkanes.** They are

▼ **FIGURE 7-3**

a Your hair is made of proteins that are made from smaller organic compounds called amino acids. Serine is an example of an amino acid.

d Caffeine is an organic compound that contains nitrogen.

b This shirt and the paper are both made of cellulose. Cellulose is made from chains of glucose molecules.

c Citrus fruits contain citric acid, an organic acid.

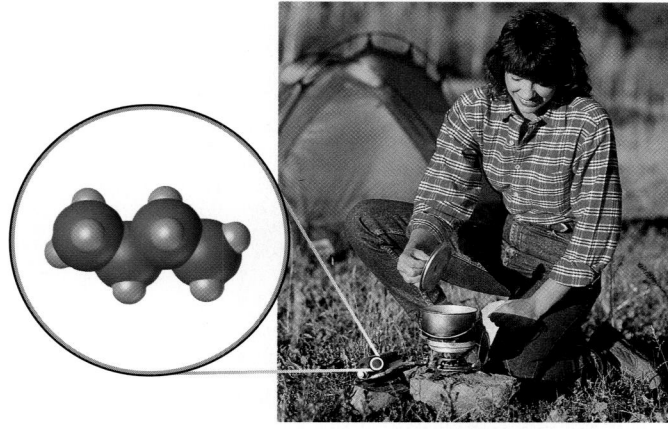

FIGURE 7-4 ◄

Butane is a hydrocarbon that is frequently used as a fuel for outdoor cooking stoves.

TEACHING TIP

Designing a Model Divide students into groups of three. Give each group the following instructions:

Draw 20 4 × 4 cm squares on a sheet of paper. Draw a circle about 2 cm in diameter in each square. Write the letter *C* in six of the circles. In each of these squares, draw four lines, each going from the center of the circle to the center of a side. In the other 14 squares, write an *H* in the circle and draw one line from the bottom of the circle to the center of the bottom of the square. Cut the squares apart. Acknowledge that the circles and letters represent atoms and that the lines represent bonds. Develop as many different molecules as possible in 5 minutes, using all the atoms and all the bonds. Sketch each molecule as it is formed, and do not repeat any molecules.

Have students compare and discuss results. To save time, you may want to prepare the "atoms" and "bonds" in advance. Five isomers exist that have the formula C_6H_{14}. If students find more than five, have them examine their sketches to determine which are duplicates.

the major components in petroleum. The carbon atoms in alkanes are connected only by single bonds. Butane is a simple example of an alkane.

$$
\begin{array}{cccc}
& H & H & H & H \\
| & | & | & | \\
H-C&-C&-C&-C-H \\
| & | & | & | \\
& H & H & H & H
\end{array}
$$
Butane

isomers

compounds with the same number and types of atoms but differing geometric arrangements

alkene

a hydrocarbon that contains one or more double bonds

Butane has four C atoms and 10 H atoms. These same atoms, shown in the structural formula for butane above, can also be arranged in the structure of 2-methylpropane, shown below and in **Figure 7-5.**

$$
\begin{array}{ccc}
H & H & H \\
| & | & | \\
H-C&-C&-C-H \\
| & | & | \\
H & H-C-H & H \\
& | & \\
& H &
\end{array}
$$
2-methylpropane

When the same number and type of atoms can be arranged in different structures, the different molecules are called **isomers.** Isomers are different compounds that have somewhat different physical and chemical properties. For the formula C_4H_{10}, there are two isomers: butane and 2-methylpropane. The number of isomers grows as the number of carbon atoms increases. $C_{10}H_{22}$ has 75 possible isomers, and $C_{20}H_{42}$ has more than 100 000 possible isomers.

The second class of hydrocarbons comprises the **alkenes.** Alkenes are hydrocarbons that contain at least one double bond between two carbon atoms. You have already learned that hydrocarbons are fairly unreactive due to the strong bonds between carbon atoms. The bond energy for a C—C single bond in ethane is 376 kJ/mol. The bond energy for a C=C double bond in ethene is 720 kJ/mol. If each component of the double bond were as strong as a single bond (376 kJ/mol), the bond energy of the double bond would be twice that of a single bond, or 752 kJ/mol.

FIGURE 7-5 ▲

These two isomers show that hydrocarbons can be either linear, also called straight-chain, like butane, or branched, like 2-methylpropane.

VISUAL STRATEGY

Figure 7-5 Use the figure and Demonstration 1 to explain to students why isomers such as butane and methylpropane differ in properties, such as boiling point, melting point, and density. Remind students that the melting point and boiling point of a substance depend on the intermolecular forces of attraction holding the molecules together.

CARBON AND ORGANIC COMPOUNDS   **237**

DEMONSTRATION 1

Isomers and Properties

Approximate time: 10 minutes

1. Use longer Velcro strips to represent molecules of butane and shorter strips to represent the shorter parent chain of methylpropane.

2. Have a student volunteer pull the strips apart and explain to other students which strips took less energy to separate (*the shorter strips*).

3. Ask students to explain what the demonstration indicates about the melting and boiling points of the two compounds. (*The melting and boiling points of methylpropane would be lower than those of butane because there is less attraction between the methylpropane molecules.*)

Disposal
Save the Velcro for later use.

Additional Application

Compounds known as pyrethrins contain the cyclopropane group. These compounds form the natural insecticides found in chrysanthemums. Scientists are studying these compounds with hopes that they can be effectively used with other types of plants, cutting down on the use of synthetic insecticides. Synthetic insecticides are usually more toxic than natural insecticides and may persist in the environment, causing pollution.

Historical Connection

Michael Faraday, the famous electrochemist discussed in Chapter 17, discovered benzene in 1825 as a component of the oily residue found in London gas mains.

▶ **FIGURE 7-6**

Limonene, also called oil of lemon, is an alkene.

alkyne

a hydrocarbon with one or more triple bonds

benzene

a six-membered ring of carbon atoms pictured with alternating double and single bonds, indicating delocalized electrons

▼ **FIGURE 7-7**

Electron orbitals in benzene overlap to form continuous orbitals, or delocalized clouds.

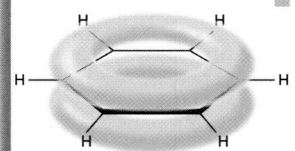

The actual bond energy for the double bond is less than this value. Each of the two components of the double bond is weaker than a single bond. Therefore, alkenes are much more reactive than alkanes.

Oxyacetylene torches are used to weld and cut metal. In these torches, the fuel gas ethyne, commonly called acetylene, burns in pure oxygen to produce a very hot flame. Ethyne, $H-C \equiv C-H$, is the simplest member of the third class of hydrocarbons, known as **alkynes.** The triple bond is even more reactive than the double bond of an alkene. Therefore, the triple bond of alkynes is the least stable of the three types of bonds. Alkynes are the most reactive of all hydrocarbons.

Carbon atoms can form rings

Carbon atoms that bond covalently to one another can also form ring structures. Recall the structure of butane from page 237. Four carbon atoms can also form a ring structure. Cyclobutane is the name of the ring compound with four carbon atoms. Its structure is shown below. Cyclobutane is an example of a *cycloalkane,* a hydrocarbon with a ring structure that contains only single bonds.

Benzene, C_6H_6, is one of the most important organic ring compounds. The following structures depict a benzene ring with alternating single and double bonds. All of these bonds are equivalent.

Benzene exhibits resonance as described in Chapter 6. The delocalized clouds of electrons are depicted in **Figure 7-7.** These delocalized electrons

ALTERNATIVE ASSESSMENT

Finding Patterns

Have students create a table similar to the one at right that goes all the way up to decane. They should try to fill in all of the empty boxes to discover the pattern of C_xH_y for alkanes, alkenes, and alkynes.

Carbon atoms	Alkane	Alkene	Alkyne
1	CH$_4$		
2	C$_2$H$_6$		
3		C$_3$H$_6$	
4			C$_4$H$_6$

Ans. alkane: C_nH_{2n+2}, alkene: C_nH_{2n}, alkyne: C_nH_{2n-2}

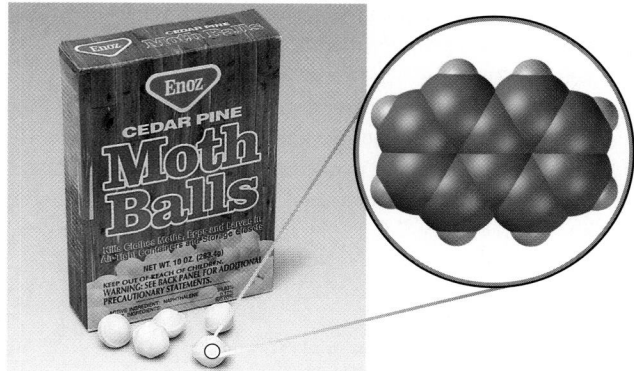

FIGURE 7-8 ◄

Naphthalene, used as a moth repellent, is made from two benzene rings fused together.

lead to extra stability of the compound. Consequently, in most of its reactions, benzene does not react the way an alkene would. It behaves more like an alkane. To designate the presence of delocalized electrons, benzene is commonly represented by a hexagon with a ring inside it. Notice that the hydrogen atoms attached to each corner of the hexagon are not shown in this simplified representation.

Benzene is the basis of a class of organic compounds called **aromatic compounds.** Included in this class are naphthalene, which is found in mothballs, and benzaldehyde, which is used in synthetic flavorings.

CONCEPT CHECK

1. Draw a structural formula for the straight-chain hydrocarbon with the molecular formula C_3H_6. Is this an alkane, alkene, or alkyne?
2. Can molecules with the molecular formulas C_4H_{10} and $C_4H_{10}O$ be isomers of one another? Why or why not?
3. Give the structural formulas for an alkane, an alkene, and an alkyne, each containing seven carbon atoms.
4. What are cycloalkanes?

Other organic compounds

Many organic compounds, including those in living things, contain at least one carbon atom that is covalently bonded not to hydrogen but to atoms of elements other than hydrogen, especially oxygen and nitrogen, but also sulfur and the halogens. These groups of atoms that include elements other than carbon and hydrogen constitute **functional groups.** Each functional group has unique chemical properties. For example,

CARBON AND ORGANIC COMPOUNDS 239

---

internetconnect

SCI LINKS
NSTA

TOPIC: Aromatic compounds
GO TO: www.scilinks.org
KEYWORD: HW073

aromatic compound

a compound containing a ring of carbon atoms pictured with alternating single and double bonds with delocalized electrons that provide great stability

functional group

a group of atoms that give characteristic properties to organic compounds

---

ANSWERS

CONCEPT CHECK

1. H—C—C=C ; an alkene
   (with H H H on top and H H on bottom)

2. no, because they contain different types of elements

3. Student answers may vary but might include the following.

   alkane:

   H—C—C—C—C—C—C—C—H
   (with H atoms above and below each carbon)

   Any structure that contains 7 C atoms, 14 H atoms, and only single bonds is correct.

   alkene:

   H—C—C—C—C=C—C—C—H
   (with H atoms above and below each carbon)

   Any structure that contains 7 C atoms, an appropriate number of H atoms, and at least one double bond is correct.

   alkyne:

   H—C—C—C—C≡C—C—C—H
   (with H atoms above and below)

   Any structure that contains 7 C atoms, an appropriate number of H atoms, and at least one triple bond is correct.

4. Cycloalkanes contain carbon atoms bonded together in a ring, two hydrogen atoms bonded to each carbon, and only single bonds.

ethers are polar, but not as polar as water. They have low boiling points, and they do not form hydrogen bonds with themselves but form weak ones with water.

Many common organic functional groups can be seen in **Figure 7-9.** Organic compounds are commonly classified by the functional groups they contain. **Table 7-1** gives an overview of some common classes of organic compounds and their functional groups; Table 7-1 includes the molecules shown in Figure 7-9.

▼ FIGURE 7-9

a Esters are common in plants and are responsible for some distinctive flavors and odors, such as the flavor of pineapple.

b Like esters, aldehydes and ketones, such as the benzaldehyde found in almonds, are responsible for many odors and flavors.

c Nutmeg contains a carboxylic acid named myristic acid.

d Ethanol is used as a solvent for many extracts and flavorings, such as vanilla extract.

240 CHAPTER 7

GRAPHIC ORGANIZER

	Elements Contained in the Compound		
	C, H, O	C and H only	C, H, N
Class of compound	alcohols	hydrocarbons	amines
	aldehydes		
	carboxylic acids		
	esters		
	ethers		
	ketones		

TABLE 7-1   Classes of Organic Compounds

Class	Functional group	Example
Alcohol	—OH	H H H—C—C—OH H H ethanol
Aldehyde	O ‖ —C—H	O ‖ C—H benzaldehyde
Halide	—F, Cl, Br, I	Cl | F—C—Cl | Cl trichlorofluoromethane (Freon 11)
Amine	—N—	H₃C N—C caffeine
Carboxylic acid	O ‖ —C—OH	H H H H H H H H H H H H H O H—C—C—C—C—C—C—C—C—C—C—C—C—C—C—OH H H H H H H H H H H H H H tetradecanoic acid (myristic acid)
Ester	O ‖ —C—O—	H H H O H H H—C—C—C—C—O—C—C—H H H H H H ethyl butanoate
Ether	—O—	O—CH₃ methyl phenyl ether (anisole)
Ketone	O ‖ —C—	H O H H—C—C—C—H H H propanone (acetone)

HISTORICAL CONNECTION

Obtaining organic compounds from natural sources can be costly and often yields amounts too small to be of practical use. Many organic compounds used as medicines are synthesized in a laboratory. In 1945, Dorothy Hodgkin determined the structure of penicillin, thus providing a crucial step toward its synthesis. In 1957, John Sheehan and his co-workers synthesized penicillin after a 9-year effort.

RESOURCE LINK

ChemFile Teaching Resources CD-ROM
Career Extension
Assign Occupational Applications Worksheet 12: *Perfumer* to emphasize relevant applications of text concepts.

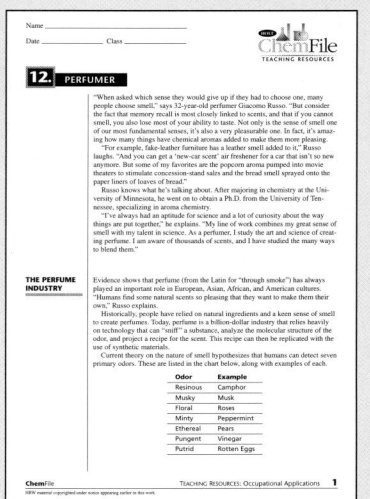

Functional groups determine properties

The presence of a functional group in an organic compound causes the compound to have chemical and physical properties that differ greatly from those of the corresponding hydrocarbon. Compare the structural formulas of the molecules shown in **Table 7-2.** Each of these compounds has four carbon atoms, but each compound has very different properties.

Compare the boiling point of butane with that of the other compounds in Table 7-2. Butane is a gas at room temperature. Butane contains only C—C single bonds and C—H bonds. The molecule is nonpolar. Butane has no strong intermolecular forces, so it has a very low boiling point and a lower density than all of the other 4-carbon molecules.

Now compare 1-butanol with diethyl ether. Both compounds have the same molecular formula, $C_4H_{10}O$. The only difference is the way the atoms are arranged; they are isomers. Yet this small structural difference makes a huge difference in the physical and chemical properties of the compounds. The compound 1-butanol boils at a higher temperature than water, at 117.5°C, and can be used to dissolve varnish. On the other hand, diethyl ether boils just below body temperature, at 34.5°C, and was once used as an anesthetic. The 1-butanol has the higher boiling point because the alcohol molecules form hydrogen bonds, which cause greater attraction between molecules. Butanoic acid also forms strong hydrogen bonds.

TABLE 7-2 Comparing Different Classes of Organic Compounds

Name	Structural formula	Melting point (°C)	Boiling point (°C)	Density (g/mL)
Butane		−138.4	−0.5	0.5788
1-butanol		−89.5	117.2	0.8098
Butanoic acid		−4.5	165.5	0.9577
2-butanone		−86.3	79.6	0.8054
Diethyl ether		−116.2	34.5	0.7138

2-methyl-1-propanol
(isobutyl alcohol)

1-butanol

FIGURE 7-10 ◄

Both of these molecules are alcohols. They are isomers because they both have the molecular formula $C_4H_{10}O$.

The compounds within each class have similar physical and chemical properties. For example, many alcohols, aldehydes, and ketones are soluble in water because they are very polar and can form hydrogen bonds with water molecules. Examine the two molecules in **Figure 7-10.** Isobutyl alcohol boils at 108°C and has a density of 0.8018 g/mL. 1-butanol is the molecule shown in Table 7-2. It boils at 117°C and has a density of 0.8098 g/mL. These two alcohols are isomers, just as 1-butanol and diethyl ether are isomers. However, because they are both alcohols, they are more similar in their properties, even though their atoms are arranged differently.

SECTION REVIEW

Total recall

1. What is an alkane? an alkene? an alkyne?
2. Draw the resonance structures for benzene.
3. In addition to carbon and hydrogen atoms, list four elements that can bond to carbon in organic compounds.
4. How are organic compounds classified?
5. Give two examples of covalent network solids.

Critical thinking

6. Explain why some alcohols and organic acids can be soluble in water, whereas hydrocarbons are virtually insoluble.
7. Compare and contrast the structures of an alcohol, an aldehyde, and an organic acid, all of which contain oxygen and hydrogen in their functional groups.
8. **Story Clue** Polyethylene is a long alkane chain. Why is the polyethylene in trash bags so unreactive?

Practice problems

9. Identify all of the functional groups in the following molecules:
   a. cinnamaldehyde   **b.** salicylic acid

10. State the class of organic compound for each of the following structural formulas:
    a.   O
          ‖
       H—C—OH

    b.   H H   H H
          | | | |
       H—C—C—O—C—C—H
          | | | |
          H H   H H

    c.   H O H O H
          | ‖ | ‖ |
       H—C—C—C—C—C—H
          | | |
          H   H   H

    d.   H   H
          | |
       H—C—N
          | |
          H   H

    e.   H
          |
       H—C—H
          |
          Cl

11. **Interpreting Tables** State the class of each molecule in Table 7-2.

2.

10. **a.** carboxylic acid
    b. ether
    c. ketone
    d. amine
    e. halide

11. In order: alkane, alcohol, carboxylic acid, ketone, ether

---

SECTION 7-1

ANSWERS

SECTION REVIEW

Total recall

1. All are hydrocarbons. Alkanes contain only single bonds. Alkenes contain at least one double bond. Alkynes contain one or more triple bonds.
2. *See below.*
3. Answers should include four of the following: oxygen, nitrogen, phosphorus, sulfur, and the halogens.
4. Organic compounds are classified according to structure and composition, including types of bonds and functional groups.
5. diamond and graphite

Critical thinking

6. Alcohols and acids are polar and form hydrogen bonds with water molecules. Hydrocarbons are nonpolar and do not form hydrogen bonds with water.
7. The functional group of an alcohol consists of an H atom bonded to an O atom. The functional group of an aldehyde consists of a C atom double bonded to an O atom and also to an H atom. The functional group of an organic acid is identical to that of an aldehyde except the C atom is bonded to an —OH group instead of to the H atom.
8. Alkanes are unreactive because of strong carbon-carbon bonds. Because polyethylene is a giant alkane, polyethylene is also unreactive.

Practice problems

9. **a.**   O
          ‖
       —C—H, aldehyde
    b. —OH, alcohol;
          O
          ‖
       —C—OH, carboxylic acid

SECTION 7-2

How are carbon compounds named and drawn?

OBJECTIVES

▶ ***Name*** a simple hydrocarbon, given its structural formula.

▶ ***Draw*** the structural formula for a simple organic compound, given the compound's name.

▶ ***Decipher*** different models for organic structures to identify functional groups, and determine molecular formulas.

Naming straight-chain hydrocarbons

Inorganic carbon compounds, such as carbon *di*oxide, CO_2, are named using the system of prefixes and suffixes introduced in Chapter 6. Organic compounds have their own systematic naming scheme. This naming scheme includes suffixes and prefixes that denote the class of organic compound.

The names of all alkanes end with the suffix *-ane*. The simplest alkane is methane, which is the main component of natural gas. The names and formulas for the first 10 straight-chain alkanes are given in **Table 7-3.** Notice that the first four do not have prefixes that denote the number of carbon atoms in the chain. For molecules of five or more carbon atoms, the prefix makes clear the number of carbon atoms in the chain. The names of the straight-chain alkanes are the basis for naming most other organic compounds.

TABLE 7-3   **Straight-Chain Alkane Nomenclature**

Number of carbon atoms	Name	Formula
1	methane	CH_4
2	ethane	CH_3-CH_3
3	propane	$CH_3-CH_2-CH_3$
4	butane	$CH_3-CH_2-CH_2-CH_3$
5	pentane	$CH_3-CH_2-CH_2-CH_2-CH_3$
6	hexane	$CH_3-CH_2-CH_2-CH_2-CH_2-CH_3$
7	heptane	$CH_3-CH_2-CH_2-CH_2-CH_2-CH_2-CH_3$
8	octane	$CH_3-CH_2-CH_2-CH_2-CH_2-CH_2-CH_2-CH_3$
9	nonane	$CH_3-CH_2-CH_2-CH_2-CH_2-CH_2-CH_2-CH_2-CH_3$
10	decane	$CH_3-CH_2-CH_2-CH_2-CH_2-CH_2-CH_2-CH_2-CH_2-CH_3$

The names of alkenes and alkynes are based on the names of alkanes

Hydrocarbons that contain double or triple bonds are called **unsaturated hydrocarbons.** Unsaturated hydrocarbons with at least one double bond are alkenes. The names of alkenes end in the suffix *-ene*. The simplest alkene is *ethene*, C_2H_4, commonly called ethylene. The next simplest alkene has three carbon atoms. Note that the alk*ane* with three carbon atoms is called prop*ane*. Likewise, the alk*ene* with three carbon atoms is called prop*ene*. The naming of all simple alkenes works this same way; the *-ane* suffix from the name of the alkane with the same number of carbon atoms is replaced by *-ene*.

Unsaturated hydrocarbons with triple bonds, alkynes, are named using the same system of prefixes and suffixes. The names of alkynes end in *-yne,* so the proper chemical name of acetylene, which has two carbon atoms, is *ethyne*. Besides being used in welding and cutting metals, ethyne is used in the manufacture of some plastics.

Ethene and ethyne have only one position in the molecule that can contain the multiple bond. It may appear that the double bond of propene can be at either of two locations, but these two locations are equivalent. The position of a double or triple bond must be specified for a longer hydrocarbon chain. To do this, you first number the carbon atoms in the chain. You can begin numbering from either end of the chain. The multiple bond must have the lowest possible number. Look at the following ways of numbering butene. Which numbering system do you think is correct?

The correct name of the above alkene is 1-butene; 1 is a lower number than 3, so the molecule is correctly numbered from right to left.

unsaturated hydrocarbon

a hydrocarbon that has at least one double or triple bond between carbon atoms

TEACHING TIP

Vocabulary Strategy Emphasize to students that *unsaturated* means "able to hold more." An unsaturated sponge can hold more water; an unsaturated saltwater solution can hold more salt. Unsaturated compounds can hold more hydrogen. An unsaturated hydrocarbon contains fewer hydrogen atoms than does a saturated hydrocarbon with the same number of carbon atoms.

CHAPTER CONNECTION

The terms *saturated* and *unsaturated* will be covered again in Chapter 13 in reference to saturated and unsaturated solutions.

FIGURE 7-11

Ethyne, commonly called acetylene, is practically the only alkyne that is commercially important.

CARBON AND ORGANIC COMPOUNDS **245**

GRAPHIC ORGANIZER

Hydrocarbon	Bonding	Suffix	General formula
Alkane	all single bonds	*-ane*	C_nH_{2n+2}
Alkene	at least one double bond	*-ene*	C_nH_{2n}
Alkyne	at least one triple bond	*-yne*	C_nH_{2n-2}

246

ANSWERS

CONCEPT CHECK

1. a. 1, 3-butadiene
  b. 1-pentyne
  c. 2-butyne

2. a.

$$H-C\equiv C-\overset{\overset{\displaystyle H}{|}}{\underset{\underset{\displaystyle H}{|}}{C}}-H$$

b.

$$H-\overset{\overset{\displaystyle H}{|}}{\underset{\underset{\displaystyle H}{|}}{C}}-\overset{\overset{\displaystyle H}{|}}{C}=\overset{\overset{\displaystyle H}{|}}{C}-\overset{\overset{\displaystyle H}{|}}{\underset{\underset{\displaystyle H}{|}}{C}}-\overset{\overset{\displaystyle H}{|}}{\underset{\underset{\displaystyle H}{|}}{C}}-H$$

c.

$$H-C\equiv C-\overset{\overset{\displaystyle H}{|}}{\underset{\underset{\displaystyle H}{|}}{C}}-\overset{\overset{\displaystyle H}{|}}{\underset{\underset{\displaystyle H}{|}}{C}}-\overset{\overset{\displaystyle H}{|}}{C}-C\equiv C-H$$

3.

$$H-\overset{\overset{\displaystyle H}{|}}{\underset{\underset{\displaystyle H}{|}}{\overset{1}{C}}}-\overset{\overset{\displaystyle H}{|}}{\underset{\underset{\displaystyle H}{|}}{\overset{2}{C}}}-\overset{3}{C}\equiv\overset{4}{C}-\overset{\overset{\displaystyle H}{|}}{\underset{\underset{\displaystyle H}{|}}{\overset{5}{C}}}-\overset{\overset{\displaystyle H}{|}}{\underset{\underset{\displaystyle H}{|}}{\overset{6}{C}}}-\overset{\overset{\displaystyle H}{|}}{\underset{\underset{\displaystyle H}{|}}{\overset{7}{C}}}-\overset{\overset{\displaystyle H}{|}}{\underset{\underset{\displaystyle H}{|}}{\overset{8}{C}}}-H$$

If there is more than one multiple bond in a molecule, *di-, tri-,* etc. are used to denote the number of multiple bonds. For example, the following molecule is called 1,3-pentadiene.

$$\overset{\overset{\displaystyle H}{|}}{\underset{\underset{\displaystyle H}{|}}{C}}=\overset{\overset{\displaystyle H}{|}}{C}-\overset{\overset{\displaystyle H}{|}}{C}=\overset{\overset{\displaystyle H}{|}}{C}-\overset{\overset{\displaystyle H}{|}}{\underset{\underset{\displaystyle H}{|}}{C}}-H$$

CONCEPT CHECK

1. Name the following compounds.

  a.
$$H-\overset{\overset{\displaystyle H}{|}}{C}=\overset{\overset{\displaystyle H}{|}}{C}-\overset{\overset{\displaystyle H}{|}}{C}=\overset{\overset{\displaystyle H}{|}}{C}$$

  b.
$$H-C\equiv C-\overset{\overset{\displaystyle H}{|}}{\underset{\underset{\displaystyle H}{|}}{C}}-\overset{\overset{\displaystyle H}{|}}{\underset{\underset{\displaystyle H}{|}}{C}}-\overset{\overset{\displaystyle H}{|}}{\underset{\underset{\displaystyle H}{|}}{C}}-H$$

  c.
$$H-\overset{\overset{\displaystyle H}{|}}{\underset{\underset{\displaystyle H}{|}}{C}}-C\equiv C-\overset{\overset{\displaystyle H}{|}}{\underset{\underset{\displaystyle H}{|}}{C}}-H$$

2. Draw the structural formulas for the following hydrocarbons.

  a. propyne   **b.** 2-hexene   **c.** 1, 6-heptadiyne

3. Correctly number the carbon atoms in the following compound.

$$H-\overset{\overset{\displaystyle H}{|}}{\underset{\underset{\displaystyle H}{|}}{C}}-\overset{\overset{\displaystyle H}{|}}{\underset{\underset{\displaystyle H}{|}}{C}}-C\equiv C-\overset{\overset{\displaystyle H}{|}}{\underset{\underset{\displaystyle H}{|}}{C}}-\overset{\overset{\displaystyle H}{|}}{\underset{\underset{\displaystyle H}{|}}{C}}-\overset{\overset{\displaystyle H}{|}}{\underset{\underset{\displaystyle H}{|}}{C}}-\overset{\overset{\displaystyle H}{|}}{\underset{\underset{\displaystyle H}{|}}{C}}-H$$

Naming nonlinear hydrocarbons

Nonlinear hydrocarbons include cyclic hydrocarbons and branched hydrocarbons. The cyclic alkanes are named according to the number of carbon atoms in the largest ring, as if they were straight chains, but the name is preceded by the prefix *cyclo-,* as in cyclobutane.

When you are faced with trying to name a hydrocarbon that is not a simple straight chain or ring, you should first determine the number of carbon atoms in the longest carbon chain. This is the *parent* compound, and this chain takes its name from the corresponding alkane in Table 7-3. Keep in mind that this chain may not appear straight in a structural formula. For example, consider the following alkane.

$$H-\overset{\overset{\displaystyle H}{|}}{\underset{\underset{\displaystyle H}{|}}{C}}\underset{\underset{\displaystyle H-\overset{2}{C}-H}{|}}{\overset{\overset{\displaystyle H}{|}}{\underset{\underset{\displaystyle \underset{\displaystyle H-\overset{1}{C}-H}{|}}{}}{\overset{3}{C}}}}\overset{\overset{\displaystyle H}{|}}{\underset{\underset{\displaystyle H}{|}}{\overset{4}{C}}}\overset{\overset{\displaystyle H}{|}}{\underset{\underset{\displaystyle H}{|}}{\overset{5}{C}}}\overset{\overset{\displaystyle H}{|}}{\underset{\underset{\displaystyle H}{|}}{\overset{6}{C}}}\overset{\overset{\displaystyle H}{|}}{\underset{\underset{\displaystyle H}{|}}{\overset{7}{C}}}-H$$

The longest chain contains seven carbon atoms. You must now assign numbers to the carbon atoms along the chain. Number the carbon atoms in the chain so that the branch or branches attached to the chain have the lowest numbers possible. There is a —CH$_3$ *alkyl* group attached to the third carbon from the left side of the chain in this example. This branch has one carbon atom. Alkyl groups are named using the same prefixes used to name alkanes. It is called a *methyl* group. The name of this compound is *3-methylheptane*.

If there is more than one group attached to the chain, the position of attachment of *each* group is given. The prefixes *di-, tri-, tetra-*, etc., are used if the same group is attached more than once.

With alkenes that have alkyl groups attached to the chain, the longest chain containing the double bond is the parent compound. This chain is numbered just as it would be if the branches were not there.

ADDITIONAL APPLICATION

Natural rubber, seen on page 253, is a polymer made from the isoprene molecules shown in Figure 7-12.

VISUAL STRATEGY

Figure 7-12 Make sure students recognize that the isoprene structure shown in the figure is numbered from right to left so that the double bonds and the functional group have the lowest possible numbers.

FIGURE 7-12 ▲

The haze that settles over the Blue Ridge Mountains of Virginia and North Carolina contains 2-methyl-1, 3-butadiene, also called *isoprene*.

To correctly name the above compound, number the chain from left to right. The correct name is *2-ethyl-1-pentene*.

   Name branched hydrocarbons

Many organic structural formulas look quite confusing, but keep in mind that the name will be based on one of the simple alkane names in Table 7-3. By following the steps below, you can correctly name many complicated molecules.

1. Identify and name the parent hydrocarbon chain

▶ Because there are no multiple bonds and the longest continuous chain has five carbon atoms, the parent chain is *pentane*.

HOW TO

ADDITIONAL EXAMPLES

Name each of the following compounds.

a.

Ans. 3-ethyl-4-methylhexane

b.

Ans. 5-butyl-2, 2-dimethylnonane

c.

Ans. 2, 3, 4, 5-tetramethylhexane

2 Number the longest chain so that the branches are attached to the lowest possible numbers

▸ The chain should be numbered from the left to the right so that the locations of the branches are at carbon atoms 2, 2, and 4.

3 Name the groups that make up the branches

▸ There are three alkyl groups with one carbon atom each. These are methyl groups.

4 Name the molecule

▸ The molecule has three methyl groups at locations 2, 2, and 4 on a pentane chain. Use prefixes to denote the number of alkyl groups. Therefore, the name of the molecule is 2,2,4-trimethylpentane.

The names of most organic compounds with functional groups are based on their parent hydrocarbon

Compounds with functional groups are named using the same system used for hydrocarbons with branched chains. The parent, or longest, chain is named first; then a suffix or prefix indicating the functional group is added to the hydrocarbon name. **Table 7-4** lists the suffixes and prefixes for some of the functional groups you have learned about.

When necessary, the location of the functional group is noted in the same way that the location of hydrocarbon branches is noted. Aldehyde and acid groups are always on the end of a molecule, so a number is not usually given in the name. Following are a few typical compounds and their proper names. The system for determining the proper names of organic compounds was developed by the International Union of Pure and Applied Chemistry (IUPAC). Keep in mind that chemists still use common names for many compounds, such as acetylene for ethyne. Common names are given below the proper ones in these examples.

TABLE 7-4	Naming Functional Groups

Class of compound	Suffix or prefix
Alcohol	*-ol*
Aldehyde	*-al*
Amine	*amino-*
Carboxylic acid	*-oic acid*
Ketone	*-one*

2-propanol
isopropyl alcohol

Propanone
acetone

Ethanoic acid
acetic acid

ALTERNATIVE ASSESSMENT

Nomenclature

1. Name the following compound.

Ans. 3-ethyl-2, 4, 5-trimethyloctane

2. Draw the structural formula for 3, 3-diethyl-2, 5-dimethylnonane.

Ans.

Fats can be *saturated* or *unsaturated*

A fat is an ester made from glycerol, correctly named 1,2,3-propanetriol, and a carboxylic acid called a *fatty acid*. Fatty acids are long straight chains of carbon and hydrogen with a carboxylic acid group on the end of the molecule. A saturated fatty acid is a fatty acid that contains only single bonds between the carbon atoms. Hexadecanoic acid, commonly called palmitic acid, shown below, is one such fatty acid.

Some people eat foods containing too much **saturated fat.** The animal fats found in butter, milk, and meat are significant sources of saturated fats, but animal fats are not the only source of saturated fats. Tropical oils, such as coconut oil and palm-kernel oil, have even larger proportions of saturated fats. Consumption of saturated fats can cause health problems because these fats can be stored by the body and lead to weight and cholesterol problems.

An unsaturated fatty acid is a fatty acid that contains one or more double bonds. Oleic acid, shown below, is an unsaturated fatty acid.

Nutritionists usually recommend that people try to eat foods that contain **unsaturated fats.** A general rule of thumb for good nutrition is to try to use fats that contain a high proportion of unsaturated fatty acids, such as canola oil and olive oil. Fats are a necessary part of the diet. For example, linoleic acid is a vital raw material for the construction of cell membranes. It is an essential fatty acid in the human diet because the body cannot make linoleic acid on its own.

saturated fat

a fat primarily containing saturated fatty acids

unsaturated fat

a fat primarily containing unsaturated fatty acids

CONCEPT CHECK

1. Name the following compound.

2. Draw the structural formula for 2,3,4-trimethylnonane.
3. Draw the structural formulas for the following organic compounds.
   a. 1,2,3-propanetriol, or glycerol
   b. hexanal
   c. 2-octanone

2.

ANSWERS

CONCEPT CHECK

1. 2, 3-dimethylpentane

2. *See below.*

3. **a.**

b.

c.

RESOURCE LINK

ChemFile Lab D
Consumer Lab
Have students do Experiment 7: *All Fats Are Not Equal!*

ChemFile Teaching Resources CD-ROM
Supplemental Reading Projects
Assign the guided reading worksheets for John Emsley's *Consumer's Good Chemical Guide,* Chapter 4, "Cholesterol, Fat, and Fibre," for cross-curricular connections to language arts.

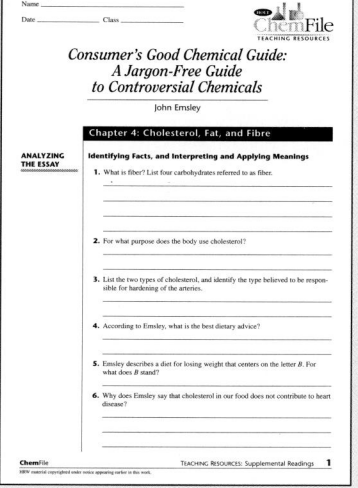

DISCUSSION STRATEGY

Have students discuss other examples of how something can be represented in more than one way. One example is found in music. The desired sounds can be represented as single notes on a staff if the music is to be sung or played on certain instruments. If the music is to be played on other instruments, such as a guitar, letters that represent groups of notes, or chords, may represent the sounds used.

In math, the process of multiplication can be represented by several different symbols—a multiplication sign, a dot, parentheses, or just two symbols written side by side—depending on what is being multiplied. Emphasize to students that molecules can be represented in different ways as well.

TABLE 7-5 Advantages and Disadvantages of Molecular Models

Type of model	Example	Advantages	Disadvantages
Chemical formula	C_6H_{12}	shows numbers of atoms in a molecule	does not show bonds, atom sizes, or shape
Structural formula		shows arrangement of all atoms and bonds in a molecule	does not show actual shape of molecule or atom sizes; larger molecules can be too complicated to easily draw
Skeletal structure		shows arrangements of carbon chains; is simple	does not show actual shape or atom sizes; does not show all atoms or bonds
Space-filling model		shows three-dimensional shape of molecule; shows most of the space taken by electrons	uses false colors to differentiate between elements; bonds are not clearly indicated; parts of large molecules may be hidden

Representing organic molecules

Table 7-5 shows four ways of representing an organic molecule, in this case cyclohexane.

Each type of model used to represent a molecule has both advantages and disadvantages. Each type highlights a different feature of a molecule, from the number and kind of atoms in the simple chemical formula to the three-dimensional shape in the space-filling model.

One disadvantage shared by all of these models is that they portray a three-dimensional object on a flat surface. Another disadvantage of the models is that they cannot show the internal motion within molecules. The atoms within each molecule are constantly vibrating—stretching, compressing, bending, and twisting. Today, molecular modeling is often done on computers so that chemists can look at a molecule from a variety of angles and examine its internal motion.

Organic structural formulas can be drawn in a simplified form

Throughout most of this text you have seen structural formulas used to represent organic molecules. Organic structures are sometimes represented by what are called *skeletal structures,* which leave out some of the carbon and hydrogen atoms. This style shows the carbon framework of a molecule only as lines representing bonds. Carbon atoms are

DEMONSTRATION 2

Unsaturated Fats

Approximate time: 10 minutes

1. Under a fume hood, prepare an iodine solution by dissolving 1.5 g of iodine in 50 mL of mineral oil.

2. Pour 10 mL of cooking oil into a 50 mL beaker.

3. Put the beaker on an overhead projector, and project the image onto a screen.

4. Add 3 mL of the iodine solution to the cooking oil, and stir thoroughly. The color will disappear, indicating that iodine has been added to the double bonds of the oil.

5. Ask students to use these results to determine whether mineral oil and cooking oil are saturated or unsaturated (*mineral oil, saturated; cooking oil, unsaturated*).

FIGURE 7-13 ▼

a The chemical name for aspirin is acetylsalicylic acid.

b Because the complete structural formula of acetylsalicylic acid is complex, . . .

c . . . chemists usually draw its skeletal structure instead. The presence of a benzene ring indicates that it is an aromatic compound.

understood to be at the intersection of these lines together with enough hydrogen atoms to satisfy carbon's need to form four bonds. You are already familiar with the skeletal structure for benzene. **Figure 7-13** uses both a structural formula and a skeletal structure to represent aspirin. Notice that the skeletal structure is simpler and quicker to draw than the complete structural formula.

Atoms other than carbon and hydrogen are always shown; this emphasizes the presence of any functional groups. Carbon atom chains are shown in a zigzag pattern to indicate the tetrahedral arrangement of bonds between a carbon atom and other atoms.

HOW TO   Decipher skeletal structures

Unlike most other amino acids, tryptophan, shown below, cannot be manufactured by the human body, so it must be available in the diet. For this reason, tryptophan is called an essential amino acid. What is the molecular formula for tryptophan?

1 Place carbon atoms at all unmarked bond junctions.

HOW TO

ADDITIONAL EXAMPLES

Write molecular formulas for each of the following compounds.

a. Thyroxine, a thyroid hormone

Ans. $C_{15}H_{11}NI_4O_4$

b. Penicillin G

Ans. $C_{16}H_{18}N_2O_4S$

c. Vitamin A

Ans. $C_{20}H_{30}O$

RESOURCE LINK

ChemFile Teaching Resources CD-ROM
Supplemental Reading Projects
Assign the guided reading worksheets for Roald Hoffmann's *The Same and Not the Same*; Essay 10, "Molecular Mimicry," for cross-curricular connections to language arts.

Safety
Wear safety goggles, gloves, and a lab coat or apron.

Disposal
Add sufficient cooking oil to the mineral-oil-and-iodine mixture to react with the iodine. Combine all liquids, and store them in a labeled container for disposal by the school waste contractor.

ANSWERS

SECTION REVIEW

1. Answer should indicate that these models reflect a three-dimensional object on a flat surface, and they cannot show internal motion in a molecule.

2. acetylene

3. Unsaturated fatty acids contain at least one multiple bond. Saturated fatty acids contain only single bonds.

4. –al

5. 7

6. alkanes

Critical thinking

7. Aldehyde and acid functional groups are always on the end of a molecule.

8. Number the carbon atoms in the longest chain so that the branches attached to the chain have the lowest numbers possible.

9. Fats supply some raw materials that the body cannot make and that are not supplied by other compounds.

10. Unsaturated fats do not cause the weight and cholesterol problems that are caused by saturated fats because they are more easily broken down by the body.

Practice problems

11. a.

Cl–C–C–C–C–C–C–H (with H atoms: H H H H H H on top; H H H Cl H H on bottom)

b.

H–C–C–C–C–C–H (with H O H H H on top, double bond O on second C; H, H H H on bottom)

c.

H–C–C–C–C–C–C–C–H (with H Br H Cl H H H on top; H H H H H H H on bottom)

d.

H–C–C–C≡C–C–C–C–C–H (with Cl H on first carbons, H H H H on top right; H H on bottom left, H H H H on bottom right)

12. a. 2, 4-dimethylpentane
    b. 1, 2-dibromobutane

---

2 Place enough hydrogen atoms on carbon atoms so that each carbon atom has four bonds.

3 To determine the molecular formula, count the number of atoms of each element. List carbon first, followed by hydrogen. Other atoms are listed alphabetically.
$C_{11}H_{12}N_2O_2$

SECTION REVIEW

Total recall

1. What is the primary disadvantage of the four models that are used to represent a molecule?

2. What is the common name for ethyne?

3. How does an unsaturated fatty acid differ from a saturated fatty acid?

4. What is the suffix used to identify an aldehyde?

5. How many carbon atoms are present in heptene?

6. Which class of organic compounds forms the basis for naming most other carbon compounds?

Critical thinking

7. Why do the names of aldehydes and organic acids not always contain numbers indicating the position of the aldehyde and acid groups?

8. What are the rules for assigning numbers to carbon atoms when naming branched hydrocarbons?

9. Why must your diet contain some fats?

10. Why are unsaturated fatty acids a better dietary choice than saturated fatty acids?

Practice problems

11. Draw the structural formula for each of the following compounds.
    a. 1,4-dichlorohexane
    b. 2-pentanone
    c. 2-bromo-4-chloroheptane
    d. 1-chloro-3-octyne

12. Name each of the following compounds.
    a.

    b.

What is a polymer?

OBJECTIVES

▶ **Describe** the formation of a polymer from monomers.

▶ **Distinguish** between addition polymers and condensation polymers.

▶ **Name** at least two natural polymers and two synthetic polymers.

▶ **Describe** the properties of elastomers, fibers, and plastics, and give an example of each.

Polymer basics

In Chapter 2 you learned how accidental discoveries can have an effect on the progress of science and technology. The development of a field of science known as polymer chemistry was the result of several accidental discoveries that took place over a number of years. The discovery of Teflon in 1938, which you read about in Chapter 2, was one such discovery. But the first accidental discovery that helped to develop the field of polymer chemistry was made in 1839, almost 100 years before the discovery of Teflon. That year, an American inventor named Charles Goodyear found a way to make rubber, a natural polymer, stronger and more durable.

Rubber is a natural product obtained from trees, such as the one shown in **Figure 7-14.** But because it is soft and weak, natural rubber is of little practical use. Goodyear was working with natural rubber mixed with sulfur when he accidentally dropped some of his mixture onto a hot stove. He noticed that the rubber did not melt but instead got much

internet**connect**

SC*LINKS.*
NSTA
TOPIC: Polymers
GO TO: www.scilinks.org
KEYWORD: HW075

FIGURE 7-14 ◀

The fluid flowing from this *Hevea brasiliensis,* or rubber tree, is a suspension of rubber particles in water. This suspension is called a latex.

CARBON AND ORGANIC COMPOUNDS   253

LESSON WARM-UP

Group Strategy Show students different types of polymers. Examples might include plastic wrap; rubber tubing; polyester thread; nylon pantyhose; foam cups; trash bags; a plastic that is firm but flexible, such as a margarine container; and a rigid, inflexible plastic, such as the material used to make a telephone.

Tell students that all of the examples are made up of the same type of compound. Ask groups of students to write down what they think the items have in common. Save the polymer samples and student answers for the Alternative Assessment on page 262.

RESOURCE LINK

Chem**File** Lab D
Consumer Lab
Have students do Experiment 8:
Polymers as Straws.

TEACHING TIP

Vocabulary Strategy Emphasize to students that the prefix *poly-* in the term *polygon* means "many." Have students think of other examples of terms in which *poly-* has the same meaning. Examples might include math terms, such as *polygon, polyhedron,* or *polynomial.* Other familiar terms might include *polygamy, polygraph,* or *polysyllabic.*

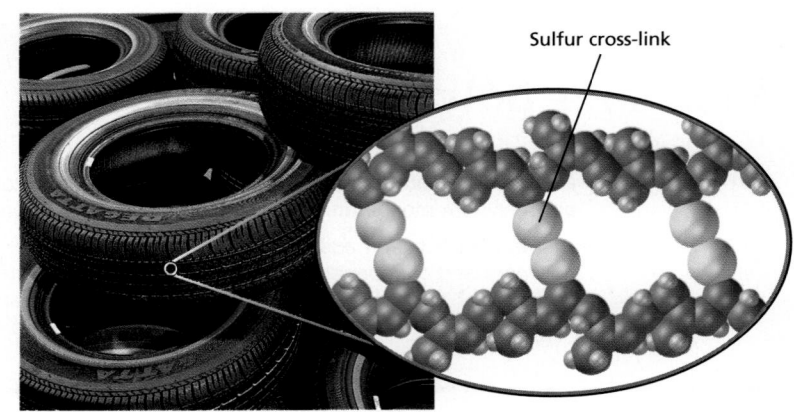

▶ **FIGURE 7-15**

The vulcanization of rubber by Charles Goodyear made automobile tires possible. Goodyear's name has now become an emblem of the tire industry.

Sulfur cross-link

▲ **FIGURE 7-16**

Nylon 66, shown here being wound onto a stirring rod, is made from the reaction of hexanedioic acid, also called adipic acid, and 1,6-diaminohexane.

polymer

a large organic molecule composed of smaller units bonded together

stronger. What Goodyear accidentally discovered is known today as *vulcanized* rubber, shown in **Figure 7-15.** The vulcanization process makes rubber stronger by joining the polymer chains together with sulfur links. Vulcanized rubber is a compound used today to make tires, rain gear, and rubber bands.

Polymers move into the 20th century

In 1907, a Belgian-born American chemist named Leo Baekeland was experimenting with reactions between certain organic compounds. In the past, chemists had thrown away what they considered to be the waste byproducts of these reactions. Baekeland, however, decided to investigate a byproduct that was formed by a reaction between two organic compounds, phenol and formaldehyde. He exposed the byproduct to high pressure and high temperature. He found that he could not soften or dissolve the substance after it had been exposed to these conditions. What Baekeland had accidentally discovered became known as Bakelite®, a compound used today to make billiard balls, telephones, and electrical insulators. Bakelite was also used to form the handles of pots and pans because it is a good heat insulator.

In the late 1930s, Wallace Carothers, a chemist working for the Dupont company, mixed two organic compounds to produce a substance that was sticky and that easily fell apart. Because of these physical properties, Carothers thought the substance was of little practical use. But one of his co-workers, Julian Hill, put a small ball of this sticky substance on the end of a glass rod. He then slowly pulled the rod away from the sticky mass and observed how easily the material could be stretched into long, silky fibers, as you can see in **Figure 7-16.** What Carothers and Hill discovered was nylon 66, a compound woven into sheer hosiery for women.

254 CHAPTER 7

RESOURCE LINK

Chem**File** Lab D
Consumer Lab
Have students do Experiment 9: *The Slime Challenge.*

Vulcanized rubber, Bakelite, and nylon 66 are only a few of the polymers that have become an integral part of our daily lives. A **polymer** is a large chainlike molecule that is built from smaller units. Because of their large size, polymers are also known as *macromolecules*. To appreciate their size, consider the molecular masses of polymers; some are in the range of 50 000 amu. Compare this with the molecular mass of water, which is 18 amu.

Polymers are made up of subunits called monomers

Many macromolecules are found in living things. These include proteins, carbohydrates, and nucleic acids. Because they are present in living things, these macromolecules are known as *natural polymers*. The rubber that Goodyear worked with was a natural polymer. In Figure 7-3, on page 236, you saw that paper and cotton clothing are made of cellulose, a natural polymer. In fact, cellulose is the most abundant natural polymer in the world. **Figure 7-17** better illustrates the cellulose polymer.

Baekeland and Carothers were among the first to make *synthetic polymers*. Today, synthetic polymers are an important part of our economy. Nearly half the industrial chemists employed in the United States work in some area of polymer chemistry. In 1996, more than 120 kg, or 270 lb, of plastic, one type of synthetic polymer, was produced per person in the United States. **Figure 7-18** shows just some of the many consumer products that contain plastic.

FIGURE 7-17 ▲

Cellulose is the polymer found in cotton. Hydrogen bonds hold the long chains of glucose monomers together in a large network.

FIGURE 7-18 ◄

How many different plastic items can you spot in this photo? There are at least 10.

VISUAL STRATEGY

Figure 7-17 Sketch the following diagram on the board to illustrate how hydrogen bonds hold the cellulose polymers together.

Cellulose chains linked by hydrogen bonds

Glucose monomer

Cellulose

Figure 7-18 Students should at least identify the CD jewel cases, the CDs themselves, the portable stereo, the telephone, the Magic 8 ball, the mirror handle, the container on the floor, and many plastic items in the container.

CARBON AND ORGANIC COMPOUNDS 255

monomer
the small unit from which polymers form

addition polymer
a polymer formed by chain addition reactions between monomers that contain a double bond

▼ **FIGURE 7-19**

Polyvinyl acetate, an addition polymer, is used in latex paints.

Whether natural or synthetic, polymers have similar basic structures. This structure was first proposed in 1920 by the German chemist Hermann Staudinger. Before Staudinger proposed his theory of polymer structure, most chemists believed that these large molecules were made of smaller molecules that were held together by weak attractions, such as the London forces you studied in Chapter 6. Staudinger, however, suggested that polymers were built from smaller units, known as **monomers,** held together by strong chemical bonds. At the time, his idea did not receive much support from other chemists. Gradually, however, experimental evidence was obtained that supported Staudinger's position. In 1953, he was awarded the Nobel Prize in chemistry for his work on polymer structure, something he had proposed more than 30 years earlier.

Some polymers form by addition

Although all polymers are formed from monomers bonded to one another, there are two ways in which this process can occur. One leads to the formation of an addition polymer. An **addition polymer** forms when monomers combine end to end. Two monomers simply join to form a dimer. Next a third monomer is added, then a fourth, a fifth, and so on. This process continues until the polymer is complete.

Consider how polyethylene is made. The monomer from which polyethylene is made is ethene, C_2H_4. Recall from Section 7-2 that ethene is commonly called ethylene, hence the name polyethylene for the polymer it forms. In forming a polymer, ethene molecules join together. As you can see in the following equation, each time two ethene molecules are joined together, the double bond present in each molecule changes to two single bonds. The equation below is written using condensed structures. The atoms are all shown, but the bonds between the carbon and hydrogen atoms are not shown.

$$CH_2{=}CH_2 + CH_2{=}CH_2 \longrightarrow -CH_2-CH_2-CH_2-CH_2-$$

Notice the open single bonds at each end of the product where additional ethene molecules can connect. The process of adding an ethene molecule continues until polyethylene is eventually produced. Polyethylene is a very long alkane polymer chain.

Because thousands of ethene molecules are joined to form polyethylene, the formula for the polymer is written using a shorthand form of notation. The formula for polyethylene is written as $\text{-}(CH_2{-}CH_2)_n$. This formula shows n units of the polymer chain. The subscript n represents the number of ethene monomers

DEMONSTRATION 3

Polyethylene

Approximate time: 5 minutes

1. Take a black plastic garbage bag, and cut bow-tie shaped strips about 18 cm long. If possible, make enough strips for each student to have one.

2. Have students firmly grasp the two ends of the strip and slowly pull apart.

3. Students should see horizontal lines forming in the plastic. Tell them these lines show the alignment of the polyethylene chains.

that were joined to form the polymer. In the case of polyethylene, n is a number in the thousands.

The process of joining monomers to form an addition polymer is not perfect. Occasionally, a monomer may be added so that the chain branches. For example, an ethene monomer is sometimes added to form a side chain, as you can see in the following structural formula.

$$-CH_2-CH_2-CH-CH_2-$$
$$\begin{array}{c} | \\ CH_2 \\ | \\ CH_3 \end{array}$$

A polymer with many side chains cannot pack tightly. This type of polyethylene is known as a low-density polyethylene, LDPE. LDPE is used primarily to manufacture tough, transparent film for wrapping a wide variety of consumer products, such as the one shown in **Figure 7-20.**

Polymers with very few side chains can pack tightly together. This type of polyethylene is known as high-density polyethylene, HDPE. Because of its higher density, HDPE has greater strength and rigidity than LDPE. The major use of HDPE is in the manufacture of plastic bottles for juices, milk, shampoos, bleaches, and other liquids. Unlike LDPE, HDPE is recycled in most communities.

CONSUMER ACTIVITY

QUICKLAB

Properties of Polymers

How can you differentiate between HDPE and LDPE? Think about the properties of these two types of plastics.

Materials   2 plastic pieces (2 × 2 in.) labeled A and B

Problem   You know the basic structures of the two types of polyethylene. How do these structural differences translate into differences in physical properties? Use the following three tests to determine which piece is LDPE and which is HDPE. To test the rigidity of A and B, try to bend both pieces. To test hardness, press into the plastic squares with your fingernail and try to make a permanent indentation. Finally, test strength by attempting to tear each plastic piece. If the pieces do not tear, try cutting each piece with a pair of scissors.

Analysis
1. Which piece of plastic is more rigid?
2. Which piece is harder?
3. Can you tear either piece? Is one piece easier to cut than the other?
4. Using your observations in items 1, 2, and 3, which piece of plastic is LDPE and which is HDPE?

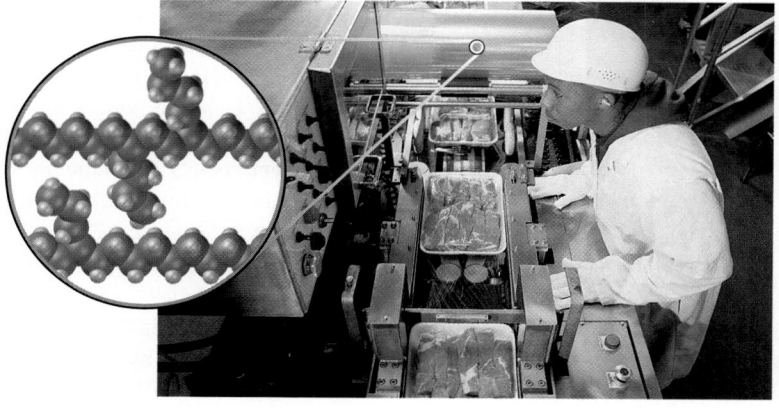

FIGURE 7-20 ◄

LDPE plastic wrap protects meat from spoiling. It also prevents food-borne illness by keeping harmful bacteria away from the meat.

QUICKLAB

A piece of a plastic milk bottle can be used for HDPE, and a piece of a plastic food-storage container lid can be used for LDPE. If you are unsure as to whether a piece of plastic is HDPE or LDPE, refer to its recycling code. HDPE is number 2; LDPE is number 4. Answers below are based on the HDPE being labeled *A* and the LDPE being labeled *B*.

Analysis

1. A

2. A

3. A will not rip. B may rip, but most likely will stretch. B was easier to cut.

4. A is HDPE, and B is LDPE.

This experiment can also be extended to test the resistance of HDPE and LDPE bags against rupturing. Have one student hold the plastic bags stretched out tight, and have the other student drop large screws and bolts on the plastic. Most grocery-store bags are HDPE, and dry-cleaning bags and trash-can liners are LDPE.

Some polymers form through condensation

You saw in Figure 7-3, on page 236, that proteins are made of small molecules called amino acids. When proteins are formed, water is released as two amino acids bond together. These natural macromolecules are known as **condensation polymers.** A condensation polymer is made when monomers are joined, and water or another small molecule, such as HCl, is produced as a byproduct. The synthesis of proteins generally occurs in the cell where amino acids are linked into long chains. The bonds linking the amino acids are called **peptide bonds.** When a small number of amino acids condense, the product is a *polypeptide*. The following chemical equation illustrates a condensation reaction between the amino acids alanine and serine. Notice that a molecule of water is split off in the reaction, as shown in red.

Many synthetic polymers also are condensation polymers. Consider how a common type of polyester named polyethylene terephthalate, PET, is synthesized. PET is frequently used to make permanent-press clothing and soda bottles. The monomers used to make polyester are ethylene glycol (1,2-ethanediol) and terephthalic acid, as shown below.

How is a condensation polymer similar to the addition polymer polyethylene? How is it different? Both polymers are made by joining small molecules together into a long chain. When polyethylene is made from ethene molecules, a double bond breaks and new single bonds form between the molecules. When PET is made, water splits out from between the acid and the alcohol, forming an ester linkage between the monomers. Recall that esters contain the functional group

Therefore, PET is a polyester.

Another synthetic polymer that is synthesized through a condensation reaction is nylon 66. You read earlier that Carothers and Hill discovered

DID YOU KNOW?

A process called *cold drawing*, the stretching of cold fibers, can increase the strength of nylon and other polymers. Cold drawing lines up the polymer molecules.

TEACHING TIP

Vocabulary strategy Have students note that the peptide bond is the same type as the bond that forms between monomers in nylon. Both proteins and nylon are called *polyamides*.

condensation polymer

a polymer formed by reactions in which water or another small molecule is a byproduct

peptide bond

the bond formed between the carboxylic acid group of one amino acid and the amine group of another amino acid

▼ **FIGURE 7-21**

This thread is made from polyester. The thread can be woven into polyester fabrics that are used to make many types of clothing.

this polymer in the late 1930s. They combined two compounds, 1,6-diaminohexane and hexanedioic acid, or adipic acid, whose condensed structures are shown in the reaction below. Again, the —H and —OH to form water are shown in red.

$$nH-\underset{\underset{H}{|}}{N}-CH_2-CH_2-CH_2-CH_2-CH_2-CH_2-\underset{\underset{H}{|}}{N}-H + nHO-\underset{\underset{O}{\|}}{C}-CH_2-CH_2-CH_2-CH_2-\underset{\underset{O}{\|}}{C}-OH \longrightarrow$$

1,6-diaminohexane   Adipic acid

$$\left(\underset{\underset{H}{|}}{N}-CH_2-CH_2-CH_2-CH_2-CH_2-CH_2-\underset{\underset{H}{|}}{N}-\underset{\underset{O}{\|}}{C}-CH_2-CH_2-CH_2-CH_2-\underset{\underset{O}{\|}}{C}\right)_n + 2nH_2O$$

Nylon 66

Look at the structure of the nylon 66 polymer molecule. There are six carbon atoms on each side of the monomer. This accounts for the 66 label following the nylon name.

CONCEPT CHECK

1. What do the letters LDPE represent?
2. Would it be possible to have an addition reaction between two different monomers? Why or why not?
3. Why can a molecule with only one functional group *not* undergo a condensation reaction to form a polymer?
4. What two functional groups are in an amino acid?

Types of Polymers

Synthetic polymers are classified on the basis of their elasticity, or ability to stretch and snap back to their original shape. Those that can be highly stretched and return to their original shape are known as **elastomers.** Some elastomers can be stretched to more than 10 times their normal length and still snap back to their original shape. The vulcanized rubber that Goodyear made is an example of an elastomer. Polymers that exhibit little or no elasticity are classified as **fibers.** Cellulose is an example of a fiber. Those synthetic polymers that are more elastic than fibers but less elastic than elastomers are classified as **plastics.** Bakelite is an example of a plastic.

Elastomers mimic a natural polymer

Rubber is a good example of an elastomer. You read earlier that rubber is a natural polymer. Natural rubber is an addition polymer made from the monomer 2-methyl-1,3-butadiene, commonly called isoprene.

$$2nH_2C=\underset{\underset{CH_3}{|}}{C}-CH=CH_2 \longrightarrow \left[\begin{array}{c} \underset{H_2C}{\overset{H_3C}{}}C=C\underset{CH_2-CH_2}{\overset{H}{}} \quad \underset{CH_2}{\overset{H_3C}{}}C=C\overset{H}{} \end{array}\right]_n$$

Isoprene   Polyisoprene

elastomer

a polymer that has elastic properties similar to rubber

fiber

a polymer that has a threadlike structure and is highly resistant to being stretched

plastic

a polymer that is able to be shaped or molded without destroying the macromolecule

ANSWERS

CONCEPT CHECK

1. low-density polyethylene
2. It would be possible as long as each monomer contained a double or triple bond.
3. The molecule must contain a functional group on each end; each functional group must contribute to the formation of the small molecule produced.
4. the amine group, —N, and the carboxylic acid group, $-\underset{\underset{\|}{O}}{C}-OH$

GRAPHIC ORGANIZER

Types:	Elastomers	Fibers	Plastics
Elasticity:	Returns to shape after being stretched	Exhibits little or no elasticity	More elastic than fibers; less elastic than elastomers
Example:	Rubber	Nylon	Polyethylene

Polymers

RESOURCE LINK

IN-TEXT LAB

Skills Development

Have students do Exploration 7A on page 736 to develop their skills working with polymeric materials.

259

After World War II, the demand for natural rubber went into sharp decline as synthetic rubbers with superior properties were invented. That pattern changed in the early 1970s because of the reduced availability of petroleum, from which synthetic rubbers are made; a large increase in the amount of land planted with rubber trees; and changes in tire technology that called for natural rubber over synthetic rubber. Today, SBR, a common synthetic rubber, makes up about 71% of the rubber market in the United States, and natural rubber makes up about 23%.

💡 DID YOU KNOW?

Some synthetic and natural fibers appear similar. However, some of their properties differ. An easy way to distinguish between synthetic and natural fibers is to hold each in a flame. When a synthetic fiber is exposed to a flame, it melts and then burns. A natural fiber does not melt; it chars. The demonstration at the bottom of the page shows this difference.

During World War II, the Japanese army occupied much of the Far East, where rubber plantations were commonly found. As a result, the United States launched a massive effort to develop synthetic rubber that could be used to make the tires needed for military vehicles. One type of synthetic rubber is made from an addition polymerization reaction between two monomers—styrene and 1,3-butadiene, shown below.

$$n\text{CH=CH}_2 + n\text{CH}_2\text{=CH-CH=CH}_2 \longrightarrow \text{(CH}_2\text{-CH=CH-CH}_2\text{-CH-CH}_2)_n$$

Styrene   1,3-butadiene   Polystyrene butadiene (SBR)

Today synthetic rubber, also known as SBR, styrene butadiene rubber, accounts for approximately 50% of the world's total rubber production.

Fibers are used in clothing

Each year, billions of kilograms of fibers are produced in the United States, most of it for the clothing we wear. Some of these macromolecules are derived from cellulose, a natural fiber, and are known as semisynthetic fibers because they are made by modifying cellulose in some way.

Most of the fibers made today are truly synthetic. You are probably wearing some article of clothing that contains a synthetic fiber. It may be the nylon in the blouse you are wearing, the acrylic fibers in the sweater you got for your birthday, or the polyester in your pants.

Nylon was the first fiber to result from a deliberate effort to create a synthetic polymer. As women's dresses became shorter during the early 1900s, stockings became more fashionable. However, silk, the main material used to make stockings, was expensive. You read earlier how Carothers and Hill succeeded in making nylon 66. This synthetic polymer was in such high demand that nylon stockings had to be rationed when they were first sold to the public in 1939. **Figure 7-22** illustrates some of the modern uses for nylon.

Other common synthetic fibers include acrylic and polyester. Acrylic, which is sold under the trade name Orlon®, is a synthetic fiber that feels like wool but is less expensive and can be machine-washed with-

▶ **FIGURE 7-22**

Today nylon is used to make ropes, fishing line, nets, and even clothing such as waterproof jackets and vests.

DEMONSTRATION 4

What Type of Fiber Is It?

Approximate time: 10 minutes

1. Use tongs to hold a square of a synthetic fabric, such as nylon, in a flame for 2 seconds.

2. Remove the fabric from the flame. Blow out any flame if the fabric is burning.

3. Have students carefully observe the odor and appearance of the results.

4. Repeat steps 1–3 for a square of a natural fabric, such as cotton.

5. Have students compare the results. Students should notice that the synthetic fabric gives off a "chemical" odor and appears to melt. The natural fabric gives off an odor similar to that of burning paper or hair and appears to char.

FIGURE 7-23 ◀

Acrylic sweaters have a texture similar to wool, but they are machine-washable.

out shrinking. As a result, Orlon has become a useful fabric for winter clothing. Polyester has now become a more popular synthetic fiber than nylon. The best known polyester is Dacron®, a fiber used extensively in clothing and to make sails for boats.

All three of these synthetic fibers have raised concerns about flammability when they are used to make clothing, especially children's clothing. The heat energy from a fire breaks the bonds that hold the monomers together. The fragments that are produced then react with oxygen in the air to continue the combustion reaction, or burning, often adhering to the skin of the person wearing the clothing. To safeguard against this danger, these fibers are often made flame retardant. One way to reduce flammability is to change the fibers that are at the surface of the material. In flame-retardant clothing, the surface fibers are extensively cross-linked to one another, making it harder to break the bonds that hold them together. As a result, the fibers char as a group rather than burn as fragments. The charred fibers on the surface serve to insulate the fibers that are underneath.

FIGURE 7-24 ▼

b Polyamide fibers can also be linked together to form a material that is so strong it can be used to make bulletproof vests. This material is called Kevlar®.

a Polyamide fibers similar to nylon can be linked to form a material that can protect firefighters from flames. This material is called Nomex®.

VISUAL STRATEGY

Figure 7-24 The Kevlar® fiber is so strong because of its regular structure. In most fibers, the strands are random and irregularly arranged. In Kevlar, the strands have such a strong attraction for each other that they line up in parallel rows, forming flat sheets that pack as layers.

ADDITIONAL APPLICATION

Kevlar is now commonly used in sports equipment, such as tennis rackets, and in Formula One racing cars to protect the drivers. Its strength and flame-resistant properties make it useful for conveyor belts, industrial hoses, and mooring ropes for oil tankers. Kevlar is so resistant to weathering that it is used to coat optical fibers that are exposed to extreme weather conditions. Airplane manufacturers sometimes use Kevlar to line the engine compartment of airplanes in order to limit damage that occurs when a part of a turbine flies off. It is being considered as a liner for airplane baggage compartments to minimize damage that could occur if a bomb explodes there.

RESOURCE LINK

ChemFile Lab A
Skills Development
Have students do Experiment 25: *Polymers.*

CARBON AND ORGANIC COMPOUNDS   **261**

Safety
Wear safety goggles and a lab apron. Do not inhale fumes from the burning fabrics. Students should be at least 3 m from the demonstration while the fabrics are in the flames.

Disposal
Throw the fabric squares into the trash can once they are completely cooled.

TEACHING TIP

Vocabulary Strategy Fractional distillation is the process often used to separate petroleum into its component parts. The word *petroleum* comes from the Latin words *petra,* which means "a rock," and *oleum,* which means "oil." *Distillation* comes from the Latin *de,* which means "down," and *stillare,* which means "to drop." Have students use these word origins and their knowledge of the meaning of the word *fraction* to explain what is involved in the fractional distillation of petroleum.

CNN **Science in the News**

PRESENTS **Feature story 18**

Chemical Separation Techniques for Plastics See the Science in the News video guide for more details.

Plastics are made from petroleum

Also known as crude oil, petroleum originally came from marine life, both plant and animal. Over millions of years, intense pressure and high temperature transform the decaying matter into petroleum. The time it takes for crude oil to be formed is important because if we exhaust our supply of this natural resource, it will be impossible to replace. Petroleum is the source of a number of compounds that we have come to rely on, including the gasoline that drives our cars and the plastics that can be found in nearly every consumer product. **Table 7-6** lists a few of the compounds obtained from petroleum and their uses.

In 1912, Fritz Klatte, a German chemist, made an accidental polymer discovery. Before the advent of electric lighting, many houses were lit using acetylene, or ethyne, gas. After electricity took the place of acetylene, researchers tried to find new uses for the leftover fuel. Klatte mixed acetylene with hydrochloric acid and found that he had made vinyl chloride (the third entry in Table 7-6). He left the product sitting on a shelf, and after a short while it polymerized. The pure polyvinyl chloride, PVC, that Klatte had made was a hard, brittle solid that decomposed easily. There were no practical applications for this polymer. Fourteen years

TABLE 7-6 Organic Chemicals from Petroleum

Compound	Formula	Common name	Major uses	Production (in metric tons per year)
Benzene	(benzene ring structure)	benzene	plastics, dyes	7.77×10^6
1,4-benzene-dicarboxylic acid	$HO-\overset{O}{\overset{\|}{C}}-\bigcirc-\overset{O}{\overset{\|}{C}}-OH$	terephthalic acid	plastics	3.61×10^6
Chloroethene	$CH_2=CH-Cl$	vinyl chloride	plastics	7.54×10^6
1,2-dichloroethane	$Cl-CH_2-CH_2-Cl$	ethylene dichloride	plastics, solvents	1.19×10^7
1,2-ethanediol	$HO-CH_2-CH_2-OH$	ethylene glycol	plastics, antifreeze	3.53×10^6
Ethene	$CH_2=CH_2$	ethylene	plastics, solvents	2.32×10^7
Ethenyl-benzene	$CH=CH_2$ (with benzene ring)	styrene	plastics	5.16×10^6
Methanol	CH_3-OH	methyl alcohol	plastics, solvents	9.69×10^6
Propene	$CH_2=CH-CH_3$	propylene	plastics	1.25×10^7

ALTERNATIVE ASSESSMENT

Group Strategy

Show students the polymer samples they saw while doing the Lesson Warm-up on page 253. Hand back to students their responses from that activity. Have the student groups reclassify the polymers based on what they now know about fibers, elastomers, and plastics.

FIGURE 7-25 ◄

In many parts of the United States, old water pipes are being replaced by PVC pipes. These new pipes can safely deliver water without the danger of corrosion and breakage that characterizes old metal pipes.

later, in 1926, Waldo Semon, an American chemist, discovered that the addition of certain compounds, now called *plasticizers,* made PVC flexible and heat-resistant.

Because the amount of petroleum available is limited, a conscious effort should be made to recycle plastics whenever possible. If we do not reduce our use of petroleum, there will eventually be no petroleum resources left. Products that require petroleum as a raw material, including most synthetic plastics and many pharmaceuticals, will become difficult to make. Recycling not only will help protect our environment and save our natural resources but also will save many non-natural resources on which our society has become dependent.

internetconnect

SCILINKS
NSTA

TOPIC: Recycling codes
GO TO: www.scilinks.org
KEYWORD: HW076

SECTION REVIEW

Total recall

1. Name the three types of synthetic polymers.

2. In addition to the polymer, what other product is formed when a condensation polymer forms?

3. What raw material is used to synthesize most plastics?

4. Write the structural formula for the monomer used to synthesize polyethylene.

Critical thinking

5. How would polymers be different if their monomers were held together by weak attractions, as scientists first suggested?

6. Why is petroleum a nonrenewable raw material?

7. How do the physical properties of polyethylene depend on the side chains that form when its monomers are joined?

8. Copolymers are made from two different monomers. For example, some plastic food wrap is an addition polymer made from 1,1-dichloroethene and chloroethene. Draw a possible structure for this copolymer showing a structure that is four monomers in length.

9. **Story Clue** Draw the skeletal structure of part of a polyethylene molecule. The molecule should be eight monomers long.

ANSWERS

SECTION REVIEW

Total recall

1. elastomers, fibers, and plastics

2. a small molecule, such as water or HCl

3. petroleum

4.

Critical thinking

5. The polymers would not be strong or rigid. The weak bonds would enable the monomers to be easily pulled apart.

6. Although petroleum is made from plant material, it takes millions of years to form. Therefore, it cannot be easily regenerated.

7. When polyethylene contains a lot of side chains, the polymer molecules cannot pack tightly together. The result is tough and flexible. When polyethylene contains few side chains, the polymer molecules can pack closely together, forming a material that is stronger and more rigid.

8.

9.

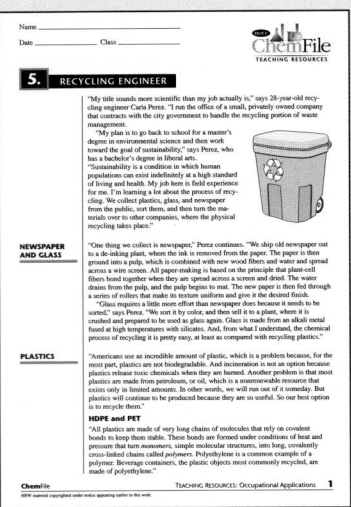
CONSUMER FOCUS

RECYCLING CODES FOR PLASTIC PRODUCTS

Sorting your plastics

More than half the states in the United States have enacted laws that require plastic products to be labeled with numerical codes that identify the type of plastic used in them. These codes are shown in the following table. Used plastic products can be sorted by these codes and properly recycled or processed. Only Codes 1 and 2 are widely accepted for recycling. Codes 3 and 6 are rarely recycled. Find out what types of plastics are recycled in your area. Knowing what the numerical codes mean will give you an idea of how successfully a given plastic product can be recycled. This may affect your decision to buy or not buy particular items.

Recycling Codes for Plastic Products

Recycling code	Type of plastic	Physical properties	Examples	Uses for recycled products
1	polyethylene terephthalate (PET)	tough, rigid; can be a fiber or a plastic; solvent resistant; sinks in water	soda bottles, clothing, electrical insulation, automobile parts	backpacks, sleeping bags, carpet, new bottles, clothing
2	high density polyethylene (HDPE)	rough surface; stiff plastic; resistant to cracking	milk containers, bleach bottles, toys, grocery bags	furniture, toys, trash cans, picnic tables, park benches, fences
3	polyvinyl chloride (PVC)	elastomer or flexible plastic; tough; poor crystallization; unstable to light or heat; sinks in water	pipe, vinyl siding, automobile parts, clear bottles for cooking oil, blister packaging	toys, playground equipment
4	low density polyethylene (LDPE)	moderately crystalline, flexible plastic; solvent resistant; floats on water	shrink wrapping, trash bags, dry-cleaning bags, frozen-food packaging, meat packaging	trash cans, trash bags, compost containers
5	polypropylene (PP)	rigid, very strong; fiber or flexible plastic; light-weight; heat- and stress-resistant	heatproof containers, rope, appliance parts, outdoor carpet, luggage, diapers, automobile parts	brooms, brushes, ice scrapers, battery cable, insulation, rope
6	polystyrene (P/S, PS)	somewhat brittle, rigid plastic; resistant to acids and bases but not organic solvents; sinks in water, unless it is a foam	fast-food containers, toys, videotape reels, electrical insulation, plastic utensils, disposable drinking cups, CD jewel cases	insulated clothing, egg cartons, thermal insulation

LOOKING BACK

What determines whether something is biodegradable?

To be broken down in the soil, organic substances must have bonds that can be broken by microorganisms. Food and lawn trimmings contain such bonds.

Over the past few years, some biodegradable plastics have been developed. One of these materials is polycaprolactone, a polyester. The $-\overset{\overset{\displaystyle O}{\|}}{C}-O-$ groups are attacked by microorganisms much more rapidly than the C—C or C—H bonds in polyethylene. Some biodegradable bags available today are made from nearly 100% cornstarch, a naturally biodegradable substance.

What is the structure of polyethylene?

Polyethylene contains chains of thousands of single carbon-carbon bonds. In polyethylene, each carbon atom is also bonded to at least two hydrogen atoms. Polyethylene is a giant alkane chain.

Why is polyethylene so stable?

Alkanes are very unreactive. The long chains of unreactive bonds make the decomposition of polyethylene extremely difficult. Consequently, most plastics will remain in the environment for a long time. In the pie chart below, you can see that plastics make up about 12% of the contents of landfills.

If biodegradable material is inside plastic bags, it is essentially nonbiodegradable. The need for environmentally friendly plastic bags has become even greater now that several states require communities to cut down on the amount of waste going into landfills. The price of biodegradable trash bags is slightly higher than the traditional polyethylene bags, but composting is much cheaper than maintaining a landfill or incinerator. Furthermore, the environmental cost of growing landfills is very high.

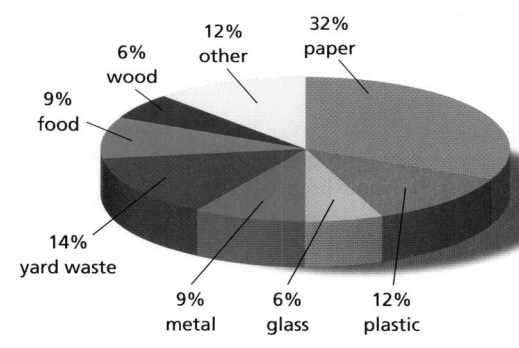

Pie chart:
- 32% paper
- 12% other
- 6% wood
- 9% food
- 14% yard waste
- 9% metal
- 6% glass
- 12% plastic

STORY CONCLUSION

Have students use the pie chart on this page and the information on page 233 to determine the maximum number of metric tons of each type of trash that might be placed daily in Fresh Kills landfill *(5760 metric tons of paper, 2160 metric tons of plastic, 1620 metric tons of metal, 1080 metric tons of glass, 2520 metric tons of yard waste, 1620 metric tons of food, 1080 metric tons of wood and 2160 metric tons of miscellaneous material)*. How many tons are definitely biodegradable? *(10 980 metric tons)* How many might not be biodegradable? *(7020 metric tons)*

RESOURCE LINK

ChemFile Teaching Resources CD-ROM

Career Extension

Assign Occupational Applications Worksheet 13: *Organic Composter* to emphasize relevant applications of text concepts.

Assimilating Knowledge

Have students return to their list of things that they want to know about carbon and organic compounds, which they created on page 232. Have them place a check mark next to each question that they are now able to answer. Students should finish by making a list of what they've learned. Have students identify unanswered questions as well as new questions they may have. These questions could be used as the basis for a research project.

REVIEW & ASSESS ASSIGNMENT GUIDE

Term Review
Assign after Section 7-3.

Concept & Skills Review

Section 7-1
▶ Items 1–9, 11–14

Section 7-2
▶ Items 10, 15–29

Section 7-3
▶ Items 30–41

Linking Chapters

Section 7-1
▶ Item 2

Section 7-3
▶ Item 1, 3

Alternative Assessments
Assign after Section 17-3.

Test Prep
Assign prior to the chapter test.

KEY TERMS

7-1
alkane
alkene
alkyne
allotropes
aromatic compound
benzene
covalent network solid

functional group
hydrocarbon
isomers

7-2
saturated fat
unsaturated fat
unsaturated hydrocarbon

7-3
addition polymer
condensation polymer
elastomer
fiber

monomer
peptide bond
plastic
polymer

KEY CONCEPTS

7-1 What kinds of covalent compounds can carbon form?

▶ Carbon, with its ability to form four covalent bonds, can form molecules and network solids in a variety of shapes.

▶ Hydrocarbons, the simplest organic compounds, contain just carbon and hydrogen atoms.

▶ The alkanes, alkenes, and alkynes are hydrocarbons. Organic compounds containing rings with delocalized electrons are aromatic hydrocarbons.

▶ Organic compounds are named and identified by functional groups, which are groups of atoms responsible for a molecule's distinctive chemical and physical properties.

▶ Classes of organic compounds include alcohols, ethers, aldehydes, organic acids, esters, ketones, and amines.

7-2 How are carbon compounds named and drawn?

▶ The names of the alkanes form the basis for naming most other organic compounds.

▶ In naming an organic compound, the carbon atoms are numbered so that any multiple bonds or branches have the lowest possible numbers.

▶ Unsaturated fats, with at least one double bond between the carbon atoms, are a better choice for diets than saturated fats, which contain only single bonds between the carbon atoms.

▶ Organic molecules can be represented in various ways, and each model has advantages and disadvantages.

7-3 What is a polymer?

▶ A polymer is a large chainlike macromolecule made by bonding thousands of monomers together.

▶ Addition polymers form by combining monomers end to end.

▶ Condensation polymers form when monomers are joined, and a small molecule is also produced.

▶ Natural polymers include proteins, nucleic acids, cellulose, and rubber.

▶ Synthetic polymers are classified as elastomers, fibers, or plastics, based on their elasticity.

KEY SKILLS

Review the following models before your exam. Be sure you can solve these types of problems.

How To Name branched hydrocarbons (p. 247)

How To Decipher skeletal structures (p. 251)

TERM REVIEW

1. An organic compound that contains a benzene ring is known as an ———.
(aromatic compound, alkane)

2. When a(n) ——— forms, a small molecule such as water is also produced.
(addition polymer, condensation polymer)

3. If a triple bond is present between two carbon atoms, then the hydrocarbon is classified as an ———.
(alkene, alkyne, alkane)

4. Diamond and graphite are examples of ———.
(hydrocarbons, covalent network solids)

5. A fat formed from fatty acids that have carbon-carbon double bonds is known as a(n) ———.
(unsaturated fat, saturated fat)

6. The unit that forms a polymer is known as a(n) ———.
(monomer, elastomer)

7. A(n) ——— is a polymer that is highly resistant to being stretched.
(plastic, fiber, elastomer)

8. Some elements exist in more than one physical form. Each of these forms is known as an ———.
(isomer, allotrope)

CONCEPT & SKILLS REVIEW

CARBON COMPOUNDS

1. a. Draw two isomers that have the molecular formula C_3H_6O.
  b. Classify each isomer based on the functional group it contains.

2. Explain why triple bonds are easier to break than single bonds.

3. a. Why does carbon form more compounds than chlorine?
  b. Why is diamond hard and strong?
  c. Why is graphite slippery?

4. Silicon, like diamond, can form covalent network solids. What property do these two elements share that gives them this common chemical property?

5. Aldehydes and ketones contain the $-\overset{\displaystyle O}{\overset{\|}{C}}-$ functional group. What makes them different?

6. Suggest a reason why diamond is less reactive chemically than graphite.

7. When ethene is mixed with Br_2, the double bond in the hydrocarbon is broken and the two bromine atoms are added to the molecule. Draw the structure that forms.

8. Explain why ethane does not react like ethene when it is mixed with Br_2 under the same conditions.

9. Br_2 reacts with benzene by replacing one of its hydrogen atoms.
  a. Draw the structural formula of the compound that forms in this chemical reaction.
  b. Explain why this is known as a substitution reaction.

10. When propyne reacts with H_2 under the proper conditions, the triple bond is broken and hydrogen atoms are added to the alkyne. An alkane is formed.
  a. Draw the structural formula for the alkane that forms.
  b. What is the name of this alkane?

Practice Problems

11. Draw two structural formulas for an alcohol with the molecular formula C_3H_8O.

TERM REVIEW

1. aromatic compound

2. condensation polymer

3. alkyne

4. covalent network solids

5. unsaturated fat

6. monomer

7. fiber

8. allotrope

CONCEPT & SKILLS REVIEW

1. a.

  b. aldehyde, ketone

2. The triple bond is the least stable of the three types of carbon-carbon bonds. Therefore, it is the easiest to break.

3. a. Answers may include the following: carbon contains four electrons available for bonding (chlorine has only one); carbon forms strong carbon-carbon bonds; carbon can form single, double, and triple bonds; and carbon compounds are relatively unreactive.
  b. In diamond, carbon atoms are arranged in a tetrahedral network; the bonding occurs in three dimensions.
  c. Graphite is bonded in a hexagonal pattern with the hexagons lying in planes. The planes are weakly held together and can slip past each other.

4. Silicon also contains four valence electrons that can bond with other silicon atoms.

5. The carbon atom that is double bonded to an oxygen atom is bonded to only one carbon atom in an aldehyde. It is bonded to two other carbon atoms in a ketone.

6. The tetrahedral bonding pattern of diamond is more stable than the hexagonal-planar pattern of graphite. Also, diamond contains only single bonds; graphite contains double bonds.

7.

$$\begin{array}{ccc} & Br & H \\ & | & | \\ H- & C- & C-H \\ & | & | \\ & H & Br \end{array}$$

8. Ethane contains no double bonds; it contains only single bonds. Thus, ethane is less reactive than ethene.

9. a.

b. The bromine atom substitutes for a hydrogen atom in the compound.

10. a.

$$\begin{array}{ccc} H & H & H \\ | & | & | \\ H-C-C-C-H \\ | & | & | \\ H & H & H \end{array}$$

b. propane

11. *See page 271A.*

12. Possible structures:

It is classified as an alkene because it contains a double bond.

13. a. organic acid
  b. aldehyde
  c. ether

14. −OH, alcohol group; and $-\overset{|}{N}-$, amine group

15.

$$\begin{array}{ccccc} H & H & H & H & H \\ | & | & | & | & | \\ HO-C-C-C-C-C-H \\ | & | & | & | & | \\ H & H & H & H & H \end{array}$$

−OH group attached to an end carbon in 1-pentanol

$$\begin{array}{ccccc} H & H & H & H & H \\ | & | & | & | & | \\ H-C-C-\ \ -C-C-C-H \\ | & | & | & | & | \\ H & OH & H & H & H \end{array}$$

−OH group attached to a carbon that is second along the chain in 2-pentanol

12. Draw the structure of a straight-chain hydrocarbon with the formula C_5H_{10}. Is it classified as an alkene or an alkyne? Explain your choice.

13. Classify the organic compounds shown below by their functional groups.

a.

b.

c.

14. What functional groups are present in a molecule of adrenaline, whose structural formula is shown below?

ORGANIC NOMENCLATURE

15. Draw structural formulas that show the difference between 1-pentanol and 2-pentanol.

16. Use Table 7-4 to identify the functional group from the name for each of the following organic compounds:
  a. propanol
  b. ethanoic acid
  c. propanal
  d. hexanone

17. When propene reacts with water, the double bond is broken and an −OH group is added to the middle carbon atom, and −H is added to an end carbon.
  a. Draw the structural formula of the organic compound that forms.
  b. Name the molecule that is the product of this reaction.

18. When 2-methylpropene is mixed with HI, 2-iodo-2-methylpropane is produced.
  a. Draw the structural formula of the organic reactant.
  b. Draw the structural formula of the product.

19. Use Table 7-3 to name the following straight-chain alkanes:
  a. C_7H_{16} **c.** $C_{10}H_{22}$
  b. C_4H_{10} **d.** C_3H_8

20. Name the following organic compounds:
  a.
  b.
  c.
  d. Write molecular formulas for the compounds shown in (a), (b), and (c).

21. Name the following organic compounds:
  a.
  b.
  c. Write molecular formulas for the compounds shown in (a) and (b).

22. Name the following compounds:
  a.

$$\begin{array}{cc} & CH_3 \\ & | \\ CH_3-C=CH-C-CH_3 \\ & | \quad\quad | \\ & CH_3 \quad CH_3 \end{array}$$

  b.

$$\begin{array}{c} CH_3 \\ | \\ CH_3-CH_2-C-C\equiv C-CH_3 \\ | \\ CH_3 \end{array}$$

  c.

$$\begin{array}{c} CH_3-CH_2-C=CH-CH_2-CH_3 \\ | \\ CH_2-CH_3 \end{array}$$

  d.

$$\begin{array}{c} CH_3-CH=C-CH_2-CH_2-CH_2-CH_3 \\ | \\ CH_2-CH_2-CH_3 \end{array}$$

23. Draw the structural formula for each of the following compounds:
  a. 1,4-dichlorohexane
  b. 2-bromo-4-chloroheptane

REPRESENTATIONS OF ORGANIC MOLECULES

24. a. Draw a structural formula for an alkene with 15 carbon atoms. What is the chemical formula of this compound?
  b. Draw a structural formula for an alkyne with 19 carbon atoms. What is the chemical formula of this compound?

25. Compare the advantages of structural formulas with those of chemical formulas.

Practice Problems

26. Convert the following structural formula to its simplified version:

Maltose

27. Draw structural formulas for the following:
   a. butanoic acid, a component of butter
   b. 1-nonanol, used in making artificial lemon oil
   c. 2-pentanone, a solvent
   d. Write molecular formulas for the compounds in (a), (b), and (c).

28. The skeletal structure for vitamin A is shown below. Draw its structural formula.

29. The skeletal structure for proline, an amino acid, is shown below. Draw its structural formula.

POLYMERS

30. What are two types of reactions by which polymers can be formed?

31. What is the structural requirement for a molecule to be a monomer in an addition polymer?

32. Explain the molecular difference between HDPE and LDPE.

33. Could ethanoic acid be used as a monomer in a condensation polymer? Why or why not?

34. A process that adds strength to polymers is known as cross-linking. This process involves the creation of covalent bonds between adjacent linear polymer chains. For example, the sulfur added in the vulcanization of rubber forms covalent bridges between adjacent chains. Predict how cross-linking would affect the elasticity of a polymer.

35. Cross-linking a polymer will also decrease a polymer's flammability. Suggest a reason for this change in a polymer's chemical property.

36. The following is the structural formula for vinyl acetate.

   a. Predict how this monomer polymerizes to form polyvinylacetate, a polymer used in latex paints. Will the polymer be an addition polymer or a condensation polymer? (Hint: Only the ethene group forms the polymer chain.)
   b. Draw a structural formula of two vinyl acetate monomers in the polymer.

Practice Problems

37. Ethylene glycol, $HO-CH_2-CH_2-OH$, is a monomer that forms a condensation polymer used as a car wax. Draw a portion of this wax polymer showing four molecules of the monomer that have combined.

38. Polymethyl methacrylate, sold under the trade names Plexiglass® and Lucite®, is an addition polymer made from the monomer methyl methacrylate, whose structural formula is shown below.

Draw a portion of a Plexiglass polymer showing four monomers that have combined.

16. a. $-OH$, alcohol
   b.

$-C-OH$, carboxylic acid
   c.

$-C-H$, aldehyde
   d.

$-C-$, ketone

17. a.

   b. 2-propanol

18. a.

   b.

19. a. heptane
   b. butane
   c. decane
   d. propane

20. a. 1-nonanol
   b. 1-aminobutane
   c. hexanoic acid
   d. $C_9H_{20}O$, $C_4H_{11}N$, $C_6H_{12}O_2$

21. a. butanone
   b. butanal
   c. Both formulas are C_4H_8O.

22. a. 2,4,4-trimethyl-2-pentene
   b. 4,4-dimethyl-2-hexyne
   c. 3-ethyl-3-hexene
   d. 3-propyl-2-heptene

23. a.

   b.

24. *See page 271A.*

25. Chemical formulas show relative numbers and types of atoms in a molecule, but they do not show how the atoms are arranged or bonded. Structural formulas show not only the numbers and types of atoms in a molecule but also how the atoms are arranged and bonded.

26. See page 271A.

27. See page 271A.

28. See page 271A.

29.

H–C–C O
H–C   C–C–OH
  N
H H
H

H H H
(structure with carbon ring)

30. addition and condensation

31. Monomers must contain a double or triple bond.

32. During the polymerization process for LDPE, a relatively large number of side chains form. These side chains prevent the polymer from packing closely. During the polymerization process for HDPE, few side chains form, and the polymer packs closely.

33. No. In order for a condensation polymer to form, the monomer or monomers must have two functional groups that can react to release a small molecule. With only one functional group, this molecule could react to form a dimer, but no chain growth could occur.

34. Cross-linking increases the elasticity of a polymer. Without the cross-linkings, the polymer molecules would pull apart and remain apart rather than stretch and return to their original shape.

35. In a fire, many polymers will melt or the bonds will break, causing the polymer to fall apart. The resulting fragments will burn easily. Cross-linking makes it harder for the bonds to break or for the polymer to melt. A crosslinked polymer will char as a whole rather than burn in fragments.

Answers continue on page 271A.

39. The Kevlar that is used in bulletproof vests is a condensation polymer that could be made from the following monomer:

H₂N–⟨ ⟩–C–OH
          ‖
          O

Draw a portion of a Kevlar polymer showing four molecules of a monomer that have combined.

40. Draw the structural formula showing how three molecules of the following monomer would combine to form a condensation polymer:

H H O
HO–C–C–C–OH
H H

41. An organic acid, lactic acid, is used as a monomer to form a polyester that is used to make surgical sutures that will dissolve in the body. The formula for lactic acid is shown below.

H H O
H–C–C–C–OH
H OH

Draw the structure that forms when two molecules of a lactic acid monomer combine to begin forming a condensation polymer.

LINKING CHAPTERS

1. Theme: Classification and trends
Polymers are also classified on the basis of their response to heat. Those that soften upon heating but remain chemically unchanged are known as thermoplastic polymers. Those that change chemically on heating are classified as thermosetting polymers. Suggest how a thermoplastic polymer might differ structurally from a thermosetting polymer to account for their differences in response to heating.

2. Lewis structures
Draw the Lewis structures for ethane, ethene, and ethyne.

3. Hydrogen and the halogens
Explain why replacing hydrogen atoms with halogen atoms will reduce the flammability of a polymer.

ALTERNATIVE ASSESSMENTS

Performance assessment

1. Devise an experiment to study how well biodegradable plastics break down. If your teacher approves your plan, conduct a class experiment to test the procedure on products labeled "biodegradable."

Portfolio projects

1. Chemistry and you
Make a record of the foods you consume in a single day. Compare the content labels from the foods, and list the chemicals in them. With the aid of your teacher and some reference books, try to classify the organic chemicals by their functional groups.

2. Research and communication
Covalently bonded solids, such as silicon, an element used in computer components, are harder than some pure metals. Research theories that explain the hardness of covalently bonded solids and their usefulness in the computer industry. Present your findings to the class.

3.

internet**connect**

SCLINKS
NSTA

TOPIC: Recycling plans
GO TO: www.scilinks.org
KEYWORD: HW077

Research and communication
Many everyday materials can be reused or recycled. However, recyclable products are continually deposited into landfills like Fresh Kills. Research the waste-management methods of your community. Write local waste-management officials to find out what has been done to reduce the amount of landfill space needed for your community's refuse. With your class, organize a plan to publicize the recycling programs available in your area.

1. Which of the following hydrocarbons must be an alkane?
   a. CH_4
   b. C_5H_{10}
   c. C_7H_{12}
   d. $C_{14}H_{26}$

2. The functional group that classifies an organic compound as an organic acid is _____.
   a.   O
        ‖
        −C−OH
   b. −OH
   c. −CH_3
   d.   O
        ‖
        −C−H

3. An alkane with the formula C_8H_{18} is called _____.
   a. octene
   b. octyne
   c. octane
   d. propane

4. During a condensation polymerization, _____.
   a. single bonds replace all double bonds that are present in the monomer
   b. water is often produced
   c. alcohol groups are formed
   d. an aldehyde group is changed to a ketone group

5. In naming an organic compound, _____.
   a. the locations of all functional groups are omitted
   b. the number of carbon atoms in the molecule is not a factor to consider
   c. begin by identifying and naming the longest hydrocarbon chain
   d. use side chains as the basis for naming the molecule

6. Which of the following would have the greatest number of isomers?
   a. C_2H_6
   b. C_3H_8
   c. C_6H_6
   d. $C_{20}H_{42}$

7. Which of the following could *not* exist as isomers?
   a. C_7H_{16}
   b. C_5H_{10}
   c. C_3H_8
   d. $C_6H_{12}O_6$

8. Examine the following structural formula:

   The correct name for this organic compound is _____.
   a. 2,2-dimethylbutane
   b. 2,2-dimethylpropane
   c. 2,2-dimethylnonane
   d. 3,3-dimethylbutane

9. Examine the following skeletal structure:

   The correct chemical formula for this compound is _____.
   a. $C_2H_4O_2$
   b. $C_5H_4O_2$
   c. $C_5H_8O_2$
   d. CHO

10. Which of the following is an aromatic compound?
    a.
    b.
    c.
    d.

Answers:
1. a
2. a
3. c
4. b
5. c
6. d
7. c
8. a
9. b
10. a

Answers from page 267

11.

H H H
H–C–C–C–OH,
H H H

H H H
H–C–C–C–H
H OH H

Answers from page 268

24. a. Sample structure:

H H H H H   H H H H H H H H H
H–C–C–C–C–C=C–C–C–C–C–C–C–C–C–H
H H H H   H H H H H H H H H H

$C_{15}H_{30}$

b. Sample structure:

H H H H   H H H H H H H H H H H H H
H–C–C–C–C–C≡C–C–C–C–C–C–C–C–C–C–C–C–H
H H H H   H H H H H H H H H H H H H

$C_{19}H_{36}$

Answers from page 269

26.

OH ... OH
HO ... O ... O ... OH
HO OH HO OH

27. a.

H H H O
H–C–C–C–C–OH
H H H

b.

H H H H H H H H H
HO–C–C–C–C–C–C–C–C–C–H
H H H H H H H H H

c.

H O H H H
H–C–C–C–C–C–H
H H H H

d. $C_4H_8O_2$, $C_9H_{20}O$, $C_5H_{10}O$

28.

(structure)

36. a. The carbon-carbon double bond in the monomer changes to two single bonds. These molecules can then combine in an addition polymerization.

b.

H
H–C–H
C=O
H O H H
–C–C–C–C–
H H H O
C=O
H–C–H
H

37. $-O-CH_2-CH_2-O-CH_2-CH_2-O-CH_2-CH_2-O-CH_2-CH_2-$

38.

(structure)

Answers from page 270

39.

(structure)

40.

H H O   H H   H H O
–C–C–C–O–C–C–C–O–C–C–C–O–
H H   H H O   H H

41.

H
H–C–H   H O
–C–C–O–C–C–O–
H O H–C–H
H

LINKING CHAPTERS

1. Thermoplastic polymers are either linear or branched, which allows them to soften when heated. Thermosetting polymers are cross-linked, and they retain their shape.

2. ethane:

$$H:\overset{\displaystyle H}{\underset{\displaystyle H}{C}}:\overset{\displaystyle H}{\underset{\displaystyle H}{C}}:H \quad \text{or} \quad H-\overset{\displaystyle H}{\underset{\displaystyle H}{C}}-\overset{\displaystyle H}{\underset{\displaystyle H}{C}}-H$$

ethene:

$$H:\overset{\displaystyle H}{C}::\overset{\displaystyle H}{C}:H \quad \text{or} \quad H-\overset{\displaystyle H}{C}=\overset{\displaystyle H}{C}-H$$

ethyne: $H:C :: C:H$ or $H-C{\equiv}C-H$

3. Halogen atoms are larger than hydrogen atoms, insulating the carbon atoms from contact with oxygen. Also, because halogens are more reactive than hydrogen, their compounds are more stable and therefore less likely to react with oxygen in a fire.

ALTERNATIVE ASSESSMENTS

Performance assessment

1. Be sure students observe all safety practices and have their procedure approved before proceeding. Check procedures to see that all factors other than biodegradability are held constant.

Portfolio projects

1. You may choose to provide students with lists of some compounds present in fresh foods, such as fresh fruits, vegetables, meats, and poultry.

2. Encourage students to use the Internet to gather information.

3. Students may want to work in groups to contact various local agencies. Encourage students to E-mail as well as write to these officials.

The Mole

CLASSROOM RESOURCES

SECTIONS	TEACHER'S DEMONSTRATIONS	PROBLEM SOLVING ■ *Text* ◆ *ChemFile Mini-Guide*	LABORATORIES ■ *Text* ◆ *ChemFile Manuals: A, B, C, D*
8-1 **How are atoms counted and measured?** Section Review, p. 283	**Demo 1** Finding the Mass of One Item, p. 282	◆ **Chapter 1** Conversions ■ **Sample Problem 8A** Converting amount in moles to number of atoms, p. 277 ■ **Sample Problem 8B** Converting number of atoms to an amount in moles, p. 277 ■ **Sample Problem 8C** Calculating average atomic mass, p. 279 ■ **Sample Problem 8D** Converting amount in moles to mass, p. 281 ■ **Sample Problem 8E** Converting mass to amount in moles, p. 281 ◆ **Chapter 5** Mole Concept ■ **Sample Problem 8F** Finding the mass of an atom, p. 282	
8-2 **How is the mole concept related to chemical formulas?** Section Review, p. 297	**Demo 2** Determine an Empirical Formula, p. 290	■ **Sample Problem 8G** Calculating molar mass, p. 287 ■ **Sample Problem 8H** Calculating molar mass of compounds, p. 288 ◆ **Chapter 6** Percentage Composition ■ **Sample Problem 8I** Determining an empirical formula from composition data, p. 290 ■ **Sample Problem 8J** Calculating empirical formulas from percentage composition, p. 291 ◆ **Chapter 7** Empirical Formulas ■ **Sample Problem 8K** Determining a molecular formula from an empirical formula, p. 293 ■ **Sample Problem 8L** Using a chemical formula to determine percentage composition, p. 295 ■ **Sample Problem 8M** Determining the percentage composition of hydrates, p. 296	◆ **EXP. 5A** Percent Composition of Hydrates, p. 730 ◆ **A7** Water of Hydration

SECTIONS	VIDEOS/VIDEODISC *Holt Chemistry Videodisc* CNN PRESENTS *Science in the NEWS*	CHEMFILE CD-ROMs ● *Teaching Resources* ◆ *Interactive Tutor*	OVERHEADS ● *Color Transparencies* ◆ *Transparency Masters*
8-1	Using Avogadro's number Conversion between moles and mass Solving mole problems	● Skills Review: Operations with Scientific Notation	● **16** Solving Mole Problems
8-2	Comparing formulas Empirical formula determination	● Supplemental Reading: *The Same and Not the Same* "In Praise of Synthesis" ● Skills Review: Percentages	● **39** Mole–Mass Calculations ● **40** Percentage Composition Calculations

ASSESSMENT RESOURCES

ALTERNATIVE ASSESSMENTS	CHAPTER TESTING	SCORING RUBRICS *Holt ChemFile Teaching Resources CD-ROM*
Student Text Performance assessments, p. 304 Portfolio projects 1–3, p. 304 **Teacher's Edition** Group Strategy, p. 278 **Study Guide** Sections 8-1 to 8-2	**Student Text** Test Preparation, p. 305 **Holt Chemistry:** **Visualizing Matter** **Chapter 8 Test** (blackline masters) **Holt ChemFile Test Generator** **for Macintosh and Windows**	**Lab Work** Student-Designed Experiments Rubric Performance Tasks Scoring Rubric Assessment for Structured Inquiry Assessment for Open-Ended Inquiry **Portfolio Projects** Evaluating Concept Maps Assessing Portfolios Portfolio Assignment Student Evaluation Form

CHAPTER 8

The Mole

SIR HUGH'S BOOK

In 1951, Sir Hugh Beaver of Ireland had a disagreement with his friends over which bird flew the fastest. Sir Hugh searched many reference books but could find nothing to resolve the argument. As a result, he created a book that would be an official list of the largest, the tallest, the smallest, the most, the hottest, and so on—the extremes of everything that could be measured.

Beaver was also the managing director of the Guinness Brewing Company, so with the backing of his company, the first *Guinness Book of World Records* was published in 1955 and has been updated every year since then. Today you can learn the following from this book:

▶ The largest pumpkin on record weighed 481 kg.

▶ The longest model train to run under its own power has 650 cars, four engines, and a length of 70 m.

▶ The heaviest mammal ever found was a blue whale that weighed 172 000 kg.

▶ A man in California did 46 001 push-ups in 24 hours.

▶ The United States gold reserve in 1996 was over 8 000 000 kg in mass.

▶ The largest diamond ever found weighed 3106 carats, or 621.2 g.

▶ The distance from Earth to the farthest known galaxy is 13.1 billion light-years, or 1.24×10^{23} km.

▶ The rarest element in Earth's crust is astatine, with an estimated mass of 0.16 g in the entire crust.

Quantities such as 1.24×10^{23} km are truly astronomical; the word *astronomic* is applied to numbers so huge that it is hard to imagine what they mean.

Extremely small quantities are also difficult to imagine. A common soil bacterium might be 1/1 000 000 m (1×10^{-6} m) in length, with a volume close to $(1 \times 10^{-6}$ m$)^3$, or 1×10^{-18} m^3. One of these bacteria is much too small to see with the unaided eye, but 84 billion copper atoms or about 30 billion water molecules would fit into the same space.

Because atoms, ions, and molecules are so small, an invisible quantity of matter may contain many billions of these particles. Chemists must have a way to count particles that are too small to be seen. Using a balance to find the mass is the most practical way to measure a small quantity of matter. In this chapter, you will learn how chemists use the simple relationship between the enormous number of atoms in a mole and the mass of those atoms to describe elements and compounds quantitatively.

CHAPTER LINKS

How can chemists count atoms by using a balance?

How many astatine atoms exist in Earth's crust?

If you traveled to the farthest galaxy, how many atoms of carbon would you have to drop per kilometer to use up all of the atoms in the largest diamond?

Students may think that extremely large and small numbers do not apply to their daily lives. These concepts seem abstract because students cannot directly measure the quantities or count the numbers involved. Use the following example which applies to the human body, to emphasize that extremely large and small numbers do affect students.

The average human body contains about 10^{14} cells. Each cell membrane has a thickness of 7×10^{-9} m. Of the cells in the human body, about 2.5×10^{12} are red blood cells. Each red blood cell has a diameter of about 7.5×10^{-6} m and a thickness of about 2×10^{-6} m. Each milliliter of blood contains about 5×10^{9} red blood cells. Because some cells die every moment, the human body replenishes itself with red blood cells at a rate of about 3×10^{6} each second.

CONCEPT PREVIEW

Section 8-1
Counting atoms and measuring their masses
▶ the mole
▶ Avogadro's constant
▶ average atomic mass
▶ molar mass

Section 8-2
Moles and chemical formulas
▶ molar mass
▶ empirical formulas
▶ molecular formulas
▶ hydrates

SECTION 8-1

How are atoms counted and measured?

OBJECTIVES

▶ **Explain** the relationship between atomic mass and atomic mass units.

▶ **Use** a periodic table to determine the relative atomic masses of elements.

▶ **Solve** problems involving moles, atoms, and molar mass.

▶ **Calculate** the mass of individual atoms.

Avogadro's constant and the mole

As you read in Chapter 3, atoms are extremely small. Macroscopic samples of elements contain an enormous number of individual atoms. For convenience, chemists created a quantity to represent the number of particles in a sample of a given substance. The quantity is the *amount of substance* or simply *amount*. A new unit was created to express the amount of substance. This unit, called the *mole* (mol), is defined as the number of atoms in exactly 12 g of carbon-12.

The number of particles in a mole is called Avogadro's constant or number. The most recent measurement of Avogadro's constant gave $6.022\,1367 \times 10^{23}$ per mole. Avogadro's constant may be used to measure any kind of particle, such as the atoms, ions, or molecules shown in **Figure 8-1** as well as electrons and even bonds. For the calculations in this text, Avogadro's constant will be rounded to 6.022×10^{23}/mol.

▼ **FIGURE 8-1**

One mole represents 6.022×10^{23} particles. The particles can be atoms in elements, molecules in molecular compounds, or ions in ionic compounds. Examples of a variety of molar quantities are shown.

AVOGADRO'S CONSTANT 6.022×10^{23}

Element	Molecular compound	Ionic compound
Carbon, C 12.01 g 6.022×10^{23} atoms	Water, H_2O 18.02 g 6.022×10^{23} molecules	Sodium chloride, NaCl 58.44 g 6.022×10^{23} Na^+ ions 6.022×10^{23} Cl^- ions
Copper, Cu 63.55 g 6.022×10^{23} atoms	Sucrose, $C_{12}H_{22}O_{11}$ 342.34 g 6.022×10^{23} molecules	Potassium dichromate, $K_2Cr_2O_7$ 294.2 g 1.240×10^{24} K^+ ions. 6.02×10^{23} $Cr_2O_7^{2-}$ ions

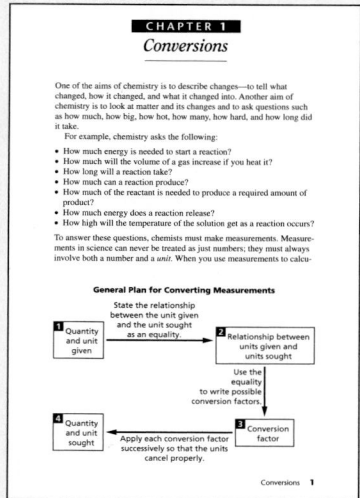
TABLE 8-1 **Counting Units**

Unit	Example	Unit	Example
1 dozen	12 objects	1 ream	500 sheets of paper
1 score	20 objects	1 hour	60 seconds
1 gross	144 objects	1 mole	6.022×10^{23} particles

Keep in mind that the mole is a counting unit used for measuring an amount of a substance in the same way that a dozen represents 12 of something. **Table 8-1** shows you examples of other familiar counting units.

Amount in moles can be converted to number of atoms

Avogadro's constant can be used to convert an amount in moles to an equivalent number of atoms. The conversion is similar to changing 20 dozen eggs into the equivalent number of individual eggs. The conversion factor is the number of eggs per dozen.

$$20 \text{ dozen} \times \frac{12 \text{ eggs}}{1 \text{ dozen}} = 240 \text{ eggs}$$

The same logic process is used to convert 2.66 mol of an element to the equivalent number of atoms. The conversion factor, Avogadro's constant, is the number of objects, in this case atoms, per 1 mol.

$$2.66 \text{ mol} \times \frac{6.022 \times 10^{23} \text{ atoms}}{1 \text{ mol}} = 1.60 \times 10^{24} \text{ atoms}$$

This answer makes sense because when you start with more than 1 mol, you should end up with more than 6.022×10^{23} atoms.

The reverse calculation is similar, only the conversion factor is inverted. Suppose you have a sample of iron that contains 2.54×10^{24} atoms. How many moles is that? The setup is as follows.

$$2.54 \times 10^{24} \text{ atoms} \times \frac{1 \text{ mol Fe}}{6.022 \times 10^{23} \text{ atoms}} = 4.22 \text{ mol Fe}$$

This answer makes sense because there are more than 6.022×10^{23} atoms, so there will be more than 1 mol.

You can use **Figure 8-2** to help you remember how to convert the number of atoms to an amount in moles, or an amount in moles to the number of atoms.

internet**connect**

SC**LINKS**

NSTA

TOPIC: Avogadro's constant
GO TO: www.scilinks.org
KEYWORD: HW081

VISUAL STRATEGY

Figure 8-2 Have students interpret the figure in their own words. Ask them how to determine the number of atoms when given the amount in moles, and vice versa.

FIGURE 8-2 ◄

By using Avogadro's constant, 6.022×10^{23} mol, you can convert from amounts to numbers, or vice versa.

RESOURCE LINK

Chem**File** Mini-Guide to Problem Solving
Assign Chapter 1: *Conversions* for additional practice.

THE MOLE 275

ANSWERS

CONCEPT CHECK

1. A mole represents the amount of a substance.
2. 6.022×10^{23} /mol
3. Because there are $2K^+$ ions for every dichromate ion in the formula unit for the compound, 1 mol of the compound yields 2 mol, or $2(6.022 \times 10^{23})$ of K^+ ions.

The sample problems throughout this book are set up to help you learn to solve problems efficiently. Most sample problems are divided into three steps. Each step emphasizes a specific set of activities that will help you develop your problem-solving skills.

1 List what you know
Don't start using your calculator yet.
A big mistake that beginning chemistry students make is to take the numbers from a problem statement and begin using the calculator before they know what the problem means. First, you must find out what information is given in the problem statement.

▶ Read the problem twice.

▶ List the quantities given in the statement of the problem. Always include the units with each value.

▶ Determine what is being asked for, including units.

2 Set up the problem

▶ First analyze what needs to be done to get the answer. Use the values and units given in the problem as your starting point. Then determine the relationships needed to get from the given values to the answer.

▶ Determine and list any other information that is needed, such as conversion factors or atomic masses obtained from the periodic table.

▶ Write down your setup with all the conversion factors. Check to see how the units cancel. If they cancel to give the units needed for your answer, the setup is most likely correct.

3 Calculate and verify

▶ Make a quick estimate of the answer by rounding the numbers in the setup and making a quick calculation.

▶ Do the calculation. Do not round off between steps—round off the answer at the end of the calculation.

▶ Check the size of the answer. Should it be larger or smaller than the value given? Ask yourself, Is this answer reasonable? For example, if the number of atoms is less than 1, the answer cannot possibly be correct.

CONCEPT CHECK

1. What quantity is represented by the mole?
2. What value should you use for Avogadro's constant in your calculations?
3. **Critical Thinking**   In Figure 8-1, why is the number of potassium ions greater than 6.022×10^{23}?

SAMPLE PROBLEM 8A — Converting amount in moles to number of atoms

Determine the number of atoms present in 2.5 mol of silicon.

1 **List what you know**
- ▶ amount of Si = 2.5 mol
- ▶ number of Si atoms = ? atoms

2 **Set up the problem**
- ▶ Use Figure 8-2 to determine which factor will take you from moles to the number of atoms.

$$\text{Avogadro's constant} = \frac{6.022 \times 10^{23} \text{ atoms}}{1 \text{ mol}}$$

- ▶ Multiply the number of moles by this factor.

3 **Calculate and verify**

$$2.5 \text{ mol Si} \times \frac{6.022 \times 10^{23} \text{ atoms Si}}{1 \text{ mol Si}} = 1.5 \times 10^{24} \text{ atoms Si}$$

The answer has the correct units and is greater than Avogadro's constant, which makes sense because you started with more than 1 mol.

SAMPLE PROBLEM 8B — Converting number of atoms to an amount in moles

Convert 3.01×10^{23} atoms of silicon to moles of silicon.

1 **List what you know**
- ▶ number of Si atoms = 3.01×10^{23}
- ▶ amount of Si = ? mol

2 **Set up the problem**

Use Figure 8-2 to determine which factor will take you from the number of atoms to moles. The following factor will give you the correct unit.

$$\frac{1 \text{ mol}}{6.022 \times 10^{23} \text{ atoms}}$$

Multiply this factor by the number of silicon atoms to get moles of silicon.

$$3.01 \times 10^{23} \text{ atoms Si} \times \frac{1 \text{ mol Si}}{6.022 \times 10^{23} \text{ atoms Si}} = ? \text{ mol Si}$$

3 **Calculate and verify**

Solve and cancel like units in the numerator and denominator.

$$3.01 \times 10^{23} \text{ atoms Si} \times \frac{1 \text{ mol Si}}{6.022 \times 10^{23} \text{ atoms Si}} = 0.500 \text{ mol Si}$$

The answer has the correct units and is less than 1 mol, which makes sense because you started with less than Avogadro's constant of atoms.

THE MOLE 277

TEACHING TIP

Designing a Model   Have students use egg cartons and individual items, such as pennies, to help them visualize the relationship between counting units, such as dozens, and counting individual items within a unit. For example, if a student has 20 pennies, filling one egg carton with one penny per section and placing the other eight pennies in another carton shows that 20 pennies is the same as one and two-thirds dozen pennies. Relate this model to Avogadro's constant and the number of moles.

RESOURCE LINK

ChemFile Teaching Resources CD-ROM
Skills Review
Assign Math Skills Worksheet 4: *Operations with Scientific Notation* to review or reteach this skill.

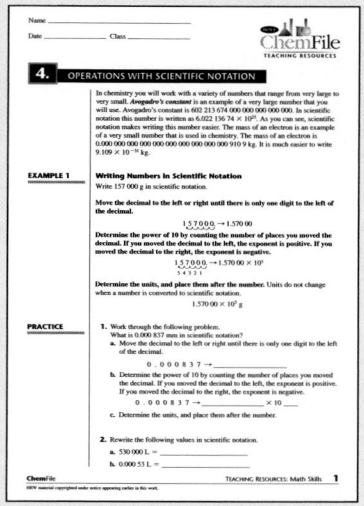

ANSWERS

PRACTICE PROBLEM 8A & 8B

1. $3.7 \text{ mol Na} \times \dfrac{6.022 \times 10^{23} \text{ Na atoms}}{\text{mol}}$

   $= 2.2 \times 10^{24} \text{ Na atoms}$

2. $155 \text{ mol As} \times \dfrac{6.022 \times 10^{23} \text{ As atoms}}{\text{mol}}$

   $= 9.33 \times 10^{25} \text{ As atoms}$

3. $5.66 \times 10^{26} \text{ Xe atoms} \times$

   $\dfrac{1 \text{ mol Xe}}{6.022 \times 10^{23} \text{ Xe atoms}} = 940. \text{ mol Xe}$

4. $2.888 \times 10^{15} \text{ Ag atoms} \times$

   $\dfrac{1 \text{ mol Ag}}{6.022 \times 10^{23} \text{ Ag atoms}} = 4.796 \times$

   10^{-9} mol Ag

ADDITIONAL EXAMPLES

SAMPLE PROBLEM 8A & 8B

1. How many atoms are present in each of the following?
   a. 4.3 mol of tungsten
      Ans. 2.6×10^{24} atoms

   b. 2.45×10^{-6} mol of nickel
      Ans. 1.48×10^{18} atoms

   c. 0.923 mol of tin
      Ans. 5.56×10^{23} atoms

2. How many moles are equivalent to each of the following?
   a. 7.95×10^{24} copper atoms
      Ans. 13.2 mol

   b. 6.93×10^{23} thallium atoms
      Ans. 1.15 mol

   c. 1.974×10^{14} calcium atoms
      Ans. 3.278×10^{-10} mol

▼ PRACTICE PROBLEMS

1. How many atoms are present in 3.7 mol of sodium?

2. How many atoms are present in 155 mol of arsenic?

3. How many moles of xenon is 5.66×10^{26} atoms?

4. How many moles of silver is 2.888×10^{15} atoms?

Relative atomic mass and the periodic table

▼ **FIGURE 8-3**

Pure copper is a mixture of two isotopes. In any sample of copper, 69.17% of the atoms are copper-63 and 30.83% of the atoms are copper-65.

Copper-65
LIBERTY
IN GOD WE TRUST
1982
Copper-63

STUDY SKILLS

WORKING PRACTICE PROBLEMS

Always review the chapter's sample problems. Work all the problems you can to prepare for the test. Answers to selected problems are in the back of your book so that you can see if you are on the right track. Never spend more than 15 minutes trying to solve a problem—get help! You won't pass the test if you can't work the problems.

At the time of Mendeleev, chemists knew the relative masses of atoms for most of the known elements. Unfortunately, chemists had no idea what the actual masses of atoms were; they knew only that they were very small and that even a microgram of an element contained an enormous number of atoms.

Why are relative atomic masses not exact whole numbers? In other words, why isn't the relative atomic mass of sodium exactly 23? One reason is that the sum of the masses of an appropriate number of neutrons, protons, and electrons is not a whole number. The constituent particles of atoms have the following relative masses.

Proton	1.00742 amu
Neutron	1.008665 amu
Electron	0.0005484 amu

From these masses you can see that sodium, with 11 protons, 11 electrons, and 12 neutrons could not have an atomic mass that is a whole number, though it would be close to a whole number. Another reason atomic masses are not whole numbers is that even though the atomic mass scale is based on the mass of carbon-12, the mass of sodium shown on the periodic table reflects the mass of a mixture of sodium isotopes. Most elements are mixtures of isotopes. Let's look at how the presence of several isotopes for an element affects its atomic mass.

Copper has a relative atomic mass of 63.54 amu. In nature, copper consists of a mixture of two isotopes, copper-63 and copper-65. The abundance of the copper-63 atom is 69.17% and that of copper-65 atom is 30.83%. The relative atomic mass of copper is a weighted average of these two isotopes. The following sample problem shows how the average atomic mass of an element is calculated from data for each of its isotopes.

ALTERNATIVE ASSESSMENT

Group Strategy

To be certain that students understand the concept of a weighted average, have them find some grade averages. For example, assume a student has 4 A's, 6 B's, 3 C's, and 1 D.

an A is worth 4 points
a B is 3 points
a C is 2 points
a D is 1 point

The total number of points is (4 A's) (4 points/A) + (6 B's)(3 points/B) + (3 C's)

(2 points/C) + (1 D) (1 point/D) = 16 points + 18 points + 6 points + 1 point = 41 points

The weighted average of the grades is

$\dfrac{41 \text{ points}}{14 \text{ grades}} = 2.9$ points/grade

Emphasize that the weighted average considers both the point value of each letter grade and its frequency.

SAMPLE PROBLEM 8C   Calculating average atomic mass

The mass of a copper-63 atom is 62.94 amu and that of a copper-65 atom is 64.93 amu. Using this data and the abundance of these two isotopes, determine the average atomic mass of native copper. The abundance of copper-63 is 69.17%. The abundance of copper-65 is 30.83%.

1   **List what you know**

- ▶ mass of a copper-63 atom = 62.94 amu
- ▶ abundance of copper-63 = 69.17%
- ▶ mass of copper-65 = 64.93 amu
- ▶ abundance of copper-65 = 30.83%
- ▶ average atomic mass of Cu = ? g

2   **Calculate and verify**

The average atomic mass of copper is the sum of the contribution of the masses of each isotope to the total mass. This type of average is called a *weighted average*. Each isotope contributes a mass equal to its mass multiplied by its fraction (or decimal equivalent) of all naturally occurring copper atoms. The fraction or decimal equivalent of each isotope is the percentage of that isotope divided by 100. Therefore, the decimal fraction is found by moving the decimal point of the percentage two places to the left.

Isotope	Percentage		Decimal equivalent
copper-63	69.17%	=	0.6917
copper-65	30.83%	=	0.3083

The decimal equivalents of the isotopes are multiplied by the mass of the isotope then added together to determine the average atomic mass.

$$\underset{\text{copper-63}}{(62.94\ \text{amu})(0.6917)} + \underset{\text{copper-65}}{(64.93\ \text{amu})(0.3083)} = 63.55\ \text{amu}$$

Verify your answer by comparing the result with the average atomic mass of copper given on the periodic table. Both are 63.55, so the result is correct.

PRACTICE PROBLEMS

1. Calculate the average atomic mass for silicon if 92.21% of its atoms have a mass of 27.98 amu, 4.70% have a mass of 28.98 amu, and 3.09% have a mass of 29.97 amu.

2. Calculate the average atomic mass of oxygen. Oxygen has three naturally occurring isotopes: oxygen-16, with a mass of 15.99 amu; oxygen-17, with a mass of 17.00 amu; and oxygen-18, with a mass of 18.00 amu. The relative abundances are 99.76%, 0.038%, and 0.20%, respectively.

3. Calculate the average atomic mass for iron. Iron has four naturally occurring isotopes. Iron-54 has a relative abundance of 5.90% and a mass of 53.94 amu. Iron-56 has a relative abundance of 91.72% and a mass of 55.93 amu. Iron-57 has a relative abundance of 2.10% and a mass of 56.94 amu. Iron-58 has a relative abundance of 0.280% and a mass of 57.93 amu.

THE MOLE   **279**

ANSWERS

PRACTICE PROBLEM 8C

1. (27.98 amu)(0.9221) + (28.98 amu)(0.047) + (29.97 amu)(0.0309) = 28.09 amu

2. (15.99 amu)(0.9976) + (17.00 amu)(0.00038) + (18.00 amu)(0.0020) = 15.99 amu

3. (53.94 amu)(0.0590) + (55.93 amu)(0.9172) + (56.94 amu)(0.0210) + (57.93 amu)(0.00280) = 55.84 amu

ADDITIONAL EXAMPLES

SAMPLE PROBLEM 8C

1. Chlorine exists as chlorine-35, which has a mass of 34.969 amu and makes up 75.8% of chlorine atoms. The rest of naturally occurring chlorine is chlorine-37, with a mass of 36.996 amu. What is the average atomic mass of chlorine?

   Ans. 35.460 amu

2. Uranium-234 makes up 0.005% of uranium atoms and has a mass of 234.041 amu. Uranium-235 makes up 0.720% and has a mass of 235.044 amu. Uranium-238 has a mass of 238.051 amu and makes up 99.275%. What is the average atomic mass of uranium?

   Ans. 238.029 amu

3. Carbon-12 makes up 98.90% of existing carbon. Carbon-13, with a mass of 13.003, makes up 1.10%. Traces of carbon-14 also exist. What is the average atomic mass of carbon?

   Ans. 12.011 amu

GRAPHIC ORGANIZER

VISUAL STRATEGY

Figure 8-5 After they are rounded off, molar masses of elements have three to five significant digits. Remind students that when they are adding numbers, decimals are aligned and the numbers are added. When determining significant figures, the number of places to the right of the decimal point in the sum should equal the least number of places to the right of the decimal point in the addends.

► **FIGURE 8-4**

By using the molar mass of a substance, you can convert between the amount in moles and the mass in grams of the substance.

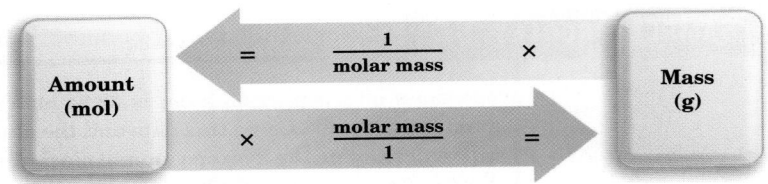

Molar mass relates moles to grams

During your study of chemistry, there will be many situations when you will need to know either the mass in grams of a given number of moles of a substance or the number of moles in a given mass of a substance. Fortunately, the mole is defined in a way that makes these conversions easy.

Suppose you need to find the mass in grams of 1 mol of helium atoms. You know that there are 6.022×10^{23} helium atoms in 1 mol. Using the periodic table, you round off the atomic mass of helium to 4.00 amu. Recall from Chapter 3 that 1 amu is approximately 1.66×10^{-24} g. You can use this information in the following calculation to find the mass of 1 mol of helium atoms.

$$1 \text{ mol He} \times \frac{6.022 \times 10^{23} \text{ atoms He}}{1 \text{ mol He}} \times \frac{4.00 \text{ amu}}{1 \text{ atom He}} \times \frac{1.66 \times 10^{-24} \text{ g He}}{1 \text{ amu}} = 4.00 \text{ g He}$$

The mass in grams of 1 mol of an element or compound is numerically equal to the atomic or formula mass. This relationship holds true for all elements. The **molar mass** of an element is numerically equal to the element's atomic mass and has the unit grams per mole (g/mol). Note: For calculations throughout this text, atomic masses are rounded to two places to the right of the decimal point. Thus, the molar mass of carbon is 12.01 g/mol, and the molar mass of iron is 55.85 g/mol.

These molar masses are used as conversion factors. **Figure 8-4** shows the relationship between moles and the mass in grams of a substance. Suppose you must determine the mass in grams of 3.50 mol of the element copper. By checking the periodic table, you find the atomic mass of copper. This mass, 63.546, is rounded to 63.55 amu. Therefore, the molar mass of copper will be given as 63.55 g/mol in your calculations.

molar mass

the mass in grams equal to the sum of all the atomic masses of the component atoms of a substance

► **FIGURE 8-5**

For consistency, molar masses from the periodic table in this text are rounded to two places to the right of the decimal point.

1 H Hydrogen 1.00794 $1s^1$	11 Na Sodium 22.989768 $[Ne]3s^1$	17 Cl Chlorine 35.4527 $[Ne]3s^23p^5$
1.00794 rounds to 1.01	22.989768 rounds to 22.99	35.4527 rounds to 35.45

SAMPLE PROBLEM 8D   Converting amount in moles to mass

Determine the mass in grams of 3.50 mol of copper.

1 **List what you know**
- ▶ amount of Cu = 3.50 mol
- ▶ mass of Cu = ? g

2 **Set up the problem**
- ▶ Use Figure 8-4 to determine which factor will take you from the number of moles to the number of grams. That factor is the molar mass of copper.

$$\frac{63.55 \text{ g Cu}}{1 \text{ mol Cu}}$$

Multiply the number of moles by this factor.

$$3.50 \text{ mol Cu} \times \frac{63.55 \text{ g Cu}}{1 \text{ mol Cu}} = ? \text{ g Cu}$$

3 **Calculate and verify**
- ▶ Solve and cancel like units in the numerator and denominator.

$$3.50 \text{ mol Cu} \times \frac{63.55 \text{ g Cu}}{1 \text{ mol Cu}} = 222 \text{ g Cu}$$

- ▶ The answer has the units requested in the problem. An answer of more than 63.55 g (the molar mass) makes sense because you started with more than 1 mol. The answer is rounded to three places to conform to the least precise measurement in the problem.

SAMPLE PROBLEM 8E   Converting mass to amount in moles

Determine the number of moles represented by 237 g of copper.

1 **List what you know**
- ▶ mass of Cu = 237 g
- ▶ amount of Cu = ? mol

2 **Set up the problem**
- ▶ Use Figure 8-4 to determine which factor will take you from the number of grams to moles. That factor is the molar mass of copper.

$$\frac{1 \text{ mol Cu}}{63.55 \text{ g Cu}}$$

- ▶ Multiply the number of grams by this factor.

$$237 \text{ g Cu} \times \frac{1 \text{ mol Cu}}{63.55 \text{ g Cu}} = ? \text{ mol Cu}$$

3 **Calculate and verify**
- ▶ Solve and cancel like units in the numerator and denominator.

$$237 \text{ g Cu} \times \frac{1 \text{ mol Cu}}{63.55 \text{ g Cu}} = 3.73 \text{ mol Cu}$$

SECTION 8-1

ADDITIONAL EXAMPLES

SAMPLE PROBLEM 8D AND 8E

1. Determine the mass in grams of each of the following amounts:

   a. 2.64 mol tellurium

   Ans. 337 g

   b. 4.96 mol titanium

   Ans. 237 g

   c. 2.00×10^{-3} mol uranium

   Ans. 0.476 g

2. Determine the amount in moles represented by each of the following masses:

   a. 54.3 g cobalt

   Ans. 0.921 mol

   b. 245 g oxygen

   Ans. 15.3 mol

   c. 0.0923 g fluorine

   Ans. 4.86×10^{-3} mol

ADDITIONAL EXAMPLES

SAMPLE PROBLEM 8F

Find the mass of a single atom of each of the following elements:

1. helium

Ans. 6.64×10^{-24} g

2. tungsten

Ans. 3.053×10^{-22} g

3. potassium

Ans. 6.493×10^{-23} g

RESOURCE LINK

ChemFile Mini-Guide to Problem Solving
Assign Chapter 5: *Mole Concept* for additional practice.

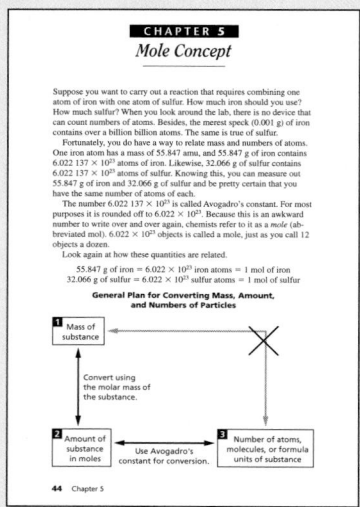

The average mass of atoms can be calculated from molar mass

Now that you know how to convert between moles, Avogadro's constant, and molar mass, you can calculate the average mass of an atom of any element. The process is no different from finding the mass of a single egg when you know the mass of a dozen eggs. For example, the mass shown on a package of a dozen eggs is 720.6 g. How do you find the mass of one egg? The answer is simple. Divide 720.6 g by 12 eggs to get the mass per egg.

$$\frac{720.6 \text{ g}}{12 \text{ eggs}} = 60.05 \text{ g/egg}$$

Using factor-label analysis, the problem would be set up as follows.

$$\frac{720.6 \text{ g}}{\text{doz}} \times \frac{1 \text{ doz}}{12 \text{ eggs}} = 60.05 \text{ g/egg}$$

The same process is applied to finding the mass of a single atom in Sample Problem 8F. In this case, instead of a dozen, you will work with Avogadro's constant for the number of atoms.

SAMPLE PROBLEM 8F | Finding the mass of an atom

Find the mass of a single silicon atom.

1 List what you know

- molar mass of silicon = 28.09 g/mol
- Avogadro's constant = 6.022×10^{23}/mol
- mass of one silicon atom = ?

2 Set up the problem

- You know the number of atoms in 28.09 g. You can divide the mass by the number of atoms to get the mass per atom. Or you can express the relationships above as factors that will give g/atom as an answer.

$$\frac{28.09 \text{ g Si}}{\text{mol Si}} \quad \text{and} \quad \frac{1 \text{ mol Si}}{6.022 \times 10^{23} \text{ atoms Si}}$$

3 Calculate and verify

- Solve and cancel like units in the numerator and denominator.

$$\frac{28.09 \text{ g Si}}{\text{mol Si}} \times \frac{1 \text{ mol Si}}{6.022 \times 10^{23} \text{ atoms Si}} = 4.665 \times 10^{-23} \text{ g/atom Si}$$

- The answer has the units specified by the problem. A very small value for mass makes sense because you are calculating the mass of a single atom. More than 99% of the mass of a silicon atom is due to the protons and neutrons in its nucleus. The electrons that occupy most of the volume of the atom contribute very little to the atom's mass.

282 CHAPTER 8

DEMONSTRATION 1

Finding the Mass of One Item

Approximate time: 10 minutes

1. Obtain a handful of identical items, such as paper clips, buttons, or pennies. Count how many items you have.

2. Find the mass of a sealable plastic bag.

3. Place the items in the bag, and seal it. Then find the mass of the bag and the items, and calculate the mass of the items by difference.

4. From the mass and the number of items, calculate the mass of one item. Use a sensitive balance to confirm your answer.

Safety
No specific safety cautions are needed.

Disposal
Save all materials for reuse.

Total recall

1. What is a weighted average? How is a weighted average calculated? How is a percentage converted to its decimal equivalent?

2. Why does the atomic mass of an element as given on the periodic table often differ from the mass of any of the element's known isotopes?

3. How is a mole defined?

4. Why is it incorrect to say that a mole is a quantity?

Critical thinking

5. **Interpreting Graphics** Use Figure 8-2 to explain how amount in moles can be converted to a number of atoms and how a number of atoms can be converted to an amount in moles.

6. **Interpreting Graphics** Use Figure 8-4 to explain how amount in moles can be converted to mass in grams and how mass in grams can be converted to amount in moles.

7. What is the relationship between atomic mass and atomic mass units?

8. **Interpreting Graphics** Use the models shown in Figure 8-2 and Figure 8-4 to develop your own graphic model for finding the mass of an atom. Your model should also include how to find the molar mass of an element, given the mass of a single atom.

Practice problems

9. Find the mass in grams of 8.6 mol of bromine atoms.

10. Find the mass in grams of 7.55 mol of silicon atoms.

11. How many moles are in 38 g of carbon atoms?

12. How many moles are in 2.0 g of hydrogen atoms?

13. Determine the number of moles represented by each of the following masses:
    a. 0.3545 g chlorine
    b. 184.2 g sodium
    c. 0.320 g copper
    d. 282.4 g iron

14. Element X has two naturally occurring isotopes. The isotope with a mass number of 10 has a relative abundance of 20.%. The isotope with a mass number of 11 has a relative abundance of 80.%. Use these figures to estimate the average atomic mass for element X. Identify element X and state its atomic number.

15. Calculate the mass in grams of each of the following:
    a. 1.38 mol N
    b. 6.022×10^{23} atoms of Ag
    c. 2.57×10^8 mol S
    d. 1.20×10^{15} atoms O

16. Calculate the number of atoms present in each of the following:
    a. 2 mol Fe
    b. 40.1 g Ca
    c. 4.5 mol boron-11
    d. 184.2 g Na

17. **Interpreting Graphics** Determine the following:
    a. the average mass of a hydrogen atom in grams
    b. the average mass of a europium atom in grams
    c. the average mass of a platinum atom in grams

ANSWERS

SECTION REVIEW

Total recall

1. A weighted average is the sum of the contribution of each item. It is found by multiplying the value of each item by its relative abundance and then finding the sum of all these products. A percentage is converted to its decimal equivalent when it is divided by 100.

2. The mass of an element as reported on the periodic table is a weighted average of the masses of the element's known isotopes.

3. A mole is the number of atoms in exactly 12 g of carbon-12.

4. A *mole* is a unit for the *quantity*— the amount of a substance.

Critical thinking

5. To convert moles to number of atoms, multiply moles by 6.022×10^{23} atoms/1 mol. When the number of atoms is divided by 6.022×10^{23} atoms/1 mol, the number of moles is found.

6. When moles are multiplied by the molar mass, the mass in grams of the substance is found. When the mass of a substance is divided by molar mass, the amount in moles is found.

7. The atomic mass unit (amu) is the unit used for atomic mass.

8. Student models should show that when the molar mass of an element is divided by Avogadro's constant, the mass of one atom of that element is found. When the mass of one atom of an element is multiplied by Avogadro's constant, the molar mass is found.

Practice problems

9. $8.6 \text{ mol Br} \times \dfrac{79.90 \text{ g Br}}{\text{mol Br}} = 690 \text{ g Br}$

10. $7.55 \text{ mol Si} \times \dfrac{28.09 \text{ g Si}}{\text{mol Si}} = 212 \text{ g Si}$

11. $38 \text{ g C} \times \dfrac{1 \text{ mol C}}{12.01 \text{ g C}} = 3.2 \text{ mol C}$

12. $2.0 \text{ g H} \times \dfrac{1 \text{ mol H}}{1.01 \text{ g H}} = 2.0 \text{ mol H}$

13. a. $0.3545 \text{ g Cl} \times \dfrac{1 \text{ mol Cl}}{35.45 \text{ g Cl}} = 0.0100 \text{ mol Cl}$

    b. $184.2 \text{ g Na} \times \dfrac{1 \text{ mol Na}}{22.99 \text{ g Na}} = 8.012 \text{ mol Na}$

    c. $0.320 \text{ g Cu} \times \dfrac{1 \text{ mol Cu}}{63.55 \text{ g Cu}} = 0.005 \text{ mol Cu}$

    d. $282.4 \text{ g Fe} \times \dfrac{1 \text{ mol Fe}}{55.85 \text{ g Fe}} = 5.056 \text{ mol Fe}$

14. $(0.20)(10 \text{ amu}) + (0.80)(11 \text{ amu}) = 10.8 \text{ amu}$, 5, boron

15. a. $1.38 \text{ mol N} \times \dfrac{14.01 \text{ g N}}{\text{mol N}} = 19.3 \text{ g N}$

    b. $6.022 \times 10^{23} \text{ Ag atoms} = 1 \text{ mol Ag} = 107.9 \text{ g Ag}$

    c. $2.57 \times 10^8 \text{ mol S} \times \dfrac{32.07 \text{ g S}}{\text{mol S}} = 8.24 \times 10^9 \text{ g S}$

    d. $1.20 \times 10^{15} \text{ O atoms} \times \dfrac{1 \text{ mol O}}{6.022 \times 10^{23} \text{ O atoms}} \times$
    $\dfrac{16.00 \text{ g O}}{\text{mol O}} = 3.19 \times 10^{-8} \text{ g O}$

Answers continue on page 305A.

▶ **List** the information you can derive about a compound from its chemical formula.

▶ **Determine** the molar mass and percentage composition of a compound from its formula.

▶ **Derive** a compound's empirical formula from its percentage composition.

▶ **Calculate** the molecular formula of a compound from its empirical formula and its formula mass.

Chemical formulas and moles

After studying Section 8-1, you may think that moles are useful for counting only the number of atoms in a sample of an element, but that is not so! Moles can be used to count molecules and ions as well. In fact, moles are especially useful when dealing with compounds. They allow us to look at the composition of a compound in a quantitative way.

Formulas reveal composition

A chemical formula tells you what elements are present in a compound. The formula for KBr, shown in **Figure 8-6,** reveals that the compound contains the elements potassium and bromine.

A formula also tells you the ratio of atoms or ions in the compound. The formula KBr indicates that potassium bromide is made of ions in the ratio of one potassium cation, K^+, for each bromide anion, Br^-. Just as the formula H_2O indicates that water contains hydrogen and oxygen atoms in a 2:1 ratio, so the formula for strontium chloride, $SrCl_2$, indicates that there is one Sr^{2+} cation for every two Cl^- anions, a 1:2 ratio.

▶ **FIGURE 8-6**

Though any sample of a compound contains many atoms and ions, the chemical formula gives the simplest ratio of those atoms or ions.

FIGURE 8-7 ◀

When you read a chemical formula, think about how the atoms are organized. Notice that polyatomic ions are distinct groups of atoms bound together. Each is treated as a unit.

DISCUSSION STRATEGY

Have students discuss when it is important to consider polyatomic ions as units and when it is important to recognize that these ions are made up of individual atoms. Student responses should indicate that it is important to treat polyatomic ions as units when writing formulas or naming ionic compounds that contain them. When determining molar mass or percentage composition from chemical formulas, you must consider all atoms separately.

The meaning of a formula does not change when polyatomic ions are involved. Potassium nitrate has the formula KNO_3. Just as the formula for the binary salt, KBr, indicates a 1:1 ratio of K^+ cations to Br^- anions, the formula KNO_3 indicates a ratio of one K^+ cation to one NO_3^- anion. This formula also illustrates why it is important to be able to recognize polyatomic ions at a glance. If you realize immediately that NO_3 in a formula is a nitrate ion, NO_3^-, you won't have to wonder whether KNO_3 consists of a KN^+ and an O_3^- ion. Similarly, if you recognize that NH_4 in a formula represents the ammonium ion NH_4^+ and that NO_3 represents the nitrate ion, you can see why the formula of ammonium nitrate is written NH_4NO_3 instead of, say, $H_4N_2O_3$. The formula NH_4NO_3 shows immediately that ammonium nitrate consists of ammonium and nitrate ions in a 1:1 ratio. When a compound contains polyatomic ions, you should think of it as cations and anions, like those compounds shown in **Figure 8-7.**

Each polyatomic ion consists of a specific number of atoms with an overall electric charge. Except for coulombic attraction, ions are independent of one another. For these reasons, the formula of ammonium sulfate is written as $(NH_4)_2SO_4$. This formula clearly indicates that ammonium sulfate consists of two ammonium ions for each sulfate ion. If the formula were written as $N_2H_8SO_4$, the number of atoms would be correct but the formula would no longer clearly show the identity of the ions in the substance.

internet**connect**

SCI**LINKS**

NSTA

TOPIC: Chemical formulas
GO TO: www.scilinks.org
KEYWORD: HW082

Formulas are used to calculate molar masses

Because a formula tells you what atoms (or ions) are present in a compound, you are able to determine the mass of a mole of the compound. The simplest formula for most elements is denoted by the element's symbol, for example, the symbol for silver, is Ag. A mole of the elements Ag, Na, Mg, or Ne contains 6.022×10^{23} atoms of that element. The molar mass of most elements equals the atomic mass of the element expressed in grams. Molecular forms of elements, such as H_2, O_3, and P_4 have molar masses equal to the sum of the masses of the number of atoms in the formula.

TEACHING TIP

Determining Numbers of Atoms in a Formula It is a good idea to practice counting atoms in a molecule before attempting to determine molar mass. Write the following formulas on the board, and ask students how many atoms of each element are present: $CaSO_3$, $K_2Cr_2O_7$, $Al(NO_3)_3$, $Al_2(SO_3)_3$, and $CuSO_4 \cdot 5H_2O$.

formula unit

the unit of an ionic compound that represents the simplest ratio of cations to anions

We also use the simplest formula to represent a mole of a compound. Chemists often use the term *formula unit* when referring to ionic compounds because ionic compounds do not have a molecular composition. A **formula unit** of an ionic compound is the unit that represents the simplest ratio of cations to anions. A formula unit of NaCl consists of one Na^+ and one Cl^- ion. One mole of an ionic compound consists of 6.022×10^{23} of these formula units. One mole of a molecular compound, like H_2O, consists of 6.022×10^{23} molecules. The molar mass of an ionic compound or molecular compound is the sum of the masses of all the atoms in the formula expressed in grams. For example, the molar mass of KNO_3 is found by adding the atomic masses of one potassium atom, one nitrogen atom, and three oxygen atoms and then expressing the numerical sum in grams. The molar mass of H_2O is found by adding the atomic masses of two hydrogen atoms and one oxygen atom and then expressing the numerical sum in grams. **Table 8-2** compares the formula units and molar masses of three ionic compounds. Sample Problem 8G shows you how to calculate the molar mass.

TABLE 8-2 **Calculating Molar Mass for Ionic Compounds**

Formula	Formula unit	Calculation of molar mass
$ZnCl_2$	Zn^{2+} Cl^- Cl^-	1 Zn = 1 × 65.39 g/mol 2 Cl = 2 × 35.45 g/mol $ZnCl_2$ = 136.29 g/mol
$ZnSO_4$	Zn^{2+} SO_4^{2-}	1 Zn = 1 × 65.39 g/mol 1 S = 1 × 32.07 g/mol 4 O = 4 × 16.00 g/mol $ZnSO_4$ = 161.46 g/mol
$(NH_4)_2SO_4$	NH_4^+ NH_4^+ SO_4^{2-}	2 N = 2 × 14.01 g/mol 8 H = 8 × 1.01 g/mol 1 S = 1 × 32.07 g/mol 4 O = 4 × 16.00 g/mol $(NH_4)_2SO_4$ = 132.17 g/mol

SAMPLE PROBLEM 8G — Calculating molar mass

Calculate the molar mass of barium nitrate, $Ba(NO_3)_2$.

1 List what you know
- formula of barium nitrate: $Ba(NO_3)_2$
- formula mass of $Ba(NO_3)_2 = ?$ g

2 Set up the problem
- Determine the amount in moles for each element in 1 mol of barium nitrate. Each mole of $Ba(NO_3)_2$ contains:

$$1 \text{ mol Ba}$$
$$2 \text{ mol N}$$
$$6 \text{ mol O}$$

- Use the periodic table to find the molar mass of each element in the formula.

molar mass of Ba = 137.33 g/mol (rounded masses)
molar mass of N = 14.01 g/mol
molar mass of O = 16.00 g/mol

3 Calculate and verify
- Multiply each mass by the correct number of moles for each atom. Add the masses to determine the molar mass of $Ba(NO_3)_2$.

$$
\begin{array}{l}
\text{mass of 1 mol Ba} = 137.33 \text{ g/mol} \\
\text{mass of 2 mol N} = 28.02 \text{ g/mol} \\
\underline{\text{mass of 6 mol O} = 96.00 \text{ g/mol}} \\
\text{molar mass of } Ba(NO_3)_2 = 261.35 \text{ g/mol}
\end{array}
$$

- The answer has the correct units. The sum of the molar masses can be approximated as 140 + 30 + 100 = 270, which is very near the calculated value.

SAMPLE PROBLEM 8H — Calculating molar mass of compounds

Glycerol, a common ingredient in cosmetics, has the structural formula shown below. Calculate the molar mass of glycerol.

$$
\begin{array}{ccccc}
\text{H} & & \text{H} & & \text{H} \\
| & & | & & | \\
\text{H--C} & \text{---} & \text{C} & \text{---} & \text{C--H} \\
| & & | & & | \\
\text{OH} & & \text{OH} & & \text{OH}
\end{array}
$$

1 List what you know
- Analyze the structural formula to determine the numbers of each atom.

3 atoms of carbon
3 atoms of oxygen
8 atoms of hydrogen

Thus, the formula of glycerol can be written as $C_3H_8O_3$.
- molar mass of $C_3H_8O_3 = ?$ g/mol

ADDITIONAL EXAMPLES

SAMPLE PROBLEM 8G & 8H

Calculate the molar mass of each of the following compounds:

1. KNO_3
   Ans. 101.11 g/mol

2. Na_2SO_4
   Ans. 142.05 g/mol

3. $Ca(OH)_2$
   Ans. 74.10 g/mol

4. $(NH_4)_2SO_3$
   Ans. 116.17 g/mol

5. $Ca_3(PO_4)_2$
   Ans. 310.18 g/mol

6. $Al_2(CrO_4)_3$
   Ans. 401.96 g/mol

SECTION 8-2

ANSWERS

PRACTICE PROBLEM 8G & 8H

1. a. 122.55 g/mol
   b. 234.06 g/mol
   c. 158.04 g/mol
   d. 72.17 g/mol
   e. 60.06 g/mol
   f. 74.14 g/mol
   g. 206.31 g/mol
   h. 58.32 g/mol
   i. 131.07 g/mol
   j. 92.15 g/mol
   k. 300.06 g/mol

2. a. $NaHCO_3$, 84.01 g/mol
   b. $K_2Cr_2O_7$, 294.20 g/mol
   c. $Mg(ClO_4)_2$, 223.20 g/mol
   d. $Al_2(SO_4)_3$, 342.17 g/mol
   e. $Fe(OH)_3$, 106.88 g/mol
   f. $SnCl_2$, 189.61 g/mol
   g. $HClO_4$, 100.46 g/mol
   h. $NiCl_2 \cdot 6H_2O$, 237.71 g/mol

RESOURCE LINK

ChemFile Teaching Resources CD-ROM
Supplemental Reading Projects
For cross-curricular connections to language arts, assign the guided reading worksheets for Roald Hoffmann's essay "In Praise of Synthesis" in *The Same and Not the Same.*

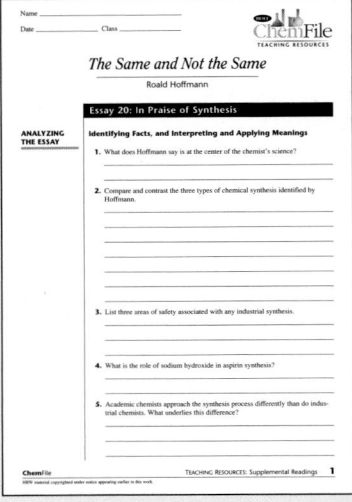

---

2 **Set up the problem**

Determine the molar masses for all atoms involved.
▸ molar mass of carbon = 12.01 g/mol
▸ molar mass of oxygen = 16.00 g/mol
▸ molar mass of hydrogen = 1.01 g/mol

3 **Calculate and verify**

▸ Multiply each mass by the correct number of moles for each atom. Add the masses to determine the molar mass of $C_3H_8O_3$.

$$
\begin{aligned}
\text{mass of 3 mol C} &= 36.03 \text{ g/mol} \\
\text{mass of 8 mol H} &= 8.08 \text{ g/mol} \\
\text{mass of 3 mol O} &= 48.00 \text{ g/mol} \\
\hline
\text{molar mass of } C_3H_8O_3 &= 92.11 \text{ g/mol}
\end{aligned}
$$

▸ The answer has the correct units. The sum of the molar masses can be approximated as 40 + 10 + 50 = 100, which is very near the calculated value.

PRACTICE PROBLEMS

1. Calculate the molar mass of each of the following compounds:
   a. $KClO_3$
   b. $Ca(H_2PO_4)_2$
   c. $KMnO_4$
   d. $CH_3CH_2CH_2CH_2CH_3$
   e. Acetic acid
   f. (structural formula, 4-carbon chain)
   g. Ibuprofen
   h. $Mg(OH)_2$
   i. $(NH_4)_2PO_4$
   j. Toluene
   k. Cisplatin

2. Write the formula and then calculate the molar mass of each of the following compounds:
   a. sodium hydrogen carbonate
   b. potassium dichromate
   c. magnesium perchlorate
   d. aluminum sulfate
   e. iron(III) hydroxide
   f. tin(II) chloride
   g. perchloric acid
   h. nickel(II) chloride hexahydrate

Fe₂O₃

FeO

FIGURE 8-8 ▲

Iron forms two different compounds with oxygen. The ratios of atoms in the formulas differ, so the two compounds have different percentage compositions.

Using analytical data

Some chemists carry out chemical reactions called *syntheses* (singular: *synthesis*) to produce new compounds for many different uses. Chemists must be able to determine the identities of the substances they have synthesized. One procedure that chemists use to identify an unknown substance is *elemental analysis.* This technique tells chemists what elements are present in the compound and their percent by mass. The information gained from this analysis is the **percentage composition** of the substance. For example, a compound that is 88.7% oxygen and 11.3% hydrogen has a percentage composition that matches that of water, H_2O. A compound that is 60.7% chlorine and 39.3% sodium has a percentage composition that matches that of sodium chloride, $NaCl$. These data along with further tests are used to identify an unknown compound. **Figure 8-8** shows a percentage composition comparison for two iron oxide compounds.

Empirical formulas can be determined from elemental analysis data

Percentage composition data allow you to calculate the *simplest* ratio among the elements of a compound. A formula that represents this simplest ratio is called an **empirical formula.** For example, ammonium nitrite has the true formula NH_4NO_2 and consists of ammonium, NH_4^+, and nitrite, NO_2^-, ions in a 1:1 ratio. Using data from an elemental analysis, a chemist would calculate the empirical formula to be NH_2O because this formula represents the *simplest* ratio of elements.

For many compounds, the empirical formula and the true formula are the same. To calculate an empirical formula from the percentage composition, convert the mass percent of each element to grams and then to moles. Then, as was done in Sample Problem 8I, compare the amounts to find the simplest whole-number ratio among the elements in the compound. The method is to divide each amount by the smallest of all the amounts. This process will give a coefficient of 1 for the atoms present in the smallest amount. After this step, additional multiplication may be necessary to convert all the coefficients to the smallest whole numbers. These numbers are the subscripts in the empirical formula.

percentage composition

the percentage by mass of each element in a compound

empirical formula

a formula that represents the simplest ratio among the elements of a compound

SECTION 8-2

ADDITIONAL APPLICATION

The percentage composition of any pure substance is always constant, regardless of the source or sample size. Therefore, percentage composition is an identifying characteristic of any substance. For that reason, percentage composition is used by investigators in many different fields—from analytical chemistry to criminal forensics—to determine the identity of unknown materials.

TEACHING TIP

Vocabulary Strategy Have students look up the meaning of the word *empirical* in the dictionary. Have them use the definition to explain where information is obtained about an empirical formula. Their explanations should reflect that empirical formulas are determined from experimental data.

RESOURCE LINK

ChemFile Teaching Resources CD-ROM
Skills Review
Assign Math Skills Worksheet 7: *Percentages* to review or reteach this skill.

Natural compounds that have medicinal applications often exist in minute amounts or are extremely expensive to extract. For that reason, chemists strive to reproduce these substances in a laboratory. Before chemists can synthesize a compound, they must first determine the chemical formula for it. One way to determine the formula of a compound is to find its percentage composition. Once the formula is determined, chemists can then investigate ways of producing it. Synthetic compounds are often as effective as, less expensive than, and more abundant than their natural counterparts. Insulin is an example of a compound that was once only available from natural sources and is now commonly synthesized in a laboratory.

SAMPLE PROBLEM 8I   Determining an empirical formula from composition data

One of the substances in a new alkaline battery is composed of 63.0% manganese and 37.0% oxygen by mass. Determine the empirical formula of the compound in the battery.

1 List what you know
- percentage Mn = 63.0%
- percentage O = 37.0%
- empirical formula = $Mn_?O_?$

2 Set up the problem
- Convert the given percentages to grams by assuming that you have exactly 100 g of the unknown substance.

$$63.0\% \text{ Mn} \times 100 \text{ g} = 63.0 \text{ g Mn}$$
$$37.0\% \text{ O} \times 100 \text{ g} = 37.0 \text{ g O}$$

- To convert the mass of each element into amount in moles, determine the molar masses of Mn and O from the periodic table.

$$\text{molar mass Mn} = 54.94 \text{ g/mol}$$
$$\text{molar mass O} = 16.00 \text{ g/mol}$$

3 Calculate
- Calculate the amounts of Mn and O in moles. Round your answers to the correct number of significant figures.

$$63.0 \text{ g Mn} \times \frac{1 \text{ mol Mn}}{54.94 \text{ g Mn}} = 1.146705497 \text{ mol Mn (calculator answer)}$$

$$= 1.15 \text{ mol Mn}$$

$$37.0 \text{ g O} \times \frac{1 \text{ mol O}}{16.00 \text{ g O}} = 2.3125 \text{ in mol O (calculator answer)}$$

$$= 2.31 \text{ mol O}$$

- To determine the simplest ratio of moles in the compound, divide the amount of each element by the smallest amount. The smallest amount in this case is 1.15.

$$\frac{1.15 \text{ mol Mn}}{1.15} = 1.00 \text{ mol Mn}$$

$$\frac{2.31 \text{ mol O}}{1.15} = 2.01 \text{ mol O}$$

- Slight deviations from exact whole numbers should be expected because you are working with analytical data.

$$\text{mol ratio} = \frac{1.00 \text{ mol Mn}}{2.01 \text{ mol O}} = \frac{1 \text{ mol Mn}}{2 \text{ mol O}}$$

- Write the empirical formula of the compound by using the smallest whole number ratio of manganese to oxygen.

$$MnO_2$$

DEMONSTRATION 2

Determine an Empirical Formula
Approximate time: 20 minutes

Other class work can be done while waiting for the crucible to cool.

Magnesium burns in air to form MgO and Mg_3N_2. Water and Mg_3N_2, when heated, produce MgO and NH_3. When only MgO remains in the crucible (NH_3 gas escapes), students can use the data from the demonstration to calculate the empirical formula.

1. Find the mass of a crucible. Then find the mass of the crucible and 65 cm of magnesium ribbon. Calculate the mass of the magnesium.

2. Roll the magnesium loosely, and place it in the crucible. Place the crucible on a clay triangle that is sitting on an iron ring that is attached to a ring stand.

SAMPLE PROBLEM 8J Calculating empirical formulas from percentage composition

Chemical analysis of a clear liquid shows that it is 60.0% C, 13.4% H, and 26.6% O. Calculate the empirical formula of this substance.

1 List what you know

▶ percentage C = 60.0%
▶ percentage H = 13.4%
▶ percentage O = 26.6%
▶ empirical formula = $C_2H_?O_?$

2 Set up the problem

▶ Assume that you have a 100.0 g sample of the liquid, and convert the percentages to grams.

$$60.0\% \text{ C} \times 100.0 \text{ g} = 60.0 \text{ g C}$$
$$13.4\% \text{ H} \times 100.0 \text{ g} = 13.4 \text{ g H}$$
$$26.6\% \text{ O} \times 100.0 \text{ g} = 26.6 \text{ g O}$$

▶ To convert the mass of each element into amount in moles, determine the molar masses of C, H, and O from the periodic table.

molar mass of C: 12.01 g/mol
molar mass of H: 1.01 g/mol
molar mass of O: 16.00 g/mol

3 Calculate and verify

▶ Calculate the amounts of C, H, and O in moles. Round your answers to the correct number of significant figures.

$$60.0 \text{ g C} \times \frac{1 \text{ mol C}}{12.00 \text{ g C}} = 5.00 \text{ mol C}$$

$$13.4 \text{ g H} \times \frac{1 \text{ mol H}}{1.01 \text{ g H}} = 13.3 \text{ mol H}$$

$$26.6 \text{ g O} \times \frac{1 \text{ mol O}}{16.00 \text{ g O}} = 1.66 \text{ mol O}$$

▶ At this point you could write the formula as $C_5H_{13.3}O_{1.66}$, but you know that subscripts in chemical formulas are always whole numbers.

▶ The empirical formula is the simplest whole-number ratio of the atoms. To find the simplest ratio, divide the amount of each element by the amount of the least-abundant element, in this case 1.66.

$$\frac{1.66 \text{ mol O}}{1.66} = 1.00 \text{ mol O}$$

$$\frac{5.00 \text{ mol C}}{1.66} = 3.012048193 \text{ mol C} = 3.01 \text{ mol C}$$

$$\frac{13.3 \text{ mol H}}{1.66} = 8.012048193 \text{ mol H} = 8.01 \text{ mol H}$$

▶ The calculation shows that the ratio of atoms in the compound is 3C : 8H : 1O. Therefore, the empirical formula for the clear liquid is C_3H_8O. To verify, use the empirical formula and relative molar masses to calculate the percent composition of this compound. The results should be very near the values given in the problem.

THE MOLE 291

SECTION 8-2

ADDITIONAL EXAMPLES

SAMPLE PROBLEM 8I AND 8J

For each of the following examples, find the empirical formula for a compound with the given composition.

1. 63.52% Fe, 36.48% S

   Ans. FeS

2. 26.56% K, 35.41% Cr, 38.03% O

   Ans. $K_2Cr_2O_7$

3. 32.38% Na, 22.65% S, 44.99% O

   Ans. Na_2SO_4

4. 74.51% Pb, 25.49% Cl

   Ans. $PbCl_2$

5. 52.546% Ba, 10.72% N, 36.73% O

   Ans. BaN_2O_6

6. 29.15% N, 8.407% H, 12.50% C, 49.94% O

   Ans. $N_2H_8CO_3$

---

3. Carefully light the magnesium, and allow it to burn completely. **CAUTION: *Do not look directly at the burning magnesium.***

4. After the crucible has cooled, powder the residue. Add several drops of distilled water to the residue to moisten it.

5. Heat the crucible until its contents are dry.

6. After the crucible has cooled, find the mass of the crucible and the magnesium oxide. Calculate the mass of the product by the difference.

7. Use the masses of the magnesium and the magnesium oxide to find the mass of the oxygen used in the reaction.

8. Have students use the calculated masses and the molar masses to find the empirical formula for magnesium oxide.

Safety

Wear safety goggles and a lab apron. Use caution when burning the magnesium. Do

CONTINUED ON PAGE 292

RESOURCE LINK

IN-TEXT LAB

Skills Development

Have students do Exploration 5A on page 730 to develop their skills using percentage composition.

ANSWERS

PRACTICE PROBLEM 8I & 8J

1. $70.0 \text{ g Mn} \times \dfrac{1 \text{ mol Mn}}{54.94 \text{ g Mn}} =$

   1.27 mol Mn

   $30.0 \text{ g O} \times \dfrac{1 \text{ mol O}}{16.00 \text{ g O}} = 1.875 \text{ mol O}$

   $\dfrac{1.27 \text{ mol Mn}}{1.27} = 1 \times 2 = 2$

   $\dfrac{1.875 \text{ mol O}}{1.27} = 1.56 \times 2 \approx 3$

   Mn_2O_3

2. $38.77 \text{ g Cl} \times \dfrac{1 \text{ mol Cl}}{35.45 \text{ g Cl}} = 1.094 \text{ mol Cl}$

   $61.23 \text{ g O} \times \dfrac{1 \text{ mol O}}{16.00 \text{ g O}} = 3.827 \text{ mol O}$

   $\dfrac{1.094 \text{ mol Cl}}{1.094} = 1 \times 2 = 2$

   $\dfrac{3.827 \text{ mol O}}{1.094} = 3.49 \times 2 = 7$

   Cl_2O_7

RESOURCE LINK

ChemFile Mini-Guide to Problem Solving
Assign Chapter 7: *Empirical Formulas* for additional practice.

CHAPTER 7
Empirical Formulas

Suppose you analyze an unknown compound that is a white powder and find that it is composed of 36.5% sodium, 38.1% oxygen, and 25.4% sulfur. You can use those percentages to determine the mole ratios among sodium, sulfur, and oxygen and write a formula for the compound.

To begin, the mass percentages of each element can be interpreted as "grams of element per 100 grams of compound." To make things simpler, you can assume you have a 100 g sample of the unknown compound. The unknown compound contains 36.5% sodium by mass. Therefore 100.0 g of the compound would contain 36.5 g of sodium. You already know how to convert mass of a substance into number of moles, so you can calculate the number of moles of sodium in 36.5 g. After you find the number of moles of each element, you can look for a simple ratio among the elements and use this ratio of elements to write a formula for the compound.

The chemical formula obtained from the mass percentages is in the simplest form for that compound. The mole ratios for each element, which you determined from the analytical data given, are reduced to the smallest whole numbers. This simplest formula is also called the empirical formula. The actual formula for the compound could be a multiple of the empirical formula. For instance, suppose you analyze a compound and find that it is composed of 40.0% carbon, 6.7% hydrogen, and 53.3% oxygen. If you determine the formula for this compound based only on the analytical data, you will determine the formula to be CH₂O. There are, however, other possibilities for the formula. It could be C₂H₄O₂ and still have the same percentage composition. In fact, it could be any multiple of CH₂O.

It is possible to convert from the empirical formula to the actual chemical formula for the compound as long as the molar mass of the compound is known. Look again at the CH₂O example. If the true compound were CH₂O, it would have a molar mass of 30.03 g/mol. If you do more tests on the unknown compound and find that its molar mass is 60.06, you know that CH₂O is not its true identity. The molar mass 60.06 is twice the molar mass of CH₂O. Therefore, you know that the true chemical formula must be twice the empirical formula, (CH₂O) × 2, or C₂H₄O₂. Any correct molecular formula can be determined from an empirical formula and a molar mass in this same way.

Empirical Formulas **73**

---

1. A dead alkaline battery is found to contain a compound of manganese and oxygen. Its percentage composition is 70.0% Mn and 30.0% O. What is the empirical formula of this substance?

2. What is the empirical formula for a compound that contains 38.77% Cl and 61.23% O?

Molecular formulas are multiples of empirical formulas

For some compounds, the empirical formula is the same as the molecular formula. Such is the case with water, H_2O, and nitric acid, HNO_3. But for most compounds, the **molecular formula** is a whole-number multiple of the empirical formula.

molecular formula
type and actual number of atoms in a compound

Consider the three molecular compounds in **Table 8-3.** The first compound, formaldehyde, is toxic and can cause cancer. The second, acetic acid, gives vinegar its sour taste. The third, glucose, is a type of sugar found in sports drinks and other foods.

Molecular formulas are calculated using the empirical formulas and molar mass data. The empirical formula is a multiple of the molecular formula as shown by the following relationship.

$$n(\text{empirical formula}) = \text{molecular formula}$$

Note that n is always a whole number, and it is occasionally a very large number. With formaldehyde, $n = 1$; for acetic acid, $n = 2$; and for glucose, $n = 6$. Likewise, the true molar mass of the compound must be a whole-number multiple of the molar mass of the empirical formula.

TABLE 8-3   Comparing Empirical and Molecular Formulas

Compound	Empirical formula	Molecular formula	Molar mass (g)	Space-filling model
Formaldehyde	CH_2O	CH_2O (same as empirical formula)	30.03	
Acetic acid	CH_2O	$C_2H_4O_2$ (2 × empirical formula)	60.06	
Glucose	CH_2O	$C_6H_{12}O_6$ (6 × empirical formula)	180.18	

DEMONSTRATION 2   *CONTINUED*

not look directly at the burning magnesium. Students must be 10 ft or more from the demonstration.

Disposal

Place the product in a sealable plastic bag. Contact your local regulatory agency to find out whether or not it is allowable in your area to throw out the product.

FIGURE 8-9 ◀

The formula for glucose, which is found in many sports drinks, can be shown in several different ways.

Ball and stick model

Space fill model

CH₂OH

$$H \quad \overset{\text{CH}_2\text{OH}}{C} \quad O \quad OH$$

Structural formula

$C_6H_{12}O_6$

Molecular formula

CH_2O

Empirical formula

Different representations for the formula of glucose are shown in **Figure 8-9.** It has the same empirical formula, CH_2O, but a different molecular formula than the other compounds listed in Table 8-3. Because their structures and molecular formulas are entirely different, these compounds have quite different chemical and physical properties.

If you know both the empirical formula and the molar mass of a compound, you can determine its molecular formula. Fortunately, there are experimental methods for determining molar mass, even though the formula of the compound is not known.

SAMPLE PROBLEM 8K | Determining a molecular formula from an empirical formula

The empirical formula of a compound is found to be P_2O_5. The molar mass of the compound is 284 g/mol. Determine the molecular formula of the compound.

1 **List what you know**
- empirical formula = P_2O_5
- molar mass = 284 g/mol
- molecular formula = ?

2 **Set up the problem**
- Look up the molar masses of the elements on the periodic table. You will need these values to determine the molar mass of the empirical formula.

molar mass of P = 30.97 g P

molar mass of O = 16.00 g O

THE MOLE 293

GRAPHIC ORGANIZER

Molecular mass ÷ Mass of empirical formula × Subscripts in the empirical formula = Molecular formula

PRACTICE PROBLEM 8K

1. $\dfrac{78 \text{ g/mol}}{13.02 \text{ g/mol}} = 6,\ C_6H_6$

2. $\dfrac{214 \text{ g/mol}}{70.11 \text{ g/mol}} = 3.1,\ C_9H_{18}N_6$

ADDITIONAL EXAMPLES

SAMPLE PROBLEM 8K

Determine the molecular formula for each of the following compounds:

1. Molar mass: 232.41 g/mol; empirical formula: OCNCl

   Ans. $O_3C_3N_3Cl_3$

2. Molar mass: 32.06 g/mol; empirical formula: NH_2

   Ans. N_2H_4

3. Molar mass: 120.12 g/mol; empirical formula: CH_2O

   Ans. $C_4H_8O_4$

---

3 **Calculate**

▶ Calculate the molar mass of a compound with the empirical formula P_2O_5.

$$\begin{aligned}\text{mass of 2 mol P} &= 61.94 \text{ g/mol} \\ \text{mass of 5 mol O} &= 80.00 \text{ g/mol} \\ \hline \text{molar mass of } P_2O_5 &= 141.94 \text{ g/mol}\end{aligned}$$

▶ Solve for n, the factor relating the empirical and molecular formulas.

$$n = \frac{\text{molar mass of compound}}{\text{molar mass of empirical formula}}$$

▶ Substitute the molar masses into the equation above, and solve for n.

$$n = \frac{\text{molar mass of compound}}{\text{molar mass of empirical formula}} = \frac{284 \text{ g/mol}}{141.94 \text{ g/mol}} = 2.001 \cong 2$$

▶ Once the value of n has been calculated, multiply the empirical formula by that value to get the molecular formula.

$$n \text{ (empirical formula)} = 2(P_2O_5) = P_4O_{10}$$

▶ To verify your answer, calculate the molar mass for the molecular formula, and compare it with the given experimental formula mass.

PRACTICE PROBLEMS

1. Determine the molecular formula of a compound having an empirical formula of CH and an experimental molar mass of 78 g/mol.

2. The empirical formula of the anticancer drug altretamine is $C_3H_6N_2$. A chemist experimentally determines its molar mass to be 214. What is the molecular formula for this drug?

Percentage composition can be calculated from a chemical formula

If you want to know the percentage composition of a compound, calculate the composition from the chemical formula of the compound. Remember that the percentage of a component part is found using the following equation.

$$\% = \frac{\text{mass of component}}{\text{mass of whole}} \times 100$$

Look back at the iron examples in Figure 8-8. The percentages shown were calculated as follows.

$$\begin{aligned}\text{mass of 2 mol Fe atoms} &= 2 \text{ mol} \times 55.85 \text{ g/mol} = 111.7 \text{ g} \\ \text{mass of 3 mol O atoms} &= 3 \text{ mol} \times 16.00 \text{ g/mol} = 48.00 \text{ g} \\ \hline \text{total mass of } Fe_2O_3 &= 159.7 \text{ g}\end{aligned}$$

$$\% \text{ Fe} = \frac{111.7 \text{ g Fe}}{159.7 \text{ g } Fe_2O_3} \times 100 = 69.9\%$$

$$\% \text{ O} = \frac{48.00 \text{ g O}}{159.7 \text{ g } Fe_2O_3} \times 100 = 30.1\%$$

Sample Problem 8K shows this process for another compound.

Calculate the percentage composition of copper(I) sulfide, a copper ore called chalcocite.

1 **List what you know**

▶ the name of the compound and its formula: copper(I) sulfide, Cu_2S

▶ percentage composition = ?% Cu, ?% S

2 **Set up the problem**

▶ To determine the molar mass of Cu_2S, find the molar mass of each element on the periodic table.

$$\text{molar mass of Cu} = 63.55 \text{ g/mol}$$
$$\text{molar mass of S} = 32.07 \text{ g/mol}$$

▶ Determine the molar mass of the compound Cu_2S.

$$\text{mass of 2 mol Cu} = 2 \text{ mol Cu} \times 63.55 \text{ g/mol Cu} = 127.10 \text{ g}$$
$$\underline{\text{mass of 1 mol S} = \ \ \ 32.07 \text{ g}}$$
$$\text{molar mass of Cu}_2\text{S} = 159.17 \text{ g/mol}$$

▶ To find the fraction that each element contributes to the molar mass, divide the total mass of that element by the total mass of the compound. Change to percent by multiplying by 100.

$$\text{mass \% Cu} = \frac{\text{mass of 2 mol Cu}}{\text{molar mass of Cu}_2\text{S}} \times 100$$

$$\text{mass \% S} = \frac{\text{mass of 1 mol S}}{\text{molar mass of Cu}_2\text{S}} \times 100$$

3 **Calculate and verify**

▶ Substitute the masses into the equations shown above. Round the calculator result to the correct number of significant figures.

$$\text{mass \% Cu} = \frac{127.10 \text{ g Cu}}{159.17 \text{ g Cu}_2\text{S}} \times 100 = 79.8517308\% \text{ (calculator answer)}$$
$$= 79.852\%$$

$$\text{mass \% S} = \frac{32.07 \text{ g S}}{159.17 \text{ g Cu}_2\text{S}} \times 100 = 20.14826915\% \text{ (calculator answer)}$$
$$= 20.15\%$$

▶ Verify by adding the percentages. They should total $100.00\% \pm 0.02\%$.

$$79.852\% + 20.15\% = 100.00\%$$

▶ The answers are correct. Percentage composition values of more-complex compounds sometimes do not add to exactly 100.00% because of rounding errors.

PRACTICE PROBLEMS

1. Calculate the percentage composition of glucose, $C_6H_{12}O_6$.

2. Calculate the percentage composition of sucrose, $C_{12}H_{22}O_{11}$.

ANSWERS

PRACTICE PROBLEM 8L

1. $\dfrac{72.06 \text{ g C}}{180.18 \text{ g C}_6\text{H}_{12}\text{O}_6} \times 100 = 39.99\% \text{ C}$

$\dfrac{12.12 \text{ g H}}{180.18 \text{ g C}_6\text{H}_{12}\text{O}_6} \times 100 = 6.73\% \text{ H}$

$\dfrac{96.00 \text{ g O}}{180.18 \text{ g C}_6\text{H}_{12}\text{O}_6} \times 100 = 53.28\% \text{ O}$

2. $\dfrac{144.12 \text{ g C}}{342.34 \text{ g C}_{12}\text{H}_{22}\text{O}_{11}} \times 100 = 42.10\% \text{ C}$

$\dfrac{22.22 \text{ g H}}{342.34 \text{ g C}_{12}\text{H}_{22}\text{O}_{11}} \times 100 = 6.49\% \text{ H}$

$\dfrac{176.00 \text{ g O}}{342.34 \text{ g C}_{12}\text{H}_{22}\text{O}_{11}} \times 100 = 51.41\% \text{ O}$

ADDITIONAL EXAMPLES

SAMPLE PROBLEM 8L

Determine the percentage composition of the following compounds:

1. NaClO

   Ans. 30.88% Na, 47.62% Cl, 21.49% O

2. H_2SO_3

   Ans. 2.46% H, 39.07% S, 58.47% O

3. C_2H_5COOH

   Ans. 48.63% C, 8.18% H, 43.19% O

ADDITIONAL EXAMPLES

SAMPLE PROBLEM 8M

Determine the percentage of water in each of the following hydrates:

1. $ZnSO_4 \cdot 7H_2O$

   Ans. 43.86%

2. $CaSO_4 \cdot 2H_2O$

   Ans. 20.93%

3. $MgBr_2 \cdot 6H_2O$

   Ans. 37.00%

RESOURCE LINK

ChemFile Lab A
Skills Development

Have students do Experiment A7: *Water of Hydration.*

SAMPLE PROBLEM 8M — Determining the percentage composition of hydrates

Determine the percentage of water by mass in sodium carbonate decahydrate, $Na_2CO_3 \cdot 10H_2O$.

1 List what you know

▶ hydrate formula = $Na_2CO_3 \cdot 10H_2O$
▶ percentage water = ?% H_2O

2 Set up the problem

▶ Start by determining the molar mass of Na_2CO_3 alone. Obtain the molar masses of the elements from the periodic table.

$$
\begin{aligned}
2 \text{ mol Na} &= 2 \times 22.99 \text{ g/mol} = 45.98 \text{ g Na} \\
1 \text{ mol C} &= 12.01 \text{ g C} \\
3 \text{ mol O} &= 3 \times 16.00 \text{ g/mol} = 48.00 \text{ g O} \\
\hline
\text{molar mass of } Na_2CO_3 &= 105.99 \text{ g/mol}
\end{aligned}
$$

▶ Determine the mass of 10 mol H_2O.

$$
\begin{aligned}
20 \text{ mol H} &= 20 \times 1.01 \text{ g/mol} = 20.2 \text{ g H} \\
10 \text{ mol O} &= 10 \times 16.00 \text{ g/mol} = 160.0 \text{ g O} \\
\hline
\text{mass of 10 mol } H_2O &= 180.2 \text{ g}
\end{aligned}
$$

▶ Determine the molar mass of $Na_2CO_3 \cdot 10H_2O$.

$$
\begin{aligned}
1 \text{ mol } Na_2CO_3 &= 105.99 \text{ g} \\
10 \text{ mol } H_2O &= 180.2 \text{ g} \\
\hline
\text{molar mass } Na_2CO_3 \cdot 10H_2O &= 286.2 \text{ g/mol}
\end{aligned}
$$

▶ Write the equation for the percentage of water in $Na_2CO_3 \cdot 10H_2O$.

$$
\text{mass \% } H_2O = \frac{\text{mass of 10 mol } H_2O}{\text{molar mass of } Na_2CO_3 \cdot 10H_2O} \times 100
$$

3 Calculate and verify

▶ Substitute your values, and calculate the answer.

$$
\begin{aligned}
\text{mass \% } H_2O &= \frac{180.2 \text{ g } H_2O}{286.2 \text{ g } Na_2CO_3 \cdot 10H_2O} \times 100 \\
&= 62.9629629\% \text{ (calculator answer)} \\
&= 62.96\% \; H_2O
\end{aligned}
$$

▶ The calculation can be approximated as $200/300 \times 100 = 66.7$, which is near the answer obtained.

SECTION REVIEW

Total recall

1. What is a formula unit?

2. Explain how an empirical formula differs from a molecular formula.

3. In addition to the empirical formula, what other information is needed to determine the molecular formula of a compound?

Critical thinking

4. Write the empirical formula for each of the following:
   a. $C_6H_8O_6$
   b. S_2O_4
   c. $C_2H_5O_2N$
   d. $(CH_2)_2(OH)_2$
   e. $CH_3(CH_2)_2COOH$

5. Why does a laboratory analysis not yield exact whole numbers when you are determining the empirical formula of a compound from its percentage composition?

6. Identify the ions that make up one formula unit of each of the following:
   a. $MgCO_3$
   b. ammonium sulfite
   c. chromium(III) nitrate

Practice problems

7. Calculate the molar mass of each of the following:
   a. calcium acetate
   b. iron(II) phosphate
   c. $C_7H_5NO_3S$, saccharin, an artificial sweetener
   d. $C_9H_8O_4$, acetylsalicylic acid
   e. 3,3-dimethylbutane

8. Calculate the empirical formula for each of the following compounds, whose percentage compositions are given.
   a. 87.42% N, 12.58% H
   b. 13.2% B, 86.8% Cl
   c. 14.6% C, 39.0% O, 46.3% F

d. 21.56% Zn, 36.23% Mn, 42.21% O
e. 58.77% C, 13.81% H, and 27.42% N

9. Determine the molecular formula for each of the following:
   a. a compound with the empirical formula CHO and a molar mass of 116.1 g/mol
   b. a compound with the empirical formula BCl_2 and a molar mass of 163 g/mol
   c. a compound with the empirical formula $NPCl_2$ and a molar mass of 347.66 g/mol

10. Calculate the percentage composition of each of the following compounds:
    a. $SrBr_2$
    b. $CaSO_4$
    c. $Mg(CN)_2$
    d. $Pb(CH_3COO)_2$

11. Determine the formula and then calculate the molar mass of each of the following compounds:
    a. strontium sulfide
    b. ammonium fluoride
    c. zinc acetate
    d. mercury(II) bromate

12. Determine the percentage composition of each of the following compounds:
    a. lead(II) chlorate
    b. dinitrogen pentoxide
    c. $Fe_2(SO_4)_3$
    d. $CuSO_4 \cdot 5H_2O$
    e. COOH

13. Anhydrous $CaCl_2$ is used as a drying agent because it forms hydrates such as $CaCl_2 \cdot 6H_2O$. How many grams of $CaCl_2$ would it take to absorb 33.5 g of water if all of the $CaCl_2$ were converted to $CaCl_2 \cdot 6H_2O$?

ANSWERS

SECTION REVIEW

Total recall

1. A formula unit is the unit of an ionic compound that represents the simplest ratio of anions to cations.

2. An empirical formula represents the simplest ratio among the elements of a compound. A molecular formula is a whole-number multiple of the empirical formula that represents the actual composition of the molecule.

3. In addition to its empirical formula, a compound's molar mass is needed to determine its molecular formula.

Critical thinking

4. **a.** $C_3H_4O_3$
   b. SO_2
   c. $C_2H_5O_2N$
   d. CH_3O
   e. C_2H_4O

5. Inaccuracies are introduced when numbers are rounded off.

6. **a.** Mg^{2+}, CO_3^{2-}
   b. $2NH_4^+$, SO_3^{2-}
   c. Cr^{3+}, $3NO_3^-$

Practice problems

7. **a.** 158.18 g/mol
   b. 357.49 g/mol
   c. 183.2 g/mol
   d. 180.17 g/mol
   e. 86.20 g/mol

8. **a.** $\dfrac{87.42 \text{ g N}}{14.01 \text{ g/mol}} = 6.24 \text{ mol N}$

   $\dfrac{12.58 \text{ g H}}{1.01 \text{ g/mol}} = 12.46 \text{ mol H}$

   $\dfrac{6.24 \text{ mol N}}{6.24} = 1$

   $\dfrac{12.46 \text{ mol H}}{6.24} = 2$

   NH_2

b. $\dfrac{13.2 \text{ g B}}{10.81 \text{ g/mol}} = 1.22 \text{ mol B}$

$\dfrac{86.8 \text{ g Cl}}{35.45 \text{ g/mol}} = 2.45 \text{ mol Cl}$

$\dfrac{1.22 \text{ mol B}}{1.22} = 1 \qquad \dfrac{2.45 \text{ mol Cl}}{1.22} = 2$

BCl_2

c. $\dfrac{14.6 \text{ g C}}{12.01 \text{ g/mol}} = 1.22 \text{ mol C}$

$\dfrac{39.0 \text{ g O}}{16.00 \text{ g/mol}} = 2.44 \text{ mol O}$

$\dfrac{46.3 \text{ g F}}{19.00 \text{ g/mol}} = 2.44 \text{ mol F}$

$\dfrac{1.22 \text{ mol C}}{1.22} = 1 \qquad \dfrac{2.44 \text{ mol O}}{1.22} = 2$

$\dfrac{2.44 \text{ mol F}}{1.22} = 2$

CO_2F_2

Answers continue on page 305A.

Making up 25.7% of the Earth's crust by weight, silicon is exceeded in abundance only by oxygen. Silicon is present in the sun and stars, and it is a principal component of aerolites, a class of meteorites. Silicon is not found free in nature. It occurs primarily as an oxide and as silicates. The oxide of silicon appears in the form of sand, quartz, rock crystal, amethyst, flint, and opal, to name a few. Granite and asbestos are two examples of the numerous silicate minerals.

Silicon is very useful. It is used in the form of sand and clay to make concrete and bricks, and it is used in the form of silicates to make enamels and pottery. As sand, silica is a principal ingredient of glass, an inexpensive material with excellent mechanical, optical, thermal, and electrical properties. Silicon is also an important component of steel.

TEACHING TIP

Vocabulary Strategy Have students infer the meaning of the word *doped* from its use in the text. Discuss with them that doping refers to the process of adding impurities in the form of atoms of other elements to a semiconductor, such as silicon, to increase its electrical conductivity. The elements used in doping have an electron structure that combines with the electron structure of the silicon to provide electrons that move when voltage is applied.

ELEMENT SPOTLIGHT

14
Si
Silicon
28.0855
[Ne]$3s^2 3p^2$

Silicon's most familiar use is in the production of microprocessor chips.

WHERE IS IT?

Earth's Crust
27.72% by mass

internetconnect

SCLINKS
NSTA
TOPIC: Silicon
GO TO: www.scilinks.org
KEYWORD: HW083

Silicon and semiconductors

Computer microprocessor chips are made from thin slices, or wafers, of a pure silicon crystal. The wafers are doped with elements such as boron, phosphorus, and arsenic in order to confer semiconducting properties on the silicon. A photographic process places patterns for several chips onto one wafer. Gaseous compounds of metals are allowed to diffuse into the open spots in the pattern, and then the pattern is removed. This process is repeated several times to build up complex microdevices on the surface of the wafer. When the wafer is finished and tested, it is cut into individual chips.

Industrial Uses

◗ Silicon and its compounds are used to add strength to alloys of aluminum, magnesium, copper, and other metals.

◗ When doped with elements of Group 13 or Group 15, silicon becomes a semiconductor. This property is important in the manufacture of computer chips and photovoltaic cells.

◗ Silicon dioxide (quartz) crystals are used for piezoelectric crystals for radio-frequency control oscillators and digital watches and clocks.

◗ Organic compounds containing silicon, carbon, chlorine, and hydrogen are used to make silicone polymers, which are used in water repellents, electrical insulation, hydraulic fluids, lubricants, and caulks.

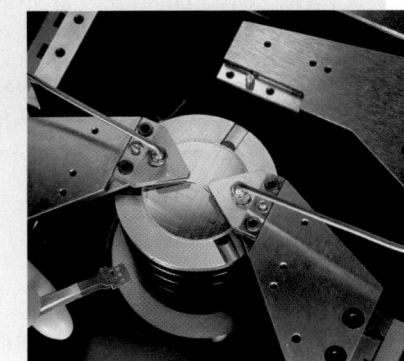

A large number of integrated circuit chips can be produced on the same silicon wafer. The wafer will be cut up into individual chips.

A BRIEF HISTORY

1811: Joseph Louis Gay-Lussac and Louis Thenard prepare impure amorphous silicon from silicon tetrafluoride.

1854: Henri S. C. Deville prepares crystalline silicon.

1800

1824: Jöns Jacob Berzelius prepares pure amorphous silicon and is credited with the discovery of the element.

1958: Jack Kilby and Robert Noyce produce the first integrated circuit on a silicon chip.

1900

1904: F. S. Kipping produces the first silicone compound.

1943: Commercial production of silicone rubber, oils, and greases begins in the United States.

Some events or objects designated in the *Guinness Book of World Records* are the largest and the smallest. You have learned in this chapter that chemists work with large numbers of very small things. They have learned that it is possible to "count" atoms by using the mass of a substance. The relationship between mass and the number of atoms is based on Avogadro's constant. Now that you have completed the chapter, you should be able to answer questions about numbers of atoms.

LOOKING BACK

How can chemists count atoms by using a balance?

Chemists have created the periodic table which lists the average atomic masses of all elements. One interpretation of the atomic mass is that it is the mass in grams of one mole of the element, consisting of 6.022×10^{23} atoms. Therefore, the number of atoms in a sample of a substance is given by

$$\text{number of atoms} = \frac{(\text{mass of sample, in g})(6.022 \times 10^{23}/\text{mol})}{(\text{atomic mass, in g/mol})}$$

How many astatine atoms exist in Earth's crust?

The molar mass of astatine is 210 g/mol, but only 0.16 g is present in Earth's crust, which is 0.16/210 mol = 0.000 76 mol. The relationship above, therefore, gives the number of astatine atoms on Earth as

$$\frac{(0.16 \text{ g})(6.022 \times 10^{23} \text{ At atoms/mol})}{210 \text{ g/mol}} =$$
$$4.6 \times 10^{20} \text{ At atoms}$$

This value is the same as 460 billion billion.

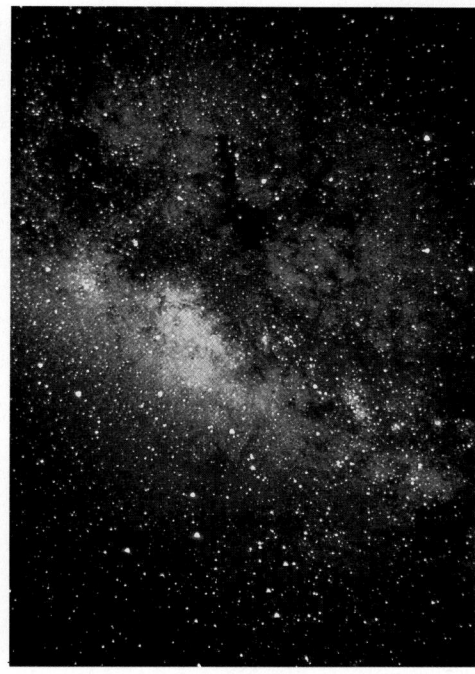

If you traveled to the farthest galaxy, how many atoms of carbon would you have to drop per kilometer to use up all of the atoms in the largest diamond?

The mass of the largest diamond is 621.2 g and because the diamond is pure carbon, the number of carbon atoms it contains is

$$\frac{621.2 \text{ g C}}{12.01 \text{ g/mol C}} \times \frac{6.022 \times 10^{23} \text{ C atoms}}{\text{mol}}$$
$$= 3.115 \times 10^{25} \text{ C atoms}$$

The farthest galaxy is 1.24×10^{23} km away, so for every kilometer you travel, you have to drop the following.

$$\frac{3.115 \times 10^{25} \text{ C atoms}}{1.24 \times 10^{23} \text{ km}} = 251 \text{ atoms/km}$$

READING STRATEGY

Assimilating Knowledge

Have students return to their lists of questions they want answered about how atoms are counted and how their masses are measured, which they created on page 272. Have them place check marks next to the questions that they are now able to answer. Students should finish by making a list of what they've learned. Have students identify unanswered questions as well as new questions they may have. These questions could be used as the basis for a research project.

REVIEW & ASSESS ASSIGNMENT GUIDE

Term Review

Assign after Section 8-2.

Concept and Skills Review

Section 8-1
▶ Items 1–24

Section 8-2
▶ Items 25–55

Linking Chapters

Section 8-1
▶ Items 1–2

Section 8-2
▶ Items 3–4

Alternative Assessments

Assign after Section 8-2.

Test Prep

Assign before the chapter test.

KEY TERMS

8-1
molar mass

8-2
empirical formula
formula unit
molecular formula
percentage composition

KEY CONCEPTS

8-1 How are atoms counted and measured?

▶ Amounts of substances are measured in moles. Amount is the quantity; mole is the unit used to express that quantity.

▶ Avogadro's constant 6.022×10^{23}/mol, expresses a number of things—atoms, molecules, ions, particles, formula units, etc.—in one mole.

▶ Conversions made between the amount in moles and the number of atoms require the use of Avogadro's constant.

▶ The average atomic mass of an element is the weighted average of the masses of the element's isotopes.

▶ Conversions made between moles and mass in grams require the use of molar mass.

8-2 How is the mole concept related to chemical formulas?

▶ An empirical formula shows the elements and the ratio of atoms or ions that are present in a compound.

▶ The molar mass of a compound can be calculated from its chemical formula.

▶ If the percent composition of a compound is known, then its empirical formula can be determined; if its molecular or empirical formula is known, then its percentage composition can be calculated.

▶ The molecular formula of a compound can be determined from its empirical formula and molar mass.

▶ The molar mass of a hydrate includes the mass of the water of hydration.

KEY SKILLS

Review the following models before your exam. Be sure you can solve these types of problems.

Sample Problem 8A: Converting amount in moles to number of atoms (p. 277)

Sample Problem 8B: Converting number of atoms to amount in moles (p. 277)

Sample Problem 8C: Calculating average atomic mass (p. 279)

Sample Problem 8D: Converting amount in moles to mass (p. 281)

Sample Problem 8E: Converting mass to amount in moles (p. 281)

Sample Problem 8F: Finding the mass of an atom (p. 282)

Sample Problem 8G: Calculating molar mass (p. 287)

Sample Problem 8H: Calculating molar mass of compounds (p. 288)

Sample Problem 8I: Determining an empirical formula from composition data (p. 290)

Sample Problem 8J: Calculating empirical formulas from percentage composition (p. 291)

Sample Problem 8K: Determining a molecular formula from an empirical formula (p. 293)

Sample Problem 8L: Using a chemical formula to determine percentage composition (p. 295)

Sample Problem 8M: Determining the percentage composition of hydrates (p. 296)

TERM REVIEW

1. A formula expressing the simplest ratio of cations to anions in an ionic compound is known as a(n) ———.
(empirical formula, formula unit)

2. The number of particles in 1 mol of a substance is known as ———.
(Avogadro's constant, molar mass)

3. ——— is the mass in grams of 1 mol of a substance. (Average atomic mass, Molar mass)

4. The simplest ratio among the elements represents the compound's ———.
(empirical formula, percentage composition)

5. ——— represents the number of atoms in exactly 12 g of carbon-12.
(One mole, Avogadro's constant)

CONCEPT & SKILLS REVIEW

RELATING MOLES TO NUMBER OF ATOMS

1. Relate the mole to two other counting units.

2. How would you determine the number of atoms in 2 mol of gallium?

3. How is Avogadro's constant related to moles?

4. Why are moles used to represent the number of atoms in a sample of a given substance?

Practice Problems

5. How many atoms of oxygen enter your lungs when you inhale 5.00×10^{-2} mol of oxygen atoms? **(Hint: See Sample Problem 8A.)**

6. How many atoms are in the 6.75×10^{-2} mol of mercury within the bulb of a thermometer?
(Hint: See Sample Problem 8A.)

7. Assume that you have 2.59 mol of aluminum foil. How many atoms of aluminum do you have? **(Hint: See Sample Problem 8A.)**

8. How many moles of gold are in 1.00 L of sea water if there are 1.50×10^{17} atoms in the sample? **(Hint: See Sample Problem 8B.)**

9. How many moles are in a copper penny containing 1.80×10^{21} atoms? **(Hint: See Sample Problem 8B.)**

AVERAGE ATOMIC MASS

10. How is the carbon-12 atom used to define atomic mass units?

11. Why is the atomic mass of nitrogen 14.0067 and not 14.?

12. If you examine a periodic table, you will see that several elements have atomic masses very close to whole numbers. What is the likely cause?

Practice Problems

13. The lithium found in a hearing-aid battery has two naturally occurring isotopes. Lithium-6 has a mass of 6.015121 amu and an abundance of 7.42%. Lithium-7 has a mass of 7.016003 amu and an abundance of 92.58%. Calculate the average atomic mass of lithium. **(Hint: See Sample Problem 8C.)**

14. Silver found in most jewelry has two naturally occurring isotopes. Silver-107 has a mass of 106.905092 amu and an abundance of 51.35%. Silver-109 has a mass of 108.904757 amu and an abundance of 48.65%. Calculate the average atomic mass of silver. **(Hint: See Sample Problem 8C.)**

RELATING AMOUNT TO MASS

15. How are moles related to atomic mass?

16. How is molar mass related to average atomic mass?

17. Describe how you would determine the number of moles present in a given mass of a known substance.

TERM REVIEW

1. formula unit
2. Avogadro's constant
3. Molar mass
4. empirical formula
5. One mole

CONCEPT & SKILLS REVIEW

1. Student answers may include that the mole is a counting unit representing 6.022×10^{23} of something, just like a dozen represents 12 of something and a gross represents 144 of something.

2. Multiply 2 mol times 6.022×10^{23} atoms per mole.

3. Avogadro's constant is the number of items in a mole.

4. The mass of a mole of a substance equals the formula mass of the substance in grams.

5. 5.00×10^{-2} mol $O_2 \times$
$$\frac{6.022 \times 10^{23} \text{ atoms } O_2}{1 \text{ mol } O_2} =$$
3.01×10^{22} O_2 atoms

6. 6.75×10^{-2} mol Hg $\times$
$$\frac{6.022 \times 10^{23} \text{ atoms Hg}}{1 \text{ mol Hg}} =$$
4.06×10^{22} Hg atoms

7. 2.59 mol Al $\times$
$$\frac{6.022 \times 10^{23} \text{ atoms Al}}{1 \text{ mol Al}} =$$
1.56×10^{24} Al atoms

8. 1.50×10^{17} atoms Au $\times$
$$\frac{1 \text{ mol Au}}{6.022 \times 10^{23} \text{ atoms Au}} =$$
2.49×10^{-7} mol Au

9. 1.80×10^{21} atoms Cu $\times$
$$\frac{1 \text{ mol Cu}}{6.022 \times 10^{23} \text{ atoms Cu}} =$$
2.99×10^{-3} mol

10. One amu equals 1/12 the mass of a carbon-12 atom.

11. The atomic mass of nitrogen is a weighted average of the mass of all isotopes of nitrogen. Not all nitrogen atoms are nitrogen-14, so the atomic mass is not 14.

12. Most of the atoms of the element consist of one isotope.

13. (6.015121 amu)(0.0742) + (7.016003 amu)(0.9258) = 6.941738 amu

14. (106.905092 amu)(0.5135) + (108.904757 amu)(0.4865) = 107.877929 amu

15. The atomic mass of an element in grams contains 1 mol of atoms.

16. Average atomic mass in grams equals molar mass.

17. To determine the number of moles present in a known mass of a substance, divide the known mass by the molar mass of the substance, or multiply the mass by the inverse of the molar mass.

18. 4.50×10^{-2} mol Ne $\times \dfrac{20.18 \text{ g Ne}}{\text{mol Ne}} =$ 0.908 g Ne

19. 2.00 mol P $\times \dfrac{30.97 \text{ g P}}{\text{mol P}} = 61.9$ g P

20. 7.2 mol NaCl $\times \dfrac{58.44 \text{ g NaCl}}{\text{mol NaCl}} =$ 42.0 g NaCl

21. 35.0 mg Na $\times \dfrac{1 \text{ mol Na}}{22.99 \text{ g Na}} \times$ $\dfrac{1 \text{ g}}{1000 \text{ mg}} = 1.52 \times 10^{-3}$ mol Na

22. 290 mg Ca $\times \dfrac{1 \text{ mol Ca}}{40.08 \text{ g Ca}} \times$ $\dfrac{1 \text{ g}}{1000 \text{ mg}} = 7.24 \times 10^{-3}$ mol Ca

23. 325 mg $C_9H_8O_4 \times$ $\dfrac{1 \text{ mol } C_9H_8O_4}{120.21 \text{ g } C_9H_8O_4} \times \dfrac{1 \text{ g}}{1000 \text{ mg}} =$ 1.80×10^{-3} mol acetylsalicylic acid

24. a. $\dfrac{196.97 \text{ g/mol Au}}{6.022 \times 10^{23} \text{ atom/mol}} =$ 3.271×10^{-22} g/atom Au

Practice Problems

18. A neon sign contains 4.50×10^{-2} mol of neon. How many grams of Ne gas are in this sign? **(Hint: See Sample Problem 8D.)**

19. How many grams are in the 2.00 mol of phosphorus used to coat your television screen? **(Hint: See Sample Problem 8D.)**

20. How many grams are present in 7.2 mol of table salt, NaCl? **(Hint: See Sample Problem 8D.)**

21. A cup of hot chocolate contains 35.0 mg of sodium. How many moles of sodium are in the hot chocolate? **(Hint: See Sample Problem 8E.)**

22. One cup of whole milk contains 290. mg of calcium. How many moles of calcium are in the milk? **(Hint: See Sample Problem 8E.)**

23. An aspirin tablet contains 325 mg of acetylsalicylic acid, $C_9H_8O_4$. How many moles of acetylsalicylic acid are in each tablet? **(Hint: See Sample Problem 8E.)**

24. Calculate the mass of the following atoms by using Avogadro's constant and the atomic masses from the periodic table.
    a. Au   d. argon
    b. Ag   e. astatine
    c. Hg   f. aluminum
    (Hint: See Sample Problem 8F.)

25. What is the molar mass of barium carbonate? **(Hint: see Sample Problem 8G.)**

26. Calculate the molar mass of TNT. The chemical formula for TNT is $C_6H_2CH_3(NO_2)_3$. **(Hint: See Sample Problem 8G.)**

27. Calculate the molar masses of each of the following organic molecules. **(Hint: See Sample Problem 8H.)**

    a.
    Alanine

    c.
    2-ethyl-3-methyl-1-butene

    b.
    Pentanoic acid

    d.
    Cyclopropane

DERIVING FORMULAS FROM PERCENTAGE COMPOSITION

28. When purifying metals from mined ores, why is it important to know the percentage composition of the ore?

Practice Problems

29. During winter vacation, you work at a ski resort covering icy sidewalks with a substance containing 26.2% N, 7.5% H, and 66.3% Cl. What is the formula for this compound? **(Hint: See Sample Problem 8I.)**

30. Magnetite is an iron ore with natural magnetic properties. It contains 72.4% Fe and 27.6% O. What is the formula for magnetite? **(Hint: See Sample Problem 8I.)**

31. Phosphorus forms two oxides. One has 56.34% P and 43.66% O. The other has 43.64% P and 56.36% O. What are the empirical formulas for these compounds? **(Hint: See Sample Problem 8I.)**

32. A 175.0 g sample of the flavor enhancer monosodium glutamate, MSG, contains 56.15 g C, 9.43 g H, 74.81 g O, 13.11 g N, and 21.49 g Na. What is its empirical formula? **(Hint: See Sample Problem 8I.)**

33. Vanillin is a common flavoring agent used in foods. This compound consists of 63.15% C, 5.30% H, and 31.55% O. Its molar mass is 152 g/mol. Determine both its empirical formula and its molecular formula. **(Hint: See Sample Problem 8J.)**

34. Acetylene is a colorless gas used as a fuel in welding torches. Its empirical formula is CH, and its molar mass is 26.04 g/mol. What is its molecular formula? **(Hint: See Sample Problem 8K.)**

35. *Para*-dichlorobenzene is an ingredient in mothballs that has a molar mass of 147.00 g/mol and an empirical formula of C_3ClH_2. What is its molecular formula? **(Hint: See Sample Problem 8K.)**

EMPIRICAL AND MOLECULAR FORMULAS

36. What does an empirical formula represent?

37. Write both the empirical formula and the molecular formula for ascorbic acid, commonly known as vitamin C. A molecule of ascorbic acid contains six carbon atoms, eight hydrogen atoms, and six oxygen atoms.

38. The full name for the active ingredient in a bleaching compound used on hair is dihydrogen dioxide. What is the molecular formula for this compound? What is its empirical formula?

39. Determine the molecular formula for each of the following:
a. a compound with the empirical formula CoC_4O_4 and a molar mass of 341.94 g/mol
b. a compound with the percent composition 74.03% C, 8.70% H, and 17.27% N, and a molar mass of 162 g/mol

Practice Problems

40. Oleic acid has the following composition: 76.54% C, 12.13% H, 11.33% O. If the experimental molar mass is 282 g/mol, what is the molecular formula of oleic acid?

DETERMINING PERCENTAGE COMPOSITION

41. What information can be determined about a compound from its percentage composition?

42. What information is needed to calculate the percentage composition of a compound?

Practice Problems

43. What is the percentage composition of ammonium nitrate, NH_4NO_3, a common fertilizer? **(Hint: See Sample Problem 8L.)**

44. Tin(IV) oxide, SnO_2, is the ingredient that gives fingernail polish its characteristic luster. What is the percentage composition of SnO_2? **(Hint: See Sample Problem 8L.)**

45. Some antacids use compounds of calcium, a mineral that is often lacking in the diet. What is the percentage composition of calcium carbonate, a common antacid ingredient? **(Hint: See Sample Problem 8L.)**

46. A superconductor has the formula $YBa_2Cu_3O_7$. What is the percentage composition of the substance? **(Hint: See Sample Problem 8L.)**

47. Which iron ore has more pure iron per kilogram of ore, Fe_2O_3 or Fe_3O_4? **(Hint: See Sample Problem 8L.)**

48. What percentage of ammonium carbonate, $(NH_4)_2CO_3$, an ingredient in smelling salts, is the ammonium ion, NH_4^+? **(Hint: See Sample Problem 8L.)**

49. Which yields a higher percentage of pure aluminum per gram, aluminum phosphate or aluminum chloride? **(Hint: See Sample Problem 8L.)**

WATER OF HYDRATION

50. How does the formula mass of a hydrate differ from that of the anhydrous form of the same compound?

Practice Problems

51. What percentage of $CoCl_2 \cdot 6H_2O$, which is used as a humidity indicator, is $CoCl_2$? **(Hint: See Sample Problem 8M.)**

52. What percentage of the paint pigment blue-violet hydrated chromium(III) sulfate, $Cr_2(SO_4)_3 \cdot 18H_2O$, is $Cr_2(SO_4)_3$? **(Hint: See Sample Problem 8M.)**

53. Soil in several regions has a reddish tinge due to the presence of iron in the form of limonite, $Fe_2O_3 \cdot \frac{3}{2}H_2O$. What percentage of limonite is water? **(Hint: See Sample Problem 8M.)**

54. Which substance, anhydrous cobalt(II) chloride, $CoCl_2$, or anhydrous magnesium chloride, $MgCl_2$, will absorb the most water per gram if both form a hexahydrate with 6 mol of water per mole of salt?

55. Aluminum chlorohydrate is an ingredient used in some antiperspirants. In its anhydrous

---

Complete worked-out solutions for these problems can be found on the teacher's interleaved pages at the end of this chapter.

b. $\dfrac{107.87 \text{ g/mol Ag}}{6.022 \times 10^{23} \text{ atom/mol}} = 1.791 \times 10^{-22} \text{ g/atom Ag}$

c. $\dfrac{200.59 \text{ g/mol Hg}}{6.022 \times 10^{23} \text{ atom/mol}} = 3.331 \times 10^{-22} \text{ g/atom Hg}$

d. $\dfrac{39.95 \text{ g/mol Ar}}{6.022 \times 10^{23} \text{ atom/mol}} = 6.634 \times 10^{-23} \text{ g/atom Ar}$

e. $\dfrac{209.99 \text{ g/mol At}}{6.022 \times 10^{23} \text{ atom/mol}} = 3.487 \times 10^{-22} \text{ g/atom At}$

f. $\dfrac{26.98 \text{ g/mol Al}}{6.022 \times 10^{23} \text{ atom/mol}} = 1.68 \times 10^{-24} \text{ g/atom Al}$

25. $BaCO_3$, 197.34 g/mol

26. 227.15 g/mol

27. a. 89.11 g/mol
b. 102.15 g/mol
c. 98.21 g/mol
d. 42.09 g/mol

28. The percentage composition enables prediction of how much metal could be produced from the ore. Refining methods can be evaluated if the actual amount is much less than the predicted amount.

29. $\dfrac{26.2 \text{ g N}}{14.01 \text{ g/mol}} = 1.87 \text{ mol N}$

$\dfrac{7.5 \text{ g H}}{1.01 \text{ g/mol}} = 7.4 \text{ mol H}$

$\dfrac{66.3 \text{ g Cl}}{35.45 \text{ g/mol}} = 1.87 \text{ mol Cl}$

$\dfrac{1.87 \text{ mol N}}{1.87} = 1$

$\dfrac{7.4 \text{ mol H}}{1.87} \approx 4$

$\dfrac{1.87 \text{ mol N}}{1.87} = 1$

NH_4Cl

Answers continue on page 305B.

LINKING CHAPTERS

1. (203.973 amu)(0.014) +
(205.974 amu)(0.241) +
(206.976 amu)(0.221) +
(207.977 amu)(0.524) =
207.217 amu

2. Their positions in the table would
be reversed. The elements would
not be in columns that contain
other elements with similar
properties.

3. C and O are covalently bonded in
CO_3^-, as are H and O in H_2O. Ionic
bonds exist between Na^+ and
CO_3^{2-}. Bonds of an ionic nature
exist between Na^+ and the negative end of the H_2O molecule and
between CO_3^{2-} and the positive
end of the H_2O molecule.

4. The law of multiple proportions
states that the mass ratios of elements in a compound are in small,
whole numbers. This law is true for
empirical and molecular formulas.

ALTERNATIVE ASSESSMENTS

Performance assessment

1. Student procedures should include
finding the mass of the hydrate,
heating the hydrate to drive off
the water, and finding the mass of
the dehydrated salt. Students may
mention that the hydrates will
change in appearance as they lose
water. The percentage of water is
found by dividing the mass of the
dehydrated salt by the mass of the
hydrate and then multiplying by
100%. Student results can be
checked by finding the percentage
of water in the hydrate by using
formula masses. Be sure that you
approve all plans and that proper
safety precautions are observed
during the experiment.

Continued on page 305.

form, it has 30.93% Al, 45.86% O, 20.32% Cl,
and 2.89% H.

a. What is the empirical formula for aluminum chlorohydrate?

b. Aluminum chlorohydrate forms a hydrated
compound with 2.00 mol H_2O/1.00 mol
compound. What is the percentage composition of the hydrate?

LINKING CHAPTERS

1. Isotopes
Table 3-3, on page 90, lists the stable isotopes
of lead and their atomic masses. Calculate the
average atomic mass for lead.

2. Theme: Classification and trends
Mendeleev organized his periodic table by arranging the elements according to their atomic
masses. This resulted in some elements being
misplaced. For example, locate the elements K
and Ar on a periodic table. If these two elements were arranged according to their atomic
masses, what impact would this have?

3. Chemical bonds
Describe the bond types that are present in a
hydrated salt, such as $Na_2CO_3 \cdot 10H_2O$.

4. Atomic theory
Explain how empirical and molecular formulas
support the law of multiple proportions.

ALTERNATIVE ASSESSMENTS

Performance assessment

1. Your teacher will give you a note card with
one of the following formulas on it:

$NaCH_3COO \cdot 3H_2O$
$MgCl_2 \cdot 6H_2O$
$MgSO_4 \cdot 7H_2O$
$LiC_2H_3O_2 \cdot 2H_2O$

Design an experiment to determine the percentage of water by mass in the hydrated salt
described by the formula. Be sure to explain

what steps you will take to ensure that the
salt is completely dry. If your teacher approves your design, obtain the salt. What percentage of water does it contain?

2. Using a hydrated salt, design an experimental
procedure that supports the law of conservation of mass. If your teacher approves your design, carry out the experiment.

Portfolio projects

1. Research and communication
Research some methods chemists initially
used to arrive at Avogadro's constant. Then
compare these methods with modern methods.

2. Chemistry and you
Sulfuric acid has a great affinity for water.
Because of this property, sulfuric acid is used
as a drying, or dehydrating, agent in the manufacture of a number of consumer products.
Search the Internet for information on the use
of sulfuric acid as a dehydrating agent. Present your findings to the class.

3. internet**connect**

SC**LINKS**   **TOPIC:** Mass spectrometry
NSTA   **GO TO:** www.scilinks.org
KEYWORD: HW084

Research and communication
The most accurate method for determining
the mass of an element involves the use of
a device known as a mass spectrometer.
This instrument is also used to determine
the isotopic composition of a natural element. Check the library and the Internet
for information on how a mass spectrometer operates. Draw a model that illustrates
its operation, and present the model to the
class.

1. Which of the following molar masses should be used in a problem with hydrated copper(II) sulfate pentahydrate, $CuSO_4 \bullet 5H_2O$?
   a. 159.62 g/mol
   b. 177.64 g/mol
   c. 249.72 g/mol
   d. 339.82 g/mol

2. One mole of NaCl contains 6.022×10^{23} ——.
   a. atoms
   b. molecules
   c. formula units
   d. ions

3. The molecular formula for acetylene is C_2H_2; the molecular formula for benzene is C_6H_6. The empirical formula for both these compounds is ——.
   a. CH
   b. C_2H_2
   c. C_6H_6
   d. $(CH)_2$

4. If the empirical formula of a compound is known, then ——.
   a. its true formula is also known
   b. its percentage composition can be calculated
   c. the arrangements of its atoms is also known
   d. the percentage water in the compound can be determined

5. To calculate the average atomic mass of an element, which of the following must be known?
   a. the atomic number and the atomic mass of each isotope
   b. the atomic mass and the symbol of each isotope
   c. the number of atoms present in each isotope
   d. the atomic mass and relative abundance of each isotope

6. The units for molar mass are ——.
   a. g/mol
   b. atoms/mol
   c. g/atoms
   d. mol/g

7. Which of the following compounds has the highest percentage composition of oxygen?
   a. CH_4O
   b. CO_2
   c. H_2O
   d. Na_2CO_3

8. The molar mass of a compound is calculated by ——.
   a. adding the number of atoms present in the compound
   b. adding the atomic masses of all the atoms in the compound and expressing that value in grams
   c. multiplying Avogadro's constant times the number of atoms present in the compound
   d. dividing the number of grams of the sample by Avogadro's constant

9. The formula for a compound that consists of 1.2% H, 42.0% Cl, and 56.8% O is ——.
   a. HClO
   b. $HClO_2$
   c. $HClO_3$
   d. $HClO_4$

10. The percentage composition of H_2SO_4 is ——.
    a. 2.5% H, 39.1% S, 58.5% O
    b. 2.1% H, 32.7% S, 65.2% O
    c. 28.6% H, 14.3% S, 57.1% O
    d. 33.3% H, 16.7% S, 50% O

11. To calculate the mass of an atom, which of the following must be known?
    a. the atomic mass and the symbol of each isotope
    b. the atomic number of the symbol of each isotope
    c. the atomic mass and Avogadro's constant
    d. the atomic mass and the number of isotopes for the element

12. To calculate the amount of a compound in moles, which of the following must be known?
    a. the atomic mass and the symbol of each isotope
    b. the mass of the compound and its molar mass
    c. the atomic mass and Avogadro's constant
    d. the formula and Avogadro's constant

1. c	5. d	9. c
2. c	6. a	10. b
3. a	7. c	
4. b	8. b	

Continued from page 304.

2. Student procedures could include finding the mass of the hydrate, then heating the hydrate to drive off the water. The water vapor driven off is collected and cooled to condense to liquid water. The mass of the dehydrated salt and the water should equal the mass of the hydrate. Be sure that you approve all plans and that proper safety precautions are observed during the experiment.

Portfolio projects

1. Historical results might include those of Avogadro, who worked with gases, and those of Jean Baptiste Perrin, who measured the displacement of colloidal particles and first calculated a value of Avogadro's constant that is close to its currently accepted value.

2. Student information may include using sulfuric acid to remove water from gases it does not react with, and using dehydrated sugar and certain other organic compounds to produce carbon.

3. Student research should show that in a mass spectrometer a beam of electrons ionizes a gaseous-element sample. A magnet deflects these ions according to their mass. The results are recorded on a detector, such as a photographic plate.

Answers from page 283

16. a. $12 \text{ mol Fe} \times \dfrac{6.022 \times 10^{23} \text{ Fe atoms}}{\text{mol Fe}} = 1 \times 10^{24} \text{ atoms}$

b. $40.1 \text{ g Ca} \times \dfrac{1 \text{ mol Ca}}{40.08 \text{ g Ca}} \times \dfrac{6.022 \times 10^{23} \text{ atoms Ca}}{\text{mol Ca}} =$
$6.02 \times 10^{23} \text{ atoms}$

c. $4.5 \text{ mol B} \times \dfrac{6.022 \times 10^{23} \text{ atoms B}}{\text{mol B}} =$
$2.7 \times 10^{24} \text{ atoms}$

d. $184.2 \text{ g Na} \times \dfrac{6.022 \times 10^{23} \text{ atoms Na}}{\text{mol Na}} \times$
$\dfrac{1 \text{ mol Na}}{22.99 \text{ g Na}} = 4.825 \times 10^{24} \text{ atoms}$

17. a. $\dfrac{1.01 \text{ g H}}{6.022 \times 10^{23} \text{ H atoms}} = 1.68 \times 10^{-24} \text{ g/H atom}$

b. $\dfrac{151.97 \text{ g Eu}}{6.022 \times 10^{23} \text{ Eu atoms}} = 2.523 \times 10^{-22} \text{ g/Eu atom}$

c. $\dfrac{195.08 \text{ g Pt}}{6.022 \times 10^{23} \text{ Pt atoms}} = 3.239 \times 10^{-22} \text{ g/Pt atom}$

Answers from page 297

d. $\dfrac{21.56 \text{ g Zn}}{65.39 \text{ g/mol}} = 0.3297 \text{ mol Zn}$

$\dfrac{36.23 \text{ g Mn}}{54.94 \text{ g/mol}} = 0.6594 \text{ mol Mn}$

$\dfrac{42.21 \text{ g O}}{16.00 \text{ g/mol}} = 2.638 \text{ mol O}$

$\dfrac{0.3297 \text{ mol Zn}}{0.3297} = 1$

$\dfrac{0.6594 \text{ mol Mn}}{0.3297} = 2$

$\dfrac{2.638 \text{ mol O}}{0.3297} = 8$

$ZnMn_2O_8$

e. $\dfrac{58.77 \text{ g C}}{12.01 \text{ g/mol}} = 4.89 \text{ mol C}$

$\dfrac{13.81 \text{ g H}}{1.01 \text{ g/mol}} = 13.67 \text{ mol H}$

$\dfrac{27.42 \text{ g N}}{14.01 \text{ g/mol}} = 1.957 \text{ mol N}$

$\dfrac{4.89 \text{ mol C}}{1.957} = 2.5 \times 2 = 5$

$\dfrac{13.67 \text{ mol H}}{1.957} \approx 7 \times 2 = 14$

$\dfrac{1.957 \text{ mol N}}{1.957} = 1 \times 2 = 2$

$C_5H_{14}N_2$

9. a. $\dfrac{1161 \text{ g/mol}}{29.02 \text{ g/mol}} = 4,\ C_4H_4O_4$

b. $\dfrac{163 \text{ g/mol}}{81.71 \text{ g/mol}} \approx 2,\ B_2Cl_4$

c. $\dfrac{347.66 \text{ g/mol}}{115.88 \text{ g/mol}} = 3,\ N_3P_3Cl_6$

10. a. $\dfrac{87.62 \text{ g Sr}}{247.42 \text{ g SrBr}_2} \times 100 = 35.41\% \text{ Sr}$

$\dfrac{159.80 \text{ g Br}}{247.42 \text{ g SrBr}_2} \times 100 = 64.59\% \text{ Br}$

b. $\dfrac{40.08 \text{ g Ca}}{136.15 \text{ g CaSO}_4} \times 100 = 29.44\% \text{ Ca}$

$\dfrac{32.07 \text{ g S}}{136.15 \text{ g CaSO}_4} \times 100 = 23.55\% \text{ S}$

$\dfrac{64.00 \text{ g O}}{136.15 \text{ g CaSO}_4} \times 100 = 47.01\% \text{ O}$

c. $\dfrac{24.30 \text{ g Mg}}{76.34 \text{ g Mg(CN)}_2} \times 100 = 31.83\% \text{ Mg}$

$\dfrac{24.02 \text{ g C}}{76.34 \text{ g Mg(CN)}_2} \times 100 = 31.46\% \text{ C}$

$\dfrac{28.02 \text{ g N}}{76.34 \text{ g Mg(CN)}_2} \times 100 = 36.70\% \text{ N}$

d. $\dfrac{207.2 \text{ g Pb}}{325.3 \text{ g Pb(CH}_3\text{COO)}_2} \times 100 = 63.70\% \text{ Pb}$

$\dfrac{48.04 \text{ g C}}{325.3 \text{ g Pb(CH}_3\text{COO)}_2} \times 100 = 14.77\% \text{ C}$

$\dfrac{6.06 \text{ g H}}{325.3 \text{ g Pb(CH}_3\text{COO)}_2} \times 100 = 1.86\% \text{ H}$

$\dfrac{64.00 \text{ g O}}{325.3 \text{ g Pb(CH}_3\text{COO)}_2} \times 100 = 19.67\% \text{ O}$

11. a. SrS, 119.69 g/mol
b. NH_4F, 37.05 g/mol
c. $Zn(CH_3COO)_2$, 183.49 g/mol
d. $Hg(BrO_3)_2$, 456.39 g/mol

12. a. $\dfrac{207.2 \text{ g Pb}}{374.1 \text{ g Pb(ClO}_3)_2} \times 100 = 55.39\% \text{ Pb}$

$\dfrac{70.90 \text{ g Cl}}{374.1 \text{ g Pb(ClO}_3)_2} \times 100 = 18.95\% \text{ Cl}$

$\dfrac{96.00 \text{ g O}}{374.1 \text{ g Pb(ClO}_3)_2} \times 100 = 25.66\% \text{ O}$

b. $\dfrac{28.02 \text{ g N}}{108.02 \text{ g N}_2\text{O}_5} \times 100 = 25.94\% \text{ N}$

$\dfrac{80.00 \text{ g O}}{108.02 \text{ g N}_2\text{O}_5} \times 100 = 74.06\% \text{ O}$

c. $\dfrac{111.7 \text{ g Fe}}{399.91 \text{ g Fe}_2(\text{SO}_4)_3} \times 100 = 27.93\% \text{ Fe}$

$\dfrac{64.14 \text{ g S}}{399.91 \text{ g Fe}_2(\text{SO}_4)_3} \times 100 = 24.05\% \text{ S}$

$\dfrac{192.00 \text{ g O}}{399.91 \text{ g Fe}_2(\text{SO}_4)_3} \times 100 = 48.00\% \text{ O}$

d. $\dfrac{63.55 \text{ g Cu}}{249.2 \text{ g CuSO}_4 \cdot 5\text{H}_2\text{O}} \times 100 = 25.45\% \text{ Cu}$

$\dfrac{32.07 \text{ g S}}{249.2 \text{ g CuSO}_4 \cdot 5\text{H}_2\text{O}} \times 100 = 12.84\% \text{ S}$

$\dfrac{144.00 \text{ g O}}{249.2 \text{ g CuSO}_4 \cdot 5\text{H}_2\text{O}} \times 100 = 57.66\% \text{ O}$

$\dfrac{10.1 \text{ g H}}{249.2 \text{ g CuSO}_4 \cdot 5\text{H}_2\text{O}} \times 100 = 4.04\% \text{ O}$

e. $\dfrac{84.07 \text{ g C}}{123.14 \text{ g C}_6\text{H}_6\text{COOH}} \times 100 = 68.27\% \text{ C}$

$\dfrac{7.07 \text{ g H}}{123.14 \text{ g C}_6\text{H}_6\text{COOH}} \times 100 = 5.74\% \text{ H}$

$\dfrac{32.00 \text{ g O}}{123.14 \text{ g C}_6\text{H}_6\text{COOH}} \times 100 = 25.98\% \text{ O}$

13. $\dfrac{33.5 \text{ g H}_2\text{O}}{18.02 \text{ g/mol}} = 1.86 \text{ mol H}_2\text{O}$

$1.86 \text{ mol H}_2\text{O} \times \dfrac{1 \text{ mol CaCl}_2}{6 \text{ mol H}_2\text{O}} = 0.310 \text{ mol CaCl}_2$

$0.310 \text{ mol CaCl}_2 \times \dfrac{100.98 \text{ g CaCl}_2}{1 \text{ mol}} = 34.4 \text{ g CaCl}_2$

Answers from page 303

30. $\dfrac{72.4 \text{ g Fe}}{55.8 \text{ g/mol}} = 1.30 \text{ mol Fe}$

$\dfrac{27.6 \text{ g O}}{16.00 \text{ g/mol}} = 1.725 \text{ mol O}$

$\dfrac{1.30 \text{ mol Fe}}{1.30} = 1 \times 3 = 3$

$\dfrac{1.725 \text{ mol O}}{1.30} = 1.3 \times 3 = 4$

Fe_3O_4

31. $\dfrac{56.34 \text{ g P}}{30.97 \text{ g/mol}} = 1.852 \text{ mol P}$

$\dfrac{43.66 \text{ g O}}{16.00 \text{ g/mol}} = 2.72 \text{ mol O}$

$\dfrac{1.82 \text{ mol P}}{1.82} = 1 \times 2 = 2$

$\dfrac{2.72 \text{ mol O}}{1.82} \approx 1.5 \times 2 = 3$

$\dfrac{43.64 \text{ g P}}{30.97 \text{ g/mol}} = 1.41 \text{ mol P}$

$\dfrac{56.36 \text{ g O}}{16.00 \text{ g/mol}} = 3.52 \text{ mol O}$

$\dfrac{1.41 \text{ mol P}}{1.41} = 1 \times 2 = 2$

$\dfrac{3.52 \text{ mol O}}{1.41} \approx 2.5 \times 2 = 5$

$\text{P}_2\text{O}_3, \text{P}_2\text{O}_5$

32. $\dfrac{56.15 \text{ g C}}{12.01 \text{ g/mol}} = 4.68 \text{ mol C}$

$\dfrac{9.43 \text{ g H}}{1.01 \text{ g/mol}} = 9.34 \text{ mol H}$

$\dfrac{74.81 \text{ g O}}{16.00 \text{ g/mol}} = 4.68 \text{ mol O}$

$\dfrac{13.11 \text{ g N}}{14.01 \text{ g/mol}} = 0.936 \text{ mol N}$

$\dfrac{21.49 \text{ g Na}}{22.99 \text{ g/mol}} = 0.935 \text{ mol Na}$

$\dfrac{4.68 \text{ mol C}}{0.935} \approx 5$

$\dfrac{9.34 \text{ mol H}}{0.935} \approx 10$

$\dfrac{4.68 \text{ mol O}}{0.935} \approx 5$

$\dfrac{0.936 \text{ mol N}}{0.935} \approx 1$

$\dfrac{0.935 \text{ mol Na}}{0.935} = 1$

$\text{C}_5\text{H}_{10}\text{O}_5\text{NNa}$

33. $\dfrac{63.15 \text{ g C}}{12.01 \text{ g/mol}} = 5.258 \text{ mol C}$

$\dfrac{5.30 \text{ g H}}{1.01 \text{ g/mol}} = 5.25 \text{ mol H}$

$\dfrac{31.55 \text{ g O}}{16.00 \text{ g/mol}} = 1.972 \text{ mol O}$

$\dfrac{5.258 \text{ mol C}}{1.972} \approx 2.66 \times 3 \approx 8$

$\dfrac{5.25 \text{ mol H}}{1.972} \approx 2.66 \times 3 \approx 8$

$\dfrac{1.972 \text{ mol O}}{1.972} = 1 \times 3 = 3$

$\text{C}_8\text{H}_8\text{O}_3, \text{C}_8\text{H}_8\text{O}_3$

34. $\dfrac{26.04 \text{ g/mol}}{13.02 \text{ g/mol}} = 2$

C_2H_2

35. $\dfrac{147.00 \text{ g/mol}}{73.50 \text{ g/mol}} = 2$

$C_6Cl_2H_4$

36. An empirical formula represents the simplest ratio among the elements of a compound.

37. $C_3H_4O_3$ empirical, $C_6H_8O_6$ molecular

38. H_2O_2 molecular, HO empirical

39. a. $\dfrac{341.94 \text{ g/mol}}{170.97 \text{ g/mol}} = 2$

$Co_2C_8O_8$

b. $\dfrac{74.03 \text{ g C}}{12.01 \text{ g/mol}} = 6.164 \text{ mol C}$

$\dfrac{8.70 \text{ g H}}{1.01 \text{ g/mol}} = 8.61 \text{ mol H}$

$\dfrac{17.27 \text{ g N}}{14.01 \text{ g/mol}} = 1.232 \text{ mol N}$

$\dfrac{6.164 \text{ mol C}}{1.232} \approx 5$

$\dfrac{8.61 \text{ mol H}}{1.232} \approx 7$

$\dfrac{1.232 \text{ mol N}}{1.232} = 1$

C_5H_7N

empirical formula

$\dfrac{162 \text{ g/mol}}{81.13 \text{ g/mol}} = 2$

$C_{10}H_{14}N_2$

40. $\dfrac{76.54 \text{ g C}}{12.01 \text{ g/mol}} = 6.373 \text{ mol C}$

$\dfrac{12.13 \text{ g H}}{1.01 \text{ g/mol}} = 12.01 \text{ mol H}$

$\dfrac{11.33 \text{ g O}}{16.00 \text{ g/mol}} = 0.7081 \text{ mol O}$

$\dfrac{6.373 \text{ mol C}}{0.7081} \approx 9$

$\dfrac{12.01 \text{ mol H}}{0.7081} \approx 17$

$\dfrac{0.7081 \text{ mol O}}{0.7081} = 1$

$C_9H_{17}O$ empirical formula

$\dfrac{2.82 \text{ g/mol}}{141.26 \text{ g/mol}} \approx 2$

$C_{18}H_{34}O_2$ molecular formula

41. The relative percentage of each element in a compound can be determined from the percentage composition of the compound.

42. The chemical formula of the compound and the atomic mass of each element in the compound are needed to calculate its percentage composition.

43. $\dfrac{28.02 \text{ g N}}{80.06 \text{ g NH}_4\text{NO}_3} \times 100 = 35.00\% \text{ N}$

$\dfrac{4.04 \text{ g H}}{80.06 \text{ g NH}_4\text{NO}_3} \times 100 = 5.05\% \text{ H}$

$\dfrac{48.00 \text{ g O}}{80.06 \text{ g NH}_4\text{NO}_3} \times 100 = 59.96\% \text{ O}$

44. $\dfrac{118.71 \text{ g N}}{150.71 \text{ g SnO}_2} \times 100 = 78.77\% \text{ Sn}$

$\dfrac{32.00 \text{ g O}}{150.71 \text{ g SnO}_2} \times 100 = 21.23\% \text{ O}$

45. $\dfrac{40.08 \text{ g Ca}}{100.09 \text{ g CaCO}_3} \times 100 = 40.04\% \text{ Ca}$

$\dfrac{12.01 \text{ g C}}{100.09 \text{ g CaCO}_3} \times 100 = 12.00\% \text{ C}$

$\dfrac{48.00 \text{ g O}}{100.09 \text{ g CaCO}_3} \times 100 = 47.96\% \text{ O}$

46. $\dfrac{88.91 \text{ g Y}}{666.22 \text{ g YBa}_2\text{Cu}_3\text{O}_7} \times 100 = 13.22\% \text{ Y}$

$\dfrac{274.66 \text{ g Ba}}{666.22 \text{ g YBa}_2\text{Cu}_3\text{O}_7} \times 100 = 40.86\% \text{ Ba}$

$\dfrac{190.65 \text{ g Cu}}{666.22 \text{ g YBa}_2\text{Cu}_3\text{O}_7} \times 100 = 29.25\% \text{ Cu}$

$\dfrac{112.00 \text{ g O}}{666.22 \text{ g YBa}_2\text{Cu}_3\text{O}_7} \times 100 = 16.66\% \text{ O}$

47. Fe_3O_4; see Figure 8-8

48. $\dfrac{36.1 \text{ g NH}_4^+}{96.11 \text{ g (NH}_4)_2\text{CO}_3} \times 100 = 37.56\% \text{ NH}_4^+$

49. $AlPO_4$

$\dfrac{26.98 \text{ g Al}}{121.95 \text{ g AlPO}_4} \times 100 = 22.1\% \text{ Al}$

$AlCl_3$

$\dfrac{26.98 \text{ g Al}}{133.33 \text{ g AlCl}_3} \times 100 = 20.23\% \text{ Al}$

aluminum phosphate

50. The formula mass of a hydrate is greater; it contains the mass of the number of water molecules that are present in each formula unit of the hydrate.

51. $\dfrac{129.83 \text{ g CoCl}_2}{237.95 \text{ g CoCl}_2 \cdot 6H_2O} \times 100 = 54.56\% \text{ CoCl}_2$

52. $\dfrac{392.21 \text{ g Cr}_2(SO_4)_3}{716.57 \text{ g Cr}_2(SO_4)_3 \cdot 18H_2O} \times 100 = 54.73\% \text{ Cr}_2(SO_4)_3$

53. $\dfrac{27.03 \text{ g H}_2O}{186.73 \text{ g Fe}_2O_3 \cdot 3/2H_2O} \times 100 = 14.48\% \text{ H}_2O$

54. $MgCl_2$

55. a. $\dfrac{30.93 \text{ g Al}}{26.98 \text{ g/mol}} = 1.146 \text{ mol Al}$

$\dfrac{45.86 \text{ g O}}{16.00 \text{ g/mol}} = 2.866 \text{ mol O}$

$\dfrac{20.32 \text{ g Cl}}{35.45 \text{ g/mol}} = 0.5732 \text{ mol Cl}$

$\dfrac{2.89 \text{ g H}}{1.01 \text{ g/mol}} = 2.86 \text{ mol H}$

$\dfrac{1.146 \text{ mol Al}}{0.5732} \approx 2$

$\dfrac{2.866 \text{ mol O}}{0.5732} = 5$

$\dfrac{0.5732 \text{ mol Cl}}{0.5732} = 1$

$\dfrac{2.86 \text{ mol H}}{0.5732} \approx 5$

$Al_2O_5ClH_5$

b. $Al_2O_5ClH_5 \cdot 2H_2O$

$\dfrac{53.96 \text{ g Al}}{210.50 \text{ g Al}_2O_5ClH_5 \cdot 2H_2O} \times 100 = 25.63\% \text{ Al}$

$\dfrac{112.00 \text{ g O}}{210.50 \text{ g Al}_2O_5ClH_5 \cdot 2H_2O} \times 100 = 53.21\% \text{ O}$

$\dfrac{35.45 \text{ g Cl}}{210.50 \text{ g Al}_2O_5ClH_5 \cdot 2H_2O} \times 100 = 16.84\% \text{ Cl}$

$\dfrac{9.09 \text{ g H}}{210.50 \text{ g Al}_2O_5ClH_5 \cdot 2H_2O} \times 100 = 4.32\% \text{ H}$

Chapter 9 Planning Guide

Chemical Equations

CLASSROOM RESOURCES

SECTIONS	TEACHER'S DEMONSTRATIONS	PROBLEM SOLVING ■ Text ◆ ChemFile Mini-Guide	LABORATORIES ■ Text ◆ ChemFile Manuals: A, B, C, D
9-1 **What is a chemical reaction?** Section Review, p. 311	**Demo 1** Production of Copper(II) Sulfide, p. 308		◆ **A5** Evidence for Chemical Change
9-2 **How are chemical equations for reactions written?** Section Review, p. 317	**Demo 2** Electrolysis of Water, p. 314	■ **Sample Problem 9A** Balancing chemical equations, p. 315	
9-3 **What does a chemical equation tell you?** Section Review, p. 324	**Demo 3** Exothermic and Endothermic Processes, p. 322	■ **Sample Problem 9B** Balancing chemical equations, p. 323	◆ **Exp. 5C** Chemical Reactions and Solid Fuel
9-4 **How are chemical reactions classified?** Section Review, p. 330	**Demo 4** Displacement of Silver with Copper, p. 328	■ **Sample Problem 9C** Using the activity series, p. 328	◆ **B9** Colored Precipitates ◆ **B10** Simple Qualitative Analysis

TECHNOLOGY RESOURCES

See Page 306 for a listing of Internet Resources

SECTIONS	VIDEOS/VIDEODISC *Holt Chemistry Videodisc* CNN *Science in the NEWS*	CHEMFILE CD-ROMs ● *Teaching Resources* ◆ *Interactive Tutor*	OVERHEADS ● *Color Transparencies* ◆ *Transparency Masters*
9-1	Hydrogen Combustion Bond Breaking and Bond Formation Iron(III) Chloride Synthesis Iron(III) Hydroxide Precipitation Nitrogen Dioxide Synthesis	● Occupational Application: Book Conservationist	◆ **42A** Elements That Normally Exist as Diatomic Molecules
9-2		◆ **Module 5** Equations and Stoichiometry **Topic** Balancing equations	● **42** Interpreting a Chemical Equation ◆ **43A** Symbols Used in Chemical Equations
9-3			● **41** Methane Combustion
9-4	Propane Combustion Phosphorus Trichloride Synthesis Phosphorus Combustion Methanol Combustion Zinc Sulfide Synthesis Aluminum Bromide Synthesis Magnesium/Zinc–Hydrochloric Acid Reaction Copper–Silver Nitrate Reaction Silver Chloride Precipitation Lead(II) Iodide Precipitation	● Supplemental Reading: *The Pale Horse*	● **43** Determining Reaction Types ◆ **44A** Activity Series

ASSESSMENT RESOURCES

ALTERNATIVE ASSESSMENTS	CHAPTER TESTING	SCORING RUBRICS *Holt ChemFile Teaching Resources CD-ROM*
Student Text Performance assessments, p. 340 Portfolio projects 1–3, p. 340 **Teacher's Edition** Chemistry in Your Community, p. 311 Group Strategies, pp. 316, 320, 326 **Study Guide** Sections 9-1 to 9-4	**Student Text** Test Preparation, p. 341 **Holt Chemistry:** **Visualizing Matter** **Chapter 9 Test** (blackline masters) **Holt ChemFile Test Generator** **for Macintosh and Windows**	**Lab Work** Student-Designed Experiments Rubric Performance-Tasks Scoring Rubric Assessment for Structured Inquiry Assessment for Open-Ended Inquiry **Portfolio Projects** Evaluating Concept Maps Assessing Portfolios Portfolio Assignment Student Evaluation Form

Chemical Equations

Establishing Prior Knowledge

Make certain students understand the following concepts.

▶ Chapter 1: definition of reactants and products
▶ Chapter 2: the joule as a unit of energy
▶ Chapter 5: ions; writing and recognizing names and chemical formulas of compounds
▶ Chapter 7: polymerization
▶ Chapter 8: the mole

READING STRATEGY

Assimilating Knowledge

Before students read this chapter, have them write a short list of all the things they already know (or think they know) about chemical reactions and chemical equations. Then have students list the things they might want to know about chemical reactions and equations.

If students are having trouble, offer the following suggestions to get them on track:

▶ What do you think happens during a chemical reaction?
▶ How do you know whether two substances will react with each other or not?
▶ What characteristics are common to all equations?

Have students save their list for later use in the Reading Strategy on page 335.

ABOUT THE ILLUSTRATION

The formation of the green patina on the surface of the statue's copper metal is due to the chemical reaction of copper with ions in water and air to form copper carbonate.

internet**connect**

Holt Chemistry: Visualizing Matter
On-Line Resources
go.hrw.com
Visit the HRW Web site for a variety of resources related to this chapter. Just type in the keyword HW0 Chapt9.

SC LINKS
NSTA

National Science Teachers Association
On-Line Resources: www.scilinks.org
The following Scilinks Internet resources can be found in the student text for this chapter:

Page 309
TOPIC: Chemical reactions
KEYWORD: HW091

Page 322
TOPIC: Endothermic/ Exothermic reactions
KEYWORD: HW092

Page 327
TOPIC: Combustion
KEYWORD: HW093

Page 328
TOPIC: Activity series
KEYWORD: HW094

Page 331
TOPIC: Fire extinguishers
KEYWORD: HW095

Page 333
TOPIC: Protease inhibitors
KEYWORD: HW096

REACTIVITY AND THE STATUE OF LIBERTY

One day in 1985, several people climbed inside the Statue of Liberty even though it was closed to visitors. A man scoured the inside of the statue with white powder. What was he doing? Why?

The man was part of a team working with the National Park Service on an $85 million project to restore the 100-year-old statue which had become damaged by corrosion.

He sprayed sodium hydrogen carbonate, $NaHCO_3$, from a combination pressure sprayer/vacuum cleaner to remove a layer of tar from inside the statue. The tar had prevented salt water from leaking into the statue. Over time, the tar had deteriorated and the statue leaked.

A team of workers searched for something rough enough to remove the tar but gentle enough to avoid damaging the statue's thin copper coating. The team tried ground walnut shells, corncobs, glass beads, rice, and sugar. $NaHCO_3$ was chosen because it is a mildly corrosive substance that effectively removed tar without damaging the underlying copper layer. Forty tons of $NaHCO_3$ was used to scour all 300 sheets of copper in the statue.

The French sculptor Frederic Bartholdi chose copper for the statue's exterior because of the metal's softness and malleability, the same properties that make the statue difficult to clean. Copper sheets were shaped and hung on a framework of 1800 iron bars. Iron was used to build the statue's framework because it was the strongest and most flexible material available at a reasonable cost.

Copper and iron, like most other metals, can react to form ionic compounds. The copper shell reacted with moisture and oxygen in the air to produce several green compounds, including $CuCO_3 \cdot Cu(OH)_2$, $CuSO_4 \cdot 3Cu(OH)_2$, and $CuSO_4 \cdot 2Cu(OH)_2$. These compounds constitute the green coating, or *patina,* on the outside of the statue.

By 1985, the iron supports had also reacted with moisture and air to form rust, which consists of hydrated oxides, such as $Fe_2O_3 \cdot 3H_2O$. Some of the iron bars had rusted to half their original thickness.

In this chapter, you will study chemical reactions. This information will enable you to appreciate the solution to the corrosion of the Statue of Liberty.

CHAPTER LINKS

Why did the iron support beams corrode much more than the thin copper coating?

What types of chemical reactions had taken place?

How could corrosion be prevented in the future?

STORY BACKGROUND

The restoration of the Statue of Liberty was initiated by the National Park Service in 1981, the hundredth anniversary of the statue's construction. The project was completed in 1986.

Many chemical factors involving both the statue's deterioration and its endurance had to be considered. For instance, while formation of iron(III) oxide led to the rusting of the iron ribs, the formation of the patina on the copper skin protected the skin from any further degradation. This protection was the result of a balanced mixture of the compounds brochantite, $CuSO_4 \cdot 3Cu(OH)_2$, and antlerite, $CuSO_4 \cdot 2Cu(OH)_2$. Yet changes observed in the proportions of these two compounds suggest that the patina, and thus the few millimeters of copper skin beneath it, might be endangered. The statue's north side has a higher concentration of antlerite, which is more susceptible to dust erosion. Debate continues on whether or not this degradation is caused by acid rain.

SECTION 9-1

What is a chemical reaction?

OBJECTIVES

▶ **List** evidence that suggests a chemical reaction might have occurred and evidence that proves a chemical reaction has occurred.

▶ **Describe** a chemical reaction using a word equation.

▶ **Describe** endothermic and exothermic reactions in terms of bond energies.

▶ **Relate** conservation of mass to the rearrangement of atoms in a chemical reaction.

▶ **Explain** how a nonspontaneous reaction can occur.

▶ **Explain** why reactants must be brought into contact for a reaction to occur.

Chemical change

You see chemical changes taking place all the time—in iron that rusts, in leaves that change color, in milk that sours, and in a car engine that converts gasoline and air into energy and exhaust fumes. Chemical changes also happen inside you. Both digestion and respiration involve chemical changes.

A *chemical reaction* describes a change in composition—the process by which one or more substances are changed into one or more different substances. Recall from Chapter 1 that in any chemical reaction the original substances, which can be elements or compounds, are known as *reactants*. The substances created are called *products*. One chemical reaction that you probably see quite often is shown in **Figure 9-1.**

Evidence of a chemical change

To understand what is involved in a chemical reaction, consider the safety match. When a match is struck against the matchbook cover, several observations can be made. Heat and light are released as a flame, and the match head changes color. In addition, a puff of smoke rises from the match and a hissing sound is heard.

How do you know what has happened to the match? It appears to have undergone a chemical change because the materials left after it has burned appear very different from those present at the beginning.

Observations that suggest a chemical reaction is taking place are the evolution of energy as heat, light, or sound; the production of a gas; the formation of a precipitate; or a change in color.

Though this kind of evidence suggests that a chemical change has taken place, it is not conclusive. For real proof, you need to analyze the

Light
Heat
Formation of gas
Change in color

▲ **FIGURE 9-1**

Chemical changes occur as a match burns.

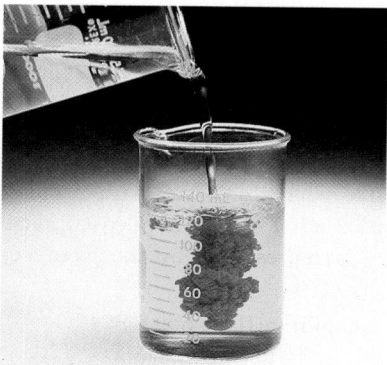

FIGURE 9-2 ◀

When two solutions are mixed, a color change and the formation of a solid precipitate are indications that a chemical reaction has probably occurred.

1. production of heat and light, formation of a gas, formation of a precipitate, and a change in color

2. The atoms in the reactants are rearranged to form the products.

3. The identity of the products is different from the identity of the reactants.

products and demonstrate that at least one new substance is present. **Figure 9-2** shows another example of noticeable changes that indicate a chemical reaction may have occurred—the formation of a precipitate.

Sometimes changes occur that appear to be chemical but are not. If analysis of the product reveals that it has the same chemical composition and molecular structure as the reactant, then the process is classified as a *physical change* rather than a *chemical reaction*. Condensation, melting, and crystallization are physical changes that at first glance can appear to be chemical reactions.

Reactions involve rearrangements of atoms

In chemical reactions, reactants are converted into products. The law of conservation of mass states that mass cannot be created or destroyed. This means that *the products of a reaction are made up of the same number and kinds of atoms as were present in the reactants*. A chemical reaction is the following process.

$$\text{Set of atoms in a particular arrangement} \longrightarrow \text{Same set of atoms in a different arrangement}$$

In chemical reactions, atoms do not become other kinds of atoms, nor do they appear or disappear. *The bonding patterns among the atoms are merely rearranged*. Sometimes few atoms are involved, but even when thousands of atoms are involved in a reaction, there are always the same number and kinds of atoms after the reaction as there were before the reaction.

---

internetconnect

SCINKS
NSTA

TOPIC: Chemical reactions
GO TO: www.scilinks.org
KEYWORD: HW091

CONCEPT CHECK

1. List four observations that signify a chemical change.
2. Describe what happens to atoms during a chemical reaction.
3. What *proves* that a chemical reaction has taken place?

RESOURCE LINK

Chem**File** Teaching Resources CD-ROM
Career Extension
Assign Occupational Applications Worksheet 2: *Book Conservationist* to emphasize relevant applications of text concepts.

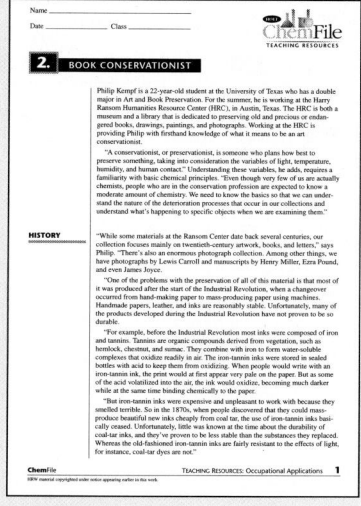

Safety

Safety goggles and a lab apron must be worn. Students must be at least 3 m from the reaction. Steps 4 and 5 must be performed in a properly operating fume hood. If the sulfur vapors catch on fire in the test tube, cover the tube with a glass plate until the fire goes out.

Disposal

Clean the copper with steel wool, and save it for reuse. Dispose of the CuS, the steel fragments from cleaning, and the ruined test tube in the trash can.

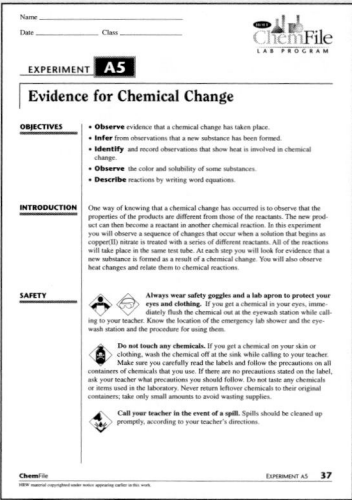

Chemical reactions release or absorb energy

Why are heat, light, and sound considered strong indicators that a chemical change has occurred? Each is evidence that energy has been liberated. Most chemical reactions occurring at mild temperatures release energy in some form. For example, when iron reacts with oxygen to produce 1 mol of iron(III) oxide, 1652 kJ of energy is released, usually as heat. This exothermic reaction is represented by the word equation shown below.

$$\text{iron} + \text{oxygen} \longrightarrow 1 \text{ mol of iron(III) oxide} + 824 \text{ kJ}$$

Unlike exothermic reactions, endothermic reactions rarely occur at room temperature. Only mildly endothermic reactions occur spontaneously at room temperature because the energy needed can be continuously supplied by the surroundings. One that does occur is the decomposition of dinitrogen pentoxide to nitrogen dioxide and oxygen gas.

$$1 \text{ mol of dinitrogen pentoxide} + 52.3 \text{ kJ} \longrightarrow$$
$$\text{dinitrogen tetroxide} + \text{oxygen gas}$$

When a reaction is said to occur naturally, it is implied that the process happens unaided. At times something, such as a spark, is required to initiate a reaction, but once the reaction is in progress it continues to generate products *as long as reactants are supplied.* The scientific term for a process like this is *spontaneous reaction.* A forest fire is an example of a spontaneous exothermic reaction, whereas the decomposition reaction above is an example of a spontaneous endothermic reaction.

A nonspontaneous reaction can occur when it is linked to an energy source

▼ **FIGURE 9-3**

Breaking down water by electrolysis requires an input of energy because the reaction is endothermic.

Hydrogen and oxygen react to produce water in a spontaneous exothermic reaction. In the electrolysis experiment illustrated in **Figure 9-3,** the reverse reaction occurs.

$$\text{water} + 572 \text{ kJ} \longrightarrow \text{hydrogen} + 1 \text{ mol oxygen}$$

At mild temperatures the breakdown of water will never occur spontaneously. Energy must be supplied to drive the endothermic reaction. In the experiment, a battery supplies this energy in the form of an electric current.

Exothermic reactions yield stronger bonds

In Chapter 1, you read that the energy changes in a chemical reaction involve breaking and forming bonds. For exothermic reactions, such as the synthesis of water from hydrogen and oxygen, energy is released because the bonds holding the products together are *stronger* than those in the reactants. The stronger a bond is, the

310 CHAPTER 9

GRAPHIC ORGANIZER

Energy is absorbed to break bonds in the reactants.

Energy is released to form bonds in the products.

more energy released when the bond forms. The energy released is then available to break additional bonds in the reactants, driving the reaction toward more product formation.

Particles must collide for a chemical reaction to occur

When a safety match is lit, one reactant, potassium chlorate, $KClO_3$, is on the match head, and the other reactant, phosphorus, P_4, is on the matchbook's striking surface. The reaction begins when the two substances are brought together by striking the match head across the striking surface, as shown in **Figure 9-4.**

When reactants are brought together, collisions occur between the reactant particles. If these collisions happen with enough energy, the bonds in the reactants are broken, allowing new bonds to form. If the collisions are too gentle, the particles may bounce off one another unchanged. In the match example, friction from sliding the match across the striking surface produces the energy needed to induce the forceful collisions that start the reaction. Increasing the temperature of a system can also provide the energy needed to induce forceful collisions.

FIGURE 9-4 ▲

The chemical reactants for igniting safety matches are $KClO_3$, on the match head, and P_4, on the striking surface.

SECTION REVIEW

Total recall

1. What is a chemical reaction?

2. What is the only way to prove that a chemical reaction has occurred?

3. In an exothermic reaction, are the bonds in the products stronger or weaker than the bonds in the reactants?

4. In an exothermic reaction, are the bonds in the products higher or lower in energy than those in the reactants?

Critical thinking

5. At what point will a spontaneous reaction stop?

6. What drives the decomposition of water in an electrolysis experiment?

7. What is the role of collisions in chemical reactions?

8. Decide whether the reactions that occur in each of the following situations are exothermic or endothermic. Explain your choice.
   a. the burning of gasoline in a car's engine
   b. fireworks exploding in the sky

9. When an orange compound is heated, it reacts by giving off nitrogen gas, green crystals of chromium(III) oxide, and water vapor. What elements were contained in the original compound?

10. In item 9, was the change chemical or physical? How do you know?

11. **Story Clue** What evidence indicated that chemical reactions had taken place inside the Statue of Liberty?

ANSWERS

SECTION REVIEW

Total recall

1. the process by which one or more substances are changed into one or more different substances

2. Analyze the products to determine if they are different from the reactants.

3. stronger

4. lower

Critical thinking

5. when it runs out of at least one reactant

6. input of energy from electric current

7. Collisions can provide the energy needed for a reaction to occur.

8. a. exothermic; energy is released as heat and light
   b. exothermic; energy is released as heat, light, and sound

9. nitrogen, chromium, oxygen, hydrogen

10. chemical; the reactants and the products have different compositions

11. The original copper and iron reacted with other materials and changed identity, becoming substances with different properties.

ALTERNATIVE ASSESSMENT

Chemistry in Your Community

Have students examine warning labels on bottles of liquid bleach, paying special attention to warnings not to mix the bleach with any cleaner containing ammonia. Have them research the active ingredients in bleach and in an ammonia cleaner, and find out what is formed when they react. Also have them research statistics on the number of people who are injured yearly from breathing the products of this reaction. Their results should show that sodium hypochlorite and ammonia gas react to form chloramines, such as NH_2Cl, which can damage lungs.

SECTION 9-2

How are chemical equations for reactions written?

LESSON WARM-UP

An Equation Analogy Write the following items on the board:

1 center + 2 guards + 2 forwards ⟶
                1 basketball team

9 girls + 14 boys ⟶
           10 lab pairs + 1 group of three

Point out to students that the same number of people are represented on both sides of the arrow. They are just arranged differently. Discuss with students that the same principle applies to atoms represented in a chemical reaction.

Module 5: Stoichiometry
Topic: Balancing Equations
This engaging tutorial reviews and reinforces balancing equations through modeling and guided practice.

OBJECTIVES

▶ ***Translate*** word equations into formula equations.

▶ ***Relate*** conservation of mass to a balanced equation.

▶ ***Write*** a balanced chemical equation for a reaction.

▶ ***Distinguish*** between coefficients in a chemical equation and subscripts in a chemical formula.

Constructing a chemical equation

You know that symbols represent elements and formulas represent compounds. In the same way, equations are used to represent chemical reactions. A correctly written **chemical equation** describes the type and number of atoms that are rearranged during a reaction.

A word equation describes a reaction

In Section 9-4 you will learn about five types of chemical reactions. One of these is called combustion, and it occurs when oxygen reacts with another substance. **Figure 9-5** shows ethanol reacting with oxygen in a combustion reaction. Water and carbon dioxide are produced. This chemical reaction can be represented by a *word equation*.

$$\text{ethanol} + \text{oxygen} \longrightarrow \text{carbon dioxide} + \text{water}$$

In word equations, the arrow means "react to form" and the plus sign means "and."

A word equation translates into a formula equation

The formulas for ethanol, oxygen gas, carbon dioxide, and water can replace the words in the word equation to make a *formula equation*. The word *ethanol* carries no quantitative meaning, but the formula CH_3CH_2OH does—it means one molecule of ethanol. The word *ethanol* can be replaced by CH_3CH_2OH. Question marks are used in the equation below to signify that the number of ethanol molecules is not yet known. The other three words in the word equation are also replaced by the corresponding formula preceded by a question mark. This gives the following *unbalanced formula equation*.

$$?CH_3CH_2OH + ?O_2 \longrightarrow ?CO_2 + ?H_2O$$

chemical equation

an expression showing the formulas and the relative amounts of the reactants and products in a chemical reaction

▼ **FIGURE 9-5**

The combustion of ethanol is part of a cooking process known as flambé.

TABLE 9-1   Testing an Equation for Balance

	Reactants	Products	Balance?
Unbalanced formula equation	$CH_3CH_2OH + O_2$	$CO_2 + H_2O$	
Carbon atoms	2	1	no
Hydrogen atoms	6	2	no
Oxygen atoms	3	3	yes

Balancing requires patience

The number of atoms of each element is conserved during a chemical reaction. A correctly written chemical equation reflects this observation. To satisfy the law of conservation of mass, you should insert **coefficients** into a chemical equation. This process is referred to as *balancing* an equation. *There are equal numbers of atoms for each element on each side of the equation when an equation is balanced.* The procedure shown in **Table 9-1** can be used to test whether an equation is balanced or not. Count the atoms of each element on both sides of the equation.

There are two carbon atoms in the reactant column and only one in the product column of Table 9-1. How can the carbon atoms be balanced? To balance the number of carbon atoms, you need to double the number of carbon dioxide molecules in the products.

$$CH_3CH_2OH + ?O_2 \longrightarrow 2CO_2 + ?H_2O$$

The 2 is called a coefficient and indicates that there are two carbon dioxide molecules. Coefficients are normally integers. When a coefficient is equal to 1, the 1 is omitted for simplicity.

$$CH_3CH_2OH \text{ \textit{not} } 1CH_3CH_2OH$$

Coefficients are written in front of a formula and multiply the entire formula. Now count the atoms of the trial equation, as in **Table 9-2.**

The carbon atoms now balance, but the hydrogen atoms do not. In addition, the oxygen atoms have been thrown out of balance. It is easiest

TABLE 9-2   Testing a Trial Equation

	Reactants	Products	Balance?
Trial equation	$CH_3CH_2OH + O_2$	$2CO_2 + H_2O$	
Carbon atoms	2	2	yes
Hydrogen atoms	6	2	no
Oxygen atoms	3	5	no

coefficient

numeral used in a chemical equation to indicate relative amounts of reactants or products

ADDITIONAL APPLICATION

The optimum oxygen to acetylene ratio (5:2) of an oxy-acetylene torch, which is used for cutting and welding metals, can be determined by looking at the balanced equation below.

$$2C_2H_2 + 5O_2 \longrightarrow 4CO_2 + 2H_2O$$

COMMON MISCONCEPTION

Because we give students a specific order to follow when writing formulas (metal or element with positive oxidation state first), they may think that there is a correct order for equations. Let them know that $CH_3CH_2OH + O_2$ is no different from $O_2 + CH_3CH_2OH$. The same principle holds for writing the products of the reaction.

CHEMICAL EQUATIONS   313

GRAPHIC ORGANIZER

```
                    Numbers with Formulas
           ┌───────────────┼───────────────┐
     Coefficients       Subscripts      Superscripts
        show              show             show
  ┌──────────────┐  ┌──────────────┐  ┌──────────────┐
  │   Relative   │  │  Number of   │  │  Amount and  │
  │ amounts of   │  │ each type of │  │ type of charge│
  │ reactants    │  │ atom in a    │  │   on an ion  │
  │ or products  │  │  formula     │  │              │
  │ in a balanced│  │              │  │              │
  │   equation   │  │              │  │              │
  └──────────────┘  └──────────────┘  └──────────────┘
  Example: 3NaOH    Example: H₂O      Example: SO₄²⁻, K⁺
```

Coefficients show **Relative amounts of reactants or products in a balanced equation** — Example: $3NaOH$

Subscripts show **Number of each type of atom in a formula** — Example: H_2O

Superscripts show **Amount and type of charge on an ion** — Example: SO_4^{2-}, K^+

VISUAL STRATEGY

Figure 9-6 Stress the advantage of using whole numbers of coefficients, as they reflect the fundamental nature of the component materials. For example, half a molecule will not be involved in a reaction.

Tables 9-2 to 9-4 Be sure students recognize that the numbers in the tables represent numbers of atoms, not coefficients.

TABLE 9-3 | Second Trial Equation

	Reactants	Products	Balance?
Trial equation	$CH_3CH_2OH + O_2$	$2CO_2 + 3H_2O$	
Carbon atoms	2	2	yes
Hydrogen atoms	6	6	yes
Oxygen atoms	3	7	no

to begin by balancing elements that occur in only one reactant and one product. Therefore, hydrogen should be balanced before oxygen.

There are six hydrogen atoms in the reactants and two in the products. An easy way to balance these atoms is to find the lowest common multiple of the numbers, which in this case is 6. To have six hydrogen atoms on each side of the equation, multiply the water molecule by 3. Test out the new equation, as in **Table 9-3.**

The oxygen atoms still are not balanced. Multiplying the number of oxygen molecules by three results in an equal number of oxygen atoms on both sides of the equation. Test it out as in **Table 9-4.**

TABLE 9-4 | Third Trial Equation

	Reactants	Products	Balance?
Trial equation	$CH_3CH_2OH + 3O_2$	$2CO_2 + 3H_2O$	
Carbon atoms	2	2	yes
Hydrogen atoms	6	6	yes
Oxygen atoms	7	7	yes

There are equal numbers of carbon, hydrogen, and oxygen atoms on both sides of the equation; the equation is balanced. Replacing the question marks in the formula equation with the appropriate coefficients now gives the correct chemical equation.

$$CH_3CH_2OH + 3O_2 \longrightarrow 2CO_2 + 3H_2O$$

► **FIGURE 9-6**

When there are equal numbers of each type of atom on both sides of an equation, the equation is balanced.

Ethanol   Oxygen gas   Carbon dioxide gas   Water

DEMONSTRATION 2

Electrolysis of Water

Approximate time: 20 minutes

1. Pour 350 mL of 0.01 M aqueous Na_2SO_4 into a 600 mL beaker.

2. Fill two small test tubes with the solution from the beaker. Cover the ends of the tubes, and carefully invert them into the solution. Be sure there are no air bubbles in the test tubes.

3. Immerse a 9 V battery into the solution, and position the battery upright in the center of the beaker.

4. Place the open mouth of each test tube over one terminal of the battery, and allow the gases to collect.

This balanced equation is represented by models in **Figure 9-6.** Count the number of atoms for each element on each side of the arrow. Are they equal?

Tips on balancing chemical equations are summarized in **Figure 9-7.**

Tips for Balancing Equations

1. Delay the balancing of elements (often hydrogen and oxygen) that occur in several reactants or products.

2. If the same polyatomic ions appear on both sides of the equation, treat them as single units, like monatomic ions.

3. After considering tips 1 and 2, balance the elements left to right.

4. Remember, balancing one element may unbalance others.

5. For ionic equations, be sure charges are balanced.

FIGURE 9-7 ◄

Use these tips to organize your approach to balancing equations.

SAMPLE PROBLEM 9A   Balancing chemical equations

The first step in the commercial production of nitric acid is the combustion of ammonia in the presence of a catalyst. The exothermic reaction produces nitrogen monoxide and water vapor. Write and balance the equation for this reaction.

1   Write the word equation

ammonia + oxygen $\longrightarrow$ nitrogen monoxide + water + heat

2   Write the unbalanced formula equation

$?NH_3 + ?O_2 \longrightarrow ?NO + ?H_2O$

3   Count the number of atoms for each element

	Reactants	Products	Balance?
Trial equation	$NH_3 + O_2$	$NO + H_2O$	
Nitrogen atoms	1	1	yes
Oxygen atoms	2	2	yes
Hydrogen atoms	3	2	no

CHEMICAL EQUATIONS   **315**

SECTION 9-2

TEACHING TIP

Correct Formulas Lead to Correct Equations   Stress to students that equations with incorrect formulas cannot be balanced correctly. All of the skill and practice that students have from writing formulas in Chapters 5, 6, and 7 will be put to the test in this chapter.

Show the balanced equation for the synthesis of sodium chloride.

$2Na + Cl_2 \longrightarrow 2NaCl$

What would happen if the formula for salt were incorrectly written as Na_2Cl? The balanced equation would then be $4Na + Cl_2 \longrightarrow 2Na_2Cl$, which does not represent the reaction.

Remind students that using oxidation numbers correctly is essential to writing correct formulas.

5. Students will observe that twice as much H_2 as O_2 is produced. Relate this observation to the balanced chemical equation for the reaction.

Safety
Wear safety goggles and a lab apron.

Disposal
Pour the liquid down the drain. Dry the battery, and save it for reuse. Put tape over the terminals before storing the battery.

ANSWERS

PRACTICE PROBLEM 9A

1. **a.** $2ZnS + 3O_2 \longrightarrow 2ZnO + 2SO_2$
   b. $2C_2H_2 + 5O_2 \longrightarrow 4CO_2 + 2H_2O$
   c. $CS_2 + 3O_2 \longrightarrow CO_2 + 2SO_2$
   d. $N_2O_5 + NO \longrightarrow 3NO_2$

ADDITIONAL EXAMPLES

SAMPLE PROBLEM 9A

Write word equations and balanced chemical equations for each of the following:

a. Magnesium metal and water react to form magnesium hydroxide and hydrogen gas.

> **Ans.** magnesium + water $\longrightarrow$
> magnesium hydroxide +
> hydrogen;
> $Mg + 2H_2O \longrightarrow$
> $Mg(OH)_2 + H_2$

b. When ethane burns, it combines with oxygen to form water and carbon dioxide.

> **Ans.** ethane + oxygen $\longrightarrow$
> water + carbon dioxide;
> $2C_2H_6 + 7O_2 \longrightarrow$
> $6H_2O + 4CO_2$

c. Iron metal and aluminum oxide form when aluminum metal reacts with iron(III) oxide.

> **Ans.** aluminum + iron(III)
> oxide $\longrightarrow$ iron + aluminum
> oxide;
> $2Al + Fe_2O_3 \longrightarrow 2Fe + Al_2O_3$

4 **Insert coefficients for atoms one element at a time**

Note that hydrogen occurs in only one substance in the products and reactants, but it occurs in the reactants' side in odd numbers and on the products' side in even numbers. To get an even number on the reactants' side, use a trial coefficient of 2 in front of NH_3. Then balance the nitrogen and hydrogen on the products' side.

	Reactants	Products	Balance?
Trial equation	$2NH_3 + O_2$	$2NO + 3H_2O$	
Nitrogen atoms	2	2	yes
Oxygen atoms	2	5	no
Hydrogen atoms	6	6	yes

We now have the same odd-even problem with oxygen. There are an even number of oxygen atoms on the products' side and an odd number on the reactants' side. By doubling all coefficients, you will have an even number of oxygen atoms on both sides.

	Reactants	Products	Balance?
Trial equation	$4NH_3 + 2O_2$	$4NO + 6H_2O$	
Nitrogen atoms	4	4	yes
Oxygen atoms	4	10	no
Hydrogen atoms	12	12	yes

As a final step, change the coefficient for oxygen gas to 5 so that the oxygen atoms balance.

	Reactants	Products	Balance?
Trial equation	$4NH_3 + 5O_2$	$4NO + 6H_2O$	
Nitrogen atoms	4	4	yes
Oxygen atoms	10	10	yes
Hydrogen atoms	12	12	yes

5 **Check to be sure that the number of atoms of each element is equal on both sides of the equation.**

$$4NH_3 + 5O_2 \longrightarrow 4NO + 6H_2O$$

PRACTICE PROBLEMS

1. Balance the following equations:
   a. $? \, ZnS + ? \, O_2 \longrightarrow ? \, ZnO + ? \, SO_2$
   b. $? \, C_2H_2 + ? \, O_2 \longrightarrow ? \, CO_2 + ? \, H_2O$
   c. $CS_2 + O_2 \longrightarrow CO_2 + SO_2$
   d. $N_2O_5 + NO \longrightarrow NO_2$

ALTERNATIVE ASSESSMENT

Group Strategy

Have students use models of atoms to balance chemical equations. Have each group choose a different chemical equation and then make a model of each type of atom present in the equation. Students should then model the formula units for each reactant and product, arranging them in the order in which they appear in the equation. Have students add formula units to each side of their model equation until an equal number of each type of atom is present.

Balancing ionic equations

In addition to mass and number of atoms, electric charge is conserved in a chemical reaction. Equal positive and negative charges are produced when a cat is stroked, generating static electricity. A similar reaction occurs when hydrogen chloride gas dissolves in water.

$$HCl + H_2O \longrightarrow Cl^- + H_3O^+$$

It is important to realize that while positive and negative charges are produced, the total charge on the reactant side must equal the total charge on the product side. In this example, the sum of electric charges on each side is zero. There is no charge on the left side of the equation, and on the right side 1+ plus 1− equals zero.

FIGURE 9-8 ▲

Positive and negative charges in the girl's hair cause the strands to stand apart.

SECTION REVIEW

Total recall

1. Explain the differences between a word equation, an unbalanced formula equation, and a chemical equation.

2. When balancing an equation, should the coefficients or the subscripts be adjusted to balance the equation?

3. List the steps in balancing a chemical equation.

4. In an ionic equation, what must be balanced in addition to the number and type of atoms?

Critical thinking

5. Use diagrams of particles to explain why four atoms of silver can produce only two molecules of silver sulfide, even when there is an excess of sulfur atoms.

6. Indicate which of the numbers in the following equation are coefficients and which are subscripts.

$$3H_2SO_4 + 2Al \rightarrow Al_2(SO_4)_3 + 3H_2$$

Practice problems

7. Write the following reactions as word equations and then as formula equations.

   a. Hydrogen reacts with chlorine to produce hydrogen chloride.

   b. Aluminum and iron(III) oxide react to produce aluminum oxide and iron.

   c. Potassium chlorate decomposes to yield potassium chloride and oxygen.

   d. Calcium hydroxide and hydrochloric acid react to produce calcium chloride and water.

8. Balance all of the equations you wrote for item 7.

9. Balance the following equations.

   a. $CaSi_2 + SbCl_3 \longrightarrow Si + Sb + CaCl_2$
   b. $Al + CH_3OH \longrightarrow (CH_3O)_3Al + H_2$
   c. $P_4 + O_2 \longrightarrow P_2O_5$
   d. $Fe + O_2 \longrightarrow Fe_2O_3$

10. **Story Clue** Write balanced equations for the following reactions.

    a. Copper and oxygen form copper(II) oxide.

    b. Iron and oxygen form iron(II) oxide.

SECTION REVIEW

Total recall

1. A word equation uses names of elements and compounds to describe reactants and products in a chemical reaction. In a formula equation, the formulas for the reactants and products replace the names used in the word equation. A chemical equation includes coefficients with the formula equation to describe the number of atoms involved in the reaction.

2. the coefficients

3. Write the word equation; replace the words with formulas; count the number of atoms for each element; use coefficients to equalize the number of atoms for each element; repeat this process until the number of atoms of each element is conserved; make sure that there are an equal number of atoms of each element on both sides of the equation.

4. charge

Critical thinking

5. Student diagrams should show four Ag atoms and more than two S atoms. When each of two S atoms combines with the Ag atoms, no more Ag atoms are available to react with the surplus S atoms.

6. The 3, 2, and 3 that are written to the left of formulas are coefficients. All other numbers are subscripts.

Practice problems

7. **a.** hydrogen + chlorine ⟶ hydrogen chloride;
   $H_2 + Cl_2 \longrightarrow HCl$

   b. aluminum + iron(III) oxide ⟶

                                       aluminum oxide + iron;

   $Al + Fe_2O_3 \longrightarrow Al_2O_3 + Fe$

   c. potassium chlorate ⟶

                       potassium chloride + oxygen;

   $KClO_3 \longrightarrow KCl + O_2$

   d. calcium hydroxide + hydrochloric acid ⟶

                               calcium chloride + water;

   $Ca(OH)_2 + HCl \longrightarrow CaCl_2 + H_2O$

8. **a.** $H_2 + Cl_2 \longrightarrow 2HCl$
   b. $2Al + Fe_2O_3 \longrightarrow Al_2O_3 + 2Fe$
   c. $2KClO_3 \longrightarrow 2KCl + 3O_2$
   d. $Ca(OH)_2 + 2HCl \longrightarrow CaCl_2 + 2H_2O$

9. **a.** $3CaSi_2 + 2SbCl_3 \longrightarrow 6Si + 2Sb + 3CaCl_2$
   b. $2Al + 6CH_3OH \longrightarrow 2(CH_3O)_3Al + 3H_2$
   c. $P_4 + 5O_2 \longrightarrow 2P_2O_5$
   d. $4Fe + 3O_2 \longrightarrow 2Fe_2O_3$

10. **a.** $2Cu + O_2 \longrightarrow 2CuO$
    b. $2Fe + O_2 \longrightarrow 2FeO$

SECTION 9-3

What does a chemical equation tell you?

OBJECTIVES

▶ **Describe** how the conditions for a chemical reaction can be specified in the chemical equation.

▶ **Include** information about the states of reactants and products in a chemical equation.

▶ **Interpret** a chemical equation in terms of the relative numbers of molecules involved.

▶ **Determine** whether a reaction is endothermic or exothermic using information from a chemical equation.

▶ **Derive** mole ratios from a balanced chemical equation.

▶ **Calculate** energy changes in reactions using mole ratios and ΔH values.

Equations and recipes

Equations describe a system that rearranges atoms and bonds to make new substances. Formulas are used to represent the products and reactants in a reaction. Equations can also contain much more information.

Figure 9-9 shows the ingredients in store-bought bread. This listing differs from a recipe. The ingredients list does not tell you that the bread needs to bake in the oven at a specific temperature. The order in which the ingredients should be mixed is not specified, and the amount of each ingredient is missing.

The recipe shown in Figure 9-9 contains the information needed to produce a loaf of bread and tells the number of loaves the recipe will yield. Like a recipe, many chemical equations contain more than just the identities of reactants and products.

▼ **FIGURE 9-9**

To make bread, you need a recipe. Like a recipe, a chemical equation can contain instructions and can show the conditions under which a reaction will occur.

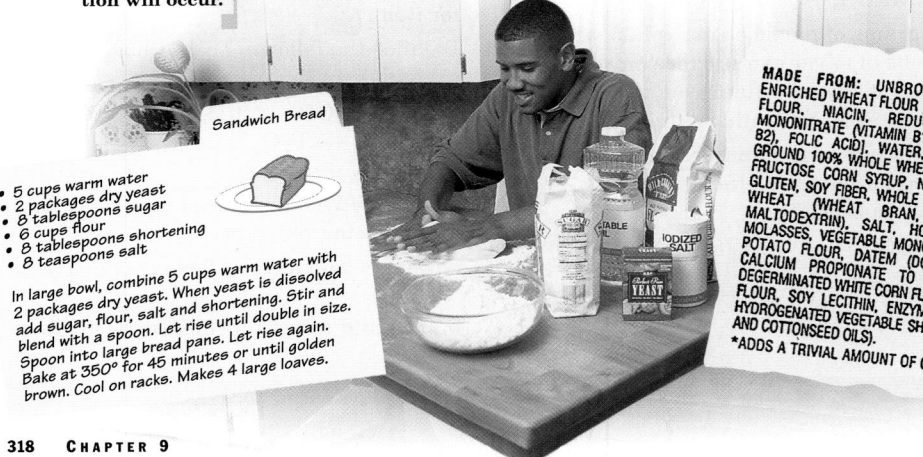

Sandwich Bread

- 5 cups warm water
- 2 packages dry yeast
- 8 tablespoons sugar
- 6 cups flour
- 8 tablespoons shortening
- 8 teaspoons salt

In large bowl, combine 5 cups warm water with 2 packages dry yeast. When yeast is dissolved add sugar, flour, salt and shortening. Stir and blend with a spoon. Let rise until double in size. Spoon into large bread pans. Let rise again. Bake at 350° for 45 minutes or until golden brown. Cool on racks. Makes 4 large loaves.

MADE FROM: UNBROMATED UNBLEACHED ENRICHED WHEAT FLOUR [FLOUR, MALTED BARLEY FLOUR, NIACIN, REDUCED IRON, THIAMIN MONONITRATE (VITAMIN B1), RIBOFLAVIN (VITAMIN B2), FOLIC ACID], WATER, UNBROMATED STONE GROUND 100% WHOLE WHEAT FLOUR, YEAST, HIGH FRUCTOSE CORN SYRUP, NONFAT MILK*, WHEAT GLUTEN, SOY FIBER, WHOLE WHEAT FLAKES, SPENT WHEAT (WHEAT BRAN, WHEAT PROTEIN, MALTODEXTRIN), SALT, HONEY, UNSULPHURED MOLASSES, VEGETABLE MONO AND DIGLYCERIDES, POTATO FLOUR, DATEM (DOUGH CONDITIONER), CALCIUM PROPIONATE TO RETARD SPOILAGE, DEGERMINATED WHITE CORN FLOUR, GUAR GUM, SOY FLOUR, SOY LECITHIN, ENZYMES AND PARTIALLY HYDROGENATED VEGETABLE SHORTENING (SOYBEAN AND COTTONSEED OILS).
*ADDS A TRIVIAL AMOUNT OF CHOLESTEROL

TABLE 9-5   Arrow Labels That Show Reaction Conditions

Symbol	Meaning
$\longrightarrow$	"produces" or "yields," indicating result of reaction
$\overset{\longrightarrow}{\longleftarrow}$	reaction in which products can reform into reactants; final result is a mixture of products and reactants
$\overset{\Delta}{\longrightarrow}$ or $\overset{heat}{\longrightarrow}$	reactants are heated; temperature is not specified
$\overset{0°C}{\longrightarrow}$	specific temperature at which reaction is carried out
$\overset{1.0 \times 10^8 \text{ kPa}}{\longrightarrow}$	pressure at which reaction is carried out
$\overset{Pd}{\longrightarrow}$	chemical formula of a catalyst, a substance added to speed up a reaction

Reaction conditions and physical states are shown in equations

Information about *the conditions under which a reaction occurs* is often found above or below the arrow. Examples of reaction conditions depicted in equations are shown in **Table 9-5.**

An equation can show the physical state of the reactants and products, as in **Table 9-6.** If an element or compound exists in more than one form but retains the same formula, the form is often indicated in parentheses. For example, C(*graph*) indicates carbon in the form of graphite, while C(*diamond*) indicates carbon in the form of diamond.

An example of the use of state symbols in an equation is the conversion of ethane to ethene and hydrogen.

$$C_2H_6(g) \xrightarrow[Cr_2O_3]{800 \text{ K}} C_2H_4(g) + H_2(g)$$

This equation tells you that the reaction proceeds at 800 K and in the presence of chromium(III) oxide, a catalyst. In addition, you are told that the reactant and products are in the gaseous state.

TABLE 9-6   State Symbols

Symbol	Meaning
(*s*) or (*cr*)	solid or crystal
(*l*)	liquid
(*g*)	gas
(*aq*)	in aqueous solution (dissolved in water)
↓	solid precipitate product
↑	gaseous product

VISUAL STRATEGY

Table 9-5   The symbols in the table are shown to familiarize students with additional information that can be included in an equation. There is no need for students to memorize these symbols. They need only be aware that the symbols are used in chemical literature.

Table 9-6   Encourage students to use state symbols in writing equations and to think about the nature of the chemicals represented when they see an equation in the text.

ANSWERS

CONCEPT CHECK

1. above or below the arrow

2. Answers could include any five symbols from Tables 9-5 and 9-6 along with the meaning for each symbol.

CONCEPT CHECK

1. In a chemical equation, where can you find information about the conditions of the reaction?

2. Cite five symbols used in chemical reactions to describe the formula of a product, and explain what each means.

When converting from molecules to moles, students should recall that a mole is simply 6.022×10^{23} particles. Therefore, the ratio of particles for each component of the reaction can always be considered the same as a mole ratio.

VISUAL STRATEGY

Table 9-7 Review all of the information about a system that students can derive from a balanced equation.

TEACHING TIP

Proportions in Equations Make a point of reviewing the proportionality of the ratios in chemical equations. Have students derive the number of moles of O_2, CO_2, and H_2O needed and produced if they have 5 mol, 10 mol, and 25 mol of $C_6H_{12}O_6$.

RESOURCE LINK

ChemFile Lab C
Skills Development
Have students do Exploration C5: *Chemical Reactions and Solid Fuel.*

| TABLE 9-7 | Interpreting a Balanced Chemical Equation |

Equation	$C_6H_{12}O_6$	+	$6O_2$	→	$6CO_2$	+	$6H_2O$
Moles	1		6	→	6		6
Molecules	$(6.02 \times 10^{23}) \times 1$		$(6.02 \times 10^{23}) \times 6$	→	$(6.02 \times 10^{23}) \times 6$		$(6.02 \times 10^{23}) \times 6$
Molar mass (g/mol)	180.18		32.00		44.01		18.02
Mass (g)	180.18		192.00	→	264.06		108.12
(Total mass (g)	372.18			→	372.18		

Quantitative relationships

Equations reveal the number of formula units involved

Using coefficients from a balanced equation, you can predict how much of each reactant is needed to make a certain amount of product. Consider the equation for cellular respiration.

$$C_6H_{12}O_6(aq) + 6O_2(g) \longrightarrow 6CO_2(g) + 6H_2O(l) + \text{energy}$$

This equation can be read in terms of formula units or molecules as well as in terms of moles, as you can see in **Table 9-7.**

For this reaction, you know that mass is conserved and that atoms are conserved. But the total number of moles and molecules do not necessarily remain the same on both sides of an equation because molecules are created and destroyed as atoms are rearranged.

Balanced equations show proportions

What would happen if you had 3 moles of glucose instead of one? How many moles of CO_2 and H_2O would form? One mole of glucose would require 6 moles of O_2 molecules and would produce 6 moles of CO_2 molecules and 6 moles of H_2O molecules. Two moles of glucose would require 12 moles of O_2 molecules and would produce 12 moles of CO_2 molecules and 12 moles of H_2O molecules. The reaction of 3 moles of glucose molecules would require 18 moles of O_2 and would produce 18 moles each of CO_2 and H_2O.

Rather than counting all of the reactants and products or running the reaction one mole at a time, imagine that the entire equation has been multiplied by three. If an entire equation is multiplied by a number, it is basically the same equation, but proportionately larger. Notice that the mole ratio stays constant.

$$C_6H_{12}O_6 + 6O_2 \longrightarrow 6CO_2 + 6H_2O$$

| 1 mol | 6 mol | 6 mol | 6 mol |
| 3 mol | 18 mol | 18 mol | 18 mol |

ALTERNATIVE ASSESSMENT

Group Strategy

Provide students with a list of balanced equations that use the symbols from Tables 9-5 and 9-6. Students should work in groups and read the equations in sentence form, expressing every item in the equation. For example, the equation $2KClO_3(s) + 156 \text{ kJ} \longrightarrow 2KCl(s) + 3O_2(g)$ could be read, "When 156 kilojoules of energy is applied to two moles of solid potassium chlorate, two moles of solid potassium chloride and three moles of oxygen gas are formed."

Relative amounts in equations can be expressed in moles

The molar interpretation of the cellular respiration reaction, shown in Table 9-7, can be expressed as ratios of reactants and products.

$$1 \text{ mol } C_6H_{12}O_6 : 6 \text{ mol } O_2 : 6 \text{ mol } CO_2 : 6 \text{ mol } H_2O$$

For any pair of molecules or formula units, a *mole ratio* can be determined by comparing the coefficients from the balanced chemical equation. Mole ratios should be expressed as the lowest whole number ratios. For example, the mole ratio of glucose to carbon dioxide would be 1:6.

$$1 \text{ mol } C_6H_{12}O_6 : 6 \text{ mol } CO_2$$

Mole ratios can be used like conversion factors to compare amounts of substances. In this way, you can determine exactly how much of a reactant is needed for the reaction or how much of a product can be expected. For example, 3 mol of $C_6H_{12}O_6$ would create 18 mol of CO_2.

$$3 \text{ mol } C_6H_{12}O_6 \times \frac{6 \text{ mol } CO_2}{1 \text{ mol } C_6H_{12}O_6} = 18 \text{ mol } CO_2$$

CONCEPT CHECK

1. Calculate the number of moles of H_2O produced by 4 mol of O_2 in the cellular respiration reaction.
2. How many moles of glucose would it take to produce 24 moles of CO_2 in the cellular respiration reaction?
3. What quantities are represented by coefficients in a chemical equation?

Energy changes in equations

The decomposition reaction of ethane to produce ethene and hydrogen is an endothermic reaction, which means that energy is absorbed. The quantity of energy involved can be written as part of the equation for the reaction.

$$C_2H_6(g) + 137 \text{ kJ} \longrightarrow C_2H_4(g) + H_2(g)$$

This equation tells you that 137 kJ of energy is required to convert all the molecules in 1 mol of ethane to form 1 mol of ethene and 1 mol of hydrogen gas. Because energy must be added to ethane for the endothermic reaction to occur, the energy is written on the reactant side of the equation. Because energy is released in an exothermic reaction, like the one in **Figure 9-10**, it is considered a product and is written on the right side of the equation, as shown for the following reaction.

$$2Al(s) + 3Br_2(g) \longrightarrow 2AlBr_3(s) + 252 \text{ kJ}$$

TEACHING TIP

Including Energy Though the major focus of this chapter is to develop the skill of balancing equations, be sure students recognize the importance of representing energy in the overall process.

ANSWERS

CONCEPT CHECK

1. 4 mol
2. 4 mol
3. relative number of particles; how much of each reactant is needed to make a certain amount of product

FIGURE 9-10 ▲

The reaction of aluminum and bromine is exothermic.

Figure 9-11 Point out that the amount of time required to expend a certain amount of energy is inversely proportional to how strenuous the task is. Power is a rate of energy use (usually expressed in joules per second). Multiplying power by a time period gives the amount of energy used during that time period.

enthalpy
the total energy content of a system

internet**connect**

SC**LINKS**
NSTA
TOPIC: Endothermic/Exothermic reactions
GO TO: www.scilinks.org
KEYWORD: HW092

▼ **FIGURE 9-11**

The energy potential contained in a 57 g (2.0 oz) candy bar is the same as the energy used during 24 minutes of basketball.

The amount of energy released or absorbed in a chemical reaction is often expressed as ΔH, where Δ stands for "change in," and H represents **enthalpy,** the total energy content of a system. In Chapter 11 you will study how ΔH values are determined. For now you need to know that in exothermic reactions, ΔH values are negative because energy is released when the stronger bonds of the products are created. In endothermic reactions, energy is added to the system and ΔH values are positive because the energy needed to break the bonds increases the total energy of the system. For the $AlBr_3$ exothermic reaction, $\Delta H = -252$ kJ, and for the endothermic decomposition of ethane, $\Delta H = +137$ kJ.

Energy depends on the states of the reactants and products; the states must be specified, as the following examples demonstrate.

$$2H_2(g) + O_2(g) \longrightarrow 2H_2O(g) + 484 \text{ kJ}$$
$$2H_2(g) + O_2(g) \longrightarrow 2H_2O(l) + 572 \text{ kJ}$$

The second reaction, which shows product formation in the liquid state, is more exothermic because energy is released as water vapor condenses.

Consider the following reaction, which essentially represents what happens when iron rusts.

$$4Fe(s) + 3O_2(g) + 6H_2O(g) \longrightarrow 2(Fe_2O_3 \cdot 2H_2O)(s) + 1648 \text{ kJ}$$

Here 1648 kJ means that 1648 kilojoules are released when 4 mol of Fe and 3 mol of O_2 are converted into 2 mol of Fe_2O_3. If you want to know the amount of energy released *per mole of iron,* then divide the energy released in the reaction by 4, because the equation involves 4 mol of Fe.

$$\frac{1648 \text{ kJ}}{4 \text{ mol Fe}} = \frac{412 \text{ kJ}}{\text{mol Fe}}$$

Getting a "feel" for energies

Perhaps you don't have much of an idea what a joule, kilojoule, or megajoule is. In Chapter 2, a joule was stated as the amount of energy needed to bring a cheeseburger to one's mouth. A joule is also roughly the energy expended in one beat of your heart. A kilojoule is the energy that a 45 kg (100 lb) person expends climbing a flight of stairs.

The energy that your body receives when you eat a 57 g (2.0 oz) candy bar, which is made mainly of sucrose, $C_{12}H_{22}O_{11}$, is the energy needed to sustain you in the activity shown in **Figure 9-11.** That energy can be calculated from the following chemical equation.

$$C_{12}H_{22}O_{11}(s) + 12O_2(g) \longrightarrow 12CO_2(g) + 11H_2O(l) + 5645 \text{ kJ}$$

The recommended energy intake is 9 MJ per day for an average 18-year-old female and 12 MJ per day for an average male. Because 1 food calorie is equal to 4.184 J, the recommended energy intake in calories is approximately 2100 cal for a female and 2800 cal for a male.

DEMONSTRATION 3

Exothermic and Endothermic Processes

Approximate time: 5 minutes

This demonstration shows the energy changes that result from the solution process. Be sure students realize that the terms *endothermic* and *exothermic* refer to the respective energy changes.

1. Add 50 mL of water to each of two 125 mL Erlenmeyer flasks.

2. Have two students measure the temperature of the water in the flasks and record each temperature on the board.

3. Add 2 g of solid NaOH to one flask, and add 10 g of solid NH_4Cl to the other flask. Let the solids dissolve for 2 minutes. Stir the solutions with stirring rods to speed up the solution process.

Energy can be expressed as part of a mole ratio

Let's return to the reaction of glucose and oxygen to form carbon dioxide and water. How much energy does this reaction release? The ΔH value for this reaction is given along with the balanced equation.

$$C_6H_{12}O_6(aq) + 6O_2(g) \longrightarrow 6CO_2(g) + 6H_2O(l)$$

$$\Delta H = -2870 \text{ kJ/mol glucose}$$

Notice that this ΔH value is expressed in kilojoules per *mole of glucose*. This ΔH value is for the combustion of glucose. For every mole of glucose combusted, 2870 kJ of heat energy is released. This can be shown by the following ratios:

2870 kJ : 1 mol $C_6H_{12}O_6$: 6 mol O_2 : 6 mol CO_2 : 6 mol H_2O

Thus, you can calculate the energy released by the reaction that produces 24 mol of H_2O.

$$24 \text{ mol } H_2O \times \frac{2870 \text{ kJ}}{6 \text{ mol } H_2O} = 11\,500 \text{ kJ}$$

In a similar way, the energy produced or consumed for any amount of reactant or product can be calculated for any chemical reaction. All that is needed is the chemical equation for the reaction and the corresponding ΔH.

SECTION 9-3

ADDITIONAL EXAMPLES

SAMPLE PROBLEM 9B

Find the amount of energy released when 100. g of each of the following compounds is formed from the free elements that compose it:

a. $CaCl_2(\Delta H = 795.8 \text{ kJ/mol})$

Ans. 717 kJ

b. $CH_4(\Delta H = 74.9 \text{ kJ/mol})$

Ans. 467 kJ

c. $SnCl_4(\Delta H = 511.3 \text{ kJ/mol})$

Ans. 196 kJ

SAMPLE PROBLEM 9B   Calculating energy for a specific reaction

Calculate the energy liberated when 100. g of glucose undergoes cellular respiration.

1 **List what you know**

▸ Mass of $C_6H_{12}O_6$ = 100. g

▸ Energy liberated = ?

2 **Set up the problem**

Start with a balanced equation. The respiration equation follows:

$$C_6H_{12}O_6(aq) + 6O_2(g) \longrightarrow 6CO_2(g) + 6H_2O(l) + 2870 \text{ kJ}$$

To calculate the amount of reactant, you'll need to find the molar mass of $C_6H_{12}O_6$ by using the atomic masses from the periodic table.

$$6 \times 12.01 \text{ g/mol} = 72.06 \text{ g/mol}$$
$$12 \times 1.01 \text{ g/mol} = 12.12 \text{ g/mol}$$
$$\underline{6 \times 16.00 \text{ g/mol} = 96.00 \text{ g/mol}}$$
$$= 180.18 \text{ g/mol}$$

To calculate the amount of glucose, divide the given mass of $C_6H_{12}O_6$ by the molar mass of $C_6H_{12}O_6$.

$$\text{Amount of } C_6H_{12}O_6 = \frac{100. \text{ g } C_6H_{12}O_6}{180.18 \text{ g/mol } C_6H_{12}O_6} = 0.555 \text{ mol } C_6H_{12}O_6$$

---

4. Have the students measure the new temperatures and record them on the board. You may want students to carefully feel the outside of each flask as you hold it.

Safety

The teacher and the participating students should wear lab aprons, safety goggles, and gloves. The rest of the class must be 3 m from the demonstration. In case of an alkali spill, dilute the spill with water and, while wearing gloves, soak up the spill with cloth or paper

towels. Do not stir the solutions with the thermometers.

Disposal

Neutralize the NaOH solution with 1 M HCl, and flush the liquid mixture down the drain. Pour the NH₄Cl solution down the drain with plenty of water. If towels were used to clean up an alkali spill, rinse the towels, neutralize the rinsings with 1 M HCl.

SECTION REVIEW

Total recall

1. The recipe describes the process for making the bread in addition to listing the ingredients. It includes the specific temperature at which the bread needs to bake, the order for mixing the ingredients, and the amount of each ingredient.

2. $\downarrow$, (s)

3. Compare the coefficients.

4. right

Critical thinking

5. a and d

6. **a.** solid reactant, solid KCl and gaseous O_2
   b. solid reactant, solid CaO and gaseous CO_2
   c. solid reactant, gaseous products
   d. All are gaseous.

7. **a.** 2 mol $KClO_3$: 2 mol KCl : 3 mol O_2
   b. 1 mol $CaCO_3$: 1 mol CaO : 1 mol CO_2
   c. 1 mol NH_4NO_3 : 1 mol N_2O : 2 mol H_2O
   d. 1 mol N_2 : 3 mol H_2 : 2 mol NH_3

Practice problems

8. **a.** 16 mol KCl, 24 mol O_2
   b. 6 mol CaO, 6 mol CO_2
   c. 7 mol N_2O, 14 mol H_2O
   d. 6 mol NH_3, assuming sufficient N_2 is present

---

3 **Calculate the energy for the amount given**

The respiration equation lists the energy output as 2870 kJ/mol. Because the coefficient of $C_6H_{12}O_6$ in the equation is 1, the value is 2870 kJ/mol of $C_6H_{12}O_6$.

For 0.555 mol:
$$\text{energy liberated} = 0.555 \text{ mol } C_6H_{12}O_6 \times \frac{2870 \text{ kJ}}{1 \text{ mol } C_6H_{12}O_6} = 1590 \text{ kJ}$$

4 **Verify your answer**

100. g is a little more than half the mass of 1 mol of glucose, so the value 0.555 mol is reasonable. We expect the energy output to be a little more than half of 2870 kJ, which is close to 1590 kJ.

SECTION REVIEW

Total recall

1. What does the bread recipe tell you that the ingredients label on the bread package does not?

2. What symbols are used in a chemical equation to indicate the formation of a solid precipitate?

3. Given a chemical equation, how do you determine a mole ratio?

4. In a chemical equation describing an exothermic reaction, is the energy written to the right or to the left of the arrow?

Critical thinking

5. Which of the following equations represent exothermic reactions?
   a. $H_2(g) + Cl_2(g) \longrightarrow 2HCl(g) + 185 \text{ kJ}$
   b. $2Al_2O_3(s) + 3351.4 \text{ kJ} \longrightarrow$
   $$4Al(s) + 3O_2(g)$$
   c. $C(s) + H_2O(g) \longrightarrow CO(g) + H_2(g)$
   $\Delta H = +131.3 \text{ kJ}$
   d. $SnCl_2(s) + Cl_2(g) \longrightarrow SnCl_4(l)$
   $\Delta H = -186.2 \text{ kJ}$

6. Describe the states of the reactants and products in each of the following equations.
   a. $2KClO_3(s) \longrightarrow 2KCl(s) + 3O_2(g) + 78 \text{ kJ}$
   b. $CaCO_3(s) + 178 \text{ kJ} \longrightarrow CaO(s) + CO_2(g)$
   c. $NH_4NO_3(s) \longrightarrow$
   $$N_2O(g) + 2H_2O(g) + 36 \text{ kJ}$$
   d. $N_2(g) + 3H_2(g) \longrightarrow 2NH_3(g) + 92.0 \text{ kJ}$

7. Write the mole ratios for each of the reactions in item 6.

Practice problems

8. Using the mole ratios in item 7, determine the number of moles of each product could be formed given the following reactant amounts.
   a. reaction 6a with 16.0 mol $KClO_3$
   b. reaction 6b with 6.00 mol $CaCO_3$
   c. reaction 6c with 7.00 mol NH_4NO_3
   d. reaction 6d with 9.00 mol H_2 and an excess of N_2

9. For each of the equations in item 6 and amounts in item 8, calculate the energy for each reaction. Also indicate whether the reaction is exothermic or endothermic.

---

9. **a.** $16.0 \text{ mol } KClO_3 \times$
   $$\frac{78 \text{ kJ}}{2 \text{ mol } KClO_3} = +624 \text{ kJ; endothermic}$$

   b. $6.00 \text{ mol } CaCO_3 \times \frac{178 \text{ kJ}}{1 \text{ mol } CaCO_3} = +1070 \text{ kJ;}$
   endothermic

   c. $7.00 \text{ mol } NH_4NO_3 \times \frac{36 \text{ kJ}}{1 \text{ mol } NH_4NO_3} = -252 \text{ kJ;}$
   exothermic

   d. $9.00 \text{ mol } H_2 \times \frac{92.0 \text{ kJ}}{3 \text{ mol } H_2} = -276 \text{ kJ; exothermic}$

How are chemical reactions classified?

OBJECTIVES

▶ **Classify** a given reaction as a combustion, decomposition, double-displacement, displacement, or synthesis reaction.

▶ **Write** chemical equations representing each type of chemical reaction.

▶ **Use** the activity series to predict whether a given reaction will occur and what its products will be.

▶ **Write** total and net ionic equations for double-displacement reactions.

Reaction types

The number of different chemical reactions is astronomical. When many reactions are similar, it is convenient to give a name to that type of reaction. You should be acquainted with five general types of reactions. Not every reaction can be classified under one of these headings because some reactions fit into more than one category.

internet connect

SC*LINKS*
NSTA

TOPIC: Combustion
GO TO: www.scilinks.org
KEYWORD: HW093

Oxygen combines with other elements in combustion

Many substances, including almost all organic compounds, will react with oxygen, often producing oxide compounds. These reactions are usually highly exothermic, releasing a large amount of energy as light, heat, or sound. Such reactions are known as **combustion** reactions. Like the pressure needed to create friction between a match and a matchbook, an initial "push" is often required to start combustion. **Figure 9-12** shows a familiar example of combustion—a Bunsen burner flame consuming natural gas (methane, CH_4) and oxygen and producing carbon dioxide and water vapor.

$$CH_4(g) + 2O_2(g) \longrightarrow CO_2(g) + 2H_2O(g) + 803 \text{ kJ}$$

Oxygen participates in oxidation reactions

Not all reactions with oxygen are as dramatic as combustion. One such reaction is called *oxidation*. The rusting of iron, which you read about earlier, is an oxidation reaction.

$$4Fe(s) + 3O_2(g) + 4H_2O(g) \longrightarrow 2(Fe_2O_3 \cdot 2H_2O)(s)$$

combustion

a violently exothermic reaction, usually with oxygen, to form oxide(s)

FIGURE 9-12 ◀

The complete combustion of any hydrocarbon, such as methane, yields only carbon dioxide and water. Incomplete combustion can yield carbon monoxide, CO.

SECTION 9-4

LESSON WARM-UP

Group Strategy Ask groups of about four students to describe what the terms *synthesis, decomposition,* and *displacement* mean to them. All are terms that have common usage. Students should associate synthesis with making something, decomposition with things breaking down, and displacement with movement from one place to another. Have groups compare their descriptions and discuss any similarities and any differences.

ADDITIONAL APPLICATION

If air is used instead of pure oxygen in the combustion process, nitrogen-oxygen compounds—many of which are poisonous—are produced. Some nitrogen-oxygen compounds are also light sensitive and turn brown when exposed to sunlight, causing the brown smog that appears in some cities.

In 1869, John Wesley Hyatt (1837–1920), in an attempt to find a substitute for the fragile ivory in billiard balls, discovered the first synthetic polymer. Called celluloid, it is a material that can be molded into shape. In 1884, Louis M. H. Bernigaud pushed the same substance through tiny holes in a nozzle, making small threads that he called rayon.

TEACHING TIP

Designing a Model Have students use foam balls and toothpicks to model a simple synthesis reaction. Then have them model the corresponding decomposition reaction.

CHAPTER CONNECTION

Polymerization will be covered in more detail in Chapter 7. Oxidation will be covered in detail in Chapter 17.

RESOURCE LINK

ChemFile Teaching Resources CD-ROM
Supplemental Reading Projects
Assign the guided reading worksheets for Agatha Christie's *Pale Horse* for cross-curricular connections to language arts.

Another example of an oxidation reaction is the souring of alcohol in wines by the formation of acetic acid.

$$C_2H_5OH(aq) + O_2(aq) \longrightarrow CH_3COOH(aq) + H_2O(l)$$

The word *oxidation* has a more general meaning that will be addressed in Chapter 17.

Compounds are made in synthesis reactions

synthesis
chemical reaction in which atoms or simple molecules combine to form a compound that is more complex

In **synthesis** reactions, complex molecules are made from simpler substances, as shown by the following example.

$$6CO_2(g) + 6H_2O(l) \longrightarrow C_6H_{12}O_6(aq) + 6O_2(g)$$

Plants can synthesize complex molecules, such as starch, caffeine, and chlorophyll, starting from the simple molecules CO_2 and H_2O and a few common ions. The reaction shown above is the synthesis of glucose from carbon dioxide and water.

Polymerization reactions are a form of synthesis

In *polymerization,* a series of synthesis reactions takes place to produce a very large molecule. Recall from Chapter 7 that the trick to making these big molecules is to take special small molecules called monomers and connect them to make a *polymer*. The simplest polymer is polyethylene, which is made by combining thousands of ethene molecules.

$$nC_2H_4(g) \longrightarrow (C_2H_4)_n(s)$$

The petrochemical industry manufactures large quantities of polyethylene ("polythene") and other related polymers. Some of these are itemized in **Figure 9-13.**

▶ **FIGURE 9-13**

Artificial polymers are used in many consumer products.

Nylon-66 polyamide in the shorts

Polystyrene foam (Styrofoam) in the helmet

Styrene-butadiene rubber in the tires

Polyethylene terephthalate (Dacron) in the shirt

Polytetrafluoroethylene (Teflon) in the lubricants

Polyethylene (plastic) in the water bottle

326   CHAPTER 9

ALTERNATIVE ASSESSMENT

Group Strategy

Have pairs of students play a game of concentration. Have them take 10 index cards and write an example equation on each card. There should be two cards for each of the five types of reactions. Then have them shuffle and deal the cards upside down in two rows of five cards each. Taking turns, each player then turns over any two cards, trying to match the two equations that are of the same reaction type. If the cards don't match, they are kept in the same position and turned back over. When a player turns over a pair of matching cards, the player removes and keeps the pair. The player that ends up with the most pairs wins.

Compounds are broken down during decomposition

A reaction in which a compound is broken down into smaller substances is known as **decomposition.** The following reactions are decomposition reactions.

$$CH_3OH(g) \longrightarrow CO(g) + 2H_2(g)$$
$$Al_2(SO_4)_3(s) \longrightarrow Al_2O_3(s) + 3SO_3(g)$$

CONCEPT CHECK

1. Cite two examples of oxidation reactions.
2. Polymerization reactions are a subclass of what type of chemical reaction?
3. Contrast synthesis and decomposition reactions.

Displacement reactions
Elements trade places in displacement reactions

When a piece of aluminum foil is added to a solution of copper(II) chloride, reddish copper metal starts to form on the aluminum foil, and some of it falls to the bottom of the container. Aluminum is *displacing* copper in the solution to form copper metal.

$$2Al(s) + 3CuCl_2(aq) \longrightarrow 2AlCl_3(aq) + 3Cu(s)$$

One way to think of this reaction is as a **displacement reaction.** Before the reaction begins, aluminum atoms are in the elemental form, and copper(II) ions are in solution. After the reaction, the copper atoms are in elemental form and aluminum ions are with chloride ions in solution. In effect, the aluminum atoms and copper ions switch places.

The activity series ranks reactivity

Experiments involving displacement reactions have been summarized in the **activity series,** shown in **Table 9-8.** The activity series is a list of elements organized according to their tendency to react (their "activity"). The more readily an element reacts with other substances, the greater its activity.

The more-active elements tend to be more stable as cations in aqueous solution than in elemental form. If a more-active element, such as potassium, and a compound containing a less-active element, such as H₂O (which contains hydrogen), are brought together, the more-active element will replace the less-active element in the compound, as shown below.

$$2K(s) + 2HOH(l) \longrightarrow 2KOH(s) + H_2(g)$$

decomposition
chemical reaction in which a single compound is broken down to produce two or more simpler substances

displacement reaction
chemical reaction in which one element replaces another element in a compound that is in solution

activity series
arrangement of elements in the order of their tendency to react with water and acids

TABLE 9-8

Activity Series

Element	Reactivity
Li Rb K Ba Sr Ca Na	react with cold water and acids, replacing hydrogen; react with oxygen, forming oxides
Mg Al Mn Zn Cr Fe Cd	react with steam (but not cold water) and acids, replacing hydrogen; react with oxygen, forming oxides
Co Ni Sn Pb	do not react with water; react with acids, replacing hydrogen; react with oxygen, forming oxides
H₂ Sb Bi Cu Hg	react with oxygen, forming oxides
Ag Pt Au	fairly unreactive; form oxides only indirectly

ANSWERS

CONCEPT CHECK

1. Answers will vary but may include rusting or a cut apple turning brown.

2. synthesis

3. In synthesis reactions, complex molecules are made from simpler substances. In decomposition reactions, a compound is broken down into simpler substances.

RESOURCE LINK

ChemFile Lab B
Microscale Lab
Have students do Experiment B9: *Colored Precipitates.*

ChemFile Lab B
Microscale Lab
Have students do Experiment B10: *Simple Qualitative Analysis.*

GRAPHIC ORGANIZER

In the activity series elements are arranged in order of activity, with the most active element at the top. *In general, an element can displace those below it from compounds in solution but not those above it.*

In addition to predicting displacement reactions, the activity series can help predict some synthesis and decomposition reactions. In general, compounds of active metals are readily synthesized, but such compounds do not easily decompose to re-form the metal. On the other hand, compounds of less active metals decompose readily but are difficult to make. For example, the synthesis of potassium compounds from their elements can be carried out more easily than the synthesis of compounds of nickel or tin.

Along with predicting whether a reaction will occur, the activity series provides indications of how easily and quickly the reaction will proceed. *In general, the farther apart two elements are on the activity series, the more likely it is that the higher one will quickly displace the lower one in compounds.*

internet**connect**

SCI**LINKS**

NSTA

TOPIC: Activity series
GO TO: www.scilinks.org
KEYWORD: HW094

SAMPLE PROBLEM 9C Using the activity series to write equations

Write a balanced chemical equation for the reaction that will occur if the metals copper and zinc are placed in a solution containing copper (II) and zinc cations. $Cu(s)$, $Zn(s)$, $Cu^{2+}(aq)$, and $Zn^{2+}(aq)$ are present.

1 **Check the activity series for the more reactive metal**

Zinc is higher on Table 9-8 than copper. This means that zinc metal will form a zinc cation as the product, displacing the copper ion from the solution. So the zinc metal and copper(II) ion will be the reactants.

$$Zn(s)\ Cu^{2+}(aq) \longrightarrow Cu(s) + Zn^{2+}(aq)$$

2 **Check other combinations of reactants for reactions**

The reaction of Cu with Cu^{2+} and the reaction of Zn with Zn^{2+} will not produce any new compounds. Furthermore, because Cu is lower than Zn on the activity series, it will not replace Zn ions. Thus, no other combination of reactants will result in a reaction.

PRACTICE PROBLEMS

1. Rank the following in order of increasing activity: aluminum, barium, copper, iron, and zinc.

2. Using Table 9-8, arrange the following reactions in order of decreasing tendency to occur. Indicate which would not occur at all. For those reactions that would occur, predict the products that would be formed.
   a. $Zn(s) + Cu^{2+}(aq) \longrightarrow$
   b. $Mg(s) + Pb^{2+}(aq) \longrightarrow$
   c. $Ni(s) + Al^{3+}(aq) \longrightarrow$
   d. $Cu(s) + Ag^{+}(aq) \longrightarrow$

DEMONSTRATION 4

Displacement of Silver with Copper

Approximate time: 5 minutes

This demonstration provides a vivid example of a displacement reaction.

1. Place a Petri dish on the overhead projector.
2. Pour a 0.1 M $AgNO_3$ solution into the dish until it is about half full.
3. Cut six 1 cm^2 pieces of copper foil.
4. Add the copper foil to the silver nitrate solution.

5. Have students note what happens. They should observe that the solution becomes blue as the reaction continues and that silver crystals form on the pieces of copper.

Safety

Safety goggles and a lab apron must be worn. Students must be at least 3 m from the demonstration. Skin should not come in

In double-displacement reactions, atoms appear to be exchanged between compounds

The reaction shown in **Figure 9-14** is the product of two colorless solutions being mixed. Where they react, a bright yellow solid forms. A reaction commonly described as a **double-displacement reaction** is occurring. The colorless solutions were prepared by dissolving potassium iodide, KI, in water and dissolving lead(II) nitrate, $Pb(NO_3)_2$, in water. The product of the reaction that forms the yellow precipitate is the salt lead(II) iodide, PbI_2, which is an insoluble yellow ionic compound. The reaction that formed this precipitate resulted from the interaction of lead(II) cations and iodide anions.

$$Pb^{2+}(aq) + 2I^-(aq) \longrightarrow PbI_2(s)$$

Nitrate anions and the potassium cations play no role in the reaction and remain dissolved in the solution, so they are not shown in the equation above.

A century ago, it was not realized that when salts dissolve in water, their ions become completely separated. Chemists at the time wrote the equation for the reaction shown in Figure 9-14 as follows.

$$2KI(aq) + Pb(NO_3)_2(aq) \longrightarrow PbI_2(s) + 2KNO_3(aq)$$

When written this way, it looks like the two cations have changed partners and for that reason, such a precipitation reaction was called a double-displacement reaction. The products' side of the equation shows that lead(II) ions bond with iodide ions, and potassium ions bond with nitrate ions. The two cations have *displaced* each other in the reaction. But the formula $KNO_3(aq)$ really represents separated K^+ ions and NO_3^- ions that are dispersed throughout the solution. It is important to remember what the symbol (aq) means when it follows the formula for an ionic compound. Though it is no longer accepted that an equation written in this way best describes the reaction, the term double-displacement is still used.

Double-displacement reactions are more accurately written as net ionic equations

When ionic compounds such as KI and $Pb(NO_3)_2$ dissolve in water, the solutions are mixtures of ions and water molecules.

$$KI(aq) = K^+(aq) + I^-(aq)$$

$$Pb(NO_3)_2(aq) = Pb^{2+}(aq) + 2NO_3^-(aq)$$

The reaction is better represented by listing all of the ions in the reactants and products as a total ionic equation.

$$2K^+(aq) + 2I^-(aq) + Pb^{2+}(aq) + 2NO_3^-(aq) \longrightarrow PbI_2(s) + 2K^+(aq) + 2NO_3^-(aq)$$

double-displacement reaction

chemical reaction in which ions from two compounds interact in solution to form a product

FIGURE 9-14 ▲

The yellow cloud of lead(II) iodide precipitate is formed as a product of the double-displacement reaction.

TEACHING TIP

Vocabulary Strategy One common example of a double-displacement reaction is an acid-base reaction. Acid-base reactions fall under the category of neutralization reactions because the two components neutralize each other's properties, producing a salt and water.

CHEMICAL EQUATIONS **329**

---

contact with the silver nitrate solution for even a short time, or skin will be stained.

Disposal

Filter the copper and silver out of the solution. Rinse the solids and the filter paper well. Store the metals for later use. Throw away the filter paper. Let the rinse water and the silver nitrate solution evaporate completely. Store and label the residue for future use.

ANSWERS

SECTION REVIEW

Total recall

1. water, carbon dioxide

2. starch, sugar, chlorophyll

3. A more active element will replace a less active element in a compound. The farther apart the elements are, the more readily the reaction occurs. Active metals undergo synthesis readily, and compounds of less active metals decompose readily.

4. K^+, NO_3^-

Critical thinking

5. **a.** $Ba(s) + H_2O(l) \longrightarrow BaO(s) + H_2(g)$
   b. $2Rb(s) + H_2O(l) \longrightarrow$
   $$Rb_2O(s) + H_2(g)$$
   c. $Zn(s) + H_2O(g) \longrightarrow$
   $$ZnO(s) + H_2(g)$$

6. **a.** $Cu(s) + O_2(g) \longrightarrow CuO(s)$
   b. $2Mn(s) + O_2(g) \longrightarrow 2MnO(g)$
   c. $2Pb(s) + O_2(g) \longrightarrow 2PbO(g)$

7. **a.** $Cl_2(g) + 2Br^-(aq) \longrightarrow$
   $$2Cl^- + Br_2(l);$$
   displacement
   b. $CaO(s) + H_2O(l) \longrightarrow Ca(OH)_2(aq);$
   synthesis
   c. $2Ag^+(aq) + SO_4^{2-}(aq) \longrightarrow$
   $$Ag_2SO_4(s);$$
   double displacement
   d. $Zn(s) + Cu^{2+}(aq) \longrightarrow$
   $$Zn^{2+}(aq) + Cu(s);$$
   displacement

Practice problems

8. **a.** $H_2O(l) + SO_3(g) \longrightarrow H_2SO_4(aq)$
   b. $2C_4H_{10}(g) + 13O_2(g) \longrightarrow$
   $$8CO_2(g) + 10H_2O(l)$$
   c. $2KClO_3(s) \longrightarrow 2KCl(g) + 3O_2(g)$
   d. $Zn(s) + CuSO_4(aq) \longrightarrow$
   $$ZnSO_4(aq) + Cu(s)$$
   e. $Ag^+(aq) + Cl^-(aq) \longrightarrow AgCl(s)$

9. **a.** no reaction
   b. $Mg(s) + Cu^{2+}(aq) \longrightarrow$
   $$Mg^{2+}(aq) + Cu(s)$$
   c. $2Ba(s) + O_2(g) \longrightarrow 2BaO(s)$
   d. $H^+(aq) + OH^-(aq) \longrightarrow H_2O(l)$

---

spectator ion

ion that remains unchanged in a chemical reaction

net ionic equation

an equation that includes only those compounds and ions that are involved in a chemical change in a reaction

When these four ions are mixed, two of them, Pb^{2+} and I^-, bond to form a solid, PbI_2. The other two ions, K^+ and NO_3^- appear on both sides of the total ionic equation. Because they remain unchanged in the reaction, they are called **spectator ions.** Double-displacement reactions are often written using **net ionic equations,** which only show the ions involved in the reaction. Spectator ions, such as K^+ and NO_3^-, are omitted from net ionic equations. That is why the ionic equation is written as the following net ionic equation.

$$\cancel{2K^+(aq)} + 2I^-(aq) + Pb^{2+}(aq) + \cancel{2NO_3^-(aq)} \longrightarrow PbI_2(s) + \cancel{2K^+(aq)} + \cancel{2NO_3^-(aq)}$$

$$Pb^{2+}(aq) + 2I^-(aq) \longrightarrow PbI_2(s)$$

SECTION REVIEW

Total recall

1. What two compounds are generally produced when organic compounds burn?

2. Name three complex molecules synthesized by plants.

3. Explain how to use the activity series to predict chemical behavior.

4. What are the spectator ions in the reaction that precipitates PbI_2?

Critical thinking

5. Assume that a displacement reaction occurs between H_2O and the following metals, and write a balanced chemical equation for the reaction. Remember that H_2O can be written as HOH.
   a. Ba   **b.** Rb   **c.** Zn

6. Assume that a synthesis reaction occurs between $O_2(g)$ and the following metals, and write a balanced chemical equation for the reaction.
   a. Cu   **b.** Mn   **c.** Pb

7. Balance each of the following equations, and indicate the class of reaction each belongs in.

   a. $?Cl_2(g) + ?Br^-(aq) \longrightarrow ?Cl^-(aq) + ?Br_2(l)$
   b. $?CaO(s) + ?H_2O(l) \longrightarrow ?Ca(OH)_2(aq)$
   c. $?Ag^+(aq) + ?SO_4^{2-}(aq) \longrightarrow ?Ag_2SO_4(s)$
   d. $?Zn(s) + ?Cu^{2+}(aq) \longrightarrow ?Zn^{2+}(aq) + ?Cu(s)$

Practice problems

8. Write balanced chemical equations for the following reactions:
   a. synthesis of sulfuric acid, H_2SO_4, from water and sulfur trioxide
   b. combustion of butane, C_4H_{10}
   c. decomposition of potassium chlorate to form potassium chloride and oxygen
   d. displacement reaction for zinc and copper(II) sulfate in aqueous solution
   e. double-displacement reaction for silver nitrate and sodium chloride in aqueous solution

9. Predict whether a reaction would occur when the materials indicated are brought together. For each reaction that would occur, complete and balance the equation, omitting any spectator ions.
   a. $?Ni(s) + ?H_2O(l) \longrightarrow$
   b. $?Mg(s) + ?Cu(NO_3)_2(aq) \longrightarrow$
   c. $?Ba(s) + ?O_2(g) \longrightarrow$
   d. $?H_2SO_4(aq) + ?KOH(aq) \longrightarrow$

CONSUMER FOCUS

FIRE EXTINGUISHERS

A fire is a combustion reaction in progress. Three things are needed for a combustion reaction to occur: a fuel, an oxidizer, and an ignition source. If any one of these three is absent, combustion cannot occur. Hence, to fight a fire, the goal is to remove one or more of these parts. To prevent air from reaching the combustible material, a layer of some nonflammable substance, often a gas, can be applied. Because fires are accelerated by high temperatures, another tactic would be to cool the burning material to reduce the fire's severity.

Types of fires

Different types of fuels require different firefighting methods. Fire extinguishers display codes indicating which types of fires they can put out. Water is used on Class A fires involving solid fuels, such as wood. The water cools the fuel so that it does not react as readily. The steam that is produced helps to displace the air around the fire. A Class B fire, in which the fuel is a liquid or gas, is best put out by carbon dioxide, CO_2. Because carbon dioxide is more dense than air, it forms a layer underneath the air, cutting off the O_2 supply for the combustion reaction. While the CO_2 in the fire extinguisher is in the liquid state, it is delivered as a cloud in which grains of solid CO_2 are mixed with the cold gas.

Dry chemical extinguishers

Class C fires involving a "live" electric circuit can also be extinguished by CO_2. Liquid water cannot be used, or there will be a danger of electric shock. Some Class C fire extinguishers contain a dry chemical that smothers the fire by interrupting the chain reaction that is occurring. For example, a competing reaction may take place with the con-

internet**connect**

SCI**LINKS**
NSTA

TOPIC: Fire extinguishers
GO TO: www.scilinks.org
KEYWORD: HW095

tents of the fire extinguisher and the intermediates of the reaction. Class C fire extinguishers usually contain compounds such as ammonium dihydrogen phosphate, $NH_4H_2PO_4$, or sodium hydrogen carbonate, $NaHCO_3$.

Finally, Class D fires involve burning metals. These fires cannot be extinguished with CO_2 or water because these compounds may react with some hot metals. For these fires, nonreactive dry powders are used to cover the metal and keep it separate from oxygen. One kind of powder contains finely ground sodium chloride crystals mixed with a special polymer that allows the crystals to adhere to any surface, even a vertical one. Another is finely ground graphite powder, which not only cuts off the oxygen supply but also absorbs heat. Most fire extinguishers can be used with more than one type of fire. Check the fire extinguishers in your home and school to find out the kinds of fires they are designed to put out.

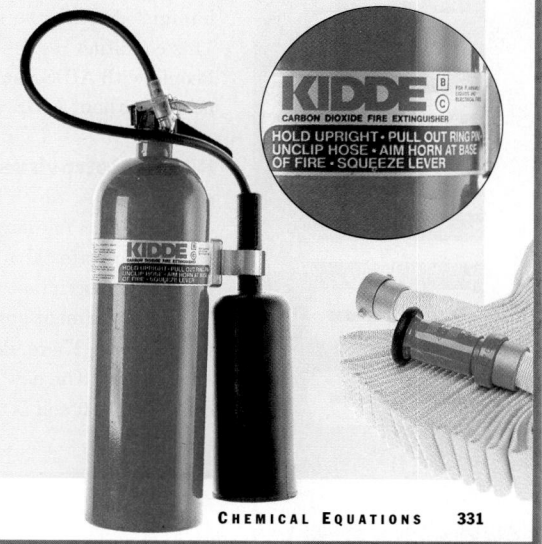

KIDDE
CARBON DIOXIDE FIRE EXTINGUISHER
HOLD UPRIGHT · PULL OUT RING PIN
UNCLIP HOSE · AIM HORN AT BASE
OF FIRE · SQUEEZE LEVER

CHEMICAL EQUATIONS 331

Review the characteristics of retro-viruses and the workings of the human immune system. Students will have encountered this information in biology class.

- retroviruses contain RNA instead of DNA as the genetic material
- retroviruses contain the enzyme *reverse transcriptase,* which is used in the production of viral DNA
- *reverse transcriptase* reverses the normal process of transcription, in which RNA is a template for DNA
- HIV evolves rapidly from protein mutations, making vaccine develop-ment and drug treatment difficult
- AIDS symptoms result from the breakdown of the immune system

Ask students for a definition of the term *inhibitor.* In this case the pro-tease inhibitor interferes with the action of reverse transcriptase, thus blocking the formation of new viruses.

AIDS treatment currently requires a combination of drugs to overcome the effects of resistance to the virus. Students should come away from this article with a new apprecia-tion for the molecular basis of life and for disease research.

SCIENCE & TECHNOLOGY

PROTEASE INHIBITORS: CONTROLLING REACTIONS

Viruses

HIV, or human immunodeficiency virus, is the virus that causes AIDS by severely weakening the human im-mune system. Since the discovery of HIV in 1983, scientists have searched for drugs that will combat the growth of the virus in human cells. Protease inhibitors are one of the newest classes of drugs to be developed in this fight.

Viruses are not living cells, but they are bits of genetic material (RNA or DNA) combined with protein mol-ecules, including enzymes. Viruses enter (infect) cells and release their ge-netic material. The host cell uses this genetic material as a code to produce more viruses.

HIV are shown here as red spheres on T-cells.

HIV and the Immune System   HIV has a particular affinity for a type of white blood cell called a *helper T-cell.* Each of these helper T-cells is vital in reg-ulating the activity of many other blood cells that destroy invading pathogens. This response to pathogens is called the immune response; it enables humans to fight off bacterial and viral diseases. Destruction of many T-cells weakens immune defenses so much that the body fails to ward off common infections. This condition results in active acquired immunodeficiency syndrome, or AIDS. People with AIDS usually die from infections that would cause little problem in people without AIDS.

HIV: A Retrovirus   The HIV virus is classified as a *retrovirus,* a virus that contains RNA, which it carries into the cell along with an enzyme called *reverse transcriptase.* You may recall from your biology class that a cell's master copy of its genetic material is DNA that remains in the nucleus. The HIV virus uses the reverse transcriptase enzyme to make a DNA copy of the RNA genetic pattern. The DNA segment enters the cell's nucleus, where it becomes a part of the cell's genetic code. There, it causes the cell to produce all of the parts needed to make new viruses. The new viruses are assembled and leave the host cell to infect new cells. The host cell is usually destroyed in the process.

Drugs for HIV Infection

Inhibiting Viral Reproduction Most of the drugs that have been used to treat HIV infections are compounds that inhibit the reverse transcriptase enzyme, in turn preventing the RNA segment from forming a DNA copy. The new protease inhibitors do their work after the parts of the virus have been produced. The proteins that are needed to assemble new viruses are made in long chains that must be cut apart into the individual proteins. Protease is an enzyme that breaks the chains in the right places. Inhibiting protease keeps many of the new viruses from assembling.

Treatment But Not a Cure Not even these new protease inhibitors can completely rid a person of HIV infection. However, combinations of drugs that inhibit the HIV reproduction process have proven successful in maintaining high T-cell levels and very low virus levels. With such treatment, many patients are able to lead essentially normal, productive lives.

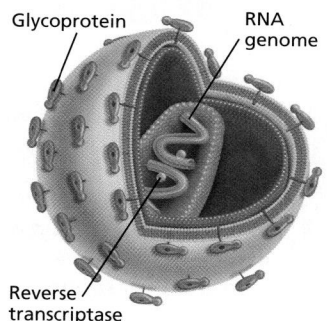

HIV Virus

Glycoprotein

RNA genome

Reverse transcriptase

HIV contains RNA in its core.

internet**connect**

SCi**LINKS** NSTA

TOPIC: Protease inhibitors
GO TO: www.scilinks.org
KEYWORD: HW096

ADDITIONAL APPLICATION

Displacement reactions are slowly destroying marble statues, monuments, and metal bridges. Have students determine where any old statues, monuments, or bridges are located in your area, and have them gather enough information to perform the following tasks:

1. Learn what materials were used in building or sculpting the structures. Find out when they were built.

2. Use the information in item 1 along with library research to suggest causes of the deterioration.

3. Write equations for the chemical reactions that are taking place during the deterioration.

4. Perform additional research to discover what measures are being taken to slow these reactions and what steps are being used to restore and repair the decaying or broken items.

CAREER APPLICATION

What would it be like to ...

▶ diagnose diseases and provide individualized care for patients?

▶ treat patients and prescribe medications?

▶ counsel families who have members with severe illnesses?

Science/Math Career Preparation	
High School	**College**
Biology	Biology
Chemistry	Chemistry
Mathematics	Mathematics
Physics	Physics

Nurse Practitioner

A nurse practitioner does all of the things that registered nurses in hospitals or physicians' offices do. In fact, most nurse practitioners (NPs) begin as nurses and after a few years of experience study to become a nurse practitioner. Nurse practitioners have some of the same responsibilities as physicians. NPs can perform extensive diagnoses of disease, carry out medical tests, counsel families, and in some cases, prescribe medicine. They often have specialties, such as pediatrics, mental health, and geriatrics. For some families, the NP is the primary health care provider.

People who choose this profession generally study biology, chemistry, physics, and mathematics. In college, the nursing candidates study analytical and organic chemistry, physics, and biology courses. After graduating, a person gains experience in the profession, takes advanced courses, and works under the supervision of a physician or other NP. Finally, an NP must pass a certification exam.

Nurse practitioners can provide very personalized care.

At the beginning of this chapter you read about problems associated with the restoration of the Statue of Liberty.

LOOKING BACK

Why did the iron support beams corrode much more than the thin copper coating?

When the tar coating wore away, salt water acted as an electrical conductor between the copper and iron. Because copper is below iron in the activity series, iron corroded preferentially. The rust that formed crumbled easily. The patina, which consists of ionic copper compounds, is insoluble in water and therefore protected the remaining copper from reacting with substances in the air and rain.

What types of chemical reactions had taken place?

The iron and copper had been oxidized by oxygen and rainwater. Rainwater is slightly acidic, and its acidity increases from pollutants in the atmosphere. The acidity may have aided the oxidation of iron, as you can see from the activity series.

How could corrosion be prevented in the future?

When considering replacement materials, the restoration team had to choose materials that resist oxidation more effectively. Two alloys, or mixtures of metals, were used to replace the rusted iron bars. One of them, *ferallium,* is a very strong iron-aluminum alloy that resists corrosion. It was used to connect the framework to the statue's structural tower. The twisting framework required a more flexible, corrosion-resistant alloy. In those cases, *316L stainless steel,* an alloy of metals such as Cr, Fe, and Ni was used.

In addition, the bars of the structure were painted with sealants to prevent corrosion. To make the top coat resistant to graffiti, an undercoat containing potassium silicate and zinc dust was applied. An epoxy polyamide polymer was used on top of that.

To keep the copper shell from touching the new frame, a layer of solid polytetrafluoroethylene (Teflon) was inserted between the shell and the frame. Finally, the cracks between the copper sheets were sealed to keep out sea spray. A silicone sealant was used for this because silicone withstands changes in temperature, and doesn't corrode or discolor the statue's copper coating.

KEY TERMS

9-2
chemical equation
coefficient

9-3
enthalpy

9-4
activity series

combustion
decomposition
displacement reaction
double-displacement
reaction

net ionic equation
spectator ion
synthesis

KEY CONCEPTS

9-1 What is a chemical reaction?

▶ A chemical reaction involves the rearrangement of atoms from the reactants into new substances, also called the products.

▶ The only way to prove that a change is a chemical change is to demonstrate that the new substances produced have chemical properties different from those of the reactants.

▶ A nonspontaneous reaction can be made to occur by linking it to an energy source.

▶ Reactants must collide with sufficient energy and the correct orientation for a reaction to occur.

9-2 How are chemical equations for reactions written?

▶ A formula equation uses atomic symbols to describe the rearrangement of atoms of the reactants to form the products in a chemical reaction.

▶ The mass, number, and types of atoms remain the same on both sides of a balanced equation.

▶ Coefficients indicating amounts of reactants and products can be adjusted to balance a chemical equation. Subscripts within a chemical formula cannot be changed.

▶ The charge must also balance in an ionic equation.

9-3 What does a chemical equation tell you?

▶ Notations in a chemical equation can indicate conditions required for a reaction to occur as well as the states of matter for the substances in the reaction.

▶ The coefficients in a balanced equation can be interpreted in terms of formula units, number of molecules, atoms, or ions, or as a mole ratio.

▶ Chemical equations may describe energy changes in a reaction. ΔH indicates the energy absorbed as heat for the overall reaction.

9-4 How are chemical reactions classified?

▶ Five basic types of chemical reactions include combustion, synthesis, decomposition, displacement, and double displacement.

▶ An activity series predicts displacement reactions. Any element on the list will displace elements below it from compounds that are in solution.

▶ Double-displacement reactions can be represented by net ionic equations indicating only the ions that are changed by the reaction.

KEY SKILLS

Review the following models before your exam. Be sure you can solve these types of problems.

Sample Problem 9A: Balancing chemical equations (p. 315).

Sample Problem 9B: Calculating energy for a specific reaction (p. 323).

Sample Problem 9C: Using the activity series to write equations (p. 328).

REVIEW & ASSESS

TERM REVIEW

1. chemical equation
2. synthesis
3. single-displacement
4. spectator ion
5. coefficients
6. combustion
7. net ionic equation
8. decomposition
9. activity series
10. monomers
11. double displacement
12. enthalpy

CONCEPT & SKILLS REVIEW

1. a. products, because more energy was released in forming new bonds than was absorbed in breaking old bonds
   b. change in energy and properties, reactant atoms rearranged to form products

2. Naturally occurring reactions tend to form more stable products. The lower the energy of a bond is, the more stable the bond is. A reaction that progresses from reactants with higher-energy bonds to products with lower-energy bonds is exothermic.

3. a. In a chemical reaction, atoms are neither destroyed nor created; they are simply rearranged. Energy is not created. It is released from the formation of products whose bonds have less energy than did the bonds of the reactants.
   b. The correct statement should read, "The atoms of the reactants were rearranged to form the products. Energy was released in the process."

4. a. Molecules in a liquid move more freely than those in a solid, so more atoms can collide with each other and react. Gas molecules move most freely and have the greatest probability of colliding to form products.

TERM REVIEW

1. When written correctly, a ——— describes which and how many atoms are rearranged in a reaction.
   (coefficient, double-displacement reaction, chemical equation)

2. Simple molecules combine to make more-complex ones in a ——— reaction.
   (decomposition, synthesis, transfer)

3. In a ——— reaction, one element replaces another in a compound that is in solution.
   (displacement, double-displacement, polymerization)

4. A ——— does not appear in a net ionic equation because it remains unchanged in the chemical reaction.
   (coefficient, monomer, spectator ion)

5. In a chemical equation, ——— indicate the relative amount of reactants and products in a chemical reaction.
   (coefficients, spectator ions, monomers)

6. Oxygen participates in ——— reactions, which produce oxides.
   (decomposition, combustion, transfer)

7. Ions that remain unchanged in a reaction in aqueous solution do not appear in a ———.
   (chemical equation, net ionic equation, coefficient)

8. A single compound is broken down into simpler substances in a ——— reaction.
   (double-displacement, combustion, decomposition)

9. If you want to predict whether a displacement reaction will occur, you can look at the ———.
   (coefficient, formula, activity series)

10. A polymer is made up of many ———.
    (coefficients, monomers, spectator ions)

11. Ions from two compounds in solution interact to form at least one new product in a ——— reaction.
    (displacement, double-displacement, synthesis)

12. The total energy content of a system is called the ———.
    (chemical equation, enthalpy, coefficient)

CONCEPT & SKILLS REVIEW

CHEMICAL REACTIONS

1. Calcium oxide, CaO, is an ingredient in cement mixes. When water is added, CaO reacts in an exothermic reaction to form calcium hydroxide, $Ca(OH)_2$. The properties of CaO are different from those of $Ca(OH)_2$.
   a. Are the bonds stronger in the reactants or in the products? Explain your answer.
   b. What evidence is there that this is a chemical reaction?

2. Use the concepts of bond energy and stability to explain why most naturally occurring chemical reactions are exothermic.

3. A student writes the following statement in a lab report: The atoms of the reactants are destroyed, and the atoms of the products are created; energy is also created.
   a. Explain the scientific inaccuracies in the student's statement.
   b. How could the student correct the inaccurate statement?

4. Considering that reactants must collide for a reaction to occur, answer the following:
   a. Why do liquids generally react faster than solids, and why do gases generally react faster than liquids?
   b. Why do gasoline pumps display labels warning against smoking while pumping gas?

c. Why is this precaution not a major concern around a solid flammable substance, such as a block of candle wax or wood?

5. What evidence can you provide that chemical reactions are responsible for the growth process that a human body undergoes?

6. If you allow a sample of ocean water to evaporate, all that is left is a mixture of salts. Why is this process not a chemical reaction even though a visible change has occurred?

BALANCING CHEMICAL EQUATIONS

7. Differentiate between formula equations and balanced chemical equations.

8. Why can coefficients, but not subscripts, be changed to balance a chemical equation?

9. The white paste that lifeguards rub on their nose to prevent sunburn contains zinc oxide, $ZnO(s)$, as an active ingredient. Zinc oxide is produced by burning zinc sulfide.

$$2ZnS(s) + 3O_2(g) \longrightarrow 2ZnO(s) + 2SO_2(g)$$

a. What is the coefficient for sulfur dioxide?
b. What is the subscript for oxygen gas?
c. How many atoms of oxygen react?
d. How many atoms of oxygen appear in the total number of sulfur dioxide molecules?

10. The following equations are balanced for mass, but they are still not written correctly. Explain why.

$$Cd(s) + 2OH^- \longrightarrow Cd(OH)_2$$

$$2NH_4^+(aq) \longrightarrow 2NH_3(g) + H_2(g)$$

INFORMATION IN CHEMICAL EQUATIONS

11. What is the significance of the positive or negative sign before the ΔH value in a chemical reaction?

12. Describe the information provided in the following equation.

$$Si(s) + 2CH_3Cl(g) \xrightarrow[300°C]{Cu\ powder} (H_3C)_2SiCl_2(l)$$

13. Dinitrogen monoxide, commonly known as laughing gas, is made by heating a solution of the salt ammonium nitrate. Water is also produced in this reaction. Write a balanced equation for this reaction, including all the appropriate notations.

14. Methyl alcohol, CH_3OH, is a clean-burning fuel. The alcohol can be made by reacting carbon monoxide and hydrogen gas.
a. What is the mole ratio of substances in this reaction?
b. How many moles of methanol can be made from 500 mol of hydrogen gas and more than enough carbon monoxide?
c. How many moles of carbon monoxide would actually react in item (b)?

15. To obtain pure silicon for use in semiconductors, silicon tetrachloride gas is reacted with magnesium metal. The products are magnesium chloride salt and solid silicon.
a. Write a balanced equation for this reaction, including all the appropriate notations.
b. The reaction releases 625.6 kJ of heat energy. How many kilojoules of heat energy are released per mole of magnesium metal in this reaction?

CLASSIFYING CHEMICAL REACTIONS

16. Explain the difference between displacement and double-displacement reactions.

17. Use Table 9-8 to predict which of the following metals would be the best to plate metal components of a boat to prevent corrosion.
a. Rb   b. Cr   c. Ba

18. Use Table 9-8 to predict which of the following metals would be the best choice as a container for concentrated sulfuric acid, H_2SO_4.
a. Sn   b. Mn   c. Pt

19. How do total and net ionic equations differ?

20. Which ions in a total ionic equation are called spectator ions? Why?

21. What other reaction type(s) can be used to categorize combustion reactions? Explain why combustion reactions also fall under these categories.

b. Vapors from gasoline move freely through the air. Because they are mixed with oxygen molecules in the air, they need little additional energy to react, and the reaction is extremely exothermic.
c. Solids do not release as many particles into the air. Thus, an ignitable gaseous mixture is not formed.

5. During growth, the human body increases in mass. Because the body does not create atoms, atoms in substances from food must be rearranged to form new compounds that the body uses, and energy is released.

6. The identity of the salt and of the water have not changed.

7. A formula equation shows formulas for the reactants and the products in a reaction. A balanced chemical equation adds the amount of each reactant and product to the formula equation.

8. Formulas for reactants and products must not change; they would change, however, if subscripts were changed. Changing coefficients in front of a formula changes the number of units but does not change the identity of the substance.

9. a. 2   c. 6
    b. 2   d. 4

10. Charge is not balanced.

11. A positive sign means that the reaction is endothermic. A negative sign means that the reaction is exothermic.

12. One mole of solid Si will react with 2 mol of gaseous CH_3Cl in the presence of powdered Cu, which acts as a catalyst, at a temperature of 300°C to form 1 mol of liquid $(CH_3)_2SiCl_2$.

13. $NH_4NO_3(s) + \text{energy} \longrightarrow$
    $\qquad N_2O(g) + 2H_2O(g)$

14. a. 1 mol CO : 2 mol H_2 :
    1 mol CH_3OH
    b. 250 mol
    c. 250 mol

15. a. $SiCl_4(g) + 2Mg(s) \longrightarrow$
$\qquad 2MgCl_2(s) + Si(s) + 625.6 \text{ kJ}$
b. 312.8 kJ

16. A displacement reaction involves one element taking the place of an ion within a compound. A double-displacement reaction involves two ions from different compounds forming a precipitate or a molecule.

17. b, Cr

18. c, Pt

19. Total ionic equations include all ions present when the reaction takes place. Net ionic equations do not include spectator ions.

20. Spectator ions are present on both the product side and the reactant side of the equation. They are called spectator ions because they are unchanged by the reaction.

21. A combustion reaction is also an oxidation reaction. Any reaction that involves combining a substance with oxygen is an oxidation reaction, and combustion is a rapid combination of a substance and oxygen. Combustion can also be a synthesis reaction if only one compound is formed, as in the combustion of pure carbon to form carbon dioxide.

22. Possible answers include the following:
a. A chemical reacts rapidly and exothermically with oxygen.
b. Two or more substances form a more complex substance.
c. A more complex substance breaks down into two or more simpler substances.
d. An element in a compound is replaced by another element.
e. Two ions from two different compounds react to form a precipitate or a molecule.

23. b

24. The first reaction will not occur because Ni is less active than Mg. The other two reactions will occur because Mg is more active than Cr and because Ba is more active than H.

---

22. What are some of the characteristics of each of these five common chemical reactions?
a. combustion
b. synthesis
c. decomposition
d. displacement
e. double-displacement

23. The saline solution used to soak contact lenses is primarily NaCl dissolved in water. Which of the following ways to designate the solution is incorrect?
a. NaCl(*aq*) b. NaCl(*s*)
c. Na$^+$(*aq*) + Cl$^-$(*aq*)

24. Use Table 9-8 to predict whether the following reactions are possible. Explain your answers.
a. $Ni(s) + MgSO_4(aq) \longrightarrow NiSO_4(aq) + Mg(s)$
b. $3Mg(s) + Cr_2(SO_4)_3(aq) \longrightarrow$
$\qquad 3MgSO_4(aq) + 2Cr(s)$
c. $Ba(s) + 2H_2O(l) \longrightarrow Ba(OH)_2(aq) + H_2(g)$

25. When heated, tungsten metal usually forms an oxide compound in a synthesis reaction. Light bulb filaments are made of tungsten. Use the information in the diagram to explain why the light bulb filament does not form an oxide compound.

Tungsten filament

Ar, N$_2$

Practice Problems

26. Balance the following equations.
a. $CaH_2(s) + H_2O(l) \longrightarrow Ca(OH)_2(aq) + H_2(g)$
b. $CH_3CH_2CCH(g) + Br_2(l) \longrightarrow$
$\qquad CH_3CH_2CBr_2CHBr_2(l)$
c. $Pb^{2+}(aq) + OH^-(aq) \longrightarrow Pb(OH)_2(s)$
d. $NO_2(g) + H_2O(l) \longrightarrow HNO_3(aq) + NO(g)$

27. Translate the following word equations into balanced chemical equations.
a. silver nitrate + potassium iodide $\longrightarrow$
$\qquad$ silver iodide + potassium nitrate

---

b. nitrogen dioxide + water $\longrightarrow$
$\qquad$ nitric acid + nitrogen monoxide
c. silicon tetrachloride + water $\longrightarrow$
$\qquad$ silicon dioxide + hydrochloric acid
d. ammonium dichromate $\longrightarrow$
$\qquad$ nitrogen + chromium(III) oxide + water
e. iron(III) oxide + magnesium $\longrightarrow$
$\qquad$ magnesium oxide + iron

28. Molecular models of unbalanced chemical equations are pictured below. On your own sheet of paper, draw molecular diagrams corrected to reflect the balanced equations.
a. $CH_4 + O_2 \longrightarrow CO_2 + H_2O$

CH$_4$ $\qquad$ O$_2$ $\qquad$ CO$_2$ $\qquad$ H$_2$O

b. $Sb + I_2 \longrightarrow SbI_3$

Sb $\qquad$ I$_2$ $\qquad$ SbI$_3$

c. $H_2 + N_2 \longrightarrow NH_3$

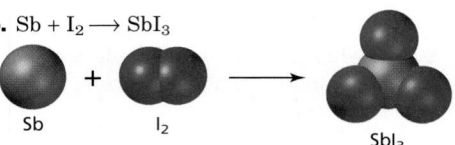

H$_2$ $\qquad$ N$_2$ $\qquad$ NH$_3$

29. Balance the following ionic equations for mass and charge.
a. $Ag^+(aq) + Cu(s) \longrightarrow Cu^{2+}(aq) + Ag(s)$
b. $Sn^{+2}(aq) + Ag^+(aq) \longrightarrow Sn^{4+}(aq) + Ag(s)$
c. $Al(s) + Fe^{2+}(aq) \longrightarrow Al^{3+}(aq) + Fe(s)$

30. Carbon tetrachloride is used as an intermediate chemical in the manufacture of other chemicals. It is prepared by allowing chlorine gas to react with methane. Hydrogen chloride is also formed in this reaction. Write the balanced chemical equation for the production of carbon tetrachloride. (**Hint: See Sample Problem 9A.**)

31. Sodium hydroxide is produced commercially by the electrolysis of aqueous sodium chloride. Hydrogen and chlorine gases are also produced. Write the balanced chemical equation for the production of sodium hydroxide. (**Hint: See Sample Problem 9A.**)

32. List the product that is missing in each of the following equations.
a. $MgO + 2HCl \longrightarrow MgCl_2 + ?$
b. $NH_4NO_3 \longrightarrow 2H_2O + ?$

33. Iron(III) chloride, $FeCl_3$, is a chemical used in photography. It can be produced by reacting iron and chlorine. Identify the chemical equation that is balanced, and explain what is wrong with the two that are not.
  a. $Fe(s) + Cl_3(g) \longrightarrow FeCl_3(s)$
  b. $2Fe(s) + 3Cl_2(g) \longrightarrow 2FeCl_3(s)$
  c. $Fe(s) + 3Cl_2(g) \longrightarrow Fe_2Cl_3(s)$

34. List the reactant that is missing in the following equations.
  a. $Na_2SO_4(aq) + ? \longrightarrow BaSO_4(s) + 2NaCl(aq)$
  b. $? \longrightarrow 2H_2O(l) + O_2(g)$

35. How many moles of HCl can be made from 6.15 mol of H_2 and an excess of Cl_2?

36. Aluminum sulfate, $Al_2(SO_4)_3$, is used to fireproof fabrics. It can be formed from a reaction with H_2SO_4.

$$Al_2O_3(s) + 3H_2SO_4(aq) \longrightarrow$$
$$Al_2(SO_4)_3(aq) + 3H_2O(l)$$

  a. How many moles of $Al_2(SO_4)_3$ would be produced if 6 mol of H_2SO_4 reacted with an excess of Al_2O_3?
  b. How many moles of Al_2O_3 are required to make 2 mol of H_2O?
  c. If 588.0 mol of Al_2O_3 react with excess H_2SO_4, how many moles of each of the products would be produced?

37. Copper(II) nitrate, $Cu(NO_3)_2$, is used to give a dark finish to items made of copper metal, making them appear antique. Copper(II) nitrate can be produced by reacting copper metal with nitric acid. Complete the following table for this reaction.

$$3Cu(s) + 8HNO_3(aq) \longrightarrow$$
$$3Cu(NO_3)_2(aq) + 4H_2O(l) + 2NO(g)$$

Equation	Cu	HNO_3	$Cu(NO_3)_2$	H_2O	NO
State					
Moles					
Molar mass					
Total mass					

38. 1,3-butadiene gas is an intermediate in the production of synthetic rubber, which is widely used in many products, from electrical insulation to car tires. This gas can be obtained by putting butane gas under high pressure and heat. Refer to the word equation below to answer the following questions.

$$\text{heat energy} + \text{butane} \xrightarrow{\text{Catalyst}}$$
$$\text{1,3-butadiene} + \text{hydrogen}$$

  a. Is this reaction exothermic or endothermic?
  b. If 236.5 kJ of heat are absorbed, what would be ΔH for the reaction?
  c. Write the full equation for the reaction, along with the ΔH value.

39. Write the balanced chemical equation for the synthesis of the antacid magnesium oxide from magnesium metal and oxygen gas. **(Hint: See Sample Problem 9A.)**

40. Write the balanced chemical equation for the synthesis of the pollutant nitrogen dioxide from nitrogen monoxide and oxygen gas. **(Hint: See Sample Problem 9A.)**

41. Sucrose, $C_{12}H_{22}O_{11}$, is the sugar used to sweeten many foods. Inside the body, it is broken down to produce H_2O and CO_2.

$$C_{12}H_{22}O_{11} + 12O_2 \longrightarrow 12CO_2 + 11H_2O$$
$$\Delta H = -5.65 \times 10^3 \text{ kJ/mol } C_{12}H_{22}O_{11}$$

  a. List all of the ratios that can be derived from this equation.
  b. Three teaspoons (0.0695 mol) of table sugar are mixed in a glass of iced tea. How much energy will the person drinking this iced tea gain from the sugar? **(Hint: See Sample Problem 9B.)**

42. Write a balanced chemical equation for the reaction that will occur if the following ingredients are mixed together. **(Hint: See Sample Problem 9C.)**

$$Pb(s), Pb^{2+}(aq), Zn(s), \text{ and } Zn^{2+}(aq)$$

43. Write the balanced equation for each of the following reactions:
  a. the combustion of propane gas, C_3H_8, to produce water and carbon dioxide
  b. the decomposition of magnesium carbonate to produce magnesium oxide and carbon dioxide

25. The filament has no contact with oxygen and thus cannot react with it. Tungsten does not react with Ar or N_2, even at high temperatures.

26. a. $CaH_2(s) + 2H_2O(l) \longrightarrow$
$$Ca(OH)_2(aq) + 2H_2(g)$$
  b. $CH_3CH_2CCH(g) + 2Br_2(g) \longrightarrow$
$$CH_3CH_2CBr_2CHBr_2(l)$$
  c. $Pb(NO_3)_2(aq) + 2NaOH(aq) \longrightarrow$
$$Pb(OH)_2(s) + 2NaNO_3(aq)$$
  d. $3NO_2(g) + H_2O(l) \longrightarrow$
$$2HNO_3(aq) + NO(g)$$

27. a. $AgNO_3 + KI \longrightarrow AgI + KNO_3$
  b. $3NO_2 + H_2O \longrightarrow 2HNO_3 + NO$
  c. $SiCl_4 + 2H_2O \longrightarrow SiO_2 + 4HCl$
  d. $(NH_4)_2Cr_2O_7 \longrightarrow$
$$N_2 + Cr_2O_3 + 4H_2O$$
  e. $Fe_2O_3 + 3Mg \longrightarrow 3MgO + 2Fe$

28. Check student drawings to ensure all atoms are accounted for.
  a. $CH_4 + 2O_2 \longrightarrow CO_2 + 2H_2O$
  b. $2Sb + 3I_2 \longrightarrow 2SbI_3$
  c. $3H_2 + N_2 \longrightarrow 2NH_3$

29. a. $2Ag^+(aq) + Cu(s) \longrightarrow$
$$Cu^{2+}(aq) + 2Ag(s)$$
  b. $Sn^{2+}(aq) + 2Ag^+(aq) \longrightarrow$
$$Sn^{4+}(aq) + 2Ag(s)$$
  c. $2Al(s) + 3Fe^{2+}(aq) \longrightarrow$
$$2Al^{3+}(aq) + 3Fe(s)$$

30. $CH_4(g) + 4Cl_2(g) \longrightarrow$
$$CCl_4(l) + 4HCl(g)$$

31. $2NaCl(aq) + 2H_2O(l) \longrightarrow$
$$2NaOH(aq) + H_2(g) + Cl_2(g)$$

32. a. H_2O **b.** N_2O

33. Equation (b) is balanced. Equation (a) uses the wrong formula for chlorine gas. Equation (c) has a different number of atoms of each type on each side and shows the wrong formula for iron(III) chloride.

34. a. $BaCl_2$ **b.** $2H_2O_2$

35. 12.3 mol

36. a. 2 mol
  b. 2/3 mol, or 0.66 mol
  c. 588.0 mol of $Al_2(SO_4)_3$ and 1764 mol of H_2O

37. State: solid, in solution, in solution, liquid, gas; Moles: 3, 8, 3, 4, 2; Molar mass: 63.55 g/mol, 63.02 g/mol, 187.57 g/mol, 18.02 g/mol, 30.01 g/mol; Total mass: 190.65 g, 504.16 g, 562.71 g, 72.08 g, 60.02 g

38. a. endothermic

b. $\Delta H = +236.5$ kJ/mol

c. $C_4H_{10}(g) + 236.5$ kJ $\longrightarrow$
$\qquad C_4H_6(g) + 2H_2(g)$;
Note: Catalyst, heat, and pressure should be indicated above or below the arrow.

39. $2Mg(s) + O_2(g) \longrightarrow 2MgO(s)$

40. $2NO(g) + O_2(g) \longrightarrow 2NO_2(g)$

41. a. 1 mol $C_{12}H_{22}O_{11}$: 12 mol O_2 :
12 mol CO_2 : 11 mol H_2O :
5.65×10^3 kJ

b. 393 kJ

42. $Zn(s) + Pb^{2+}(aq) \longrightarrow$
$\qquad Pb(s) + Zn^{2+}(aq)$

43. a. $C_3H_8(g) + 5O_2(g) \longrightarrow$
$\qquad 4H_2O(g) + 3CO_2(g)$

b. $MgCO_3(s) \longrightarrow MgO(s) + CO_2(g)$

c. $Cu^{2+}(aq) + S^{2-}(aq) \longrightarrow CuS(s)$

d. $HCl(g) + NH_3(g) \longrightarrow NH_4Cl(s)$

e. $Pt(s) + 2F_2(g) \longrightarrow PtF_4(s)$

44. $C_8H_6O_4(s) + C_2H_6O_2(l) \longrightarrow$
$\qquad C_{10}H_{10}O_5(s) + H_2O(l)$

45. Total: $Al^{3+}(aq) + 3OH^-(aq) +$
$3H^+(aq) + 3Cl^-(aq) \longrightarrow$
$\qquad Al^{3+}(aq) + 3Cl^-(aq) + 3H_2O(l)$
Net: $OH^-(aq) + H^+(aq) \longrightarrow H_2O(l)$

a. Al^{3+} and Cl^-

b. When $NaHCO_3$ is used, gas (CO_2) is formed in the stomach, causing discomfort.

LINKING CHAPTERS

1. The higher-energy reactants are converted into more stable (lower-energy) products during the reaction. The extra energy that was contained in the bonds of the reactants is released as heat and light.

2. a.

b. C_4H_5Cl

3. Cesium would be in the highest reactivity group of the activity series, where the other alkali metals are listed.

Continued on page 341.

c. the double-displacement reaction between copper(II) nitrate and ammonium sulfide

d. the transfer of a proton in a water solution from HCl to NH_3

e. the synthesis of platinum(IV) fluoride from platinum and fluorine gas

44. Terephthalic acid and ethylene glycol, shown below, can combine to synthesize a dimer molecule of the polyethylene terephthalate polymer used in film production. During the reaction, a molecule of water is formed. Write the balanced equation for this reaction.

Terephthalic acid $\qquad$ Ethylene glycol

45. Write the total and net ionic equations for the reaction in which the antacid $Al(OH)_3$ neutralizes the stomach acid HCl. This reaction is a double-displacement reaction.

$NaHCO_3(aq) + HCl(aq) \longrightarrow$
$\qquad NaCl(aq) + H_2O(aq) + CO_2(g)$

a. Identify the spectator ions in this reaction.

b. What would be the advantages of using $Al(OH)_3$ as an antacid rather than $NaHCO_3$, which undergoes the following reaction with stomach acid?

LINKING CHAPTERS

1. Theme: Conservation of energy
When wood is burned, energy is released in the form of heat and light. Explain why this change does not violate the law of conservation of energy.

2. Theme: Structural formulas
Neoprene is a polymer used to make shoes and gloves.

a. Identify the monomer in a neoprene molecule by drawing its Lewis structure.

b. What is the empirical formula of neoprene?

3. Theme: Classifications and trends
Although cesium is not included in the activity series in Table 9-8, where would you expect it to appear based on its position in the periodic table?

ALTERNATIVE ASSESSMENTS

Performance assessment

1. Design an experiment to test different antacids on the market. Include $NaHCO_3$, $Mg(OH)_2$, $CaCO_3$, and $Al(OH)_3$ in your data. Discover which one neutralizes the most acid and what byproducts are formed. Show your experiment to your teacher for approval. If your experiment is approved, obtain the necessary chemicals from your teacher and test your procedure.

Portfolio projects

1. Chemistry and you
For one day, record situations that show evidence of a chemical change. Identify the reactants and the products, and determine whether there is proof of a chemical reaction. Classify each of the chemical reactions according to the five common reaction types in the chapter.

2. Chemistry and you
Research safety tips for dealing with fires. Create a poster or brochure about fire safety that explains both these tips and their basis in science.

3. Research and communication
Many products are labeled biodegradable. Choose several biodegradable items on the market, and research the decomposition reactions involved. Be sure to take into account any special conditions that must occur for the substance to biodegrade. Present your information to the class to help inform the students about what products are best for the environment.

1. According to the law of conservation of matter, the total mass of the reacting substances is _____.
   a. always more that the total mass of the products
   b. always less than the total mass of the products
   c. sometimes more and sometimes less than the total mass of the products
   d. always equal to the total mass of the products

2. In a chemical equation, the symbol (aq) indicates that the substance is _____.
   a. water
   b. dissolved in water
   c. an acid
   d. insoluble

3. The ratio of chlorine to hydrogen chloride in the reaction $H_2(g) + Cl_2(g) \longrightarrow 2HCl(g)$ is _____.
   a. 1:1
   b. 1:2
   c. 2:1
   d. 2:2

4. The tendency for a displacement reaction to occur increases as the _____.
   a. interval between any two elements in the activity series decreases
   b. temperature decreases
   c. valence electrons are used up
   d. interval between any two atoms in the activity series increases

5. The coefficients in a chemical equation _____.
   a. show the number of grams of each substance that would react
   b. indicate the number of moles of each substance
   c. are the molar masses of the substances
   d. show the valence electrons for each atom

6. A reaction in which the ions of two compounds exchange places in aqueous solution to form two new compounds is called a(n) _____.
   a. synthesis reaction
   b. double-displacement reaction
   c. decomposition reaction
   d. combustion reaction

7. To balance a chemical equation, it is permissible to adjust the _____.
   a. coefficients
   b. subscripts
   c. formulas of the products
   d. number of products

8. The use of a double arrow in a chemical equation indicates that the reaction _____.
   a. is reversible
   b. requires heat
   c. is written backwards
   d. has not been confirmed in the laboratory

9. When reading a word equation, the plus sign, +, represents the word _____.
   a. *and*
   b. *heat*
   c. *react*
   d. *yield*

10. Negative changes in enthalpy indicate that a reaction is _____.
    a. endothermic
    b. exothermic
    c. nonspontaneous
    d. a synthesis reaction

11. The formation of polymers is a type of reaction called _____.
    a. decomposition
    b. displacement
    c. synthesis
    d. oxidation

12. Net ionic equations accurately represent _____ involving ionic compounds in solution.
    a. double displacement reactions
    b. oxidation reactions
    c. synthesis reactions
    d. all of the above

13. Elements in the activity series are arranged by _____.
    a. atomic number
    b. position in the family
    c. ionization energy
    d. experimentally determined order

1. d	6. b	10. b
2. b	7. a	11. c
3. b	8. a	12. a
4. d	9. a	13. d
5. b		

Continued from page 340.

ALTERNATIVE ASSESSMENTS

Performance assessment

1. Answers will vary. Be sure that students' testing schemes are logical and that proper laboratory procedures are followed.

Portfolio projects

1. Answers will vary. Some examples are fires or car engines combusting gasoline.

2. Answers will vary. Evaluate students' responses with respect to scientific accuracy and the feasibility of the safety measure.

3. Answers will vary. Be sure students consider reaction conditions such as light, heat, and moisture.

CHAPTER 10 PLANNING GUIDE

Stoichiometry

CLASSROOM RESOURCES

SECTIONS	TEACHER'S DEMONSTRATIONS	PROBLEM SOLVING ■ *Text* ◆ *ChemFile Mini-Guide*	LABORATORIES ■ *Text* ◆ *ChemFile Manuals: A, B, C, D*
10-1 **How much can a reaction produce?** Section Review, p. 356	**Demo 1** Stoichiometry of a Reaction, p. 344	■ **Sample Problem 10A** Mass-mass stoichiometry, p.351 ■ **Sample Problem 10B** Mole-mass stoichiometry, p. 353 ■ **Sample Problem 10C** Stoichiometric calculations with density, p. 355 ◆ **Chapter 8** Stoichiometry	■ **EXP. 10A** Decomposition of Baking Soda
10-2 **How much does a reaction really produce?** Section Review, p. 366	**Demo 2** Limiting Reactants, p.357	■ **Sample Problem 10D** Determining the limiting reactant, p. 359 ■ **Sample Problem 10E** Calculating percent yield, p. 363 ■ **Sample Problem 10F** Using percent yield, p. 365 ◆ **Chapter 9** Limiting Reactants ◆ **Chapter 10** Percent yield	■ **EXP. 10B** Stoichiometry and Gravimetric Analysis ■ **INV. 10B** Gravimetric Analysis—Hard Water Testing ■ **EXP. 10C** Stoichiometry of Reactions ■ **INV. 10C** Stoichiometry—Viral Disease Alert
10-3 **How can stoichiometry be used?** Section Review, p. 374	**Demo 3** Acid and Marble Chips, p. 367	■ **Sample Problem 10G** Air bag stoichiometry and density, p. 369 ■ **Sample Problem 10H** Stoichiometric calculations: air-fuel ratio, p. 371 ■ **Sample Problem 10I** Calculating yields: pollution, p. 374	

SECTIONS	VIDEOS/VIDEODISC *Holt Chemistry Videodisc* CNN PRESENTS *Science in the NEWS*	CHEMFILE CD-ROMS ● *Teaching Resources* ◆ *Interactive Tutor*	OVERHEADS ● *Color Transparencies* ◆ *Transparency Masters*
10-1	Solving Stoichiometry Problems Solving Mass-Mass Stoichiometry Problems Vinegar-Baking Soda Reaction	● Supplemental Reading Project: Chapter 5 of Consumer's Good Chemical Guide, "Painkillers and Painful Decision" ● Math Skills: Ratios ◆ **Module 5** Equations and Stoichiometry **Topic** Balancing Equations **Topic** Stoichiometry	● **44** Solving Mass-Mass Stoichiometry Problems ● **45** Solving Stoichiometry Problems with Moles or Grams ● **47** Stoichiometry Calculations
10-2	Limiting Reactants	● Math Skills: Percentage ◆ **Module 5** Equations and Stoichiometry **Topic** Limiting Reagents	
10-3	Methanol Combusting		

ASSESSMENT RESOURCES

ALTERNATIVE ASSESSMENTS	CHAPTER TESTING	SCORING RUBRICS *Holt ChemFile Teaching Resources CD-ROM*
Student Text Performance assessments, p. 380 Portfolio projects 1–4, p. 380 **Teacher's Edition** Discussion Strategy, p. 349 Group Strategy, p. 351 Percentage Yield, p. 362 **Study Guide** Sections 10-1 to 10-3	**Student Text** Test Preparation, p. 381 **Holt Chemistry: Visualizing Matter Chapter 10 Test** (blackline masters) **Holt ChemFile Test Generator for Macintosh and Windows**	**Lab Work** Student-Designed Experiments Rubric Performance-Tasks Scoring Rubric Assessment for Structured Inquiry Assessment for Open-Ended Inquiry **Portfolio Projects** Evaluating Concept Maps Assessing Portfolios Portfolio Assignment Student Evaluation Form

Establishing Prior Knowledge

Make certain students understand the following concepts:
- Chapter 1: conversion factors
- Chapter 2: significant digits, density
- Chapter 7: nomenclature and structures of organic compounds
- Chapter 8: conversion between grams and moles, molar masses, three-step method of problem solving
- Chapter 9: balanced chemical equations

READING STRATEGY

Assimilating Knowledge

Before reading this chapter, have students write a short list of all the things they know about how the mass of the reactants affects the mass of the products. When students finish their list, ask them to contribute their entries to a group list on the board. Then have students list the things they want to know about how the mass of the reactants affects the mass of the products.

If students are having trouble coming up with questions, offer the following suggestions to get them on track:

- What do you know about the total mass of reactants compared with the total amount of product?
- What does a balanced chemical equation tell you about the ratio of the amount of reactants to the amount of products in the reaction?

Have students save their lists for later use in the Reading Strategy on page 376.

ABOUT THE ILLUSTRATION

Stoichiometry can be used to estimate mass and amount quantities in a chemical reaction.

reactants

products

 internetconnect

Holt Chemistry: Visualizing Matter
On-Line Resources
go.hrw.com
Visit the HRW Web site for a variety of resources related to this chapter. Just type in the keyword HW0 Chapt10.

SC LINKS
NSTA

National Science Teachers Association
On-Line Resources: www.scilinks.org
The following Scilinks Internet resources can be found in the student text for this chapter:

Page 346
TOPIC: Aldehydes/ Ketones
KEYWORD: HW101

Page 368
TOPIC: Air bags
KEYWORD: HW102

Page 373
TOPIC: Catalytic converters
KEYWORD: HW103

MASS RELATIONSHIPS AND FEEDING THE ARMY

> At dinnertime, the soldiers were miles from a field kitchen. They each pulled out a meal pouch, inserted it into a small bag, and added water. Within 15 minutes, the soldiers were eating hot meals.

The dinner is one of the U.S. Army's "Meal, Ready-to-Eat," or MRE, rations. Each MRE is a main dish within a pouch made of aluminum foil and plastic. In 1985, researchers at the Army's Natick Research, Development, and Engineering Center invented a way to heat MREs using a special "Flameless Ration Heater," or FRH.

Each FRH is a plastic sleeve that holds a pad containing metal particles embedded in a polymeric matrix. The metal is an alloy of 90% magnesium and 10% iron. The entire package has a mass of 20.0 g, of which about 8.1 g is magnesium.

In the FRH, the water reacts with magnesium in an exothermic reaction.

$$Mg(s) + 2H_2O(l) \longrightarrow$$
$$Mg(OH)_2(s) + H_2(g) + 349 \text{ kJ}$$

The energy released by this reaction warms the meal to 60°C. To speed the reaction, iron was added to the FRH. Both iron and magnesium react readily with warm water but since iron is a less active metal than magnesium, the magnesium first reacts. Earlier models of the FRH used more than 60 mL of water, but the latest version requires only 45 mL.

Before the FRH was developed, the Army issued bars of trioxane, $C_3H_6O_3$, to warm meals. The bars came in 15 g and 30 g sizes and were burned in a combustion reaction, releasing about 500 kJ of energy for a 30 g bar.

The necessity of heating meals with equipment that is lightweight and easy to use is one shared by the Army and by people involved in outdoor activities such as camping. A heater similar to the FRH is available for campers. It uses the energy released when water reacts with calcium oxide.

$$CaO(s) + H_2O(l) \longrightarrow Ca(OH)_2(s) + 65.2 \text{ kJ}$$

How do the amounts and masses of substances in a reaction compare? In this chapter, you will learn how to determine the amount of reactant needed for a reaction and how to predict the amount of product that is made. You can apply these same principles to determine the most effective way to heat an MRE.

CHAPTER LINKS

Why was the magnesium-water reaction of the FRH chosen over trioxane and calcium oxide?

Why is there a difference between the amount of water that is added and the amount of water that the reaction requires?

STORY BACKGROUND

The Flameless Ration Heater was developed jointly by the U.S. Army and Zesto Therm, a company based in Cincinnati, Ohio, as an environmentally safe method of preparing hot meals outdoors. Soldiers were able to use the FRH to heat their meals in the 1990–1991 Desert Storm conflict.

To achieve the high exothermic reaction needed to warm food, the magnesium undergoes a supercorrosion process, shown by the equation on page 343.

NaCl is used in the FRH to enhance the corrosion of magnesium, which is naturally protected by an oxide coating. The Cl^- ion in NaCl reacts with $Mg(OH)_2$ to form MgOHCl. The magnesium oxide coating is soluble in the MgOHCl, so it dissolves. Once the coating is gone, water can continue to react with the magnesium.

RESOURCE LINK

Supplemental Reading Projects Guided reading worksheets for Chapter 5 of *Consumer's Good Chemical Guide,* "Painkillers and Painful Decisions," can be found on the Holt ChemFile Teaching Resources CD-ROM.

CONCEPT PREVIEW

Section 10-1
Mass-mole relationships in a chemical reaction
- mass-mass stoichiometry
- mass-mole stoichiometry
- effect of density

Section 10-2
How much a reaction actually produces
- limiting reactants
- theoretical yield
- actual yield
- percentage yield

Section 10-3
Uses of stoichiometry
- automobile air bags
- fuel delivery systems
- pollution control

SECTION 10-1

LESSON WARM-UP

Mass Relationships in a Chemical Reaction

Use the demonstration on this page to trace mass relationships in a simple reaction. Tell students that you are going to demonstrate the following reaction.

$$Na_2CO_3(s) + 2HCl(aq) \longrightarrow$$
$$2NaCl(aq) + H_2O(l) + CO_2(g)$$

How much can a reaction produce?

OBJECTIVES

▶ **Distinguish** between composition stoichiometry and reaction stoichiometry.

▶ **Apply** a three-step method to solve stoichiometry problems.

▶ **Use** mole ratios and molar masses to create conversion factors for solving stoichiometry problems.

Stoichiometry

In Chapter 9, you learned that reactions can be used to make new products, to break down reactants, and to provide a source of energy. But the predictions you made in Chapter 9 relate only to the *identities* and *relative amounts* of the products and reactants. It is also very useful to predict exactly *how much mass* of a substance will be involved in a reaction. Such predictions are a part of chemistry known as **stoichiometry.**

stoichiometry

mass and amount relationships between reactants and products in a chemical reaction

Moles: the language of equations

When calculating masses of reactants or products, keep in mind that *balanced* equations give the relative numbers of moles of substances involved in the reaction and not the actual amounts of substances present. *When solving stoichiometry problems, you must start from a balanced equation.* Consider the reaction between ammonia and oxygen, as shown by the following equation.

$$4NH_3(g) + 5O_2(g) \longrightarrow 4NO(g) + 6H_2O(g)$$

The equation states that 4 mol NH_3 react with 5 mol O_2 to produce 4 mol NO and 6 mol H_2O. See the space-filled model in **Figure 10-1.**

▼ **FIGURE 10-1**

Equations show the relative, not actual, quantities of substances present.

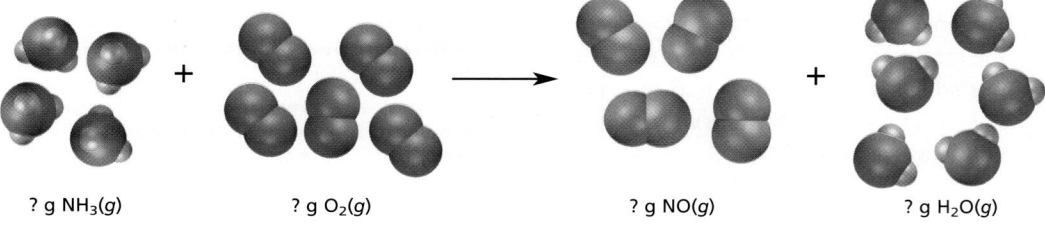

| ? g $NH_3(g)$ | ? g $O_2(g)$ | ? g $NO(g)$ | ? g $H_2O(g)$ |

DEMONSTRATION 1

Stoichiometry of a Reaction

Approximate time: 20 minutes

1. Weigh the mass of a Pyrex evaporating dish to the thousandth of a gram. Record the mass on the board.

2. Add 1 g of anhydrous Na_2CO_3 to the dish. Determine and record the total mass of the dish and the salt.

3. Add 1 M HCl one drop at a time until the bubbling stops. Then add about two more drops of HCl to make sure the reaction goes to completion.

4. Clamp a ring to a ring stand. Make sure you perform this part of the demonstration underneath a fume hood. Place a wire gauze and the evaporating dish on the ring. Heat the dish gently with a lab burner until none of the liquid remains.

Suppose you have only 2.4 mol NH_3. How many mol O_2 are needed? You need to carry out a mole-to-mole conversion.

$$\text{mol } NH_3 \longrightarrow \text{mol } O_2$$

Recall from Chapter 9 that coefficients in chemical equations provide mole ratios that can be used as conversion factors. Because the amount of O_2 is asked for, the conversion factor you set up should have moles of O_2 in the numerator. You are given the amount of NH_3, so the denominator of your conversion factor should include the amount of NH_3 relative to moles of O_2, as shown in the balanced chemical equation on page 344.

$$\frac{5 \text{ mol } O_2}{4 \text{ mol } NH_3}$$

Use this information to carry out the conversion.

$$2.4 \text{ mol } NH_3 \times \frac{5 \text{ mol } O_2}{4 \text{ mol } NH_3} = 3.0 \text{ mol } O_2$$

All stoichiometric calculations involving equations use mole ratios at some point.

Making chemicals in large amounts

The makers of artificial flavors for products, such as banana ice cream and banana-flavored bubble gum, use stoichiometry in synthesizing the flavors. The substance providing most of the taste and smell of bananas is 3-methylbutyl acetate, or isoamyl acetate. Isoamyl acetate belongs to the group of organic compounds known as esters. **Esters** are among the organic chemicals responsible for the aromas and flavors of fruits. The ester functional group is indicated in red on the structure of isoamyl acetate in **Figure 10-2**.

Because there are so many compounds in a banana, it is difficult to isolate and purify natural flavoring. It is more cost-effective to

ester

an organic compound often responsible for the aromas and flavors of fruits

HISTORICAL CONNECTION

The word *stoichiometry* is from the Greek work *stoicheion*, which means "to measure the elements." Joseph Black (1728–1799) and his student Daniel Rutherford studied quantitatively the forward and reverse of the following reaction to measure the redistribution of mass during the course of a reaction:

$$CaCO_3(s) \quad CaO(s) + CO_2(g)$$

Their findings laid the groundwork for modern stoichiometry.

VISUAL STRATEGY

Figure 10-2 Use the structural formula in this figure to review with students how to write a chemical formula from a structural one. Students should realize that $C_6H_{14}COO$ is equivalent to the structural formula for isoamyl acetate.

Acetic acid   Isoamyl alcohol   Isoamyl acetate   Water

Isoamyl acetate

FIGURE 10-2 ◄

Isoamyl acetate is the compound primarily responsible for a banana's fruity flavor. It is used in a variety of artificially flavored products.

5. Weigh and record the mass of the dish and the dried NaCl.

6. Have students compare the mass of the Na_2CO_3 with the mass of the NaCl. The mass of NaCl will be greater. Ask students to explain this result and what happens to the excess HCl.

7. Save the results for Section 10-2, when theoretical yield, actual yield, and percentage yield are discussed.

Safety

Wear safety goggles and a lab apron at all times. Use tongs when handling hot glassware. Do not breathe HCl fumes. Students should stand 3 m from the demonstration.

Disposal

Wrap the NaCl in newspaper, and put it in the trash.

In a spacecraft, the carbon dioxide exhaled by astronauts is removed by its reaction with lithium hydroxide according to the following chemical equation.

$$CO_2(g) + 2LiOH(s) \longrightarrow Li_2CO_3(s) + H_2O(l)$$

However, excess mass is a serious consideration in a spacecraft. Scientists must therefore estimate how much carbon dioxide will be exhaled and provide only enough LiOH to react with that amount. Stoichiometry provides a means of estimating this amount.

VISUAL STRATEGY

Figure 10-3 Be sure students are aware that a carbon atom exists at each corner of the cyclic parts of the structural formulas. These carbon atoms are bonded to the appropriate number of hydrogen atoms. Have students rewrite the bottom two formulas to show all of the hydrogen and carbon atoms.

Ethyl butyrate

Ethyl acetate

Benzaldehyde

4-(4-hydroxyphenyl) 2-butanone
or raspberry ketone

▲ **FIGURE 10-3**

Many flavors and aromas are attributed to organic chemicals such as esters, aldehydes, alcohols, and ketones.

synthesize isoamyl acetate in the lab using the reaction shown on page 345. The other flavor chemicals shown in **Figure 10-3** are also often synthesized as artificial flavorings.

Consider the following question: *If a flavoring manufacturer has 450. g isoamyl alcohol and more than enough acetic acid to react with all of it, what is the maximum mass of banana flavoring that can be made?* Questions that deal with masses involved in reactions are examples of *reaction stoichiometry.*

Organize what you already know

When faced with a problem like this one, a good way to start is to make a table or list of all of the information given in the problem as well as the answer you are trying to find. *Remember to include units for all quantities.* The sections of **Table 10-1** include this initial information. The question mark in the table indicates the answer that is sought. Problems like this are often called *mass-mass problems* because the data given and the answer sought are mass amounts.

Start by figuring out more than just what the problem tells you. Determine the molecular formulas from the structural formulas for isoamyl alcohol and acetic acid shown on page 345.

In Chapter 5, you learned how to use the periodic table to calculate molar masses of reactants and products. Such calculations are called *composition stoichiometry* because they describe the mathematical relationships among the elements that make up a substance. The values for molar mass are shown in Table 10-1. *For almost all chemistry problems of this type, you will need the molar masses of the substances involved.*

The most important piece of information that you need now is the balanced chemical equation for the reaction. Because a balanced chemical equation provides mole ratios for the substances in the reaction, you

TABLE 10-1	Some Data for the Banana-Flavoring Problem		
Reactants and products	**Amount**	**Molecular formula**	**Molar mass**
Isoamyl alcohol	450. g	$C_5H_{11}OH$	88.17 g/mol
Acetic acid	excess	$C_2H_4O_2$	60.06 g/mol
Isoamyl acetate	? g	$CH_3COOC_5H_{11}$	130.21 g/mol
Water	not given	H_2O	18.02 g/mol

can compare relative amounts of the reactants and products. In the balanced equation for isoamyl acetate synthesis, all of the coefficients are 1, so all of the mole ratios are 1:1.

$$C_5H_{11}OH(l) + CH_3COOH(l) \xrightarrow{\text{HCl}} CH_3COOC_5H_{11}(l) + H_2O(l)$$

In the equation, hydrochloric acid, HCl, is added to speed up the reaction and therefore is written above the arrow. The equation shows that 1 mol isoamyl alcohol and 1 mol acetic acid react to make 1 mol isoamyl acetate and 1 mol water. *For almost all chemistry problems, you need a balanced chemical equation so that you can find the mole ratios.* Because the problem gives and asks for mass, you must first convert the given mass to amount, use the mole ratio to get moles of the unknown, then convert from amount to mass of the unknown. Remember that mole ratios can only be used to convert amount. Mass, volume, and other quantities must be converted to moles before a mole ratio can be used.

$$g \text{ of } A \longrightarrow mol \text{ of } A \longrightarrow mol \text{ of } B \longrightarrow g \text{ of } B$$

Divide the calculation into steps.

1. Calculate moles of isoamyl alcohol

You are given 450. g of isoamyl alcohol, shown in **Figure 10-4,** and you need to convert from grams of alcohol to moles of alcohol. This requires multiplication by a conversion factor as yet unknown.

$$450. \text{ g } C_5H_{11}OH \times ? \longrightarrow mol \text{ } C_5H_{11}OH$$

The units on both sides must match, so moles of alcohol must be introduced in the numerator on the left, and grams of alcohol must be in the denominator to cancel the unit grams of alcohol.

$$450. \text{ g } \cancel{C_5H_{11}OH} \times \frac{1 \text{ mol } C_5H_{11}OH}{? \text{ g } \cancel{C_5H_{11}OH}} = ? \text{ mol } C_5H_{11}OH$$

This step makes the units equal on both sides of the equation. Now you need to figure out the actual conversion factor needed. It is the inverse of the molar mass, which you calculated for Table 10-1.

$$450. \text{ g } \cancel{C_5H_{11}OH} \times \frac{1 \text{ mol } C_5H_{11}OH}{88.14 \text{ g } \cancel{C_5H_{11}OH}} = 5.10 \text{ mol } C_5H_{11}OH$$

TEACHING TIP

Conversion Factors Remind students that all conversion factors are equal to 1. To determine which conversion factor to use to solve a stoichiometry problem, students should assign the given unit as the denominator so that the unit will cancel. The numerator of the conversion factor should contain the unit the student is trying to find.

FIGURE 10-4 ◄

The molar mass of isoamyl alcohol, one of the reactants in the banana-flavoring synthesis reaction, is 88.14 g/mol.

RESOURCE LINK

ChemFile Teaching Resources CD-ROM
Skills Review
Assign Math Skills Worksheet 5: *Ratios* to review or reteach this skill.

▶ **FIGURE 10-5**

Besides being used as a flavoring agent, isoamyl acetate is also used as an ingredient in air fresheners, as a solvent, and as an ingredient in the manufacture of artificial leather, artificial pearls, and waterproof varnishes.

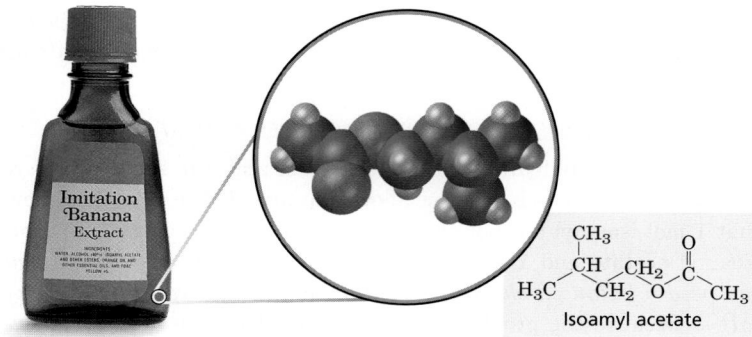

Isoamyl acetate

2. Use the mole ratio to calculate amount of isoamyl acetate

You know from the equation that 1 mol of isoamyl alcohol produces 1 mol of isoamyl acetate, shown in **Figure 10-5.** So, just as before, use the mole ratio in the equation to convert from the amount of one substance to the amount of another.

$$5.10 \text{ mol } C_5H_{11}OH \times \frac{1 \text{ mol } CH_3COOC_5H_{11}}{1 \text{ mol } C_5H_{11}OH} = 5.10 \text{ mol } CH_3COOC_5H_{11}$$

3. Use molar mass to calculate mass of isoamyl acetate

You now know the amount of isoamyl acetate, but you were asked to find the mass of this product. Just as before, you need a conversion factor. Use units to determine it. The unit *g CH₃COOC₅H₁₁* needs to be in the numerator, and *mol CH₃COOC₅H₁₁* must be in the denominator in order to produce the correct units for the answer. The molar mass of the isoamyl acetate can then be calculated.

$$5.10 \text{ H}_3COOC_5H_{11} \times \frac{130.19 \text{ g } CH_3COOC_5H_{11}}{\text{H}_3COOC_5H_{11}} =$$

$$664 \text{ g } CH_3COOC_5H_{11}$$

Verify your answer. The units are correct, and there are three significant figures. Because the molar mass of the acetate is larger than that of the alcohol, the product mass should be larger. 664 g is larger than the 450. g alcohol used, so the answer is probably correct.

4. Combine all the steps

All of these calculations can be combined rather than done separately. If you keep steps separate, make sure to round only the final answer, not the intermediate steps, to the correct number of significant digits.

$$450. \text{ g } C_5H_{11}OH \times \frac{1 \text{ mol } C_5H_{11}OH}{88.14 \text{ g } C_5H_{11}OH} \times \frac{1 \text{ mol } CH_3COOC_5H_{11}}{1 \text{ mol } C_5H_{11}OH} \times$$

$$\frac{130.19 \text{ g } CH_3COOC_5H_{11}}{1 \text{ mol } CH_3COOC_5H_{11}} = 664 \text{ g } CH_3COOC_5H_{11}$$

Three-step method

In solving stoichiometry problems, it is important to think about what the problem means, rather than just multiplying and dividing the given values with your calculator. In Chapter 8 you learned about the three-step method used in solving the Sample Problems. Because the ability to solve stoichiometry problems is crucial to your success in chemistry, the method is repeated here for you to review before working with the Sample Problems that follow. As you work through your homework problems, it may be useful to refer to this page for suggestions. The Sample Problems that follow can also provide helpful hints.

Remember that *the way to convert from one substance to another is to relate the reaction stoichiometry **in moles.*** For this you need to start with a balanced equation. Use the mole ratios from the balanced equation to convert substances. If your data from the problem are in grams, convert them to moles first. If they are in kilograms, convert to grams before proceeding.

Module 5: Equations and Stoichiometry
Topic: Balancing Equations
This engaging tutorial reviews the rules for balancing equations through modeling and guided practice.

HOW TO — Solve stoichiometry problems

1 List what you know
- Read the problem carefully.
- Organize the information from the problem statement in a list or table.
- Identify what you are asked to find, and write down the units for the answer.
- If there is a reaction, write an equation for it, making sure that it is balanced so that you'll have the correct mole ratios.
- List any conversion factors that you might need, such as molar masses, mole ratios, and unit conversions.

2 Set up the problem
- First analyze what needs to be done to get to the answer. See if there is any information not given in the problem that you need for the answer.
- Write the formulas for all substances you will be working with, and determine their molar masses. Use a periodic table where necessary.
- Identify which value given in the problem can be used as a starting point. Write it on a sheet of paper. Write an equals sign to the right of the starting point and then a question mark with the units of the answer. Fill in the units of the conversion factors and the actual numerical values necessary to convert from what is given in the problem to what is sought in the answer.
- Many chemistry problems (and virtually all stoichiometry problems) require the quantities of substances to be in moles, so use the molar masses from step (1) to convert the mass into moles, if necessary.

STOICHIOMETRY 349

> ▶ If you need to change from the amount of one substance to the amount of another substance, use mole ratios derived from the coefficients of the balanced chemical equation. Remember that the mole ratio is not always 1:1.

> ▶ Be sure to convert the data into appropriate units, such as *grams* instead of *kilograms,* or vice versa, depending on what units you are given and want to find.

> ▶ When you have finished writing down your plan with all of the conversion factors, as shown in **Figure 10-6,** check to see how the units cancel each other. If they all cancel to give you the units you need for the answer, the setup is probably correct.

3 Calculate and verify

> ▶ Begin your calculations by working through the setup in step (2). In the examples in this book, numbers are not rounded off between steps in calculations.

> ▶ When you have finished your calculations, remember to round off and make sure that the answer has the correct number of significant figures.

> ▶ Always report the answer with the correct units. Do not write the answer as just a number.

> ▶ Verify your answer by estimating. One way to do this is to round off the numbers in the problem setup and make a quick calculation. Another excellent aid is to compare conversion factors in the setup and decide whether the answer should be bigger or smaller than the initial value.

> ▶ Make sure your answer is reasonable. For example, if you began with 5.3 mg of one reactant and your answer is that it will make 725 g of a product, you know that you need to double-check all of your work.

▼ FIGURE 10-6

Most stoichiometry problems can be solved using this flowchart.

Mass-Mass Stoichiometry

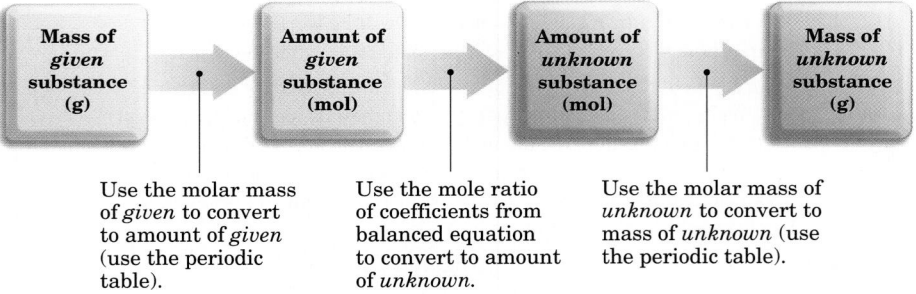

| Mass of *given* substance (g) | → | Amount of *given* substance (mol) | → | Amount of *unknown* substance (mol) | → | Mass of *unknown* substance (g) |

Use the molar mass of *given* to convert to amount of *given* (use the periodic table).

Use the mole ratio of coefficients from balanced equation to convert to amount of *unknown*.

Use the molar mass of *unknown* to convert to mass of *unknown* (use the periodic table).

GRAPHIC ORGANIZER

For the equation A + B ⟶ C + D

Mass of A   +   Mass of B   =   Mass of C   +   Mass of D

Students can use this flow diagram to check calculations if all masses are known.

SAMPLE PROBLEM 10A   Mass-mass stoichiometry

A hungry soldier is ready to prepare one of his MREs. How many grams of water must he add to ensure that all of the 8.1 g magnesium used in an FRH react to produce heat?

$$Mg(s) + 2H_2O(l) \longrightarrow Mg(OH)_2(s) + H_2(g) + 353 \text{ kJ}$$

1 **List what you know**

▶ Mass of magnesium used: 8.1 g
   Mass of water needed: ? g

2 **Set up the problem**

▶ To solve the problem, you will need the molar masses and mole ratio of magnesium and water.
   molar mass of magnesium: Mg, 24.30 g/mol
   molar mass of water: H_2O, 18.02 g/mol
▶ To convert from the mass of Mg given to the mass of H_2O needed, first convert to moles and use the mole ratio to link the two amounts. This is a problem of the type already considered.

$$\text{g of Mg} \longrightarrow \text{mol of Mg} \longrightarrow \text{mol of } H_2O \longrightarrow \text{g of } H_2O$$

Therefore, you use the procedure in Figure 10-6. First convert the grams of magnesium into moles, then convert moles of magnesium to moles of water, and finally convert moles of water into grams of water.

$$8.1 \text{ g Mg} \times \frac{1 \text{ mol Mg}}{24.30 \text{ g Mg}} \times \frac{2 \text{ mol } H_2O}{1 \text{ mol Mg}} \times \frac{18.02 \text{ g } H_2O}{1 \text{ mol } H_2O} = ? \text{ g } H_2O$$

3 **Calculate and verify**

▶ Use your calculator to work through the setup. Be sure to round to the correct number of significant figures, which is two.
   Calculator answer: 12.01333 g H_2O
   Answer to two significant figures: 12 g H_2O
▶ Verify your answer by rounding the numbers in the setup and estimating.
   If the units are correct and the number is close to the estimate, the answer is probably correct.

PRACTICE PROBLEMS

1. Tin(II) fluoride, also known as stannous fluoride, is added to some dental products to help prevent cavities. What mass of tin(II) fluoride can be made from 55.0 g of hydrofluoric acid, HF, if there is more than enough tin?

$$Sn(s) + 2HF(aq) \longrightarrow SnF_2(aq) + H_2(g)$$

COMMON MISCONCEPTION

Many students use their calculators incorrectly with numbers that are multiplied in the denominator of fractions. Many students will work out problems such as

$$\frac{67 \times 70}{15 \times 35}$$

by dividing the product of the numerator by 15 then multiplying by 35. Tell them that if the number is in the numerator, it is multiplied, and if it is in the denominator, it is divided. The problem can be worked on a calculator by pressing $67 \times 70 \div 15 \div 35 = 8.9$.

CHEMISTRY INTERACTIVE TUTOR

Module 5: Equations and Stoichiometry
Topic: Stoichiometry
This engaging tutorial reviews stoichiometry concepts through modeling and guided practice.

ALTERNATIVE ASSESSMENT

Group Strategy

Allow students to work in small groups. Have each group calculate the amount in grams of each product produced from the 8.1 g of magnesium and the 12 g of water in Sample Problem 10A.

Ans. 19 g Mg(OH)$_2$ and 0.67 g H$_2$

After students finish their calculations, have them each write a short paragraph explaining how the amounts of reactants and products in a chemical reaction can be used to explain the law of conservation of mass.

Note: Students may mention that the total masses of reactants and products are close but that they differ by 0.4 g. Ask students why this difference exists. Have students rework the problems using three significant digits to show that the totals become closer as more significant digits are used.

ANSWERS

PRACTICE PROBLEM 10A

1. $55.0 \text{ g HF} \times \dfrac{1 \text{ mol HF}}{20.01 \text{ g HF}} \times$

   $\dfrac{1 \text{ mol SnF}_2}{2 \text{ mol HF}} \times \dfrac{156.7 \text{ g SnF}_2}{1 \text{ mol SnF}_2} =$

   215 g SnF_2

2. $40.0 \text{ g C}_6\text{H}_6 \times \dfrac{1 \text{ mol C}_6\text{H}_6}{78.11 \text{ g C}_6\text{H}_6} \times$

   $\dfrac{1 \text{ mol C}_6\text{H}_5\text{Cl}}{1 \text{ mol C}_6\text{H}_6} \times \dfrac{112.6 \text{ g C}_6\text{H}_5\text{Cl}}{1 \text{ mol C}_6\text{H}_5\text{Cl}} =$

   $57.6 \text{ g C}_6\text{H}_5\text{Cl}$

3. $25\,000 \text{ g C}_6\text{H}_6\text{O}_2 \times$

   $\dfrac{1 \text{ mol C}_6\text{H}_6\text{O}_2}{110.11 \text{ g C}_6\text{H}_6\text{O}_2} \times \dfrac{1 \text{ mol C}_{20}\text{H}_{12}\text{O}_5}{2 \text{ mol C}_6\text{H}_6\text{O}_2} \times$

   $\dfrac{332.31 \text{ g C}_{20}\text{H}_{12}\text{O}_5}{1 \text{ mol C}_{20}\text{H}_{12}\text{O}_5} \times \dfrac{1 \text{ kg}}{1000 \text{ g}} =$

   $37.72 \text{ kg C}_{20}\text{H}_{12}\text{O}_5$

ADDITIONAL EXAMPLES

SAMPLE PROBLEM 10A

Balance the equation for each of the following problems, and then solve.

a. Limestone ($CaCO_3$) will react with most acids to form a calcium salt, water, and carbon dioxide. What mass of water is produced if 65.2 g of calcium carbonate reacts with phosphoric acid that is in excess? What salt is formed?

   Ans. $3CaCO_3(s) + 2H_3PO_4(aq) \longrightarrow$
   $Ca_3(PO_4)_2(s) + 3H_2O(l) + 3CO_2(g)$;
   11.7 g H_2O; Calcium phosphate is the salt formed.

b. Oxygen and potassium chloride are formed when potassium chlorate decomposes. What mass of oxygen is produced when 49.89 g of potassium chlorate decomposes?

   Ans. $2KClO_3(s) \longrightarrow 2KCl(s) +$
   $3O_2(g)$; 19.54 g O_2

c. What mass of ammonia is formed when 7.50 g of nitrogen gas reacts with enough hydrogen gas?

   Ans. $N_2(g) + 3H_2(g) \longrightarrow 2NH_3(g)$;
   9.12 g NH_3

2. Chlorobenzene, C_6H_5Cl, is used in the production of many important chemicals, such as aspirin, dyes, and disinfectants. What mass in grams of chlorobenzene can be made from 40.0 g of benzene if more than enough chlorine is present?

$$C_6H_6(l) + Cl_2(g) \longrightarrow C_6H_5Cl(s) + HCl(g)$$

3. What mass of fluorescein can be made from 25.00 kg resorcinol?

| Two resorcinol | One phthalic anhydride | One fluorescein | Two water |

Other stoichiometric calculations

Problems with amounts in moles

Some stoichiometry problems involve data or answers in mole quantities instead of mass quantities. These problems can be solved with an approach similar to that used to solve the problems having both data and answers in grams. But there are fewer steps with this approach because one or both molar mass conversions are unnecessary, as shown in **Figure 10-7,** which has some of the same steps as **Figure 10-6.** If both the answer and the given data are in moles, the only conversion factor necessary to solve the problem is the mole ratio.

► **FIGURE 10-7**

If a stoichiometry problem involves quantities in moles, it can be solved in fewer steps than are required to solve problems with quantities in grams.

| Mass of given | Amount of given | Amount of unknown | Mass of unknown |

Mass-to-Mass Problem-Solving Plan
1. Always begin with a balanced chemical equation.
2. Use the molar mass of the given substance to convert from mass of given to amount of given.
3. Use the mole ratio of coefficients from the balanced chemical equation to change from amount of given to amount of unknown.
4. Use the molar mass of unknown to convert from amount of unknown to mass of unknown.

Mole-to-Mass Problem-Solving Plan
1. Always begin with a balanced chemical equation.
2. Use the mole ratio of coefficients from the balanced chemical equation to change from amount of given to amount of unknown.
3. Use the molar mass of the unknown substance to convert from amount of unknown to mass of unknown.

SAMPLE PROBLEM 10B   Mole-mass stoichiometry

The human body needs at least 1.03×10^{-2} mol O_2 every minute. If all of this oxygen is used for the cellular respiration reaction that oxidizes glucose to carbon dioxide and water, what mass of glucose does the human body consume each minute?

$$C_6H_{12}O_6(aq) + 6O_2(aq) \longrightarrow 6CO_2(aq) + 6H_2O(l)$$

1 List what you know

▸ Amount of O_2 used each minute: 1.03×10^{-2} mol O_2
▸ Mole ratio: 1 mol $C_6H_{12}O_6$:6 mol O_2
▸ Mass of glucose needed each minute: ? g

Because oxygen is already given in a mole amount, the molar mass of O_2 is unnecessary.

2 Set up the problem

▸ Calculate molar mass from the periodic table.
  molar mass of $C_6H_{12}O_6$: 180.16 g/mol
▸ Analyze what needs to be done to get the answer. You are given moles of oxygen, so you can immediately convert to moles of glucose using the mole ratio from the balanced equation. Then you can use the molar mass to determine the mass in grams of the glucose.

$$1.03 \times 10^{-2} \text{ mol } O_2 = ? \text{ g } C_6H_{12}O_6$$

You need to go from moles of O_2 to moles of glucose to grams of glucose using two conversions.

$$1.03 \times 10^{-2} \text{ mol } O_2 \times \frac{1 \text{ mol } C_6H_{12}O_6}{6 \text{ mol } O_2} \times \frac{180.16 \text{ g } C_6H_{12}O_6}{1 \text{ mol } C_6H_{12}O_6} = ? \text{ g } C_6H_{12}O_6$$

3 Calculate and verify

▸ Use your calculator to work through the setup. Be sure to round to the correct number of significant figures, which is three.
  Calculator answer: 0.3092747 g of glucose
  Answer to three significant figures: 0.309 g of glucose
▸ Verify your answer by rounding off the numbers in the setup and estimating.

PRACTICE PROBLEMS

1. Use the information in Sample Problem 10B to determine the mass of carbon dioxide that would be produced each minute.

2. Use the information in Sample Problem 10B to determine the mass of water that would be produced each minute.

3. Calculate the mass of isoamyl acetate which can be produced when 6 mol of isoamyl alcohol are reacted with 6 mol of acetic acid.

$$C_5H_{11}OH(l) + CH_3COOH(l) \xrightarrow{\text{HCl}} CH_3COOC_5H_{11}(l) + H_2O(l)$$

ANSWERS

PRACTICE PROBLEM 10B

1. $0.0103 \text{ mol } O_2 \times \dfrac{31.999 \text{ g } O_2}{1 \text{ mol } O_2} =$

   $0.3296 \text{ g } O_2$

   $0.3296 \text{ g } O_2 \times \dfrac{1 \text{ mol } O_2}{31.999 \text{ g } O_2} \times$

   $\dfrac{6 \text{ mol } CO_2}{6 \text{ mol } O_2} \times \dfrac{44.01 \text{ g } CO_2}{1 \text{ mol } CO_2} =$

   $0.453 \text{ g } CO_2$

2. $0.3296 \text{ g } O_2 \times \dfrac{1 \text{ mol } O_2}{31.999 \text{ g } O_2} \times$

   $\dfrac{6 \text{ mol } H_2O}{6 \text{ mol } O_2} \times \dfrac{18.015 \text{ g } H_2O}{1 \text{ mol } H_2O} =$

   $0.186 \text{ g } H_2O$

3. $6 \text{ mol } CH_3COOH \times$

   $\dfrac{60.05 \text{ g } CH_3COOH}{1 \text{ mol } CH_3COOH} =$

   $360.3 \text{ g } CH_3COOH$

   $360.3 \text{ g } CH_3COOH \times$

   $\dfrac{1 \text{ mol } CH_3COOH}{60.05 \text{ g } CH_3COOH} \times$

   $\dfrac{6 \text{ mol } CH_3COOC_5H_{11}}{6 \text{ mol } CH_3COOH} \times$

   $\dfrac{130.2 \text{ g } CH_3COOC_5H_{11}}{1 \text{ mol } CH_3COOC_5H_{11}} =$

   $781 \text{ g } CH_3COOC_5H_{11}$

ADDITIONAL EXAMPLES

SAMPLE PROBLEM 10B

Balance the equation for each of the following problems, and then solve.

a. Propane, C_3H_8, burns in oxygen to produce carbon dioxide and water. What mass of propane could be combusted by 8.35 mol of oxygen?

Ans. $C_3H_8(g) + 5O_2(g) \longrightarrow 3CO_2(g) + 4H_2O(g)$;
73.7 g C_3H_8

b. Limestone, $CaCO_3$, can be decomposed with heat to form lime, CaO, and carbon dioxide. What amount of lime would be formed from the decomposition of 20.1 kg of limestone?

Ans. $CaCO_3(s) \longrightarrow CaO(s) + CO_2(g)$;
201 mol $CaCO_3$

c. Oxygen gas was discovered by Joseph Priestley in 1774 when he decomposed mercury(II) oxide, HgO, into its constituent elements by heating it. What amount of oxygen could Priestley have produced if he had decomposed 216.59 g of HgO?

Ans. $2HgO(s) \longrightarrow 2Hg(l) + O_2(g)$; 0.50000 mol HgO

Use this flow chart to solve stoichiometric calculations involving density.

Volume-Molecule Stoichiometry

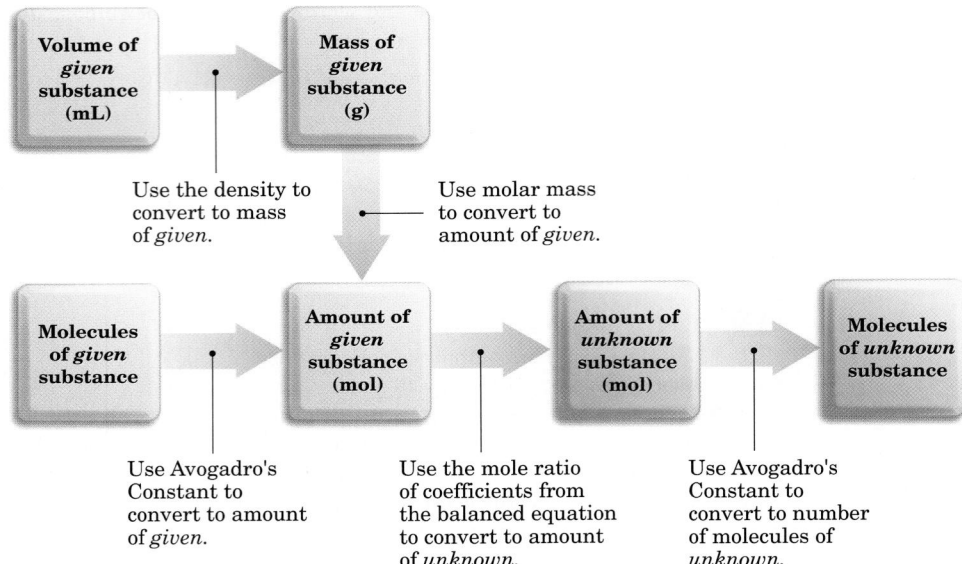

VISUAL STRATEGY

Figure 10-8 Go through the flowchart with students. Make sure students understand how the chart is organized and how it can be used to solve different problems. Visual algorithms can help students recognize the overall process of solving a multi-step stoichiometry problem.

TEACHING TIP

Extending the Flowchart Diagram Using **Figure 10-8** as an example, have students make a model flowchart in which they are given the volume of one substance and are solving for the volume of an unknown.

Using density with stoichiometry

Remember that the key to solving any reaction stoichiometry problem is to convert to amount and to use the balanced equation to change from the amount of one substance to the amount of another. Once the amount is determined, conversion factors such as molar mass can be used to convert to the mass in grams. Similarly, once the volume is known, the density can be used to convert to mass, and if mass is known, the density of a substance can be used to convert from mass to volume. Converting between mass and volume adds one or more steps to stoichiometric calculations. Look at the flow diagram shown in **Figure 10-8.** This solution scheme can be used as a guide for solving most stoichiometry problems involving density or to calculate the number of molecules. If the units for the given quantity is in mL, start with the volume box from the diagram. If the units for the given quantity is molecules, formula units, or atoms, start with the molecule box from the diagram. Follow the arrows and operations to the box in the diagram that yields the answer.

Recall from Chapter 2 that density is defined as the mass of a substance per unit volume expressed mathematically as $D = m/V$. Use the density value to set up a conversion factor that will cancel the units in the measurement you have and leave the units of the measurement for the answer, as shown in Sample Problem 10C on page 355.

SAMPLE PROBLEM 10C   Stoichiometric calculations with density

In space shuttles, the CO_2 that the crew exhales is removed from the air by a reaction within canisters of lithium hydroxide, LiOH. On average, each astronaut exhales about 20.0 mol of CO_2 daily. What volume of water will be produced from 20.0 mol of CO_2 if an excess of LiOH is present? (Hint: the density of water is about 1.00 g/mL.)

$$CO_2(g) + 2LiOH(s) \longrightarrow Li_2CO_3(aq) + H_2O(l)$$

1 List what you know

- Amount of CO_2: 20.0 mol CO_2
- Density of H_2O: 1.00 g/mL
- Mole ratio: 1 mol CO_2:1 mol H_2O
- Volume of H_2O produced: ? mL

2 Set up the problem

- Calculate molar mass using the periodic table.
  molar mass of H_2O: 18.02 g/mol
- Analyze what needs to be done to get the answer. You are given moles of CO_2, so you first convert to moles of water using the mole ratio. Then use the molar mass to find out the mass of water.

$$20.0 \text{ mol } CO_2 \times \frac{1 \text{ mol } H_2O}{1 \text{ mol } CO_2} \times \frac{18.02 \text{ g } H_2O}{1 \text{ mol } H_2O} \times \underline{\quad} = ? \text{ mL } H_2O$$

- Next convert from the mass of H_2O to the volume of H_2O using the inverse of the density as the conversion factor. The correct conversion factor will have g H_2O in the denominator and mL H_2O in the numerator.

$$20.0 \text{ mol } \cancel{CO_2} \times \frac{1 \text{ mol } \cancel{H_2O}}{1 \text{ mol } \cancel{CO_2}} \times \frac{18.02 \text{ g } \cancel{H_2O}}{1 \text{ mol } \cancel{H_2O}} \times \frac{1 \text{mL } H_2O}{1.00 \text{ g } \cancel{H_2O}} = ? \text{ mL } H_2O$$

3 Calculate and verify

- Use your calculator to work through the setup. Be sure to round to the correct number of significant figures, which is three.
  Calculator gives: 360.3 mL H_2O
  Answer to three significant figures: 360. mL H_2O
- Verify your answer by rounding off the numbers in the setup and estimating.

PRACTICE PROBLEMS

1. Calculate the mass of lithium hydroxide used to obtain 1.5 L of water.

2. The reaction that causes cake batter to rise involves the production of CO_2 from $NaHCO_3$ when the $NaHCO_3$ reacts with an acid, such as acetic acid, CH_3COOH (vinegar.) What volume of CO_2 gas will be created when 15.0 g $NaHCO_3$ are used? (Note: at baking temperature, the density of CO_2 is about 1.10 g/L.)

$$NaHCO_3(s) + CH_3COOH(aq) \longrightarrow CH_3COONa(aq) + H_2O(l) + CO_2(g)$$

STOICHIOMETRY   355

Answers continue on page 381A.

ANSWERS

SECTION REVIEW

Total recall

1. $CH_3COOH(l) + C_5H_{11}OH(l) \xrightarrow{HCl}$
$C_6H_{14}COO(l) + H_2O(l)$

2. $\dfrac{6.022 \times 10^{23} \text{ atoms}}{1 \text{ mol}}$

3. Moles provide a way of equating numbers of particles. One mole of one substance has the same number of particles as 1 mol of another substance. Equal amounts in grams of two substances will not have equal numbers of particles because the types of particles have different masses.

4. **a.** $1200. \text{ kg } N_2H_4 \times \dfrac{1000 \text{ g}}{1 \text{ kg}} \times$
$\dfrac{1 \text{ mol } N_2H_4}{32.05 \text{ g } N_2H_4} \times \dfrac{3 \text{ mol } N_2O_4}{2 \text{ mol } N_2H_4} =$
$5.616 \times 10^4 \text{ mol } N_2O_4$

   b. $56\,160 \text{ mol } N_2O_4 \times$
$\dfrac{1 \text{ mol } (CH_3)_2N_2H_2}{3 \text{ mol } N_2O_4} \times$
$\dfrac{60.099 \text{ g } (CH_3)_2N_2H_2}{1 \text{ mol } (CH_3)_2N_2H_2} =$
$1.125 \times 10^6 \text{ g } (CH_3)_2N_2H_2$

   c. $56\,160 \text{ mol } N_2O_4 \times \dfrac{6 \text{ mol } N_2}{3 \text{ mol } N_2O_4} \times$
$\dfrac{6.022 \times 10^{23} \text{ molecules } N_2}{1 \text{ mol } N_2} =$
$6.764 \times 10^{28} \text{ molecules of } N_2$

5. $0.35 \text{ g } C_9H_8O_4 \times \dfrac{1 \text{ mol } C_9H_8O}{180.16 \text{ g } C_9H_8O} \times$
$\dfrac{1 \text{ mol } C_7H_6O_3}{1 \text{ mol } C_9H_8O} \times \dfrac{138.12 \text{ g } C_7H_6O_3}{1 \text{ mol } C_7H_6O_3} =$
$0.27 \text{ g of salicylic acid}$

6. $8.1 \text{ g } Mg \times \dfrac{1 \text{ mol } Mg}{24.305 \text{ g } Mg} \times \dfrac{1 \text{ mol } H_2}{1 \text{ mol } Mg} \times$
$\dfrac{2.0159 \text{ g } H_2}{1 \text{ mol } H_2} \times \dfrac{1 \text{ L } H_2}{0.073 \text{ g } H_2} = 9.2 \text{ L } H_2$

Answers continue on page 381A.

Calculating the number of atoms or formula units

Just as molar mass, density, and mole ratios can be used as conversion factors in problems, Avogadro's constant, 6.022×10^{23}, can be used to calculate the number of atoms or formula units involved in a reaction. This approach was shown in Figure 10-8. The two points to remember are the same as with other stoichiometry problems.

▶ Be certain that you work with moles.

▶ Make sure that you set up the conversion factors so that the quantity sought is in the numerator and the quantity given is in the denominator.

SECTION REVIEW

Total recall

1. Write the chemical equation describing the synthesis of artificial banana flavoring.

2. What conversion factor is used to determine the number of atoms participating in a reaction?

Critical thinking

3. Why do you need to use amount to solve stoichiometry problems? Why can't you just convert from mass to mass?

4. Use the three-step method to solve the following problems. The equation below shows the use of the reactants hydrazine, N_2H_4, and dimethylhydrazine, $(CH_3)_2N_2H_2$, as rocket propellants. For each problem, assume that you start with 1200. kg of N_2H_4 and that it is completely used up by the reaction.

$2N_2H_4(l) + (CH_3)_2N_2H_2(l) + 3N_2O_4(l) \longrightarrow$
$6N_2(g) + 2CO_2(g) + 8H_2O(g)$

   a. Calculate how many moles of N_2O_4 are needed.

   b. Calculate how many grams of $(CH_3)_2N_2H_2$ are needed.

   c. Calculate how many molecules of N_2 are produced.

5. Aspirin is made by allowing salicylic acid to react with acetic anhydride.

$C_7H_6O_3 + C_4H_6O_3 \xrightarrow{HCl} C_9H_8O_4 + C_2H_4O_2$
Salicylic   Acetic   Aspirin   Acetic
  acid   anhydride   acid

What mass of salicylic acid is needed to make one aspirin tablet, which is 0.35 g?

6. **Story Clue** At the temperature within an FRH, 60°C, the density of hydrogen gas is 0.073 g/L. How many liters of H_2 gas are produced by an FRH?

7. **Story Clue** Take a look at the amount of heat energy produced per gram of reactants for each of the magnesium and calcium oxide reactions on page 343. If the mass of the reactants were the deciding factor, which reaction would be most effective? (Hint: Remember to include the mass of water necessary for the two reactions.)

How much does a reaction really produce?

OBJECTIVES

▶ **Distinguish** between a limiting reactant and an excess reactant.

▶ **Identify** the limiting reactant in a problem, and calculate the theoretical yield.

▶ **Distinguish** between theoretical yield and actual yield.

▶ **Calculate** the percentage yield, given the actual yield and the quantity of the limiting reactant.

▶ **Use** percentage yield to calculate actual yield.

Leftover reactants

You now know how to use mole ratios and other conversion factors to figure out how much of a product is produced by a chemical reaction. All previous reactions and calculations described an *ideal situation*. Some assumptions were made: there were always enough reactants so that none were left over, and all reactions went to completion, producing only the products indicated in the equation. The reactions proceeded exactly as written; no unwanted or unexpected products were formed.

These assumptions are useful when learning how reactions and equations work and how to make predictions from them. But to treat real reactions accurately, you must take additional factors into account, such as the amounts of all reactants, the completeness of the reaction, and the product lost in the process.

Reactants combine in specific whole-number ratios

Have you ever tried to assemble a bicycle only to discover that you didn't have enough nuts for the bolts that were supplied, as shown in **Figure 10-9**? For every bolt, you needed a nut, so the shortage of nuts limited what you could do. Or have you ever been in a car that ran out of gas? The car needed both gas and oxygen from the air to run. Once the gas was gone, it wouldn't run, no matter how much oxygen was present.

A similar limitation occurs in all chemical reactions. When a chemical reaction occurs, the reactants are seldom present in ratios of amounts equal to their mole ratios. There may be too much of one reactant or too little of another. For example, reconsider the reaction used to make the banana-flavored ester, isoamyl acetate.

FIGURE 10-9 ▼

With only one nut, you can make only a single nut-bolt pair, no matter how many bolts you have. Similarly, when one reactant in a chemical reaction is used up, the reaction can no longer proceed.

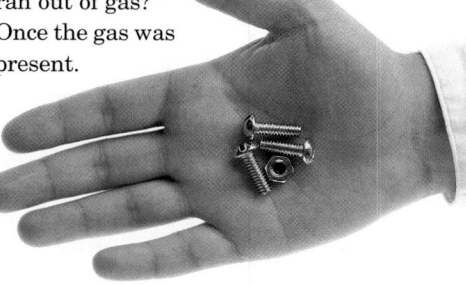

STOICHIOMETRY 357

LESSON WARM-UP

Limiting Reactants
Use the demonstration on this page to introduce the concept of limiting reactants. Various amounts of CO_2 gas will be produced, showing the need for correct proportions of reactants.

TEACHING TIP

Designing a Model Provide students with items they can use to model everyday examples of limiting and excess materials. Examples include graham crackers, marshmallows, and chocolate squares for "s'mores"; nuts and bolts; and index cards that are labeled *center, guard,* and *forward,* to represent a basketball team. Be sure to have some items in excess and one item that is limited. For example, 14 graham cracker squares, 5 marshmallows, and 6 chocolate squares will make 5 s'mores. The marshmallows are limiting, and there are 4 excess graham crackers and 1 excess chocolate square. This modeling can be done either by students or as a demonstration.

DEMONSTRATION 2

Limiting Reactants
Approximate time: 15 minutes

Note: Before class, determine if the mass specified will work with the size of balloons you use. Change amounts accordingly.

1. Before class, obtain three 2 L plastic bottles. Remove the labels, and number the bottles *1, 2,* and *3.* Stretch three 9 to 12 in. balloons by inflating them and deflating them several times. Measure out 4 g, 7.5 g, and 10 g samples of baking soda.

2. Pour 100 mL of vinegar into each bottle.

3. Add a baking soda sample to each of the three balloons. With a permanent marker, label each balloon with the mass of the sample size it contains. Twist each balloon to seal in the sample. In the order the samples were listed in step 1, attach

CONTINUED ON PAGE *358*

The reactants   **The products**   **Excess reactants**

▲ **FIGURE 10-10**

Making a cheeseburger can be an analogy for a reaction with limiting reactants. The number of cheeseburgers you can make is limited by the one critical ingredient.

According to the following equation, for every mole of acetic acid, a mole of isoamyl alcohol is needed. What mass of isoamyl acetate could be made if there were 20 mol of acetic acid and only 1 mol of isoamyl alcohol?

$$H_3C-\overset{\displaystyle O}{\overset{\|}{C}}-OH \;+\; HO-\overset{\displaystyle CH_3}{\underset{CH_2}{\overset{|}{CH_2-CH}}}-CH_3 \;\longrightarrow\; H_3C-\overset{\displaystyle O}{\overset{\|}{C}}-O-\overset{\displaystyle CH_3}{\underset{CH_2}{\overset{|}{CH_2-CH}}}-CH_3 \;+\; H_2O$$

Acetic acid   Isoamyl alcohol   Isoamyl acetate   Water

One mole of acetic acid reacts with 1 mol of isoamyl alcohol. After that, the isoamyl alcohol reactant is used up, and none is available to react with the other 19 mol of acetic acid. Obviously, the reaction would stop after forming only 1 mol of each product even though there were 20 mol of one reactant at the start. An excess of this reactant would be left over, as in the analogy illustrated in **Figure 10-10**.

excess reactant

reactant that will not be completely used up in a reaction that goes to completion

An **excess reactant** is not completely used up in a chemical reaction. In the preceding example, acetic acid is the excess reactant. Some of this reactant will be left over when the reaction is complete. On the other hand, isoamyl alcohol is known as the **limiting reactant.** A limiting reactant is used up first and thus limits the amount of other reactants that can participate in a chemical reaction. The limiting reactant also limits the amount of product that can be formed.

limiting reactant

reactant that is consumed completely in a reaction that goes to completion

Determining the limiting reactant

Determining the limiting reactant in this case was fairly straightforward because the mole ratio in the balanced equation was 1:1. You could easily determine which reactant would be totally used up after the reaction was complete. For more complicated problems, first determine the number of moles of each reactant, as shown in Sample Problem 10D. Then use the mole ratios to determine how much of the other reactants would be needed by each reactant. *Whichever reactant runs out first will be the limiting reactant and should be used in stoichiometric calculations to determine the maximum amount of product possible.*

DEMONSTRATION 2 CONTINUED

the balloons to the tops of bottles 1–3, respectively.

4. Secure the balloons to the bottle tops with tape or a twist tie. Untwist the balloons, and shake the baking soda into the vinegar.

The reaction in Sample 1 should produce the least gas. Samples 2 and 3 should produce about the same amount. Bottle 1 has limited baking soda. Bottle 2 has the correct stoichiometric mass to completely react. Even though bottle 3 had more baking soda, there was not enough vinegar to react with the excess.

Safety

Wear safety goggles and a lab apron. Students should remain at least 3 m from the demonstration. Stay back from the balloons as they fill with gas in case one bursts.

Disposal

Pour the solutions down the drain with plenty of water. Throw the balloons in the trash. Rinse the bottles, and save them for later use.

Carbon monoxide can be combined with hydrogen to produce methanol, CH_3OH. Methanol is used as an industrial solvent, as a reactant in synthesis, and as a clean-burning fuel for some race cars. If you had 152.5 g CO and 24.50 g H_2. What mass of CH_3OH could be produced?

1   List what you know

▶ Mass of CO: 152.5 g CO
▶ Mass of H_2: 24.50 g H_2
▶ Mass of CH_3OH produced: ? g CH_3OH

2   Set up the problem

▶ Balance the chemical equation for the reaction:

$$CO(g) + 2H_2\ (g) \longrightarrow CH_3OH(l)$$

▶ Calculate molar masses using the periodic table.
 molar mass of CO: 28.01 g/mol
 molar mass of H_2: 2.02 g/mol
 molar mass of CH_3OH: 32.05 g/mol

3   Calculate and verify

▶ To determine which reactant is the limiting reactant, first figure out how many moles of each reactant are present.

$$152.5\ \text{g CO} \times \frac{1\ \text{mol CO}}{28.01\ \text{g CO}} = 5.444\ \text{mol CO present}$$

$$24.50\ \text{g H}_2 \times \frac{1\ \text{mol H}_2}{2.02\ \text{g H}_2} = 12.1\ \text{mol H}_2\ \text{present}$$

▶ Then figure out how much of the first reactant would be needed to use up all of the second reactant. Compare this with the amount actually present.

$$12.1\ \text{mol H}_2 \times \frac{1\ \text{mol CO}}{2\ \text{mol H}_2} = 6.06\ \text{mol CO needed}$$

Because the amount of CO present is not enough to react with all the H_2, CO is the limiting reactant.

▶ Use the limiting reactant to set up the stoichiometric calculation.

$$5.444\ \text{mol CO} \times \frac{1\ \text{mol CH}_3\text{OH}}{1\ \text{mol CO}} \times \frac{32.05\ \text{g CH}_3\text{OH}}{1\ \text{mol CH}_3\text{OH}} = ?\ \text{g CH}_3\text{OH}$$

▶ Calculate, and round to the correct number of significant digits.
 Calculator answer: 174.4802 g CH_3OH
 Answer to four significant figures: 174.5 g CH_3OH

▶ Verify your answer by rounding off the numbers in the setup and estimating.

$$5.5 \times \frac{1}{1} \times \frac{30}{1} \approx 150$$

Module 5: Equations and Stoichiometry
Topic: Limiting Reagents
This engaging tutorial reviews the concept of limiting reagents through modeling and guided practice.

ANSWERS

PRACTICE PROBLEM 10D

1. No, there is not enough $Al(OH)_3$

$$34.0 \text{ g HCl} \times \frac{1 \text{ mol HCl}}{36.46 \text{ g HCl}} \times$$

$$\frac{1 \text{ mol Al(OH)}_3}{1 \text{ mol HCl}} \times \frac{78.004 \text{ g Al(OH)}_3}{1 \text{ mol Al(OH)}_3} =$$

$$78.0 \text{ g Al(OH)}_3$$

2. N_2 is the limiting reactant

$$92.7 \text{ kg N}_2 \times \frac{1000 \text{ g}}{1 \text{ kg}} \times \frac{1 \text{ mol N}_2}{28.01 \text{ g N}_2} =$$

$$3.31 \times 10^3 \text{ mol N}_2 \text{ present}$$

$$265.8 \text{ kg H}_2 \times \frac{1000 \text{ g}}{1 \text{ kg}} \times \frac{1 \text{ mol H}_2}{2.0159 \text{ g H}_2} =$$

$$1.319 \times 10^5 \text{ mol H}_2 \text{ present}$$

$$131\,900 \text{ mol H}_2 \times \frac{1 \text{ mol N}_2}{3 \text{ mol H}_2} =$$

$$4.397 \times 10^4 \text{ mol N}_2 \text{ needed}$$

ADDITIONAL EXAMPLES

SAMPLE PROBLEM 10D

Balance the chemical equation for each of the following problems, and then solve.

a. Zinc citrate, $Zn_3(C_6H_5O_7)_2$, an ingredient in toothpaste, is made by reacting zinc carbonate and citric acid, $C_6H_8O_7$. The other products are water and carbon dioxide. If there are 6.0 mol of $ZnCO_3$ and 10.0 mol of $C_6H_8O_7$, which is the limiting reactant?

Ans. $3ZnCO_3(s) + 2C_6H_8O_7(aq) \longrightarrow$
$Zn_3(C_6H_5O_7)_2(s) + 3H_2O(l) +$
$3CO_2(g)$; $ZnCO_3$ is the limiting reactant.

Answers continue on page 381A.

---

1. Hydrochloric acid, $HCl(aq)$, secreted in your stomach can be neutralized in a double-displacement reaction by taking an antacid such as aluminum hydroxide, $Al(OH)_3$. If 34.0 g HCl are secreted and 12.0 g $Al(OH)_3$ are taken, is there enough $Al(OH)_3$ to react with all of the HCl?

2. Ammonia, NH_3, is used throughout the world as a fertilizer. To manufacture ammonia, nitrogen, N_2, is combined with hydrogen, H_2, in a synthesis reaction. If 92.7 kg N_2 and 265.8 kg H_2 are used, which is the limiting reactant?

Cost is a factor in selecting the limiting reactant

In industry, the least expensive reactant is usually used as the excess reactant. In this way, the expensive reactant is more completely used up, while some of the cheaper reactant is left over.

In addition to being cost-effective, this practice can be used to control which reactions happen. One example is the production of cider vinegar, shown in **Figure 10-11,** from apple juice. At first, the original apple juice is kept where there is no oxygen. When no oxygen is present, the microorganisms in the apple juice cannot use the cellular respiration reaction as a source of energy. Instead, they use an alternative pathway in which the glucose is fermented, or broken down, into molecules of ethanol. The resulting solution is hard cider.

Excess oxygen is used in the next step in the production of cider vinegar. Once the ethanol in hard cider is exposed to air, the organisms use atmospheric oxygen to produce acetic acid, resulting in cider vinegar. Because the oxygen in the air costs nothing and is abundant, the makers of cider vinegar pump air through hard cider as they make it into vinegar. In this way, oxygen is not the limiting reactant. Ethanol is the limiting reactant, so it is entirely consumed in the reaction.

Similarly, the manufacturers of the banana flavoring discussed at the beginning of the chapter use acetic acid as the excess reactant because it costs much less than isoamyl alcohol. For example, acetic acid costs about $11 for 500 mL (525 g), while 500 mL (406 g) of isoamyl alcohol costs about $16. When compared mole for mole, isoamyl alcohol is almost three times as expensive as acetic acid. With an excess of acetic acid, none of the more expensive isoamyl alcohol is wasted.

▼ **FIGURE 10-11**

Makers of cider vinegar use special tanks and equipment to pump air through hard cider so that oxygen, O_2, is the excess reactant.

A chemical equation tells what could happen

Although equations tell you what *should* happen, they can't always tell you what *will* happen. For example, a reaction will stop once the limiting reactant has been used up, regardless of how much of the other reactants is present.

TABLE 10-2 Predictions and Measurements for Isoamyl Acetate Synthesis

Reactants	Formula	Mass	Amount present	Amount needed for reaction
Isoamyl alcohol	$C_5H_{11}OH$	500.0 g	5.67 mol (limiting reactant)	5.67 mol
Acetic acid	CH_3COOH	1.25×10^3 g	20.8 mol	5.67 mol

Products	Formula	Amount expected	Theoretical yield (mass expected)	Actual yield (mass produced)
Isoamyl acetate	$CH_3COOC_5H_{11}$	5.67 mol	738 g	590 g
Water	H_2O	5.67 mol	102 g	81.6 g

CHAPTER CONNECTION
When students study chemical equilibrium in Chapter 14, they will learn more about reactions that proceed in the opposite direction, thus reducing the amount of actual product and the percentage yield.

Sometimes reactions don't match the proportions of reactants consumed and products generated defined by equations. The mass of product expected from stoichiometric calculations is called the **theoretical yield.** But in most cases, the **actual yield,** the mass of product actually obtained, is less than expected. An actual yield can be much less than the theoretical yield. How can this be? Reconsider the banana-flavoring problem.

When a worker at the flavoring factory mixes 500.0 g isoamyl alcohol with 1.25×10^3 g acetic acid, the stoichiometric calculations that account for isoamyl alcohol being a limiting reactant give the results summarized in the second half of **Table 10-2.** But when the actual yield is measured, it is less than was expected. What went wrong?

As mentioned, some reactions do not go to completion. As reactants form products, some of the products react to re-form the original reactants. Because this reverse reaction is occurring, some of the reactants are always present. When the forward reaction occurs at the same rate as the reverse reaction, the system is said to be in **chemical equilibrium.** In a chemical equation, chemical equilibrium is indicated by double arrows, as shown below. You will study chemical equilibrium in more detail in Chapters 12 and 14.

theoretical yield

calculated maximum amount of product possible from a given amount of reactant

actual yield

measured amount of product experimentally produced from a given amount of reactant

chemical equilibrium

condition where the forward reaction occurs at the same speed as the reverse reaction, and all reactants and products are present

Acetic acid   Isoamyl alcohol   Isoamyl acetate   Water

Percentage yield is a way to describe reaction efficiency

There is a way of relating the theoretical yield of a reaction to its actual yield. This ratio describes reaction efficiency. For example, a worker in the flavoring factory kept track of the results of several attempts to make isoamyl acetate, as shown in **Table 10-3.**

RESOURCE LINK

Skills Development
Have students do Exploration 10C on page 750 to further develop their skills using reaction-stoichiometry techniques.

Self-Directed Inquiry
Have students do Investigation 10C: *Gravimetric Analysis—Viral Disease Alert* on page 754 to design an experiment for the concept of reaction-stoichiometry concepts.

Most industrial processes that involve chemical reactions rely heavily on the concepts presented in this chapter. For example, factory owners must know how much of each reactant to order to produce the required amount of product. Percentage yield is constantly determined along with new methods to increase it. Students will learn more about the importance of limiting and excess reactants when they study equilibrium and factors that affect it in Chapter 14.

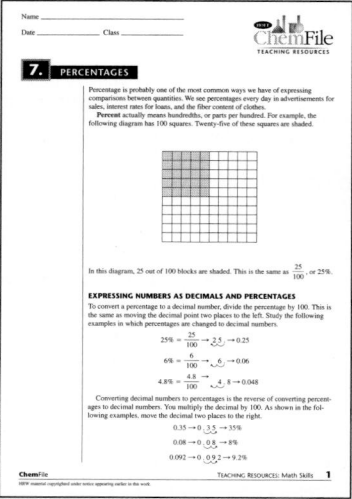
TABLE 10-3	Data from Several Trials of Isoamyl Acetate Synthesis	
Mass of isoamyl alcohol used (g)	Theoretical yield of isoamyl acetate (g)	Actual yield of isoamyl acetate (g)
500.	738	590
500.	738	599
500.	738	579
500.	738	582
500.	738	603

percentage yield

ratio of actual yield to the theoretical yield multiplied by 100

As you can see, the actual yields are close. The **percentage yield** describes how close actual yield is to the theoretical yield.

$$\text{percentage yield} = \frac{\text{actual yield}}{\text{theoretical yield}} \times 100$$

The percentage yield figures for the values shown in Table 10-3 are 79.9%, 81.2%, 78.5%, 78.9%, and 81.7%. These values are all close, but why aren't they equal? Competing side reactions and purification techniques are two ways in which products can be lost. In addition, products that form as gases are often hard to collect, thus lowering percentage yields. While these factors all result in product loss, they are not exact processes, and the mass of product lost almost always varies from day to day. So to determine a general figure for predicting reaction yields, the percentage yield figures are usually averaged over several different trials. For this set of values, the average is 80.0%.

Describing yields in this way is similar to using statistics to describe how frequently a player scores in sports. For example, if you try 20 layups during a basketball game, your theoretical score is 40 points. However, if you make only 10 of those shots, your actual score is 20 points. Your shooting percentage is 50%.

Actual percentage yields must be measured experimentally. However, after closely observing many different reactions, experienced chemists can recognize patterns and reaction types that allow them to make pretty good *estimates* of percentage yield.

The batting average shown on the back of baseball cards, like the one in **Figure 10-12,** is similar to percentage yield because it is a ratio of the number of hits to the number of times at bat.

▼ **FIGURE 10-12**

A baseball player's batting average is similar to percentage yield because it is a ratio of the number of hits achieved and the number of hits possible.

1997 American League Batting Average

Player	Team	Average
Frank Thomas	Chicago	.347
Edgar Martinez	Seattle	.330
David Justice	Cleveland	.329
Bernie Williams	New York	.328
Manny Ramirez	Cleveland	.328

ALTERNATIVE ASSESSMENT

Percentage Yield

Have students brainstorm about situations that are analogous to calculating percentage yield, where they compare actual results with theoretical results. Examples might include finding a batting average (the number of hits compared with the number of times at bat), as shown in Figure 10-12, or calculating a percentage average for a test (the number of correct answers compared with the number of possible answers, multiplied by 100%).

Have students then make up problems for their own situations, trade the problems, and discuss how the situations are similar to calculating percentage yield.

SAMPLE PROBLEM 10E Calculating percentage yield

A student is synthesizing aspirin by adding 200.0 g of salicylic acid to an excess of acetic anhydride. Calculate the percentage yield if 231 g of aspirin is produced. (Hint: Before you can determine the percentage yield, you must first calculate the theoretical yield of aspirin based on the amount of the limiting reactant supplied.)

1 List what you know

- Mass of limiting reactant: 200.0 g $C_7H_6O_3$
- Mole ratio: l mol $C_7H_6O_3$: l mol $C_9H_8O_4$
- Actual yield: 231 g $C_9H_8O_4$
- Theoretical yield: ? g $C_9H_8O_4$
- Percentage yield: ? %

2 Set up the problem

- Write and balance the chemical equation:

$$C_7H_6O_3 + C_4H_6O_3 \longrightarrow C_9H_8O_4 + C_2H_4O_2$$

- Calculate molar masses using the periodic table.
  molar mass of limiting reactant: 138.12 g/mol $C_7H_6O_3$
  molar mass of product: 180.16 g/mol $C_9H_8O_4$

3 Calculate and verify

- Before you can calculate percentage yield, you must calculate theoretical yield by using the molar masses and mole ratios in a mass-mass conversion.

$$200.0 \text{ g } C_7H_6O_3 \times \frac{1 \text{ mol } C_7H_6O_3}{138.12 \text{ g } C_7H_6O_3} \times \frac{1 \text{ mol } C_9H_8O_4}{1 \text{ mol } C_7H_6O_3} \times \frac{180.16 \text{ g } C_9H_8O_4}{1 \text{ mol } C_9H_8O_4}$$
$$= ? \text{ g } C_9H_8O_4$$

Calculator answer: 260.8746018 g $C_9H_{10}O_4$
Rounded answer: 260.9 g $C_9H_{10}O_4$

- Calculate percentage yield from the actual and theoretical yields.

$$\frac{231 \text{ g actual}}{260.9 \text{ g theoretical}} \times 100 = ? \% \text{ yield}$$

Calculate, and round to the correct number of significant digits, which is three.
Calculator answer: 88.539670% yield
Rounded answer: 88.5% yield

- Verify your answer by rounding the numbers in the setup and estimating.

$$200 \times \frac{1}{150} \times \frac{1}{1} \times \frac{200}{1} = \frac{4}{3} \times 200 \approx 250$$

$$\frac{230}{250} \times 100 \approx 90\%$$

ALTERNATIVE ASSESSMENT

Have students determine the theoretical yield for the reaction from the Demonstration on page 344. Use this value and the results that were saved to calculate the percentage yield for the reaction.

GRAPHIC ORGANIZER

ANSWERS

PRACTICE PROBLEM 10E

1. $550 \text{ g C}_7\text{H}_8 \times \dfrac{1 \text{ mol C}_7\text{H}_8}{92.141 \text{ g C}_7\text{H}_8} \times$

   $\dfrac{1 \text{ mol C}_7\text{H}_7\text{NO}_2}{1 \text{ mol C}_7\text{H}_8} \times$

   $\dfrac{137.14 \text{ g C}_7\text{H}_7\text{NO}_2}{1 \text{ mol C}_7\text{H}_7\text{NO}_2} =$

   $818.6 \text{ g C}_7\text{H}_7\text{NO}_2$

   $\dfrac{305 \text{ g actual}}{819 \text{ g theoretical}} \times 100 = 37.2\% \text{ yield}$

2. $\dfrac{468 \text{ g actual}}{819 \text{ g theoretical}} \times 100 = 51.7\% \text{ yield}$

ADDITIONAL EXAMPLES

SAMPLE PROBLEM 10E

a. Nitrogen and hydrogen at high temperatures and pressures are converted into ammonia using the Haber process. The process was developed by Fritz Haber (1868–1934), and it allowed Germany to manufacture explosives during World War II. When 400. kg of H_2 is added to an excess of N_2, 1040 kg of NH_3 is produced. What is the percentage yield of the reaction?

   Ans. 46.2%

b. A standard laboratory preparation of iodine is the following reaction.

   $\text{NaI} + \text{MnO}_2 + \text{H}_2\text{SO}_4 \longrightarrow$
   $\quad \text{Na}_2\text{SO}_4 + \text{MnSO}_4 + \text{H}_2\text{O} + \text{I}_2$

   Balance the equation, then find the percentage yield of I_2 if the actual yield of I_2 was 39.78 g when the amount of NaI used was 62.55 g.

   Ans. $2\text{NaI} + \text{MnO}_2 + 2\text{H}_2\text{SO}_4 \longrightarrow$
   $\text{Na}_2\text{SO}_4 + \text{MnSO}_4 + 2\text{H}_2\text{O} + \text{I}_2$;
   75.11%

c. A 15 g sample of magnesium reacts with hydrochloric acid to form magnesium chloride and hydrogen. During the reaction, 46.6 g of magnesium chloride was formed. What was the percentage yield?

   Ans. 79.3%

PRACTICE PROBLEMS

1. One step in making *para*-aminobenzoic acid, PABA, an ingredient in some suntan lotions, involves replacing one of the hydrogen atoms in a toluene molecule with an —NO$_2$ group directly opposite the —CH$_3$ group. Calculate the percentage yield if 550.0 g of toluene added to an excess of nitric acid provides 305 g of the ρ-nitrotoluene product.

Toluene C_7H_8	Nitric acid	ρ-Nitrotoluene $C_7H_7NO_2$	Water

2. One reason for the low yield in the reaction shown above is a competing side reaction that produces a nitrotoluene product that cannot be used to make PABA. After 550.0 g of toluene reactant was used with an excess of nitric acid, 468 g of this other product remained. Calculate its percentage yield.

Toluene C_7H_8	Nitric acid	o-Nitrotoluene $C_7H_7NO_2$	Water

Percentage yield figures can be used to predict actual yield

Take another look at the banana-flavoring reaction. The worker in the flavoring factory is concerned with the efficiency of the reaction. Recall from pages 362-363 that the ratio of the theoretical yield of the reaction to the actual yield can be used to calculate efficiency of a reaction.

After calculating the theoretical yield of the reaction in the usual way, you can use the percentage yield as a conversion factor. The easiest way to do this is to rewrite the percentage as the number of grams of actual yield per 100 g of theoretical yield. Suppose the reaction for synthesizing artificial banana flavoring gives the product, isoamyl acetate, in 61.7% yield.

$$61.7\% \text{ yield} = \frac{61.7 \text{ g actual yield}}{100 \text{ g theoretical yield}} \times 100$$

Theoretically, 150.0 g of isoamyl alcohol should provide 221.4 g of isoamyl acetate. But you know from the equation with the percentage yield to expect only about 61.7% of that isoamyl acetate to actually be formed. What does this tell the worker about the efficiency of the reaction? That 150.0 g of isoamyl alcohol actually provides 136.6 g of isoamyl acetate.

$$61.7\% = \frac{? \text{ g actual yield}}{221.4 \text{ g theoretical yield}} \times 100$$

A more-efficient way to synthesize the compound that was used to produce PABA for suntan lotion involves a slightly different starting material known as isopropylbenzene. This reaction usually has a 91% yield because the bulky isopropyl group hinders the nitro group from entering the ring next to it. What mass of the product, *para*-nitro-isopropylbenzene, can you expect if 775 g of isopropylbenzene reacts with an excess of nitric acid?

| Isopropylbenzene | Nitric acid | | ρ-Nitro-isopropylbenzene | Water |

1 List what you know

▸ This is a case in which a table for organizing data is useful.

Substance	Formula	Molar mass	Mass	Mole ratio
Isopropylbenzene	C_9H_{12}	? g/mol	775 g	1
para-nitro-isopropylbenzene	$C_9H_{11}NO_2$	? g/mol	? g	1

Percentage yield: 91%

2 Set up the problem

▸ Calculate molar masses using the periodic table.
molar mass of isopropylbenzene: 120.21 g/mol
molar mass of *para*-nitro-isopropylbenzene: 165.21 g/mol
First set up the calculation for theoretical yield. Then use the percentage yield as a conversion factor to calculate actual yield.

$$775 \text{ g } C_9H_{12} \times \frac{1 \text{ mol } C_9H_{12}}{120.21 \text{ g } C_9H_{12}} \times \frac{1 \text{ mol } C_9H_{11}NO_2}{1 \text{ mol } C_9H_{12}} \times$$

$$\frac{165.21 \text{ g } C_9H_{11}NO_2}{1 \text{ mol } C_9H_{11}NO_2} \times \frac{91 \text{ g actual}}{100 \text{ g theoretical}} = ? \text{ g } C_9H_{11}NO_2$$

3 Calculate and verify

▸ Calculate, and round to the correct number of significant figures, which is two.
Calculator answer: 969.25673 g $C_9H_{11}NO_2$
Rounded answer: 970 g $C_9H_{11}NO_2$
▸ Verify your answer by rounding off the numbers in the setup and estimating.

$$800 \times \frac{1}{120} \times \frac{1}{1} \times \frac{160}{1} \times 0.9 \approx 960$$

ADDITIONAL EXAMPLES

SAMPLE PROBLEM 10F

a. Huge quantities of sulfur dioxide are produced from zinc sulfide when it reacts with oxygen. The other product is zinc oxide. If the typical yield is 86.78%, what mass of SO_2 should be expected if 4897 g of ZnS is used?

Ans. 2793 g S

b. Methanol, CH_3OH, can be produced through the reaction of CO and H_2 in the presence of a catalyst. If 75.0 g of CO is used and the typical yield is 79.8%, what mass of methanol is likely to be produced?

Ans. 68.5 g CH_3OH

c. Aluminum reacts with excess copper(II) sulfate to produce copper and aluminum sulfate. If 1.85 g of Al reacts and the percent yield of Cu is 56.6%, what mass of copper is produced?

Ans. 3.70 g Cu

ANSWERS

SECTION REVIEW

Total recall

1. The limiting reactant is completely used up during a chemical reaction. Some of the excess reactant is left over when the reaction reaches completion. Usually, the more expensive reactant is chosen as the limiting reactant.

2. Chemical equilibrium is the state in which the forward reaction occurs at the same rate as the reverse reaction. It is indicated by double arrows.

3. percent yield

Practice problems

4. **a.** $TiCl_4$ is the limiting reactant
O_2 is the excess reactant

$$4.5 \text{ mol } O_2 \times \frac{1 \text{ mol } TiCl_4}{1 \text{ mol } O_2} = 4.5 \text{ mol } TiCl_4$$

b. .992 mol O_2 will remain

$$3.5 \text{ mol } TiCl_4 \times \frac{189.7 \text{ g } TiCl_4}{1 \text{ mol } TiCl_4} = 663.95 \text{ g } TiCl_4$$

$$663.95 \text{ g } TiCl_4 \times \frac{1 \text{ mol } TiCl_4}{189.69 \text{ g } TiCl_4} \times$$

$$\frac{1 \text{ mol } O_2}{1 \text{ mol } TiCl_4} \times \frac{32.100 \text{ g } O_2}{1 \text{ mol } O_2} = 112.36 \text{ g } O_2$$

$$4.5 \text{ mol } O_2 \times \frac{31.999 \text{ g } O_2}{1 \text{ mol } O_2} = 144.10 \text{ g } O_2$$

$$144.10 \text{ g } O_2 - 112.35 \text{ g } O_2 = 31.75 \text{ g } O_2$$

$$31.75 \text{ g } O_2 \times \frac{1 \text{ mol } O_2}{31.999 \text{ g } O_2} = 0.992 \text{ mol } O_2$$

$$3.5 \text{ mol } TiCl_4 \times \frac{1 \text{ mol } O_2}{1 \text{ mol } TiCl_4} = 3.5 \text{ mol } O_2$$

c. $3.5 \text{ mol } TiCl_4 \times \dfrac{2 \text{ mol } Cl_2}{1 \text{ mol } TiCl_4} = 7.0 \text{ mol } Cl_2$

Answers continue on page 381A.

Total recall

1. Distinguish between the limiting reactant and the excess reactant in a chemical reaction. How do chemists decide which reactant to use as the limiting reactant in a chemical reaction?

2. What is chemical equilibrium, and how is it indicated in a chemical equation?

3. What number describes a reaction's efficiency?

Practice problems

4. Titanium(IV) oxide, TiO_2, is used as a pigment in paints and as a whitening and coating agent for paper. It can be made by reacting O_2 with $TiCl_4$.

$$TiCl_4(g) + O_2(g) \longrightarrow TiO_2(s) + 2Cl_2(g)$$

a. If 3.5 mol of $TiCl_4$ reacts with 4.5 mol of O_2, identify both the limiting and excess reactants.

b. What amount of excess reactant will remain if the reaction goes to completion?

c. What amount of each product should be formed if the reaction goes to completion?

5. When phosphorus burns in the presence of oxygen, P_4O_{10} is produced. In turn, P_4O_{10} reacts with water to produce phosphoric acid, H_3PO_4.

$$P_4O_{10}(g) + H_2O(l) \longrightarrow H_3PO_4(aq)$$

a. Write a balanced chemical equation for the reaction shown above.

b. When 100.0 g of P_4O_{10} reacts with 200.0 g of H_2O, what is the theoretical yield of phosphoric acid?

c. If the actual yield is 126.2 g of H_3PO_4, what is the percentage yield for this reaction?

6. Quicklime, CaO, can be prepared by roasting limestone, $CaCO_3$, according to the chemical equation below. When 2.00×10^3 g of $CaCO_3$ are heated, the actual yield of CaO is 1.05×10^3 g. What is the percentage yield?

$$CaCO_3(s) \longrightarrow CaO(s) + CO_2(g)$$

7. Aluminum reacts with an aqueous solution containing excess copper(II) sulfate. If 1.85 g of Al reacts and the percentage yield of Cu is 56.6%, what mass of Cu is produced? (Hint: Remember to balance the equation.)

$$Al(s) + CuSO_4(aq) \longrightarrow Cu(s) + Al_2(SO_4)_3$$

8. If 50.0 g of benzaldehyde reacts with acetaldehyde, which is in excess, to make cinnamaldehyde and the percentage yield is 94.5%, how many grams of cinnamaldehyde will be produced?

9. **Story Clue** When using an FRH, soldiers add 45 mL of water. What volume of water is theoretically necessary for the reaction of the 10.1 g of magnesium in the FRH? (Hint: the density of water is 1.0 g/mL.)

10. **Story Clue** Using your answer to Practice Problem 9, state whether water or magnesium is the limiting reactant.

How can stoichiometry be used?

OBJECTIVES

▶ **Relate** volume calculations in stoichiometry to the inflation of automobile safety air bags.

▶ **Use** the concept of limiting reactants to explain why fuel-

air ratios affect engine performance.

▶ **Compare** the efficiency of pollution-control mechanisms in cars using percentage yield.

Stoichiometry and cars

So far in your study of stoichiometry, you have examined a number of chemical reactions with practical applications—from banana flavoring to cosmetics to aspirin. Here's one more application that you might not know about. During the 1960s, automobile manufacturers introduced driver safety air bags for protection. Air bags have saved the lives of thousands of drivers and passengers involved in accidents. The functioning of an air bag depends on stoichiometry.

Air-bag design depends on stoichiometric precision

Air bags are designed to protect occupants in a car from injuries during a high-speed front-end collision, as shown in **Figure 10-13.** When inflated, air bags slow the motion of the occupants so that they do not strike the steering wheel, windshield, or instrument panel as hard as they would without the air bag.

Stoichiometry is used by air-bag designers to ensure that air bags do not underinflate or overinflate. Bags that underinflate do not provide enough protection for the occupants, and bags that overinflate can cause injury and can even rupture, making them useless. To protect occupants adequately, air bags must fully inflate within one-tenth of a second after impact. The systems that make an air bag work this quickly are shown in **Figure 10-14.** A front-end collision transfers energy to a crash sensor that signals the firing of an igniter, which is similar to a small blasting cap. The igniter provides heat energy to start a reaction in a mixture called the *gas generant,* which forms a gaseous product. The igniter also raises the temperature and

FIGURE 10-13 ▼

When used in combination with seat belts, air bags can lessen the severity of injuries in a front-end collision.

LESSON WARM-UP

Air Bag Safety

Find out how many students' families have cars with air bags. Ask the following questions to facilitate the discussion:

▶ How does an air bag work?

▶ Where does the gas that inflates the bag comes from?

Refer to these responses as you cover the stoichiometry of the air bag in this section.

VISUAL STRATEGY

Figure 10-13 Make students aware that cars are made to absorb some force of a crash, reducing the amount of force that the human body absorbs. Fortunately, people suffer fewer injuries in crashes today. Unfortunately, the cars sustain more damage.

DEMONSTRATION 3

Acid and Marble Chips

Approximate time: 15 minutes

1. Place a Petri dish on an overhead projector, and add 1 M HCl until the dish is half-full.

2. Have a student determine the mass of 5–10 marble chips to the nearest thousandth of a gram. Record this mass on the board.

3. Place the marble chips in the Petri dish. Ask what gas makes up the bubbles that

are given off (CO_2). While the reaction is proceeding, have students do Additional Example 10G on pages 369–370 in the Teacher's Edition wrap.

CONTINUED ON PAGE 368

► **FIGURE 10-14**

A series of events takes place, eventually producing the nitrogen gas that inflates the air bag.

Storage for uninflated bag

Inflator/igniter

Crash sensor (one of several on auto)

Backup power supply in case of battery failure

pressure within the inflator, a metal vessel, so that the reaction occurs at a rate fast enough to fill the bag before the occupant strikes it. The inflator releases the gas into the bag while a high-efficiency filter keeps the reactants and the solid products away from the occupant.

For most current systems, the gas generant is a solid mixture of sodium azide, NaN_3, and an oxidizer. The gas that inflates the bag is almost pure nitrogen gas, N_2, which is produced in the following decomposition reaction.

$$2NaN_3(s) \longrightarrow 2Na(s) + 3N_2(g)$$

However, this reaction alone cannot inflate the bag fast enough, and the sodium metal produced is a dangerously reactive substance. Oxidizers such as ferric oxide, Fe_2O_3, are included in the gas generant so that they can react immediately with the sodium metal. This exothermic reaction raises the temperature more than a hundred degrees so that the gas fills the bag faster.

$$6Na(s) + Fe_2O_3(s) \longrightarrow 3Na_2O(s) + 2Fe(s) + 418 \text{ kJ}$$

But even sodium oxide is unsafe because it is an extremely corrosive substance. Eventually, it reacts with carbon dioxide, CO_2, and moisture from the air to form sodium hydrogen carbonate, or baking soda.

$$Na_2O(s) + 2CO_2(g) + H_2O(g) \longrightarrow 2NaHCO_3(s)$$

internetconnect

SC*LINKS*
NSTA

TOPIC: Air bags
GO TO: www.scilinks.org
KEYWORD: HW102

The amount of gas needed to fill an air bag of a certain volume depends on the volume of gas available and the density of the gas. Gas density, in turn, depends on temperature. To calculate the amount of gas generant necessary, air-bag designers must know the stoichiometry of the reactions and account for energy changes in the reactions, which may change the temperature and thus the density of the gas.

368 CHAPTER 10

DEMONSTRATION 3 *CONTINUED*

4. Have students answer the following questions.
- How do you know when the reaction is finished? *(No more bubbles are given off.)*
- Look at what remains in the Petri dish. What was the limiting reactant? *(whatever is used up, probably HCl)* What was the excess reactant? *(whatever is left over, probably the marble chips)*
- How could you find out the theoretical yield of CO_2? *(Dry the leftover marble chips. Record their mass again, and sub-*

tract this from the original mass of the chips to find out how much of the marble reacted. Use this mass and the stoichiometry of the reaction to predict the grams of CO_2 that could possibly be produced.) the actual yield? *(Collect the gas given off and find its mass.)* the percentage yield? *(Divide the actual yield by the theoretical yield, and multiply by 100%.)*
- How does this demonstration show the effect of acid rain on marble? *(The acid reacts with the marble, causing damage.)*

SAMPLE PROBLEM 10G   Air-bag stoichiometry and density

Assume that 65.1 L of N_2 gas is needed to inflate an air bag to the proper size. What mass of NaN_3 must be included in the gas generant to generate this volume of N_2? (Hint: The density of N_2 gas at this temperature is about 0.916 g/L.)

1 List what you know
- Volume of N_2: 65.1 L N_2
- Density of N_2: 0.916 g/L
- Mass of reactant: ? g NaN_3

2 Set up the problem
- Write and balance the chemical equation.
  balanced chemical equation: $2NaN_3(s) \longrightarrow 2Na(s) + 3N_2(g)$
- Calculate molar masses using the periodic table.
  molar mass of NaN_3: 65.02 g/mol
  molar mass of N_2: 28.02 g/mol
- First the product amount must be converted from a volume to a mass using density. Then it must be converted from a mass to an amount in moles using molar mass. Next the mole ratio is used to determine moles of reactant needed. Then the mass of reactant is calculated using molar mass as a conversion factor.

$$mL\ N_2 \longrightarrow g\ N_2 \longrightarrow mol\ N_2 \longrightarrow mol\ NaN_3 \longrightarrow g\ NaN_3$$

$$65.1\ \text{L}\ N_2 \times \frac{0.916\ \text{g}\ N_2}{1\ \text{L}\ N_2} \times \frac{1\ \text{mol}\ N_2}{28.02\ \text{g}\ N_2} \times \frac{2\ \text{mol}\ NaN_3}{3\ \text{mol}\ N_2} \times \frac{65.02\ \text{g}\ NaN_3}{1\ \text{mol}\ NaN_3} = ?\ \text{g}\ NaN_3$$

3 Calculate and verify
- Calculate, and round to the correct number of significant digits.
  Calculator answer: 92.2495035 g NaN_3
  Answer to three significant figures: 92.2 g NaN_3
- Verify your answer by rounding the numbers in the setup and estimating.

PRACTICE PROBLEMS

1. Calculate the number of grams of Fe_2O_3 that must be added to the gas generant for this mass of NaN_3.

2. Calculate the mass of sodium hydrogen carbonate produced in the air-bag reaction.

3. The density of $NaHCO_3$ is 2.20 g/mL. What volume of $NaHCO_3$ is produced by the reaction?

4. What mass of water and of sodium acetate would be produced by the reaction of $NaHCO_3$ and CH_3COOH to fill the above air bag with CO_2? Recall the volume of the air bag is 65.1 L. (Hint: The density of CO_2 at room temperature is 2.68 g/L.)

STOICHIOMETRY   369

ANSWERS

PRACTICE PROBLEM 10G

1. $65.1\ \text{L}\ N \times \dfrac{0.916\ \text{g}\ N_2}{1\ \text{L}} \times \dfrac{1\ \text{mol}\ N_2}{28.02\ \text{g}\ N_2} \times$
   $\dfrac{2\ \text{mol}\ Na}{3\ \text{mol}\ N_2} \times \dfrac{22.9898\ \text{g}\ Na}{1\ \text{mol}\ Na} =$
   $\qquad\qquad 32.6\ \text{g}\ Na$

   $32.6\ \text{g}\ Na \times \dfrac{1\ \text{mol}\ Na}{22.9898\ \text{g}\ Na} \times$
   $\dfrac{1\ \text{mol}\ Fe_2O_3}{6\ \text{mol}\ Na} \times \dfrac{159.89\ \text{g}\ Fe_2O_3}{1\ \text{mol}\ Fe_2O_3} =$
   $\qquad\qquad 37.8\ \text{g}\ Fe_2O_3$

2. $32.6\ \text{g}\ Na \times \dfrac{1\ \text{mol}\ Na}{22.9898\ \text{g}\ Na} \times$
   $\dfrac{3\ \text{mol}\ Na_2O}{6\ \text{mol}\ Na} \times \dfrac{61.98\ \text{g}\ Na_2O}{1\ \text{mol}\ Na_2O} =$
   $\qquad\qquad 43.9\ \text{g}\ Na_2O$

   $43.9\ \text{g}\ Na_2O \times \dfrac{1\ \text{mol}\ Na_2O}{61.98\ \text{g}\ Na_2O} \times$
   $\dfrac{2\ \text{mol}\ NaHCO_3}{1\ \text{mol}\ Na_2O} \times \dfrac{84.007\ \text{g}\ NaHCO_3}{1\ \text{mol}\ NaHCO_3} =$
   $\qquad\qquad 119\ \text{g}\ NaHCO_3$

3. $119\ \text{g}\ NaHCO_3 \times \dfrac{1\ \text{mL}\ NaHCO_3}{2.20\ \text{g}\ NaHCO_3} =$
   $\qquad\qquad 54.1\ \text{mL}\ NaHCO_3$

4. $65.1\ \text{L}\ CO_2 \times \dfrac{2.68\ \text{g}\ CO_2}{1\ \text{L}} =$
   $\qquad\qquad 174.5\ \text{g}\ CO_2$

   $174.5\ \text{g}\ CO_2 \times \dfrac{1\ \text{mol}\ CO_2}{44.01\ \text{g}\ CO_2} \times$
   $\dfrac{1\ \text{mol}\ H_2O}{1\ \text{mol}\ CO_2} \times \dfrac{18.015\ \text{g}\ H_2O}{1\ \text{mol}\ H_2O} =$
   $\qquad\qquad 71.43\ \text{g}\ H_2O$

   $174.5\ \text{g}\ CO_2 \times \dfrac{1\ \text{mol}\ CO_2}{44.01\ \text{g}\ CO_2} \times$
   $\dfrac{1\ \text{mol}\ CH_3COONa}{1\ \text{mol}\ CO_2} \times$
   $\dfrac{82.034\ \text{g}\ CH_3COONa}{1\ \text{mol}\ CH_3COONa} =$
   $\qquad\qquad 325\ \text{g}\ CH_3COONa$

ADDITIONAL EXAMPLES

SAMPLE PROBLEM 10G

a. Marble, $CaCO_3$, reacts with hydrochloric acid and is changed to calcium chloride, water, and carbon dioxide. If the density of carbon dioxide is 1.997 g/L, what volume of carbon dioxide is produced when 4.000 g of marble is reacted with

Safety
Wear safety goggles and a lab apron. Students should remain at least 3 m from the reaction. Avoid getting acid on your skin or breathing the acid fumes.

Disposal
Decant the liquid, and wash any remaining chips. Combine the washings with the decanted liquid. Test the pH of the solution. If the pH is 3 or below, neutralize the liquid with 1 M NaOH, and pour the mixture down the drain with plenty of water. Save leftover chips.

HCl? (See Demonstration 3 on page 367.)

Ans. 0.8807 L CO_2

b. Assume that the gas in Problem 1 is warmed and has a density of 1.797 g/L. What volume will the gas occupy?

Ans. 0.9787 L

c. How many grams of $NaHCO_3$ and acetic acid, CH_3COOH, would be needed to inflate an air bag to a volume of 65.1 L? CO_2 gas has a density of 2.68 g/L at that temperature. The other products are sodium acetate and water.

Ans. 333 g $NaHCO_3$, 238 g CH_3COOH

VISUAL STRATEGY

Figure 10-16 Make sure students are aware that liquid gasoline is not normally present in the cylinders. In order for the gas to explode, it must be in the gaseous state. The carburetor mixes oxygen with gasoline, which is volatile, to make a vapor mixture for the cylinder explosion.

▲ **FIGURE 10-15**

Isooctane, one of the components found in gasoline, has properties that are similar to those of gasoline, which is a mixture.

Engine efficiency depends on reactant proportions

The gasoline used for automobiles can be treated as if it were pure isooctane, (2,2,4-trimethylpentane), whose structure is shown in **Figure 10-15**. This molecule has a molar mass that is about the same as the weighted average of the molecules within the gasoline. The other reactant in gasoline combustion is oxygen, which is only 20.9% of air by volume. The reaction for gasoline combustion can be written as follows.

$$2C_8H_{18}(l) + 25O_2(g) \longrightarrow 16CO_2(g) + 18H_2O(g) + 10\ 900\ kJ$$

For efficient combustion, the two reactants must be mixed in a mole ratio that is close to the one shown in the balanced chemical equation. If either reactant is restricted too much, the engine might stall. If you pump the gas pedal too much before starting, the mixture will contain almost entirely gasoline, and the lack of oxygen may prevent the mixture from burning. This is referred to as "flooding the engine." On the other hand, if there is too much oxygen and not enough gasoline, the engine will stall just as if the car were out of gas. These situations are illustrated in the model carburetor in **Figure 10-16.**

▼ **FIGURE 10-16**

Engine running at normal speeds

Air inlets

Fuel inlet

Engine starting

Air inlet

Fuel inlet

Engine idling

Air inlet

Fuel inlet

O_2 Fuel

1:16 fuel-oxygen ratio by mass

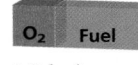

O_2 Fuel

1:2 fuel-oxygen ratio by mass

O_2 Fuel

1:9 fuel-oxygen ratio by mass

a Under ordinary running conditions, an engine's fuel-oxygen ratio is maintained by the carburetor at 1:16, instead of the 1:12.5 (2:25) stoichiometric mole ratio. The mixture is slightly "lean," meaning that gasoline is the limiting reactant. Oxygen is in excess.

b When an engine is starting, the mixture is very "rich," with a 1:12 mole ratio of fuel to oxygen. Oxygen is the limiting reactant, and gasoline is in excess.

c When an engine is idling, the reaction mixture is kept rich at a 1:9 fuel-oxygen mole ratio. Oxygen is the limiting reactant. This ensures that there will always be plenty of fuel for the combustion reaction.

What volume of air must react with 1.00 L of isooctane for combustion to occur completely? At 20°C, the density of isooctane is 0.692 g/mL and the density of oxygen is 1.33 g/L. (Hint: Air is 21% O_2, so use the conversion factor 21 L O_2 / 100 L air.)

1 List what you know

▶ Make a table to organize the data.

Reactant	Formula	Molar mass	Density	Volume
Isooctane	C_8H_{18}	? g/mol	0.692 g/mL	1.00 L
Oxygen	O_2	? g/mol	1.33 g/L	? L

Percentage of oxygen in air: 21% oxygen
Volume of air needed: ? L

2 Set up the problem

▶ Write and balance the chemical equation:

$$2C_8H_{18} + 25O_2 \longrightarrow 16CO_2 + 18H_2O$$

▶ Calculate molar masses.
molar mass of isooctane: 114.26 g/mol
molar mass of oxygen: 32.00 g/mol

▶ The volume of isooctane must be converted to mass and then to moles. Then the mole ratio is used to convert to moles of oxygen. The moles of oxygen must be converted to mass and then to volume of oxygen. Then the percentage of oxygen in air is used to convert to volume of air.

$$1.00 \text{ L } C_8H_{18} \times \frac{1000 \text{ mL}}{1 \text{ L}} \times \frac{0.692 \text{ g } C_8H_{18}}{1 \text{ mL } C_8H_{18}} \times \frac{1 \text{ mol } C_8H_{18}}{114.26 \text{ g } C_8H_{18}} \times$$

$$\frac{25 \text{ mol } O_2}{2 \text{ mol } C_8H_{18}} \times \frac{32.00 \text{ g } O_2}{1 \text{ mol } O_2} \times \frac{1 \text{ L } O_2}{1.33 \text{ g } O_2} \times \frac{100 \text{ L air}}{21 \text{ L } O_2} = ? \text{ L air}$$

3 Calculate and verify

▶ Calculate, and round off correctly.
Calculator answer: 8.6736307×10^3 L air
Rounded answer: 8.7×10^3 L air

PRACTICE PROBLEMS

1. Figure 10-16a describes the fuel-air *mole* ratio necessary for ordinary running conditions. Indicate what volume of the limiting reactant would need to be added to bring the following fuel volume ratios to the proper stoichiometric ratio.
   a. 3.00 L of isooctane: 35 000.0 L of air
   b. 24.75 L of isooctane: 2.00×10^5 L of air
   c. 57.3 mL of isooctane: 400.0 L of air

2. What volume of liquid water is produced from the combustion of 1.0 L of 2,2,4-trimethylpentane, C_8H_{18}?

ANSWERS

PRACTICE PROBLEM 10H

1. **a.** $3.00 \text{ L } C_8H_{18} \times \frac{1000 \text{ mL}}{1 \text{ L}} \times$

    $\frac{0.692 \text{ g } C_8H_{18}}{1 \text{ mL}} = 2076 \text{ g } C_8H_{18}$

    $2076 \text{ g } C_8H_{18} \times \frac{1 \text{ mol } C_8H_{18}}{114 \text{ g } C_8H_{18}} =$
    $18.21 \text{ mol } C_8H_{18}$

    $35\,000 \text{ L air} \times \frac{21 \text{ L } O_2}{100 \text{ L air}} \times$

    $\frac{1.33 \text{ g } O_2}{1 \text{ L } O_2} = 9775.5 \text{ g } O_2$

    $9775.5 \text{ g } O_2 \times \frac{1 \text{ mol } O_2}{31.999 \text{ g } O_2} =$
    $305 \text{ mol } O_2$

    $305 \text{ mol } O_2 \times \frac{2 \text{ mol } C_8H_{18}}{25 \text{ mol } O_2} =$
    $24 \text{ mol } C_8H_{18}$

    $24 \text{ mol } C_8H_{18} \times \frac{114 \text{ g } C_8H_{18}}{1 \text{ mol } C_8H_{18}} \times$

    $\frac{1 \text{ mL } C_8H_{18}}{0.692 \text{ g } C_8H_{18}} \times \frac{1 \text{ L}}{1000 \text{ mL}} =$
    $3.95 \text{ L } C_8H_{18}$

    $3.95 \text{ L } C_8H_{18} - 3.00 \text{ L } C_8H_{18} =$
    $0.950 \text{ L isooctane}$

    b. $24.75 \text{ L } C_8H_{18} \times \frac{1000 \text{ mL}}{1 \text{ L}} \times$

    $\frac{0.692 \text{ g } C_8H_{18}}{1 \text{ mL}} = 17\,121 \text{ g } C_8H_{18}$

    $17\,121 \text{ g } C_8H_{18} \times \frac{1 \text{ mol } C_8H_{18}}{114 \text{ g } C_8H_{18}} =$
    $150 \text{ mol } C_8H_{18}$

    $200\,000 \text{ L air} \times \frac{21 \text{ L } O_2}{100 \text{ L air}} \times$

    $\frac{1.33 \text{ g } O_2}{1 \text{ L } O_2} = 55\,860 \text{ g } O_2$

    $55\,860 \text{ g } O_2 \times \frac{1 \text{ mol } O_2}{31.999 \text{ g } O_2} =$
    $1745.7 \text{ mol } O_2$

    $150 \text{ mol } C_8H_{18} \times \frac{25 \text{ mol } O_2}{2 \text{ mol } C_8H_{18}} =$
    $1875 \text{ mol } O_2$

    $1875 \text{ mol } O_2 \times \frac{31.999 \text{ g } O_2}{1 \text{ mol } O_2} \times$

    $\frac{1 \text{ L } O_2}{1.33 \text{ g } O_2} \times \frac{100 \text{ L air}}{21 \text{ L } O_2} =$
    $214\,816 \text{ L air}$

    $214\,816 \text{ L air} - 200\,000 \text{ L air} =$
    $1.5 \times 10^4 \text{ L air}$

Answers continue on page 381B.

ADDITIONAL EXAMPLES

SAMPLE PROBLEM 10H

At 20°C, the density of O_2 is 1.331 g/L, and the density of propane, C_3H_8, is 1.83 g/L. Air is 20.9% O_2.

a. Plumbers use propane torches to solder copper tubing. How much air is required to react with 2.00 L of propane?

Ans. 47.7 L of air

b. Determine how many grams of O_2 must be provided by a car's carburetor or fuel-injection system to ensure that 528.7 g of C_8H_{18} would be completely combusted.

Ans. 1851 g O_2

c. How many grams of air are needed in problem 2?

Ans. 8860 g air

DID YOU KNOW?

Los Angeles often experiences thermal inversions that trap the photochemical smog above the city. When this happens, the smog continues to build up until it is eventually blown eastward into the mountains. Thermal inversions occur when a layer of warm air forms over a layer of cooler air.

TABLE 10-4	Clean Air Act Standards for 1996 Air Pollution*		
Pollutant	**Cars**	**Light trucks**	**Motorcycles**
Hydrocarbons	0.25 g/km	0.50 g/km	5.0 g/km
Carbon monoxide	2.1 g/km	2.1–3.1 g/km, depending on truck size	12 g/km
Oxides of nitrogen (NO, NO₂)	0.25 g/km	0.25–0.68 g/km, depending on truck size	not regulated

*Note: Excludes standards for diesel-powered vehicles. EPA standards for cars and light trucks are actually expressed in grams per mile at 75°F.

Car designers use stoichiometry to control pollution

Automobiles are the primary source of air pollution in many parts of the world. The Clean Air Act was enacted in 1968 to address the issue of the amount of photochemical smog, as shown in **Figure 10-17**, and other pollution caused by automobile exhaust. This act was amended in 1990 to set new, more-restrictive emission control standards for automobiles driven in the United States. **Table 10-4** lists the latest standards for automobile exhaust. The standards are issued by the U.S. Environmental Protection Agency. The maximum allowable amount of pollutant the vehicle can produce per kilometer driven is shown in Table 10-4.

The equation for the combustion of isooctane shows most of what happens when gasoline burns but it does not tell the whole story. For example, if the fuel-air mixture is improperly balanced and there is not enough oxygen, as when a car is started, some carbon monoxide will be produced instead of carbon dioxide. In cold weather, cars need even more fuel to start than usual, so unburned hydrocarbons come out as exhaust and more carbon monoxide is formed. In addition, the high-temperature environment of the engine promotes the formation of nitrogen oxides from the nitrogen and oxygen in air.

One of the Clean Air Act standards limits the amount of nitrogen oxides, NO and NO_2, that a car can emit. Such compounds can combine with oxygen and water in the atmosphere to produce nitric acid, a constituent of acid rain. In addition, these compounds can react with oxygen to produce another harmful chemical, ozone. Because these chemicals are produced in reactions that are catalyzed by energy from the sun's ultraviolet light, they form what is referred to as photochemical smog. Although photochemical smog is easy to detect around many cities, it is caused by very small amounts of pollutants.

▼ FIGURE 10-17

Smog is a problem for many cities in the world. It not only is unpleasant to look at but also can make breathing difficult for many people.

GRAPHIC ORGANIZER

Formation of Photochemical Smog

From exhaust fumes

$NO_2(g)$ —*Ultraviolet light*→ $NO(g)$ + $O(g)$

$O_2(g)$ +

$O_3(g)$ — Ozone

FIGURE 10-18

The catalytic converters used in automobiles effectively decrease nitrogen oxides, carbon monoxide, and hydrocarbons in exhaust, unless the converter is exposed to leaded gasoline or conditions of extreme heat.

Catalytic converter containing ceramic pellets coated with platinum, palladium, or rhodium catalysts

Formation of photochemical smog begins when NO_2 molecules absorb light. The NO_2 decomposes as it absorbs this energy and produces oxygen *atoms* and nitrogen(II) oxide molecules. In turn, the oxygen atoms produced by the NO_2 decomposition react with oxygen molecules in the air to produce ozone.

$$NO_2(g) \xrightarrow{\text{ultraviolet light}} NO(g) + O(g)$$

$$O_2(g) + O(g) \longrightarrow O_3(g)$$

You may already know that ozone in the upper atmosphere serves as a protective shield against the sun's ultraviolet rays. But closer to Earth, ozone is a very reactive molecule that can crack rubber, corrode metals, and damage living tissues. In addition, ozone can undergo a complex series of reactions with any hydrocarbons that are not completely burned by a car's engine. The products of these reactions also contribute to photochemical smog.

Automobile manufacturers use stoichiometry to predict when adjustments will be necessary to keep exhaust emissions within legal limits. Because the units in Table 10-4 are *grams per kilometer,* auto manufacturers must consider how much fuel the vehicle will burn to move a certain distance. Automobiles with better gas mileage will use less fuel per kilometer. Cars that are more fuel efficient should also have slightly lower emissions per kilometer.

Most cars have catalytic converters, like the one shown in **Figure 10-18,** to treat the exhaust before it is released into the air. The platinum, palladium, or rhodium found in these converters assists in the decomposition of NO_2 into N_2 and O_2, harmless gases already found in the air. Catalytic converters also decrease emissions of CO and hydrocarbons. But catalytic converters perform at their best in warm weather and when the ratio of fuel to air in the engine is very close to the proper stoichiometric ratio. Newer cars include on-board computers and oxygen sensors to make sure the proper ratio is maintained so that the engine and the catalytic converter work at top efficiency.

internetconnect

SCLINKS
NSTA

TOPIC: Catalytic converters
GO TO: www.scilinks.org
KEYWORD: HW103

SAMPLE PROBLEM 10I

Race cars often burn ethanol, C_2H_5OH, for added performance. The products are carbon dioxide and water. The density of ethanol is 0.816 g/mL, the density of CO_2 is 1.997 g/L, and the density of O_2 is 1.331 g/L.

a. If the car holds 100. L of ethanol and all of the carbon in it forms carbon dioxide, what volume of carbon dioxide is added to the air?

Ans. 78×100 L of CO_2

b. What volume of oxygen is needed to react with 78.3 L of ethanol?

Ans. 1.00×10^5 L of O_2

c. If all of the carbon dioxide from item (a) mixes with water to form carbonic acid, what mass of carbonic acid is formed?

Ans. 220 000 g of H_2CO_3

ANSWERS

SECTION REVIEW

Total recall

1. decomposition

2. Chemicals are formed in the air in reactions that are catalyzed by energy from the sun's ultraviolet light.

3. platinum, palladium, or rhodium

Practice problems

4. $22.4 \text{ g NaN}_3 \times \dfrac{1 \text{ mol NaN}_3}{65.01 \text{ g NaN}_3} \times$

$\dfrac{3 \text{ mol N}_2}{2 \text{ mol NaN}_3} \times \dfrac{28.01 \text{ g N}_2}{1 \text{ mol N}_2} =$

14.5 g N_2

$14.5 \text{ g N}_2 \times \dfrac{1 \text{ L}}{0.916 \text{ g N}_2} = 15.8 \text{ L N}_2$

5. $18.3 \text{ g O} \times \dfrac{1 \text{ mol O}}{15.999 \text{ g O}} \times \dfrac{1 \text{ mol O}_2}{1 \text{ mol O}} \times$

$\dfrac{31.999 \text{ g O}_2}{1 \text{ mol O}_2} = 36.6 \text{ g O}_2$

Answers continue on page 381B.

SAMPLE PROBLEM 10I Calculating yields: pollution

What mass of ozone, O_3, could be produced from 3.50 g of NO_2 contained in a car's exhaust? The net equation for this reaction is shown.

$$NO_2(g) + O_2(g) \longrightarrow NO(g) + O_3(g)$$

1 List what you know

▶ Balanced equation: $NO_2(g) + O_2(g) \longrightarrow NO(g) + O_3(g)$
▶ Mass of reactant: 3.50 g NO_2
▶ Mass of product: ? g O_3

2 Set up the problem

▶ Calculate molar masses.
  molar mass for NO_2: 46.01 g/mol
  molar mass for O_3: 48.00 g/mol
▶ First the mass of NO_2 must be converted to moles. Then the mole ratio is used to convert to moles of ozone. The moles of ozone are then converted to mass of ozone.

$$3.50 \text{ g NO}_2 \times \frac{1 \text{ mol NO}_2}{46.01 \text{ g NO}_2} \times \frac{1 \text{ mol O}_3}{1 \text{ mol NO}_2} \times \frac{48.00 \text{ g O}_3}{1 \text{ mol O}_3} = ? \text{ g O}_3$$

3 Calculate

▶ Calculate, and round off correctly.
Calculator answer: 3.651380135 g O_3
Correct answer: 3.65 g O_3

SECTION REVIEW

Total recall

1. What type of reaction is used to produce the nitrogen gas used in air bags?

2. How is photochemical smog produced?

3. What substances are used in catalytic converters to eliminate CO and hydrocarbons?

Practice problems

4. What volume of N_2 gas is produced if 22.4 g of NaN_3 were placed inside an air-bag igniter.

5. What mass of O_2 could react with 18.3 g of O produced from the NO_2 emitted in a car's exhaust.

6. What mass of O_3 would be produced by the O_2 and O in item 5?

7. Assume that 74.0 g of isooctane must be combusted to drive a car for 1.0 km. Assume that all of the carbon atoms in the isooctane form CO. What mass of CO is produced?

At the beginning of this chapter, you learned about how the Army invented a way to make sure soldiers get hot meals without the use of combustion.

LOOKING BACK

Why was the magnesium-water reaction of the FRH chosen over trioxane and calcium oxide?

Soldiers have a great deal of equipment to carry. The less mass devoted to warming equipment, the better. Soldiers also operate under hectic conditions. The simpler the process used for meal preparation, the better. From the story, you know that the reaction of 1 mol of Mg produces more than five times as much energy as the reaction of 1 mol of CaO. When equal masses are compared, the advantage is even greater. But mole for mole and gram for gram, trioxane releases far more energy than does the Mg reaction. Why was this method discarded?

Trioxane must be used outside, it must be lit with matches or a lighter, and it takes longer to heat a meal. Conversely, an FRH can be used safely in vehicles, tents, ships, planes, and buildings. Furthermore, the energy released in the combustion of trioxane cannot be directly used to heat MREs. Instead, the burning trioxane has to heat a metal cup of water containing the MRE pouch.

Why is there a difference between the volume of water that is added and the volume of water the reaction requires?

To warm a meal in the FRH, 45 mL of water is added, even though the balanced chemical equation requires only 12 mL. Because it is inexpensive and readily available, water is used in excess. Thus, the more expensive magnesium is the limiting reactant and is completely consumed in the reaction. The extra water also provides efficient heat transfer over a larger area and makes up for any water absorbed by the porous pad.

The designers of this system had to consider how varying quantities of water would affect the reaction. If too little water was added, the reaction would not go to completion, some magnesium would be wasted, and not as much energy would be generated. On the other hand, excess water would absorb heat that could be warming the meal. A balance between these competing concerns provided the most efficient FRH.

CONCLUSION

Before the development of the FRH, soldiers heated their meals using the combustion reaction of a compound called trioxane. Mole for mole and gram for gram, trioxane releases far more energy than does the Mg method or the CaO method. However, trioxane must be used outside, it must be lit with a flame, and it takes longer to heat a meal. It was difficult to use in some of the situations the soldiers encountered.

CHAPTER 10
Highlights

HIGHLIGHTS

CHAPTER

10

READING STRATEGY

Assimilating Knowledge

Have students return to the list of things they wanted to know about how the mass of the reactants affects the mass of the products, which they created on page 342. Have them place check marks next to the questions that they are now able to answer. Students should finish by making a list of what they've learned. Have students identify unanswered questions as well as new questions they may have. These questions could be used as the basis for a research project.

REVIEW & ASSESS ASSIGNMENT GUIDE

Term Review

Concepts & Skills Review

Section 10-1
- Items 1–7

Section 10-2
- Items 8–20

Section 10-3
- Items 21–29

Linking Chapters

Section 10-1
- Item 1

Section 10-2
- Item 2

Alternative Assessments

Assign after Section 10-3.

Test Prep

Assign prior to chapter test.

KEY TERMS

10-1
ester
stoichiometry

10-2
actual yield
chemical equilibrium

excess reactant
limiting reactant

percentage yield
theoretical yield

KEY CONCEPTS

10-1 **How much can a reaction produce?**
- Reaction stoichiometry compares the mass and amount of substances in a chemical reaction.
- Composition stoichiometry describes the relationship among the elements within a substance.
- Stoichiometry problems can be solved with conversion factors created from mole ratios, molar masses, density, and Avogadro's constant.

10-2 **How much does a reaction really produce?**
- Once the limiting reactant has been used up, no more product can be formed, no matter how much of the other reactant(s) remains.
- The theoretical yield is the calculated maximum mass of product possible from a given mass of reactants.

- The actual yield is the mass of product experimentally measured after the reaction of a given mass of reactants.
- Percentage yield is 100 times the ratio of actual yield to theoretical yield. Percentage yield describes reaction efficiency.

10-3 **How can stoichiometry be used?**
- Stoichiometry is used by automobile designers to maximize a car's safety and performance while minimizing its environmental impact.
- Engineers apply stoichiometry to automobile air bags, fuel delivery systems, and pollution control devices.

KEY SKILLS

Review the following models before your exam. Be sure you can solve these types of problems.

How To Solve stoichiometry problems (p. 349)

Sample Problem 10A: Mass-mass stoichiometry (p. 351)

Sample Problem 10B: Mole-mass stoichiometry (p. 353)

Sample Problem 10C: Stoichiometric calculations with density (p. 355)

Sample Problem 10D: Determining the limiting reactant (p. 359)

Sample Problem 10E: Calculating percentage yield (p. 363)

Sample Problem 10F: Using percentage yield (p. 365)

Sample Problem 10G: Air-bag stoichiometry and density (p. 369)

Sample Problem 10H: Stoichiometric calculations: air-fuel ratio (p. 371)

Sample Problem 10I: Calculating yields: pollution (p. 374)

TERM REVIEW

1. If the forward reaction is occurring at the same speed as the reverse reaction, a chemical reaction is said to be in ——.
(stoichiometry, limiting reactant, chemical equilibrium)

2. A(n)—— is often responsible for the flavor of a fruit.
(organic acid, ester, limiting reactant)

3. When a reaction goes to completion, the —— is not totally consumed.
(limiting reactant, excess reactant, actual yield)

4. You can determine the maximum amount of product expected from a reaction by calculating the ——.
(actual yield, percentage yield, theoretical yield)

5. If you want to know how much mass of a substance will be involved in a reaction, you should look at the reaction's ——.
(stoichiometry, actual yield, chemical equilibrium)

6. The relationship between actual yield and theoretical yield is expressed as the ——.
(differential yield, stoichiometry, percentage yield)

7. In a chemical reaction, the —— is consumed when the reaction goes to completion.
(excess reactant, limiting reactant, actual yield)

8. The —— is what chemists observe in a laboratory.
(actual yield, stoichiometry, theoretical yield)

CONCEPT & SKILLS REVIEW

STOICHIOMETRY

1. Explain the difference between reaction stoichiometry and composition stoichiometry.

2. Why is a balanced chemical equation required to solve stoichiometry problems?

3. A reaction between hydrazine, N_2H_4, and dinitrogen tetroxide, N_2O_4, has been used to launch rockets into space. The reaction produces nitrogen gas and water vapor, as shown in the unbalanced equation below.

$$N_2H_4(l) + N_2O_4(l) \longrightarrow N_2(g) + H_2O(g)$$

a. Write the balanced chemical equation for the reaction.
b. What is the mole ratio of N_2H_4 to N_2?
c What is the mole ratio of N_2O_4 to H_2O?
d. What amount of water will be produced from 14 000 mol of hydrazine used by a rocket?

Practice Problems

4. Various processes, including gasoline combustion in automobiles and industrial burning of fossil fuels, can result in the production of sulfur dioxide, SO_2. The SO_2 can undergo a series of reactions with oxygen and water in the air to form sulfuric acid eventually, as shown in the equation below. This acid mixes with moisture to form acid precipitation. If 0.500 g of sulfur dioxide from pollutants reacts with excess water and oxygen found in the air, what mass of sulfuric acid can be produced? **(Hint: See Sample Problem 10A.)**

$$2H_2O(l) + O_2(g) + 2SO_2(g) \longrightarrow 2H_2SO_4(aq)$$

5. Oxygen gas can be produced by decomposing potassium chlorate using the reaction below. If 125 g of $KClO_3$ is heated and decomposes completely. What amount of oxygen gas is produced? **(Hint: See Sample Problem 10B.)**

$$2KClO_3(s) \longrightarrow 2KCl(s) + 3O_2(g)$$

6. Oxygen gas and water are produced by the decomposition of hydrogen peroxide. If 10.0 mol of H_2O_2 decomposes, what volume of oxygen will be produced? Assume the density of oxygen is 1.429 g/L. **(Hint: See Sample Problem 10C.)**

$$2H_2O_2(aq) \longrightarrow 2H_2O(l) + O_2(g)$$

STOICHIOMETRY **377**

Complete worked-out solutions for these problems can be found on the teacher's interleaved pages at the end of this chapter.

TERM REVIEW

1. chemical equilibrium
2. ester
3. excess reactant
4. theoretical yield
5. stoichiometry
6. percent yield
7. limiting reactant
8. actual yield

CONCEPT & SKILLS REVIEW

1. Reaction stoichiometry deals with the relative amounts of products and reactants. Composition stoichiometry deals with the identity of one substance.

2. The coefficients in a balanced chemical equation give the mole ratios needed for stoichiometry calculations.

3. a. $2N_2H_4(l) + N_2O_4(l) \longrightarrow$
$\qquad 3N_2(g) + 4H_2O(g)$
b. 2 mol N_2H_4 : 3 mol N_2
c. 1 mol N_2O_4 : 4 mol H_2O
d. 28 000 mol H_2O

4. 0.765 g H_2SO_4

5. 1.53 mol O_2

6. 112 L O_2

7. 560 L NO

8. A limiting reactant is used up before the excess reactant and thus limits a reaction.

9. The only reactions without limiting reactants are those that have precise proportions of different reactant amounts that match the mole ratios.

10. 63.4 g Ag

11. 58.2 g methylbutanoate

Complete worked-out solutions for these problems can be found on the teacher's interleaved pages at the end of this chapter.

12. a. limiting reactant, firewood; excess reactant, oxygen
   b. limiting reactant, food; excess reactant, stomach acid
   c. limiting reactant, silver; excess reactant, sulfur compounds
   d. limiting reactant, NO_2 gas; excess reactants, oxygen and water

13. a. Theoretical yield is the maximum calculated amount of product that could be produced, while actual yield is the measured amount actually produced.
   b. Precise actual yields are mass measurements from a balance.
   c. Theoretical yield is calculated from the balanced chemical equation for the reaction.

14. If the reverse reaction occurs, reactants are re-formed from the products. Other side reactions may also occur, forming other products.

15. 73.1%

16. 99%

17. .714 g CH_4

18. 1.748 g CH_4

19. 75.0%

20. a. No, the theoretical yield is the maximum amount that can be obtained. Thus, actual yield will always be less.
   b. Answers will vary but may include contamination of the product, or human or instrument error.

21. a. The ratio of gasoline to air is too high. The combustion reaction will not take place.
   b. The ratio of air to gasoline is too high. The combustion reaction will not take place.

22. Twice as much material will produce twice as much energy in the form of light.

23. 10.7 g of baking powder

24. 1.3 g of $C_6H_{12}O_6$

25. 3130 L of H_2O

7. One of the intermediate steps in the production of nitric acid is the reaction between ammonia and oxygen. If 25 mol of ammonia gas react with excess oxygen, how many liters of NO will be produced? Assume the density of NO is 1.340 g/L. **(Hint: See Sample Problem 10C.)**

$$4NH_3(g) + 5O_2(g) \longrightarrow 4NO(g) + 6H_2O(g)$$

LIMITING REACTANTS

8. Differentiate a limiting reactant from an excess reactant.

9. Do all reactions have a limiting reactant? Explain.

10. When copper metal is added to a silver nitrate solution, silver metal and copper(II) nitrate are produced. If 100.0 g of copper metal is added to a solution containing 100.0 g of silver nitrate, what mass of silver metal will be produced? **(Hint: See Sample Problem 10D.)**

11. A fruit-scented air freshener can be made by reacting butanoic acid with methanol to produce methyl butanoate and water. How many grams of methyl butanoate can be produced if 50.0 g of butanoic acid reacts with 40.0 g of methanol? **(Hint: See Sample Problem 10D.)**

Butanoic acid   +   Methanol $\longrightarrow$

Methyl butanoate   +   Water

12. Identify the limiting reactant and the excess reactant in the following situations:
   a. firewood burning in a campfire
   b. stomach acid reacting with a tablet of $Mg(OH)_2$
   c. sulfur compounds from the air tarnishing silver
   d. NO_2 gas reacting with oxygen and water vapor in air to produce acid rain

PERCENTAGE YIELD

13. a. Differentiate theoretical yield from actual yield.
   b. How is actual yield determined?
   c. How is theoretical yield determined?

14. Why do many chemical reactions produce less than the amount of product predicted by stoichiometry?

15. Magnesium metal is usually obtained from dissolved magnesium ions in sea water. A series of reactions produces magnesium chloride. Electrolysis is used to decompose the magnesium chloride into magnesium metal and chlorine gas, as shown by the equation below. If 185 g of magnesium is recovered from 1000.0 g of magnesium chloride, what is the percentage yield for this reaction? **(Hint: See Sample Problem 10E.)**

$$MgCl_2(l) \longrightarrow Mg(l) + Cl_2(g)$$

16. The combustion of methane produces carbon dioxide and water. Assume that 2.0 mol of CH_4 burned in the presence of excess air. What is the percentage yield if the reaction produces 87.0 g CO_2? **(Hint: See Sample Problem 10E.)**

$$CH_4(g) + 2O_2(g) \longrightarrow CO_2(g) + 2H_2O(g)$$

17. Coal gasification is a process that converts coal into methane gas. If this reaction has a percentage yield of 85%, how much methane can be obtained from 1.255 g of coal? (Assume coal to be 100% carbon.)

$$2C(s) + 2H_2O(l) \longrightarrow CH_4(g) + CO_2(g)$$

18. If the percentage yield for the coal gasification process in item 17 is increased to 95.0%, how much methane can be obtained from 2.75 g of carbon?

19. A sandpaper company uses silicon carbide, SiC, to make its product. Reacting silicon dioxide with graphite yielded 30.0 kg of SiC. The theoretical yield is 991 mol. What is the percentage yield?

20. a. Can actual yield ever exceed theoretical yield? Explain.
   b. In the lab, you run an experiment that appears to have a percentage yield of 115%. Propose possible reasons for this result.

PRACTICAL USES OF STOICHIOMETRY

21. Use stoichiometry to explain the following problems that a lawn mower may have:
   a. A lawn mower fails to start because the engine floods.
   b. A lawn mower stalls after starting cold and idling.

22. Use stoichiometry to explain why a 4.00 kg firework would produce more light than a 2.00 kg firework containing the same proportion of reactants.

Practice Problems

23. Phosphate baking powder is a mixture of starch, sodium hydrogen carbonate, and calcium dihydrogen phosphate. When mixed with water, phosphate baking powder releases carbon dioxide gas, causing a dough or batter to bubble and rise.

$$2NaHCO_3(aq) + Ca(H_2PO_4)_2(aq) \longrightarrow 2Na^+(aq) + Ca^{2+}(aq) + 2HPO_4^{2-}(aq) + 2CO_2(g) + 2H_2O(l)$$

If 0.750 L of CO_2 is needed for a cake and each kilogram of baking powder contains 168 g of $NaHCO_3$, what mass of baking powder must be used to generate this amount of CO_2? The density of CO_2 at baking temperature is about 1.25 g/L. **(Hint: See Sample Problem 10G.)**

24. The addition of yeast can make bread rise because the yeast produces CO_2 from glucose, $C_6H_{12}O_6$, according to the equation below. Assume that 0.50 L of carbon dioxide is required for a loaf of bread. What mass of $C_6H_{12}O_6$ must be broken down by yeast to produce this amount of CO_2? The density of CO_2 at baking temperature is about 1.25 g/L. **(Hint: See Sample Problem 10G, and balance the equation.)**

$$C_6H_{12}O_6(s) \longrightarrow C_2H_5OH(l) + CO_2(g)$$

25. Plaster of Paris, $CaSO_4 \cdot \frac{1}{2}H_2O$, has many uses, including castings and dental cement. It can be obtained by heating gypsum, $CaSO_4 \cdot 2H_2O$. How many liters of water vapor evolve when 5.00 L of gypsum is heated at 110°C to produce plaster of Paris? At 110°C the density of $CaSO_4 \cdot 2H_2O$ is 2.32 g/mL, and the density of water vapor is 0.581 g/L. **(Hint: See Sample Problem 10H.)**

$$2CaSO_4 \cdot 2H_2O(s) \longrightarrow 2CaSO_4 \cdot \tfrac{1}{2}H_2O(s) + 3H_2O(g)$$

26. Builders and dentists must store plaster of Paris, $CaSO_4 \cdot \frac{1}{2}H_2O$, in airtight containers to prevent it from absorbing water vapor and changing back into gypsum, $CaSO_4 \cdot 2H_2O$. If 7.50 kg of plaster of Paris absorbed excess water vapor, what volume of gypsum would form? The density of $CaSO_4 \cdot 2H_2O$ is 2.32 g/mL. **(Hint: See Sample Problem 10H.)**

$$2CaSO_4 \cdot \tfrac{1}{2}H_2O(s) + 3H_2O(g) \longrightarrow 2CaSO_4 \cdot 2H_2O(s)$$

27. Gold can be recovered from sea water by reacting the water with an active metal such as zinc, which is refined from zinc oxide. The zinc displaces the gold in the water. What mass of gold can be recovered if 2.00 g of ZnO and an excess of sea water are available? **(Hint: See Sample Problem 10I.)**

$$2ZnO(s) + C(s) \longrightarrow 2Zn(s) + CO_2(g)$$

$$2Au^{3+}(aq) + 3Zn(s) \longrightarrow 3Zn^{2+}(aq) + 2Au(s)$$

28. Explain the stoichiometry involved in blowing air on the base of a dwindling campfire to keep the coals burning.

29. Why would it be unreasonable for an amendment to the Clean Air Act to call for 0% pollution emissions from cars with combustion engines?

LINKING CHAPTERS

1. Recognizing reaction types
Determine the conversion factors needed for the following problems. Be sure to write a balanced equation first.
   a. What mass of oxygen gas is evolved from the decomposition of a known amount of water?
   b. What amount of hydrochloric acid is needed to completely react with a known mass of zinc in a single-displacement reaction?

Complete worked-out solutions for these problems can be found on the teacher's interleaved pages at the end of this chapter.

26. 3.83 L of $CaSO_4 \cdot 2H_2O$

27. 3.23 g of Au

28. Near the center of the fire, oxygen is the limiting reactant. The added oxygen from your breath reacts with the wood to produce more heat.

29. 0% pollution emissions from cars with combustion engines would require 100% yield for the combustion reaction of gasoline. This requirement does not take into account the actual yield or the stoichiometry of nitrogen from the air reacting in the hot engine.

LINKING CHAPTERS

1. a. $2H_2O(l) \longrightarrow 2H_2(g) + O_2(g)$

$$\text{mol } H_2O \times \frac{1 \text{ mol } O_2}{2 \text{ mol } H_2O} \times \frac{32.00 \text{ g } O_2}{1 \text{ mol } O_2}$$

b. $2HCl(aq) + Zn(s) \longrightarrow ZnCl_2(aq) + H_2(g)$

$$\text{g Zn} \times \frac{1 \text{ mol Zn}}{65.39 \text{ g Zn}} \times \frac{2 \text{ mol HCl}}{1 \text{ mol Zn}}$$

c. $Ca(NO_3)_2(aq) + K_2CO_3(aq) \longrightarrow 2KNO_3(aq) + CaCO_3(s)$

$$\text{g Ca(NO}_3)_2 \times \frac{1 \text{ mol Ca(NO}_3)_2}{164.10 \text{ g Ca(NO}_3)_2} \times \frac{1 \text{ mol CaCO}_3}{1 \text{ mol Ca(NO}_3)_2}$$

2. Both the synthesis reaction and the dissolution of sugar involve reversible processes. At equilibrium, the forward reaction occurs at the same rate as the reverse reaction, so no net change is visible.

ALTERNATIVE ASSESSMENTS

Performance assessment

1. For all parts, student procedures should include using the mass of the limiting reactant to determine the theoretical yield of the easiest product to isolate and measure. The procedure should also include finding the actual yield by rinsing, drying, and measuring the mass of the product. The actual yield

Complete worked-out solutions for these problems can be found on the teacher's interleaved pages at the end of this chapter.

divided by the theoretical yield times 100% is the percentage yield. When doing the experiments, be sure sufficient excess reactants are used for the reaction to go to completion. Below are some specific hints for each part.

a. Let Zn be the limiting reactant. $ZnCl_2$ should be the product. Be sure students do the drying process in a fume hood, as excess HCl will be driven off also.

b. By drying the product solution, the Na_2CO_3 can be obtained.

c. Choose one reactant to be limiting. Use the mass of a sample of it to determine how much of the other reactant will react with it. Use more than that amount so that it will be in excess. Filter out and rinse the solid $CaCO_3$.

d. Let NaOH be the limiting reactant. Heat the product solution to drive off the water and leave the NaCl behind. Be sure the students do the drying process in a fume hood, as excess HCl will be driven off also.

2. Gases to be collected should differ in density from air so that they can be collected easily. Hydrogen (less dense) and carbon dioxide (more dense) are ideal. Oxygen and nitrogen can be collected, but they are more difficult to collect because they are similar in density to air. Be sure students do not use gases such as H_2S or SO_2. These gases are unsafe and are a hazard to students. Hydrogen can be prepared by reacting a safe, active metal, such as magnesium, with dilute HCl. CO_2 can be prepared by reacting a carbonate with dilute acid. A gas of low density should be collected with an inverted container placed over the reaction. Allowing the gas to fall into the collection container can be used to collect a gas of high density.

Answers continue on page 381D.

c. What amount of calcium carbonate is produced in a double-displacement reaction between a known mass of calcium nitrate and potassium carbonate?

2. **Theme: Equilibrium and change**
In some reactions the products react to reform the reactants. How is this reversal of a reaction similar to the dissolution and recrystallization of sugar from a saturated solution of sugar in iced tea?

ALTERNATIVE ASSESSMENTS

Performance assessment

1. Design an experiment to measure the percentage yields for the reactions listed below. If your teacher approves your design, acquire the necessary materials, and carry out your plan to obtain percentage yield data.
   a. $Zn(s) + 2HCl(aq) \longrightarrow ZnCl_2(aq) + H_2(g)$
   b. $2NaHCO_3(s) \longrightarrow Na_2CO_3 + H_2O(g) + CO_2(g)$
   c. $CaCl_2(aq) + Na_2CO_3(aq) \longrightarrow$
   $\qquad\qquad\qquad\qquad CaCO_3(s) + 2NaCl(aq)$
   d. $NaOH(aq) + HCl(aq) \longrightarrow NaCl(aq) + H_2O(l)$
   (Note: use only dilute NaOH and HCl, less concentrated that 1.0 mol/L.)

2. Your teacher will give you an index card specifying a volume of a gas. Reactants to make the gas will also be listed. Describe exactly how you would make the gas from the reactants. Include a method of collecting the gas without allowing it to mix with the air. Then specify how much of each reactant you need.

Choose a limiting reactant and explain your choice. If your teacher approves your plan, obtain the necessary materials and make the gas. (Hint: Look up the density of the gas in a chemical handbook.)

Portfolio projects

1. **Research and communication**
Research the composition of gasoline sold in your area. Contact a gasoline company to discover what formulations are used. Investigate whether the mixtures change by season or by geographic area. Find out if your area has any guidelines regarding gasoline additives that reduce air pollution. Present your findings in the class.

2. **Cooperative activity**
Investigate corporate, governmental, or private use of alternative fuel sources for vehicles. Hold a class debate to compare the costs and environmental effects of these alternative fuels.

3. **Chemistry and you**
Visit a car maintenance shop to find out how you can help reduce air pollution by increasing your car's efficiency. Make a checklist of tasks to perform regularly to help meet this goal.

4. **Research and communication**
Research the production of the following pollutants: methane, CH_4; mercury, Hg; lead, Pb; chlorine, Cl_2; and sulfur oxides, SO_X. Determine the stoichiometry involved in the production of each of these chemicals. Contact the EPA, and gather information on what you can do to help reduce pollution by these chemicals.

1. Stoichiometry problems require the use of a
   _____.
   a. table of bond energies
   b. Lewis structure
   c. chart of electron configurations
   d. mole ratio

2. In the chemical equation $A + B \longrightarrow C + D$, if
   you know the mass of A, you can determine
   _____.
   a. the mass of any of the other reactants and
      products
   b. only the mass of C and D combined
   c. only the mass of B
   d. only the mass of A and B combined

3. In order to solve a mass-mass stoichiometry
   problem it is necessary to know the _____.
   a. coefficients of the balanced equation
   b. phases of the reactants and products
   c. rate at which the reaction occurs
   d. chemical names of the reactants and
      products

4. For the reaction $N_2 + 3H_2 \longrightarrow 2NH_3$, _____ mol
   of N_2 is required to produce 18 mol of NH_3.
   a. 9   c. 18
   b. 27   d. 36

5. If a chemical reaction involving substances A
   and B stops when B is completely used, then
   B is referred to as the _____.
   a. excess reactant
   b. primary reactant
   c. limiting reactant
   d. primary product

6. The measured amount of a product obtained
   from a chemical reaction is called the _____.
   a. mole ratio
   b. theoretical yield
   c. percentage yield
   d. actual yield

7. If a chemist calculates the maximum amount
   of product that might be obtained in a chemical reaction, he or she is calculating the _____.
   a. theoretical yield   c. percentage yield
   b. mole ratio   d. actual yield

8. Knowing the mole ratio of a reactant and
   product in a chemical reaction would allow
   one to determine _____.
   a. the energy released in the reaction
   b. the mass of the product produced from a
      known mass of reactant
   c. the speed of the reaction
   d. whether the reaction was reversible

9. In stoichiometry, chemists are mainly concerned with _____.
   a. the types of bonds found in compounds
   b. energy changes occurring in chemical
      reactions
   c. mass relationships in chemical reactions
   d. speed with which chemical reactions occur

10. In the reaction $6CO_2 + 6H_2O \longrightarrow C_6H_{12}O_6 + 6O_2$, the mole ratio of CO_2 to $C_6H_{12}O_6$ is _____.
    a. 1:2   c. 6:1
    b. 1:1   d. 1:4

11. In a chemical reaction, the reactant remaining
    after all of the limiting reactant is completely
    used is referred to as the _____.
    a. product
    b. controlling reactant
    c. excess reactant
    d. catalyst

1. d
2. a
3. a
4. a
5. c
6. d
7. a
8. b
9. c
10. c
11. c

Answers from page 355

SAMPLE PROBLEM 10C

Ans. $C_6H_4(NO_2)COOH(s) + 3H_2(g) \longrightarrow NH_2C_6H_4COOH(s) + 2H_2O(l)$;
648 g $NH_2C_6H_4COOH$

e. When pentane, C_5H_{12}, burns in oxygen, it produces carbon dioxide and water. If 85.5 g of pentane is burned, what volume of carbon dioxide is produced? Assume the CO_2 cools to room temperature, where its density is 1.997 g/L.

Ans. $C_5H_{12}(g) + 8O_2(g) \longrightarrow 5CO_2(g) + 6H_2O(g)$; 131 L CO_2

f. Magnesium burns in oxygen to produce magnesium oxide. What mass of magnesium will burn in the presence of 189 mL of oxygen? The density of oxygen is 1.429 g/L.

Ans. $2Mg(s) + O_2(g) \longrightarrow 2MgO(s)$; 0.410 g Mg

Answers from page 356

7. The magnesium reaction releases 5.78 kJ/g.

$[24.305 \text{ g} + (18.015 \text{ g} \times 2)] = 60.335$ g
349 kJ ÷ 60.335 g = 5.78 kJ/g

The calcium oxide reaction releases 0.880 kJ/g.

40.078 g + 15.999 g + 18.015 g = 74.092 g
65.2 kJ ÷ 74.092 g = 0.880 kJ/g

The magnesium reaction is more effective.

Answers from page 360

SAMPLE PROBLEM 10D

b. Hydrogen sulfide gas is formed when HCl reacts with FeS. $FeCl_2$ is the other product. What mass of H_2S is formed when 130.5 g of FeS is mixed with 70.4 g of HCl in solution?

Ans. $FeS(s) + 2HCl(aq) \longrightarrow H_2S(g) + FeCl_2(aq)$; 32.9 g H_2S

c. Iron(III) oxide reacts with carbon monoxide to form molten iron and carbon dioxide. If you have 180.0 kg of iron(III) oxide and 110.0 kg of carbon monoxide, what mass of iron is produced?

Ans. $Fe_2O_3(s) + 3CO(g) \longrightarrow 2Fe(s) + 3CO_2(g)$; 125.9 kg Fe

Answers from page 366

5. a. $P_4O_{10}(g) + 6H_2O(l) \longrightarrow 4H_3PO_4(aq)$

b. $100 \text{ g } P_4O_{10} \times \dfrac{1 \text{ mol } P_4O_{10}}{283.9 \text{ g } P_4O_{10}} \times \dfrac{4 \text{ mol } H_3PO_4}{1 \text{ mol } P_4O_{10}} \times$

$\dfrac{97.995 \text{ g } H_3PO_4}{1 \text{ mol } H_3PO_4} = 138.1 \text{ g } H_3PO_4$ theoretical yield

$100 \text{ g } P_4O_{10} \times \dfrac{1 \text{ mol } P_4O_{10}}{283.9 \text{ g } P_4O_{10}} = 0.35 \text{ mol } P_4O_{10}$ limiting reactant

$200 \text{ g } H_2O \times \dfrac{1 \text{ mol } H_2O}{18.015 \text{ g } H_2O} = 3.60 \times 10^3 \text{ mol } H_2O$ excess reactant

c. $\dfrac{126.2 \text{ g actual}}{138.1 \text{ g theoretical}} \times 100 = 91.4\%$ yield

6. $2000 \text{ g } CaCO_3 \times \dfrac{1 \text{ mol } CaCO_3}{100.09 \text{ g } CaCO_3} \times \dfrac{1 \text{ mol } CaO}{1 \text{ mol } CaCO_3} \times$

$\dfrac{56.08 \text{ g } CaO}{1 \text{ mol } CaO} = 1.12 \times 10^3 \text{ g } CaO$ theoretical yield

$\dfrac{1050 \text{ g actual}}{1120 \text{ g theoretical}} \times 100 = 93.8\%$ yield

7. $Al(s) + 3CuSO_4(aq) \longrightarrow 3Cu(s) + Al(SO_4)_3(aq)$

$1.85 \text{ g Al} \times \dfrac{1 \text{ mol Al}}{26.981 \text{ g Al}} \times \dfrac{3 \text{ mol Cu}}{1 \text{ mol Al}} \times \dfrac{65.546 \text{ g Cu}}{1 \text{ mol Cu}} = 13.5 \text{ g Cu}$

$13.5 \text{ g Cu} \times \dfrac{56.6\%}{100\%} = 7.64 \text{ g Cu}$

8. $50.0 \text{ g } C_7H_6O \times \dfrac{1 \text{ mol } C_7H_6O}{106.12 \text{ g } C_7H_6O} \times \dfrac{1 \text{ mol } C_9H_8O}{1 \text{ mol } C_7H_6O} \times \dfrac{132.16 \text{ g } C_9H_8O}{1 \text{ mol } C_9H_8O} =$

$62.3 \text{ g } C_9H_8O$

$62.3 \text{ g } C_9H_8O \times \dfrac{94.5\%}{100\%} = 58.8 \text{ g } C_9H_8O$

9. $10.1 \text{ g Mg} \times \dfrac{1 \text{ mol Mg}}{24.31 \text{ g Mg}} \times \dfrac{2 \text{ mol } H_2O}{1 \text{ mol Mg}} \times \dfrac{18.02 \text{ g } H_2O}{1 \text{ mol } H_2O} = 15.0 \text{ g } H_2O$

$15.0 \text{ g } H_2O \times \dfrac{1 \text{ mL}}{1.0 \text{ g}} = 15.0 \text{ mL } H_2O$

10. Mg is the limiting reactant.
H_2O is the excess reactant.

$10.1 \text{ g Mg} \times \dfrac{1 \text{ mol Mg}}{24.31 \text{ g Mg}} = 0.415 \text{ mol Mg}$

$15.0 \text{ g } H_2O \times \dfrac{1 \text{ mol } H_2O}{18.02 \text{ g } H_2O} = 0.832 \text{ mol } H_2O$

$0.832 \text{ mol } H_2O \times \dfrac{1 \text{ mol Mg}}{2 \text{ mol } H_2O} = 0.416 \text{ mol Mg}$

PRACTICE PROBLEM 10H

c. $57.3 \text{ mL } C_8H_{18} \times \dfrac{0.692 \text{ g } C_8H_{18}}{1 \text{ mL}} = 39.652 \text{ g } C_8H_{18}$

$39.652 \text{ g } C_8H_{18} \times \dfrac{1 \text{ mol } C_8H_{18}}{114 \text{ g } C_8H_{18}} = 0.348 \text{ mol } C_8H_{18}$

$400 \text{ L air} \times \dfrac{21 \text{ L } O_2}{100 \text{ L air}} \times \dfrac{1.33 \text{ g } O_2}{1 \text{ L } O_2} = 112 \text{ g } O_2$

$112 \text{ g } O_2 \times \dfrac{1 \text{ mol } O_2}{31.999 \text{ g } O_2} = 3.50 \text{ mol } O_2$

$0.348 \text{ mol } C_8H_{18} \times \dfrac{25 \text{ mol } O_2}{2 \text{ mol } C_8H_{18}} = 4.350 \text{ mol } O_2$

$4.350 \text{ mol } O_2 \times \dfrac{31.999 \text{ g } O_2}{1 \text{ mol } O_2} \times \dfrac{1 \text{ L } O_2}{1.33 \text{ g } O_2} \times \dfrac{100 \text{ L air}}{21 \text{ L } O_2} = 498.4 \text{ L air}$

$498.4 \text{ L air} - 400 \text{ L air} = 98.4 \text{ L air}$

2. $1 \text{ L } C_8H_{18} \times \dfrac{1000 \text{ mL}}{1 \text{ L}} \times \dfrac{0.692 \text{ g } C_8H_{18}}{1 \text{ mL}} \times \dfrac{1 \text{ mol } C_8H_{18}}{114 \text{ g } C_8H_{18}} \times$

$\dfrac{18 \text{ mol } H_2O}{2 \text{ mol } C_8H_{18}} \times \dfrac{18.015 \text{ g } H_2O}{1 \text{ mol } H_2O} = 984 \text{ g } H_2O$

6. $36.6 \text{ g } O_2 \times \dfrac{1 \text{ mol } O_2}{32.0 \text{ g } O_2} \times \dfrac{1 \text{ mol } O_3}{1 \text{ mol } O_2} \times \dfrac{48.0 \text{ g } O_3}{1 \text{ mol } O_3} = 54.9 \text{ g } O_3$

7. $74.0 \text{ g } C_8H_{18} \times \dfrac{1 \text{ mol } C_8H_{18}}{114 \text{ g } C_8H_{18}} \times \dfrac{16 \text{ mol CO}}{2 \text{ mol } C_8H_{18}} \times \dfrac{28.01 \text{ g CO}}{1 \text{ mol CO}} = 145 \text{ g CO}$

CONCEPT & SKILLS REVIEW

4. $500 \text{ g } SO_2 \times \dfrac{1 \text{ mol } SO_2}{64.06 \text{ g } SO_2} \times \dfrac{2 \text{ mol } H_2SO_4}{2 \text{ mol } SO_2} \times \dfrac{98.08 \text{ g } H_2SO_4}{1 \text{ mol } H_2SO_4} = 0.765 \text{ g } H_2SO_4$

5. $125 \text{ g } KClO_3 \times \dfrac{1 \text{ mol } KClO_3}{122.55 \text{ g } KClO_3} \times \dfrac{3 \text{ mol } O_3}{2 \text{ mol } KClO_3} = 1.53 \text{ mol } O_2$

6. $10.0 \text{ mol } H_2O_2 \times \dfrac{1 \text{ mol } O_2}{2 \text{ mol } H_2O_2} \times \dfrac{32.0 \text{ g } O_2}{1 \text{ mol } O_2} \times \dfrac{1 \text{ L } O_2}{1.429 \text{ g } O_2} = 112 \text{ L } O_2$

7. $25 \text{ mol } NH_3 \times \dfrac{4 \text{ mol NO}}{4 \text{ mol } NH_3} \times \dfrac{30.01 \text{ g NO}}{1 \text{ mol NO}} \times \dfrac{1 \text{ L NO}}{1.340 \text{ g NO}} = 560 \text{ L NO}$

10. $100 \text{ g Cu} \times \dfrac{1 \text{ mol Cu}}{63.5 \text{ g Cu}} = 1.57 \text{ mol Cu}$

$100 \text{ AgNO}_3 \times \dfrac{1 \text{ mol } AgNO_3}{170 \text{ g } AgNO_3} = 0.588 \text{ mol } AgNO_3$

$0.588 \text{ mol } AgNO_3 \times \dfrac{2 \text{ mol Ag}}{2 \text{ mol } AgNO_3} \times \dfrac{107 \text{ g Ag}}{1 \text{ mol Ag}} = 63.4 \text{ g Ag}$

11. $50 \text{ g } C_4H_8O_2 \times \dfrac{1 \text{ mol } C_4H_8O_2}{88.11 \text{ g } C_4H_8O_2} = 0.57 \text{ mol } C_4H_8O_2$

$40 \text{ g } CH_3OH \times \dfrac{1 \text{ mol } CH_3OH}{32.04 \text{ g } CH_3OH} = 1.25 \text{ mol } CH_3OH$

$0.57 \text{ mol } C_4H_8O_2 \times \dfrac{1 \text{ mol } C_5H_{10}O_2}{1 \text{ mol } C_4H_8O_2} \times \dfrac{102 \text{ g } C_5H_{10}O_2}{1 \text{ mol } C_5H_{10}O_2} = 58.2 \text{ g } C_5H_{10}O_2$

Answers from page 378

15. $1000 \text{ g MgCl}_2 \times \dfrac{1 \text{ mol MgCl}_2}{95 \text{ g MgCl}_2} \times \dfrac{1 \text{ mol Mg}}{1 \text{ mol MgCl}_2} \times \dfrac{24 \text{ g Mg}}{1 \text{ mol Mg}} = 253.0 \text{ g Mg}$

$\dfrac{185 \text{ g Mg actual}}{253 \text{ g Mg theoretical}} \times 100 = 73.1\%$

16. $2.0 \text{ mol CH}_4 \times \dfrac{1 \text{ mol CO}_2}{1 \text{ mol CH}_4} \times \dfrac{44 \text{ g CO}_2}{1 \text{ mol CO}_2} = 88 \text{ g CO}_2$

$\dfrac{87 \text{ g CO}_2 \text{ actual}}{88 \text{ g CO}_2 \text{ theoretical}} \times 100 = 99\%$

17. $1.255 \text{ g C} \times \dfrac{1 \text{ mol C}}{12.01 \text{ g C}} \times \dfrac{1 \text{ mol CH}_4}{2 \text{ mol C}} \times \dfrac{16.04 \text{ g CH}_4}{1 \text{ mol CH}_4} = 0.84 \text{ g CH}_4$

$0.84 \text{ g CH}_4 \times \dfrac{85}{100} = 0.714 \text{ g CH}_4$

18. $2.75 \text{ g C} \times \dfrac{1 \text{ mol C}}{12.011 \text{ g C}} \times \dfrac{1 \text{ mol CH}_4}{2 \text{ mol C}} \times \dfrac{16.04 \text{ g CH}_4}{1 \text{ mol CH}_4} = 1.84 \text{ g CH}_4$

$1.84 \text{ g CH}_4 \times \dfrac{95}{100} = 1.748 \text{ g CH}_4$

19. $30\,000 \text{ g SiC} \times \dfrac{1 \text{ mol SiC}}{40.097 \text{ g SiC}} = 748 \text{ mol SiC}$

$\dfrac{748 \text{ mol SiC actual}}{991 \text{ mol SiC theoretical}} \times 100 = 75\%$

23. $0.750 \text{ L CO}_2 \times \dfrac{1.25 \text{ g CO}_2}{1 \text{ L}} \times \dfrac{1 \text{ mol CO}}{44.01 \text{ g CO}_2} \times \dfrac{2 \text{ mol NaHCO}_3}{2 \text{ mol CO}_2} \times$

$\dfrac{84.007 \text{ g NaHCO}_3}{1 \text{ mol NaHCO}_3} \times \dfrac{1 \text{ kg baking powder}}{168 \text{ g NaHCO}_3} \times \dfrac{1000 \text{ g}}{1 \text{ kg}} = 10.7 \text{ g baking powder}$

24. $.50 \text{ L CO}_2 \times \dfrac{1.25 \text{ g CO}_2}{1 \text{ L}} \times \dfrac{1 \text{ mol CO}_2}{44.01 \text{ g CO}_2} \times \dfrac{2 \text{ mol C}_6\text{H}_{12}\text{O}_6}{4 \text{ mol CO}_2} \times$

$\dfrac{180.16 \text{ g C}_6\text{H}_{12}\text{O}_6}{1 \text{ mol C}_6\text{H}_{12}\text{O}_6} = 1.3 \text{ g C}_6\text{H}_{12}\text{O}_6$

Answers from page 379

25. $5.00 \text{ L CaSO}_4 \cdot 2\text{H}_2\text{O} \times \dfrac{1000 \text{ mL}}{1 \text{ L}} \times \dfrac{2.32 \text{ g CaSO}_4 \cdot 2\text{H}_2\text{O}}{1 \text{ mL}} \times$

$\dfrac{1 \text{ mol CaSO}_4 \cdot 2\text{H}_2\text{O}}{172.17 \text{ g CaSO}_4 \cdot 2\text{H}_2\text{O}} \times \dfrac{3 \text{ mol H}_2\text{O}}{2 \text{ mol CaSO}_4 \cdot 2\text{H}_2\text{O}} \times \dfrac{18.015 \text{ g H}_2\text{O}}{1 \text{ mol H}_2\text{O}} \times$

$\dfrac{1 \text{ L H}_2\text{O}}{0.581 \text{ g H}_2\text{O}} = 3134 \text{ L H}_2\text{O}$

26. $7.50 \text{ kg CaSO}_4 \cdot \tfrac{1}{2}\text{H}_2\text{O} \times \dfrac{1 \text{ mol CaSO}_4 \cdot \tfrac{1}{2}\text{H}_2\text{O}}{145.15 \text{ g CaSO}_4 \cdot \tfrac{1}{2}\text{H}_2\text{O}} \times \dfrac{2 \text{ mol CaSO}_4 \cdot 2\text{H}_2\text{O}}{2 \text{ mol CaSO}_4 \cdot \tfrac{1}{2}\text{H}_2\text{O}} \times$

$\dfrac{172.17 \text{ g CaSO}_4 \cdot 2\text{H}_2\text{O}}{1 \text{ mol CaSO}_4 \cdot 2\text{H}_2\text{O}} \times \dfrac{1 \text{ mL CaSO}_4 \cdot 2\text{H}_2\text{O}}{2.32 \text{ g CaSO}_4 \cdot 2\text{H}_2\text{O}} \times \dfrac{1 \text{ L}}{1000 \text{ mL}} =$

$3.83 \text{ L CaSO}_4 \cdot 2\text{H}_2\text{O}$

27. $2.00 \text{ g ZnO} \times \dfrac{1 \text{ mol Zn}}{81.23 \text{ g ZnO}} \times \dfrac{2 \text{ mol Zn}}{2 \text{ mol ZnO}} \times \dfrac{65.39 \text{ g Zn}}{1 \text{ mol Zn}} = 1.61 \text{ g Zn}$

$1.61 \text{ g Zn} \times \dfrac{1 \text{ mol Zn}}{65.39 \text{ g Zn}} \times \dfrac{2 \text{ mol Au}}{3 \text{ mol Zn}} \times \dfrac{196.97 \text{ g Au}}{1 \text{ mol Au}} = 3.23 \text{ g Au}$

Portfolio projects

1. Encourage students to use a variety of methods to contact the companies. Letters, phone calls, and e-mail all are effective. Contact information should be available from local gasoline stations. Students will probably find out that have wide yearlong temperature ranges.

2. Alternative fuel sources should include biomass fuels, such as ethanol; solar energy; and fuel cells. Research can be done from recent printed matter and Internet sources.

3. Student findings might include using the correct grade of gasoline for a car's engine, checking for proper tire inflation, replacing the air filter regularly, and properly adjusting carburation.

4. Students will determine that the amount of each pollutant produced depends on the reactions that occur and the amounts of reactants involved. Most large cities have an EPA office that can be contacted by phone of letter. The EPA can be contacted at www.epa.gov on the Internet.

Causes of Change

CLASSROOM RESOURCES

SECTIONS	TEACHER'S DEMONSTRATIONS	PROBLEM SOLVING ■ *Text* ◆ *ChemFile Mini-Guide*	LABORATORIES ■ *Text* ◆ *ChemFile Manuals: A, B, C, D*
11-1 **How does heat differ from other forms of energy?** Section Review, p. 391	**Demo 1** Inexpensive Hand Warmer, p. 384 **Demo 2** Molar Heat Capacity, p. 386	■ **Sample Problem 11A** Calculating the molar heat capacity of a substance, p. 388	■ **QuickLab** A Randomness Model, p. 386 ◆ **A16** Temperature of a Bunsen Burner Flame ◆ **Exp. C6** Specific Heat Capacity ◆ **Inv. C6** Specific Heat Capacity—Terrorist Investigation
11-2 **How does temperature affect enthalpy and entropy** Section Review, p. 395		■ **Sample Problem 11B** Calculating molar enthalpy change, p. 393	◆ **A14** Energy and Entropy ◆ **Exp. C7** Constructing a Heating and Cooling Curve ◆ **Inv. C7** Constructing a Heating and Cooling Curve—Melting Oils for Soap Production
11-3 **What happens during a change of state?** Section Review, p. 401	**Demo 3** An Interesting State Change, p. 396 **Demo 4** Boiling Water in a Paper Cup, p. 398 **Demo 5** Synthesis of Copper(II) Sulfide, p. 400		◆ **A10** Molar Heat of Fusion of Ice ◆ **Exp. C8** Heat of Fusion
11-4 **How does thermodynamics apply to reactions and nutrition?** Section Review, p. 413	**Demo 6** Hess's Law and the Enthalpy of Neutralization for NaOH, p. 406	■ **Sample Problem 11C** Calculating change in enthalpy, p. 405 ■ **Sample Problem 11D** Calculating change in entropy, p. 406 ■ **Sample Problem 11E** Calculating change in molar Gibbs energy, p. 407 ◆ **Chapter 19** Thermochemistry	■ **Exp. 11A** Calorimetry and Hess's Law, p. 756 ◆ **A18** Heat of Combustion ■ **Exp. 11B** Kitchen Calorimetry, p. 761 ◆ **Exp. C9** Heat of Solution ◆ **D10** Counting Calories

TECHNOLOGY RESOURCES

See page 382 for a listing of Internet resources.

SECTIONS	VIDEOS/VIDEODISC *Holt Chemistry Videodisc* CNN PRESENTS *Science in the NEWS*	CHEMFILE CD-ROMS ● *Teaching Resources* ◆ *Interactive Tutor*	OVERHEADS ● *Color Transparencies* ◆ *Transparency Masters*
11-1	Heat and Temperature: Hot Metal in Water Heat and Temperature: Microscopic View	● Occupational Application: Firefighter ● Basic Skills: Graphing ● Internet Activity 11: Fuel Cells	● **92** Combustion Calorimeter
11-2	CNN PRESENTS Segment 19 Icebergs Entropy: Hydrogen Combustion Entropy of Reaction Low Entropy/High Entropy		● **94** Low Entropy and High Entropy Systems
11-3	Boiling of Water Evaporation of Liquids States of Matter Sublimation of Iodine	◆ **Module 1:** States of Matter **Topics:** Solids, Liquids, Gases; and Changes of State	● **61** Change of State Models for Water ● **58** Sodium as a Solid, Liquid, and Gas ● **63** Exothermic and Endothermic Changes of State ● **93** Calculating Energy Changes for a Heating Curve ◆ **96A** Relating Enthalpy and Entropy to Spontaneity
11-4	CNN PRESENTS Segment 20 What Is a Calorie? Bomb Calorimeter Calorimeter		● **92** Combustion Calorimeter ● **95** Calculations Involving Energy ◆ See also **92A, 93A, 94A.**

ASSESSMENT RESOURCES

ALTERNATIVE ASSESSMENTS	CHAPTER TESTING	SCORING RUBRICS *Holt ChemFile Teaching Resources CD-ROM*
Student Text Performance assessments, p. 419 Portfolio projects, p. 420 **Teacher's Edition** Specific Heat Capacity, p. 389 Group Strategy, p. 404 **Study Guide** Sections 11-1 to 11-4	**Student Text** Test Preparation, p. 421 **Holt Chemistry: Visualizing Matter Chapter 11 Test** (blackline masters) **Holt ChemFile Test Generator for Macintosh and Windows**	**Lab Work** Student-Designed Experiments Rubric Performance-Tasks Scoring Rubric Assessment for Structured Inquiry Assessment for Open-Ended Inquiry **Portfolio Projects** Evaluating Concept Maps Assessing Portfolios Portfolio Assignment Student Evaluation Form

Causes of Change

Establishing Prior Knowledge

Make certain students understand the following concepts.

▶ Chapter 2: potential and kinetic energy, systems, heat, and temperature
▶ Chapter 8: measuring amounts in moles
▶ Chapter 9: balancing chemical equations

 ## READING STRATEGY

Assimilating Knowledge

Before reading this chapter, have students write a short list of all the things they already know or think they know about heat, entropy, changes of state, and energy from food. When students finish their lists, ask them to contribute their entries to a group list on the board or on an overhead projector. Then have students list the things they might want to know about heat and energy. If students have trouble coming up with questions, ask the following to get them on track:

▶ What sort of energy changes and temperature changes take place as ice at 0°C melts?
▶ Which has the greater disorder, a substance in the liquid state or the same substance in the gaseous state?
▶ How is the fuel value of food determined?

ABOUT THE ILLUSTRATION

The eruption of a volcano is a spontaneous change that results in an increase of disorder. The photo depicts a spectacular change of state from liquid magma to solid rock. Students generally think of freezing as a change of state associated with low temperature. Point out that low temperature is not necessary to cause a substance to solidify.

---

 internetconnect

***Holt Chemistry:
Visualizing Matter***
On-Line Resources
go.hrw.com
Visit the HRW Web site for a variety of resources related to this chapter. Just type in the keyword HW0 Chapt11.

SCLINKS SM
NSTA

National Science Teachers Association
On-Line Resources: www.scilinks.org
The following Scilinks Internet resources can be found in the student text for this chapter:

Page 385
TOPIC: Heat/Temperature
KEYWORD: HW111

Page 391
TOPIC: Entropy
KEYWORD: HW112

Page 393
TOPIC: Enthalpy
KEYWORD: HW113

Page 411
TOPIC: Nutrition/
Thermodynamics
KEYWORD: HW114

Page 414
TOPIC: Hydrogen
KEYWORD: HW115

Page 420
TOPIC: Alternative fuels
KEYWORD: HW116

ENERGY AND LOW-EMISSION CARS

Engineers have long been searching for alternative energy sources to replace petroleum products in automobiles. Petroleum-based fuels produce toxic emissions, and petroleum reserves will eventually be exhausted.

Engineers have investigated solar-powered and battery-powered vehicles as well as internal-combustion engines that burn substances not made from fossil fuels. Hydrogen is one of the most promising alternative energy sources examined so far.

Hydrogen gas has two big advantages as a fuel. When compared to gasoline it produces few toxic emissions. The combustion of gasoline produces hydrocarbons and nitrogen and carbon oxides. These compounds contribute to acid rain, photochemical smog, and the greenhouse effect. When hydrogen is burned, no hydrocarbons or carbon oxides are emitted, and only small quantities of nitrogen oxides are produced. Second, the energy available from 1 g of hydrogen gas far exceeds that given off by other fuels, as shown in the table. Hydrogen gas has three times the energy content of gasoline.

So why aren't hydrogen-powered cars on the roads? One reason is the high cost of making such a car. Another reason is the ex-pense of producing and distributing huge supplies of hydrogen gas.

Some people worry about the danger of storing hydrogen gas because it is highly reactive. But it is no more dangerous than storing gasoline or natural gas, which also react with oxygen. A serious obstacle to using hydrogen gas as a fuel is that it *cannot easily be liquefied*. There is no economical way to cool the gas to its boiling point of 20 K (−253°C). As a gas at ordinary pressure, nearly 3000 L of H_2 is needed to match the energy equivalent of 1 L of gasoline. Vehicles could carry compressed H_2, but that would require using unacceptably heavy cylinders.

Fuel (1 g)	Energy (kJ/g)
Methanol, $CH_3OH(l)$	23
Ethanol, $C_2H_5OH(l)$	30
Gasoline (octane), $C_8H_{18}(l)$	48
Propane, $C_3H_8(g)$	50
Natural gas (methane), $CH_4(g)$	56
Hydrogen, $H_2(g)$	142

CHAPTER LINKS

What drives the H_2 combustion reaction?

Is there a safe and economical way to carry H_2 in a car?

Would the use of hydrogen-powered cars lead to less pollution?

STORY BACKGROUND

Gasoline, diesel, and steam engines are called heat engines because the heat produced by fuel combustion is used to expand gases, which in turn push on pistons or turn turbines. The maximum theoretical efficiency of a heat engine, including an engine that uses hydrogen as a fuel, is between 25% and 40%. Electric motors are about 90% efficient in practice and would seem to provide a high-efficiency alternative to fuel-burning engines. Attempts to market electric cars have been only partially successful primarily because the cars have a limited range with today's battery technology and because they lack sufficient power. In addition, the electricity to charge batteries must sometimes be generated at fuel-burning power plants. Work continues on developing vehicles that use a hydrogen/oxygen fuel cell to supply electricity.

RESOURCE LINK

ChemFile Teaching Resources CD-ROM
Internet Activity
Assign Internet Activity 11: *Fuel Cells* to emphasize relevant applications of text concepts.

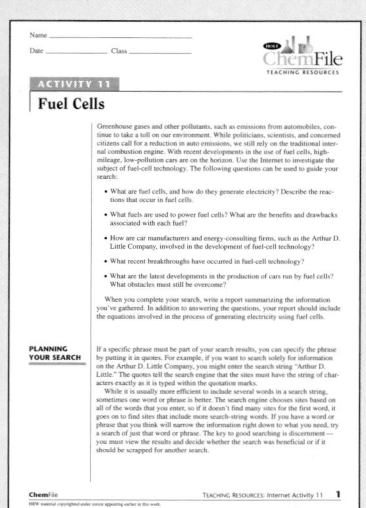

CONCEPT PREVIEW

Section 11-1
Changes in heat and disorder
▸ heat and temperature
▸ heat and kinetic energy
▸ molar heat capacity
▸ entropy

Section 11-2
Thermodynamic properties
▸ effect of temperature on molar enthalpy and entropy changes

Section 11-3
State changes
▸ pattern of enthalpy and entropy changes during a state change
▸ effects of pressure on state changes
▸ Gibbs energy and spontaneity

Section 11-4
Measuring enthalpy changes
▸ calorimetry
▸ using Hess's law in enthalpy and entropy calculations
▸ calculating Gibbs energy changes

Thermodynamics of nutrition
▸ photosynthesis and cellular respiration
▸ diet and energy

How does heat differ from other forms of energy?

OBJECTIVES

▶ *Cite* the two principles that govern most natural events.

▶ *Distinguish* between heat and temperature.

▶ *Propose* a qualitative explanation of entropy.

▶ *Define* molar heat capacity, and **calculate** its value from temperature measurements taken during heating experiments.

Governing principles

This chapter explores the driving forces behind chemical reactions and explains why reactions occur. Because chemical reactions are natural events, their driving forces may be found by examining other events in nature. Natural events are often accompanied by a decrease in energy, an increase in disorder, or both. For example, think about the water flow in a waterfall. Water that has fallen to the foot of a waterfall has a lower potential energy than it had at the top. Another example is a spinning wheel, which loses kinetic energy as it gradually slows down and stops. Of course the energy lost in these examples does not disappear. It becomes another form of energy, usually heat.

A natural event that is accompanied by an increase in disorder is the release of gas into the atmosphere. When gases are discharged into the atmosphere, they mix with the air and disperse. Another example of a natural event accompanied by increased disorder is seen in autumn, when leaves change color, fall, and scatter. This entropy increase is illustrated in **Figure 11-1.** In both of these examples the

▶ **FIGURE 11-1**

Falling leaves are an example of a natural event accompanied by an increase in disorder.

LESSON WARM-UP

Demonstration 1 Discussion
Remind students that they learned about energy changes in chemical reactions in Chapter 9. Then perform Demonstration 1 on this page. Point out that the reaction in the demonstration is the same as the rusting of iron.

$$4Fe + 3O_2 \longrightarrow 2Fe_2O_3 + heat$$

You may want to compare the demonstration results with an even more rapid oxidation of iron that occurs when a tuft of fine steel wool held with tongs burns over a burner flame.

Vermiculite is a mineral that consists of hydrated magnesium-aluminum-iron silicate. Vermiculite serves two functions: It disperses the iron-salt mixture over a large surface area and entraps air, and it acts as an insulator preventing the mixture from cooling too quickly.

Ask students to determine whether the enthalpy change for the demonstration reaction is positive or negative and to explain its sign. *(The enthalpy change is negative because the heat that produced the reaction system goes to the surroundings.)*

DISCUSSION STRATEGY

Ask students for examples of both increasing and decreasing disorder, and list them on the board. Have students critique the lists for irrelevant or incorrect examples.

DEMONSTRATION 1

Inexpensive Hand Warmer

Approximate time: 10 minutes

The iron must be in powdered form. Iron filings will probably corrode too slowly to increase the temperature noticeably.

1. Place 25 g of iron powder in a small sealable plastic bag, add 1 g of NaCl, seal the bag, and shake to mix.

2. Add 1 tablespoon of expanded vermiculite, reseal the bag, and shake it again.

3. To activate the hand warmer, add 5 mL of water to the bag. Seal the bag, and squeeze or shake it thoroughly to mix the contents. The heat given off in the reaction will produce a noticeable temperature increase in about 1 minute.

4. Pass the bag around the class. If it begins to cool too soon, open the bag to let in fresh air, and shake or squeeze it again.

natural event results in a decrease in order. Later in the chapter, you will see that a decrease in energy and an increase in disorder govern chemical reactions. Energy and disorder in simpler processes, such as cooling and boiling, will also be examined. First you will learn the difference between heat and temperature.

Heat and temperature are different

Heat is thermal energy. Like other forms of energy, heat is measured in *joules.* A hot object has more heat than an otherwise similar cold object. When the two objects are placed in contact, energy spontaneously flows into the cooler object until the objects are the same temperature. This phenomenon is illustrated in **Figure 11-2a.** The total heat content of the two blocks shown in the diagram remains constant because the gain in thermal energy by the cool block exactly equals the loss in thermal energy by the warm block.

Certainly you have a natural sense of what is hot and what is cold. But what is *temperature*? In **Figure 11-2b,** the beaker on the left has a higher heat content than the beaker on the right, but its temperature is lower. That is because temperature represents the *intensity* of thermal energy, whereas heat indicates the *quantity* of thermal energy.

The SI temperature unit is the *kelvin,* although scientific thermometers are usually graduated in *degrees Celsius.* The interval in the two scales is the same, so a temperature *difference* has the same numerical value in kelvins and in degrees Celsius. For example, consider the temperature difference between the two blocks in Figure 11-2a.

$$\Delta T = T_{left} - T_{right} = 40°C = 40 \text{ K}$$

On the other hand, because 0.00°C is equal to 273.15 K, *individual* temperatures are different on the two scales.

$$T_{left} = 65°C = 338 \text{ K}$$
$$T_{right} = 25°C = 298 \text{ K}$$

FIGURE 11-2 ▼

a Heat always flows from a warmer object to a cooler object.

b The liquid on the left has a higher heat content than the liquid on the right. The large volume of the liquid on the left disperses the heat, so the liquid has a lower temperature.

CAUSES OF CHANGE 385

SECTION 11-1

CHAPTER CONNECTION
Kinetic-molecular theory is covered in Chapter 12. For now, students should understand that the particles of matter are in constant motion and have kinetic energy. Heat is the total of this energy, and temperature is a measure of the average kinetic energy of matter.

VISUAL STRATEGY
Figure 11-2 Emphasize that the quantity of heat depends on the quantity of matter present but that temperature does not. As long as enough matter is present, measuring its temperature does not appreciably affect its temperature.

TEACHING TIP
Particle Motion The particles in a solid are moving at a whole range of velocities, bumping into neighboring particles in the crystal. This constant colliding and bouncing *resembles* vibration. Except for a very short free path, the motion of particles in solids is no different from that in liquids and gases.

RESOURCE LINK

ChemFile Lab A
Skills Development
Have students do Experiment A16.

QUICKLAB

Analysis

1. When all arrangements are possible, there are six different arrangements. Where x is the number of possible arrangements of n things, $x = n!$, and $3! = (3 \times 2 \times 1) = 6$. If one position is restricted, the number of possibilities drops to only two because there are only two objects left to arrange. Mathematically, the number of possibilities becomes $x = (n - 1)!$.

2. The set in which all positions are possible is the most random. If a position is restricted, randomness is reduced.

3. The set in which all positions are possible models the greatest entropy. The restricted set models the least entropy.

QUICKLAB

CONSUMER ACTIVITY

A Randomness Model

In this activity, you will model the random positions of molecules by using individual playing cards to represent molecules.

Materials 3 different playing cards

Problem Obtain a set of three different playing cards from your instructor. Put the cards in as many different arrangements as you can. Record the number of possible arrangements. Next select one card to always be in the first (or leftmost) position. Record the number of possible arrangements. Repeat, this time keeping two cards in a constant position. Record the number of possible arrangements.

Analysis

1. What is the relationship between the possible number of arrangements and the number of cards that can be arranged? How does restricting the position of one card affect the number of arrangements?

2. If randomness is the number of distinguishable arrangements, which set is most random? the least random?

3. Entropy is a measure of disorder in systems. Using this definition, which set models the greatest entropy? the least entropy?

Both temperature and heat reflect kinetic energy

The atoms in a gas, liquid, or solid are in constant motion, which means they have kinetic energy. The heat, or thermal energy, of a body is the *total random kinetic energy of its atoms*. The temperature of a substance, on the other hand, reflects the *average random kinetic energy of its atoms*. Remember that kinetic energy is related to velocity. Atoms move faster at high temperatures and slower at lower temperatures. Imagine a piece of gold metal being cooled. As heat is removed, the temperature falls, and the kinetic energy of the gold atoms decreases. As the kinetic energy decreases, the velocity of the atoms decreases. In solids, atoms move by vibrating in their crystal lattice. Some of the atoms vibrate faster than others, but the average speed of the atomic vibrations falls as the temperature decreases. By the time the temperature reaches absolute zero (0.00 K), the atoms have practically stopped moving.

Can you now appreciate the importance of the Kelvin temperature scale? Its zero corresponds to the absence of motion. There are no negative temperatures on the Kelvin scale because you can't have negative motion. Always convert temperatures to the Kelvin scale before carrying out heat and temperature calculations.

Water shows a steady increase in temperature when heated

Think about how the temperature of a beaker of water changes as energy is supplied to the system by a 100 W heater. If the beaker contains 360.3 g of H_2O (20.00 mol) initially at 15°C and the heater is switched on, the water temperature starts to rise. If the temperature is recorded every 15 seconds until it reaches 30°C, you get the data in **Figure 11-3.** The recorded temperatures are converted to kelvins and graphed against time.

DEMONSTRATION 2

Molar Heat Capacity
Approximate time: 15 minutes

1. Obtain samples of aluminum, iron, and copper, or any three different metals. If possible, use uniform 2.5 cm blocks. Measure the mass of each sample, and write the mass on the board. Have students determine the amount in moles of each metal present while you continue the setup.

2. Pour equal volumes of room-temperature water into each of three 250 mL beakers (or 400 mL depending on the size of the samples). Use enough water to cover the samples by at least 1 cm. Adjust the volume as needed to cover the samples. Each beaker should have the same volume of water. Add a thermometer to each beaker, and place the beakers on folded towels to minimize heat transfer through the bottom.

After an initial lag, the temperature rises steadily with time. A straight line has been drawn through some of the data points, and its slope can be measured using the following formula.

$$\text{slope} = \frac{y_2 - y_1}{x_2 - x_1}$$

$$= \frac{T_2 - T_1}{t_2 - t_1} = \frac{\Delta T}{\Delta t}$$

You may remember the slope formula as the following.

$$\text{slope} = \frac{\text{rise}}{\text{run}}$$

Scientists use the symbol Δ as a shorthand way of writing "change in." So $\Delta T/\Delta t$ means the change in temperature, ΔT, that occurs while time is changing by an interval, Δt.

If you choose any two points on the line that are not data points and substitute them in the equation for determining slope, you can determine the rate at which the temperature increases. For example, during a time interval of 150 seconds the temperature rose 9.9 K. The rate is calculated as follows.

$$\text{slope} = \frac{\Delta T}{\Delta t} = \frac{9.9 \text{ K}}{150 \text{ s}} = 0.066 \text{ K/s}$$

The temperature increases by 0.066 kelvins per second during most of the experiment.

What energy changes occur in this experiment? The temperature increase is evidence that the thermal energy of the water increases. How much heat is required to produce a temperature rise of 1 K? That quantity depends on the substance being heated and is called a substance's *heat capacity*. You may recall that heat capacity was introduced in Chapter 2 as a property of matter. The heat capacity of an object is the thermal energy needed to raise its temperature by 1 K. Chemists are most interested in energies per mole, so they measure the **molar heat capacity** of substances. Molar heat capacity is given the symbol C and is the *heat required to increase the temperature of 1 mol of a substance by 1 K*. C is just the specific heat capacity for a substance that you learned about in Chapter 2. In the following equation, q is the heat needed to increase the temperature of n moles of a substance by ΔT.

$$q = nC\Delta T$$

You can now determine the molar heat capacity of water by using the data from the experiment and the equation for q. This process is demonstrated in Sample Problem 11A.

Change in Water Temperature on Heating

Temperature, T (K) vs *Time, t (s)*

Point 1

Point 2

FIGURE 11-3 ▲

Experimental data points cluster around a straight line when temperature is plotted against time.

molar heat capacity

the heat required to increase the temperature of 1 mol of a substance by 1 K

TEACHING TIP

Heat vs. Temperature   Help students differentiate between temperature and heat content with the following thought exercise. Ask students to imagine a bathtub filled with warm water at a temperature of 40°C and a cup filled with water at 40°C. Assume that both samples are at the same temperature, would they feel the same to you if you dipped one hand into the cup and the other hand into bathtub? (*No. The water in the bathtub has a greater quantity of heat.*) Emphasize that although two objects have the same temperature, they do not necessarily have the same heat content.

RESOURCE LINK

ChemFile Lab C
Skills Development
Have student do Exploration C6.

Self-Directed Inquiry
Have students do Investigation C6.

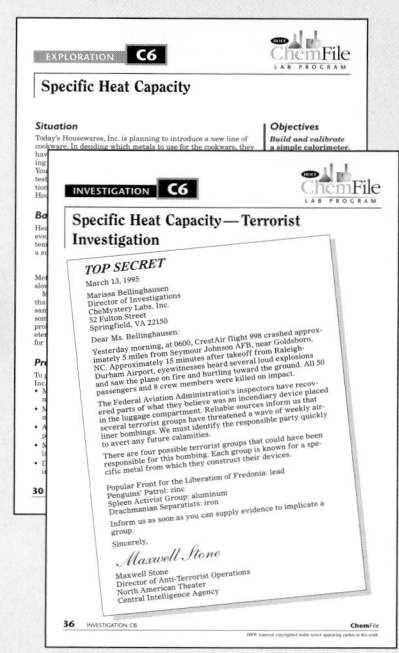

3. Use tongs to remove the samples from the beaker and lower them gently into a metal pan of boiling water on a hot plate. After the water returns to a boil, allow the samples to remain in the water for 1 minute.

4. Using tongs, quickly remove each metal sample, and *gently* return them to their beakers.

5. Have student volunteers watch the thermometers as they swirl the beakers very gently, and record the highest temperature reached by the water in each beaker.

6. Have students use their results to order the metals from highest to lowest molar heat capacity. Because the samples were all at the same temperature, and the quantity of water in each beaker was also the same, the heat capacities are proportional to ΔT/mol of metal. This ratio should be approximately equal for the metals.

7. Tell students that the molar heat capacities for the elements are about equal, and

CONTINUED ON PAGE 388

ADDITIONAL EXAMPLES

SAMPLE PROBLEM 11A

a. A 100.0 W heater is used to heat 6.00 mol of ethanol, $CH_3CH_2OH(l)$. The temperature is recorded every 15 s and the data is plotted to produce a graph similar to that in Figure 11-4. The slope of the graph is calculated to be 0.148 K/s. Calculate the molar heat capacity for ethanol.

Ans. 113 J/K•mol

b. The molar heat capacity for ethylene glycol, $HOCH_2CH_2OH(l)$, the main component of antifreeze, is 148.3 J/K•mol. What quantity of heat in kilojoules will be absorbed by 4850 g of ethylene glycol if its temperature increases from 22.0°C to 108.0°C?

Ans. 997 kJ

c. The molar heat capacity for nitrobenzene, $C_6H_5NO_2(l)$, which is sometimes used as a solvent in shoe polish, is 185.9 J/K•mol. What will be the temperature of a 50.00 g sample of nitrobenzene at 18.0°C after it absorbs 1.00×10^3 J of heat?

Ans. 31.2°C

ANSWERS

PRACTICE PROBLEM 11A

1. $90.0 \text{ g } H_2O \times \dfrac{1 \text{ mol } H_2O}{18.02 \text{ g } H_2O} \times \dfrac{76 \text{ J}}{\text{mol}\bullet\text{K}} \times$

$10 \text{ K} = 3800 \text{ J}$

2. $1.8 \text{ g } H_2O \times \dfrac{1 \text{ mol } H_2O}{18.02 \text{ g } H_2O} \times \dfrac{76 \text{ J}}{\text{mol}\bullet\text{K}} \times$

$70 \text{ K} = 530 \text{ J}$

SAMPLE PROBLEM 11A   Calculating the molar heat capacity of a substance

A 100 W heater is used to heat 20.00 mol of water. The temperature is recorded every 15 s and the data are plotted to produce the graph shown in Figure 11-3. The slope of the graph is calculated to be 0.066 K/s. Use these data to calculate the molar heat capacity for water.

1 List what you know

▶ amount of water = 20.00 mol
▶ capacity of the heater = 100. W
▶ rate of temperature increase $(\Delta T / \Delta t)$ = 0.066 K/s
▶ molar heat capacity of water = ?J/K•mol

2 Set up the problem

The molar heat capacity for water, C, is defined as the amount of heat required to raise the temperature of 1 mol of H_2O by 1 K.

$$C = \frac{q}{n\Delta T}$$

First calculate how much heat was input. One watt equals one joule per second (1 J/s). The total heat supplied by a 100 W heater over a time interval, Δt, can be found by the following equation.

$$q = (100. \text{ J/s})\Delta t$$

There are 20.00 mol of water in the beaker, n = 20.00 mol. Substitute the known values to calculate C.

$$C = \frac{q}{n\Delta T} = \frac{(100. \text{ J/s})\Delta t}{n\Delta T}$$

In the above expression you see $\dfrac{\Delta t}{\Delta T}$. This fraction is the inverse of the slope, so 1/slope is substituted into the equation.

3 Calculate and verify

$$C = \frac{q}{n\Delta T} = \frac{(100. \text{ J/s})\Delta t}{n\Delta T} = \frac{100. \text{ J/s}}{n(slope)}$$

$$= \frac{100. \text{ J/s}}{(20.00 \text{ mol})(0.066 \text{ K/s})} = 76 \text{ J/K}\bullet\text{mol}$$

Solving the expression gives an answer in J/K•mol. The unit of molar heat capacity is *joules per kelvin per mole,* so the units are correct.

PRACTICE PROBLEMS

1. Use the molar heat capacity for water from Sample Problem 11A to calculate the amount of heat energy needed to raise the temperature of 90.0 g of H_2O from 35°C to 45°C.

2. Use the molar heat capacity for water from Sample Problem 11A to calculate the amount of heat energy needed to raise the temperature of 1.8 g of H_2O from 10.0°C to 80.0°C.

DEMONSTRATION 2   *CONTINUED*

explain the different temperature increases they observed in the beakers.

Safety

Wear goggles and a lab apron. Use a metal container to boil the water to avoid breaking a glass container by dropping a metal sample. Always use tongs to handle the hot samples.

Disposal

Pour the water down the drain. Dry the samples, and save them for another use.

Molar heat capacity depends on the number of atoms

The experimental C value just calculated for water is close to the molar heat capacity value listed in **Table 11-1**. Notice the uniform heat capacities of metals and the *identical* molar heat capacities of the noble gases.

A mole of tungsten has a mass of 184 g, whereas a mole of aluminum has a mass of only about 27 g. So you might predict that more heat would be needed to increase the temperature of 1 mol of tungsten by 1 K than to increase the temperature of 1 mol aluminum by 1 K. But Table 11-1 shows that mole for mole, the same heat input is needed to raise 1 mol of either metal by 1 K. Aluminum and tungsten have the same molar heat capacity. The reason is that heat energy is taken up by increasing the kinetic energies of the atoms, and there are exactly the same number of atoms in 1 mol of each metal. The type of metal atom is largely irrelevant. It's the number of atoms that affects the molar heat capacity of a substance.

Notice that the C values in Table 11-1 for the metal chlorides are close to a 2:3:4 ratio. This is the ratio of the total numbers of ions in the formula. For example, there are 1.5 times as many ions in 1 mol of $BaCl_2$ in 1 mol of NaCl, so you would predict a 50% larger molar heat capacity for $BaCl_2$. There are twice as many ions per mole in Hg_2Cl_2 as in NaCl, so you would predict twice the molar heat capacity of Hg_2Cl_2 compared with NaCl.

TABLE 11-1 Molar Heat Capacities	
Substance	**C (J/K • mol)**
Iron, Fe(s)	25.1
Silver, Ag(s)	25.3
Tungsten, W(s)	24.2
Aluminum, Al(s)	24.2
Sodium chloride, NaCl(s)	50.5
Barium chloride, $BaCl_2$(s)	75.1
Mercury(I) chloride, Hg_2Cl_2(s)	102.0
Water, H_2O(s)	37.4
Water, H_2O(l)	75.3
Water, H_2O(g)	36.8
Octane, C_8H_{18}(l)	254.0
Helium, He(g)	20.8
Neon, Ne(g)	20.8
Argon, Ar(g)	20.8
Hydrogen, H_2(g)	28.8
Nitrogen, N_2(g)	29.1
Chlorine, Cl_2(g)	33.9

ANSWERS

CONCEPT CHECK

1. the tendency toward lower energy and the tendency to increased disorder

2. Heat is thermal energy, the kinetic energy of atoms and molecules. It is measured in joules.

3. Heat is the total kinetic energy of all the atoms in an object, whereas temperature is the average kinetic energy of those atoms.

4. The cooler block, on the right, gained energy.

5. The beaker with more liquid has more heat.

6. 303 and 323, 20°C, 20 K

CONCEPT CHECK

1. What two tendencies drive natural events?
2. What kind of energy is heat, and what unit is it measured in?
3. Distinguish between heat and temperature in terms of the kinetic energy of atoms.
4. **Interpreting Graphics** Which of the two blocks shown in Figure 11-2a gained energy?
5. **Interpreting Graphics** If the beakers in Figure 11-2b held the *same* volume of liquid but their temperatures were still as shown, which flask would contain more thermal energy?
6. **Interpreting Graphics** What are the temperatures of the liquid samples in Figure 11-2b in kelvins? What is the temperature *difference* between the liquid on the right and the liquid on the left in degrees Celsius? in kelvins?

ALTERNATIVE ASSESSMENT

Specific Heat Capacity

Ask students to look at the four metals listed in Table 11-1, then pose this question: Given equal *masses* of all four metals, which would require the smallest quantity of heat to raise its temperature? *(tungsten)* Which would require the largest quantity of heat? *(aluminum)* Ask students to explain their reasoning. *(Aluminum has the smallest molar mass, and tungsten has the largest molar mass. Equal masses would contain the largest amount of aluminum and the smallest amount of tungsten.)*

thermodynamics

the branch of science concerned with the energy changes accompanying physical and chemical processes

entropy

a measure of the randomness or disorder of a system

▼ FIGURE 11-4

Ice has a lower entropy than liquid water because it has more order.

Thermodynamics

The invention of the steam engine 200 years ago and the Industrial Revolution brought urbanization and other exciting changes to the world. These technological advances led to a new branch of science called **thermodynamics.**

Thermo- means "heat," and *dynamics* means "motion." Thermodynamics originally referred to the study of the conversion of heat into mechanical energy. Thermodynamics has since been expanded to include all energy changes that accompany physical and chemical processes.

Heat energy is disorderly atomic motion

Why is heat different from other kinds of energy? Scientists picture the thermal energy of an iron wheel, for example, as the kinetic energy of the Fe atoms randomly vibrating in their metallic lattice. When 45 kJ of heat is applied to a 10 kg wheel, the wheel gets 10 K hotter. Each atom receives about 7.5×10^{-20} J of the supplied thermal energy. The additional energy makes each Fe atom vibrate a little faster. The vibrations are random in that the direction one atom moves is not related to the directions its neighbors move. The atoms behave independently.

Consider a wheel that is rotated to produce 45 kJ of mechanical energy. As in the previous example, the energy supplied is distributed among the kinetic energies of the Fe atoms. Each atom receives approximately 7.5×10^{-20} J. This is the same amount of energy that is received when the wheel is heated. However, this time the extra kinetic energy is *concerted;* all atoms move in the same direction.

Thus, heat energy is described as energy of disorderly atomic motion, while other forms of energy are seen as orderly motion or orderly arrangements of particles. Recall that nature favors changes that proceed toward lower energy and greater disorder. The tendency toward greater disorder explains why it is easier to convert other forms of energy to heat energy and why the reverse process is inefficient.

Entropy measures disorder

Disorder is quantified as a property called **entropy.** Entropy is a measure of the total disorder in a substance or system. Chemists are mainly concerned with *molar entropy,* which is the quantity of entropy possessed by 1 mol of a substance. It is expressed in the same units used for molar heat capacity, J/K•mol, and is represented by the symbol S. **Figure 11-4** shows water in two of its three states. The molar entropies of water in its three states are very different. Molar entropies are always positive, except at 0.0 K, where they are generally zero. The entropy of a substance increases with temperature. The molar entropy of $H_2O(l)$ is 69.9 J/mol·K at 298 K. The molar entropy of $H_2O(g)$ is 188.7 J/mol·K.

The gaseous form of water has a much greater entropy than the liquid form. The liquid form has a greater entropy than ice. Atoms in the crystal lattice of a solid are highly ordered, so it makes sense that they have a low entropy. Atoms or molecules in liquids can move more freely than those in solids. Thus, liquids have greater molar entropies than solids. Atoms and molecules in the gaseous state have the most freedom to move, so their molar entropies are the greatest.

The entropy of a substance increases with temperature. With few exceptions, the entropy of a pure substance is zero at absolute zero (0 K). That is because all substances are solids, and most have perfectly ordered crystal lattices at 0 K. No disorder means no entropy.

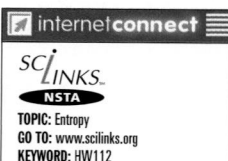

internet**connect**

SCI**LINKS**
NSTA

TOPIC: Entropy
GO TO: www.scilinks.org
KEYWORD: HW112

SECTION REVIEW

Total recall

1. **a.** Define *entropy*.
   b. Define *molar entropy*.
2. What is the SI unit for temperature?
3. Describe what happens to all atoms at 0.00 K.
4. **a.** What is the symbol for molar heat capacity?
   b. What is the symbol for molar entropy?
5. Define *thermodynamics*.
6. What is the common term used for thermal energy?

Critical thinking

7. What natural driving force causes ice to melt spontaneously at room temperature?
8. **Interpreting Tables** Examine Table 11-1. Explain why the molar heat capacity of octane is the highest value listed on this table.
9. Why is the molar entropy of water vapor higher than that of ice?

10. How is it possible that the temperature *difference* has the same numerical value in kelvins and in degrees Celsius?
11. **a.** What is the relationship between heat and kinetic energy?
    b. What is the relationship between temperature and kinetic energy?

Practice problems

12. Use Table 11-1 to predict the molar heat capacity of $AlCl_3(s)$.
13. **Story Clue** Use the table on page 383 to calculate the quantity of energy liberated when 1 mol of $H_2(g)$ is combusted.
14. Use the molar heat capacity for aluminum from Table 11-1 to calculate the amount of heat energy needed to raise the temperature of 260 g of aluminum from 0°C to 125°C.
15. Use the molar heat capacity for iron from Table 11-1 to calculate the amount of heat energy needed to raise the temperature of 260 g of iron from 0°C to 125°C.

ANSWERS

SECTION REVIEW

Total recall

1. **a.** Entropy is a measure of the total disorder of a system.
   b. Molar entropy is the entropy of one mole of a substance.
2. the kelvin
3. At 0 K, essentially all particle motion has stopped and the entropy of pure substances is zero.
4. **a.** C
   b. S
5. Thermodynamics is the branch of chemistry and physics that deals with the energy changes that accompany physical and chemical processes.
6. heat

Critical thinking

7. the tendency toward increased entropy
8. Octane has the greatest number of atoms.
9. The liquid state is more disordered than the solid state.
10. The size of the temperature increments, °C and kelvins, are the same.
11. **a.** Heat is the total of all kinetic energy in a sample.
    b. Temperature is a measure of the average kinetic energy of the particles in a sample.

Practice problems

12. The value will be approximately 4×25 J/K·mol, or 100 J/K·mol.

13. $142 \text{ kJ/g} \times \dfrac{2.20 \text{ g } H_2}{1 \text{ mol } H_2} = 286.84 \text{ kJ}$

14. $260 \text{ g Al} \times \dfrac{1 \text{ mol Al}}{26.98 \text{ g Al}} \times \dfrac{24.2 \text{ J}}{\text{mol·K}} \times$
    $125 \text{ K} = 29\,000 \text{ J, or } 29 \text{ kJ}$

15. $260 \text{ g Fe} \times \dfrac{1 \text{ mol Fe}}{55.85 \text{ g Fe}} \times \dfrac{25.1 \text{ J}}{\text{mol·K}} \times$
    $125 \text{ K} = 15\,000 \text{ J, or } 15 \text{ kJ}$

How does temperature affect enthalpy and entropy?

OBJECTIVES
- **Classify** properties of matter as extensive or intensive.
- **Describe** the temperature, enthalpy, and entropy changes in a substance when it is heated.
- **Calculate** the molar enthalpy change for a substance on heating.

Thermodynamic properties

Thermodynamics is concerned with much more than the conversion of heat into mechanical energy. Thermodynamics deals with energy transformations of all kinds. To study the relationship between energy and matter, we shall look at three properties. One of these properties is entropy. Another property is enthalpy. Enthalpy was introduced in Section 9-3. The third property used in discussing thermodynamics is called *Gibbs energy*. Gibbs energy is described in Section 11-3.

Enthalpy is the energy of an atom or molecule

You may think of enthalpy as the heat, or thermal energy, of a substance. When something is heated at constant pressure, its enthalpy increase equals the thermal energy it receives. The symbol for molar enthalpy is H because enthalpy was once called "heat content." A change in enthalpy can be measured when a substance is heated or cooled, but scientists have no way to measure the enthalpy itself. Scientists have, therefore, agreed to assign *all elements under standard conditions a molar enthalpy of zero*. Writing a small superscript zero, as in H^0, means "under standard conditions."

extensive property
a property that depends on the amount of material present

Enthalpy and entropy are extensive properties

These properties of matter—enthalpy and entropy—may be new to you, and they are easy to confuse. Think of enthalpy as the *energy* that is "inside" an object or substance. Entropy, on the other hand, measures the *amount of disorder* "inside" a body or substance and is not a form of energy.

In your study of chemistry you have come across many properties of matter. Some are listed in **Table 11-2.** The properties are divided into two groups. **Extensive properties** depend on how much of the material you're dealing

TABLE 11-2 Properties of Matter

Extensive	Intensive
Mass, m	Density, D
Volume, V	Pressure, P
Heat capacity, C	Temperature, T
Enthalpy, H	Concentration, c
Entropy, S	

GRAPHIC ORGANIZER

A Summary of Thermodynamic Quantities

Quantity	Meaning	Description
C	molar heat capacity	the amount of energy required to raise the temperature of 1 mol of a substance by 1 K
T	temperature	Kelvin temperature
ΔH	change in enthalpy	the amount of energy lost (negative) or gained (positive) by a system in a process

with, so the quantity of substance must be specified. **Intensive properties** are specific to the particular substance and do not depend on how much material is present. For example, you can say that the density of copper is 8.960 g/cm^3 because density is an intensive property. But you must specify a particular sample size when discussing the mass or volume of copper. Enthalpy and entropy are extensive properties because they depend on the amount of substance. **Table A-13** in the Appendix lists the molar enthalpies and molar entropies, which are intensive properties, for many elements and compounds.

Temperature affects molar enthalpy

Revisit the experiment described in Figure 11-3. Over a 150 second interval, 20.00 mol of water received 15.0 kJ of thermal energy. How much did the water's molar enthalpy increase? The total enthalpy increase was equal to the heat input, q. So the *molar* enthalpy increase, ΔH, can be found by dividing by n, the moles of water.

$$\Delta H = \frac{q}{n} = \frac{15.0 \text{ kJ}}{20 \text{ mol}} = 0.750 \text{ kJ/mol}$$

You saw in Section 11-1 that the amount of heat, q, delivered to n mol of a substance to raise the substance's temperature by ΔT is represented by the following equation.

$$q = nC\Delta T$$

Thus, the molar enthalpy change of a substance is related to its molar heat capacity, C, using the following equation.

$$\Delta H = \frac{q}{n} = \frac{nC\Delta T}{n} = C\Delta T$$

So the molar enthalpy change of a substance upon heating is simply the molar heat capacity multiplied by the temperature change. Use this formula to check the calculation from the experiment. In Figure 11-3, the temperature increase between Point 1 and Point 2 is 9.9 K, and the measured molar heat capacity of water is 76 J/K•mol.

$$\Delta H = (76 \text{ J/K•mol})(9.9 \text{ K}) = 750 \text{ J/mol} = 0.750 \text{ kJ/mol}$$

Both equations for ΔH produce the same result.

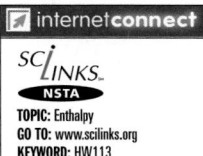

SAMPLE PROBLEM 11B Calculating molar enthalpy change

How much does the molar enthalpy change when a 92.3 g block of ice is cooled from –0.2°C to –5.4°C?

1 List what you know

▶ Mass of $H_2O(s)$ = 92.3 g
▶ Initial temperature = –0.2°C
▶ Final temperature = –5.4°C
▶ Molar enthalpy change, ΔH = ?

Quantity	Meaning	Description
ΔS	change in entropy	the change in disorder of a system during a process; increased disorder (positive), or increased order (negative)
ΔG	change in Gibbs energy	the net amount of useful energy output (negative) in a process

---

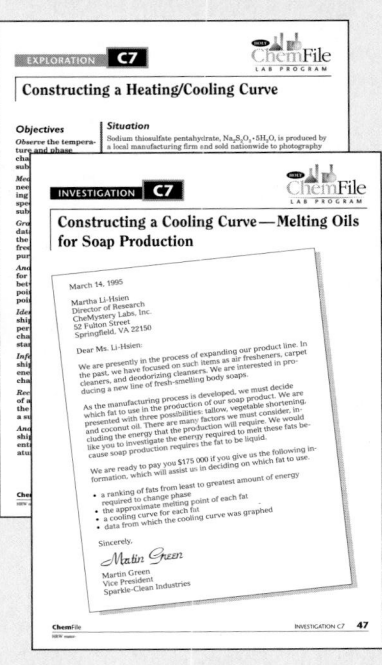

ANSWERS

PRACTICE PROBLEM 11B

1. $100. \text{ g } H_2O \times \dfrac{1 \text{ mol}}{18.02 \text{ g } H_2O} \times \dfrac{75.3 \text{ J}}{K \cdot mol} \times$

$34.5 \text{ K} = 14.4 \text{ kJ}$

2. $1 \text{ mol Al} \times \dfrac{24.2 \text{ J}}{K \cdot mol} \times -105.9 \text{ K} = -2.56 \text{ kJ}$

3. $\dfrac{618 \text{ J}}{mol} \times \dfrac{1 \text{ K} \cdot mol}{420 \text{ J}} = 1.47 \text{ K}$

ADDITIONAL EXAMPLES

SAMPLE PROBLEM 11B

a. The molar heat capacity of sodium fluoride, NaF(s), is 46.9 J/K•mol. What is the enthalpy change when 2.00 mol of NaF is heated from 5°C to 131°C?

Ans. 11 800 J, or 11.8 kJ

b. The molar heat capacity of cyclohexane, $C_6H_{12}(l)$, is 154.9 J/K•mol. What is the enthalpy change when 5.00×10^2 g of cyclohexane is cooled from 28.5°C to –18.8°C?

Ans. –43 500 J, or –43.5 kJ

RESOURCE LINK

ChemFile Lab A
Skills Development
Have students do Experiment A14.

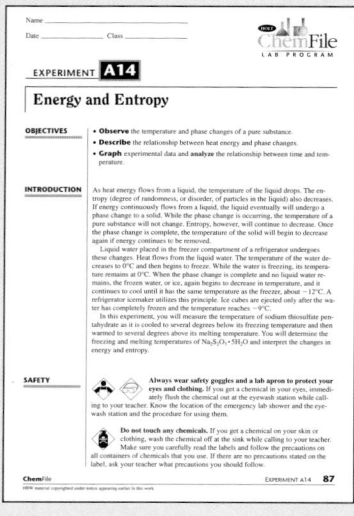

---

2 **Set up the problem**

▶ You will need the molar heat capacity of ice from Table 11-1. The unit for molar heat capacity includes kelvins, so you will have to convert the Celsius temperatures in the problem to kelvins.

$$C = 37.4 \text{ J/K} \cdot mol \text{ from Table 11-1}$$

$$(-0.2 + 273.15) \text{ K} = 273.0 \text{ K}$$

$$(-5.4 + 273.15) \text{ K} = 267.8 \text{ K}$$

▶ Calculate the temperature change.

$$\Delta T = T_{final} - T_{initial} = 267.8 \text{ K} - 273.0 \text{ K} = -5.2 \text{ K}$$

▶ The appropriate equation to calculate the molar enthalpy change is the following.

$$\Delta H = C \Delta T$$

3 **Calculate and verify**

▶ Substitute the values into the equation.

$$\Delta H = (37.4 \text{ J/K} \cdot mol)(-5.2 \text{ K})$$

▶ Solve, and cancel like units in the numerator and the denominator.

$$\Delta H = \frac{37.4 \text{ J}}{K \cdot mol} \times (-5.2 \text{ K}) = -1.9 \times 10^2 \text{ J/mol} = -0.19 \text{ kJ/mol}$$

▶ The enthalpy change is negative, which is expected for a cooling process.
▶ The temperature change is about –5 K, and the molar heat capacity is about 40 J/K•mol. Multiplying these numbers gives about –200 J/mol, which is close to the calculated answer.

PRACTICE PROBLEMS

1. Calculate ΔH when 100. mL of $H_2O(l)$ is heated from 41.7°C to 76.2°C.

2. The molar heat capacity of Al(s) is 24.2 J/K•mol. Calculate ΔH when 1 mol of Al(s) is cooled from 128.5°C to 22.6°C.

3. The molar heat capacity of $C_2H_5OH(g)$ is 420. J/K•mol. What was the temperature change if $\Delta H = 618.5$ J/mol?

Notes on Sample Problem 11B

Notice in Sample Problem 11B that the mass of the ice, though given, was not needed to solve the problem. It is common for a scientist to have more information than is needed to solve a problem. Never feel that you have to use all the data given. Second, recall that the Δ notation always means the final value minus the initial value and never the other way around, even if $T_{initial}$ is larger than T_{final}.

$$\Delta T = T_{final} - T_{initial}$$

Third, notice that because temperature differences are the same on the Kelvin and Celsius scales, you will still get the correct answer if you work in degrees Celsius rather than kelvins. However, this is not generally true in thermodynamic calculations, and you are strongly advised to adopt the good habit of *always* converting Celsius data to kelvins. Finally, note that molar heat capacities are always tabulated in units that include joules, whereas enthalpies are usually reported in terms of *kilo*joules. An easy mistake is to forget about the factor of 1000 needed to convert from one to the other.

Temperature also affects entropy

Unlike enthalpy, entropy can be measured directly. At absolute zero all substances are solids and most have perfectly ordered crystal lattices. No disorder means no entropy.

The reason entropy increases with temperature is that atoms do not share energy evenly, even in an element. At any instant, some atoms have more than the average energy while others have less. This uneven distribution of energy is an example of disorder. The more energy there is to distribute, the more opportunity there is for uneven distribution. A system with more energy has more disorder.

SECTION REVIEW

Total recall

1. Name three state properties studied in thermodynamics.

2. Classify each of the following as an extensive or intensive property of matter:
   a. melting point   **d.** ductility
   b. color   **e.** molar mass
   c. texture

3. How are enthalpy and entropy affected by an increase in temperature?

4. Should ΔH be positive or negative for an exothermic process?

5. What is the unit used to express entropy? enthalpy?

Critical thinking

6. Why are all elements under standard conditions assigned a molar enthalpy of zero?

7. Why is the molar entropy of water vapor higher than that of ice?

Practice problems

8. A block of ice is cooled from $-0.5°C$ to $-10.1°C$. Calculate the temperature change, ΔT, in degrees Celsius and in kelvins.

9. Calculate ΔH when an 80.2 g block of ice is heated from $-8.4°C$ to $-5.2°C$.

10. Calculate ΔH when 22.5 g of $H_2O(l)$ is cooled from $48.3°C$ to $25.2°C$.

11. The molar heat capacity of benzene, $C_6H_6(l)$, is 136 J/K•mol. Calculate ΔH when the temperature of 15.4 g of $C_6H_6(l)$ changes from $19.7°C$ to $46.8°C$.

12. The molar heat capacity of diethyl ether, $(C_2H_5)_2O(l)$, is 172. J/K•mol. What is the temperature change if $\Delta H = -186.9$ J/mol?

13. **Story Clue** Calculate ΔH when the temperature of 1 mol of $H_2(g)$ is increased by $25°C$. Use Table 11-1 for data.

TEACHING TIP

Entropy and Kinetic Energy To help students connect the discussion of entropy to kinetic energy, have them look at Figure 12-4 on page 426, which shows the Gaussian energy distribution curves for a collection of gas molecules at two different temperatures. Students can see that the range of probable kinetic energies available to molecules is wider for the molecules at higher temperature. Thus, it is probable that they will have greater disorder.

ANSWERS

SECTION REVIEW

Total recall

1. enthalpy, entropy, and Gibbs energy

2. **a.** intensive
   b. intensive
   c. intensive
   d. intensive
   e. intensive

3. Both the enthalpy and entropy of a system increase when temperature increases.

4. ΔH is negative.

5. enthalpy: kJ; entropy: J/K

Critical thinking

6. Scientists have no way to measure the absolute enthalpy of a substance.

7. Water molecules in the gas state are more disordered than water molecules in the liquid state.

Practice problems

8. $\Delta T = -9.6°C = -9.6$ K

9. $80.2 \text{ g } H_2O \times \dfrac{1 \text{ mol } H_2O}{18.02 \text{ g } H_2O} \times \dfrac{37.4 \text{ J}}{\text{K•mol}} \times 3.2 \text{ K}$
   $= 0.533$ kJ

10. $22.5 \text{ g } H_2O \times \dfrac{1 \text{ mol } H_2O}{18.02 \text{ g } H_2O} \times \dfrac{75.3 \text{ J}}{\text{K•mol}} \times -23.1 \text{ K}$
    $= -2.17$ kJ

11. $15.4 \text{ g } C_6H_6 \times \dfrac{1 \text{ mol } C_6H_6}{78.12 \text{ g } C_6H_6} \times$
    $\dfrac{136 \text{ J}}{\text{K•mol}} \times 27.1 \text{ K} = 0.727$ kJ

12. $\dfrac{-186.9 \text{ J}}{\text{mol}} \times \dfrac{1 \text{ K•mol}}{172 \text{ J}} = -1.09°C$

13. $1 \text{ mol } H_2 \times \dfrac{28.8 \text{ J}}{\text{K•mol}} \times 25 \text{ K} = 0.72$ kJ

LESSON WARM-UP

Changes of State

Demonstrate an example of a state change to students, such boiling in Demonstration 3. Ask students to describe what is taking place at the molecular level. Ask them also to characterize the state change as an increase or decrease in order.

VISUAL STRATEGY

Figure 11-5 Use the diagrams of the three states to discuss entropy changes. Point out that water in the solid state increases in disorder as it changes to the liquid state. The change to a gas represents another increase in disorder because the particles are now farther apart.

CHEMISTRY INTERACTIVE TUTOR

Module 1: States of Matter
Topics: Solids, Liquids, Gases and Changes of State
This engaging tutorial reviews and reinforces particles views of matter and change-of-state systems through modeling and guided practice.

What happens during a change of state?

OBJECTIVES

▶ **List** the different changes of state.

▶ **Describe** how the enthalpy and entropy of a substance are affected by melting and boiling.

▶ **Define** the quantities represented by the following symbols: ΔH_{vap}, ΔS_{fus}, and ΔG.

▶ **Calculate** T_{mp}, ΔH_{fus}, or ΔS_{fus} given the other two quantities.

▶ **Use** ΔG to predict whether a change of state will occur.

Changing states for water

You are probably most familiar with changes of state for water. The common state of water is as a liquid. The solid form is ice. The gaseous form is steam. A diagram relating *changes of state* is shown in **Figure 11-5.** You see from the diagram that most change-of-state processes have names; however, the direct conversion of a gas to a solid is not denoted by a specific term. Other changes of state, not shown on the diagram, include transitions between two different solid forms, such as the change between the gray and white varieties of tin. Though a change of state is a lot like a chemical reaction, it is considered a physical process.

▶ **FIGURE 11-5**

This map shows how change of state processes are related.

DEMONSTRATION 3

An Interesting State Change
Approximate time: 10 minutes

1. Obtain a piece of Onion's fusible metal (available from Flinn Scientific and other scientific supply houses) that has cooled to be a flat shape. While wearing gloves, show students your attempts to bend the metal.

2. Place the metal in a 150 mL beaker of boiling water. The metal should liquefy, and you can show that it has liquefied by moving it with a glass rod.

3. Pour most of the water into a waste beaker. Pour the metal *slowly* into cold water.

4. While wearing gloves, show the solidified metal to students. Metallic crystals may be seen on the surface if cooling was sufficiently slow.

Enthalpy and entropy change dramatically during a change of state

Thermal energy is needed to melt ice and to boil water. Thermal energy increases the kinetic energy of molecules, allowing them to break free of intermolecular forces. With enough added thermal energy, molecules in a solid enter the liquid phase and molecules in a liquid enter the gas phase. The added thermal energy not only causes a change of state but also increases the molar enthalpy of water.

Figure 11-6 shows enthalpy changes with temperature over a range that includes the melting and boiling points of water. Notice the sudden enthalpy increases that occur at the melting point, 273.15 K, and the boiling point, 372.78 K. The enthalpy increase for a change of state is much larger than that which occurs during the rise in temperature for the substance at each state. The slopes of the slowly rising lines in the graph are the molar heat capacities of $H_2O(s)$, $H_2O(l)$, and $H_2O(g)$. The large heat capacity of liquid water is probably due to breaking hydrogen bonds.

Entropy also changes dramatically during melting and boiling processes. A graph of the molar entropy changes for water as it changes state looks similar to Figure 11-6.

Change of state

The molar enthalpy change that occurs during melting is called the **molar enthalpy of fusion,** or *heat of fusion* (ΔH_{fus}). It is the difference between the enthalpy of 1 mol of a substance in its liquid and solid states.

$$\Delta H_{fus} = H(\text{liquid at mp}) - H(\text{solid at mp})$$

In this expression, *mp* refers to the melting point of the substance.

Similarly, the **molar enthalpy of vaporization,** or *heat of vaporization,* is the difference between the molar enthalpies of 1 mol of a substance in its gaseous and its liquid states.

$$\Delta H_{vap} = H(\text{gas at bp}) - H(\text{liquid at bp})$$

In the equation, *bp* refers to the boiling point of the substance. The molar entropies of fusion and vaporization, ΔS_{fus} and ΔS_{vap}, are defined similarly.

Molar Enthalpy Versus Temperature for Water

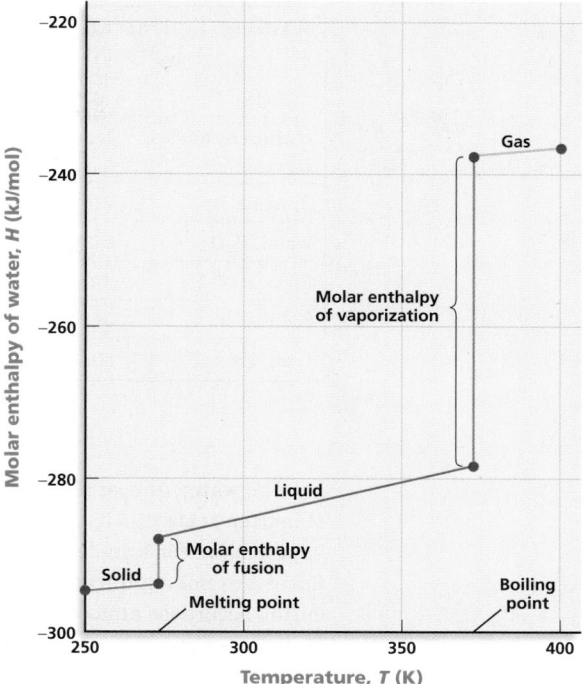

FIGURE 11-6 ▲

The molar enthalpy of water rises gently with temperature in the solid, liquid, and gaseous ranges. Sudden leaps occur at the melting and boiling temperatures.

molar enthalpy of fusion

the heat absorbed when 1 mol of a substance melts

molar enthalpy of vaporization

the heat absorbed when 1 mol of a liquid vaporizes

CAUSES OF CHANGE   **397**

VISUAL STRATEGY

Figure 11-6 Draw students' attention to the vertical segments of the graph. Ask students to speculate on what that energy is doing if it is not increasing the temperature. *(The energy is either used to do work on the molecules, moving them out of the crystal lattice at the melting point, or moving them farther from each other into the gaseous state at the boiling point.)*

COMMON MISCONCEPTION

Students may find it strange that the boiling point of water is given as 372.78 K instead of the expected 373 K (100°C). Remind them that standard pressure for measuring thermodynamic properties is 100 kPa, a little less than 101.325 kPa (1 atm). Water boils at 99.63°C (372.78 K) at this pressure.

RESOURCE LINK

ChemFile Lab A
Skills Development
Have students do Experiment A10: *Molar Heat of Fusion of Ice.*

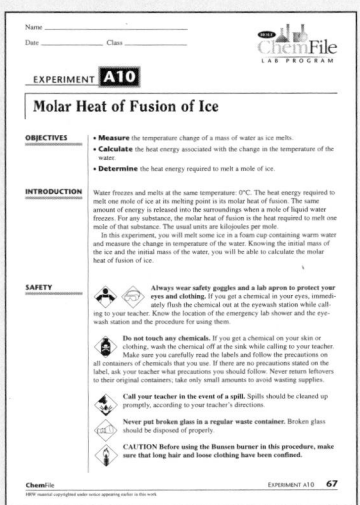

Safety

Observe all precautions described on the label and in the MSDS for Onion's fusible metal. Wear plastic or rubber gloves. Students should also wear gloves if they handle the metal.

Disposal

Save the Onion's fusible metal for another demonstration.

TABLE 11-3			Molar Enthalpies and Entropies of Fusion and Vaporization			
Substance	T_{mp} (K)	ΔH_{fus} (kJ/mol)	ΔS_{fus} (J/K•mol)	T_{bp} (K)	ΔH^0_{vap} (kJ/mol)	ΔS^0_{vap} (J/K•mol)
Nitrogen, N_2	63	0.719	11.4	77	5.59	72.2
Hydrogen sulfide, H_2S	188	2.38	12.6	213	18.7	87.8
Bromine, Br_2	270	10.57	39.8	332	29.5	88.6
Water, H_2O	273	6.01	22.0	373	40.7	108.8
Benzene, C_6H_6	279	10.59	38.0	353	30.8	87.2
Sodium, Na	371	2.60	7.0	1156	98.0	84.8
Lead, Pb	601	4.77	7.9	2023	177.8	87.9

Like water, almost all substances can exist in the three common states of matter. **Table 11-3** lists the molar enthalpies and entropies of fusion and vaporization for some elements and compounds. Because intermolecular forces are not significant in the gaseous state, a similar extent of disordering occurs for almost all substances when 1 mol of liquid is converted to 1 mol of gas. This similarity in disorder explains the similar values for ΔS_{vap}.

Enthalpy and entropy determine state

Liquid H_2O at 273.3 K will never freeze, and ice maintained at 273.0 K will never melt. Only at 273.15 K (0.00°C) can liquid and solid H_2O permanently coexist. Why is H_2O a liquid at one temperature and a solid at another?

Nature's tendency to lower energy corresponds thermodynamically to ΔH being negative. Likewise, nature's drive toward disorder corresponds to ΔS being positive. During changes of state, changes in enthalpy and entropy oppose each other. The relative values of ΔH and $T\Delta S$ determine which state is preferred. At 273.3 K, the enthalpy and entropy values for water are as follows.

$$\Delta H_{fus} = 6.009 \text{ kJ/mol} = 6009 \text{ J/mol}$$

$$T\Delta S_{fus} = (273.3 \text{ K})(22.00 \text{ J/K•mol}) = 6013 \text{ J/mol}$$

Though the values are close, the more-disordered liquid state is favored over the lower energy state of ice. Therefore, H_2O is a liquid at 273.3 K. At 273.0 K, however, the drive to decrease energy dominates, and water freezes.

$$\Delta H_{fus} = 6.009 \text{ kJ/mol} = 6009 \text{ J/mol}$$

$$T\Delta S_{fus} = (273.0 \text{ K})(22.00 \text{ J/K•mol}) = 6006 \text{ J/mol}$$

DEMONSTRATION 4

Boiling Water in a Paper Cup

Approximate time: 10 minutes

1. Place a small paper cup (like those used in restaurants to serve ketchup or tartar sauce) on a wire gauze above a bunsen burner, and watch the cup catch fire and burn.

2. Fill a second paper cup half full with water, and place it on the wire gauze. Place the lit burner under it. The water will come to a boil, and the absorption of heat will keep the temperature of the cup below the kindling temperature of paper (233°C). The cup will not burn until the water has boiled away.

3. Students may wonder if this demonstration works with polystyrene foam cups; it does not.

FIGURE 11-7 ▼

SECTION 11-3

a Water condenses on the wings of the dragonfly when $\Delta H_{vap} > T\Delta S_{vap}$.

b Water freezes on the flower when $\Delta H_{fus} > T\Delta S_{fus}$.

At high enough temperatures, $T\Delta S_{fus}$ exceeds ΔH_{fus}, so all solids eventually melt unless they decompose or sublime. The melting point is the temperature at which ΔH_{fus} equals $T\Delta S_{fus}$. In other words, the melting point of a solid equals the molar enthalpy of fusion divided by the molar entropy of fusion.

$$T_{mp} = \frac{\Delta H_{fus}}{\Delta S_{fus}}$$

Boiling occurs when the drive toward disorder overcomes the tendency to lose energy. Condensation, shown in **Figure 11-7,** occurs when the tendency to lose energy overcomes the drive to increase disorder. In other words, when $\Delta H_{vap} > T\Delta S_{vap}$, the liquid state is favored. The gas state is preferred when $\Delta H_{vap} < T\Delta S_{vap}$. The ΔH_{vap} and $T\Delta S_{vap}$ terms are equal at the boiling point of a substance and therefore:

$$T_{bp} = \frac{\Delta H_{vap}}{\Delta S_{vap}}$$

Pressure can affect change-of-state processes

Water left in an uncovered vessel slowly disappears, or *evaporates*. During **evaporation,** a liquid becomes a gas at a temperature well below its boiling point. A similar phenomenon is not seen with the solid/liquid phase transition. Ice cubes in a freezer do not melt at temperatures below water's freezing point.

The boiling point of a liquid is affected greatly by atmospheric pressure, whereas the change in freezing point is very small. In Denver,

evaporation

the process by which molecules in a nonboiling liquid escape the liquid surface and enter the gas phase

4. Ask students to speculate about why the foam would melt or catch fire although paper does not. *(Foam is an insulator, and heat transfer to the water does not take place rapidly enough to keep the foam from melting.)*

Safety
Wear safety goggles and a lab apron. Have students stand at least 10 ft from the demonstration area.

Disposal
Pour water down the drain. Put cups and residues in the trash.

Josiah Willard Gibbs (1839–1903) was little known during his lifetime of work at Yale University in Connecticut. Point out to students that Gibbs energy, sometimes called Gibbs free energy, can be viewed as the available, useful energy from a process. When Gibbs energy has a negative value, a system is giving off usable energy and the process taking place is spontaneous.

Engineers in the 19th century were interested in developing more efficient engines, usually steam engines, to power the mills that turned out mass-produced goods. They sought to maximize the useful (free) energy available from a process so that the machine could do work, such as pushing a piston to turn a wheel, most efficiently. Initially, the heat measurements and calculations of thermodynamics served only practical applications. But as the understanding of matter developed rapidly during the century, scientists found increasing applications for thermodynamics in explaining the energy changes of any chemical or physical processes.

FIGURE 11-8

A runner sweats when the body overheats as a result of exertion. As sweat evaporates, the body is cooled.

Gibbs energy

a thermodynamic property incorporating both enthalpy and entropy

FIGURE 11-9

An avalanche is a spontaneous process driven by an increase in disorder and a decrease in energy.

Colorado, where the atmospheric pressure is typically 0.84 atm, water boils at 369 K (96°C), but ice still melts at exactly 273.15 K (0.00°C).

Boiling points are pressure-dependent because pressure has a large effect on the entropy of a gas. There is always some water vapor pressure in the air. When this vapor pressure is less than the standard pressure, water's entropy of vaporization is higher than the standard value listed in Table 11-3. So the liquid-gas transition can occur at temperatures below the normal boiling point. Chapter 12 discusses vapor pressure in detail.

Evaporation is rather slow despite being a spontaneous process. There are two reasons for this. The first reason is that vaporization is an endothermic process. Evaporation removes thermal energy and produces cooling. People sweat when they are hot and when they exercise, as in **Figure 11-8.** The evaporation of sweat cools the body. At lower temperatures, evaporation is slower and less likely to occur because the average energy of random motion is lower. The second reason evaporation is slow is that the water vapor formed by evaporation can remain close to the surface and increase the local humidity. When laundry is hung out to dry, the breeze accelerates evaporation by dispersing the water vapor.

Gibbs energy determines spontaneity

The relative values of H and S determine whether a phase transition will occur. Josiah Willard Gibbs, a professor at Yale University, described a new thermodynamic property that incorporates H and S. This is called the **Gibbs energy.** For 1 mol of a substance, G is the *molar Gibbs energy,* defined by the following equation.

$$G = H - TS$$

An older name for Gibbs energy is *molar free energy.* Gibbs energy values are based on a convention similar to that used for enthalpies. Elements are assigned a Gibbs energy of zero under standard conditions.

Scientists use the word *spontaneous* to describe a process that actually occurs or is likely to occur without continuous outside assistance. For example, the melting of ice at 300 K (27°C) is a spontaneous process. The avalanche shown in **Figure 11-9** is also spontaneous. The combustion

DEMONSTRATION 5

Synthesis of Copper(II) Sulfide
Approximate time: 10 minutes

A darkened room will help students see the red glow of the exothermic reaction between copper and sulfur that forms copper(II) sulfide, CuS. In this reaction, entropy increases and ΔG is negative, so the reaction is spontaneous.

1. Cut a 1 cm × 10 cm piece of copper foil.
2. Place flowers of sulfur (the powdery form of sulfur) in a heat-resistant test tube to a

depth of 2 cm. Clamp the test tube vertically to a ring stand, and heat the bottom strongly with a burner.

3. As sulfur vapors escape from the tube, use crucible tongs to hold the copper strip over the tube so that it can be hit by the sulfur vapors. Point out that no reaction takes place.

of gasoline is a spontaneous process, even though a spark must initiate the reaction.

You can use the change in Gibbs energy to compare the change in enthalpy and the change in entropy using the following relationship.

$$\Delta G = \Delta H - T\Delta S$$

A *process is spontaneous if ΔG is negative. All spontaneous processes occur with a decrease in Gibbs energy. When ΔG is exactly zero, the system is in a state of equilibrium.*

The Gibbs energy equation applies to change-of-state processes as well as to chemical reactions. A change of state occurs spontaneously when there is a decrease in Gibbs energy.

SECTION REVIEW

Total recall

1. List the six changes of state.
2. What is ΔS_{fus} for 1 mol of benzene?
3. Write the equations that define ΔS_{fus} and ΔS_{vap}.
4. Name two properties that change dramatically during a change of state.
5. Select any example from Table 11-3 other than water, and show that the following relationship holds.

$$T_{mp} = \frac{\Delta H_{fus}}{\Delta S_{fus}}$$

6. **Interpreting Tables** Select any example from Table 11-3, and show that the following relationship holds:

$$T_{bp} = \frac{\Delta H_{vap}}{\Delta S_{vap}}$$

7. How does atmospheric pressure affect the boiling point of a substance?
8. What equation defines molar Gibbs energy?
9. For a process to be spontaneous, what must be true of the ΔG value?
10. What do the symbols ΔH_{vap} and ΔS_{fus} represent?
11. What causes a change of state?

Critical thinking

12. In terms of enthalpy and entropy, when does melting occur?
13. Explain why liquid H_2O at 273.3 K will never freeze.
14. Why is the gas state favored when $T > \dfrac{H_{vap}}{\Delta S_{vap}}$?
15. What must be true of a process if the ΔH value is positive and the $T\Delta S$ value is negative?
16. Determine the change-of-state process described by each of the following.
    a. $\Delta H_{vap} > T\Delta S_{vap}$
    b. $\Delta H_{fus} < T\Delta S_{fus}$
    c. $\Delta H_{vap} < T\Delta S_{vap}$
    d. $\Delta H_{fus} > T\Delta S_{fus}$

Practice problem

17. Consider the following change of state.

    $$Br_2(l) \longrightarrow Br_2(g)$$

    $\Delta H_{vap} = 29.5$ kJ/mol
    $\Delta S_{vap} = 88.6$ J/mol
    Calculate the boiling point of $Br_2(l)$.

ANSWERS

SECTION REVIEW

Total recall

1. melting, freezing, boiling, condensation, sublimation, and the change from gas to a liquid
2. 38.0 J/K
3. $\Delta H_{fus} = H_{liquid} - H_{solid}$
   $\Delta H_{vap} = H_{gas} - H_{liquid}$
4. enthalpy and entropy
5. Answers will depend on the substance chosen; for example, T_{mp} for N_2 = (719 J/mol)/ (11.4 J/K•mol) = 63.1 K
6. Answers will depend on the substance chosen; for example, T_{bp} for H_2S = (18 700 J/mol)/ (87.8 J/K•mol) = 213 K
7. A decrease in atmospheric pressure decreases the boiling point.
8. $\Delta G = \Delta H - T\Delta S$
9. The value of ΔG must be negative.
10. enthalpy of vaporization and entropy of fusion, respectively
11. Increases and decreases in enthalpy cause state changes.

Critical thinking

12. The melting point occurs at the temperature when $\Delta H_{fus} = T\Delta S_{fus}$. If energy is available from the surroundings, the entropy increase will be favored and the solid will spontaneously absorb energy and melt.
13. Water will not freeze at 273.3 K because $T\Delta S_{fus} > \Delta H_{fus}$, and the disordered state (liquid) is favored.
14. The temperature exceeds the boiling point, and $T\Delta S_{vap} > \Delta H_{vap}$, so the gas is favored.
15. In this case, ΔG will have a positive value and the process is nonspontaneous.
16. a. condensation   c. boiling
    b. melting   d. freezing

Practice problem

17. $\dfrac{29.5 \text{ kJ}}{\text{mol}} \times \dfrac{1 \text{ mol}}{88.6 \text{ J•K}} \times \dfrac{1000 \text{ J}}{1 \text{ kJ}} = 333$ K

---

4. Insert the strip into the hot, viscous sulfur vapors inside the test tube. The red glow shows that CuS is forming.

5. Remove the copper strip, and let it cool for inspection. Bending the strip should cause flakes of CuS to break off from the surface.

Safety
Wear safety goggles and a lab apron. Students should stand 10 ft away from the demonstration. If the sulfur vapors catch fire

at the top of the test tube, cover the tube with a glass plate to smother the flames.

Disposal
Put the damaged test tube and used copper foil in the trash.

How does thermodynamics apply to reactions and nutrition?

OBJECTIVES

▶ **Explain** the principles of calorimetry.

▶ **Use** data tables to calculate ΔH, ΔS, and ΔG for any reaction under standard conditions.

▶ **Predict** the spontaneity of any reaction for which you know ΔH and ΔS.

▶ **Classify** reactions as exothermic or endothermic, disordering or ordering, and spontaneous or nonspontaneous on the basis of thermodynamic data.

▶ **Use** Nutrition Facts data to determine the energy content of food.

LESSON WARM-UP

Exothermic Changes

Carry out some energy-yielding reactions, such as burning a piece of magnesium ribbon, a wooden splint, or a peanut held with forceps. Ask students how it would be possible to quantify the energy output of such a reaction. Remind them that energy can be detected and measured only when it interacts with other matter.

TEACHING TIP

Vocabulary Strategy The word *bomb* in bomb calorimeter refers to a container that withstands internal pressure. This meaning comes from the practice of making bombs by packing highly reactive material inside an iron container. The containers were designed to hold the reacting material inside until enough pressure built up to burst the iron container, creating a violent explosion. Often, the containers were spherical and had a hole through which the bomb could be packed and a screw-in plug with a fuse like the black bomb often pictured in comics or cartoons.

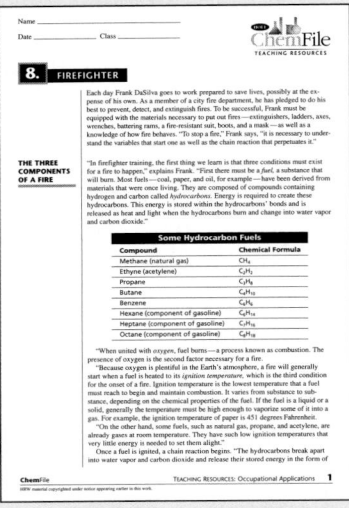
Chemical calorimetry

You already know that a negative ΔH accompanies an exothermic reaction and a positive ΔH accompanies an endothermic reaction. How are ΔH values determined? Sometimes ΔH values are calculated by using data tables that have been built over many years. ΔH values can also be measured using a device called a **calorimeter**, which is shown in **Figure 11-10.** This type of calorimeter is used to measure energy changes when substances undergo combustion. The data you get from calorimetry experiments are changes in temperature. Heat cannot be measured directly, so the change in temperature is used in an equation to determine ΔH for a reaction.

calorimeter
a device used to measure the heat absorbed or released in a chemical or physical change

▶ **FIGURE 11-10**

A bomb calorimeter is used to measure enthalpies of combustion.

Thermometer · Stirrer · Electrical leads · Insulated outer container · Sample to be burned · Steel bomb · Water · Oxygen at high pressure · Firing element

Calorimetry provides measurements used in determining ΔH

One method for measuring the ΔH of a reaction is known as **adiabatic calorimetry.** The word *adiabatic* means "not allowing heat to pass through" and refers to the fact that no energy leaves the system. In an adiabatic system, the reaction occurs in a vessel that is surrounded by a vacuum jacket similar to a thermos bottle. When the reaction occurs, the heat evolved or consumed by the reaction changes the temperature. The amount of reactant, the temperature change, and the heat capacity are used in an equation to calculate ΔH for the reaction.

The bomb calorimeter, shown in Figure 11-10, is used to measure energy transfers that result from a combustion reaction. This type of calorimeter is a useful tool for helping nutritionists determine the energy equivalent of food, as in **Figure 11-11.** In a bomb calorimeter, most organic matter, including foodstuffs, fabrics, and plastics, will ignite easily, will burn rapidly, and may even explode. The size of the sample to be burned is selected so that oxygen will be in excess during combustion. Under these conditions the combustion of organic matter is a complete reaction that yields carbon dioxide and water.

The whole "bomb" is immersed in a stirred-water bath. The water bath absorbs heat from the reaction of combustion for the substance. The energy released by the combustion equals the energy absorbed by the water and the calorimeter. The absorption of energy causes the temperature of the calorimeter and water to increase.

The temperature rise, ΔT, of the water bath in the calorimeter is used to determine the molar enthalpy.

Hess's law allows you to combine enthalpy changes

Any two processes that start with the reactants in the same condition and finish with the products in the same condition will involve the same enthalpy change. This statement is the basis of **Hess's law,** which states that the overall enthalpy change in a reaction is equal to the sum of the enthalpy changes for the individual steps in the process. If the heats of reaction for the partial reactions are known, then they can be combined to give the heat change for the overall reaction. For example, you can use Hess's law to find ΔH for the reaction that fuels the hydrogen-powered car.

$$2H_2(g) + O_2(g) \longrightarrow 2H_2O(g)$$

FIGURE 11-11 ▲

Nutritionists work with established data for ingredients to determine a recipe's calorie content. The data were collected by burning foods in a calorimeter.

adiabatic calorimetry

method of measuring the heat absorbed or released in a chemical or physical change in which no heat is allowed to enter or leave the system

Hess's law

law stating that the overall enthalpy change in a reaction is equal to the sum of the enthalpy changes of the individual steps in the process

DID YOU KNOW?

Many people have exhibited "perpetual motion" machines and have even attempted to obtain patents for them. In every case, however, examination of the machine has revealed some mechanism for obtaining energy from outside the system.

RESOURCE LINK

ChemFile Lab A
Skills Development
Have students do Experiment A18: *Heat of Combustion.*

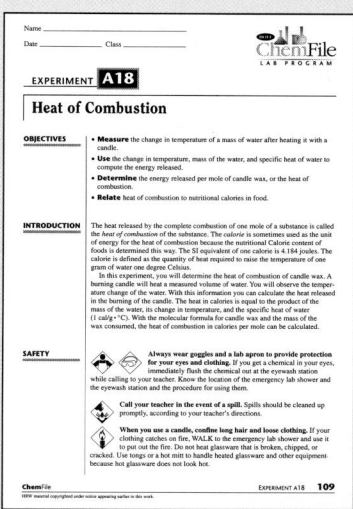

HISTORICAL CONNECTION

Germain Henri Hess (1802–1850) was a Russian chemist and professor of chemistry at the Technological Institute of St. Petersburg. He published the law that bears his name in 1840 after studying the energy changes in a great number of chemical reactions. The law seems almost absurdly logical today and is actually a statement of the law of conservation of energy to account for multi-step processes.

TEACHING TIP

Standard Thermodynamic Temperature Caution students to remember that the standard temperature for thermodynamic measurements is 25°C, not 0°C.

RESOURCE LINK

IN-TEXT LAB

Skills Development
Have students do Exploration 11A: *Calorimetry and Hess's Law,* on page 756, to develop their calorimetry skills.

Self-Directed Inquiry
Have students do Investigation 11B: *Kitchen Calorimetry* on page 761.

ChemFile Lab C

Skills Development
Have students do Exploration C9.

▶ **FIGURE 11-12**

In football, as in Hess's law, only initial and final conditions matter. If a football team gains 15 yards on a pass play but has a 10-yard penalty, the team's field position is no different than if the team had gained only 5 yards during the play.

To find ΔH for the combustion of 2 mol of H_2, start with data for the enthalpy of the reaction of hydrogen and oxygen to produce water in the *liquid* state.

$$2H_2(g) + O_2(g) \longrightarrow 2H_2O(l) \; \Delta H = -571.66 \text{ kJ}$$

You can also use data for the enthalpy of vaporization of water.

$$2H_2O(l) \longrightarrow 2H_2O(g) \; \Delta H = 88.02 \text{ kJ}$$

The principle of Hess's law allows you to add the last two equations, canceling $H_2O(l)$, which is common to both sides. The enthalpies are also added because they are part of the expressions.

$$2H_2(g) + O_2(g) \longrightarrow 2H_2O(l) \qquad \Delta H = -571.66 \text{ kJ}$$
$$2H_2O(l) \longrightarrow 2H_2O(g) \qquad \Delta H = 88.02 \text{ kJ}$$
$$\overline{2H_2(g) + O_2(g) + 2H_2O(l) \longrightarrow 2H_2O(l) + 2H_2O(g) \; \Delta H = -483.64 \text{ kJ}}$$

Thermodynamic data are compiled through experiments and the application of Hess's law

Enthalpies listed in Table A-13 of the Appendix are based on the convention that the enthalpy of all the elements at standard temperature, 298.15 K (25.00°C), is zero. The enthalpy of a compound is called the **standard enthalpy of formation,** symbolized by ΔH_f^0, because such enthalpy changes accompany the formation reaction represented below.

$$\text{elements (at 298.15 K)} \longrightarrow \text{one mole of compound (at 298.15 K)}$$

For simplicity, you can think of the entries in the table as being just molar enthalpies, H^0, under standard conditions.

It is possible to use thermodynamic data to calculate the enthalpy change for any reaction that involves compounds listed in the table. Using the data in Table A-13, you can determine if certain reactions are exothermic or endothermic. An example of this procedure is shown in Sample Problem 11C.

standard enthalpy of formation

the amount of heat released or absorbed when 1 mol of compound is made from its elements under standard conditions

404   CHAPTER 11

ALTERNATIVE ASSESSMENT

Group Strategy

Ask students to use other sports analogies to model Hess's law. Games that use goals, such as hockey, soccer, and basketball usually provide good analogies.

Calculate the change in enthalpy, ΔH^0, for the following reaction using data from Table A-13.

$$H_2(g) + CO_2(g) \longrightarrow H_2O(g) + CO(g)$$

Is the reaction exothermic or endothermic?

1 **List what you know**

▶ Products: $H_2O(g) + CO(g)$
▶ Reactants: $H_2(g) + CO_2(g)$

2 **Set up the problem**

▶ The change in enthalpy for any reaction is found by subtracting the sum of the enthalpies of the reactants from the sum of the enthalpies of the products.

$$\Delta H^0 = \text{sum of } H^0_{(products)} - \text{sum of } H^0_{(reactants)}$$

▶ Find the values from Table A-13 of the Appendix.

$$H^0_{H_2O} = -241.8 \text{ kJ/mol} \qquad H^0_{H_2} = 0$$

$$H^0_{CO} = -110.5 \text{ kJ/mol} \qquad H^0_{CO_2} = -393.5 \text{ kJ/mol}$$

▶ The coefficients in the equation are all 1's in this case. Therefore,

$$\text{sum of } H^0_{products} = [(1 \text{ mol})(-214.8 \text{ kJ/mol}) + (1 \text{ mol})(-110.5 \text{ kJ/mol})]$$

$$\text{sum of } H^0_{reactants} = [(1 \text{ mol})(-393.5 \text{ kJ/mol}) + (1 \text{ mol})(0)]$$

▶ Substitute these values in the equation.

$$\Delta H^0 = [(-241.8 \text{ kJ}) + (-110.5 \text{ kJ})] - (-393.5 \text{ kJ})$$

3 **Calculate**

$$\Delta H^0 = (-352.3 \text{ kJ}) - (-393.5 \text{ kJ}) = 41.2 \text{ kJ}$$

The reaction is endothermic because ΔH^0 is positive.

PRACTICE PROBLEMS

1. The Romans used CaO as a building material similar to mortar. CaO was mixed with water to produce $Ca(OH)_2$, which reacted slowly with CO_2 in the air to form limestone, $CaCO_3$. This reaction is represented as follows.

$$Ca(OH)_2(s) + CO_2(g) \longrightarrow H_2O(g) + CaCO_3(s)$$

Determine the ΔH value for this reaction using the data given below.

Substance	ΔH^0_f (kJ/mol)	Substance	ΔH^0_f (kJ/mol)
$Ca(OH)_2(s)$	−986.1	$H_2O(g)$	−241.8
$CO_2(g)$	−393.5	$CaCO_3(s)$	−1206.9

SECTION 11-4

ADDITIONAL EXAMPLES

SAMPLE PROBLEM 11C

Use data from Table A-13 to determine the enthalpy change in each of the following reactions.

a. $2H_2O_2(l) \longrightarrow 2H_2O(l) + O_2(g)$

Ans. −196.0 kJ

b. $HCl(g) + NH_3(g) \longrightarrow NH_4Cl(s)$

Ans. −176.2 kJ

c. $CH_4(g) + 2O_2(g) \longrightarrow$
$$CO_2(g) + 2H_2O(g)$$

Ans. −802.2 kJ

Note that H_2O is a gas.

RESOURCE LINK

ChemFile Mini-Guide to Problem Solving
Assign Chapter 19.

CHAPTER 19
Thermochemistry

Thermochemistry deals with the changes in heat energy that accompany a chemical reaction. Heat energy is measured in a quantity called *enthalpy*, represented as *H*. The change in heat energy that accompanies a chemical reaction is represented as Δ*H*. Hess's law provides a method for calculating the Δ*H* of a reaction from tabulated data. This law states that if two or more chemical equations are added, the Δ*H* of the individual equations may also be added to find the Δ*H* of the final equation. As an example of how this law operates, look at the three reactions below.

(1)	$2H_2(g) + O_2(g) \rightarrow 2H_2O(l)$	ΔH = −571.6 kJ/mol
(2)	$2H_2O_2(l) \rightarrow 2H_2(g) + 2O_2(g)$	ΔH = +375.6 kJ/mol
(3)	$2H_2O_2(l) \rightarrow 2H_2O(l) + O_2(g)$	ΔH = ? kJ/mol

When adding equations 1 and 2, the 2 mol of H₂(g) will cancel each other out, while only 1 mol of O₂(g) will cancel.

$$2H_2(g) + O_2(g) \rightarrow 2H_2O(l)$$
$$2H_2O_2(l) \rightarrow 2H_2(g) + 2O_2(g)$$

Combining what is left yields the following equation.

$$2H_2O_2(l) \rightarrow 2H_2O(l) + O_2(g)$$

Notice that this is the same equation as the third equation shown above. Adding the two ΔH values for the reactions 1 and 2 gives the ΔH value for reaction 3. Using Hess's law to calculate the enthalpy of this reaction, the following answer is obtained.

$$-571.6 \text{ kJ/mol} + 375.6 \text{ kJ/mol} = -196.0 \text{ kJ/mol}$$

Thus, the ΔH value for the reaction is −196.0 kJ/mol.
Equation 1 represents the formation of water from its elemental components. If equation 2 were written in reverse, it would represent the formation of hydrogen peroxide from its elemental components. Therefore, adding equations 1 and 2 is the equivalent of subtracting the equation for the formation of the reactants of equation 3 from the equation for the formation of the products of equation 3.

$$2H_2(g) + O_2(g) \rightarrow 2H_2O(l)$$
$$-[2H_2(g) + 2O_2(g) \rightarrow 2H_2O_2(l)]$$
$$2H_2O_2(l) \rightarrow 2H_2O(l) + O_2(g)$$

222 Chapter 19

ANSWERS

PRACTICE PROBLEM 11C

1. $[(-241.8 \text{ kJ} \cdot \text{mol}) + (-1206.9 \text{ kJ} \cdot \text{mol})] - [(-986.1 \text{ kJ} \cdot \text{mol}) + (-393.5 \text{ kJ} \cdot \text{mol})] = -69.1 \text{ kJ/mol}$

PRACTICE PROBLEM 11D

1. 146.1 J/K

2. 159.1 J/K

3. ΔS for the conversion of 1 mol of $C_{diamond}$ to 1 mol of $C_{graphite}$ is 3.3 J/K. You cannot say that the reaction is spontaneous from entropy data alone. You must also know the enthalpy change and calculate the Gibbs energy change to determine spontaneity. In this case, ΔG is negative and the reaction is spontaneous.

ADDITIONAL EXAMPLES

SAMPLE PROBLEM 11D

Use data from Table A-13 to determine the entropy change in each of the following reactions. Remind students that they must multiply the molar entropy by the number of moles of that substance in the reaction. Assume that the coefficients represent the number of moles involved in the reaction.

a. $2Na(s) + 2HCl(g) \longrightarrow$
$$2NaCl(s) + H_2(g)$$

Ans. −201.7 J/K

b. $2LiOH(s) + CO_2(g) \longrightarrow$
$$Li_2CO_3(s) + H_2O(l)$$
ΔS^0 for $Li_2CO_3(s) = 155.5$ J/K•mol

Ans. −34.3 J/K

c. $2C_6H_6(l) + 15O_2(g) \longrightarrow$
$$12CO_2(g) + 6H_2O(l)$$

Ans. −437.7 J/K

Hess's law can also be applied to entropy calculations

Table A-13 also lists molar entropy values. Entropies can be determined, so the entropy values are not based on assigning a zero entropy to the elements. The values for S^0 are given at standard temperature, 298.15 K. The data for gases are at a standard pressure of 1 atm, and the data for dissolved substances are at a standard concentration near 1 mol/L.

Hess's law can be applied to S values to calculate the overall entropy of a reaction, ΔS^0. The procedure is shown in Sample Problem 11D.

SAMPLE PROBLEM 11D | **Calculating change in entropy**

Calculate the entropy change for the following reaction using data from Table A-13.

$$H_2(g) + CO_2(g) \longrightarrow H_2O(g) + CO(g)$$

Does the reaction proceed toward a more ordered or more disordered state?

1 **List what you know**
- Products: $H_2O(g) + CO(g)$
- Reactants: $H_2(g) + CO_2(g)$

2 **Set up the problem**
- The change in entropy for any reaction is found by subtracting the sum of the entropies of the reactants from the sum of the entropies of the products.

$$\Delta S^0 = \text{sum of } S^0_{(products)} - \text{sum of } S^0_{(reactants)}$$

- Find the molar entropies from Table A-13.

$S^0_{H_2O} = 188.7$ J/K•mol $S^0_{H_2} = 130.7$ J/K•mol

$S^0_{CO} = 196.7$ J/K•mol $S^0_{CO_2} = 213.8$ J/K•mol

- Substitute the values into the equation for ΔS^0.

$\Delta S^0 = [(1 \text{ mol})(188.7 \text{ J/K•mol}) + (1 \text{ mol})(197.6 \text{ J/K•mol})] -$
$$[(1 \text{ mol})(130.7 \text{ J/K•mol}) + (1 \text{ mol})(213.8 \text{ J/K•mol})]$$

3 **Calculate and verify**

$$\Delta S^0 = 386.3 \text{ J/K} - 344.5 \text{ J/K} = 41.8 \text{ J/K}$$

- The reaction has a positive entropy; it produces a net disordering.

PRACTICE PROBLEMS

1. Using Table A-13, calculate the entropy change for the following fuel-generating reaction.

$$2Fe(s) + 3H_2O(g) \longrightarrow Fe_2O_3(s) + 3H_2(g)$$

Remember to account for coefficients in the equation when calculating. Does the reaction produce more disorder or less?

DEMONSTRATION 6

Hess's Law and the Enthalpy of Neutralization for NaOH
Approximate time: 10 minutes

The water and the acid and base solutions should all be prepared ahead of time and allowed to stand so that they will be at room temperature.

1. Write the following three equations on the board.

$NaOH(s) + H_2O(l) \longrightarrow$
$$Na^+(aq) + OH^-(aq) + H_2O(l) + \Delta H_1$$

$Na^+(aq) + OH^-(aq) + H_3O^+(aq) + Cl^-(aq) \longrightarrow$
$$2H_2O(aq) + Na^+(aq) + Cl^-(aq) + \Delta H_2$$

$NaOH(s) + H_3O^+(aq) + Cl^-(aq) \longrightarrow$
$$2H_2O(l) + Na^+(aq) + Cl^-(aq) + \Delta H_3$$

Students should note that the first two equations can be added to give the third, so the enthalpy changes of the first two equations add to give the enthalpy

2. Calcium carbonate, $CaCO_3$, decomposes into calcium oxide and carbon dioxide. What is the entropy change for this reaction?

$$CaCO_3(s) \longrightarrow CO_2(g) + CaO(s)$$

Substance	S^0(J/K•mol)
$CaCO_3(s)$	+92.9
$CO_2(g)$	+213.8
$CaO(s)$	+38.2

3. What is the entropy change for converting graphite to diamond? Is this entropy change favorable to the conversion?

graphite: $S^0 = +5.7$ J/K•mol
diamond: $S^0 = +2.4$ J/K•mol

Gibbs energy calculations are used to determine if a reaction is spontaneous

There are two ways of using thermodynamic data tables to find the change in Gibbs energy, ΔG^0, that accompanies a chemical reaction. One way is to calculate ΔH^0 and ΔS^0 and use the following equation.

$$\Delta G^0 = \Delta H^0 - T\Delta S^0$$

This method can be used when a specific temperature is given in the problem.

The second equation for calculating ΔG^0 is similar to the equation you used to calculate ΔH^0 and ΔS^0 in Sample Problems 11C and 11D. The following equation is based on the fact that ΔG^0 is a state property.

$$\Delta G^0 = \text{sum of } G^0_{(products)} - \text{sum of } G^0_{(reactants)}$$

If the calculation of ΔG^0 results in a value that is positive, the reaction is not spontaneous. If the calculation of ΔG^0 results in a value that is negative, the reaction is spontaneous. If ΔG^0 is zero, then neither the forward nor the reverse reaction is favored and the reaction system is at equilibrium. Both methods for calculating ΔG^0 are shown in Sample Problem 11E.

SAMPLE PROBLEM 11E   Calculating change in molar Gibbs energy

Calculate the change in Gibbs energy, ΔG^0, for the following reaction using data from Sample Problems 11C and 11D.

$$H_2(g) + CO_2(g) \longrightarrow H_2O(g) + CO(g)$$

Is the reaction spontaneous at 25°C?

1 **List what you know**

▶ Values of ΔH^0 and ΔS^0 have already been calculated
▶ $\Delta H^0 = 41.2$ kJ/mol
▶ $\Delta S^0 = 0.0418$ kJ/K (this value was converted from J/K)

CAUSES OF CHANGE   **407**

DISCUSSION STRATEGY

Students may better understand the connection between Gibbs energy and spontaneity by discussing the following idea.

Processes, including physical and chemical changes, are spontaneous if they increase the entropy of the universe. This is one statement of the second law of thermodynamics. The universe consists of the following: the system in which the process is taking place and the system's surroundings. The universe increases in entropy whenever work is done on it. To do work on the universe, a process must be able to supply energy to its surroundings. Gibbs energy is the usable energy available from a process. If a process outputs energy, the sign of Gibbs energy is negative and the process can do work on the surroundings. Therefore, the process is spontaneous.

change of the third. By keeping the masses of all substances the same in all three reactions, the temperature changes should be proportional to the enthalpy changes, and $\Delta T_1 + \Delta T_2 = \Delta T_3$.

2. **Reaction 1:** Pour 50 mL of distilled water into a plastic-foam cup, and record the temperature. Add 1 g of NaOH, stir until dissolved. Record the new temperature and ΔT.

3. **Reaction 2:** Pour 25 mL of 1 M HCl into a plastic-foam cup, and record the tempera-

ture. Add 25 mL of 1 M NaOH, stir, record the temperature and ΔT.

4. **Reaction 3:** Pour 25 mL of 1 M HCl into a plastic foam cup, add 25 mL of distilled water, and record the temperature. Add 1 g of NaOH pellets. Stir until dissolved, and record the temperature and ΔT.

5. Compare $\Delta T_1 + \Delta T_2$ with ΔT_3.

CONTINUED ON PAGE 408

ANSWERS

PRACTICE PROBLEM 11E

1. $\Delta G = -58.0$ kJ
   The reaction is spontaneous.
2. $\Delta G = -39.0$ kJ at 900°C
3. $T = 911$ K $= 638$°C

ADDITIONAL EXAMPLES

SAMPLE PROBLEM 11E

Use enthalpy and entropy data from Table A-13 to calculate the Gibbs energy change in each of the following reactions.

a. $2HgO(s) \longrightarrow 2Hg(l) + O_2(g)$ at 25°C

   Ans. $\Delta G = 26.3$ kJ

b. $CO(g) + H_2O(g) \longrightarrow HCOOH(l)$ at 500°C

   Ans. $\Delta G = 126.1$ kJ

c. Calculate the temperature at which the reaction in part **a** becomes spontaneous.

   Ans. $T = 146$°C

2 **Set up the problem and calculate**

▸ Substitute ΔH^0 and ΔS^0 into the equation for ΔG^0.

$$\Delta G^0 = \Delta H^0 - T\Delta S^0$$

$$\Delta G^0 = (41.2 \text{ kJ}) - [(298.15 \text{ K})(0.0418 \text{ kJ/K})] = 28.7 \text{ kJ}$$

▸ **Alternative method:** A second method of calculating ΔG^0 uses G^0 values from Table A-13 and the following equation.

$$\Delta G^0 = G^0_{\text{(products)}} - G^0_{\text{(reactants)}}$$

▸ Now use this method to determine ΔG^0 for the reaction.

$$\Delta G^0 = G^0_{\text{(products)}} - G^0_{\text{(reactants)}}$$

$$= [(1 \text{ mol})(-228.6 \text{ kJ/mol}) + (1 \text{ mol})(-137.2 \text{ kJ/mol})] -$$
$$[0 + (1 \text{ mol})(-394.4 \text{ kJ/mol})]$$

$$= 28.6 \text{ kJ}$$

▸ Both methods give practically the same answer. For this reaction, a positive value of ΔG^0 means the reaction is *not* spontaneous. Hydrogen does not react with carbon dioxide at room temperature.

PRACTICE PROBLEMS

1. Use either of the methods shown in Sample Problem 11E to calculate the Gibbs energy change for the following reaction.

$$2Fe(s) + 3H_2O(g) \longrightarrow Fe_2O_3(s) + 3H_2(g)$$

   Is this reaction spontaneous at 25°C?

2. Graphite and steam can react to produce water gas. This fuel is a mixture of several gases, but contains mostly carbon monoxide gas and hydrogen gas. When water gas is made industrially, the reaction is carried out at temperatures near 900°C. Are the products or reactants favored at this temperature? (Hint: Assume that ΔH and ΔS are constant at all temperatures.)

$$H_2O(g) + C(graphite) \longrightarrow CO(g) + H_2(g) \quad \Delta H = +135.5 \text{ kJ} \quad \Delta S = +148.8 \text{ J/K}$$

3. Holding the temperature of the reactants in the water-gas reaction, shown in item 2, at 900°C is expensive. What is the lowest temperature that could be used to produce a spontaneous reaction? (Hint: Assume that ΔS and ΔH do not change and that $\Delta G = -0.1$ kJ.)

Enthalpy and entropy together determine reaction spontaneity

Recall that Gibbs energy combines changes in enthalpy and entropy for a chemical reaction according to the following equation.

$$\Delta G = \Delta H - T\Delta S$$

The net effect of these changes determines whether the reaction is spontaneous ($-\Delta G$) or nonspontaneous ($+\Delta G$.)

DEMONSTRATION 6 *CONTINUED*

Safety

Wear safety goggles and a lab apron. Use a nonmercury thermometer. Follow first-aid instructions on the label and in the MSDS if acid or base gets in the eyes or on skin or clothing.

Disposal

Rinse out the cups, and put them in the trash. Combine all liquids, neutralize them with 1 M NaOH or 1 M HCl as appropriate, and pour down the drain.

Sometimes nature's tendency toward lower enthalpy and higher entropy act together to favor or disfavor a particular chemical reaction. The reaction of potassium with water, shown in **Figure 11-13,** occurs instantaneously due to the resulting large decrease in energy for the products. Sometimes the effects of entropy and enthalpy are in opposition. **Table 11-4** summarizes the four possible combinations of enthalpy and entropy changes for any chemical reaction. Remember how the chemist defines *spontaneous*—a reaction that is not spontaneous will *not* occur, and a reaction that is spontaneous *may* occur.

FIGURE 11-13 ◀

The spontaneous reaction between potassium metal and water is driven by a large decrease in energy.

TABLE 11-4	Relating Enthalpy and Entropy Changes to Spontaneity		
ΔH	ΔS	ΔG	Is the reaction spontaneous?
Negative (exothermic)	positive (disordering)	negative	yes, at all temperatures
Negative (exothermic)	negative (ordering)	either sign + or −	only at $T < \dfrac{\Delta H}{\Delta S}$
Positive (endothermic)	positive (disordering)	either sign + or −	only at $T > \dfrac{\Delta H}{\Delta S}$
Positive (endothermic)	negative (ordering)	positive	never

CONCEPT CHECK

1. What thermodynamic properties does the Gibbs energy equation include?
2. What does the calculation of a negative ΔG allow you to predict for a reaction?
3. What does the calculation of a positive ΔG allow you to predict for a reaction?
4. Under what conditions can an endothermic reaction be spontaneous?

TEACHING TIP

Spontaneous Reactions

Emphasize that spontaneous reactions only *may* occur and often do not. For example, the conversion of diamond to graphite is spontaneous but, for all practical purposes, does not ever occur.

VISUAL STRATEGY

Table 11-4 Help students analyze the table by asking them to use the equation $\Delta G = \Delta H - T\Delta S$ to determine why the sign of ΔG is negative in the first case and positive in the fourth case. Then help them reason out why ΔG has a negative value when T is low in the second case and T is high in the third case. You may wish to have students formulate a statement to describe the conditions that produce spontaneity in the second and third cases.

ANSWERS

CONCEPT CHECK

1. enthalpy and entropy
2. If ΔG is negative, the reaction is spontaneous.
3. If ΔG is positive, the reaction is not spontaneous.
4. An endothermic reaction can be spontaneous at temperatures above $\Delta H/\Delta S$. At such temperatures, the tendency toward increased entropy overcomes the increase in enthalpy.

The idea that green plants use energy directly from the sun to power life processes persists. Stress that once green plants manufacture glucose and starch, they carry on cellular respiration just as animals do. Reinforce this idea by pointing out the function of mitochondria in the cell.

TEACHING TIP

Photosynthesis Process Remind students that the process of photosynthesis is much more complex than its net equation indicates. Students may recall from Chapter 3 that when light interacts with matter, it usually does so by exciting electrons to higher energy states. This is the role of light in the *photo* part of photosynthesis. Excited electrons emitted when light strikes chlorophyll molecules are used in one case to reduce water to O_2 gas and H^+ ions and in another case to supply energy for the formation of ATP. These materials are then used in reactions in which CO_2 forms molecules that are assembled into glucose.

DID YOU KNOW?

The process in which glucose is oxidized to release energy is called cellular respiration and requires oxygen.

▲ FIGURE 11-14

Photosynthesis is an endothermic reaction that takes place in a chloroplast. Respiration is an exothermic reaction that takes place in a mitochondrion.

Nutrition and thermodynamics
Food energy is just another reaction enthalpy

Essentially, the food you eat is combusted to reclaim the energy that was stored in the food molecules by the plant or animal. The simplest illustration is provided by the food molecule *glucose.*

Green plants make glucose from carbon dioxide and water by the process of photosynthesis, which is shown in the following equation.

$$2870 \text{ kJ/mol} + 6CO_2(g) + 6H_2O(l) \longrightarrow C_6H_{12}O_6(s) + 6O_2(g)$$

$$\Delta H^0 = 2870 \text{ kJ}$$

$$\Delta S^0 = -259 \text{ J/K}$$

$$\Delta G^0 = 2947 \text{ kJ}$$

This reaction is endothermic, is ordering, and has a large positive Gibbs energy change; nothing favors this reaction. How does a plant make such a nonspontaneous reaction occur? The secret is the energy of sunlight, which is used to bring about a series of complicated biochemical reactions whose overall result is summarized by the equation above. A *chloroplast* is the organelle where a plant carries out photosynthesis. Of course, the plant is not making glucose for our benefit, but to power its own biochemistry. **Figure 11-14** shows a chloroplast as well as a *mitochondrion,* the organelle where the cell reoxidizes glucose for its own energy needs.

Humans use the energy in glucose and other carbohydrates for their own needs. But the reaction that goes on in your body is the same one that the glucose is destined to undergo in the mitochondria. It's an oxidation reaction that is the exact reverse of photosynthesis.

$$C_6H_{12}O_6(s) + 6O_2(g) \longrightarrow 6CO_2(g) + 6H_2O(l)$$

$$\Delta H^0 = -2870 \text{ kJ}$$

$$\Delta S^0 = 259 \text{ J/K}$$

$$\Delta G^0 = -2947 \text{ kJ}$$

Notice that this reaction is spontaneous and is strongly favored not only because it is exothermic but also because the products are at a higher state of disorder. The food energy that you get from eating glucose is exactly what the equation reports: 2870 kJ per mole of glucose, or 15.9 kJ/g.

Recall from Chapter 8 that combustion and oxidation can refer to the same chemical reaction. The distinction is solely in the burning that accompanies a combustion. The same energy is released in either case. Thus, one way to determine ΔH for glucose is to burn it in a bomb calorimeter. Glucose is a pure substance, whereas most foodstuffs are not. If a calorimeter is used to combust a peanut, the enthalpy of combustion corresponds accurately to the food energy that you would obtain from eating that peanut.

Some components of some foods are not nutritious. For example, you cannot digest cellulose, although it will combust in a bomb calorimeter. Food scientists have to make corrections to calorimetric data to allow for these situations.

Metabolic rate is a measure of your energy consumption

Your body needs energy to carry out all the tasks your daily life demands—not only to power your muscles but also to digest food, to respire, to keep you warm, and to carry out all the other biochemical processes needed to sustain your health and growth.

If you eat more food than your body needs, excess energy intake is often stored either as glycogen in the liver or as fat. To some degree, the extent of this energy storage depends on the food you eat. Fat is a more efficient storage medium than carbohydrates and protein. It has a much higher energy content per gram than other nutrients, as **Table 11-5** shows.

Of course, your energy needs depend on your activity; an athlete needs more energy than a hospital patient, for example. The digestion of food itself requires considerable energy, so a person's resting metabolic rate, or RMR, is defined as the energy he or she expends when resting or sleeping *with an empty stomach*. You expend more energy than your RMR when you carry out other activities.

A metabolic rate is a rate of energy consumption, so its SI unit is *joules per*

TOPIC: Nutrition/Thermodynamics
GO TO: www.scilinks.org
KEYWORD: HW114

TABLE 11-5	Energy Content of Carbohydrates, Proteins, and Fats	
Nutrient	**kJ/g**	**Cal/g**
Carbohydrate	17	4
Protein	17	4
Fat	38	9

TEACHING TIP

Combustion vs. Metabolism Ask students to explain how the energy available from the combustion of glucose and the energy available from the metabolism of glucose provide an example of Hess's law. In the oxidation of glucose by cellular respiration, energy is released in small quantities suitable for supplying energy to cell activities. However, the total energy available is the same as the energy obtained from the combustion of glucose in oxygen.

ADDITIONAL APPLICATION

Inform students that the word *Calorie*, when spelled with a capital *C* represents one kilocalorie of energy. It is these "big *C*" Calories that are always referred to in nutrition labeling of foods. "Small *c*" calories were once used in the physical sciences routinely, but this unit has been supplanted almost entirely by the joule.

$$1 \text{ cal} = 4.184 \text{ J}$$

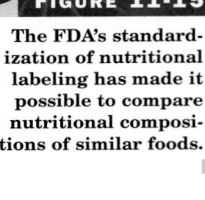

The FDA's standardization of nutritional labeling has made it possible to compare nutritional compositions of similar foods.

Serving size
Volume and mass of a standard portion

Calories
Fuel value of the food for the serving size listed

Total fat
Mass of the fat in the serving size listed with a breakdown of the mass of saturated fat

Total carbohydrate
Mass of complex carbohydrates, fiber, and sugars in the serving size listed

Calories from fat
Energy equivalent of the fat grams for the serving size listed

Sodium and potassium
Mass of each mineral in the serving size listed. One teaspoon of table salt has a mass of about 2 g.

Protein
Mass of protein in the serving size listed

Vitamins and other minerals
Values listed are the percentage of total daily requirement for that vitamin or mineral that is provided in the serving size listed.

Nutrition Facts

Serving Size 20 crackers (31 g)
Servings Per Container About 8

Amount Per Serving

Calories 130 Calories from Fat 20

	% Daily Value*
Total Fat 2.5g	4%
Saturated Fat 0g	0%
Polyunsaturated Fat 0g	
Monounsaturated Fat 1g	
Cholesterol 0mg	0%
Sodium 270mg	11%
Total Carbohydrate 23g	8%
Dietary Fiber 1g	4%
Sugars Less than 1 gram	
Protein 3g	

Vitamin A 0%	•	Vitamin C 0%
Calcium 0%	•	Iron 4%

* Percent Daily Values are based on a 2,000 calorie diet. Your daily values may be higher or lower depending on your calorie needs:

		Calories:	2,000	2,500
Total Fat	Less than		65g	80g
Sat Fat	Less than		20g	25g
Cholesterol	Less than		300mg	300mg
Sodium	Less than		2400mg	2400mg
Total Carbohydrate			300g	375g
Dietary Fiber			25g	30g

Calories per gram:
Fat 9 • Carbohydrate 4 • Protein 4

INGREDIENTS: ENRICHED WHEAT FLOUR (CONTAINS NIACIN, REDUCED IRON, THIAMINE MONONITRATE, (VITAMIN B1), RIBOFLAVIN (VITAMIN B2) FOLIC ACID), CRACKED WHEAT, VEGETABLE SHORTENING (PARTIALLY HYDROGENATED CANOLA AND/OR SOYBEAN OILS), SALT, BAKING SODA, POPPY SEEDS, BLACK PEPPER, WHEY, MALTED BARLEY FLOUR, LEMON OIL, YEAST.

CHRISTIE BROWN & CO.
2150 LAKESHORE BLVD. WEST,
ETOBICOKE, M8V 1A3 CANADA
DIVISION OF
NABISCO LTD
© 1997 ALL RIGHTS RESERVED
* Reg. U.S. Pat. & TM Off.

PRODUCT OF CANADA

second or *watts.* The usual metric unit, *kilojoules per day,* is more convenient and is used in most of the world. Instead of the kilojoule, an older unit is still used primarily in the United States. This energy unit goes by two names. It is called either a *kilocalorie* (kcal) or a *Calorie* (Cal). The Calorie is the unit used on the "Nutrition Facts" label required by law on all packaged foods. A Nutrition Facts label is shown in **Figure 11-15.** The conversions are as follows.

$$1 \text{ kcal} = 1 \text{ Cal} = 4.184 \text{ kJ}$$

You can easily find data on the energy content of most of the foods you eat. Most of the packaged food you get from the grocery store provides a lot of nutritional information. The labels in Figure 11-15 are in the style now mandated by the Food and Drug Administration (FDA).

TABLE 11-6 Energy and Nutrient Breakdown of Some Foods*

Food and measure	Calories	Kilojoules	Carbohydrate (g)	Protein (g)	Fat (g)
Apple, 1 medium	81	339	21.1	0.3	0.5
Cheeseburger, 4.1 oz	310	1297	31.2	15.0	13.8
Cola soft drink, 6 oz	72	301	19.0	0	0
French fries, 3.4 oz	320	1339	36.3	4.4	17.1
Potato, baked, 7.1 oz	220	920	51.0	4.7	0.2
Potato chips, 1 oz	150	628	15.0	1.0	10.0
Pretzels, 1 oz	110	460	22.0	2.0	2.0
Yogurt with fruit, 8 oz	240	1004	43.0	9.0	3.0
Yogurt, low-fat frozen, 3 oz	100	418	22.0	4.0	0.8

*These figures have been rounded and represent average values.

SECTION REVIEW

Total recall

1. How is Hess's law used to determine the ΔH of a reaction?

2. Predict what conditions, if any, are needed to make the following changes spontaneous.
   a. exothermic reaction with an increase in entropy
   b. reaction with an increase in both enthalpy and entropy

Practice problems

3. Using the following values, compute the ΔG value for each reaction and predict whether it will occur spontaneously.

Reaction	ΔH (kJ)	Temperature	ΔS (J/K)
1	+125	293 K	+35
2	−85.2	127 K	+125
3	−275	500°C	+450

4. **Story Clue** Hydrogen gas can be prepared for use in cars in several ways, such as by the decomposition of water or hydrogen chloride.

$$2H_2O(l) \longrightarrow 2H_2(g) + O_2(g)$$
$$2HCl(g) \longrightarrow H_2(g) + Cl_2(g)$$

Use the following data to determine whether these reactions can occur spontaneously. Assume that ΔH and ΔS are constant.

	H^0 (kJ/mol)	S^0 (J/K·mol)
$H_2O(l)$	−285.8	+70.0
$H_2(g)$	0	+130.7
$O_2(g)$	0	+205.1
$HCl(g)$	−92	+187
$Cl_2(g)$	0	+223.1

ANSWERS

SECTION REVIEW

Total recall

1. The enthalpy changes from two or more separate reactions that will lead to the desired products may be added to determine the overall enthalpy change.

2. a. No change is needed.
   b. Raise the temperature until $T\Delta S$ is greater than ΔH.
   c. Lower the temperature until ΔH is greater than $T\Delta S$.

Practice problems

3. Reaction 1: $\Delta G = 115$ kJ, not spontaneous
   Reaction 2: $\Delta G = -244$ kJ, spontaneous
   Reaction 3: $\Delta G = -623$ kJ, spontaneous

4. The reaction using H_2O is not spontaneous at 25°C because $\Delta G = 474$ kJ. The reaction using HCl is likewise not spontaneous at 25°C because $\Delta G = 134$ kJ. It would be spontaneous at temperatures above 830°C.

ELEMENT SPOTLIGHT

H
1
Hydrogen
1.00794
1s¹

While the H atom is the most abundant atom in the universe, only 3% of the atoms in the Earth's crust are hydrogen.

WHERE IS IT?

Universe
approximately 93% of all atoms

Earth's Crust
0.9% by mass

internet**connect**

SC**LINKS**
NSTA
TOPIC: Hydrogen
GO TO: www.scilinks.org
KEYWORD: HW115

A BRIEF HISTORY

Hydrogen an element unto itself

Hydrogen is a unique element in many respects. Its scarcity on Earth is partially due to the low density of hydrogen gas. The low density permits hydrogen molecules to escape the Earth's gravitational pull and drift into space.

Hydrogen does not fit comfortably anywhere in the periodic table. However, it could be placed in Group 1 because it has a single valence electron. It can also be placed with the halogens in Group 17 because it can accept an electron to produce a hydride ion, H^-, and easily forms covalent bonds with carbon.

Industrial Uses

▶ Hydrogen gas is prepared industrially by the thermal decomposition of hydrocarbons. Natural gas, oil-refinery gas, gasoline, fuel oil, and crude oil are the principal raw materials.

▶ Most of the hydrogen gas produced is used for synthesizing ammonia.

▶ Hydrogen is used in the hydrogenation of unsaturated vegetable oils to make solid fats.

▶ Liquid hydrogen is a clear, colorless liquid with a boiling point of −252.87°C, the lowest boiling point of any known liquid other than liquid helium. Because of its low temperature, liquid hydrogen is used to cool superconducting materials.

▶ Liquid hydrogen is used to fuel rockets that explore space, launch satellites, and power spacecrafts.

1766: Henry Cavendish prepares a pure sample of hydrogen and distinguishes it from other gases. He names it "inflammable air."

1937: The *Hindenburg,* a hydrogen-filled dirigible, explodes during a landing in Lakehurst, New Jersey.

1783: Jacques Charles fills a balloon with hydrogen and flies in a basket over the French countryside.

1931: Harold Urey discoveres deuterium, an isotope of hydrogen, in water.

1600	1700	1800	1900

1660: Robert Boyle prepares hydrogen from a reaction between iron and sulfuric acid.

1783: Antoine Lavoisier names hydrogen. It means "water former."

1898: James Dewar produces liquid hydrogen and develops a glass vacuum flask to hold it.

1934: Ernest Rutherford, Marcus Oliphant, and Paul Harteck discover tritium.

1996: Scientists at Lawrence Livermore National Laboratory succeed in making solid metallic hydrogen.

At the beginning of this chapter, you explored hydrogen-powered cars. Let's revisit the three questions posed at that time considering what you now know about the forces that drive chemical reactions and changes of state.

LOOKING BACK

What drives the H_2 combustion reaction?

Natural processes are driven by a decrease in enthalpy, an increase in entropy, or both. Hydrogen combustion is accompanied by a decrease in both entropy and enthalpy. Entropy decreases as three molecules become two molecules—an ordering process. As often happens the enthalpy effect far outweighs the entropy effect.

Is there a safe and economical way to carry H_2 in a car?

Yes. Hydrogen can form interstitial hydrides in which the hydrogen enters the lattice of a metallic element without forming bonds. Through simple temperature and pressure adjustments, hydrogen absorbed on the metal can be easily recovered. Unfortunately, the best metal for this purpose, palladium, is too scarce and costly to use in mass-produced automobiles. Titanium and manganese alloys with similar properties to palladium are inexpensive alternatives.

In fact, the experimental car is equipped with tanks that contain plates of a manganese/titanium alloy. The exothermic absorption of hydrogen on the metal plates in fueling and the endothermic reverse process require complex cooling and heating equipment.

Because of the complicated fuel-handling system, a hydrogen-powered car could cost 50% more to mass-produce than its gasoline-powered counterpart.

Would the use of hydrogen-powered cars lead to less pollution?

Unfortunately, one tank of absorbed hydrogen provides only as much mileage as about half a full tank of gas. As a gasoline replacement, massive quantities of H_2 would need to be produced. H_2 can easily be made by the electrolysis of water, but that requires electrical energy. An increased demand for electrical energy requires more power stations. Because most of the present-day power stations burn fossil fuels, pollution will be about the same.

There is concern that hydrogen-powered cars may merely move the pollution from the highways to the neighborhoods of electricity-generating power plants, but battery-powered cars present the same concern.

Despite obstacles, engineers at several car firms believe that use of hydrogen-powered cars will be common one day.

READING STRATEGY

Assimilating Knowledge

Have students return to their list of things they want to know about energy from chemical reactions, which they created on page 383. Have them place check marks next to the questions that they are now able to answer. Students should finish by making a list of what they've learned. Have students identify unanswered questions as well as new questions they may have. These questions could be used as the basis for a research project.

REVIEW & ASSESS ASSIGNMENT GUIDE

Term Review
Assign after Section 11-4.

Concept and Skills Review

Section 11-1
Items 1–7

Section 11-2
Items 8–18

Section 11-3
Items 19–26

Section 11-4
Items 27–37

Linking Chapters
Assign after Section 11-4.

Alternative Assessments
Assign after Section 11-4.

Test Prep
Assign prior to the chapter test.

KEY TERMS

11-1
entropy
molar heat capacity
thermodynamics

11-2
extensive property
intensive property

11-3
molar enthalpy of fusion
molar enthalpy of
   vaporization
Gibbs energy

11-4
adiabatic calorimetry
calorimeter
Hess's law
standard enthalpy of
   formation

KEY CONCEPTS

11-1 How does heat differ from other forms of energy?

▶ The two natural driving forces are a decrease in energy and an increase in disorder.

▶ Heat represents the quantity of thermal energy; temperature represents the intensity of thermal energy.

▶ An increase in the heat and temperature of a substance reflects an increase in the random kinetic energy of its atoms.

▶ The molar heat capacity of a substance is the quantity of heat required to increase the temperature of 1 mol of a substance by 1 K.

▶ The molar heat capacity depends on the number of atoms a substance contains.

▶ Entropy is the measure of the total disorder of a system.

11-2 How does temperature affect enthalpy and entropy?

▶ Enthalpy is the total energy of a substance.

▶ Absolute enthalpy, represented by H, cannot be measured; changes in enthalpy, represented by ΔH, can be measured.

▶ Absolute entropy, represented by S, and change in entropy, represented by ΔS, can be measured.

11-3 What happens during a change of state?

▶ Both enthalpy and entropy change dramatically during changes of state.

▶ The relative values of ΔH and $T\Delta S$ determine physical state.

▶ Gibbs energy combines the ΔH and $T\Delta S$ of a process and is used to predict spontaneity.

11-4 How does thermodynamics apply to reactions and nutrition?

▶ Calorimetry can be used to determine the ΔH of a reaction.

▶ Hess's law can be used to determine the ΔH for an overall reaction by adding the ΔH values for the individual steps in the overall process.

▶ Thermodynamic data can be used to determine if a reaction is endothermic ($\Delta H > 0$) or exothermic ($\Delta H < 0$), ordering ($\Delta S < 0$) or disordering ($\Delta S > 0$), and spontaneous ($\Delta G < 0$) or not ($\Delta G > 0$).

▶ Metabolic rate is the rate of energy consumption by the body.

KEY SKILLS

Sample Problem 11A: Calculating the molar heat capacity of a substance (p. 388)

Sample Problem 11B: Calculating molar enthalpy change (p. 393)

Sample Problem 11C: Calculating change in enthalpy (p. 405)

Sample Problem 11D: Calculating change in entropy (p. 406)

Sample Problem 11E: Calculating change in molar Gibbs energy (p. 407)

416 CHAPTER 11

1. The disorder possessed by 1 mol of a substance is quantified in its _____.
(molar entropy, molar heat capacity)

2. A(n) _____ is a property of matter that is independent of the quantity of matter that is present.
(extensive property, intensive property)

3. The difference between the molar enthalpy of 1 mol of a substance in its gaseous state and 1 mol in its liquid state is known as the substance's _____.
(molar enthalpy of fusion, molar enthalpy of vaporization)

4. The quantity involving both enthalpy and entropy is _____.
(the molar Gibbs energy, molar heat capacity)

5. The symbol H_f^0 represents the _____ of a compound.
(entropy, standard enthalpy of formation)

6. The ΔH of a reaction can be calculated with the help of _____.
(adiabatic calorimetry, the resting metabolic rate)

CONCEPT & SKILLS REVIEW

HEAT ENERGY AND MOLAR HEAT CAPACITY

1. Explain why the liquid in a thermometer rises when it gets hotter outdoors and drops when it gets cooler in terms of the kinetic energy of atoms in the liquid.

2. What compound unit is represented by the watt?

3. Flask A contains 500 mL of water at 25°C, and flask B contains 250 mL of water at 50°C. Which flask has a higher heat content? Explain your choice.

4. How does the number of atoms in a molecule of a substance affect its molar heat capacity?

5. Explain what happens in terms of thermal energy when ice is used to freeze a liquid.

Practice Problems

6. A student performs an experiment to determine the molar heat capacity of a sample of silica, SiO_2, with a mass of 4.0 g. The silica absorbs 121 J of heat, and its temperature increases from 0.0°C to 41.0°C. What is the molar heat capacity of the glass? **(Hint: See Sample Problem 11A.)**

7. Calculate the amount of heat energy transferred in the following situations:
   a. the temperature of 1.0 g of water rises from 22.5°C to 24.5°C
   b. the temperature of 3.0 g of silver rises from 46.0°C to 47.0°C
   c. the temperature of 7.0 g of tungsten rises from 0°C to 5°C
   d. the temperature of 11.0 g of iron rises from 240°C to 244°C

ENTROPY AND ENTHALPY

8. Why do molar entropies always have positive values?

9. Predict how the molar entropy of $CO_2(g)$ would compare with the molar entropy of $CO_2(s)$. Explain your answer.

10. The molar entropy of $C(g)$ at 298 K is 158.096 J/K•mol. The molar entropy of $CO_2(g)$ at 298 K is 213.74 J/K•mol. What does this data indicate about the relative motion of the atoms in these two gases?

11. Why are entropy and enthalpy considered extensive properties?

12. What does ΔT represent?

13. What does a positive ΔH value indicate about the temperature change in a substance?

TERM REVIEW

1. molar entropy
2. intensive property
3. molar enthalpy of vaporization
4. the molar Gibbs energy
5. standard enthalpy of formation
6. adiabatic calorimetry

CONCEPT & SKILLS REVIEW

1. As the temperature increases, the average kinetic energy of the particles of the liquid increases. As a result, the particles push one another farther apart and the liquid expands.

2. one joule per second, J/s

3. Flask A has the higher heat content, which is proportional to the Kelvin temperature, not the Celsius temperature. The difference in Kelvin temperature is not enough to overcome the difference in quantity of matter.

4. As the number of atoms increases, so does the molar heat capacity.

5. Thermal energy moves from the warmer liquid to the colder ice, raising its temperature if it is below the freezing point or melting it if the ice is at the freezing point.

6. $121 \text{ J} \times \dfrac{60.09 \text{ g/mol}}{4.0 \text{ g}} \times \dfrac{1}{41.0 \text{ K}} = 44.3 \text{ J/K•mol}$

7. a. $1.0 \text{ g } H_2O \times \dfrac{1 \text{ mol } H_2O}{18.02 \text{ g } H_2O} \times$
$\dfrac{75.3 \text{ J}}{\text{mol•K}} \times 2.0 \text{ K} = 8.4 \text{ J}$

b. $3.0 \text{ g Ag} \times \dfrac{1 \text{ mol Ag}}{107.87 \text{ g Ag}} \times \dfrac{25.3 \text{ J}}{\text{mol•K}} \times$
$1.0 \text{ K} = 0.70 \text{ J}$

c. $7.0 \text{ g W} \times \dfrac{1 \text{ mol W}}{183.84 \text{ g W}} \times \dfrac{24.2 \text{ J}}{\text{mol•K}} \times$
$5.0 \text{ K} = 4.6 \text{ kJ}$

d. $11.0 \text{ g Fe} \times \dfrac{1 \text{ mol Fe}}{55.85 \text{ g Fe}} \times \dfrac{25.1 \text{ J}}{\text{mol•K}} \times$
$4.0 \text{ K} = 19.8 \text{ J}$

8. The lowest possible entropy is 0 for a perfect crystal at 0 K. Therefore, all substances have positive entropies at temperatures above 0 K.

9. The entropy of $CO_2(g)$ would be higher because a gas is a more disordered state.

10. The motion of CO shows more randomness.

11. Both entropy and enthalpy depend on the amount of matter present.

12. change in temperature

13. The temperature is probably increasing because the system is absorbing energy.

14. Temperature may be decreasing because entropy is decreasing.

15. $AlCl_3$ has four atoms, so its molar heat capacity should be about 4 times that of a substance consisting of single atoms.

16. The enthalpy change is being calculated per mole of substance; therefore, it is independent of the amount of a sample.

17. $= \Delta H = (75.1 \text{ J/K} \cdot \text{mol})(16.0 \text{ K})$
$= 450.6 \text{ J/K} \cdot \text{mol}$

18. $\Delta H = (119.5 \text{ J/K} \cdot \text{mol})(-25.8 \text{ K})$
$= -3080 \text{ J/K} \cdot \text{mol}$

19. The identity of the substance changing state does not change.

20. The energy absorbed or released results from the state change, not from any change in temperature.

21. The enthalpy is higher because of polar attractions and hydrogen bonding between water molecules in the liquid state.

22. Work is being done on the particles to cause the change of state.

23. Entropy increases in the formation of water vapor as energy is absorbed, so enthalpy also increases.

24. When $T\Delta S > \Delta H$, the system tends toward higher entropy, and the gas state has higher entropy than the liquid state of the same substance.

25. Enthalpy decreases as the O_2 condenses and energy is given off. Entropy decreases because the liquid is a more ordered state.

14. What does a negative ΔS value indicate about the temperature change in a substance?

15. Explain why $AlCl_3$ has a molar heat capacity that is approximately four times that of a metallic crystal.

16. If the molar heat capacity and the temperature change are known, why is the mass of a substance not needed to calculate its molar enthalpy change?

Practice Problems

17. The molar heat capacity of $BaCl_2(s)$ is 75.1 J/K•mol. Calculate the ΔH value when the temperature is raised from 50°C to 66°C. **(Hint: See Sample Problem 11B.)**

18. The molar heat capacity of $(C_2H_5)_2O(g)$ is 108 75.1 J/K•mol. Calculate the ΔH value when the temperature drops from 68.5°C to 42.7°C. **(Hint: See Sample Problem 11B.)**

CHANGE OF STATE

19. Explain why changes of state are considered physical transitions and not chemical processes.

20. How does an enthalpy change that accompanies a change of state compare with an enthalpy change that accompanies the heating of an individual phase? Explain the difference.

21. What makes the molar entropy of vaporization for water higher than most other substances?

22. During melting, heat is added, the temperature does not change, yet enthalpy increases. How can this be?

23. How are entropy and enthalpy involved in the boiling process?

24. Why is the gas phase favored when $T\Delta S_{vap} > \Delta H_{vap}$?

25. Describe what happens in terms of entropy and enthalpy when $O_2(g)$ becomes $O_2(l)$.

26. **a.** What is the relation between the enthalpy change and the entropy change during a change of state?
   b. What determines the direction of the change of state?

MOLAR GIBBS ENERGY

27. Draw a graph with ΔH on the x-axis and ΔS on the y-axis. In each quadrant of the graph, indicate what conditions, if any, are necessary to make a reaction spontaneous for each combination of positive and negative ΔH and ΔS values.

28. The entropy change for the spontaneous reaction to make NOCl from its elements at a low temperature is negative. Is the enthalpy change positive or negative?

29. What drives photosynthesis, a chemical reaction with a large positive ΔH value?

30. At high temperatures, does enthalpy or entropy have a greater effect on a reaction's molar Gibbs energy? Explain your answer.

31. Nitrogen dioxide, $NO_2(g)$, has a standard enthalpy of formation of 33.1 kJ/mol. Dinitrogen tetroxide, $N_2O_4(g)$, has a standard enthalpy of formation of 9.1 kJ/mol. What is the enthalpy change for synthesizing N_2O_4 from NO_2?

Practice Problems

32. Use Hess's law to calculate the change in enthalpy for the combustion of 1 mol of carbon monoxide to form carbon dioxide. Oxygen is in elemental form. **(Hint: See Sample Problem 11C.)**

33. The diagram below represents an interpretation of Hess's law for the following reaction.

$$Sn(s) + 2Cl_2(g) \longrightarrow SnCl_4(l)$$

Use the diagram to determine ΔH for each step and the net reaction.

$Sn(s) + Cl_2(g) \longrightarrow SnCl_2(l) \qquad \Delta H = ?$
$SnCl_2(s) + Cl_2(g) \longrightarrow SnCl_4(l) \qquad \Delta H = ?$
$Sn(s) + 2Cl_2(g) \longrightarrow SnCl_4(l) \qquad \Delta H = ?$

(Hint: See Sample Problem 11C.)

34. Solid iron will slowly oxidize into iron oxide, Fe_2O_3, if it is left untreated in the open air. What is the entropy change for this reaction?

$$4Fe(s) + 3O_2(g) \longrightarrow 2Fe_2O_3(s)$$

(Hint: See Sample Problem 11D.)

Substance	S (J/K•mol)
Fe(s)	27.3
$O_2(g)$	205.2
$Fe_2O_3(s)$	87.4

35. Ammonium nitrate is a common fertilizer that can become a powerful explosive when it undergoes rapid decomposition. What is the entropy change for this reaction?

$$2NH_4NO_3(s) \longrightarrow 2N_2(g) + 4H_2O(g) + O_2(g)$$

(Hint: See Sample Problem 11D.)

Substance	S (J/K•mol)
$NH_4NO_3(s)$	151.1
$N_2(g)$	191.6
$H_2O(g)$	188.8
$O_2(g)$	205.2

36. Titanium chloride, $TiCl_4$, is an intermediate chemical formed in the production of titanium metal, a substance used extensively in aerospace technology. Will the reaction for the production of $TiCl_4$ be spontaneous if it is carried out at 100.0°C? Show your work.

$$TiO_2(s) + 2Cl_2(g) \longrightarrow TiCl_4(l) + O_2(g)$$
$$\Delta H = +140.5 \text{ kJ}$$
$$\Delta S = -38.9 \text{ J/K}$$

(Hint: See Sample Problem 11E.)

37. Will the combustion of benzene be spontaneous if the temperature is 25°C? Show your work.

$$2C_6H_6(l) + 15O_2(g) \longrightarrow 12CO_2(g) + 6H_2O(l)$$
$$\Delta H = -6535 \text{ kJ}$$
$$\Delta S = -439.1 \text{ J/K}$$

(Hint: See Sample Problem 11E.)

1. Molar mass
Specific heat capacity is the thermal energy needed to raise the temperature of 1 g of a substance by 1 K, and it has the unit J/K•g. For example, the specific heat capacity of $(CH_2OH)_2(l)$, ethylene glycol or antifreeze, is 2.42 J/K•g. Calculate the molar heat capacity of $(CH_2OH)_2(l)$.

2. Theme: Systems and interactions
The block of ice in Sample Problem 11B on page 393 constitutes a system. The negative ΔH value indicates that the system lost thermal energy. As you learned, energy cannot be created or destroyed. Where did the energy go?

3. Theme: Equilibrium and change
At 1109.15 K the reaction of oxygen gas (O_2) to form ozone (O_3) has a ΔG value of zero. What does this tell you about the reaction involving these two gases?

4. Theme: Systems and interactions
Inside a calorimeter, two systems interact. What are these two systems, and how do they interact?

Performance assessment

1. Design an experiment to measure the molar heat capacities of zinc and copper. If your teacher approves the design, obtain the materials needed and conduct the experiment. When finished, compare your experimental values with those from a chemical handbook or other reference source.

2. Develop a procedure to measure the ΔH of a reaction. If your teacher approves, test your procedure by measuring the ΔH value of the following reaction. Determine the accuracy of your method by comparing your ΔH with the accepted ΔH value.

$$CH_3COONa(s) \longrightarrow Na^+(aq) + CH_3COO^-(aq)$$

26. a. Depending on the change, both enthalpy and entropy increase or both enthalpy and entropy decrease.

b. The direction is determined by whether the conditions favor increasing order (cooler surroundings) or increasing disorder (warmer surroundings).

27. Students' labeling of their graphs should match Table 11-4.

28. negative

29. the energy of sunlight

30. Entropy change has the greater effect because $T\Delta S$ is large at high temperatures.

31. $\Delta H = -24.0$ kJ

32. $\Delta H = (-393.5 \text{ kJ}) - (-110.5 \text{ kJ}) = -283.0$ kJ

33. $\Delta H = -330$, $\Delta H = -180$ kJ, $\Delta H = -510$ kJ

34. $\Delta S = [(2 \text{ mol})(87.4 \text{ J/K•mol})] - [(4 \text{ mol})(27.3 \text{ J/K•mol}) + (3 \text{ mol})(205.2 \text{ J/K•mol})] -550.0$ J/K

35. $\Delta S = [(4 \text{ mol})(188.80 \text{ J/K•mol}) + (1 \text{ mol})(205.2 \text{ J/K•mol}) + (2 \text{ mol})(191.6 \text{ J/K•mol})] - [(2 \text{ mol})(151.1 \text{ J/K•mol})] = 1041.4$ J/K

36. $\Delta G = (140.5 \text{ kJ}) - (373 \text{ K})(-0.0389 \text{ kJ/K}) = +155$ kJ, so the reaction is not spontaneous.

37. $\Delta G = (-6536 \text{ kJ}) - (298 \text{ K})(-0.4391 \text{ kJ/K}) = -6405$ kJ, so the reaction is spontaneous.

1. You would multiply the specific heat capacity by the number of grams in 1 mol of the substance. $C = 1.50 \times 10^2$ kJ/K•mol

2. The energy was absorbed by the surroundings.

3. The reaction is in equilibrium at this temperature.

4. One system is the combustion reaction itself, and the other consists of the calorimeter and water, both of which absorb energy given off by the reaction.

CHAPTER 11
Review Answers

Performance assessment

1. Answers will vary but should include measuring the mass of samples, heating them, and determining how much they increase the temperature of a known mass of water in a calorimeter. Be sure students use a safe procedure and available materials. A calorimeter can easily be made from a foam cup.

2. Answers will vary but should include dissolving a known mass of sodium acetate in a known mass of water and measuring the resulting temperature change. Be sure students follow proper safety procedures, wear proper personal protective equipment, and follow chemical safety guidelines.

3. Answers will vary but should involve allowing ice of known mass to melt completely in an insulated cup containing a known mass of water and measuring the resulting temperature change. Students must know the actual temperature of the ice before they put it in water because it is likely to be lower than 0°C. Be sure students use a safe procedure and available materials. A calorimeter can easily be made from a foam cup.

Portfolio projects

1. Besides hand warmers that actually burn fuel, there are two basic types of chemical warmers. In one type, a salt dissolves exothermically in water. This type can be used only once. The other type contains a supersaturated solution of a salt that can be made to crystallize, giving off heat. This kind can be reused.

2. Answers will vary but should reflect the idea that a balanced diet in moderation is probably preferable to more unusual regimens.

Continued on page 421.

3. Design an experiment to determine the ΔH_{fus} for $H_2O(s)$. If your teacher approves the design, obtain the materials needed and carry out the experiment. Compare your experimental value with that listed on Table 11-3.

Portfolio projects

1. **Chemistry and you**
   Hand warmers depend on chemical reactions that have a negative ΔH value. Research these hand warmers to find out what reactions they use. Prepare a report that includes the advantages and disadvantages of each type. Experiment to see if you can prepare a more efficient or less expensive hand warmer.

2. **Chemistry and you**
   Evaluate your own diet after researching diet issues such as starchy carbohydrates versus sugary carbohydrates, complete versus incomplete proteins, and saturated versus unsaturated fats. Write a report on some of the controversies that exist regarding food choices.

3. **Cooperative activity**
   Conduct research on different mechanisms that lower the entropy of a system. Decide which are most effective. Present your findings to the class.

4.

   SCI**LINKS**
   NSTA

   TOPIC: Alternative fuels
   GO TO: www.scilinks.org
   KEYWORD: HW116

   Research and communication
   The chapter story examines one alternative fuel for cars. Conduct research on the public and private uses of alternative fuels in automobiles and other combustion engines. Determine which ones can be used and produced with the least environmental impact. Present your findings to the class.

TEST PREP

1. An adiabatic calorimeter can be used to determine the ——— of a reaction.
   a. ΔG
   b. ΔS
   c. ΔH
   d. molar Gibbs energy

2. The temperature of a substance is a measurement of the ———.
   a. total kinetic energy of its atoms
   b. entropy of the substance
   c. average kinetic energy of its atoms
   d. molar heat capacity of the substance

3. Which of the following energy conversions would be least efficient?
   a. heat energy $\longrightarrow$ mechanical energy
   b. mechanical energy $\longrightarrow$ potential energy
   c. electrical energy $\longrightarrow$ mechanical energy
   d. chemical energy $\longrightarrow$ light energy

4. An example of an intensive property in matter would be its ———.
   a. mass
   b. volume
   c. entropy
   d. temperature

5. Which of the following physical properties do all the noble gases share?
   a. molar heat capacity
   b. entropy
   c. boiling point
   d. electron configuration

6. When carrying out thermodynamic calculations, always ———.
   a. convert joules to kilojoules
   b. convert Celsius data to kelvins
   c. determine the ΔH value first
   d. convert moles to grams

7. The melting point of a solid can be defined as the ———.
   a. molar enthalpy of vaporization
   b. molar enthalpy of fusion divided by the molar entropy of fusion
   c. point at which enthalpy and entropy are equal
   d. condensation point of the gas

8. Which of the following two conditions will favor a spontaneous reaction?
   a. increase in entropy and decrease in enthalpy
   b. increase in entropy and increase in enthalpy
   c. decrease in entropy and decrease in enthalpy
   d. decrease in entropy and increase in enthalpy

9. Respiration is a spontaneous reaction as reflected by ———.
   a. $\Delta H > 0$
   b. $\Delta S < 0$
   c. $\Delta G < 0$
   d. $\Delta G > 0$

10. The gasification of coal is a method of producing methane. The overall reaction has three separate steps, with the following heats of reaction.

   Step 1: $C(s) + O_2(g) \longrightarrow CO_2(g)$
   $\Delta H_c^0 = -393.5 \text{ kJ}$
   Step 2: $2H_2(g) + O_2(g) \longrightarrow 2H_2O(l)$
   $\Delta H_c^0 = -571.6 \text{ kJ}$
   Step 3: $CH_4(g) + 2O_2(g) \longrightarrow CO_2(g) + 2H_2O(l)$
   $\Delta H_c^0 = -890.8 \text{ kJ}$

   What is the ΔH for the following overall reaction for the gasification of coal?
   $$C(s) + 2H_2(g) \longrightarrow CH_4(g)$$
   a. -393.5 kJ
   b. -74.3 kJ
   c. 0 kJ
   d. $+890.8$ kJ

1. c	4. d	7. b
2. c	5. a	8. a
3. a	6. b	9. c
		10. b

Continued from page 420.

3. Answers will vary but should include ways to increase the order of a system both with and without a temperature change.

4. Be sure students realize that "fuel" includes battery power. They should consider that electric power often must be produced in a way that contributes to pollution. Some students may want to learn about hybrid electric vehicles, which burn fuel and produce electricity.

Gases and Liquids

CLASSROOM RESOURCES

SECTIONS	TEACHER'S DEMONSTRATIONS	PROBLEM SOLVING ■ *Text* ◆ *ChemFile Mini-Guide*	LABORATORIES ■ *Text* ◆ *ChemFile Manuals: A, B, C, D*
12-1 **What are the characteristics of gases?** Section Review, p. 432	**Demo 1** Elastic and Inelastic Collisions, p. 424 **Demo 2** Atmospheric Pressure, p. 428		
12-2 **What behaviors are described by the gas laws?** Section Review, p. 444	**Demo 3** Volume Changes with a Vacuum Pump, p. 434 **Demo 4** Amount of Oxygen in Air, p. 438	■ **Sample Problem 12A:** Solving pressure-volume problems, p. 435 ■ **Sample Problem 12B:** Solving volume-temperature problems, p. 440 ■ **Sample Problem 12C:** Comparing molecular speeds, p. 443 ◆ **Chapter 11** Gas Laws	■ **QuickLab**: Pressure Relief, p. 437 ◆ **Exp. C10** Gas Pressure–Volume Relationship ◆ **A8** Boyle's Law ◆ **Inv. C10** Gas Temperature–Volume Relationship: Balloon Flight ◆ **Exp. C11** Masses of Equal Volumes of Gases ◆ **A9** Molar Volume of a Gas
12-3 **How do the gas laws fit together?** Section Review, p. 451		■ **Sample Problem 12D:** Using the ideal gas law, p. 447 ■ **Sample Problem 12E:** Using the combined gas law, p. 448 ■ **Sample Problem 12F:** Using the ideal gas law to solve stoichiometry problems, p. 450 ◆ **Chapter 12** The Ideal Gas Law ◆ **Chapter 13** Stoichiometry of Gases	◆ **B11** Generating and Collecting O_2 ◆ **B12** Generating and Collecting H_2 ◆ **B13** Testing Reaction Combinations of H_2 and O_2 ◆ **D11** Factors Affecting CO_2 Production in Yeast
12-4 **What conditions will cause a gas to condense?** Section Review, p. 458	**Demo 5** Boiling Water in a Vacuum, p. 454		

TECHNOLOGY RESOURCES

See page 422 for a listing of Internet resources.

SECTIONS	VIDEOS/VIDEODISC *Holt Chemistry Videodisc* CNN PRESENTS *Science in the NEWS*	CHEMFILE CD-ROMS ● *Teaching Resources* ◆ *Interactive Tutor*	OVERHEADS ● *Color Transparencies* ◆ *Transparency Masters*
12-1	States of matter Gas molecular speeds Ozone CNN PRESENTS Segment 21 Global Warming	● Skills Review: SI Conversions ● Supplemental Reading: *Ultraviolet Reflections: Life Under a Thinning Ozone Layer*	● **58** Sodium as a Solid, Liquid, and Gas ● **48** Relationship Between Pressure, Force, and Area ◆ **48A** Units of Pressure ● **49** Mercury Barometer
12-2	Gas laws and bicycle pumps Gas volume change Gases: Charles's law data and graph Gas pressure–temperature relationship Avogadro's law Gas diffusion: ammonium chloride ring	● Skills Review: Graphing ● Skills Review: Isolating Variables in Equations ● Supplemental Reading: *The Same and Not the Same,* "Static/Dynamic" ◆ **Module 6:** Gas Laws **Topic:** Behavior of Gases	● **50** Gas Mixtures and Dalton's Law ● **52** Avogadro's Law ● **54** Graham's Law ● **56** Diffusion ◆ *See also* **49A, 50A, 51A, 52A.**
12-3	Gas pressure–number of moles relationship		● **53** Gas Law Calculations ◆ **53A** Numerical Values of the Gas Constant
12-4	Evaporation of liquids Vapor-liquid equilibrium Boiling point of water Sublimation of iodine crystals CNN PRESENTS Segment 22 Belching Cows	● Occupational Application: Pest-Control Technician ● Occupational Application: Air Quality Specialist	● **59** Liquid-Vapor Equilibrium System ● **61** Change-of-State Models for Water ● **62** Exothermic and Endothermic Changes of State ● **63** Phase Diagram for Water

ASSESSMENT RESOURCES

ALTERNATIVE ASSESSMENTS	CHAPTER TESTING	SCORING RUBRICS *Holt ChemFile Teaching Resources CD-ROM*
Student Text Performance assessment, p. 464 Portfolio projects 1–2, p. 464 **Teacher's Edition** Group Strategies, pp. 432, 440, 442 **Study Guide** Sections 12-1 to 12-4	**Student Text** Test Preparation, p. 465 **Holt Chemistry: Visualizing Matter Chapter 12 Test** (blackline masters) **Holt ChemFile Test Generator for Macintosh and Windows**	**Lab Work** Student-Designed Experiments Rubric Performance-Tasks Scoring Rubric Assessment for Structured Inquiry Assessment for Open-Ended Inquiry **Portfolio Projects** Evaluating Concept Maps Assessing Portfolios Portfolio Assignment Student Evaluation Form

Establishing Prior Knowledge

Make certain students understand the following concepts.

▸ Chapter 2: kinetic energy, potential energy, heat, temperature
▸ Chapter 8: the mole
▸ Chapter 9: chemical equations
▸ Chapter 10: stoichiometry

READING STRATEGY

Assimilating Knowledge

Before students read this chapter, have them write a short, individual list of all the things they know about the molecular properties of gases and liquids. Encourage them to include information on their lists about the motion of gas particles; about the relationships of the temperature, pressure, and volume of a gas; and about the processes of evaporation, condensation, and boiling. Then have students list the things they might want to know about gases and about the changes in state between gases and liquids.

If students are having trouble coming up with questions, you can offer these suggestions to get them on track.

▸ Considering that all matter is made of particles, what is the fundamental difference between gases and liquids?
▸ How would you explain the properties of liquids and gases to someone by E-mail, without using pictures?
▸ What are the ways that a liquid changes to a gas?

ABOUT THE ILLUSTRATION

A gas and a liquid interact to form the bubbles on this wand. As air is blown through the hole in the wand, the soap expands into a bubble, eventually enclosing the air.

CHAPTER 12

Gases and Liquids

 internet**connect**

Holt Chemistry: Visualizing Matter
On-Line Resources
go.hrw.com
Visit the HRW Web site for a variety of resources related to this chapter. Just type in the keyword HW0 Chapt12.

SCLINKS
NSTA

National Science Teachers Association
On-Line Resources: www.scilinks.org
The following Scilinks Internet resources can be found in the student text for this chapter:

Page 429
TOPIC: Greenhouse gases
KEYWORD: HW121

Page 430
TOPIC: Ozone depletion
KEYWORD: HW122

Page 432
TOPIC: Non-CFCs
KEYWORD: HW123

Page 445
TOPIC: Nitrogen
KEYWORD: HW124

Page 453
TOPIC: Supercritical fluids
KEYWORD: HW125

ASCENT INTO THE OZONE

In the still air, the sun begins to rise above the horizon. The busy team of scientists, awake for hours, monitors atmospheric conditions to be sure they are right. Today looks like a great day for the research team— today, there will be a launch.

As the sun rises, a growing silver form appears in the distance. A strange hissing sound fills the air. The shape, now recognizable as a huge balloon, takes form as it inflates with helium.

The ground crew continues to monitor atmospheric conditions as other scientists turn their attention to the expanding balloon. When the top of the partially inflated balloon extends about 250 m into the air, it is ready for launch. Though the balloon is only a fraction of the size it will be when it is completely inflated, it is still capable of lifting a cargo of telescopes, cameras, and recording equipment with a total mass of more than 700 kg. With the data provided by these instruments, scientists can derive a clearer picture of what is happening in the upper atmosphere.

When the restraining lines are removed, the balloon ascends to about 38 000 m above Earth's surface. This mission, like many others before it, involves collecting data on the ever-changing ozone layer in the atmosphere. After collecting data for several days, the payload falls back to Earth, and the instruments are retrieved by scientists. The data collected will become part of the monthly log scientists use to determine conditions in the atmosphere and make predictions about the ozone layer.

With the advent of satellites, you might expect the use of balloons to be obsolete, but balloons offer several advantages over satellites. Balloons are much cheaper to build and launch, and a balloon can collect data from within the ozone layer, while a satellite can merely provide data from an aerial perspective above the layer.

The principles used in launching balloons were discovered nearly 150 years ago. In studying these ideas, you will find information to help you answer the following questions.

CHAPTER LINKS

Why is the balloon only partially inflated at launch?

How do scientists know how much to inflate the balloon?

Why do scientists monitor the ozone layer?

What gases are thought to be responsible for changes in the ozone layer?

What is being done to protect the ozone layer?

STORY BACKGROUND

Balloons have been used to explore the upper atmosphere since 1931, when Auguste Piccard developed an airtight pressurized cabin that allowed crews to ascend into the stratosphere. Realizing that a balloon expands in volume at higher altitudes, Piccard used a much larger balloon than had been used in previous ascents. By partially filling the larger balloon, there was enough gas to provide lift for the cabin and still enough room in the balloon for the gas to expand once the external atmospheric pressure dropped.

Currently, two types of balloons are used in stratospheric research: super-pressure balloons and zero-pressure balloons. Super-pressure balloons are fully inflated and sealed so that their volume and pressure are kept constant. The balloon ascends until the density of the air outside the balloon equals the density inside, at which point the balloon ceases to rise. Zero-pressure balloons, by contrast, have variable volumes and pressures. This allows them to float at any altitude during their flight. They are the largest balloons and thus are able to carry the heaviest payloads.

Besides being used to carry instruments to parts of the atmosphere being studied, balloons are a relatively inexpensive way of testing satellite equipment prior to launch. Because the satellite equipment is retrievable, adjustments can be made until the instrument is ready to be placed into orbit.

CONCEPT PREVIEW

Section 12-1
Properties of gases
- kinetic-molecular theory
- kinetic-molecular model of gases

Earth's atmosphere
- measuring pressure
- greenhouse effect
- ozone depletion

Section 12-2
The gas laws
- pressure-volume relationship
- partial pressures in gas mixtures
- volume-temperature relationship
- temperature-pressure relationship
- Avogadro's law
- effusion and diffusion

Section 12-3
Quantitative relationships in gases
- the ideal gas law
- the combined gas law
- stoichiometry of reactions

Section 12-4
Gas-liquid phase changes
- relationship of vapor pressure and temperature
- phase diagrams

What are the characteristics of gases?

OBJECTIVES

▶ **Describe** the general properties of gases.

▶ **Relate** the kinetic-molecular theory to the properties of an ideal gas.

▶ **Define** pressure, and give the SI unit for pressure.

▶ **Describe** the events that are believed to be responsible for global warming.

▶ **Explain** the depletion of ozone in the stratosphere.

Properties of gases

Each state of matter has its own characteristic properties. The properties of gases can be explained by a model called the **kinetic-molecular theory.** Models are used in science to make predictions. Models explain the facts available and often lead to correct predictions. The kinetic-molecular theory was developed in the mid-1800s, and it is still extremely useful as a model for predicting gas behavior. This theory makes some major assumptions about a theoretical gas often called an **ideal gas.**

kinetic-molecular theory

the theory that explains the behavior of gases at the molecular level

ideal gas

a model that effectively describes the behavior of gases under most conditions

Gases are fluids

Gases are fluids, which means that they flow just as liquids do. Gases also transmit and exert pressure equally in all directions. Gas molecules are in constant motion and frequently collide with one another and with the walls of their container, as illustrated in **Figure 12-1.** The kinetic-molecular theory assumes that collisions between ideal gas molecules are elastic. Normally, collisions between everyday objects are not elastic. A collision is said to be elastic when there is no loss in the total amount of kinetic energy involved in the collision. According to the kinetic-molecular theory, there are no net attractive or repulsive forces between ideal gas molecules, allowing collisions between these molecules to be elastic.

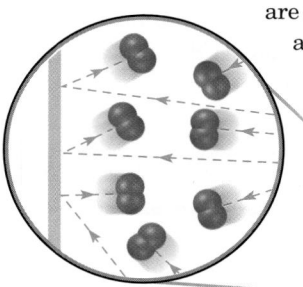

▶ **FIGURE 12-1**

Gas molecules travel in a straight-line motion until they collide with each other or the walls of their container.

LESSON WARM-UP

The Fluidity of Gases Demonstrate the fluid property of a gas by generating CO_2 in a 1 L beaker, flask, or tall cylinder. You can do this by placing a small piece of dry ice and a little warm water in the bottom of the container. As an alternative, place a heaping tablespoonful of baking soda in the container, followed by 100 mL of 1 M acetic acid. As the reaction proceeds, the container will fill with CO_2. Place a candle in the bottom of a large beaker, and light the candle. You can pour the dense CO_2 from the first container into the beaker and extinguish the candle. Students may be more impressed if you make a trough from a folded sheet of paper and pour the CO_2 down the trough and into the beaker. If the gas seems foggy, remind students that CO_2 is colorless. Droplets of water suspended in the gaseous CO_2 create the cloudy appearance.

TEACHING TIP

Elastic and Inelastic Collisions If students wonder what happens to the energy of objects in a collision, explain that energy is conserved in all collisions, both elastic and inelastic. In a perfectly elastic collision between two objects, energy is conserved as energy of motion. The sum of the kinetic energies of the two objects is the same before and after the collision. In an inelastic collision, part of the kinetic energy of the objects is converted into heat energy.

DEMONSTRATION 1

Elastic and Inelastic Collisions

Approximate time: 5 minutes

1. Obtain a set of "happy" and "sad" balls from a scientific supply house. (The "happy" ball is made of a very elastic rubber, like that used in "super balls." The "sad" ball is made of a very inelastic rubber, like that used for cushioning collisions and for making the soles of shoes.)

2. Place the "happy" ball in your left pocket and the "sad" ball in your right pocket.

3. Remove the "happy" ball, and bounce it on the table several times while initiating a discussion on elastic collisions. Return the "happy" ball to your left pocket.

4. Ask for two volunteers to help determine the ball's elasticity by measuring how high it bounces.

Figure 12-2   The drawings in Figure 12-2 are two-dimensional models of the three principal states of matter. Be sure students note the spacing of particles.

Figure 12-3   If you have a plastic syringe, demonstrate Figure 12-3, and allow students to do it themselves to feel the increase in pressure. Ask students to use the models in Figure 12-2 to explain why the compression shown in Figure 12-3 is possible. Ask them if they think the compression would be possible if a liquid were in the syringe. *(Liquids are incompressible at normal forces. The incompressibility and fluidity of liquids make hydraulic devices possible.)*

Gases have low density

Compared with liquids and solids, gases have a very low density. To explain the low density of gases, the kinetic-molecular theory states that molecules of an ideal gas are so small that the volume of the individual molecules can almost be ignored when compared with the total volume of the gas. Gases are mostly empty space, while particles in solids and liquids are in contact with each other, as shown in **Figure 12-2.** This distance between particles illustrates why a substance in the liquid or solid state always has a greater density than the same substance in the gaseous state.

Gases are highly compressible

Suppose you fill a syringe with liquid and try to push the plunger in when the opening is plugged. Nothing happens. It takes enormous pressure to reduce the volume of a liquid or solid. However, if there is a gas or mixture of gases, such as air, in the syringe, it does not take much pressure to move the plunger down and compress the gases, as shown in **Figure 12-3.**

FIGURE 12-2 ▲

Particles of sodium metal in three different states are shown. Sodium exists in a gaseous state in a sodium-vapor lamp.

FIGURE 12-3 ▼

The volume of gas in the syringe is reduced when the plunger is pushed inward.

💡 **DID YOU KNOW?**

Gas particles are approximately 10 times farther apart than the particles of a liquid or a solid. As a result, the volume of a substance in the gas state is roughly 1000 ($10 \times 10 \times 10$) times the volume of the same amount of the substance in the liquid or solid state.

5. Remove the "sad" ball from your right pocket, and hand it, rather than the "happy" ball, to one of the students. Ask the other student to hold a meter-stick while the other drops the ball, and stand back.

6. Ask students what has happened to the ball. Reveal the "happy" ball, explain how the two balls differ, and discuss the types of collisions each underwent. Ask students what happened to the kinetic energy of the inelastic ball when it hit the floor.

(It was converted to heat by internal friction as the ball became distorted.)

Safety
Safety goggles are recommended for all participants. The rest of the class must stand back at least 10 ft.

Disposal
None

The volume occupied by a gas is almost entirely empty space because the volume filled by the gas molecules is very small. You know that gases are made up of tiny particles that are far apart from each other relative to their size; therefore, it is easy to understand that applying a small pressure will move the gas molecules closer together, decreasing the volume of the gas. Steel cylinders containing gases under pressure are widely used in industry. When they are full, these cylinders may contain 100 times as many gas molecules as would be contained in nonpressurized containers of the same size.

Gases completely fill a container and exert pressure equally in all directions

A solid has a distinctive shape and volume. A liquid has a distinctive volume but assumes the shape of its container. In contrast, a gas fills the entire container and exerts pressure on the container in all directions. The pressure exerted on a container by a gas is the result of gas molecules colliding against it, as illustrated in Figure 12-1.

The temperature of a gas determines the average kinetic energy of its particles

The kinetic energy of a gas molecule can be expressed using the kinetic-energy equation that relates kinetic energy to one-half the mass, *m*, multiplied by the square of the speed, *v*.

$$KE = \tfrac{1}{2}mv^2$$

According to the kinetic-molecular theory, the average kinetic energy of gas particles depends on the temperature of the gas. Remember that the collisions of ideal gas particles are elastic and therefore do not affect the kinetic energy of the system. **Figure 12-4** shows how energy is distributed in a sample of gas molecules. Most of the gas molecules are traveling near the average speed, a few are traveling at lower speeds, and a few are traveling at very high speeds. The blue curve shows the speed of gas molecules at 25°C (298 K). The red curve shows gas molecules at a temperature 10°C higher. Notice that the shape of the curve changes when the temperature increases. As the temperature increases, the average speed increases slightly. But, as shown on the graph, the number of very high energy molecules, indicated by the shaded area, has increased greatly, perhaps doubling.

▼ FIGURE 12-4

Increasing the temperature of a sample of gas shifts the energy distribution in the direction of greater average kinetic energy.

Energy Distribution of Gas Molecules at Different Temperatures

GRAPHIC ORGANIZER

Observed behavior of gas	Property of gas
Gases can flow through pipes and from one container to another.	Gases are fluids.
The mass of a gas is much lower than the same volume of a solid or a liquid.	Gases are much less dense than solids or liquids.
Gases can be squeezed to a smaller volume.	Gases are compressible.
The air in a tire inflates the tire all the way around.	Gases exert pressure in all directions.
Unlike a liquid, which puddles in the bottom of a container, a gas will always fill the container.	Gases occupy all the space available to them.

The atmosphere is a sea of gases

The atmosphere exerts pressure on the surface of Earth

Every day you are surrounded by gases. Earth's atmosphere is a gaseous mixture of elements and compounds. The atmosphere is composed of gas molecules that have mass. As these molecules move and collide with Earth's surface, they exert pressure. You already have an idea of what pressure is, but now it must be defined more precisely.

Pressure is the force on a surface divided by the area of that surface.

$$\text{pressure} = \frac{\text{force}}{\text{area}}$$

In SI, force is measured in **newtons** (N), and the unit of area is meters squared (m^2). Therefore, the SI unit for pressure is the **pascal** (Pa) and is derived from the units of force and area.

$$1 \text{ pascal (Pa)} = 1 \text{ N/m}^2$$

There are other ways to express pressure. For example, as shown in **Figure 12-5,** the atmosphere exerts pressure on the surface of Earth. This same pressure causes a sealed column of mercury to rise in a barometer. How does this barometer measure the pressure exerted by the atmosphere? Due to its weight, the column of mercury exerts a pressure downward. The atmosphere exerts a pressure that is transmitted

pressure

the force exerted per unit area

newton

the force that will increase the speed of a 1 kg mass by 1 m/s each second that force is applied

pascal

a unit of pressure equal to the force of 1 N on 1 m^2

Force

Oxygen, O$_2$ Nitrogen, N$_2$

1 atm of pressure is the force of 101.325 kN on 1 m^2

Pressure

FIGURE 12-5 ◄

Gas molecules in air collide with Earth's surface, creating atmospheric pressure.

GASES AND LIQUIDS   427

Kinetic-molecular explanation

Particles of gases are not held in rigid position like particles of a solid are.
The distance between gas particles is very large compared with the distance between particles of a solid or a liquid.
The distance between gas particles is very large. Thus, they can be squeezed together.
Gas particles are in constant motion and collide with the walls of their container, thus exerting pressure.
Particles of gases are widely spaced, and attractive forces between gas particles are very small. Therefore, gas particles are free to spread farther apart.

CONTENT STRATEGY

Commonly encountered pressures are usually expressed in kilopascals (kPa) because the pascal (Pa) represents such a small amount of pressure.

HISTORICAL CONNECTION

In the seventeenth century, many scientists believed that liquid suspended in eudiometer tubes was held in place by invisible "ropes." Robert Boyle showed this idea to be untrue by inserting a long wire into a eudiometer tube and wiggling it back and forth. Because the wire did not catch on the rope, the rope did not exist. It is for simple and straightforward experiments such as this that Boyle is considered the father of modern chemistry.

RESOURCE LINK

ChemFile Teaching Resources CD-ROM
Skills Review
Assign Basic Skills Worksheet 5: *SI Conversions* to review or reteach this skill.

Vacuum

Pressure exerted by the column of mercury

760 mm

O₂ N₂

Atmospheric pressure

Surface of mercury

▲ **FIGURE 12-6**

In the sealed column of a mercury barometer, the mercury falls until the pressure exerted by its weight equals the atmospheric pressure.

standard temperature and pressure (STP)

standard conditions for a gas at 0°C and 1 atm

upward through the fluid mercury to the mercury in the column. The mercury in the column falls only until the pressure exerted downward by its weight is equal to the pressure exerted upward by the atmosphere. The force per unit area exerted by the atmosphere on the mercury column is called atmospheric pressure. An illustration of a mercury barometer is shown in **Figure 12-6.**

Although water could be used in a barometer, it is an impractical choice because the atmosphere would support a column of water more than 10 m high. The density of mercury is 13.7 times greater than the density of water. Because of its very high density, mercury provides a practical column height of less than 1 m. At sea level, the atmosphere maintains the mercury at an average height of 760 mm. One millimeter of mercury is called a torr, in honor of Evangelista Torricelli, the Italian physicist who invented the barometer. The pressure of one standard atmosphere is equal to 101 325 pascals, or 101.325 kilopascals. Other units of pressure include the bar and pound per square inch (psi). One goal of the scientific community is to eventually have only one unit of pressure in common use—the pascal. The units of pressure are summarized in **Table 12-1.**

To study the effects of changing temperature and pressure on a gas, it is useful to have a standard for comparison. Scientists have specified a set of standard conditions called **standard temperature and pressure,** or **STP.** This text will use the following conditions for STP.

$$STP = 0°C \text{ and } 1 \text{ atm}$$

TABLE 12-1 Pressure Units

Unit	Abbreviation	Equivalent number of pascals
Atmosphere	atm	1 atm = 101 325 Pa
Bar	bar	1 bar = 100 025 Pa
Millimeter of mercury	mm Hg	1 mm Hg = 133.322 Pa
Pascal	Pa	
Pound per square inch	psi	1 psi = $6.892\ 86 \times 10^3$ Pa
Torr	torr	1 torr = 133.322 Pa

DEMONSTRATION 2

Atmospheric Pressure

Approximate time: 5 minutes

1. Half fill a 50 mL eudiometer tube with tap water colored with food dye.

2. Cover the eudiometer tube mouth with your forefinger, invert the tube, and place it upside down in a clear 1 L cylinder or other tall container filled with similarly colored water. Ask students what they think will happen when you remove your finger

from the tube. Once the tube is submerged, uncover the tube mouth.

3. Hold the eudiometer until the 50 mL mark is level with the water level in the cylinder. Ask students what they think holds the water up in the tube. *(Atmospheric pressure acting on the surface of the water in the cylinder is transmitted throughout the water*

CONCEPT CHECK

1. Why is it more practical to use a very dense liquid rather than water in a barometer?
2. What is the SI unit of pressure, and from what units is it derived?
3. What are the conditions referred to as STP?

Earth's changing climate

If not for the sun, Earth would be a completely frozen globe. Earth receives electromagnetic radiation from the sun. The fate of this radiant energy is shown in **Figure 12-7.** Most of the visible radiation is reflected back into space by clouds, dust in the atmosphere, and the surface of Earth. About one-third of the electromagnetic radiation from the sun reaches Earth's surface and is absorbed. This absorbed radiant energy warms the surface of Earth and in turn warms the atmosphere.

Greenhouse gases trap radiant energy

All objects with a temperature above 0 K radiate energy, and this is true of Earth. The radiant energy from Earth that goes out into space is heat radiation in the infrared region of the spectrum, as shown in Figure 3-20, on page 92. Certain gases in the atmosphere, called greenhouse gases, absorb much of this infrared radiation and emit it back toward Earth's surface, causing Earth to be warmer than it otherwise might be.

internetconnect

SC**L**INKS.
NSTA

TOPIC: Greenhouse gases
GO TO: www.scilinks.org
KEYWORD: HW121

ANSWERS

CONCEPT CHECK

1. The less dense the liquid is in a barometer, the taller the barometer must be. The use of a very dense liquid, such as mercury, allows the barometer tube to be short enough to be manageable.

2. The SI unit of pressure is the pascal. The pascal $(1\ Pa = 1\ \frac{N}{m^2})$ is derived from the equation $P = \frac{F}{a}$, where force is measured in newtons and length is measured in meters (to calculate area).

3. The conditions referred to as STP are 0°C and 1 atm of pressure.

CNN **Science in the News**

PRESENTS **Feature story 21**
Global Warming. See the Science in the News video guide for more details.

FIGURE 12-7 ◄

Greenhouse gases in the atmosphere can trap radiant energy by reflecting it back to Earth.

and into the tube. This pressure provides the force that holds up the column of water.)

4. Fill the eudiometer tube completely, and invert it as in step 2. Show students that atmospheric pressure can support the entire column of water in the tube.

Safety
Wear a lab apron and a pair of safety goggles. The class must be 10 ft or more from the demonstration.

Disposal
Pour water down the drain.

TEACHING TIP

Global Warming Point out to students that global warming is not a certainty. Scientists realize that Earth has gone through many warming and cooling cycles during its existence. The expectation of global warming caused by human activities is based on the extrapolation of currently available data using a computer model of Earth. In addition to the greenhouse effect, periodic variations in solar activity and volcanic activity affect Earth's temperature. Even so, guarding against global warming by moderating greenhouse gases is advisable.

RESOURCE LINK

ChemFile Teaching Resources CD-ROM
Supplemental Reading Projects
For cross-curricular connections to language arts, assign the guided reading worksheets for Annika Nilsson's *Ultraviolet Reflections: Life Under a Thinning Ozone Layer.*

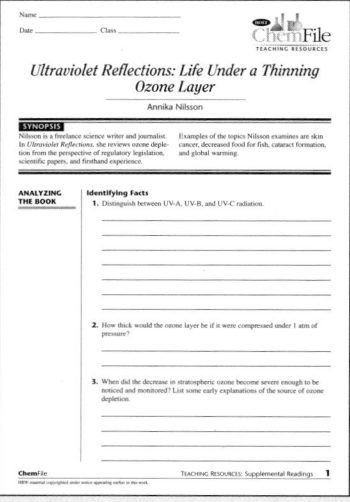

greenhouse effect

an increase in the temperature of Earth caused by reflected solar radiation that is trapped in the atmosphere

internetconnect

SCLINKS
NSTA
TOPIC: Ozone depletion
GO TO: www.scilinks.org
KEYWORD: HW122

This warming mechanism, referred to as the **greenhouse effect,** is illustrated in Figure 12-7. Natural greenhouse warming keeps Earth at a habitable temperature. Greenhouse gases include water vapor, H_2O, carbon dioxide, CO_2, methane, CH_4, dinitrogen monoxide, N_2O, and chlorofluorocarbons, CFCs.

Earth is becoming warmer

Over the past century, Earth has become warmer. In the past 100 years, the average increase in global air temperature has been about 0.6°C. This seems to be a small amount, but if you consider that the last ice age was caused by an average decrease in global temperature of about 5°C, you can begin to understand the effects this increase might have.

Many scientists who study the atmosphere believe that a primary cause of the warming is the increase in the concentration of greenhouse gases. Levels of CO_2 in the atmosphere have increased and have contributed to the warming. Some scientists believe that most of the increase in CO_2 levels is caused by combustion of fossil fuels: coal, petroleum, and natural gas. Many everyday activities involve the combustion of fossil fuels. Driving a car, cooking on an outdoor grill, and using electricity produced by coal-fired generators all involve combustion processes. Another source of CO_2 in our atmosphere comes from the burning of forests, most of them tropical rain forests.

There has also been an increase in artificial greenhouse gases. These are mostly chlorofluorocarbons once used in refrigeration and air-conditioning but now banned in the United States. The structures of two typical chlorofluorocarbons are depicted in **Figure 12-8.**

Ozone depletion allows more ultraviolet radiation to reach Earth

About 9% of the radiant energy emitted by the sun is ultraviolet radiation. Ultraviolet radiation is a mutagen because it can cause a mutation, including various forms of skin cancer, some of which can be fatal. Ozone, O_3, is an extremely good absorber of ultraviolet light, and it

► **FIGURE 12-8**

Freon-11 and Freon-12 were commonly used chlorofluorocarbon compounds.

Freon-11   Freon-12

FIGURE 12-9 ◀

The black region over Antarctica shows the area of greatest ozone depletion, called the ozone hole.

TEACHING TIP

Free Radicals   Students may think that free radicals are ions. In reality, they are uncharged. They are highly reactive because they have an unpaired electron in a position that is usually covalently bonded to another atom. Other examples of free radicals are $CH_3\bullet$, $NH_2\bullet$, $Br\bullet$, and $HO\bullet$.

DID YOU KNOW?

The United States began to phase out the use of CFCs as aerosol propellants in 1979. No CFCs have been used in aerosol products for many years. Old air-conditioning systems in cars and in buildings continue to be a source of CFCs.

Once chlorofluorocarbons, sulfur dioxide, and nitrogen oxides (yet another contributor to ozone depletion and a common gas in aircraft and automobile exhaust) are removed from the ozone layer, the high-energy ultraviolet radiation from the sun will begin to replenish the ozone layer.

blocks most of the ultraviolet light from reaching Earth. Upon absorbing ultraviolet light, ozone breaks apart into an oxygen molecule and an oxygen atom.

The ozone layer is thin and extremely fragile. Unfortunately, chlorofluorocarbons are destroying the ozone layer. The CFC molecules diffuse into the atmosphere over many years. There, the energetic ultraviolet radiation breaks them apart, liberating Cl atoms. The resulting atom is a chlorine **free radical,** $Cl\bullet$, that reacts rapidly with an ozone molecule to form molecular oxygen and chlorine monoxide, ClO, as shown by the following equation.

$$Cl\bullet(g) + O_3(g) \longrightarrow ClO(g) + O_2(g)$$

The resulting chlorine monoxide is very reactive. It reacts with O atoms formed by the decomposition of O_3 to form the more stable O_2 molecule.

$$ClO(g) + O(g) \longrightarrow Cl\bullet(g) + O_2(g)$$

The first reaction destroys the ozone. The second reaction consumes reactive O atoms needed to form ozone. The $Cl\bullet$ formed in the second reaction then becomes available to repeat the sequence. In this **chain reaction,** one $Cl\bullet$ may destroy thousands of ozone molecules before it diffuses down to the troposphere.

There has always been an annual decrease in the ozone concentration around the South Pole during September and October. But since 1977, the decrease has been so great that it is referred to as an ozone hole. This decrease in ozone level is shown in **Figure 12-9.** In recent years, the size of the ozone hole has averaged approximately 21 million square kilometers.

To halt the destruction of the ozone layer, 163 nations became parties to the Montreal Protocol, which called for ending the production of all CFCs by industrialized nations by 1996 and for banning their use in developing countries by 2010. However, CFCs already in the atmosphere continue to damage the ozone layer.

free radical

an atom or molecule that has one or more unpaired electrons and is therefore very reactive

chain reaction

a self-sustaining nuclear or chemical reaction in which the product from one step acts as a reactant for the next step

VISUAL STRATEGY

Figure 12-9   Stress that the ozone layer's formation is the result of ultraviolet radiation interacting with molecular oxygen to form O_3. Within the stratosphere, the density of oxygen is high enough for ozone to form, with the highest concentration occurring about 25 km above Earth's surface.

CONSUMER FOCUS

One of the consequences of burning carbon fuels is that sulfur impurities are released into the atmosphere, producing SO_2, a gas responsible for acid rain. Because it reflects sunlight, SO_2 helps to cool the Earth's atmosphere and partially counteracts the greenhouse warming caused by CO_2. But this effect is not a solution to the problem posed by the greenhouse effect because it affects only regions of high industrialization, while the greenhouse effect occurs throughout the atmosphere. This results in a higher overall temperature in the Southern Hemisphere than in the Northern Hemisphere, and it could result in more violent storms or droughts.

ANSWERS

SECTION REVIEW

Total recall

1. The pressure exerted on a container by a gas results from the molecules of that gas colliding with the walls of the container.

2. The conversion factor that equates pascals to atmospheres is $1.013\,25 \times 10^5$ Pa/atm.

Critical thinking

3. Temperature is a measurement of the average kinetic energy of molecules in a sample. As the temperature rises, average kinetic energy increases.

4. Fossil fuels are materials that contain carbon. When they burn, CO_2 is emitted into the atmosphere. Additional CO_2 increases the greenhouse effect and contributes to global warming.

5. At 35°C, the average kinetic energy of the sample is higher than at 25°C. Therefore, fewer particles at 35°C have values on the lower end of the kinetic energy scale than at 25°C.

CONSUMER FOCUS

NON-CFC AIR CONDITIONING

internet**connect**

SC**LINKS**
NSTA

TOPIC: Non-CFCs
GO TO: www.scilinks.org
KEYWORD: HW123

A less toxic alternative

In keeping with the limits set for CFCs by the Montreal Protocol, car manufacturers have developed new air-conditioning systems that use a hydrofluorocarbon, 1,1,1,2-tetrafluoroethane, called HFC-134a, as the **refrigerant** instead of the traditional dichlorodifluoromethane, CFC-12.

HFC-134a is believed to have low toxicity and appears to have little effect on the ozone layer. However, the chemical differences between CFC-12 and HFC-134a result in some major problems for consumers.

New air-conditioning systems required

HFC-134a *cannot* be used in an air-conditioning system that was built specifically for CFC-12.

Conversion to HFC-134a requires a complete redesign of the existing air-conditioning system. Because non-CFC air conditioning is a new technology, consumers should have work performed only at reputable service stations by knowledgeable mechanics.

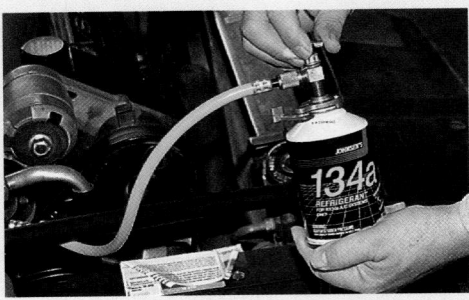

SECTION REVIEW

Total recall

1. What causes the pressure exerted by gas molecules on their container?

2. **Interpreting Tables** What is the conversion factor to change atmospheres to pascals?

Critical thinking

3. Describe the relationship between average molecular kinetic energy of gases and temperature.

4. Why are scientists concerned about burning fossil fuels?

5. **Interpreting Graphics** Notice that more molecules have a certain kinetic energy at 25° C than at 35° C at points on the graph in Figure 12-4, on page 426. Explain.

ALTERNATIVE ASSESSMENT

Group Strategy

Have students draw a representation of gas particles in a container. The drawings should show particles far apart relative to their diameters.

Ask students the following questions about the gas particles:

▶ In what sort of path do they travel? *(They travel in straight lines.)*

▶ Do they all move at the same speed? *(No, they travel at different speeds.)*

▶ When the temperature increases, what happens to the motion of the particles? *(Many of the particles move faster.)*

▶ What happens when they collide with the walls of the container? *(They bounce off at the same speed at which they collided.)*

▶ Why is it possible to compress a gas? *(Because the particles of a gas are far apart, they can be pushed closer together.)*

What behaviors are described by the gas laws?

OBJECTIVES

▶ **Relate** the ideal gas model to the observed behavior of real gases.

▶ **State** the following laws describing the behavior of gases: Boyle's law, Dalton's law, Charles's law, Avogadro's

law, Gay-Lussac's law, and Graham's law.

▶ **Use** these laws to solve problems.

▶ **Describe** the relationship between gas behavior and chemical formulas.

The gas laws

In Section 12-1 you learned how gases exert pressure. In this section you will study the mathematical relationships that relate the variables used to describe a gas under specific conditions. Each variable is represented by a symbol.

P = pressure exerted
by the particles

T = temperature in kelvins
of the particles

V = volume occupied
by the particles

n = number of moles
of the particles

The pressure and the volume of a gas are related

Recall from Section 12-1 that gases are highly compressible and exert pressure. The English scientist Robert Boyle studied the relationship between the volume and the pressure of a gas and published his results in 1662. He found that at constant temperature, all gases behave the same when compressed; that is, as increasing pressure is applied to a gas in a closed container, the volume of the gas decreases. Recall the diagram of the syringe in Figure 12-3. The volume of the syringe decreased as pressure was applied. **Table 12-2** shows pressure-volume data for an experiment similar to those performed by Boyle.

The data in Table 12-2 show that the volume is inversely proportional to the pressure. Graphing these data produces

TABLE 12-2 Pressure-Volume Data for a Gas at Constant Temperature

Pressure (kPa)	Volume (L)	PV (kPa·L)
100	0.500	50.0
150	0.334	50.1
200	0.250	50.0
250	0.200	50.0
300	0.167	50.1
350	0.142	49.7
400	0.125	50.0
450	0.111	50.0

GASES AND LIQUIDS 433

▶ How does a gas exert pressure? (A gas exerts pressure through the collision of its particles with the walls of its container.)

LESSON WARM-UP

Pressure-Volume Relationship
Repeat the demonstration of the syringe that was illustrated in Figure 12-3, on page 425, to show that when pressure increases, volume decreases. For an even more effective demonstration, obtain an ordinary T-handled cylindrical air pump like the kind used to inflate bicycle tires by hand. Pull the handle about three-fourths of the way up, and clamp the delivery hose shut with a C-clamp or a sturdy laboratory screw clamp. Demonstrate that the upward force on the piston increases as the handle is pushed down. Ask students what this increase indicates. *(It is evidence of an increase in pressure in the cylinder.)* Leave the pump set up, and let students feel the change in pressure for themselves during a free moment. Challenge students to explain why the pressure increases when the piston is pushed down. *(The decrease in volume causes an increase in gas pressure within the cylinder.)*

RESOURCE LINK

ChemFile Teaching Resources CD-ROM
Skills Review
Assign Basic Skills Worksheet 4: *Graphing* to review or reteach this skill.

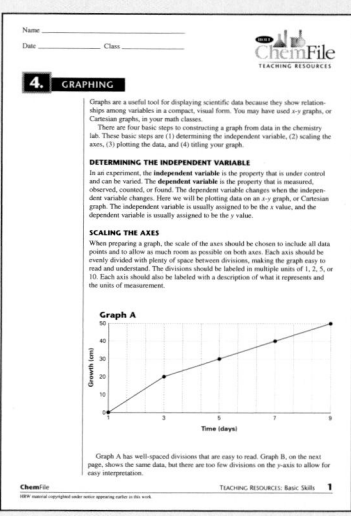

Figure 12-10 This illustration provides an example of an inverse relationship in which $V \propto 1/P$. When one variable goes up, the other goes down.

Figure 12-11 This illustration shows that the product of P and V remains constant over the range of pressures tested. Make students aware that the two graphs in Figures 12-10 and 12-11 provide the same information.

ChemFile Lab C
Skills Development
Have students do Exploration C10: *Gas Pressure–Volume Relationship.*

ChemFile Lab A
Skills Development
Have students do Experiment A8: *Boyle's Law.*

► **FIGURE 12-10**

The volume versus pressure graph represents an inverse relationship: as pressure increases, volume decreases.

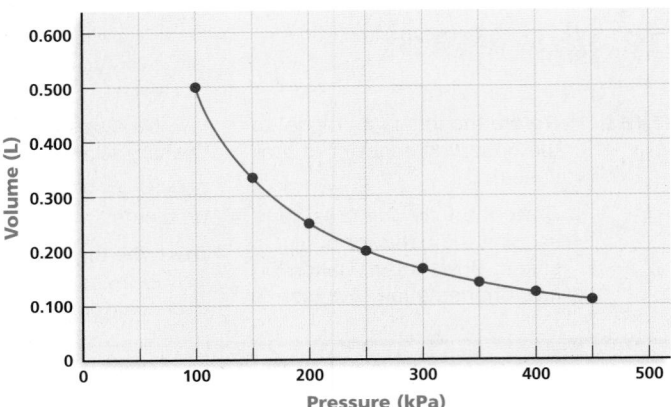

Volume vs. Pressure for a Fixed Amount of Gas at Constant Temperature

the curve shown in **Figure 12-10.** By examining the points along this curve, you can see that as the pressure of a gas increases, its volume decreases while keeping the temperature of the system constant. As the pressure of the gas decreases, its volume increases. Another way to consider the information in Table 12-2 is to plot the data in the product column, PV, against P, as in **Figure 12-11.** The horizontal line produced by the data points shows that the product of the pressure and the volume of a given sample of gas at constant temperature is a constant.

$$PV = k$$

► **FIGURE 12-11**

The product of the pressure and volume of a gas at constant temperature is a constant value.

PV vs. Pressure for a Fixed Amount of Gas at Constant Temperature

DEMONSTRATION 3

Volume Changes with a Vacuum Pump

Approximate time: 15 minutes

1. Gather the following objects to demonstrate how they are affected when air pressure is lowered around them by a vacuum pump: a balloon; shaving cream; marshmallows; jelly beans; and a piece of closed-cell plastic foam, such as the thin foam polyethylene sheets used as packing material.

2. Discuss with students what should happen to each object before it is placed in the bell jar or vacuum chamber.

3. If there is an open hole in the plate of the vacuum pump, invert a shallow container, such as half a Petri dish or a jar lid, over the hole to prevent foreign material from getting into the pump. Be sure the hole cover is

FIGURE 12-12 ▼

a Gas molecules in a car-engine cylinder expand to fill the cylinder.

b As the container volume decreases, the gas molecules move closer together, increasing their concentration and their pressure.

The relationship expressed by these data is known as **Boyle's law,** one of the oldest valid scientific laws in existence today. If the product, *PV*, is measured for a given amount of gas under one set of conditions, P_1V_1, and then under another set of conditions, P_2V_2, both products are found to be equal to the constant, *k*. Therefore, they are equal to each other. Using this information, Boyle's law can also be expressed as follows.

$$P_1V_1 = k$$
$$P_2V_2 = k$$
$$P_1V_1 = P_2V_2$$

How is this relationship explained by the kinetic-molecular theory? As mentioned in Section 12-1, gas pressure is caused by the collision of gas molecules with the walls of their container. If the volume is reduced by half, the gas concentration is doubled, and the number of collisions with the walls of the container is doubled, as shown in **Figure 12-12.** Therefore, the pressure is also doubled.

Boyle's law

the volume of a given amount of gas at constant temperature is inversely proportional to the pressure

SAMPLE PROBLEM 12A   Solving pressure-volume problems

The gas in a balloon has a volume of 7.5 L at 100 kPa. The balloon is released into the atmosphere, and the gas in it expands to a volume of 11 L. Assuming a constant temperature, what is the pressure on the balloon at the new volume?

1 **List what you know**
▶ $V_1 = 7.5$ L
▶ $P_1 = 100$ kPa
▶ $V_2 = 11$ L
▶ $P_2 = ?$ kPa

GASES AND LIQUIDS 435

SECTION 12-2

HISTORICAL CONNECTION

The English physicist James Clerk Maxwell (1831–1879) formulated the kinetic-molecular theory, which states that gases consist of a large number of randomly moving particles, in the 1860s. He and Ludwig Boltzmann (1844–1906) used the theory to derive Boyle's law mathematically.

VISUAL STRATEGY

Figure 12-12 Stress the kinetic explanation for increased pressure. Point out that the temperature of the particles has remained the same from Figure 12-12a to Figure 12-12b. Therefore, increased kinetic energy is not an explanation for increased pressure. The increased pressure is a result of the increased frequency of collisions with the wall of the container. Challenge students to explain why, if particles are in random motion, we do not detect variations in the pressure. *(The collisions are so numerous and so frequent that we experience only the average effect of them all.)*

RESOURCE LINK

ChemFile Teaching Resources CD-ROM
Skills Review
Assign Math Skills Worksheet 8: *Isolating Variables in Equations* to review or reteach this skill.

loose enough that it will not seal to the plate. The balloon is a good object to start with, followed by beakers containing the marshmallows and the shaving cream. The balloon and the marshmallows should expand quickly as the pressure is reduced. The shaving cream will expand almost to the top of the bell jar, and if the pressure is released slowly, it often goes completely back into the beaker. The plastic foam should also expand, and the jelly beans may or may not, depending on whether they contain trapped air.

Safety

Because of the possibility of the bell jar shattering at low pressures, all students must wear safety goggles. You must wear safety goggles and a lab apron. Students must be 10 ft or more from the demonstration. The use of a polycarbonate plastic vacuum chamber will greatly reduce the risk of shattering.

Disposal

Throw all tested materials in the trash.

ANSWERS

PRACTICE PROBLEM 12A

1. $P_2 = \dfrac{P_1V_1}{V_2}$

   $P_2 = \dfrac{(22.5 \text{ kPa})(155 \text{ cm}^3)}{90.0 \text{ cm}^3}$

   $P_2 = 38.8 \text{ kPa}$

2. $V_2 = \dfrac{P_1V_1}{P_2}$

   $V_2 = \dfrac{(0.500 \text{ atm})(300.0 \text{ mL})}{0.750 \text{ atm}}$

   $V_2 = 200. \text{ mL}$

3. $V_2 = \dfrac{P_1V_1}{P_2}$

   $V_2 = \dfrac{(101.3 \text{ kPa})(5.0 \text{ L})}{50.7 \text{ kPa}}$

   $V_2 = 10. \text{ L}$

4. $V_2 = \dfrac{P_1V_1}{P_2}$

   $V_2 = \dfrac{(0.947 \text{ atm})(150. \text{ mL})}{1.000 \text{ atm}}$

   $V_2 = 142 \text{ mL}$

SAMPLE PROBLEM 12A

ADDITIONAL EXAMPLES

a. A syringe has a sample of gas with a volume of 3.95 mL at a pressure of 1.00 atm. What is the pressure of the gas in the syringe if the volume is changed to 2.53 mL?

   Ans. 1.56 atm

b. A partially inflated weather balloon has a volume of 1.50×10^3 L at 98.8 kPa of pressure. What is the volume of the balloon when it is released to a height where the pressure is 44.1 kPa?

   Ans. 3.36×10^3 L

---

2 **Set up the problem**

▶ The volume of the gas has increased. Boyle's law predicts that the gas pressure will decrease.

$$P_1V_1 = P_2V_2$$
$$P_2 = \frac{P_1V_1}{V_2}$$

▶ Multiply the known pressure by the ratio of volumes that will result in a decrease in pressure.

$$P_2 = 100 \text{ kPa} \times \frac{7.5 \text{ L}}{11 \text{ L}}$$

3 **Calculate and verify**

$$P_2 = 100 \text{ kPa} \times \frac{7.5 \cancel{\text{ L}}}{11 \cancel{\text{ L}}} = 68 = 70 \text{ kPa (rounded to 1 significant figure)}$$

▶ The final pressure has decreased as predicted.

PRACTICE PROBLEMS

1. A flask contains 155 cm^3 of hydrogen collected at a pressure of 22.5 kPa. Under what pressure would the gas have a volume of 90.0 cm^3 at the same temperature? (Recall that 1 cm^3 = 1 mL.)

2. If the pressure exerted on a 300.0 mL sample of hydrogen gas at constant temperature is increased from 0.500 atm to 0.750 atm, what will be the final volume of the sample?

3. A helium balloon has a volume of 5.0 L at a pressure of 101.3 kPa. The balloon is released and reaches an altitude of 6.5 km at a pressure of 50.7 kPa. If the gas temperature remains the same, what is the new volume of the balloon? Assume that pressures are the same inside and outside the balloon.

4. A sample of oxygen gas has a volume of 150. mL at a pressure of 0.947 atm. What will the volume of the gas be at a pressure of 1.000 atm if the temperature remains constant?

---

partial pressure

the pressure of an individual gas in a gas mixture that contributes to the total pressure of the mixture

Dalton's law of partial pressures

the total pressure in a gas mixture is the sum of the partial pressures of the individual components, each behaving as if the other gases were absent

The total pressure of a mixture of gases can be calculated

Suppose you want to calculate the pressure of a mixture of gases rather than that of a single gas. An English chemist named John Dalton investigated the pressure exerted by a mixture of various gases on its container, and he presented his results in 1805. He found that in a mixture of gases, each gas exerts a pressure as if it were alone in the container. The pressure of a gas in a mixture is called the **partial pressure** of that gas. The total pressure of a mixture of gases is equal to the sum of the partial pressures of the individual gases. This statement is known as **Dalton's law of partial pressures.** Dalton's law is written as follows.

$$P_{total} = P_A + P_B + P_C$$

P_{total} is the total pressure of the mixture. P_A, P_B, and P_C are the partial pressures of the mixture's component gases, A, B, and C.

How is Dalton's law of partial pressures explained by the kinetic-molecular theory? All the gas molecules are moving about at random, and they have an equal chance to collide with the container wall. Each gas exerts a pressure on the container wall proportional to its number of molecules in the container. The presence of other gas molecules does not change this fact.

Another way to determine partial pressures

Dalton was not aware of the concept of moles. But because we are, we can use the **mole fraction** of a gas in a mixture to calculate the partial pressure of that gas. The mole fraction is the number of moles of a particular substance divided by the total number of moles in a mixture. If A, B, and C are the components of a gas mixture, then the mole fraction of gas A is represented mathematically as follows.

$$\text{mol fraction} = \frac{\text{mol A}}{\text{mol A} + B + C}$$

The air we breathe is a mixture of gases that contains 0.78 mole fraction of N_2, 0.21 mole fraction of O_2, and 0.01 mole fraction of argon, Ar. The mixture has a total pressure of 0.97 atm. What is the partial pressure of each gas in the mixture? The following equation shows that the partial pressure of a gas can be calculated by multiplying the total pressure of the system by the mole fraction of the specific gas. Accordingly, the partial pressure of nitrogen in this mixture of gases is 0.76 atm, and the partial pressures of oxygen and argon in the mixture are 0.20 atm and 0.01 atm, respectively.

$P_{total} = P_{nitrogen} + P_{oxygen} + P_{argon}$

$P_{total} = (0.97 \text{ atm} \times 0.78) + (0.97 \text{ atm} \times 0.21) + (0.97 \text{ atm} \times 0.01)$

$P_{total} = 0.76 \text{ atm} + 0.20 \text{ atm} + 0.01 \text{ atm} = 0.97 \text{ kPa}$

QUICKLAB

Pressure Relief

Pressure builds up in closed systems such as boiler tanks and pressure cookers. Relief valves allow the pressure to be released when it gets too high. In this activity, you will use pressure-volume relations to modify the balloon-in-a-bottle apparatus.

Materials round latex balloon, PET bottle, rubber band

Problem
1. Blow up the balloon and let the air out.
2. Put the round part of the balloon inside the bottle. Roll the neck of the balloon over the mouth of the bottle and secure the balloon with a rubber band.
3. Try to blow up the balloon. Record the results.
4. Answer items 1 and 2 below.
5. Design a modification to the balloon-in-a-bottle apparatus that will allow the balloon to inflate. Answer item 3 below.
6. If your teacher approves your design, try it out.

Analysis
1. What happens to air that is trapped in the bottle when you blow into the balloon?
2. What causes the balloon to expand? Why can you not blow up the balloon?
3. Describe your design modification, and include a sketch, if applicable. Explain, in terms of pressure, why your design works.

mole fraction
the number of moles of one component compared with the total number of moles in the mixture expressed as a ratio

TEACHING TIP

Partial Pressure Dalton's law may seem difficult and abstract to some students. Make the following analogy. Suppose you are given a box containing 2.00 kg of beans. Upon opening the box, you discover there are three kinds of beans mixed together. You can sort them into three piles and find the mass of each pile. The red beans have a mass of 0.85 kg; the pinto beans, 0.72 kg; and the white beans, 0.43 kg. Thus, the red beans contribute 42.5 % of the total mass; the pinto beans, 36.0 %; and the white beans, 21.5 %. Each kind of bean contributes its *partial mass* to the total mass.

QUICKLAB

This experiment works best if the bottle is much larger than the uninflated balloon.

Analysis

1. It is compressed by the inflating balloon.
2. The balloon expands because of the pressure of the air being blown into it. After the balloon expands slightly, the pressure of the air inside the bottle becomes large enough to match the person's ability to exert air pressure into the balloon.
3. Accept all plausible answers. Designs should incorporate a means for air to leave the bottle as the balloon is inflated. This could include a hole in the side or bottom or a tube that delivers air back up the neck, underneath the balloon.

TEACHING TIP

The Pressure of a Gas Ask students to list the factors that determine the pressure exerted by the randomly moving molecules of a gas. The pressure of an enclosed gas depends on two factors—the frequency of collisions and the average energy of the collisions. The energy of the collisions depends on temperature. At higher temperatures, particles move faster, so both the frequency and the average energy of the collisions are greater. At constant temperature, frequency of collisions is the only variable factor.

Charles's law

the volume of a sample of gas at constant pressure is directly proportional to the absolute temperature

RESOURCE LINK

ChemFile Lab C
Self-Directed Inquiry
Have students do Investigation C10: *Gas Temperature–Volume Relationship: Balloon Flight.*

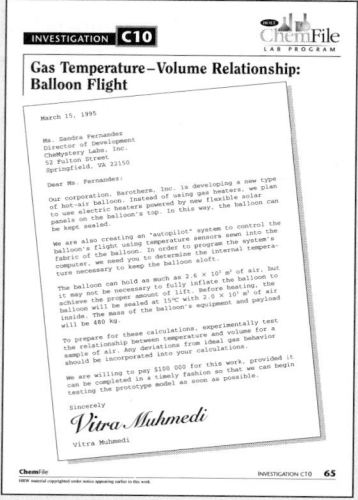

Atmospheric pressure changes with altitude

The mole fraction of oxygen in dry air at sea level is 0.21. Therefore, the oxygen partial pressure is close to 21 kPa. As the altitude increases, pressure decreases, but the composition of the air changes very little. This means that the partial pressure of oxygen also decreases with an increase in altitude. Consequently, as altitude increases, a person takes in less and less oxygen with each breath.

Gases expand greatly when heated and contract greatly when cooled

Heating a gas will make it expand. Gas molecules move faster when heat energy is added to them, causing them to strike with more force against the walls of their container. The more frequent and more forceful collisions make the volume of a yielding container, such as a balloon, increase. Likewise, gas volumes decrease greatly when the gas is cooled.

The volume change of a gas caused by a change of temperature at constant pressure is expressed by **Charles's law.** Jacques Charles discovered that the volume is directly proportional to the temperature on the Kelvin scale at constant pressure. In **Table 12-3,** each gas volume is divided by its corresponding temperature. At constant pressure, the volume of a given sample of gas divided by its absolute temperature is a constant, k. This relationship can be stated as the mathematical representation of Charles's law.

$$\frac{V}{T} = k$$

The ratio, V/T, for the same gas sample at any set of volume-temperature conditions (at constant pressure) will always equal the same constant, k. Therefore, Charles's law can also be expressed as follows.

$$\frac{V_1}{T_1} = \frac{V_2}{T_2}$$

TABLE 12-3 — Volume-Temperature Data for a Gas at a Constant Pressure

Volume (mL)	Temperature (K)	V/T (mL/K)
748	373	2.01
567	283	2.00
545	274	1.99
545	273	2.00
546	272	2.01
402	200	2.01
199	100	1.99

DEMONSTRATION 4

Amount of Oxygen in Air

Approximate time: 5 minutes for setup

1. Wet a tuft of fine steel wool, and push it into the bottom of a 100 mL or larger graduated cylinder. If the steel wool is oily, wash it with soap and water to remove the oil before putting it in the cylinder.

2. Invert the cylinder, and submerge the mouth in a beaker of water. Make sure that enough water is above the mouth of

the cylinder to fill one-fifth of its volume. Clamp the cylinder in place.

3. As the iron oxidizes, oxygen will be removed from the air. The water level will rise about one-fifth of the length of the cylinder, an amount equal to the volume occupied by the oxygen. The effect will reach completion by the next day.

Volume vs. Temperature for a Fixed Amount of Gas at Constant Pressure

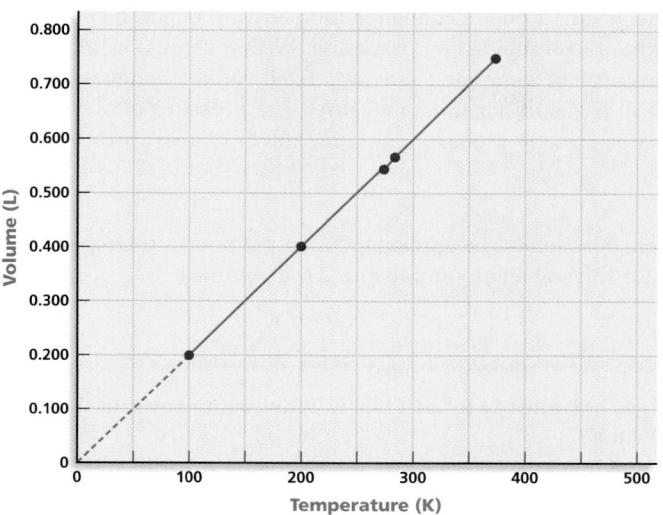

FIGURE 12-13 ◄

When kelvins are used on the temperature scale of the graph, the relationship between volume and temperature can be expressed as a direct proportion.

VISUAL STRATEGY

Figure 12-13 Students will see that if the line on the graph were extended, it would intersect with the (0, 0) point. Ask them to explain the significance of this point. *(The point represents the volume of the gas at 0 K, or absolute zero. Theoretically, the gas would have zero volume at 0 K, but in reality it would have solidified before reaching that point.)*

The volume-temperature data is graphed using the Kelvin scale in **Figure 12-13.** When the line produced in Figure 12-13 is extended to 0 K, the gas's volume becomes zero. Does a gas volume become zero at absolute zero? No. Before this temperature is reached, the gas condenses to a liquid and then freezes to a solid, which has a finite volume. Charles's law is illustrated in **Figure 12-14.**

FIGURE 12-14 ▼

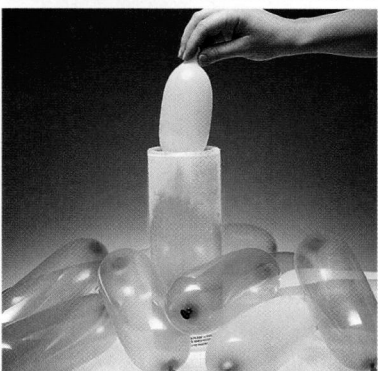

a Air-filled balloons are dipped into liquid nitrogen.

b The extremely low temperature of the nitrogen causes them to shrink in volume.

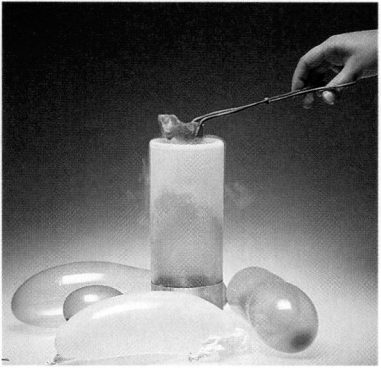

c When the balloons are removed from the liquid nitrogen, the air inside them quickly warms, and the balloons expand to their original volume.

GASES AND LIQUIDS 439

RESOURCE LINK

ChemFile Teaching Resources CD-ROM
Supplemental Reading Projects
For cross-curricular connections to language arts, assign the guided reading worksheets for Roald Hoffmann's essay "Static/Dynamic" in *The Same and Not the Same.*

4. On the following day, have students note the change in water level. Then test to see if there is any oxygen left in the tube. Place a small glass plate under the mouth of the cylinder while it is still submerged. Withdraw the cylinder, and immediately set it upright on the table with the plate still in place. Light a wooden splint, remove the cover from the cylinder, and quickly thrust the burning splint inside. The splint should go out immediately.

Safety

Safety goggles and a lab apron must be worn. Students must be 10 ft or more from the demonstration.

Disposal

Throw rusty iron into the trash.

440

HISTORICAL CONNECTION

The relationship $P/T = k$ at constant volume is called Gay-Lussac's law. Joseph Louis Gay-Lussac (1778–1850) was a French chemist and physicist who was interested in the properties of gases. He was also a pioneer in ballooning, reaching an altitude of 7000 m (4.35 mi). His law can also be stated as follows:

$$\frac{P_1}{T_1} = \frac{P_2}{T_2}$$

ANSWERS

PRACTICE PROBLEM 12B

1. $V_2 = \dfrac{T_2 V_1}{T_1}$

   $V_2 = \dfrac{(80.0 \text{ K})(2.5 \text{ L})}{300.0 \text{ K}}$

   $V_2 = 0.67 \text{ L}$

2. $P_2 = \dfrac{T_2 P_1}{T_1}$

   $P_2 = \dfrac{(325 \text{ K})(3.00 \text{ atm})}{298 \text{ K}}$

   $P_2 = 3.27 \text{ atm}$

SAMPLE PROBLEM 12B

ADDITIONAL EXAMPLES

a. A sample of gas has a volume of 852 mL at 189 K. What volume does the gas occupy at 293 K?

   Ans. 1320 mL

b. A sample of gas has a volume of 234.9 L at a temperature of 23°C. What temperature is necessary to have a volume of 200.0 L?

   Ans. 252 K, or –21°C

Gas pressure increases with an increase in temperature

You have seen that changes in temperature and pressure affect the volume of a gas. But how does a change in temperature affect the pressure of a gas when its volume is kept constant? With a change in temperature, the pressure of a sample of gas at a fixed volume behaves just as the volume of a gas at constant pressure. The pressure of a gas in a fixed volume is directly proportional to its kelvin temperature.

$$\frac{P}{T} = k$$

This relationship can also be applied to any set of pressure-temperature conditions for the same gas sample at a fixed volume.

SAMPLE PROBLEM 12B   Solving volume-temperature problems

A sample of gas occupies 24 m³ at 175.0 K. What volume would the gas occupy at 400.0 K?

1 **List what you know**

   ▸ $V_1 = 24 \text{ m}^3$ ▸ $T_2 = 400.0 \text{ K}$

   ▸ $T_1 = 175.0 \text{ K}$ ▸ $V_2 = ? \text{ m}^3$

2 **Set up the problem**

   ▸ The temperature of the gas is increased. Charles's law predicts that the gas volume will also increase.

   $$\frac{V_1}{T_1} = \frac{V_2}{T_2}; \text{ therefore } V_2 = \frac{V_1 T_2}{T_1}$$

   ▸ Multiply the known volume by the ratio of temperatures that will result in an increase in volume.

   $$V_2 = 24 \text{ m}^3 \times \frac{400.0 \text{ K}}{175.0 \text{ K}}$$

3 **Calculate and verify**

   $$V_2 = 24 \text{ m}^3 \times \frac{400.0 \text{ K}}{175.0 \text{ K}} = 55 \text{ m}^3$$

   ▸ The ratio of temperatures is greater than 1, which means the volume increases, as predicted.

PRACTICE PROBLEMS

1. Gas in a balloon occupies 2.5 L at 300.0 K. The balloon is dipped into liquid nitrogen that is at a temperature of 80.0 K. What volume will the gas in the balloon occupy at this temperature?

2. The gas in a sealed can is at a pressure of 3.00 atm at 25°C. A warning on the can tells the user not to store the can in a place where the temperature will exceed 52°C. What would the gas pressure in the can be at 52°C?

ALTERNATIVE ASSESSMENT

Group Strategy

Check students' conceptual understanding of the gas laws by asking them to determine the unknown quantity in each column without using a calculator. Students should determine the degree of change by inspection. Note that all changes are by factors of 2 or 1/2.

Condition 1	Sample 1	Sample 2	
Temperature	300 K	300 K	
Pressure	100 kPa	100 kPa	
Volume	200 mL	200 mL	
Condition 2			
Temperature	no change	no change	
Pressure	200 kPa	? kPa	
Volume	? mL	400 mL	

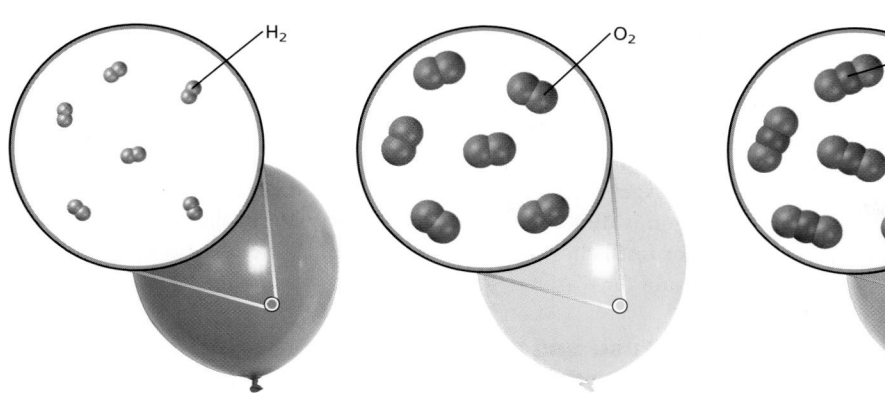
H_2 O_2 CO_2

Gas behavior and chemical formulas

Gases with equal volumes under the same conditions have an equal number of molecules

In 1811, the Italian physicist Amadeo Avogadro made a bold proposition. He proposed that equal volumes of different gases under the same conditions have the same number of molecules. This proposal is respresented in **Figure 12-15** and is known as **Avogadro's law.** Unfortunately, Avogadro's valuable insight was not recognized immediately, mainly because scientists at the time did not realize that there is a difference between atoms and molecules. In 1875, the Italian chemist Stanislao Cannizzaro made use of Avogadro's law to determine the true formulas of a number of gaseous chemical compounds.

Gases at constant temperature and pressure form compounds with each other in definite proportions

In 1808, the French scientist Joseph Gay-Lussac made an interesting discovery. If the pressure and temperature are kept constant, gases react in volume proportions that are whole numbers. This is called **Gay-Lussac's law of combining volumes.** For example, consider the formation of gaseous hydrogen chloride from the reaction of hydrogen gas and chlorine gas. One volume of hydrogen reacts with one volume of chlorine to form two volumes of hydrogen chloride. Let us use Avogadro's law and assume that two molecules of hydrogen chloride are formed, one in each of the two boxes on the right in **Figure 12-16.** Each HCl molecule must

Hydrogen gas	Chlorine gas	Hydrogen chloride gas
1 Volume	+ 1 Volume	→ 2 Volumes
1 Molecule	1 Molecule	2 Molecules

FIGURE 12-15 ▲

At the same temperature and pressure, balloons of equal volume contain equal numbers of molecules, regardless of which gas they contain.

Avogadro's law

equal volumes of different gases under the same conditions of temperature and pressure have the same number of molecules

Gay-Lussac's law of combining volumes

at constant temperature and pressure, gases react in volume proportions that are whole numbers (equivalent to the coefficients in the balanced chemical equation)

FIGURE 12-16 ◄

Hydrogen molecules combine with chlorine molecules in a 1:1 volume ratio to produce twice the volume of hydrogen chloride.

VISUAL STRATEGY

Figure 12-15 Use this diagram to remind students that both mass and velocity are factors in kinetic energy. Ask students how the average kinetic energy of the gases—H_2, O_2, and CO_2— in the three balloons varies. *(They are equal.)* Then ask how the motions of the molecules differ. *(The H_2 molecules, the lightest molecules, must be moving the fastest, and the CO_2 molecules, the heaviest molecules, must be moving the slowest.)* Only if this is true can three gases at the same temperature and pressure occupy the same volume. This is an example of the reasoning that Maxwell used in formulating the kinetic-molecular theory.

HISTORICAL CONNECTION

Comstock's Chemistry, an American chemistry textbook published in 1831, refers to water as the "protoxide of hydrogen" and suggests the formula HO.

RESOURCE LINK

ChemFile Lab C
Skills Development
Have students do Exploration C11: *Masses of Equal Volumes of Gases.*

GASES AND LIQUIDS   **441**

Sample 3	Sample 4	Sample 5	Sample 6
300 K	400 K	300 K	300 K
? kPa	100 kPa	100 kPa	100 kPa
400 mL	600 mL	400 mL	200 mL
no change	200 K	? K	150 K
200 kPa	no change	no change	? kPa
200 mL	? mL	200 mL	no change

Strictly speaking, Graham's law of effusion applies only to gases effusing into a vacuum. Experiments that show the diffusion of HCl(g) and NH$_3$(g) through air to form a cloud of NH$_4$Cl(s) do not demonstrate Graham's law. However, because both gases are diffusing through the same air, their relative rates of diffusion reflect the relative velocities predicted by the law.

COMMON MISCONCEPTION

It is unlikely that students have ever seen a demonstration of true effusion. Effusion requires that a gas effuse into a vacuum or that two gases effuse into each other with no other molecules present. Allowing air to rush through a small hole into a vacuum chamber is a reasonably accurate demonstration of effusion, and it will give students an idea of the velocities of molecules.

contain at least one atom of hydrogen and one atom of chlorine, as shown. Therefore, we need two atoms of hydrogen and two atoms of chlorine as starting materials. With one molecule of hydrogen and one molecule of chlorine, each of the molecules must be diatomic.

Using other reactions, such as the reaction of gaseous hydrogen and gaseous oxygen to form water vapor, Cannizarro was able to deduce that oxygen is diatomic and that the correct formula for water is H$_2$O. It was not until the time of the Civil War that chemists knew the correct formula for water.

Gases effuse and diffuse rapidly

effusion
the motion of a gas through a small opening

The passage of a gas through a small opening, called **effusion**, is illustrated in **Figure 12-17.** Effusion occurs, for example, when there is a small leak in a tire: the air in the tire effuses through the hole. The Scottish scientist Thomas Graham studied this gas behavior in detail. He found that at constant temperature and pressure, the rate of effusion of a gas is inversely proportional to the square root of its density; in other words, it is inversely proportional to the square root of its molar mass, M. This is stated mathematically when comparing the speed of effusion, v, of two gases, A and B.

$$\frac{v_A}{v_B} = \sqrt{\frac{M_B}{M_A}}$$

For example, compare the speed of effusion of H$_2$ with that of O$_2$.

$$\frac{v_{H_2}}{v_{O_2}} = \sqrt{\frac{M_{O_2}}{M_{H_2}}} = \sqrt{\frac{32 \text{ g/mol}}{2 \text{ g/mol}}} = \sqrt{16} = 4$$

The answer of 4 means that hydrogen gas effuses through a small opening four times as fast as oxygen. Molecules of low molar mass travel

O$_2$ N$_2$

▶ **FIGURE 12-17**

Molecules of nitrogen and oxygen from the air inside the bicycle tire effuse out through a small nail hole.

ALTERNATIVE ASSESSMENT

Group Strategy

Ask students to explain why a more massive object has greater kinetic energy than a less massive object when both are traveling at the same velocity. Ask them for examples that show the effect of an object of small mass moving at a high velocity and the effect of a massive object moving at a slow velocity. Smaller objects at high velocity could include bullets, BBs, pebbles launched from a slingshot, a baseball, and grains of sand in a sand-blaster. Massive objects at slow velocity could include a bowling ball, a car rolling slowly, a boulder rolling across a highway after falling from a cliff, and a log used as a battering ram.

faster on average than heavy molecules. Hydrogen, with the lowest molar mass, travels the fastest of any atom or molecule.

Graham's law of effusion is explained by the kinetic-molecular theory. At the same temperature, the average kinetic energy of all gases is the same. We can write the following relationship to compare the kinetic energies for molar quantities of two gases, A and B.

$$\tfrac{1}{2}M_A v_A^2 = \tfrac{1}{2}M_B v_B^2$$

The rate of effusion is proportional to the speed of the molecules because their speed determines the rate at which they hit the opening. Solving the equation on the previous page for the ratio of speeds gives the ratios of the rates of effusion.

$$\frac{v_A}{v_B} = \sqrt{\frac{M_B}{M_A}}$$

When you open a bottle of household ammonia, it doesn't take long for the odor of ammonia gas, NH_3, to fill the room. Gaseous molecules of the compounds responsible for the smell are traveling at high speeds in all directions and are mixing quickly with molecules of other gases in the air in a process called **diffusion.** Gases diffuse through each other at a very rapid rate. During diffusion a substance moves from a region of high concentration to a region of low concentration. Eventually, the mixture becomes homogeneous, as seen in the bottle of bromine gas in **Figure 12-18.**

Evaporated $Br_2(g)$ molecule diffusing into air

$O_2(g)$ molecule

$N_2(g)$ molecule

FIGURE 12-18 ◀

Gaseous bromine diffuses into the air above the surface of liquid bromine.

Graham's law of effusion

the rates of effusion for two gases are inversely proportional to the square roots of their molar masses at the same temperature and pressure

diffusion

the process by which particles mix by dispersing from regions of higher concentration to regions of lower concentration

TEACHING TIP

Graham's Law of Effusion
Mention that it is permissible to square both sides of Graham's equation to remove the square root and simplify calculations.

SAMPLE PROBLEM 12C

ADDITIONAL EXAMPLES

a. The average velocity of ammonia, NH_3, molecules at room temperature is 658 m/s. How fast would hydrogen sulfide, H_2S, molecules travel on average under the same conditions?

Ans. 465 m/s

b. The average velocity of CO_2 molecules at room temperature is 409 m/s. What is the molar mass of a gas whose molecules have an average velocity of 322 m/s under the same conditions?

Ans. 71.0 g/mol

RESOURCE LINK

ChemFile *Mini-Guide to Problem Solving*
Assign Chapter 11: *Gas Laws* for additional practice.

SAMPLE PROBLEM 12C **Comparing molecular speeds**

Oxygen molecules have an average speed of about 480 m/s at room temperature. On average, how fast are molecules of sulfur trioxide, SO_3, traveling at the same temperature?

1 **List what you know**

▸ v_{O_2} = 480 m/s
▸ v_{SO_3} = ? m/s

2 **Set up the problem**

▸ To use the equation for Graham's law, you need the molar masses of O_2 and SO_3. Calculate the molar mass of O_2 and SO_3.

mass of 2 mol O = 2(16.00 g)   mass of 1 mol S = 32.07 g
M_{O_2} = 32.00 g/mol   mass of 3 mol O = 3(16.00 g)
                                        M_{SO_3} = 80.07 g/mol

GASES AND LIQUIDS 443

CHEMISTRY TUTOR

Module 6: Gas Laws
Topic: Behavior of Gases
This engaging tutorial reviews and reinforces the behavior of gases through modeling and guided practice.

ANSWERS

SECTION REVIEW

Total recall

1. The concentration doubles.

2. The atmospheric pressure would be less in Denver than at sea level.

Critical thinking

3. CO_2 would be preferable because its molar mass is greatest, so the average velocity of CO_2 molecules would be lowest. Therefore, CO_2 would leak through a small puncture or crack more slowly than the other two would.

4. Helium atoms are much smaller than the molecules of any gas found in air, and their average velocity is also higher than molecules in the air at the same temperature.

Practice problems

5. $V_2 = \dfrac{P_1 V_1}{P_2}$

$V_2 = \dfrac{(101\,325\text{ Pa})(30.0\text{ m}^3)}{2.87 \times 10^2\text{ Pa}}$

$V_2 = 1.06 \times 10^4\text{ m}^3$

6. $v_{SO_2} = v_{Cl_2}\sqrt{\dfrac{M_{Cl_2}}{M_{SO_2}}}$

$v_{SO_2} = 0.380\text{ km/s}\sqrt{\dfrac{70.90\text{ g/mol}}{64.07\text{ g/mol}}}$

$v_{SO_2} = 0.400\text{ km/s}$

7. $v_{C_4H_{10}} = v_{Ne}\sqrt{\dfrac{M_{Ne}}{M_{C_4H_{10}}}}$

$v_{C_4H_{10}} = 800.\text{ m/s}\sqrt{\dfrac{20.18\text{ g/mol}}{58.14\text{ g/mol}}}$

$v_{C_4H_{10}} = 471\text{ m/s}$

▶ Use the equation for Graham's law, and solve for v_{SO_3}.

$$\dfrac{v_{SO_3}}{v_{O_2}} = \sqrt{\dfrac{M_{O_2}}{M_{SO_3}}} \qquad\qquad v_{SO_3} = v_{O_2}\sqrt{\dfrac{M_{O_2}}{M_{SO_3}}}$$

3 **Calculate and verify**

$$v_{SO_3} = 480\text{ m/s}\sqrt{\dfrac{32.00\text{ g/mol}}{80.07\text{ g/mol}}} = 3.0 \times 10^2\text{ m/s}$$

▶ SO_3 is heavier, so its speed is slower than that of oxygen.

SECTION REVIEW

Total recall

1. If the volume of a gas is reduced by half, what happens to the concentration of the gas?

2. In Denver, would the atmospheric pressure be greater or less than the atmospheric pressure at sea level?

Critical thinking

3. Using the ideas of the kinetic-molecular theory, which of the following gases is best for filling automobile tires: CO_2, N_2, or He? Explain your choice.

4. Inexpensive balloons filled with air deflate within a few days because the pores in the walls of these balloons are larger than most of the molecules that are found in air. Explain why helium-filled balloons collapse faster than those filled with air.

Practice problems

5. **Story Clue** At 40 km above Earth, the pressure is about 2.87×10^2 Pa. A helium balloon launched from Earth's surface at 1.000 atm of pressure has a volume of 30.0 m³. What will be the volume of the balloon at 40 km? Assume that the temperature of the He stays constant.

6. At a certain temperature, molecules of chlorine gas travel at 0.380 km/s. What is the speed of sulfur dioxide gas molecules under the same conditions?

7. Given that atoms of neon gas effuse at 800. m/s at a given temperature, calculate the rate of effusion for molecules of butane gas, C_4H_{10}, at the same temperature.

8. The average speed of helium atoms is 1.20×10^3 m/s at a certain temperature. What is the average speed of HCl molecules at the same temperature?

9. Compare the rate of effusion of molecules of water vapor with that of molecules of carbon dioxide gas at the same pressure and temperature.

10. Hydrogen sulfide, H_2S, has a very strong rotten-egg odor. Methyl salicylate, $C_8H_{10}O_3$, has a wintergreen odor. Benzaldehyde, C_7H_6O, has an almond odor. If vapors for these three substances were released at the same time from across the room, which would you smell first? Why?

8. $v_{HCl} = v_{He}\sqrt{\dfrac{M_{He}}{M_{HCl}}}$

$v_{HCl} = 1.20 \times 10^3\text{ m/s}\sqrt{\dfrac{4.00\text{ g/mol}}{36.46\text{ g/mol}}}$

$v_{HCl} = 397\text{ m/s}$

9. $\dfrac{v_{H_2O}}{v_{CO_2}} = \sqrt{\dfrac{M_{CO_2}}{M_{H_2O}}} = \sqrt{\dfrac{44.01\text{ g/mol}}{18.02\text{ g/mol}}} = 1.56$

Molecules of water vapor effuse at 1.56 times the rate of carbon dioxide molecules.

10. $M_{H_2S} = (2 \times 1.01\text{ g/mol}) + 32.07\text{ g/mol} = 34.09\text{ g/mol}$
$M_{C_7H_6O} = (7 \times 12.01\text{ g/mol}) + (6 \times 1.01\text{ g/mol}) + 16.00\text{ g/mol} = 106.13\text{ g/mol}$
$M_{C_8H_{10}O_3} = (8 \times 12.01\text{ g/mol}) + (10 \times 1.01\text{ g/mol}) + (3 \times 16.00\text{ g/mol}) = 154.18\text{ g/mol}$

H_2S is the lightest molecule, so you would smell it first.

ELEMENT SPOTLIGHT

N 7
Nitrogen
14.0067
[He]2s²2p³

Nitrogen is a colorless, odorless, and tasteless gas that makes up about four-fifths of the atmosphere.

WHERE IS IT?

Earth's Crust
<0.01% by mass

Air
75% by mass

Sea Water
0.0016% by mass

SCiLINKS
NSTA

TOPIC: Nitrogen
GO TO: www.scilinks.org
KEYWORD: HW124

Nitrogen cycle

Nitrogen gas is the most abundant gas in the atmosphere. Nitrogen is important for photosynthesis and for making the proteins, nucleic acids, vitamins, enzymes, and hormones needed by plants and animals to live. Unfortunately, plants and animals cannot directly use nitrogen gas. The nitrogen must be converted into forms they can use.

Nitrogen-fixing bacteria convert atmospheric nitrogen into substances that green plants absorb from the soil. Animals then eat these plants or eat other animals that feed on these plants. When the animals and plants die and decay, the nitrogen in the decomposed organic matter returns to the atmosphere and the soil. With the return of nitrogen to the soil as ammonium salts, the nitrogen cycle starts all over again.

Nitrogen-fixing bacteria can convert atmospheric nitrogen into chemical compounds, such as ammonia, that can be used by green plants in the formation of proteins.

Industrial Uses

▶ Nitrogen is used in the synthesis of ammonia.

▶ Ammonia is used to produce fertilizer, explosives, nitric acid, urea, hydrazine, and amines.

▶ Liquid nitrogen is used in superconductor research and as a cryogenic supercoolant for storing biological tissues.

▶ Nitrogen gas is used as an inert atmosphere for storing and processing reactive substances.

▶ Nitrogen gas, usually mixed with argon, is used for filling incandescent light bulbs.

ELEMENT SPOTLIGHT

Daniel Rutherford discovered nitrogen in 1772. From 1774 to 1777, Antoine Lavoisier researched nitrogen, and he determined that it is an element. This element accounts for 78% of the air; an estimated 4000 trillion tons of nitrogen is contained in Earth's atmosphere. Lavoisier called nitrogen *azote,* which means "without life," because it is so inert. The compounds of nitrogen, however, are so active that they are essential in the production of foods, poisons, fertilizers, and explosives.

Elemental nitrogen has several industrial applications. The largest consumer of nitrogen gas is the ammonia industry. Nitrogen gas is used in the electronics industry as an inert blanketing agent during the production of sensitive components as well as in the pharmaceutical industry for the synthesis of many drugs. Liquid nitrogen is used both as a refrigerant in the transportation of food products and as a coolant in superconductor research.

A BRIEF HISTORY

1774–1777: Antoine Lavoisier determines that nitrogen is an element.

1200   1700   1800   1900

1772: Nitrogen is discovered by Daniel Rutherford in Scotland, Joseph Priestley and Henry Cavendish in England, and Carl Scheele in Sweden.

1909: Fritz Haber, a German chemist, discovers a method for synthesizing ammonia from hydrogen gas and nitrogen gas. The method is still used today and is called the Haber-Bosch process.

SECTION 12-3

How do the gas laws fit together?

OBJECTIVES ▶ **Use** the ideal gas law and combined gas law to solve mathematical problems.

▶ **Apply** your knowledge of reaction stoichiometry to solve gas stoichiometry problems.

LESSON WARM-UP

The Ideal Gas Law The ideal gas law introduces the new variable n, which represents the number of molecules or the amount of gas in moles. Have students study the equation and conclude what will happen to P when n is increased while V and T are held constant. After they conclude that P increases, ask them to offer explanations for why it increases. The introduction of more molecules in the same space (such as by pumping more gas into an already inflated tire) results in a proportionate increase in collisions per unit time. Ask students to conclude what will happen to V as n increases and P and T are held constant. *(It will increase.)*

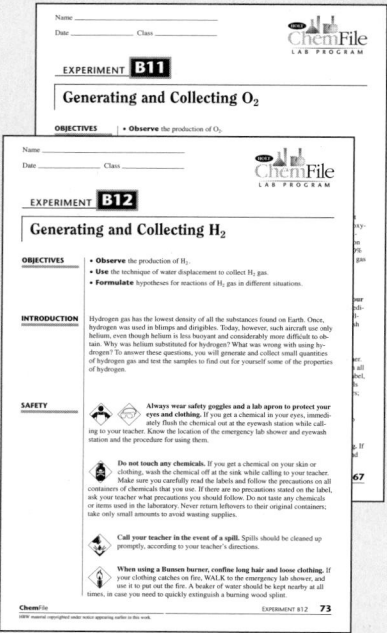

ideal gas law

the equation of state for an ideal gas in which the product of the pressure and volume is proportional to the product of the absolute temperature and the amount of gas expressed in moles

▼ **FIGURE 12-19**

Balloonists use the gas laws to predict the conditions of their flight.

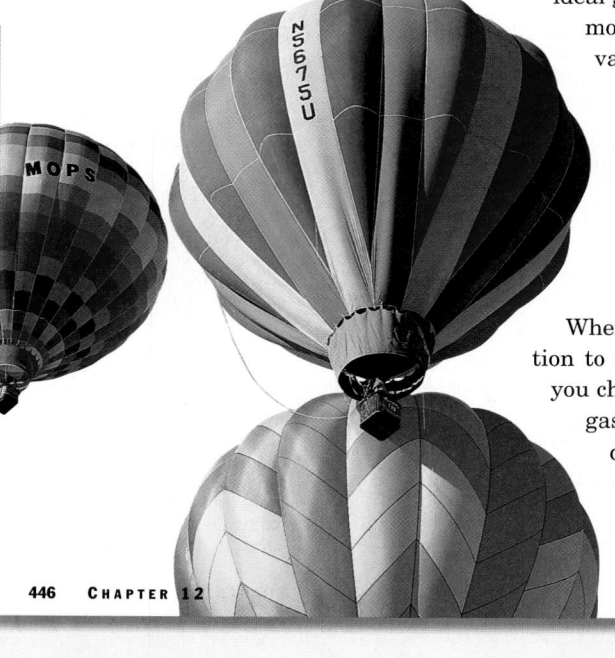

Putting it together: the ideal gas law
The ideal gas law relates all four gas variables

Boyle's law, Charles's law, and Avogadro's law can be combined into one equation that gives the relationships between P, V, T, and n for any sample of gas. This relationship is called the **ideal gas law.** When any three variables are given, the fourth can be calculated. The ideal gas law is frequently used when the pressure, volume, and temperature do not change. The ideal gas law is represented mathematically as follows.

$$PV = nRT$$

R is a proportionality constant, and the value used depends on the units for pressure and volume. The amount n is always expressed in moles, and the temperature is always in kelvins. A temperature in degrees Celsius must be converted to the Kelvin scale before the ideal gas law can be used. In this text we will almost always use kilopascals and liters, so the value you will use for R is as follows.

$$R = \frac{8.314 \text{ L} \cdot \text{kPa}}{\text{mol} \cdot \text{K}}$$

If the gas law problem gives pressure data in atmospheres, R can also be expressed as follows.

$$R = \frac{0.0821 \text{ L} \cdot \text{atm}}{\text{mol} \cdot \text{K}}$$

When using the ideal gas law, pay close attention to the units of pressure and volume so that you choose the correct value for R. Use the ideal gas law when you know three of the variables describing the gaseous state (P, V, n, T) and you wish to calculate the fourth. Sample Problem 12D shows this type of problem.

SAMPLE PROBLEM 12D   Using the ideal gas law

A sample of carbon dioxide with a mass of 0.250 g is placed in a 350.0 mL container at 400.0 K. What is the pressure exerted by the gas?

1 List what you know

▶ There is no change of conditions for the gas, so this is a straightforward ideal gas law problem.
▶ mass of CO_2 = 0.250 g
▶ P = ? kPa
▶ V = 350.0 mL
▶ T = 400.0 K
▶ n = ? mol
▶ R = 8.314 L•kPa/mol•K

2 Set up the problem

▶ The molar mass of CO_2 must be calculated.

$$\text{molar mass of } CO_2 = 44.01 \text{ g/mol}$$

▶ The mass of CO_2 in grams must be converted into moles.

$$\text{mol } CO_2 = \frac{0.250 \text{ g } CO_2}{44.01 \text{ g/mol } CO_2} = 5.68 \times 10^{-3} \text{ mol } CO_2$$

▶ The volume unit must be compatible with the value of R used; therefore, the volume must be converted from milliliters to liters.

$$\frac{1 \text{ L}}{1000 \text{ mL}} \times 350.0 \text{ mL} = 0.3500 \text{ L}$$

▶ Use the ideal gas law to find the fourth variable, pressure.

$$PV = nRT$$
$$P = \frac{nRT}{V}$$

3 Calculate

▶ Substitute the values given in the problem into the equation.

$$P = \frac{(5.68 \times 10^{-3} \text{ mol})(8.314 \text{ L•kPa/mol•K})(400.0 \text{ K})}{(0.3500 \text{ L})}$$
$$P = 54.0 \text{ kPa}$$

PRACTICE PROBLEMS

1. A 500. g block of dry ice (solid CO_2) becomes a gas at room temperature. Calculate the volume of gas produced at 25°C and 975 kPa.

2. Calculate the volume of 1.00 mol of CO_2 gas at STP.

3. The average lung capacity of humans is about 4.0 L. Assuming you are breathing pure oxygen, how many moles of oxygen gas can your lungs hold at 37°C (body temperature) and 110 kPa?

4. What mass in grams of chlorine gas, Cl_2, is contained in a 10.0 L tank at 27°C and 3.50 atm of pressure? (Assume that all Cl_2 in the tank is in gaseous form.)

GASES AND LIQUIDS   447

ANSWERS

PRACTICE PROBLEM 12D

1. $500. \text{ g } CO_2 \times \dfrac{1 \text{ mol } CO_2}{44.01 \text{ g } CO_2} =$
   11.36 mol CO_2

$$V = \frac{nRT}{P}$$
$$V =$$
$$\frac{(11.36 \text{ mol } CO_2)\left(8.314\dfrac{\text{L•kPa}}{\text{mol•K}}\right)(298 \text{ K})}{975 \text{ kPa}}$$
$$V = 28.9 \text{ L } CO_2$$

2. $V = \dfrac{nRT}{P}$
$$V =$$
$$\frac{(1.00 \text{ mol } CO_2)\left(8.314\dfrac{\text{L•kPa}}{\text{mol•K}}\right)(273 \text{ K})}{101.325 \text{ kPa}}$$
$$V = 22.4 \text{ L } CO_2$$

3. $n = \dfrac{PV}{RT}$
$$n = \frac{(110 \text{ kPa})(4.0 \text{ L})}{\left(8.314\dfrac{\text{L•kPa}}{\text{mol•K}}\right)(310 \text{ K})}$$
$$n = 0.17 \text{ mol } O_2$$

4. $n = \dfrac{PV}{RT}$
$$n = \frac{(3.50 \text{ atm})(10.0 \text{ L})}{\left(0.0821\dfrac{\text{L•atm}}{\text{mol•K}}\right)(300 \text{ K})}$$
$$n = 1.421 \text{ mol } Cl_2$$
$$1.421 \text{ mol } Cl_2 \times \frac{70.90 \text{ g } Cl_2}{1 \text{ mol } Cl_2} =$$
$$101 \text{ g } Cl_2$$

SAMPLE PROBLEM 12D

ADDITIONAL EXAMPLES

a. How many moles of gas are in a balloon that has a volume of 15.9 L at a pressure of 149 kPa and a temperature of 28°C?

Ans. 0.946 mol

b. What mass of ammonia, NH_3, is required to fill a 14.88 L bottle to a pressure of 199 kPa at 25°C?

Ans. 20.4 g NH_3

TEACHING TIP

The Combined Gas Law   Point out that the ideal gas law can be manipulated into Boyle's, Gay-Lussac's, or Charles's laws by converting it to the combined gas law, as shown on this page, and then omitting the variable (*P, V,* or *T*) that remains constant in those equations. Many students will appreciate this tip because they will no longer have to remember four different equations. The combined gas law is the one chemists use most often when converting real laboratory data to standard conditions.

RESOURCE LINK

ChemFile *Mini-Guide to Problem Solving*
Assign Chapter 12: *The Ideal Gas Law* for additional practice.

ChemFile *Mini-Guide to Problem Solving*
Assign Chapter 13: *Stoichiometry of Gases* for additional practice.

CHAPTER 12
The Ideal Gas Law

In 1811, the Italian chemist Amedeo Avogadro proposed the principle that *equal volumes of gases at the same temperature and pressure contain equal numbers of molecules.* He determined that at standard temperature and pressure, one mole of gas occupies 22.414 10 L (usually rounded to 22.4 L).

CHAPTER 13
Stoichiometry of Gases

Now that you have worked with relationships among moles, mass, and volumes of gases, you can easily put these to work in stoichiometry calculations. Many reactions have gaseous reactants, gaseous products, or both.

Reactants and products that are not gases are usually measured in grams or kilograms. As you know, you must convert these masses to amounts in moles before you can relate the quantities by using a balanced chemical equation. Gaseous products and reactants can be related to solid or liquid products and reactants by using the mole ratio, just as solids and liquids are related to each other.

Reactants and products that are gases are usually measured in liters. If the gas is measured at STP, you will need only Avogadro's law to relate the volume and amount of a gas. One mole of any gas at STP occupies 22.4 L. If the gas is not at STP, you will need to use the ideal gas law to determine the number of moles. Once volume has been converted to amount in moles you can use the mole ratios of products and reactants to solve stoichiometry problems involving multiple phases of products and reactants.

$$n = \frac{PV}{RT}$$

If the problem which you are trying to solve involves only gases, there is a simpler way of dealing with the stoichiometric amounts. Look again at the expression for the ideal gas law above; the molar amount of a gas is directly related to its volume. Therefore, the mole ratios of gases given by the coefficients in the balanced equation can be used as volume ratios of those gases to solve stoichiometry problems. No conversion from volume to amount is required to determine the volume of one gas from the volume of another gas in a balanced chemical equation.

There is one condition that must be observed. Gas volumes can be related by mole ratios only when the volumes are measured under the same conditions of temperature and pressure. If they are not, then the volume of one of the gases must be converted to the conditions of the other gas. Usually you will need to use the combined gas law for this conversion.

$$V_2 = \frac{V_1 P_1 T_2}{T_1 P_2}$$

150   Chapter 13

The combined gas law is derived from the ideal gas law

In many problems the quantity of gas does not change; that is, the number of moles remains constant. We merely change a given quantity of gas from one set of pressure, volume, and temperature conditions to another set. We can easily derive a general gas law for this circumstance by rearranging the ideal gas law.

$$R = \frac{P_1 V_1}{n_1 T_1} = \frac{P_2 V_2}{n_2 T_2}$$

combined gas law

the gas law for a given quantity of gas that is changed from one set of P, V, or T conditions to another

If the amount of gas, *n,* does not change, *n* can be canceled out of both expressions. The remaining two expressions are equal to each other because they are both equal to the product *nR.* The following relationship is often referred to as the **combined gas law,** or *general gas law.* In calculations you must make sure that the units for each variable are the same on each side of the equation.

$$\frac{P_1 V_1}{T_1} = \frac{P_2 V_2}{T_2} \quad \text{or} \quad \frac{PV}{T} = k$$

SAMPLE PROBLEM 12E   Using the combined gas law

A weather balloon containing helium with a volume of 410.0 L rises in the atmosphere and is cooled from 27°C to –27°C. The pressure on the gas is reduced from 110.0 kPa to 25.0 kPa. What is the volume of the gas at the lower temperature and pressure?

1   List what you know

- P_1 = 110.0 kPa
- V_1 = 410.0 L
- T_1 = 27°C + 273 = 300. K

- P_2 = 25.0 kPa
- V_2 = ? L
- T_2 = –27°C + 273 = 246 K

2   Set up the problem

- Because conditions change but the amount of gas does not change, use the combined gas law equation and solve for the new volume.
- In this problem the temperature change will cause the volume to decrease, and the pressure change will cause the volume to increase. Keep this in mind as you set up the problem and calculate your answer.

$$\frac{P_1 V_1}{T_1} = \frac{P_2 V_2}{T_2} \qquad V_2 = \frac{V_1 T_2 P_1}{T_1 P_2}$$

3   Calculate and verify

- Substitute the values given into the equation.

$$V_2 = 410.0 \text{ L} \times \frac{246 \text{ K}}{300. \text{ K}} \times \frac{110.0 \text{ kPa}}{25.0 \text{ kPa}}$$

$$V_2 = 1.48 \times 10^3 \text{ L}$$

- The pressure ratio is much larger than the temperature ratio, so the pressure reduction will have a greater effect on the volume than the decrease in temperature. The new volume will be larger than 410 L.

PRACTICE PROBLEMS

1. A gas occupies 2.0 m³ at 100.0 K, exerting a pressure of 100.0 kPa. What volume will the gas occupy at 400.0 K if the pressure is increased to 200.0 kPa?

2. An 8.00 L sample of neon gas at a temperature of 23°C exerts a pressure of 900.0 kPa. If the gas is compressed to 2.00 L and the temperature is raised to 225°C, what will the new pressure be?

3. A sample of methane gas that initially occupies 850.0 mL at 500.0 Pa and 500.0 K is compressed to a volume of 700.0 mL. To what temperature will the gas need to be cooled to lower the pressure of the gas to 200.0 Pa?

4. A sample of carbon dioxide gas occupies 45 m³ at 750 K and 500. kPa. What is the volume of this gas at STP?

Gas stoichiometry

Gas volumes can be determined from mole ratios in balanced equations

Avogadro's law allows us to interpret equations representing reactions of gases in terms of volumes as well as moles. His work showed us that the mole ratio of two gases at the same temperature and pressure is the same as the volume ratio. This relationship greatly simplifies the calculation of the volume of product or reactant in a chemical reaction involving gaseous reactants and products. For example, consider the following equation for the production of ammonia.

$$3H_2(g) + N_2(g) \longrightarrow 2NH_3(g)$$

Equal volumes of gases contain equal numbers of molecules at the same temperature and pressure. Therefore, 3 L of hydrogen will contain three times as many molecules as 1 L of nitrogen, and 2 L of ammonia will contain twice as many molecules as 1 L. Consequently, 3 L of H_2 will react with 1 L of N_2 to form 2 L of NH_3, and no H_2 or N_2 will be left over. Equations give ratios of moles; they also give ratios of volumes of gases.

We can ask the following question: How many liters of H_2 are needed to react completely with 22 L of N_2? By using the coefficients from the balanced equation, we arrive at the following conversion factor.

$$\frac{3 \text{ L } H_2}{1 \text{ L } N_2}$$

Therefore, the solution to the problem is as follows.

$$22 \text{ L } N_2 \times \frac{3 \text{ L } H_2}{1 \text{ L } N_2} = 66 \text{ L } H_2$$

The ideal gas law can also be used to solve gas stoichiometry problems.

STUDY SKILLS

ORGANIZING THE GAS LAWS
It may help to organize all of the gas laws introduced in this chapter into a table. For each gas law, you may want to include an explanation of the law's use, an example, and its mathematical representation. You can then use the table as a reference when working problems in the chapter and when studying for the test.

ANSWERS

PRACTICE PROBLEM 12E

1. $V_2 = \dfrac{T_2 V_1 P_1}{T_1 P_2}$

   $V_2 = \dfrac{(400.0 \text{ K})(2.0 \text{ m}^3)(100.0 \text{ kPa})}{(100.0 \text{ K})(200.0 \text{ kPa})}$

   $V_2 = 4.0 \text{ m}^3$

2. $P_2 = \dfrac{T_2 V_1 P_1}{T_1 V_2}$

   $P_2 = \dfrac{(498 \text{ K})(8.00 \text{ L})(900.0 \text{ kPa})}{(296 \text{ K})(2.00 \text{ L})}$

   $P_2 = 6.06 \times 10^3 \text{ kPa}$

3. $T_2 = \dfrac{T_1 V_2 P_2}{T_1 P_1}$

   $T_2 = \dfrac{(500.0 \text{ K})(700.0 \text{ mL})(200.0 \text{ Pa})}{(850.0 \text{ mL})(500.0 \text{ Pa})}$

   $T_2 = 164.7 \text{ K}$

4. $V_2 = \dfrac{T_2 V_1 P_1}{T_1 P_2}$

   $V_2 = \dfrac{(273 \text{ K})(45 \text{ m}^3)(500. \text{ kPa})}{(750 \text{ K})(101.325 \text{ kPa})}$

   $V_2 = 81 \text{ m}^3$

SAMPLE PROBLEM 12E

ADDITIONAL EXAMPLES

a. A gas has a volume of 18.5 L at 85.5 kPa and 296 K. What is the volume of the gas at STP?

   Ans. 14.4 L

b. A balloon full of helium gas has a volume of 132 L at 99.7 kPa and 30.°C. What temperature is required for the balloon to have a volume of 176 L at a pressure of 77.6 kPa?

   Ans. 314 K, 41°C

c. A plastic bag is inflated to a volume of 3.89 L at 1.095 atm and 23°C. If the volume drops to 3.05 L at a temperature of –4°C, what is the new pressure?

   Ans. 1.27 atm

SAMPLE PROBLEM 12F

ADDITIONAL EXAMPLES

a. In the combustion reaction of 149 g of propane with excess oxygen, what volume of carbon dioxide is produced at STP?

$$C_3H_8 + 5O_2 \longrightarrow 3CO_2 + 4H_2O$$

Ans. 227 L CO_2

b. A student wishes to prepare oxygen by using the thermal decomposition of potassium chlorate, $KClO_3$. Given that the gas will have a temperature of 700°C and a pressure of 98.6 kPa, how much potassium chlorate will be necessary to produce 125 mL of oxygen?

Ans. 0.124 g $KClO_3$

RESOURCE LINK

ChemFile Lab B

Microscale Lab

Have students do Experiment B13: *Testing Reaction Combinations of H_2 and O_2.*

ChemFile Lab D

Consumer Lab

Have students do Experiment D11: *Factors Affecting CO_2 Production in Yeast.*

SAMPLE PROBLEM 12F · Using the ideal gas law to solve stoichiometry problems

How many liters of hydrogen gas will be produced at 280.0 K and 96.0 kPa if 40.0 g of sodium react with excess water according to the following equation?

$$2Na(s) + 2H_2O(l) \longrightarrow 2NaOH(aq) + H_2(g)$$

1 List what you know

- $V = ?$ L
- $P = 96.0$ kPa
- $n = ?$ mol
- $R = 8.314$ L•kPa/mol•K
- $T = 280.0$ K

2 Set up the problem

- Use the mole ratio in the balanced chemical equation to determine the number of moles of hydrogen that can be produced. The mole ratio between Na and H_2 is

$$\frac{2 \text{ mol Na}}{1 \text{ mol } H_2}$$

- Look up the molar mass of sodium.

$$Na = 22.99 \text{ g/mol}$$

- Convert 40.0 g Na to moles using the molar mass.

$$\frac{40.0 \text{ g Na}}{22.99 \text{ g/mol}} = 1.74 \text{ mol Na}$$

- Use the correct form of the mole ratio from the balanced chemical equation to calculate the number of moles of H_2 produced.

$$1.74 \text{ mol Na} \times \frac{1 \text{ mol } H_2}{2 \text{ mol Na}} = 0.870 \text{ mol } H_2$$

- Use the ideal gas law to calculate the volume of hydrogen produced under the temperature and pressure conditions given.

$$PV = nRT$$

- Rearrange the ideal gas law by dividing both sides of the equation by P in order to solve for the volume of hydrogen gas.

$$V = \frac{nRT}{P}$$

3 Calculate

- Substitute the values given into the equation shown above. Solve for volume.

$$V = \frac{(0.870 \text{ mol } H_2)(8.314 \text{ L•kPa/mol•K})(280.0 \text{ K})}{(96.0 \text{ kPa})}$$

$$V = 21.1 \text{ L of } H_2$$

Total recall

1. What three gas laws can be combined into the ideal gas law?

2. **a.** In this text, in what units is R usually expressed?
   b. Why must the units of P, V, T, and n match up to those of R in solving problems?
   c. What would be the units for R if P is in pascals, T is in kelvins, V is in liters, and n is in moles?

3. How is the combined gas law derived, and under what circumstance is it used to solve problems?

4. How does Avogadro's law help to determine gas volumes from balanced chemical equations?

Practice problems

5. A sample of carbon dioxide has a mass of 35.0 g and occupies 2.5 L at 400 K. What pressure does the gas exert?

6. What volume is occupied by 0.45 g of nitrogen gas measured at 100. kPa and a room temperature of 20°C ?

7. A sample of nitrogen gas exerts 2.5 atm of pressure at 250 K.
   a. What is the density of the gas expressed in g/L?
   b. What is the density of the gas in g/L at STP?

8. How many moles of sulfur dioxide gas, SO_2, are contained in a 4.0 L container at 450 K and 5.0 kPa?

9. A 10.0 L tank of helium gas is filled to a pressure of 400 psi. Assuming no loss of gas, how many balloons, each containing 4.0 L of helium at 100 kPa, could you fill?

10. When heated, solid iron(III) hydroxide decomposes to produce iron(III) oxide and water vapor. If 0.75 L of water vapor is produced at 227°C and 1.0 atm.
    a. How many grams of $Fe(OH)_3$ were used?
    b. How many grams of Fe_2O_3 are produced?

11. The synthesis of hydrogen chloride occurs according to the following equation.
    $$H_2(g) + Cl_2(g) \longrightarrow 2HCl(g)$$
    If 3.0 L of H_2 are used, how many liters of HCl can be produced? What do you have to assume to answer this question?

12. In the presence of a Pt catalyst, ammonia and oxygen react to form nitrogen monoxide and water, as shown by the following equation.
    $$4NH_3(g) + 5O_2(g) \xrightarrow{\text{Pt}} 4NO(g) + 6H_2O(g)$$
    Assume that the temperature and pressure stay constant at 350.0 K and 100.0 kPa. What volume of O_2 is needed to burn 15 L of ammonia?

13. Solid LiOH has been used in spacecraft to remove exhaled CO_2 from the environment, as shown by the following equation.
    $$2LiOH(s) + CO_2(g) \longrightarrow Li_2CO_3(s) + H_2O(l)$$
    What mass of LiOH must be used to absorb the carbon dioxide that exerts a partial pressure of 5.0 kPa at 15°C in a space laboratory with dimensions of 4.0 m × 2.5 m × 8.0 m?

ANSWERS

SECTION REVIEW

Total recall

1. Boyle's law, Charles's law, and Avogadro's law are all combined to form the ideal gas law.

2. **a.** In this text R is usually expressed with the units L•kPa/mol•K.
   b. The units of P, V, T, and n must match up with those of R so that they cancel out accordingly when solving problems.
   c. The units of R would be L•Pa/mol•K.

3. The combined gas law is derived from the ideal gas law, and it is used to solve problems in which a given quantity of gas changes from one set of pressure, volume, and temperature conditions to another set.

4. Avogadro's law shows that the mole ratio of two gases at the same temperature and pressure is the same as the volume ratio.

Practice problems

5. $35.0 \text{ g CO}_2 \times \dfrac{1 \text{ mol CO}_2}{44.01 \text{ g CO}_2} =$
   0.7953 mol CO_2
   $P = \dfrac{nRT}{V}$
   $P =$
   $\dfrac{(0.7953 \text{ mol CO}_2)\left(8.314\frac{L•kPa}{mol•K}\right)(400 \text{ K})}{2.5 \text{ L}}$
   $P = 1100 \text{ kPa}$

6. $0.45 \text{ g N}_2 \times \dfrac{1 \text{ mol N}_2}{28.02 \text{ g N}_2} =$
   0.0161 mol N_2
   $V = \dfrac{nRT}{P}$
   $V =$
   $\dfrac{(0.0161 \text{ mol N}_2)\left(8.314\frac{L•kPa}{mol•K}\right)(293 \text{ K})}{100. \text{ kPa}}$
   $V = 0.39 \text{ L N}_2$

7. **a.** $n = \dfrac{PV}{RT}$
   $n = \dfrac{(2.5 \text{ atm})(1 \text{ L})}{\left(0.0821\frac{L•atm}{mol•K}\right)(250 \text{ K})}$
   $n = 0.122 \text{ mol N}_2$
   $0.122 \text{ mol N}_2 \times \dfrac{28.02 \text{ g N}_2}{1 \text{ mol N}_2} = 3.4 \text{ g N}_2$
   $D = \dfrac{m}{V} = \dfrac{3.4 \text{ g N}_2}{1 \text{ L}} = 3.4 \text{ g/L}$

   b. $n = \dfrac{PV}{RT}$
   $n = \dfrac{(1 \text{ atm})(1 \text{ L})}{\left(0.0821\frac{L•atm}{mol•K}\right)(273 \text{ K})}$
   $n = 0.0446 \text{ mol N}_2$
   $0.0446 \text{ mol N}_2 \times \dfrac{28.02 \text{ g N}_2}{1 \text{ mol N}_2} = 1.3 \text{ g N}_2$
   $D = \dfrac{m}{V} = \dfrac{1.3 \text{ g N}_2}{1 \text{ L}} = 1.3 \text{ g/L}$

Answers continue on page 465A.

SCIENCE & TECHNOLOGY

SUPERCRITICAL FLUIDS

SCIENCE & TECHNOLOGY

Supercritical CO_2 technology has many commercial applications. It is primarily used in the extraction of essential oils from spices and plants. These essential oils are then used in the production of various foods, flavorings, and fragrances. Supercritical CO_2 is important in the pharmaceutical industry because it extracts integral compounds from plants that are used to synthesize disease-fighting drugs. In the purification of manufactured polymers, supercritical CO_2 removes unreacted monomers from the reaction mix. Also, supercritical CO_2 is useful in the electronics industry because it provides a safe and effective method for cleaning expensive and highly sensitive electrical components.

The commercial application of supercritical CO_2 technology offers several advantages. The solvating power of CO_2 can be adjusted by varying the temperature and pressure of the system, allowing for some widely variable applications of this technology. This technology can be tailored to suit the needs of individual projects. The ability to change the solvating power of supercritical CO_2 ensures an optimum yield of varying products and services. Moreover, applications involving supercritical CO_2 are environmentally friendly, solvent-free processes.

New Uses for Carbon Dioxide

If the temperature and pressure of a substance are above their critical values, that substance is referred to as a supercritical fluid. In recent years, many supercritical fluids have been used for their very effective and selective ability to dissolve other substances. This is especially true of carbon dioxide. Carbon dioxide can be made into a supercritical fluid at a relatively low temperature and pressure, so little energy is used in preparing it. Supercritical CO_2 can also be used just above room temperature. It is cheap, nontoxic, nonflammable, and easily removed.

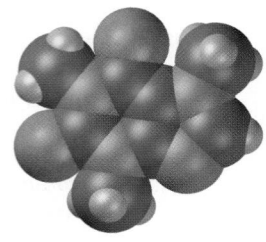

$C_8H_{10}N_4O_2$

Caffeine gives coffee its bitter taste; it also gives some people who drink coffee a feeling of restlessness.

Getting a Good Night's Sleep   Supercritical CO_2 is used to remove caffeine from coffee beans. First the green coffee beans are soaked in water. The absorbed water increases the size of the bean and also dissolves the caffeine inside the bean. The beans are then placed in the top of a 70 ft high column. Supercritical CO_2 fluid at approximately 93°C and 250 atm enters at the bottom of the

Water
Soaked beans
Carbon dioxide
Carbon dioxide and caffeine
Decaffeination column
Purification column
Water and caffeine
Processed beans

In the early 1900s, chloroform and benzene, both toxic substances, were used to remove the caffeine from coffee. One process used today dissolves the caffeine in supercritical CO_2.

column. The caffeine diffuses out of the beans and into the CO_2. The beans near the bottom of the column are in contact with the freshest supercritical CO_2. This ensures that the concentration of caffeine inside the beans is always greater than the caffeine concentration of the CO_2, forcing the dissolved caffeine within the beans to diffuse out into the CO_2. It takes about five hours for fresh beans to move down and out of the column.

The decaffeinated beans are removed from the bottom of the column, dried, and roasted as usual. The caffeine-rich CO_2 is removed at the top and passed upward through another column. Droplets of water fall through the supercritical CO_2 fluid and dissolve out the caffeine. The water solution of caffeine is then sold to soft-drink manufacturers. The CO_2, now purified, is recirculated to be used again.

internet**connect**

SCLINKS
NSTA
TOPIC: Supercritical fluids
GO TO: www.scilinks.org
KEYWORD: HW125

Other Uses Supercritical CO_2 is also used for other purposes. Some of these applications are extracting flavoring oils from various vegetable products, such as ginger oil from ginger root and spearmint oil from mint leaves; determining pesticide and PCB levels in water; and determining organic compounds in soil.

CAREER APPLICATION

What would it be like to . . .
▸ have a part in developing new foods?
▸ determine the safety of foods we eat?

Science/Math Career Preparation	
High School	**College**
Chemistry	Chemistry
Biology	Biochemistry
Mathematics	Microbiology
	Mathematics

Food Scientist

Important and rewarding professions include those of food technologists and food scientists. Food science is the study of the chemistry, microbiology, and processing of foods. Food technicians are responsible for testing foods for their quality and acceptability in carefully controlled taste tests. Microbiologists employed by the food industry monitor the safety of food products. Food analysts work in laboratories to monitor the composition of foods and the presence of pesticides. Some food scientists are involved in the creation of new food products or food ingredients, such as artificial sweeteners.

During their course of study, college students in the field of food science can gain valuable experience working for food manu-

facturers and government agencies, such as the U.S. Food and Drug Administration. This extra experience can help students find a job after graduation.

GASES AND LIQUIDS 453

SECTION 12-4

LESSON WARM-UP

Deviations from the Ideal Gas Law Theoretically, the particles of an ideal gas have zero volume and no interactive forces, and they make perfectly elastic collisions. The properties of real gases vary from these basic assumptions of the kinetic-molecular theory. Particles do have volume, collisions are not perfectly elastic, and attractive forces exist between the particles. Real gases exhibit many interactions between particles, causing deviations from the "ideal" model. In light of these differences, why is the ideal gas model used at all? At ordinary temperatures and pressures, the behavior of many real gases is close to that of an ideal gas. Also, the assumption of an ideal gas allows us to make reasonably accurate predictions about what happens to a gas when conditions, such as temperature, pressure, volume, and the number of particles, change.

RESOURCE LINK

ChemFile Teaching Resources CD-ROM
Career Extension
Assign Occupational Applications Worksheet 7: *Pest-Control Technician* to emphasize relevent applications of text concepts.

What conditions will cause a gas to condense?

OBJECTIVES

▶ **List** the conditions under which gases deviate from ideal behavior.

▶ **Relate** attractive forces to boiling point.

▶ **Interpret** a phase diagram.

▶ **Relate** vapor pressure to temperature.

▶ **Define** boiling point in terms of vapor pressure.

Forces of attraction

The gas laws described in this chapter were discovered long ago. They produced correct results, considering the methods of measurement available at the time. Later, more-careful measurements showed that real gases deviate from these ideal gas laws. **Figure 12-20** compares the behavior of an ideal gas with some real gases at different pressures. Real gases deviate particularly when the pressure is high because the molecules spend a larger fraction of time in close proximity to one another. The molecules are so close together that attractive forces become significant. Similar deviations between predicted and actual gas volumes occur at low temperatures. At low temperatures, gas molecules slow down, again making the attractive forces between them more significant.

▶ **FIGURE 12-20**

The ratio of *PV/nRT* for any ideal gas is one, which is represented by the dashed line. Using actual measurements for real gases, you can see that they deviate from the ideal.

Behavior of Real Gases vs. an Ideal Gas

DEMONSTRATION 5

Boiling Water in a Vacuum

Approximate time: 10 minutes

1. Half fill a 250 mL Erlenmeyer flask with slightly warm water, and place a nonmercury thermometer in the flask.

2. Place the flask on top of the vacuum-pump platform, and position it so that the thermometer is visible. Put some paper towels on the bottom of the platform in case some water bumps out during boiling. Cover the flask with a bell jar.

3. Ask a student to come forward and read the thermometer.

4. Run the vacuum pump until the water boils. Ask students what they believe the temperature of the water is.

5. Ask the student to read the thermometer again. Why does the water continue to cool? (*Evaporation is a cooling process.*)

At extremely high pressures, gas volumes are actually higher than calculated. The gases are more difficult to compress because the volume of molecules is now significant compared with the total volume. There is less space to compress the gas into. In both cases, the conditions allow particle size and the attractive forces between molecules to significantly affect the actual volume. Thus, low temperatures and high pressures favor deviations from the ideal gas law. In contrast, high temperatures and low pressures favor a gas's behaving more like the kinetic-molecular theory predicts it should. If the temperature is low enough and the pressure is high enough, the attractive forces between particles will be so strong that the gas will condense to form a liquid or solid. There are two assumptions made by the kinetic-molecular theory that do not represent the behavior of real gases.

‣ The volume of the gas molecules is negligible.
‣ There are no attractive forces between gas molecules.

Vapor pressure increases with temperature

A common gas that condenses easily is water vapor. This is due to the fairly strong hydrogen bonds formed between water molecules. You can see water vapor condense in clouds or on any cold surface, such as a glass with ice in it.

Though water exists mostly as a liquid at room temperature and pressure, water in an open container evaporates over a period of time until it all finally "disappears." The water vapor formed during **evaporation** is like any other gas in that it exerts pressure and it expands and contracts with temperature changes. You may have noticed that in a closed system, such as in a sealed bottle of water, water does not *appear* to evaporate.

When placed in a closed container, such as the one in **Figure 12-21**, water does evaporate until the air in the container is *saturated* with water vapor. When the air is saturated with vapor, the molecules in the vapor condense to a liquid as fast as the liquid evaporates, and the two processes of evaporation and **condensation** continue at equal rates.

$$H_2O(l) \rightleftarrows H_2O(g)$$

The two opposing arrows in the equation above represent a system in dynamic equilibrium. Recall from Chapter 8 that equilibrium describes reversible processes occurring at the same rate. The evaporation and condensation are proceeding at the same rate, so there is no net change. In a closed container, the pressure due to the water vapor reaches a maximum value (at a given temperature) called the equilibrium vapor pressure, or simply the **vapor pressure.**

FIGURE 12-21 ◄

Some molecules of a nonboiling liquid acquire enough energy to overcome intermolecular forces within the liquid and escape from the surface into the gas phase.

evaporation

the process by which particles escape from the surface of a nonboiling liquid and enter the gas state

condensation

the process by which a gas changes to a liquid

vapor pressure

the pressure exerted by a vapor in equilibrium with its liquid state at a given temperature

GASES AND LIQUIDS　455

SECTION 12-4

READING STRATEGY

Assimilating Knowledge

Give students self-stick notes, and have them mark areas of difficulty as they read Section 12-4 outside of class. Remind them to study the diagrams and graphs, particularly Figure 12-22.

Tell students that as they read they should be prepared to answer the following questions:

‣ What is the kinetic-molecular explanation of evaporation and condensation?
‣ How is the vapor pressure of a substance related to temperature? What is the kinetic-molecular explanation for this relationship?
‣ What are the conditions under which a substance boils?
‣ What happens during sublimation?

CHAPTER CONNECTION

The description of an ideal gas is very much like the description of an ideal solution, which is assumed to be infinitely dilute so that solute particles have no effect on each other and take up no space in the solution. Solutions are covered in Chapter 13.

6. Shut down the vacuum pump, and release the vacuum. Work quickly, and do not allow the water to continue boiling for more time than is required for the demonstration. Continued boiling will allow water to condense inside the pump.

7. Before you remove the flask, ask students if they think the flask is hot. Remind students that the concepts of boiling and heat do not necessarily go together.

Safety

The teacher must wear a lab apron. Everyone must wear safety goggles in case the bell jar shatters under the vacuum. Students must be at least 10 ft away from the demonstration.

Disposal

Pour water down the sink.

Pressure cookers are a necessity for cooking at high altitudes. Often the boiling point of water at high altitudes is not high enough to cook firm vegetables, pasta, eggs, and similar items in a reasonable amount of time. When water is heated in a sealed pressure cooker, the vapor pressure increases, which in turn increases the pressure inside the pot. The water must become hotter to boil under this pressure. The pressure is regulated by either a weighted seal or a mechanical valve. Many high-altitude restaurants also use pressure ovens to speed the cooking of foods such as roasts and stews.

Science in the News

PRESENTS **Feature story 22**

Belching Cows. See the Science in the News video guide for more details.

▶ **FIGURE 12-22**

A liquid boils when its vapor pressure equals the external pressure, which is usually that of the atmosphere. When the pressure is 1 atm (101.325 kPa), a liquid boils at its normal boiling point.

Vapor Pressures of Diethyl Ether, Ethanol, and Water at Various Temperatures

As the temperature of the water increases, its vapor pressure increases. **Figure 12-22** shows how the vapor pressure of three liquids increases with temperature. When the vapor pressure equals the external pressure on the liquid, the liquid begins to boil. The temperature at which boiling occurs is called the boiling point. At high altitudes, the boiling point of liquids is lower than at sea level. In Denver, Colorado, water will boil at about 94°C. Do not confuse boiling with cooking. Cooking vegetables in Denver, where water usually boils near 94°C, is a slower process because the water is at a lower temperature, even though it is boiling. Also, remember that water boiling rapidly is no hotter than water at a slow boil. The temperature of the water remains constant during the boiling process.

There are fundamental differences between evaporation and boiling. Evaporation occurs at temperatures lower than the boiling point of the liquid. Also, evaporation occurs at the *surface* of the liquid, whereas in boiling, bubbles of vapor arise *inside* the body of the liquid. For a bubble to form, the pressure of the atmosphere on the surface of the liquid must be overcome. This pressure is the total pressure of all the gases in the atmosphere, not just that of the water vapor. Whereas the vapor pressure of the liquid alone is important in evaporation, the total atmospheric pressure is what controls the boiling process.

Phase diagrams relate physical state to temperature and pressure

Think of a closed container with steam, water, ice, and air as a system. Within this system, H_2O can exist in the solid **phase,** the liquid phase, and the gas phase. A **phase diagram** is a graph that shows the temperatures and pressures at which a substance exists in different phases. The phases are at equilibrium with each other along the lines of the diagram. Look at **Figure 12-23,** the phase diagram for water. Segment AD is the vapor pressure–temperature curve for liquid water and its vapor. On segment AD, liquid and vapor coexist. Any point along segment AD represents the change of state from a liquid to a vapor and from a vapor to a liquid where the two distinct phases of liquid and vapor are in equilibrium with each other. Notice that point E, the **normal boiling point** of water, falls on segment AD. At the boiling point of water, the liquid and vapor phases are in equilibrium with each other. You can now see why boiling point can also be defined as the temperature at which the vapor pressure equals the external, or atmospheric, pressure. If the external pressure is greater than 101.325 kPa, water boils at a higher temperature. If the pressure is less than 101.325 kPa, water boils at a lower temperature.

As you increase the temperature of a liquid, its vapor pressure increases. As a result, the density of the vapor increases. At the same time, the density of the liquid decreases. Eventually, at some temperature and pressure, liquid and vapor have the same density, and vapor,

phase

any part of a system that has uniform composition and properties

phase diagram

a graphic representation of the relationships between the physical states (phases) of a substance at different pressures and temperatures

normal boiling point

the temperature at which a substance boils at 1.0000 atm of pressure

Phase Diagram for H_2O

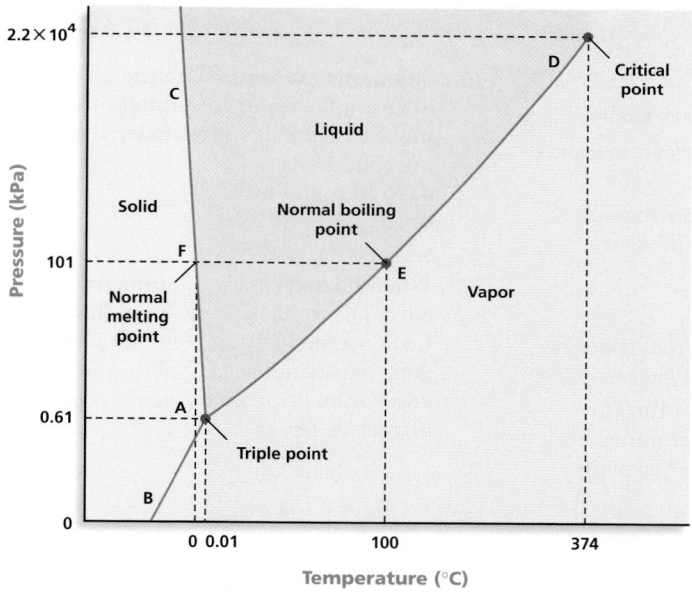

FIGURE 12-23 ◂

The phase diagram for water can be used to predict the physical state of water at different temperatures and pressures. Note that the diagram is not drawn to scale.

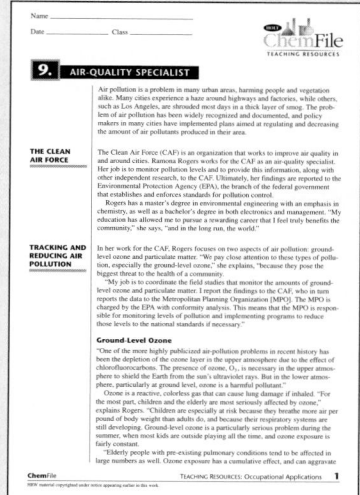

ADDITIONAL APPLICATION

Other good examples of materials that sublime are iodine crystals, mothballs, and moth flakes. Moth flakes sublime slowly in a closet or clothes bag and kill the larvae of moths that might be in wool or fur. They are also used in urinals to mask odors. They do not dissolve because they are very nonpolar. Because they sublime slowly, they freshen the air.

POSSIBLE MISCONCEPTION

Many students will have trouble understanding that all three states of matter can exist in equilibrium at the same time at the triple point. Liken the triple point to the apex of a pyramid, where a step in any direction places one on a different wall of the structure. At the triple point, a shift in any direction will result in a different physical state of the substance.

ANSWERS

SECTION REVIEW

Total recall

1. Water vapor condenses easily.

2. During evaporation, molecules randomly leave the surface of the liquid at temperatures below the boiling point. At the boiling point, the vapor pressure of the liquid equals atmospheric pressure, so bubbles of vapor can form underneath the surface of the liquid.

3. Its vapor pressure increases as well.

Critical thinking

4. Real gases behave differently from ideal gases under all conditions. They deviate from ideal most under conditions of low temperature and/or high pressure.

---

critical point

the temperature and pressure at and above which the properties of the vapor phase of a substance cannot be distinguished from those of the liquid phase

sublimation

a change of state in which a solid is transformed directly to a gas without going through the liquid state

triple point

the temperature and pressure at which three phases of a substance exist in equilibrium

---

as such, ceases to exist. This is the **critical point** of the substance, point *D*. For water the critical conditions are 374°C and 22.1 MPa (218 atm). If the pressure is high enough, it is possible to heat substances beyond the critical point to produce supercritical fluids. Among the very interesting properties of supercritical fluids is their ability to dissolve other substances.

Segment *BA* is the vapor pressure–temperature curve for the vapor phase. On segment *BA*, solid and vapor coexist. Segment *BA* represents the temperatures and pressures at which water vapor and ice are in equilibrium. Ice undergoes **sublimation** along this curve, and water vapor solidifies. Point *A* on the graph denotes coordinates of special significance. Point *A* is the **triple point** of water, that is, the point at which three phases of water exist in equilibrium. The triple point of water is 0.010°C and 0.612 kPa. The sublimation region of the graph always lies below the triple point.

Segment *CA* represents temperatures and pressures at which the liquid is in equilibrium with the solid and no vapor is present. On segment *CA*, solid and liquid coexist. For water, this line has a negative slope, meaning an increase in pressure decreases the melting point. This behavior, which differs from almost all other substances, occurs because the density of solid ice is less than the density of liquid water. Point *F* corresponds to the normal freezing/melting point, 0.000°C, for water at 1 atm (101.325 kPa).

SECTION REVIEW

Total recall

1. What common gas condenses easily?

2. What is the difference between evaporation and boiling?

3. As the temperature of water increases, what happens to its vapor pressure?

Critical thinking

4. Under what conditions do real gases behave differently from ideal gases?

5. Will turning up the heat on the stove under a pot of boiling water and pasta make the pasta cook faster? Explain your answer.

6. **Interpreting Graphics** Use the phase diagram for water to estimate the physical state of water under the following conditions.
   a. 75 kPa and 50°C
   b. 101 kPa and 80°C
   c. 25 kPa and 100°C

7. When heated slowly at standard pressure, I_2 sublimes. What does this mean? Look up the melting points of the halogens in a handbook. Explain the differences in melting point in terms of attractive forces.

---

5. Turning up the heat should have no effect because the temperature of the liquid water cannot increase above the boiling point as long as the pressure stays constant.

6. **a.** liquid
   b. liquid
   c. gas

7. Iodine molecules enter the vapor phase directly from the solid.

Halogen	Melting point
F_2	–219.6°C
Cl_2	–101.0°C
Br_2	–7.2°C
I_2	113.5°C

As attractive forces become greater, melting point increases.

In addition to collecting data on the ozone layer, balloons have been used to chart the Milky Way galaxy, collect dust from comets and meteorites, and photograph the sun. New balloons are being designed to lift a 100 cm telescope into the atmosphere to explore the center of our galaxy. These new balloons have a volume of over 1 million cubic meters and are able to lift cargos of over 3500 kg.

LOOKING BACK

Why is the balloon only partially inflated at launch?

The volume of the balloon increases as the balloon ascends into the atmosphere, and the pressure on the balloon decreases. If the balloon were completely inflated at the launch site, there would be no room for the expanding helium as the balloon ascended, and the larger volume of gas inside would burst the balloon.

How do scientists know how much to inflate the balloon?

Based on the volume they want the balloon to have at its cruising altitude, they use gas laws to calculate the mass and volume of gas needed at launch.

Why are scientists monitoring the ozone layer?

Destruction of the ozone layer increases the amount of UV radiation that reaches Earth's surface, which can result in an increased incidence of mutations and skin cancers.

How are chlorofluorocarbons responsible for changes in the ozone layer?

Chlorofluorocarbons, or CFCs, are broken apart by UV radiation in the stratosphere to form chlorine atoms that react with ozone in a chain reaction to form oxygen gas. One chlorine atom is capable of reacting with as many as 10 000 ozone molecules.

What is being done to protect the ozone layer?

The Montreal Protocol stipulates the following provisions for developed countries. Developing countries have an additional 10 years to comply.

- 100% phaseout of CCl_4 and CH_3CCl_3 in 1996
- production freeze of CFCs in 1996; 100% phaseout by 2010
- production freeze of methyl chloride in 1995

READING STRATEGY

Assimilating Knowledge

Have students return to their lists of things they want to know about gases and liquids that they created at the beginning of the chapter. Have them place check marks next to the questions that they are now able to answer. Students should finish by making a list of what they've learned. Have students identify unanswered questions as well as new questions they may have. These questions could be used as the basis for a research project.

REVIEW & ASSESS ASSIGNMENT GUIDE

Term Review
Assign after Section 12-4.

Concept & Skills Review

Section 12-1
▶ Items 9–17

Section 12-2
▶ Items 18–40

Section 12-3
▶ Items 41–54

Section 12-4
▶ Items 55–57

Linking Chapters
Assign after Section 12-4.

Alternative Assessments
Assign after Section 12-4.

Test Prep
Assign prior to the chapter test.

KEY TERMS

12-1
chain reaction
free radical
greenhouse effect
ideal gas
kinetic-molecular theory
newton
pascal
pressure
STP

12-2
Avogadro's law
Boyle's law
Charles's law
Dalton's law of partial
  pressures
diffusion
effusion
Gay-Lussac's law of com-
  bining volumes
Graham's law of effusion

mole fraction
partial pressure

12-3
combined gas law
ideal gas law

12-4
condensation
critical point

vapor pressure
evaporation
normal boiling point
phase
phase diagram
sublimation
triple point

KEY CONCEPTS

12-1 What are characteristics of gases?
▶ Gases are fluids that have very low, variable densities.
▶ The kinetic-molecular theory is a model of gas behavior based on assumptions about a theoretical gas known as an ideal gas.
▶ When released into the atmosphere, some gases lead to environmental problems.

12-2 What behaviors are described by the gas laws?
▶ Boyle's law describes the indirect proportionality between the volume and pressure of a gas.
▶ Dalton's law relates the partial pressures of the individual gases in a gas mixture to the total pressure of the mixture.
▶ Charles's law describes the direct proportionality between the volume of a gas and its temperature.
▶ Avogadro's law states that equal volumes of gases at equal temperatures and pressures contain equal numbers of molecules.

▶ Gay-Lussac's law of combining volumes states that at the same temperature and pressure, gases react in volume ratios that are whole numbers.
▶ Graham's law states that, at the same temperature and pressure, the effusion rates for two gases are inversely proportional to the square roots of their molar masses.

12-3 How do the gas laws fit together?
▶ The ideal gas law relates pressure, volume, temperature, and amount of any gas.
▶ The combined gas law relates pressure, volume, amount, and temperature of a gas sample under two sets of conditions.

12-4 What conditions will cause a gas to condense?
▶ The behavior of real gases deviates from ideal at high pressures and low temperatures.
▶ A phase diagram is a graph depicting the phases of a substance as determined by pressure and temperature.

KEY SKILLS

Sample Problem 12A: Solving pressure-volume problems (p. 435)

Sample Problem 12B: Solving volume-temperature problems (p. 440)

Sample Problem 12C: Comparing molecular speeds (p. 443)

Sample Problem 12D: Using the ideal gas law (p. 447)

Sample Problem 12E: Using the combined gas law (p. 448)

Sample Problem 12F: Using the ideal gas law to solve stoichiometry problems (p. 450)

TERM REVIEW

1. A collision is said to be _____ when there is no loss in the total kinetic energy involved in the collision.
(elastic, inelastic)

2. _____ gas molecules exert no attractive or repulsive forces on each other.
(Real, Ideal)

3. The number of moles of a particular substance divided by the total number of moles in a mixture is the _____.
(triple point, mole fraction)

4. A free radical is a very reactive substance with _____ electrons.
(paired, unpaired)

5. _____ law relates the pressure and volume of a gas at constant temperature.
(Charles's, Boyle's)

6. _____ law relates the volume and temperature of a gas at constant pressure.
(Charles's, Boyle's)

7. The passage of a gas through a small opening is called _____.
(diffusion, effusion)

8. Evaporation occurs _____ a liquid.
(inside, at the surface of)

CONCEPT & SKILLS REVIEW

DESCRIBING A GAS

9. a. What assumption does the kinetic-molecular theory make about the volume of an ideal gas particle?
b. Describe the motion of an ideal gas particle.

10. How does the combustion of a fossil fuel contribute to the greenhouse effect?

11. How would the shape of a curve showing the kinetic-energy distribution of gas molecules at 50°C compare with the blue curve in Figure 12-4?

12. a. List the four variables in the ideal gas law equation that are used to describe a gas.
b. Why must a specific temperature be stated when working with gas data?

13. a. Briefly describe how a barometer works.
b. Why is mercury used instead of water to measure atmospheric pressure?

14. What technologies have been affected by the Montreal Protocol?

15. A ball is dropped from a distance of 2.0 m above the floor.
a. If the collision is elastic, how high will the ball bounce?
b. If the collision is inelastic, will the ball bounce higher or lower than 2.0 m?

16. Gas companies often store their fuel supplies in liquid form in large storage tanks. Liquid nitrogen is used to keep the temperature low enough for the fuel to remain condensed in liquid form. Although continuous cooling is expensive, storing a condensed fuel as a liquid is still more economical than storing it as a gas. Give one reason why storing a liquid is more economical than storing a gas.

17. Below is a diagram showing the effects of pressure on a column of mercury and on a column of water. Which system is under a higher pressure? Explain your choice.

Mercury   Water

Complete worked-out solutions for these problems can be found on the teacher's interleaved pages at the end of this chapter.

TERM REVIEW

1. elastic
2. Ideal
3. mole fraction
4. unpaired
5. Boyle's
6. Charles's
7. effusion
8. at the surface of

CONCEPT & SKILLS REVIEW

9. a. It assumes that an ideal gas particle has zero volume.
   b. An ideal gas particle moves in straight lines in random directions.

10. The combustion of fossil fuel contributes to the greenhouse effect primarily by adding CO_2, a greenhouse gas, to the atmosphere.

11. The peak of the curve would be broader and lower and would be farther to the right than the red curve, which peaks at 25°C.

12. a. V, volume; P, pressure; T, Kelvin temperature; n, amount in moles
   b. A specific temperature must be stated when working with gas data because both P and V change with temperature.

13. a. The pressure of the atmosphere on a pool of liquid supports that liquid inside a column sealed at the top. The column was originally filled completely with the liquid.
   b. Mercury has a high density, so the barometer column can be of a practical height. Standard atmospheric pressure supports a column of water more than 10 m high, which is not a practical height.

14. Air conditioning, refrigeration, and aerosol-packaging technologies have been affected by the phaseout of CFCs.

CHAPTER 12
Review Answers

15. a. The ball will bounce 2.0 m high because it loses no kinetic energy.

b. The ball will bounce lower because it loses kinetic energy in the form of heat.

16. As a liquid, the fuel occupies about 0.001 of the volume it would have as a gas, so only a small number of tanks are needed. This savings more than compensates for the cost of maintaining natural gas in a liquid form.

17. The mercury barometer indicates the higher pressure. Because mercury's density is 13.7 times that of water, much more pressure is required to hold up a column at the height shown, assuming both barometers are 1 m tall.

18. a. The table shows that V/T is a constant.

b. Answers will vary. The most likely causes are human error in measurement and the lack of precision in the measuring instruments, particularly due to changing temperatures.

c. Charles's law

19. Boyle's law expresses an inverse relationship between P and V at constant temperature ($P \propto 1/V$).

20. O_2 and H_2O

21. The bubble expands, creating conditions that cause the diver to have "the bends."

22. Atmospheric pressure increases as you move to lower altitudes. The air behind the eardrums remains at the lower pressure until the pressure difference is enough to open the eustachian tubes and allow the two pressures to equalize.

23. A sample of gas expands when it is heated. With an increase in temperature, gas particles move faster and collide more forcefully with the walls of their container, resulting in an increase in volume.

BOYLE'S LAW AND CHARLES'S LAW

18. a. Describe the relationship between the volume and temperature of the gas in Table 12-3.

b. List possible reasons why the values in the V/T column of Table 12-3 are not exactly the same.

c. Which gas law is verified by the data in Table 12-3?

19. What type of relationship between pressure and volume does Boyle's law express?

20. Above 100°C and at constant pressure, two volumes of hydrogen react with one volume of oxygen to form two volumes of gaseous water. Set up a diagram similar to the one on page 441 for this reaction, and determine the molecular formulas for oxygen and water.

21. A gas bubble forms in the bloodstream of a diver at 50 m below the surface. What happens to the volume of the bubble as the diver ascends to the surface and the pressure is reduced?

22. Why do your ears sometimes pop when you drive down a steep incline or descend in an airplane?

23. Use the kinetic-molecular theory to explain Charles's law.

24. Use Charles's law to explain the danger of throwing a sealed can filled with a volatile gas into a fire.

25. In a science fiction story, the main character visits a planet where the temperature is −15 K. Use Charles's law to explain why this temperature is unrealistic.

26. Use Boyle's law to explain why "bubble wrap" pops when you squeeze it.

Practice Problems

27. A 2.00 L container has an internal pressure of 506.6 kPa at 25°C. What volume of methyl bromide is needed to fill the container at standard pressure if the temperature remains constant? **(Hint: See Sample Problem 12A.)**

28. At a deep-sea station 200. m below the surface of the Pacific Ocean, workers live in a pressurized environment. How many liters of gas

at STP on the surface must be compressed to fill the underwater environment with 2.00×10^7 L of gas at 20.0 atm? Assume that temperature remains constant. **(Hint: See Sample Problem 12A.)**

29. A child receives a balloon filled with 2.30 L of helium from a vendor at an amusement park, where the temperature is 311 K. What will the volume of the balloon be when the child brings the balloon home to an air-conditioned house at 295 K? **(Hint: See Sample Problem 12B.)**

30. A sample of hydrogen exerts a pressure of 0.329 atm at 47°C. The gas is heated to 77°C at constant volume. What will its new pressure be? **(Hint: See Sample Problem 12B.)**

DALTON'S LAW AND GRAHAM'S LAW

31. How are mole fractions used to find partial pressures of gas mixtures?

32. Use the diffusion process to explain how a perfume travels through the air.

33. Differentiate between diffusion and effusion.

34. What ratios are compared in Graham's law?

Practice Problems

35. The average speed of nitrogen molecules is 500.0 m/s at room temperature. What is the average speed of helium molecules at the same temperature? **(Hint: See Sample Problem 12C.)**

36. Carbon dioxide molecules travel at an average speed of 450. m/s at a certain temperature. How fast would oxygen molecules travel at the same temperature? **(Hint: See Sample Problem 12C.)**

37. How do the average velocities of neon molecules and krypton molecules compare when both gases are at the same temperature?

38. The refrigerant released when a typical automobile air-conditioning system is being repaired contains CCl_2F_2. If 365 g of CCl_2F_2 is released into the atmosphere from one air-conditioning unit, calculate the number of moles of chlorine atoms made available to react with ozone.

39. If one chlorine atom can destroy up to 10 000 ozone molecules, calculate the amount of ozone destroyed by the chlorine atoms from item 38.

40. A mixture of gases is under a pressure of 0.95 atm. The mixture contains 0.037 mole fraction of helium and 0.009 mole fraction of xenon. What are the partial pressures of these two gases?

IDEAL GAS LAW, COMBINED GAS LAW, AND STOICHIOMETRY

41. What determines the value for the constant R?

42. Which gas variable is held constant when the combined gas law is being used to analyze gas behavior?

43. How can a balanced chemical equation be used to determine the volume of a gas that will be produced from the represented reaction?

Practice Problems

44. Suppose you have a 500.0 mL container that holds 0.0500 mol of oxygen gas at a room temperature of 32°C. What is the pressure inside the container? **(Hint: See Sample Problem 12D.)**

45. How many grams of oxygen gas must be in a 10.0 L container to exert a pressure of 97.0 kPa at a temperature of 25°C? **(Hint: See Sample Problem 12D.)**

46. A sample of helium has a volume of 500. mL at STP. What will be its new volume if the temperature is increased to 325 K and its pressure is increased to 125 kPa? **(Hint: See Sample Problem 12E.)**

47. A 3.00 L sample of air exerts a pressure of 101 kPa at 300.0 K. What pressure will the air exert if the temperature is increased to 400.0 K and the air is allowed to expand to 15.0 L? **(Hint: See Sample Problem 12E.)**

48. How many liters of hydrogen gas can be produced at 300.0 K and 104 kPa pressure if 20.0 g of sodium metal is reacted with water according to the following equation? **(Hint: See Sample Problem 12F.)**

$$2Na(s) + 2H_2O(l) \longrightarrow 2NaOH(aq) + H_2(g)$$

49. Magnesium will burn in oxygen to form magnesium oxide as represented by the following equation.

$$2Mg(s) + O_2(g) \longrightarrow 2MgO(s)$$

What mass of magnesium will react with 500.0 mL of oxygen at 150°C and 70.0 kPa? **(Hint: See Sample Problem 12F.)**

50. A plastic weather balloon is filled with 90.0 L of hydrogen gas at ground level, where the pressure is 99.0 kPa and the temperature is 20.0°C. The balloon will burst if its volume exceeds 300.0 L. Can the balloon rise above the altitude of Mount Everest, where the pressure drops to 32.1 kPa and the temperature decreases by 64.4°C?

51. Calculate the density of helium at STP using the ideal gas law equation. Check your answer with a reference source that lists gas densities.

52. Suppose a certain automobile engine has a cylinder with a volume of 500.0 mL that is filled with air (21% oxygen) at a temperature of 55°C and a pressure of 101.0 kPa. What mass of octane must be injected to react with all of the oxygen in the cylinder?

$$2C_8H_{18}(l) + 25O_2(g) \longrightarrow 16CO_2(g) + 18H_2O(g)$$

53. Air is 20.9% oxygen by volume.
   a. How many liters of air are needed for the combustion of 25.0 L of octane vapor, $C_8H_{18}(g)$?
   b. What volume of each product is produced?

54. Methanol, CH_3OH, is made by using a catalyst to react carbon monoxide with hydrogen at high temperature and pressure. If 450.0 mL of CO and 825 mL of H_2 are allowed to react, answer the following. (Hint: First write the balanced chemical equation for this reaction.)
   a. Which reactant is in excess?
   b. How much of that reactant remains when the reaction is complete?
   c. What volume of $CH_3OH(g)$ is produced?

CONDENSATION AND LIQUIDS

55. Why do real gases deviate from ideal gas behavior?

Complete worked-out solutions for these problems can be found on the teacher's interleaved pages at the end of this chapter.

24. As the temperature increases, the pressure of the gas inside the can increases. Eventually, the gas reaches a pressure that exceeds the structural strength of the can, causing the can to explode.

25. Charles's law states that the volume of an ideal gas is proportional to the Kelvin temperature, so the volume of the gas would be zero at 0 K. A negative temperature would result in a negative volume, which is physically impossible.

26. As the bubble is squeezed to a smaller volume, the pressure of the gas inside the bubble increases until it is enough to burst the plastic film.

27. *See page 465A.*

28. *See page 465A.*

29. *See page 465A.*

30. *See page 465A.*

31. Pressure depends on the frequency of collisions and the average kinetic energy of the collisions. The molecules of all gases have the same average kinetic energy at the same temperature, so pressure depends only on the frequency of collisions. At constant temperature, the frequency of collisions is determined by the number of particles present. Therefore, any gas in a mixture contributes to the total pressure of the mixture proportionate to the gas's portion of the total number of particles, or its mole fraction.

32. The scent molecules from the perfume move randomly, colliding and changing direction. As a result, the molecules spread out in all directions.

33. Diffusion is the movement of molecules of one substance through the molecules of another substance, particularly liquids and gases. Effusion is the movement of gas molecules through a hole.

Complete worked-out solutions for these problems can be found on the teacher's interleaved pages at the end of this chapter.

34. The law compares the ratio of the velocities with the ratio of the square roots of the masses.

35. *See page 465A.*

36. *See page 465A.*

37. *See page 465A.*

38. *See page 465A.*

39. *See page 465A.*

40. *See page 465A.*

41. The value of R depends on the units of volume, pressure, and temperature used in its calculation. The value of n is always in moles.

42. n, the number of moles of gas

43. You can use stoichiometry to determine the number of moles of gas produced. Volume is easily calculated from the number of moles if conditions of temperature and pressure are known.

44. *See page 465A.*

45. *See page 465A.*

46. *See page 465B.*

47. *See page 465B.*

48. *See page 465B.*

49. *See page 465B.*

50. *See page 465B.*

51. *See page 465B.*

52. *See page 465B.*

53. *See page 465B.*

54. *See page 465B.*

55. Real gases deviate from ideal gases because attractive forces exist between particles, the particles occupy volume, and collisions are not always perfectly elastic.

56. a. point A
b. point C
c. point D
d. point B

57. a. liquid
b. all states (solid, liquid, and vapor) are in equilibrium
c. vapor
d. liquid

Answers continue on page 465B.

56. Use the following graph of the vapor pressure of water versus temperature to answer these questions:
  a. At what point(s) does water boil at standard atmospheric pressure?
  b. At what point(s) is water only in the liquid phase?
  c. At what point(s) is water only in the vapor phase?
  d. At what point(s) is liquid water in equilibrium with water vapor?

57. Use the phase diagram for water on page 455 to determine the physical state of water under the following conditions:
  a. 200 kPa and 0°C
  b. 0.61 kPa and 0.01°C
  c. 50 kPa and 200°C
  d. 50 kPa and 10°C

LINKING CHAPTERS

1. Empirical formula
An unknown gas was analyzed and found to contain 80% carbon and 20% hydrogen. Determine the empirical formula for the gas.

2. Properties related to electron configuration
In Period 2 of the periodic table, nitrogen, oxygen, fluorine, and neon are gases at STP. Neon is the only one of these elements that is not diatomic in the gaseous state. How do you explain this observation?

ALTERNATIVE ASSESSMENTS

Performance assessment

1. Design and perform an experiment to measure the molar mass of the gas found inside a disposable butane lighter. Measure the mass and volume of the gas at a known temperature and pressure. Use the ideal gas law equation, $PV = nRT$, to find molar mass. Compare your answer with the known molar mass of butane. Try different brands of lighters, and compare the results.

Portfolio projects

1. Research and writing
Hydrochlorofluorocarbons, HCFCs, are being used as alternatives to CFCs. HCFCs, which have hydrogen atoms in the molecules, decompose more readily in the atmosphere. Use library resources to find out why these compounds will also be phased out by the Montreal Protocol.

2. Chemistry and you
Locate a hot-air-balloon group, and discuss with group members how they use the gas laws to fly their balloons. The group may be willing to give a demonstration. Report your experience to your class.

1. The kinetic-molecular theory states that ideal gas molecules _____.
   a. have weight and take up space
   b. are in constant, rapid, random motion
   c. exert attractive and repulsive forces on each other
   d. have high densities compared with liquids and solids

2. Pressure can be measured in _____.
   a. grams   c. pascals
   b. meters   d. liters

3. It is thought that CFCs are harmful to the atmosphere because _____.
   a. they block the ozone in the lower atmosphere from diffusing to higher regions
   b. they do not readily decompose when exposed to sunlight
   c. they produce free radicals that break down molecules of ozone
   d. they form a layer within the atmosphere that reflects radiant energy back into space

4. A sample of oxygen gas has a volume of 150 mL when its pressure is 0.947 atm. If the pressure is increased to 0.987 atm and the temperature remains constant, the new gas volume will be _____.
   a. 140 mL   c. 200 mL
   b. 160 mL   d. 240 mL

5. A sample of neon gas occupies a volume of 752 mL at 25°C. What volume will the gas occupy at 50°C if the pressure remains constant?
   a. 694 mL
   b. 752 mL
   c. 815 mL
   d. 955 mL

6. A sample of gas in a closed container at a temperature of 100.0°C and a pressure of 3.0 atm is heated to 300.0°C. What pressure does the gas exert at the higher temperature?
   a. 2.7 atm   c. 4.6 atm
   b. 3.5 atm   d. 5.9 atm

7. Predict which gas will effuse through a small opening fastest.
   a. the gas with the greatest molecular mass
   b. the gas with the least molecular mass
   c. the most-polar gas molecules
   d. All of the gases will effuse at equal rates.

8. What is the pressure exerted by a 0.500 mol sample of nitrogen gas in a 10.0 L container at 298 K?
   a. 1.80×10^4 atm   c. 490 atm
   b. 4.90×10^2 atm   d. 1.22 atm

9. A helium-filled balloon has a volume of 50.0 L at 25°C and 1.08 atm. What volume will it have at 0.855 atm and 10.0°C?
   a. 37.6 L   c. 60.0 L
   b. 41.7 L   d. 66.5 L

10. What volume of chlorine gas at 38°C and 1.63 atm is needed to react completely with 10.4 g of sodium to form NaCl?
    a. 3.54 L   c. 7.90 L
    b. 4.45 L   d. 10.2 L

11. Potatoes will cook faster at sea level than at higher altitudes because the water used to cook them will _____.
    a. be boiling more rapidly
    b. boil at a lower temperature
    c. increase in temperature while boiling
    d. boil at a higher temperature

12. The phase diagram for water shows that _____.
    a. water can exist as a solid, liquid, and gas at the same temperature and pressure
    b. water cannot exist as a solid, liquid, and gas at the same conditions of temperature and pressure
    c. water's normal boiling point and normal melting point exist at the same temperature
    d. solid water cannot sublime to form water vapor

Assign prior to the chapter test.

1. b
2. c
3. c
4. a
5. c
6. c
7. b
8. d
9. c
10. a
11. d
12. a

GASES AND LIQUIDS 465

Answers from page 451

8. $n = \dfrac{PV}{RT}$

$n = \dfrac{(5.0 \text{ kPa})(4.0 \text{ L})}{\left(8.314 \dfrac{\text{L}\cdot\text{kPa}}{\text{mol}\cdot\text{K}}\right)(450 \text{ K})}$

$n = 5.3 \times 10^{-3} \text{ mol SO}_2$

9. $400 \text{ psi} \times \dfrac{6.892\,86 \times 10^3 \text{ Pa}}{1 \text{ psi}} \times \dfrac{1 \text{ kPa}}{1000 \text{ Pa}} = 2757 \text{ kPa}$

$V_2 = \dfrac{P_1 V_1}{P_2}$

$V_2 = \dfrac{(2757 \text{ kPa})(10.0 \text{ L He})}{100 \text{ kPa}}$

$V_2 = 275.7 \text{ L He}$

$275.7 \text{ L He} \times \dfrac{1 \text{ balloon}}{4 \text{ L He}} = 68.9 \text{ balloons}$

You could fill 68 balloons. (The calculated answer is 68.9, but you cannot fill 0.9 of a balloon.)

10. $2\text{Fe(OH)}_3 \xrightarrow{\Delta} \text{Fe}_2\text{O}_3 + 3\text{H}_2\text{O}$

a. $n = \dfrac{PV}{RT}$

$n = \dfrac{(1.0 \text{ atm})(0.75 \text{ L})}{\left(0.0821 \dfrac{\text{L}\cdot\text{atm}}{\text{mol}\cdot\text{K}}\right)(500 \text{ K})}$

$n = 0.0183 \text{ mol H}_2\text{O}$

$0.0183 \text{ mol H}_2\text{O} \times \dfrac{2 \text{ mol Fe(OH)}_3}{3 \text{ mol H}_2\text{O}} \times \dfrac{106.88 \text{ g Fe(OH)}_3}{1 \text{ mol Fe(OH)}_3} = 1.3 \text{ g Fe(OH)}_3$

b. $0.0183 \text{ mol H}_2\text{O} \times \dfrac{1 \text{ mol Fe}_2\text{O}_3}{3 \text{ mol H}_2\text{O}} \times \dfrac{159.70 \text{ g Fe}_2\text{O}_3}{1 \text{ mol Fe}_2\text{O}_3} = 0.97 \text{ g Fe}_2\text{O}_3$

11. $3.0 \text{ L H}_2 \times \dfrac{2 \text{ L HCl}}{1 \text{ L H}_2} = 6.0 \text{ L HCl}$

Assume that the volume of HCl is measured at the same conditions of temperature and pressure under which the H_2 was measured.

12. $15 \text{ L NH}_3 \times \dfrac{5 \text{ L O}_2}{4 \text{ L NH}_3} = 19 \text{ L O}_2$

13. $V = 4.0 \times 10^2 \text{ cm} \times 2.5 \times 10^2 \text{ cm} \times 8.0 \times 10^2 \text{ cm} = 8.0 \times 10^7 \text{ cm}^3$

$8.0 \times 10^7 \text{ cm}^3 \times \dfrac{1 \text{ mL}}{1 \text{ cm}^3} \times \dfrac{1 \text{ L}}{1000 \text{ mL}} = 8.0 \times 10^4 \text{ L}$

$n = \dfrac{PV}{RT}$

$n = \dfrac{(5.0 \text{ kPa})(8.0 \times 10^4 \text{ L})}{\left(8.314 \dfrac{\text{L}\cdot\text{kPa}}{\text{mol}\cdot\text{K}}\right)(288 \text{ K})}$

$n = 167 \text{ mol CO}_2$

$167 \text{ mol CO}_2 \times \dfrac{2 \text{ mol LiOH}}{1 \text{ mol CO}_2} \times \dfrac{23.95 \text{ g LiOH}}{1 \text{ mol LiOH}} = 8.0 \times 10^3 \text{ g LiOH}$

Answers from page 462

27. $V_1 P_1 = V_2 P_2$

$V_2 = \dfrac{V_1 P_1}{P_2} = \dfrac{(2.00 \text{ L})(506.6 \text{ kPa})}{101.325 \text{ kPa}} = 10.0 \text{ L}$

28. $V_1 P_1 = V_2 P_2$

$V_1 = \dfrac{V_2 P_2}{P_1} = \dfrac{(2.00 \times 10^7 \text{ L})(20.0 \text{ atm})}{1 \text{ atm}} = 4.00 \times 10^8 \text{ L}$

29. $\dfrac{V_1}{T_1} = \dfrac{V_2}{T_2}$

$V_2 = \dfrac{V_1 T_2}{T_1} = \dfrac{(2.30 \text{ L})(295 \text{ K})}{311 \text{ K}} = 2.18 \text{ L}$

30. $\dfrac{P_1}{T_1} = \dfrac{P_2}{T_2}$

$P_2 = \dfrac{P_1 T_2}{T_1} = \dfrac{(0.329 \text{ atm})(350 \text{ K})}{320 \text{ K}} = 0.360 \text{ atm}$

35. $\dfrac{v_{He}}{v_{N_2}} = \sqrt{\dfrac{M_{N_2}}{M_{He}}}$

$v_{He} = v_{N_2}\sqrt{\dfrac{M_{N_2}}{M_{He}}} = 500.0 \text{ m/s}\sqrt{\dfrac{28.02 \text{ g/mol}}{4.00 \text{ g/mol}}} = 1323 \text{ m/s}$

36. $\dfrac{v_{O_2}}{v_{CO_2}} = \sqrt{\dfrac{M_{CO_2}}{M_{O_2}}}$

$v_{O_2} = v_{CO_2}\sqrt{\dfrac{M_{CO_2}}{M_{O_2}}} = 450. \text{ m/s}\sqrt{\dfrac{44.01 \text{ g/mol}}{32.00 \text{ g/mol}}} = 528 \text{ m/s}$

37. $\dfrac{v_{Ne}}{v_{Kr}} = \sqrt{\dfrac{M_{Kr}}{M_{Ne}}} = \sqrt{\dfrac{83.80 \text{ g/mol}}{20.18 \text{ g/mol}}} = 2.04$

The average velocity of neon atoms is 2.04 times that of krypton atoms at the same temperature.

38. $365 \text{ g CCl}_2\text{F}_2 \times \dfrac{1 \text{ mol CCl}_2\text{F}_2}{120.91 \text{ g CCl}_2\text{F}_2} \times \dfrac{2 \text{ mol Cl atoms}}{1 \text{ mol CCl}_2\text{F}_2} = 6.04 \text{ mol Cl atoms}$

Answers from page 463

39. $6.04 \text{ mol Cl} \times \dfrac{6.022 \times 10^{23} \text{ Cl atoms}}{1 \text{ mol Cl}} \times \dfrac{10\,000 \text{ O}_3 \text{ molecules}}{1 \text{ Cl atom}} \times$

$\dfrac{1 \text{ mol O}_3}{6.022 \times 10^{23} \text{ O}_3 \text{ molecules}} = 60\,400 \text{ mol O}_3$

40. $P_{helium} = 0.95 \text{ atm} \times 0.037 = 0.035 \text{ atm}$

$P_{xenon} = 0.95 \text{ atm} \times 0.009 = 0.009 \text{ atm}$

44. $PV = nRT$

$P = \dfrac{nRT}{V} = \dfrac{(0.0500 \text{ mol O}_2)\left(8.314 \dfrac{\text{L}\cdot\text{kPa}}{\text{mol}\cdot\text{K}}\right)(305 \text{ K})}{0.5000 \text{ L}} = 254 \text{ kPa}$

45. $PV = nRT$

$n = \dfrac{PV}{RT} = \dfrac{(97.0 \text{ kPa})(10.0 \text{ L})}{\left(8.314 \dfrac{\text{L}\cdot\text{kPa}}{\text{mol}\cdot\text{K}}\right)(298 \text{ K})} = 0.3915 \text{ mol O}_2$

$0.3915 \text{ mol O}_2 \times \dfrac{32.00 \text{ g O}_2}{1 \text{ mol O}_2} = 12.5 \text{ g O}_2$

46. $\dfrac{V_1 P_1}{T_1} = \dfrac{V_2 P_2}{T_2}$

$V_2 = \dfrac{T_2 V_1 P_1}{T_1 P_2} = \dfrac{(325 \text{ K})(500. \text{ mL})(101.325 \text{ kPa})}{(273 \text{ K})(125 \text{ kPa})} = 482 \text{ mL He}$

47. $\dfrac{V_1 P_1}{T_1} = \dfrac{V_2 P_2}{T_2}$

$P_2 = \dfrac{T_2 V_1 P_1}{T_1 V_2} = \dfrac{(400.0 \text{ K})(3.00 \text{ L})(101 \text{ kPa})}{(300.0 \text{ K})(15.0 \text{ L})} = 26.9 \text{ kPa}$

48. $20.0 \text{ g Na} \times \dfrac{1 \text{ mol Na}}{22.99 \text{ g Na}} \times \dfrac{1 \text{ mol H}_2}{2 \text{ mol Na}} = 0.4350 \text{ mol H}_2$

$PV = nRT$

$V = \dfrac{nRT}{P} = \dfrac{(0.4350 \text{ mol H}_2)\left(8.314 \dfrac{\text{L}\cdot\text{kPa}}{\text{mol}\cdot\text{K}}\right)(300.0 \text{ K})}{104 \text{ kPa}} = 10.4 \text{ L H}_2$

49. $PV = nRT$

$n = \dfrac{PV}{RT} = \dfrac{(70.0 \text{ kPa})(0.5000 \text{ L})}{\left(8.314 \dfrac{\text{L}\cdot\text{kPa}}{\text{mol}\cdot\text{K}}\right)(423 \text{ K})} = 0.009952 \text{ mol O}_2$

$0.009952 \text{ mol O}_2 \times \dfrac{2 \text{ mol Mg}}{1 \text{ mol O}_2} \times \dfrac{24.31 \text{ g Mg}}{1 \text{ mol Mg}} = 0.484 \text{ g Mg}$

50. $\dfrac{V_1 P_1}{T_1} = \dfrac{V_2 P_2}{T_2}$

$V_2 = \dfrac{T_2 V_1 P_1}{T_1 P_2} = \dfrac{(228.6 \text{ K})(90.0 \text{ L})(99.0 \text{ kPa})}{(293 \text{ K})(32.1 \text{ kPa})} = 217 \text{ L}$

Yes. The volume will increase to only 217 L.

51. $PV = nRT$

$n = \dfrac{PV}{RT} = \dfrac{(101.325 \text{ kPa})(1.0 \text{ L})}{\left(8.314 \dfrac{\text{L}\cdot\text{kPa}}{\text{mol}\cdot\text{K}}\right)(273 \text{ K})} = 0.044642 \text{ mol He}$

$0.044642 \text{ mol He} \times \dfrac{4.00 \text{ g He}}{1 \text{ mol He}} = 0.178568 \text{ g He}$

$D = \dfrac{m}{V} = \dfrac{0.178568 \text{ g}}{1 \text{ L}} = 0.178568 \text{ g/L}$

According to the *CRC Handbook,* the density of helium at STP is 0.1785 g/L.

52. $PV = nRT$

$0.5000 \text{ L air} \times \dfrac{0.21 \text{ L O}_2}{1 \text{ L air}} = 0.105 \text{ L O}_2$

$n = \dfrac{PV}{RT} = \dfrac{(101.0 \text{ kPa})(0.105 \text{ L})}{\left(8.314 \dfrac{\text{L}\cdot\text{kPa}}{\text{mol}\cdot\text{K}}\right)(328 \text{ K})} = 0.00389 \text{ mol O}_2$

$0.00389 \text{ mol O}_2 \times \dfrac{2 \text{ mol C}_8\text{H}_{18}}{25 \text{ mol O}_2} \times \dfrac{114.26 \text{ g C}_8\text{H}_{18}}{1 \text{ mol C}_8\text{H}_{18}} = 0.036 \text{ g C}_8\text{H}_{18}$

53. a. $25.0 \text{ L C}_8\text{H}_{18} \times \dfrac{25 \text{ L O}_2}{2 \text{ L C}_8\text{H}_{18}} \times \dfrac{1 \text{ L air}}{0.209 \text{ L O}_2} = 1.50 \times 10^3 \text{ L air}$

b. $25.0 \text{ L C}_8\text{H}_{18} \times \dfrac{16 \text{ L CO}_2}{2 \text{ L C}_8\text{H}_{18}} = 200. \text{ L CO}_2(g)$

$25.0 \text{ L C}_8\text{H}_{18} \times \dfrac{18 \text{ L H}_2\text{O}}{2 \text{ L C}_8\text{H}_{18}} = 225 \text{ L H}_2\text{O}(g)$

54. $CO + 2H_2 \longrightarrow CH_3OH$

a. $450.0 \text{ mL CO} \times \dfrac{2 \text{ mL H}_2}{1 \text{ mL CO}} = 900.0 \text{ Ml H}_2$

Carbon monoxide is in excess. 900.0 mL of H_2 would be required to react with 450 mL of CO. Only 825 mL of H_2 is available.

b. $450.0 \text{ mL CO} - 412.5 \text{ mL CO} = 37.5 \text{ mL CO}$

c. $825 \text{ mL H}_2 \times \dfrac{1 \text{ mL CH}_3\text{OH}}{2 \text{ mL H}_2} = 412 \text{ mL CH}_3\text{OH}$

Answers from page 464

LINKING CHAPTERS

1. $80 \text{ g C} \times \dfrac{1 \text{ mol C}}{12.01 \text{ g C}} = 6.66 \text{ mol C}$

$20 \text{ g H} \times \dfrac{1 \text{ mol H}}{1.01 \text{ g H}} = 19.8 \text{ mol H}$

$\dfrac{6.66 \text{ mol C}}{6.66} = 1.00 \text{ mol C}$

$\dfrac{19.8 \text{ mol H}}{6.66} = 2.97 \text{ mol H}$

$\text{mol ratio} = \dfrac{1 \text{ mol C}}{3 \text{ mol H}}$

CH_3

2. Neon is a noble gas. Its atoms have a complete octet in the outer energy level, so they are unreactive and do not form bonds with other atoms.

ALTERNATIVE ASSESSMENTS

Performance assessment

1. Students' designs should include methods to collect the gas, measure its volume and its mass, and determine temperature and barometric pressure. The most common means to collect the gas is by water displacement into an eudiometer, an inverted graduated cylinder, or an inverted buret. The mass of gas is often determined by measuring the mass of the lighter before and after the experiment. Students should allow time to assure that the lighter mechanism is dry when it is weighed the second time. If reasonably accurate volume and mass measurements are made, students should subtract the vapor pressure of water from the barometer reading to arrive at the pressure of the collected butane.

Portfolio projects

1. HCFCs will be phased out by the Montreal Protocol because they also aid in the destruction of ozone, although at a much slower rate than CFCs do. The production of HCFCs will be phased out completely by the year 2030.

2. Hot-air ballooning depends on the buoyancy of the balloon, which in turn depends on the density of the gas inside the balloon. The report should include factors such as the temperature of the hot-air balloon, the average time it takes to heat the air, and the method used to determine the lifting force of the balloon.

Solutions

CLASSROOM RESOURCES

SECTIONS	TEACHER'S DEMONSTRATIONS	PROBLEM SOLVING ■ Text ◆ ChemFile Mini-Guide	LABORATORIES ■ Text ◆ ChemFile Manuals: A, B, C, D
13-1 **What is a solution?** Section Review, p. 478	**Demo 1** Liquid Mixtures, p. 468 **Demo 2** Volume of Solvent, Solute, and Solution, p. 470 **Demo 3** Separation of Substances, p. 476	■ **How To** Prepare 1.000 L of a 0.5000 M solution, p. 472 ■ **Sample Problem 13A** Calculating molarity, p. 473 ■ **Sample Problem 13B** Determining the mass of solute, p. 473 ■ **Sample Problem 13C** Using solution stoichiometry, p. 474 ◆ **Chapter 14** Concentration of Solutions ◆ **Chapter 15** Dilutions	■ **Exp. 13A** Paper Chromatography of Colored Markers, p. 765 ■ **InquiryLab** The Color of M&M® Candies, p. 477 ◆ **Exp. C2** Separation of Mixtures ◆ **Inv. C2** Separation of Mixtures—Tanker Truck Spill ◆ **D12** Solutions: Rock Formation
13-2 **Does substance A dissolve in substance B?** Section Review, p. 486	**Demo 4** Temperature and Solubility of Gases, p. 480 **Demo 5** Temperature Effects on Rates of Dissolving, p. 483 **Demo 6** Polarity, p. 484		◆ **Exp. C12** Paper Chromatography ◆ **Inv. C12** Paper Chromatography—Forensic Investigation ◆ **Exp. C13** Testing for Dissolved O_2 ◆ **Exp. C14** Solubility of Ammonia
13-3 **What causes conductivity in solutions?** Section Review, p. 494	**Demo 7** Conductance of Solutions, p. 486 **Demo 8** Conductance of Tap Water, p. 488 **Demo 9** Saturation, p. 490 **Demo 10** Supersaturation, p. 492		◆ **Exp. C9** Heat of Solution
13-4 **How are a liquid's properties changed by solutes?** Section Review, p. 501	**Demo 11** Forming an Emulsion, p. 498	◆ **Chapter 16** Colligative Properties	■ **Exp. 13B** Boiling-Point Elevation and Molar Mass, p. 768 ◆ **Exp. C16** Freezing-Point Depression—Testing De-Icing Chemicals ◆ **Inv. C16** Freezing-Point Depression—Making Ice Cream ◆ **A11** Ice-Nucleating Bacteria ◆ **D13** Soaps and Detergents

SECTIONS	VIDEOS/VIDEODISC *Holt Chemistry Videodisc* CNN *Science in the NEWS*	CHEMFILE CD-ROMS ● *Teaching Resources* ◆ *Interactive Tutor*	OVERHEADS ● *Color Transparencies* ◆ *Transparency Masters*
13-1	Particle Model for a Solution CNN Segment 23 PRESENTS New Extraction Techniques for Gold	◆ **Module 8:** Strong and Weakly Ionized Species, pH, and Titrations **Topic:** Solutions	● **64** Particle Model for a Solution ● **66** Particle Model for a Suspension ● **67** Electrolytes and Nonelectrolytes in Solution ● **76** Moles Solute vs. Volume ◆ *See also* **64A, 66A.**
13-2	Saturation Sodium Acetate Hot Pack Solubility: Iodine in Water and Carbon Tetrachloride CNN Segment 24 PRESENTS Mixing Oil and Water: Surfactants CNN Segment 25 PRESENTS Multivitamins		● **68** Saturated vs. Unsaturated Solutions ● **69** Models for Miscible and Immiscible Solutions ● **70** Hydrogen Bonding Between a Solute and a Solvent ● **71** Model for Soluble and Insoluble Substances ● **72** Solubility vs. Temperature ● **73** Predicting Solubility ◆ *See also* **65A, 67A.**
13-3	Calcium Chloride Dissociation Dissociation Formation of a Precipitate Electrolytic Strengths Hydration of a Hydrogen Ion		● **74** Energy Changes in the Solution Process ● **78** Dissociation of NaCl ● *See also* **79, 80, 81.** ◆ **67A** Solubility Guidelines
13-4	Colligative Effects on Vapor Pressure Colligative Properties		● **82** Vapor Pressures of Pure Water and a Water Solution ● **83** Osmotic Pressure ◆ *See also* **68A, 69A.**

ASSESSMENT RESOURCES

ALTERNATIVE ASSESSMENTS	CHAPTER TESTING	SCORING RUBRICS *Holt ChemFile Teaching Resources CD-ROM*
Student Text Performance assessments, p. 508 Portfolio projects 1–4, p. 508 **Teacher's Edition** Depicting Molecules in Mixtures, p. 473 **Study Guide** Sections 13-1 to 13-4	**Student Text** Test Preparation, p. 509 **Holt Chemistry: Visualizing Matter Chapter 13 Test** (blackline masters) **Holt ChemFile Test Generator for Macintosh and Windows**	**Lab Work** Student-Designed Experiments Rubric Performance-Tasks Scoring Rubric Assessment for Structured Inquiry Assessment for Open-Ended Inquiry **Portfolio Projects** Assessing Portfolios Portfolio Assignment Student Evaluation Form

CHAPTER
13

Establishing Prior Knowledge

Make sure students understand the following concepts:

▶ Chapter 5: ions and ionic compounds
▶ Chapter 6: molecular structure and properties of water
▶ Chapter 8: measuring amounts in moles
▶ Chapter 12: boiling and freezing points

READING STRATEGY

Assimilating Knowledge

Before students read this chapter, have them write a short individual list of all the things they already know about the nature of solutions and electrolytes, the factors that affect solubility, the ways that solutes change a solution's properties, and the difference between solutions and suspensions. When students have finished their lists, have them make a group list on the chalkboard or on an overhead projector. Then have students list the things they might want to know about solutions. Ask the following questions to get them started:

▶ Besides water solutions, what other kinds of solutions exist?
▶ How many ways can you express the concentration of a solution?
▶ Why does salt dissolve in water, whereas oil does not?
▶ Why does most tap water conduct electricity, whereas distilled water does not?

ABOUT THE ILLUSTRATION

Sea water is a mixture containing many forms of dissolved matter, including ions, gases, and organic molecules. These solutions are vital to the many forms of marine life shown in this picture.

CHAPTER
13   Solutions

internet connect

Holt Chemistry: Visualizing Matter
On-Line Resources
go.hrw.com
Visit the HRW Web site for a variety of resources related to this chapter. Just type in the keyword HW0 Chapt13.

SCiLINKS
NSTA

National Science Teachers Association
On-Line Resources: www.scilinks.org
The following Scilinks Internet resources can be found in the student text for this chapter:

Page 469
TOPIC: Colloids
KEYWORD: HW131

Page 484
TOPIC: Vitamins
KEYWORD: HW132

Page 494
TOPIC: Sports drinks
KEYWORD: HW133

Page 498
TOPIC: Emulsions
KEYWORD: HW134

Page 508
TOPIC: Vitamin supplements
KEYWORD: HW135

SOLUBILITY AND THE ARCTIC BEAR HUNT

In northern Canada, a helicopter hovers over the snow. Dr. Malcolm Ramsay, an ecologist at the University of Saskatchewan and an expert on polar bears, leans out of the doorway to keep a polar bear in sight. As Ramsay aims his rifle, the bear lumbers through the snow to escape. Ramsay fires, and the bear runs faster.

Ramsay signals the pilot to land in a clearing. He unloads his equipment, and the helicopter departs. By the time Ramsay reaches the bear, the tranquilizer-filled dart has done its job, and the animal lies quietly in the snow.

Ramsay begins a physical examination that will take hours. The bear is hoisted into the air to be weighed. Large syringes are filled with blood samples. A tooth is extracted; its growth rings will tell the animal's age. A sample of fat tissue is taken. As the bear begins to stir, Ramsay packs his gear and waves to the returning helicopter. The polar bear will now resume its migration to Hudson Bay.

The tissue samples are sent to a laboratory for analysis. The results Ramsay gets from the lab are worrisome. The bear's fat tissue contains polychlorinated biphenyls, better known as PCBs. Ramsay has found that the concentration of PCBs in the bear's fat tissue is 8 ppm (parts per million). Polar bears are not the only ones affected. Tissue from fish, seals, and other animals has also been found to contain PCBs. This family of synthetic nonpolar organic compounds has been used industrially in electrical and mechanical equipment for decades. Originally, scientists believed that PCBs were biologically inert, but in the 1970s they discovered that laboratory animals exposed to PCBs had higher than normal rates of birth defects and liver cancer.

With a knowledge of how oily chemicals mix and dissolve, Ramsay and other scientists believe they have found answers to some puzzling questions through their research. In this chapter, you will explore the principles of solubility, and then you will apply those principles to answer some of the questions that environmental scientists have about PCBs.

CHAPTER LINKS

Why would you not expect to find PCBs dissolved in Hudson Bay or any other body of water?

Why were the PCBs not removed from the polar bear's system by the kidneys?

How did PCBs end up in the bear's fat?

Dr. Malcolm Ramsay is a professor of vertebrate ecology at the University of Saskatchewan, in Canada, and one of Canada's leading experts on polar bears. Arctic ecological interactions are relatively simple to study, and Dr. Ramsay focuses on polar bears because of their placement at the top of the food chain. Their tissue clearly demonstrates biological amplification of pesticides and other pollutants. The polar bear's food chain consists of algae, which absorb PCBs from polluted water; plankton, which eat algae; cod, which eat plankton; seals, which eat cod; and finally, polar bears, which eat seals. At each link in the food chain, the concentration of PCBs increases.

There are more than 209 different oily synthetic polychlorinated biphenyl compounds (PCBs). They have been used as coolants and insulating materials in electrical transformers. Most are insoluble in water, soluble in fats, and resistant to biological and chemical degradation. These properties result in the biological amplification of PCBs.

Although they are now banned in North America and Western Europe, PCBs are still used in Eastern Europe. The long-range effects of PCBs and their more toxic furan impurities on people are unknown. However, in laboratory animals, high doses of PCBs produce gastric disorders, birth defects, bronchitis, miscarriages, skin lesions, and several other disorders.

CONCEPT PREVIEW

Section 13-1

The nature of solutions
▶ types of mixtures

Expressing concentration
▶ preparing molar solutions
▶ calculations using molarity

Separating mixtures
▶ filtration, evaporation, centrifuging
▶ chromatography

Section 13-2

Solubility of substances
▶ soluble and insoluble
▶ gas solubility and pressure
▶ polarity and hydrogen bonds
▶ using solubility differences

Section 13-3

Electrical conductivity
▶ electrolytes and nonelectrolytes
▶ molecular compounds

The process of dissolving
▶ dissociation and hydration
▶ energy changes
▶ solubility guidelines

Section 13-4

Solute effects on liquids
▶ boiling point elevation
▶ freezing point depression
▶ effect of concentration
▶ emulsions and surfactants

What is a solution?

OBJECTIVES	
▶ **Distinguish** between solutions, suspensions, and colloids.	▶ **Relate** various ways that concentrations may be expressed.
▶ **Explain** the role of a solute and a solvent in a solution.	▶ **Use** units of molarity in stoichiometric calculations.
▶ **Describe** some techniques chemists use to separate mixtures.	▶ **Describe** the procedure for making a solution of prescribed molarity.

LESSON WARM-UP

Discussion Strategy As students come into class, call their attention to a jar like the one shown in Figure 13-1 containing water and (if possible) a bit of potter's clay. You should be stirring the suspension continuously. Ask students to predict what will happen when you stop stirring the mixture. Introduce the word *suspension,* and ask students to name things that are suspended. Examples could include traffic lights over a street, stage scenery, and an object on a chain worn around the neck. Help them develop the sense that a suspended object is one that is held up in some way. Stop stirring the mixture, and have students watch what happens. Ask them if the solid material formed a suspension or a solution.

Mixtures

You learned in Chapter 1 about the distinction between pure substances and mixtures. Mixtures can by classified into *homogeneous* mixtures, all parts of which have the same composition, and *heterogeneous* mixtures, which are not uniform in composition, though they may appear to be. This chapter is mainly about homogeneous mixtures, or *solutions.*

The potter shown in **Figure 13-1** uses water to help sculpt the sides of a clay pot. As she dips her clay-covered fingers into a container of water, the water turns gray-brown. The clay-water mixture appears uniform. However, if the container sits overnight, the next day the potter will see a muddy layer at the bottom with clear water above. The ingredients of this type of mixture, called a **suspension,** have separated. In a suspension, the particles remain thoroughly mixed while the liquid is being stirred, but later they settle to the bottom. The clay does not dissolve in water; it merely breaks up into small pieces that are so light that, for a time, they remain buoyed up by the surrounding water.

suspension
a mixture that appears uniform while being stirred but separates into different phases when agitation ceases

VISUAL STRATEGY

Figure 13-1 Ask students how the jar would appear if its contents were a solution (transparent although perhaps colored). Point out that the clay particles are much larger than water molecules but that they can be suspended for a short time by collisions with water molecules. These collisions are not enough to overcome gravitational force, and the particles eventually fall to the bottom of the jar.

Module 8: Strong and Weakly Ionized Species, pH, and Titrations
Topic: Solutions
This engaging tutorial reviews and reinforces understanding of the nature of solutions.

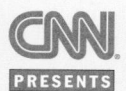 **Science in the News**
PRESENTS **Feature Story 23**
New Extraction Techniques for Gold
See the Science in the News video guide for more details.

▼ **FIGURE 13-1**

Before settling   **After settling**

a Initially, the clay-water mixture seems homogeneous, like a solution.

b Over time, however, the mixture separates into two distinct layers.

468 CHAPTER 13

DEMONSTRATION 1

Liquid Mixtures

Approximate time: 10 minutes

This demonstration should promote a discussion of solubility, suspensions, and miscibility.

1. Add 50 mL of H_2O to 50 mL of ethanol in a small Erlenmeyer flask. Stopper and shake the flask, and set it down.

2. Add 50 mL of H_2O to 50 mL of vegetable oil in an identical Erlenmeyer flask. Stopper and shake that flask, and set it down.

3. Add 5 g of sucrose to 50 mL of H_2O in a third Erlenmeyer flask. Stopper and shake the flask, and set it down.

4. Add 5 g of $Mg(OH)_2$ to 50 mL of H_2O in a fourth Erlenmeyer flask. Stopper and shake the flask, and set it down.

5. Discuss the condition of each flask, and compare the results in terms of solubility

FIGURE 13-2 ▼

a Fresh water is stable and homogeneous.

Fresh water

Saltwater solution

Sodium ion, Na⁺

Chloride ion, Cl⁻

Water

b The saltwater mixture is also stable and homogeneous because mixing occurs between molecules and ions.

Colloids are intermediate between suspensions and solutions

Milk, on the other hand, does not settle. You might be tempted to think that milk is a homogeneous mixture or even a pure substance. Under a high-powered microscope, however, you would see that milk contains globules of fat and small lumps of casein, a protein, in a clear liquid called whey. Milk is what scientists call a **colloid,** a mixture in which very small isolated regions of one component (the lumps of fat and casein) are dispersed throughout the major component (the whey). Though small, the isolated regions contain millions of molecules.

Solutions are stable, homogeneous mixtures

A student working in a pet shop is asked to prepare some water for a saltwater aquarium. She fills an aquarium with fresh water. Then she adds a carefully measured quantity of salt crystals to the aquarium, as shown in **Figure 13-2**, and stirs. These crystals are a mixture of salts formulated to produce the same composition as sea water. After stirring, the student can no longer see grains of salt that are distinct from the water. No matter how long she waits, the salt will not spontaneously separate from the water. The salt has dissolved to form a stable homogeneous mixture. The particles of each substance are dispersed throughout the mixture, making it a true solution. The dissolved particles, ions in this case, are individually in contact with the water molecules, not clustered together as they are in colloids or suspensions.

colloid

a mixture in which small particles are suspended throughout a solvent

internetconnect

SCLINKS
NSTA
TOPIC: Colloids
GO TO: www.scilinks.org
KEYWORD: HW131

SOLUTIONS 469

SECTION 13-1

TEACHING TIP

Characteristics of Colloids Point out that colloids do not settle upon standing. Also, some colloids can appear to be clear. An example is gelatin that has set. These colloids can always be identified by the Tyndall effect, the scattering of a beam of light passing through them.

To demonstrate the Tyndall effect, stir one or two drops of milk into an aquarium or other large, transparent container filled with clear water. In a darkened room, shine a focused beam from an adjustable halogen flashlight or an inexpensive laser pointer through the tank. The colloidal particles from the milk will make the beam visible. Place a small mirror on the bottom of the tank, and shine the beam at an angle toward the mirror. Students will be able to see both the incident beam and the reflected beam.

DID YOU KNOW?

Some common colloids, such as milk and mayonnaise, appear white primarily because of the complete scattering of light striking them. On the microscopic level, they generally appear to be clear droplets suspended in another clear liquid.

VISUAL STRATEGY

Figure 13-2 Help students realize that in a true solution the dissolved substance is completely separated into individual ions or molecules that are dispersed evenly throughout the solvent.

and homogeneity. Both ethanol and sucrose dissolve in water and form homogeneous mixtures. Neither oil nor Mg(OH)₂ is soluble in water (to any visible extent); they form heterogeneous mixtures with water.

Safety
Wear safety goggles and an apron; avoid flames. Students should remain at least 10 ft from the demonstration.

Disposal
Mix all liquids together, add a little liquid detergent, and shake. Dilute the mixture to five times its volume with water, stir, and pour the mixture down the drain.

HISTORICAL CONNECTION

The Swedish chemist Svante Arrhenius was working toward his Ph.D. degree in 1884 when he proposed that the salt $CuCl_2$ was pulled apart into ions when it dissolved in water. His idea was thought to be so weak that he was awarded his degree with the lowest possible grade. In 1903, Arrhenius won the Nobel Prize for this theory of ionic dissociation in water.

ANSWERS

CONCEPT CHECK

1. **a.** heterogeneous
   b. homogeneous
   c. heterogeneous
   d. heterogeneous
2. No. Any homogeneous mixture is a solution.
3. solvent: water; solute: sodium chloride (Na^+ ions and Cl^- ions)

---

solvent

the substance in which the solute dissolves to make the solution

solute

the substance dissolved in a solution

aqueous

describing a solution in which the solvent is water

concentration

the quantity of solute in a specific quantity of solvent or solution

molarity

a concentration unit, expressed as moles of solute per liter of solution

---

Solution is a broad term

Technically, any mixture that is homogeneous on a microscopic level is a solution. According to that definition, air is a solution, as are alloys, such as brass, bronze, and steel. However, when most people use the word *solution,* they are usually referring to a homogeneous *liquid* mixture. A homogeneous liquid mixture has one primary component—a liquid—as well as one or more additional ingredients that are present in smaller amounts. The primary ingredient is called the **solvent,** and the other ingredients, which may be solid, liquid, or gas in their pure state(s), are **solutes** and are said to be *dissolved* in the solvent. By far the most common solutions are those with water as the solvent. Such solutions are called **aqueous** solutions.

CONCEPT CHECK

1. Classify the following mixtures as homogeneous or heterogeneous:
   a. freshly squeezed orange juice   **c.** human blood
   b. tap water   **d.** sand
2. Does a solution have to be a liquid mixture? Explain why or why not.
3. Name the solute and the solvent in an aqueous sodium chloride solution.

Expressing concentration

Molarity is the ratio of solute amount (in moles) to solution volume (in liters)

A method is needed to express how much solute is present in a solution, either in relation to a quantity of solvent or to a quantity of solution. Such a ratio is a measure of the **concentration.** You learned in Chapter 3 that the mole is the SI unit for amounts of substances, such as the amount of reactants and products in chemical reactions. The mole is also a basis of the concentration unit called **molarity,** M.

$$\text{molarity (M)} = \frac{\text{moles of solute}}{\text{liters of solution}} = \frac{\text{mol}}{\text{L}}$$

Though determined and used as a ratio, molarity is always regarded as a quotient, as shown in the following example.

$$\frac{0.036 \text{ mol LiCl}}{0.040 \text{ L solution}} = \frac{0.90 \text{ mol LiCl}}{\text{L solution}} = 0.90 \text{ M LiCl}$$

It is easy to calculate molarity when the volume of solution is exactly 1 L. In the real world, however, most situations will involve more or less than 1 L of solution. Keep in mind that molarity is a ratio—the amount of solute divided by the volume of solution. Once you make a 0.90 M solution, the ratio of the amount of solute to the volume of solution is *constant,* regardless of how much of the solution you sample.

DEMONSTRATION 2

Volume of Solvent, Solute, and Solution

Approximate time: 10 minutes

RESOURCE LINK

ChemFile Lab D
Consumer Lab
Have students do Experiment 12:
Solutions: Rock Formation.

Use this demonstration of a discrepant event to generate interest in the mechanism of solution formation.

1. Fill a 100 mL graduated cylinder to the 100.0 mL mark with H_2O. Adjust the volume with an eyedropper.

2. Fill another 100 mL cylinder to the 100.0 mL mark with 95% ethanol (available as denatured alcohol at most pharmacies).

3. Have a student come forward to verify the cylinder readings and write them on the board in the following form.

   100.0 mL H_2O + 100.0 mL ethanol = _____ mL solution

4. Pour the contents of both cylinders into a single 250 mL cylinder, and drain them completely. Mix the contents thoroughly

A concentration can be expressed in many forms. Certain concentration measures are used in medicine, others in pollution control, and still others in biological research, as described in **Table 13-1.** It is possible to convert among all the ways of expressing concentration, but you may need to know molar masses and densities.

If you simply mixed a liter of solvent with the proper amount of solute to prepare a liter of solution of a specific concentration, the final solution would generally have a volume slightly greater or smaller than 1 L, depending on the relative densities of the solvent and the solution. The definition of *molarity* is based on the amount of solute in the final volume of the solution. To make a solution that has a volume of exactly 1.000 L when finished, you must follow the very specific procedure shown on the next page.

TEACHING TIP
Concentration and Color Display several identical flasks or beakers containing solutions of potassium permanganate of various concentrations (made by diluting a stock solution of $KMnO_4$ with varying volumes of water). Ask students which container has the solution of greatest concentration and how they made that judgment. Elicit the idea that the solutions have varying numbers of ions per unit volume, which accounts for the varying depths of color.

TABLE 13-1 Measures of Concentration

Name	Abbreviation or symbol	Units	Areas of application
Grams of solute per hundred grams of solvent	g/100 g	$\dfrac{g\ solute}{100\ g\ solvent}$	to determine solubilities; in medical products
Mass percent or weight percent	% or %w/w	$\dfrac{g\ solute}{g\ solution} \times 100$	in biological research
Parts per million	ppm*	$\dfrac{g\ solute}{1\ 000\ 000\ g\ solution}$	to express small concentrations
Parts per billion	ppb*	$\dfrac{g\ solute}{1\ 000\ 000\ 000\ g\ solution}$	to express very small concentrations, as in pollutants or contaminants
Parts per trillion	ppt*	$\dfrac{g\ solute}{1\ 000\ 000\ 000\ 000\ g\ solution}$	to express extremely small concentrations, as with isotopes used as tracers in medicine
Molarity	M	$\dfrac{mol\ solute}{L\ solution}$	in solution stoichiometry reactions
Molality	m	$\dfrac{mol\ solute}{kg\ solvent}$	with calculation of properties such as boiling-point elevation and freezing-point depression
Mole fraction	x	$\dfrac{mol\ solute}{total\ mol\ solution}$	in solution thermodynamics
Volume percent	% V/V	$\dfrac{volume\ solute}{volume\ solution} \times 100$	with liquid-liquid mixtures
Mass-volume percent	% w/v	$\dfrac{g\ solute}{mL\ solution} \times 100$	in many commercial products

*When applied to gases, ppm means mL of the solute per million mL (1 m^3) of solution, and similarly for ppb and ppt.

RESOURCE LINK

ChemFile Mini-Guide to Problem Solving
Assign Chapter 14: *Concentration of Solutions* and Chapter 15: *Dilutions* for additional practice.

CHAPTER 14
Concentration of Solutions

There are three principal ways to express solution concentration in chemistry—percentage by mass, molarity, and molality.
The following table compares these three ways of stating solution concentration. Examining the method of preparation of the three types may help you understand the differences among them.

CHAPTER 15
Dilutions

Suppose you work in the laboratory of a paint company where you use 100 mL of a 0.1 M solution of zinc chloride in a quality-control test that you carry out 10 times a day. It would be tedious and time-consuming to continually measure out small amounts of $ZnCl_2$ to make 100 mL of this solution. Of course, you could make many liters of the solution at one time, but that would require several large containers to store the solution. The answer to the problem is to make a much more concentrated solution and then dilute it with water to make the less concentrated solution that you need. The more-concentrated solution is called a *stock solution*. You could make a 1 M $ZnCl_2$ solution by measuring out 1 mol of zinc chloride, 136.3 g, and dissolving it in enough water to make a liter of solution. This solution is 10 times as concentrated as the solution you need. Every time you need the test solution, you can measure out 10 mL of the 1 M solution and dilute it to 100 mL to yield 100 mL of 0.1 M $ZnCl_2$ solution.
To make a solution by dilution, you must determine the volume of stock solution to use and the amount of solvent needed to dilute to the concentration you need. As you have learned, the molarity of a solution is its concentration in moles of solute per liter of solution. Molarity is found by dividing the moles of solute by the number of liters of solution.

$$M = \frac{moles\ solute}{liter\ solution}$$

So, for a measured volume of any solution:

amount of solute in mol = molarity $\times$ volume of solution

If this measured volume of solution is diluted to a new volume by adding solvent, the new, larger volume still contains the same number of moles of solute. Therefore, where 1 and 2 represent the concentrated and diluted solutions:

molarity$_1$ $\times$ volume$_1$ = moles solute = molarity$_2$ $\times$ volume$_2$

Therefore:

molarity$_1$ $\times$ volume$_1$ = molarity$_2$ $\times$ volume$_2$

This relationship applies whenever solution 2 is made from solution 1 by dilution.

176 Chapter 15

with a long stirring rod that can reach to the bottom of the cylinder.

5. Have the same student record the combined volume and write it on the board. The volume should be around 190 to 192 mL. Challenge students to account for the missing volume. Strong hydrogen bonding occurs among water molecules and ethanol molecules. When these molecules are combined, this bonding pulls them closer together than they were before mixing. The formation of this tighter arrangement is exothermic, as is usually evident to the touch.

Safety
Wear safety goggles and an apron. Avoid flames. Students should remain 10 ft from the demonstration.

Disposal
Mix all liquids together. Add 500 mL of water, and pour the mixture down the drain.

TEACHING TIP

Water of Hydration   Call students' attention to the fact that when solutions of hydrates are being prepared, the water of hydration must be added to the molar mass.

COMMON MISCONCEPTION

Some students have a difficult time with the idea that the concentration of a specific solution is the same regardless of the quantity present. Make 1 L of a CuSO₄ solution, as shown in the How To feature on this page. Pour samples of various volumes into several beakers. Ask students which sample contains the most solute (*the largest sample*). Then ask which sample has the highest concentration. Students should realize that all are the same concentration.

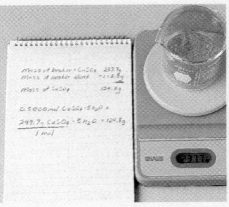

$CuSO_4 \cdot 5H_2O$ is one of the compounds used to produce the chemiluminescence in light sticks. To make this solution, each liter will require 0.5000 mol of $CuSO_4 \cdot 5H_2O$. Start by calculating the mass of copper(II) sulfate pentahydrate, $CuSO_4 \cdot 5H_2O$, needed. To convert this amount to a mass, multiply by the molar mass of $CuSO_4 \cdot 5H_2O$ (mass of $CuSO_4 \cdot 5H_2O$ = 0.5000 mol × 249.68 g/mol = 124.8 g).

Add some solvent (water) to the calculated mass of $CuSO_4 \cdot 5H_2O$ in the beaker to dissolve it, and then pour the solution into a 1.000 L volumetric flask.

Rinse the beaker with more water several times, and each time pour the rinse water into the flask until the solution almost reaches the neck of the flask.

Stopper the flask, and swirl thoroughly until all of the solid is dissolved.

Carefully fill the flask exactly to the 1.000 L mark with more water.

Restopper, and invert the flask at least 10 times to ensure complete mixing.

The resulting solution has 0.5000 mol of solute dissolved in 1.000 L of solution—a 0.5000 M concentration.

GRAPHIC ORGANIZER

Classifying Mixtures

SAMPLE PROBLEM 13A Calculating molarity

What is the molarity of a potassium chloride solution that has a volume of 400.0 mL and contains 85.0 g of KCl?

1 List what you know

- solution volume = 400.0 mL
- solute mass = 85.0 g KCl
- molarity of KCl solution = ? M

2 Set up the problem

- Calculate the molar mass of the solute, KCl.

$$\text{molar mass of KCl} = 74.55 \text{ g/mol}$$

- Because the units of molarity are mol/L, the mass must be converted to an amount in moles and the volume of solution must be converted to liters. Place the solute quantity over the solution volume, even though they are not yet in the correct units. Use the conversion factor that will change milliliters to liters. Then use the conversion factor from the molar mass that will give the amount of solute in moles.

$$\frac{\text{g KCl}}{\text{mL solution}} \times \frac{1000 \text{ mL}}{1 \text{ L}} \times \frac{1 \text{ mol KCl}}{\text{g KCl}} = \frac{\text{mol KCl}}{\text{L}}$$

3 Calculate

- Substitute the values given.

$$\frac{85.0 \text{ g KCl}}{400.0 \text{ mL}} \times \frac{1000 \text{ mL}}{1 \text{ L}} \times \frac{1 \text{ mol KCl}}{74.55 \text{ g KCl}} = \frac{2.85 \text{ mol KCl}}{\text{L}} = 2.85 \text{ M}$$

- This result can be expressed as 2.85 M, 2.85 mol/L, or 2.85 molar. They all mean the same thing.

$$\text{molar} = \text{mol/L} = \text{M}$$

SAMPLE PROBLEM 13B Determining the mass of solute

Sodium thiosulfate, $Na_2S_2O_3$, is used as a fixer when developing photographic film. What is the mass in grams of $Na_2S_2O_3$ needed to make 100.0 mL of a 0.250 M solution?

1 List what you know

- solution volume = 100.0 mL
- solution molarity = 0.250 M $Na_2S_2O_3$
- mass of $Na_2S_2O_3$ = ? g

2 Set up the problem

- Calculate the molar mass of the solute, $Na_2S_2O_3$.

$$\text{molar mass of } Na_2S_2O_3 = 158.12 \text{ g/mol}$$

SAMPLE PROBLEM 13A

ADDITIONAL EXAMPLES

a. Determine the molarity of a solution prepared by dissolving 16.9 g of NaOH in enough water to make 250.0 mL of solution.

Ans. 1.69 M

b. A solution is prepared by dissolving 30.05 g of ammonium dichromate, $(NH_4)_2Cr_2O_7$, in water and diluting it to 500.0 mL in a volumetric flask. What is the molarity of the solution?

Ans. 0.2384 M

c. A mass of 158.0 g of calcium nitrate tetrahydrate is dissolved in enough water to make 1.500 L of solution. Calculate the molarity of this solution.

Ans. 0.4460 M

ALTERNATIVE ASSESSMENT

Depicting Molecules in Mixtures

Ask students to make drawings to illustrate the following mixtures at the molecular level:

- a solution of glucose in water
- a mercury-silver dental amalgam (alloy)
- a suspension of $Al(OH)_3$ (insoluble) in water

SAMPLE PROBLEM 13B

ADDITIONAL EXAMPLES

a. What mass of $MgCl_2$ would you need in order to make 250.0 mL of a 0.200 M solution?

Ans. 4.76 g

b. What mass of nickel(II) iodide would have to be dissolved in order to make 0.500 L of a 0.0750 M solution?

Ans. 11.7 g

c. You want to make 200.0 mL of a 2.80 M solution of strontium bromide. What mass of $SrBr_2 \cdot 6H_2O$ would you need for the solution?

Ans. 199 g

▶ Remember what you are asked for and what you are given. You are trying to find out the mass in grams, given a solution volume and molarity.

▶ Set up your calculation, using the conversion factors correctly to achieve the answer. Convert the solution volume to the amount in moles using the solution molarity given. The amount in moles can then be converted to mass using the molar mass of the solute. (This problem can be done in one or several steps.)

$$\text{mL solution} \times \frac{1 \text{ L}}{1000 \text{ mL}} \times \frac{\text{mol Na}_2\text{S}_2\text{O}_3}{1 \text{ L}} \times \frac{\text{g Na}_2\text{S}_2\text{O}_3}{1 \text{ mol Na}_2\text{S}_2\text{O}_3} = \text{g Na}_2\text{S}_2\text{O}_3$$

3 Calculate

▶ Substitute the values given.

$$100.0 \text{ mL} \times \frac{1 \text{ L}}{1000 \text{ mL}} \times \frac{0.250 \text{ mol Na}_2\text{S}_2\text{O}_3}{1 \text{ L}} \times \frac{158.12 \text{ g Na}_2\text{S}_2\text{O}_3}{1 \text{ mol Na}_2\text{S}_2\text{O}_3} =$$

$$3.95 \text{ g Na}_2\text{S}_2\text{O}_3$$

SAMPLE PROBLEM 13C   Using solution stoichiometry

What volume in milliliters of a 0.500 M solution of copper(II) sulfate, $CuSO_4$, is needed to react with an excess of aluminum to provide 11.0 g of copper?

1 List what you know

▶ molarity of reactant = 0.500 M $CuSO_4$
▶ mass of product = 11.0 g Cu
▶ solution volume = ? mL

2 Set up the problem

▶ Write the balanced chemical equation for the reaction.

$$3CuSO_4(aq) + 2Al(s) \longrightarrow 3Cu(s) + Al_2(SO_4)_3(aq)$$

▶ Look up the molar mass of Cu.

$$\text{molar mass of Cu} = 63.55 \text{ g/mol}$$

▶ As in all these types of problems, remember what you are asked for and what you are given. You are trying to find the solution volume. You are given the molarity of the solution and the mass of one of the products.

▶ Set up your calculation, using the conversion factors correctly to achieve the answer. Convert the mass of Cu to moles, then use the mole ratio of $CuSO_4$: Cu from the balanced chemical equation to determine the number of moles of $CuSO_4$. The moles of $CuSO_4$ solution can be converted to volume using the reciprocal of molarity. This calculation can be done in two steps, as follows.

$$\text{g Cu} \times \frac{1 \text{ mol Cu}}{\text{g Cu}} \times \frac{\text{mol CuSO}_4}{\text{mol Cu}} = \text{mol CuSO}_4$$

$$\text{mol CuSO}_4 \times \frac{\text{L solution}}{\text{mol CuSO}_4} \times \frac{1000 \text{ mL}}{1 \text{ L solution}} = \text{mL CuSO}_4 \text{ solution}$$

Or the calculation can be combined into one step, as follows.

$$\text{g Cu} \times \frac{1 \text{ mol Cu}}{\text{g Cu}} \times \frac{\text{mol CuSO}_4}{\text{mol Cu}} \times \frac{\text{L solution}}{\text{mol CuSO}_4} \times \frac{1000 \text{ mL}}{1 \text{ L solution}} =$$

$$\text{mL CuSO}_4 \text{ solution}$$

3 Calculate

▸ Substitute the values given.

$$11.0 \text{ g Cu} \times \frac{1 \text{ mol Cu}}{63.55 \text{ g Cu}} \times \frac{3 \text{ mol CuSO}_4}{3 \text{ mol Cu}} \times \frac{1 \text{ L solution}}{0.500 \text{ mol CuSO}_4} \times$$

$$\frac{1000 \text{ mL solution}}{1 \text{ L solution}} = 346 \text{ mL CuSO}_4 \text{ solution}$$

PRACTICE PROBLEMS

1. What is the molarity of a sodium hypochlorite household bleach made from the equivalent of 125 g of NaClO in 2.0 L of solution?

2. What volume in milliliters of a 0.375 M solution of sodium hydrogen carbonate, $NaHCO_3$, is needed to provide 15.3 g of $NaHCO_3$?

3. What volume in liters of a 2.5 M solution of acetic acid, CH_3COOH, is needed to provide 256 g of acetic acid?

4. What mass in grams of copper sulfate pentahydrate, $CuSO_4 \cdot 5H_2O$, is needed to make 75.0 mL of a 0.2500 M solution?

5. What mass in kilograms of table sugar (sucrose, $C_{12}H_{22}O_{11}$) is needed to make 3.50 L of a 1.15 M solution?

6. The calcium phosphate used in fertilizers can be made according to the following unbalanced chemical equation.

$$H_3PO_4(aq) + Ca(OH)_2(s) \longrightarrow Ca_3(PO_4)_2 (aq) + H_2O(l)$$

What mass in grams of each product would be formed if 7.5 L of 5.00 M phosphoric acid reacted with an excess of calcium hydroxide? (Hint: First balance the chemical equation.)

7. What is the molarity of a solution composed of 6.25 g of HCl in 0.300 L of solution?

8. The compound $C_4H_4Au_2CaO_4S_2$ is used in the treatment of rheumatoid arthritis. What mass in milligrams of this compound is needed to make 10.0 mL of a 0.0100 M solution?

9. What is the molarity of a solution composed of 5.8 g of potassium iodide, KI, dissolved in enough water to make 0.125 L of solution?

10. **a.** How many moles of NaOH are contained in 65.0 mL of a 2.2 M solution of NaOH in water?
    b. How many grams of NaOH does this represent?

11. What volume in liters of a 1.50 M solution of NaCl is needed for a reaction that requires 146.3 g of NaCl?

12. What is the molar concentration of a solution composed of 8.210 g of potassium chromate, K_2CrO_4, dissolved in enough water to make 0.500 L of solution?

SAMPLE PROBLEM 13C

ADDITIONAL EXAMPLES

a. What volume in milliliters of a 1.50 M HCl solution would be needed to react completely with 28.4 g of Na_2CO_3 to produce water, CO_2, and NaCl?

Ans. 357 mL

b. A zinc bar is placed in 435 mL of a 0.770 M solution of $CuCl_2$. What mass of zinc would be replaced by copper if all of the copper ions were used up?

Ans. 21.9 g

c. What volume of a 0.232 M solution of barium nitrate would be needed to precipitate all of the sulfate ions in 150.0 mL of a 0.086 M solution of sodium sulfate, Na_2SO_4?

Ans. 56 mL

ANSWERS

PRACTICE PROBLEMS

1. 0.84 M
2. 486 mL
3. 1.70 L
4. 3.48 g $CuSO_4 \cdot 5H_2O$
5. 1.38 kg sucrose, $C_{12}H_{22}O_{11}$
6. 2030 g H_2O, 5820 g $Ca_3(PO_4)_2$
7. 0.571 M
8. 61 mg
9. 0.28 M
10. a. 0.14 mol
    b. 5.7 g
11. 1.67 L
12. 0.0846 M

VISUAL STRATEGY

Figure 13-3 Stress to students that all separation techniques take advantage of the properties of the materials involved. The separation of the coffee grounds is based on solubility and particle size. The separation of salt in the salt pond is based on solubility.

RESOURCE LINK

IN-TEXT LAB
Skills Development
Have students do Exploration 13A on page 765 to develop their skills using chromatographic techniques.

ChemFile Lab C
Skills Development
Have students do Exploration 2: *Separation of Mixtures*.

Self-Directed Inquiry
Have students do Investigation 2: *Separation of Mixtures—Tanker Truck Spill*.

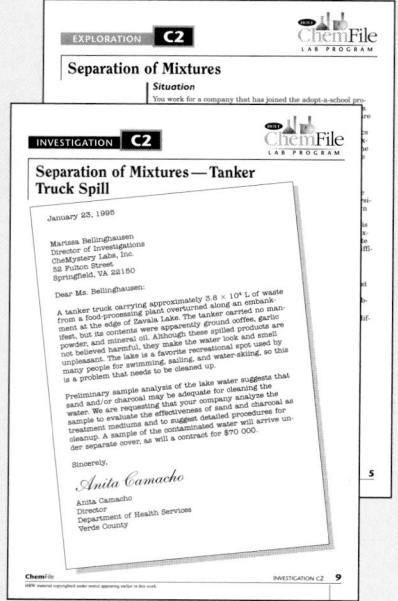

Separating mixtures

There are many ways to separate mixtures into their components. The best method to use in a particular case depends on the properties and quanities of the ingredients. The methods illustrated in **Figure 13-3a** through **Figure 13-3d** rely on the physical properties of the ingredients to effect a separation. Notice that these methods can be done outside a chemistry lab. In fact, you may use one or more of these methods right in your home. For example, you may use filtration to make coffee, and you may use evaporation when you cook.

▼ **FIGURE 13-3**

a Decanting gently separates a liquid from solids that have settled. To decant a mixture, simply pour the liquids off and leave the solids behind. First, however, the solid content of the suspension must be well settled.

b A centrifuge is a tool used to separate mixtures, the components of which have different densities. The centrifuge spins rapidly; the resulting force pushes dense matter outward.

c Ground coffee is separated from liquid coffee by filration. The filtrate—the liquid and any particles smaller than the holes in the filter—collect in the coffeepot. The solid grounds are retained in the filter.

d In saltwater ponds such as this one, sea water evaporates, and salts, mainly sodium chloride, are left behind. This simple method of salt production is still widely used.

DEMONSTRATION 3

Separation of Substances
Approximate time: 15 minutes

1. Place 4 g of NaCl and 5 g of white sand (mostly SiO_2) into 20 mL of water in a large heat-resistant test tube.

2. Ask students how they might separate the mixture based on the properties of the three substances. Ask them if filtering the sand will also separate the salt.

3. Filter the mixture, and then ask for methods to separate the salt and water. An easy method is to place the solution in an evaporating dish and to heat it gently until the water evaporates, leaving dry salt crystals. Heat *very* gently as the mixture approaches dryness.

4. Ask students how they could also recover the water that evaporated.

Chromatography is widely used in industry and research

Chromatography may be used to separate the components of a liquid or gaseous mixture so that they may be isolated or identified. The method works because different dissolved substances are attracted differently to solvents and other media, such as solid surfaces.

Paper chromatography is a powerful separation technique. It can be used to separate the dyes in ink. Water or some other solvent dissolves the ink. The solvent containing the ink travels up the paper by *capillary action,* the attraction of the surface of a liquid to the surface of a solid. The dissolved dyes from the ink travel at different rates according to the attraction that they have for the solvent or the paper, as shown in **Figure 13-4.** Those most attracted to the paper travel the slowest. They remain in a rather low position on the paper. The dyes that have the least attraction for the paper travel fastest and farthest. The resulting chromatogram displays bands of different colors.

Laboratories use chromatography to isolate and identify the agents that give foods their flavor and give perfumes their aroma. Law enforcement officers use chromatography to determine the blood alcohol level of motorists suspected of drunk driving.

INQUIRYLAB

The Color of M&M® Candies

In this activity you will investigate whether the colors of candies are single dyes or whether these candies are colored with a mixture of different dyes.

Materials   M&M candies, chromatography paper, developing solution (0.1% NaCl)

Problem   Design an experiment that will determine whether M&M candies contain mixtures of dyes or whether they are single dyes. For example, is the orange color a result of mixing two primary colors? What about the other colors?

Analysis
1. Summarize your results in a report that includes your experimental procedure, a data table that summarizes your results, and the experimental evidence.
2. Be sure to answer the questions posed in the problem statement.

INQUIRYLAB

Other candies that have deeply colored sugar coatings can be used. Students should use no more water than is necessary to dissolve the color coating. Check that they do not dissolve too much of the underlying sugar. It may interfere with the separation.

Analysis
1. Students should report each of the original colors tested and the color components that each color contains.
2. Students will find that most colors are mixtures.

chromatography

a technique for separating components of a mixture by placing the mixture in a mobile phase that is passed over a stationary phase

FIGURE 13-4 ▼

a In chromatography, ink marks are made on absorbent paper, which is then suspended in contact with a solvent.

b The finished chromatogram, shown at right, displays different dyes found in the ink sample.

Safety
Wear safety goggles and a lab apron. Tie back loose clothing and long hair.

Disposal
Save the sand for reuse at another time. Dissolve the salt in water, and pour the mixture down the drain.

ANSWERS

SECTION REVIEW

Total recall

1. Homogeneous mixtures are the same throughout in composition. In a suspension, the separate parts of the mixture are distinct.

2. Pure water can be prepared by boiling impure water and condensing the water vapor—distillation.

3. Chromatography can be used in analysis to separate the components of a mixture so that each can be identified, such as flavors and scents. It is also used to determine blood-alcohol levels.

Critical thinking

4. **a.** suspension
   b. suspension
   c. solution
   d. solution

5. **a.** solute: CO_2 (in equilibrium with H_2CO_3, HCO_3^-, and H_3O^+); solvent: H_2O
   b. solute: sugar; solvent: H_2O
   c. solutes: sugar and several soluble extracts of coffee, including caffeine; solvent: H_2O
   d. solutes: soluble components of lemon juice, including citric acid; soluble extracts of tea, including theophylline; sweetening agent aspartame; solvent: H_2O

Practice problems

6. **a.** 0.652 M
   b. 6.52 M
7. **a.** 1.5 M
   b. 0.52 mol
8. 0.282 M

Distillation can be used to separate components of a solution

distillation

a separation process in which a liquid component is evaporated from a solution and the vapor is condensed to liquid, usually for the purpose of purification

If you have ever left a pot of boiling salted water on a stove until all the liquid boils away, you have performed a **distillation.** Distillation separates components of a mixture based on their boiling points. As one component reaches its boiling point, its vapor is removed and allowed to cool and condense. This process continues until all the desired components have been separated from the mixture.

In a few locations throughout the world, distillation is used to obtain drinking water from sea water. However, because the process requires a lot of energy, it is expensive. Distillation is used on a wide scale in the petroleum industry to separate crude petroleum into its component fractions. These fractions have many uses. Gasoline, heating oil, lubricants, and raw materials used in the plastics industry are all separated from the crude-oil mixture by distillation.

SECTION REVIEW

Total recall

1. Explain why a suspension is classified as a heterogeneous mixture.

2. How is distillation used to prepare pure water from tap water?

3. Give two examples of the practical uses of chromatography.

Critical thinking

4. Identify the following as solutions or suspensions:
   a. muddy river water
   b. orange juice
   c. chlorinated water in a swimming pool
   d. diet soda

5. Name the solute(s) and solvents in the following solutions:
   a. carbonated water
   b. sugar water
   c. black coffee with sugar
   d. diet iced tea with lemon

Practice problems

6. What is the molar concentration of these solutions?
   a. 0.0750 mol of $NaHCO_3$ in 115 mL of solution
   b. 0.750 mol of $NaCH_3COO$ in 115 mL of solution

7. **a.** What is the molar concentration of a solution composed of 3.0 mol of solute in 2.0 L of solution?
   b. How many moles would there be in 350 mL of this solution?

8. What is the molar concentration of a solution composed of 5.85 g of potassium iodide, KI, dissolved in enough water to make 0.1250 L of solution?

9. Describe in your own words exactly how you would prepare 1.00 L of a 0.85 M solution of sodium chloride, NaCl.

10. **Story Clue** On page 467 you read that Dr. Ramsay's test on bear fat revealed a PCB concentration of 8 ppm. How many milligrams of PCB would there be in 35 g of bear fat?

9. Weigh a clean empty beaker, and record its mass. Pour NaCl into the beaker until the mass is increased by 49.7 g, the mass of 0.85 mol of sodium chloride. Use a funnel to pour the salt into a 1 L volumetric flask. Rinse the beaker and funnel with plenty of distilled water. Add more distilled water and swirl until thoroughly dissolved. Add more water dropwise until the flask is filled to the mark. Invert and swirl several times to ensure thorough mixing.

10. 0.28 mg PCB

Does substance A dissolve in substance B?

OBJECTIVES

▶ **Explain** why predicting solubility is difficult.

▶ **Describe** the effects of temperature on solubility.

▶ **Discuss** the features that influence whether pairs of compounds will dissolve in each other.

▶ **Relate** how molecular polarity affects solubility.

▶ **Examine** practical applications of solubility principles.

Solubility

The student pictured in **Figure 13-5** is exploring **solubility.** He has three pure compounds—water, H_2O, lithium chloride, LiCl, and toluene, $C_6H_5CH_3$—and is combining them in pairs. In two cases, nothing appears to happen. After these mixtures are shaken, two layers form, with the denser ingredient on the bottom of the test tube. In the case of

solubility

the maximum amount of a chemical that will dissolve in a given quantity of a solvent at a specified temperature while the solution is in contact with undissolved solute

Water and lithium chloride

Soluble

— Water, H_2O

— Lithium ion, Li^+

— Chloride ion, Cl^-

Toluene and lithium chloride

Insoluble

— Toluene, $C_6H_5CH_3$

— Lithium chloride, LiCl

Water and toluene

Insoluble

— Toluene, $C_6H_5CH_3$

— Water, H_2O

> **FIGURE 13-5** ◀
>
> When H_2O and LiCl are mixed, a solution forms. However, $C_6H_5CH_3$ does not form a solution with either LiCl or H_2O.

SOLUTIONS **479**

TEACHING TIP

Relative Solubility Help students understand that while the words *soluble* and *insoluble* are useful, a whole spectrum of solubilities exists. Compare this situation with the degrees of particle size in mixtures discussed in Section 13-1 and the fact that an intermediate state (colloids) exists between suspensions and solutions.

READING STRATEGY

Peer Teaching

Give students self-stick notes, and have them mark any text that is unclear as they read pages 479–483, which cover solubility and the factors that affect solubility. After students complete their reading, they should work with a partner to discuss what each did or did not understand. Have students write their remaining questions on the board for a class discussion. In this assignment, students should consider the following questions:

▸ Why are *soluble* and *insoluble* not precise words?

▸ How do pressure and temperature changes affect gas solubility?

▸ Why is gas solubility a hazard in diving?

▸ What words are used to describe mixtures of two liquids? What do the words mean?

▸ What are the influences of polarity and hydrogen bonding on solubility?

VISUAL STRATEGY

Figure 13-6 Ask students to describe what is taking place in the bottle before the cap is removed. They should understand that a stable system exists in which $CO_2(g)$ is in a dynamic equilibrium with $CO_2(aq)$.

soluble

can be dissolved in a particular solvent

insoluble

does not dissolve appreciably in a particular solvent

lithium chloride and water, a single phase is formed—a clear aqueous solution containing lithium ions, Li^+, and chloride ions, Cl^-. From the preliminary experimental results, we might say that lithium chloride is **soluble** in water but **insoluble** in toluene and that water and toluene are insoluble in each other.

But appearances can be deceptive, and you have to be cautious when discussing solubility. If you were to carefully analyze the two layers from the water-toluene mixture, you would find a very small amount of toluene in the aqueous layer and a similarly small concentration of water in the toluene layer. And if the student had chosen a slightly larger sample of lithium chloride, he would have gotten a different result in the first experiment. Not all the salt would have dissolved. Solubility is not a matter of yes or no. It is a matter of how much.

Gases can dissolve in liquids

If you look at an unopened soda bottle, the liquid inside has no bubbles. But what happens once you open an ice-cold bottle of soda? First there is a hissing sound of gas escaping. Then you can see bubbles rising in the liquid. When you first taste the soda, it is tart and there is plenty of fizz. If the soda is allowed to stand, it tastes flat. Why does this happen? Where did the bubbles come from? What can you do to keep soda from going flat? If you apply what you already know about gases and solutions, you may be able answer some of these questions.

You may already know that the bubbles in soda are carbon dioxide gas, CO_2. Because the bubbles are not visible in the unopened soda bottle, shown in **Figure 13-6a,** you know that the liquid contents of the bottle, including the CO_2, are a homogeneous solution. Part of the CO_2 reacts with water to form carbonic acid, H_2CO_3, which partially ionizes into ions that give the soda its tangy, acidic taste.

▼ **FIGURE 13-6**

CO_2 under high pressure above solvent

Air at atmospheric pressure

CO_2 gas bubble

Dissolved CO_2 molecules

a There are no bubbles in an unopened bottle of soda because carbon dioxide is dissolved in the liquid.

b When the bottle cap is removed, the pressure inside the bottle decreases rapidly. Carbon dioxide escapes due to its lowered solubility.

Dissolved CO_2 molecules

DEMONSTRATION 4

Temperature and Solubility of Gases

Approximate time: 10 minutes

1. At the beginning of class, submerge a bottle of soda in an ice bath. Place an identical bottle in a warm-water bath maintained at 37°C (body temperature). Allow a third identical bottle to stand at room temperature. Monitor the warm-water bath, and add ice to the ice bath as needed.

2. Near the end of class, turn the cap of each bottle so that the gas just begins to

escape. Have student volunteers record the time it takes for each bottle to stop hissing. Have students draw conclusions about the relationship between temperature and the solubility of CO_2.

Safety

Goggles and a lab apron should be worn by the teacher and the volunteers. Other stu-

Gas solubility depends on pressure

In an unopened bottle of soda, some carbon dioxide is in the gas above the liquid level and some is in the liquid itself. We say that the solution in the bottle is **saturated.** This means that, even though there is more CO_2 available, the liquid is holding as much carbon dioxide solute as it can under the present conditions. The concentration of the solute in the saturated solution is the solubility of the solute under the prevailing conditions of temperature and pressure.

Chemists now understand the details of the relationship between pressure and gas solubility. **Henry's law** sums up their findings. In an unopened soda bottle, there is a much higher partial pressure of carbon dioxide in the neck of the bottle, above the liquid, than there is in the air outside the bottle. This greater partial pressure causes more CO_2 to dissolve in the soda than would be possible standing in air. When the bottle is opened, much of the dissolved CO_2 escapes into the air and the partial pressure of carbon dioxide in the bottle's neck soon equals that of the CO_2 in the air. The decrease in the partial pressure of CO_2 inside the bottle causes several things to happen. The solubility of the CO_2 in the soda is reduced, and the excess CO_2 bubbles out of solution, as shown in **Figure 13-6b,** on page 480. The dissolved gas given off as foam from a **supersaturated** solution is called *effervescence*.

A special case: gas solubility and diving

The principles of gas solubility are used in a variety of situations other than soda bottling. Knowledge of these principles is a life-or-death matter for the underwater diver shown in **Figure 13-7.**

When divers are underwater, their bodies are subject to more pressure than at the surface. As a result, the pressure of the air that they breathe must be increased to force the air out of the air tank and into their lungs. Blood is a water-based mixture. Oxygen is carried by hemoglobin molecules within the blood cells in this mixture. But some of the oxygen and other gases, such as nitrogen, which makes up most of air, dissolve in the blood just as carbon dioxide dissolves in soda.

If a diver breathing pressurized air rises to the surface too quickly, decompression sickness, also called the bends, can result. What causes the bends? The sudden decrease from high pressure underwater to normal atmospheric pressure at the surface is similar to the pressure decrease that takes place when you open a soda bottle. Gases, such as nitrogen, that dissolve in blood and body fluids bubble out of solution. Such bubbles in the blood can block blood flow in smaller blood vessels, press on tissues, and affect nerve impulses, causing the intense pain that incautious divers may experience.

saturated

containing the amount of solute specified by the solubility

Henry's law

the solubility of a gas in a liquid is directly proportional to the partial pressure of that gas on the surface of the liquid

supersaturated

containing more than the amount of solute specified by the solubility at a given set of conditions

---

ADDITIONAL APPLICATION

Cold, aerated water typically forms white ice, which contains many small bubbles of gas that come out of solution as the ice freezes. This type of ice catalyzes the release of CO_2 from soda that is poured over it, causing the soda to foam and go flat. Fast-food restaurant icemakers are sometimes connected to hot-water supplies in order to make ice that is clear. Hot water contains much less dissolved gas than cold water. The clear ice allows waitstaff to fill drink containers more rapidly because less foaming occurs.

FIGURE 13-7 ▼

Underwater divers breathing pressurized air must return to the surface gradually to prevent the bends.

RESOURCE LINK

ChemFile Lab C
Skills Development
Have students do Exploration 13:
Testing for Dissolved O_2.

Skills Development
Have students do Exploration 14:
Solubility of Ammonia.

EXPLORATION C13 — ChemFile LAB PROGRAM

Testing for Dissolved Oxygen

Situation
The company you work for has been hired as an expert witness in a lawsuit. The local chapter of Bass Anglers Unlimited has been disturbed by recent declines in the population of bass in Pulaski Lake...

Objectives
Measure the concentration of oxygen in a sample of water.

EXPLORATION C14 — ChemFile LAB PROGRAM

Solubility of Ammonia

Situation
Sparkle-Clean Industries has contacted you about one of their products, a household window cleaner with ammonia, NH_3. Sparkle-Clean did not have a product for this market until they bought out a competitor. The competitor purchased gaseous NH_3 from a local gas products supplier. Then the NH_3 was dissolved in water at room temperature as the first and most difficult step in the manufacturing process.

Sparkle-Clean's manufacturing equipment has several features that the competitor did not have. One piece of equipment can maintain liquids at temperatures from 0°C to 80°C. Perhaps changing the temperature could improve the competitor's procedure so that more NH_3 would dissolve in the water. However, the equipment would need expensive adjustments to keep the hazardous NH_3 gas under control. To determine whether the savings will justify the initial expense, they want you to model the process on a small scale, determine the best temperature, and estimate how much NH_3 dissolves at that temperature.

Objectives
Prepare a small amount of ammonia gas in a container.
Calculate amount of ammonia present, given volume, temperature, and pressure.
Test how well the ammonia dissolves in water at different temperatures.
Relate changes in volume of a gas to the removal of gas particles as they dissolve in a solution.

Background
Most gases dissolve better in water at cooler temperatures, provided that the pressure remains the same. This is the opposite of the pattern observed for most solids. One example is a soda bottle, the warmer the soda, the flatter it will taste because the dissolved CO_2 that provides the "fizz" will bubble out of solution. You must test the NH_3 to see if it follows this same pattern. Measuring how long it takes for a given amount of NH_3 to dissolve can also provide a rough measure of how much more efficient the process will be at a different temperature.

Problem
To determine the optimum temperature for this procedure, you must do the following.
• Prepare some NH_3 gas by heating a solution of aqueous NH_3.
• Test the NH_3 by dissolving it in water at various temperatures.
• Compare efficiencies of the dissolving process for the NH_3 in the different water samples by measuring the time for it to dissolve completely.

86 EXPLORATION C14   ChemFile

SOLUTIONS 481

---

dents should remain 10 ft from the demonstration. Do not allow anyone to drink the sodas.

Disposal
Pour the sodas and the water down the drain.

▶ **FIGURE 13-8**

When oil and water are mixed, they do not form a solution. Instead, the less dense oil forms a layer on top of the water.

miscible
indicates liquids that will dissolve in each other

immiscible
indicates liquids that will not dissolve appreciably in each other

One solution is to rise to the surface slowly, but today most deep-sea divers prevent the bends by breathing an oxygen-helium mixture instead of compressed air that contains nitrogen. Because helium is less soluble than nitrogen, less of it dissolves in the body tissues, so if a diver has to return to the surface rapidly, there is less gas bubbling out of the diver's blood.

Gas solubility decreases with increasing temperature

After your soda bottle is open and the soda is allowed to warm, the soda forms fewer bubbles and tastes flat. Even if you compare the taste of a newly opened warm soda with that of a newly opened cold soda, you will find that the warm soda will taste somewhat flat. Warm soda tastes flat because there is less CO_2 dissolved in it. Chemists have found that other gases behave similarly; their solubility in liquids decreases with increasing temperature.

Liquids and miscibility

Certain pairs of liquids form a single phase—a solution—when they are mixed, no matter what the relative amounts of the liquids are. These liquids are **miscible.** A mixture of ethylene glycol and water is an example. Ethylene glycol, which is commonly called glycol, is the most common antifreeze, a substance added to radiator water to prevent it from freezing in cold climates or overheating in warm climates.

Certain other pairs of liquids, such as the oil and water shown in **Figure 13-8,** scarcely mix at all. They are **immiscible.** Each liquid is almost insoluble in the other; instead they form two layers, with the denser liquid on the bottom.

Polarity of the solvent and solute is important

When treating solubilities, a rule of thumb is "like dissolves like." You learned in Chapter 6 that molecules can be polar or nonpolar. Generally speaking, polar solvents dissolve polar compounds, and nonpolar solvents dissolve nonpolar compounds. **Figure 13-9** shows a sugar cube, which is made of polar sucrose molecules, dissolving in water, a polar solvent.

In the dissolving process, attractive forces between solute particles are disrupted and replaced by new attractions between solute and solvent. If the new solvent-solute attractions are similar to the attractive forces in the solute, the energy needed to form the solution is low. The

GRAPHIC ORGANIZER

Comparing Electrolytes

	Activity in water	Kind of electrolyte	Examples
Molecular compounds	Ionize completely	Strong electrolyte	HCl, HNO$_3$
	Ionize slightly	Weak electrolyte	CH$_3$COOH, NH$_3$
	Do not ionize	Nonelectrolyte	CH$_3$CH$_2$OH, C$_{12}$H$_{22}$O$_{11}$
Ionic compounds	Soluble (dissociates)	Strong electrolyte	NaCl, KNO$_3$
	Insoluble (does not dissociate)	Strong electrolyte to the degree that it dissolves	AgCl, BaSO$_4$

enthalpy factor is usually favorable for one substance to dissolve in another. This means that the dipole forces between polar solvent molecules easily replace the similar forces between polar solute molecules and form a solution. Also, the London forces between nonpolar solvent molecules require little energy to replace similar forces between nonpolar solute molecules.

To understand the dissolving process, you must also consider entropy. There is a natural tendency for substances to mix. Imagine a container with gas A on one side of a partition and gas B on the other side. If you were to remove the partition, molecules of A and of B eventually would be thoroughly mixed because of this natural tendency for disorder. The dissolution of one substance in another requires a negative free energy change. This usually, but not always, results from a negative enthalpy change and a positive entropy change.

Hydrogen bonding also plays a role

You encountered hydrogen bonding in Chapter 6. High solubility is expected when hydrogen bonds form between solute and solvent molecules. If molecule A forms hydrogen bonds with other A molecules but not with molecules of B, it is very probable that substance A will not mix with substance B.

In summary, there are two guidelines that can be used to predict the mutual solubility of pairs of compounds.

1. Two compounds that are both polar or both nonpolar are likely to be miscible.

2. Two compounds that can form hydrogen bonds with each other are likely to be miscible.

However, the most reliable way to tell if two compounds are mutually soluble is to follow the example of the student in Figure 13-5 on page 479, that is, to mix the compounds and observe the result.

FIGURE 13-9

You can see the sucrose in the sugar cube going into solution with the surrounding water solvent.

CONCEPT CHECK

1. Why are gas bubbles not visible in an unopened bottle of soda?
2. Explain what happens to gases dissolved in the blood when a diver rises to the water's surface very quickly.
3. Identify the following pairs of compounds as miscible or immiscible:
   a. antifreeze and water
   b. ethanol and water
   c. toluene and water
   d. acetic acid and water
4. How does rising temperature affect the solubility of gases in water?

DEMONSTRATION 5

Temperature Effects on Rates of Dissolving

Approximate time: 10 minutes

1. Fill a 400 mL beaker with hot water. Fill an identical beaker with ice-cold water. Place the two beakers on the overhead projector.

2. Place two tea bags inside each beaker. Observe the difference in the rate of color change in the two beakers. Have students draw conclusions about the relationship between temperature and the solubility of tea.

Safety
Wear goggles and a lab apron. Do not allow anyone to drink the tea.

Disposal
Throw the tea bags in the trash can, and pour the tea down the drain.

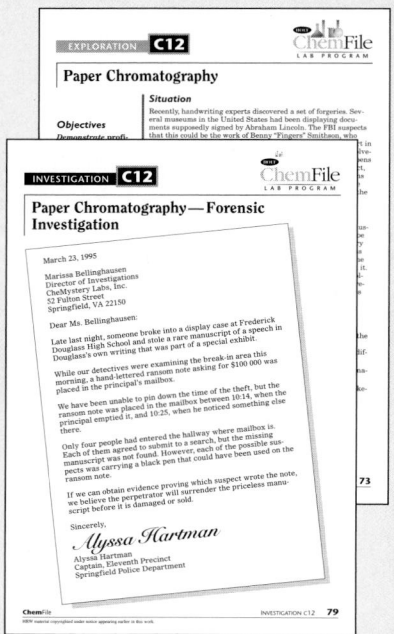
Solubility principles at work

Dry cleaners use solubility principles to remove stains

Why do some clothes need to be dry-cleaned, while others do not? Washing with water and detergents cleans most clothes. But there are three situations in which dry cleaning may be necessary—if your clothes have a stubborn stain, such as ink or rust; if you have spilled something greasy on your clothes; or if the label on the clothing recommends dry cleaning.

In spite of its name, dry cleaning does involve liquids. The process uses a nonpolar liquid solvent—tetrachloroethylene, C_2Cl_4 (also known as perchloroethylene, shown in **Figure 13-10**). As you now know, nonpolar solvents will dissolve nonpolar materials. Fats, greases, and oils fall into that category and are notoriously difficult to remove from fabrics by water-based washing.

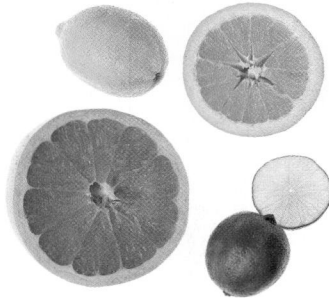

▲ **FIGURE 13-10**

The most commonly used dry-cleaning solvent is tetrachloroethylene, C_2Cl_4.

Vitamin C dissolves in water

The human body needs vitamins. Vitamins control chemical reactions within the body. Not getting enough of a vitamin can make you sick, but so can getting too much. The reasons relate to solubility.

People who have poor diets have suffered from scurvy since at least the time of the Crusades, nearly 1000 years ago. Soldiers and sailors were especially susceptible to scurvy, which causes fatigue and bleeding of the gums and prevents wounds from healing.

The first controlled study of the effects of diet on scurvy was in 1747 when James Lind, a doctor in the British Royal Navy, compared the reactions of sailors suffering from scurvy when given cider, garlic, mustard, vinegar, ocean water, oranges, or lemons. The sailors who received citrus fruits recovered. We now know that citrus fruits are rich in vitamin C. **Figure 13-11** illustrates important information about vitamin C.

internetconnect

SCLINKS
NSTA
TOPIC: Vitamins
GO TO: www.scilinks.org
KEYWORD: HW132

▼ **FIGURE 13-11**

a Lemons, oranges, grapefruits, and limes are rich sources of vitamin C.

b The most common form of vitamin C is ascorbic acid, shown here.

c Because ascorbic acid is highly polar, it is very soluble in water but insoluble in fat and oil.

DEMONSTRATION 6

Polarity

Approximate time: 15 minutes

This demonstration should provoke discussion about solvent-solute interactions.

1. Place 10 mL of H_2O and 10 mL of ethanol in separate test tubes. Use forceps to add no more than two crystals of I_2 to each tube.

2. Stopper and shake each tube. The nonpolar iodine should give a brown color to the less polar ethanol but not to the very polar water.

3. Add a few small crystals of KI to the tube with the water. Stopper and shake the tube. The KI will cause the iodine to dissolve, forming a brown solution. This occurs because of a chemical interaction between the I^- ions and the I_2 molecules to form I_3^- and other polyiodide ions.

Researchers have found that vitamin C has several vital functions, the most important being its role in the synthesis of collagen. Collagen is the protein that makes up tendons, gives strength to teeth and bones, and most importantly, knits endothelial cells together to make blood vessels.

To synthesize collagen where it is needed, vitamin C must be distributed throughout the body. Vitamin C is easily transported by the blood because it is water-soluble.

In the belief that vitamin C combats the common cold, some people prefer to take it in large doses. Is it possible to take too much? Probably not. When intake increases, the vitamin C level rises, but then the kidneys begin excreting the vitamin faster. Your kidneys are so good at regulating water-soluble vitamins that overdosing on vitamin C is very unlikely.

Vitamin A dissolves in oils and fats

For decades, children have been told, "Eat your carrots so you will have good vision." There is some truth to the saying because carrots, and some other vegetables, contain carotenes that your body easily converts into vitamin A. If you do not get enough vitamin A, you may lose your ability to see at night due to a disorder called night blindness.

Vitamin A affects vision because the human body uses it to make a pigment called visual purple, one of the vital light-sensitive molecules in the retina. Vitamin A is also needed for normal growth of the skin, respiratory tract, cornea, and other epithelial tissues, as well as for bone growth and tooth development. Fortunately, most people get enough vitamin A from the variety of foods that they eat. Some sources of vitamin A and its structure are shown in **Figure 13-12.**

FIGURE 13-12 ▼

a Sources of vitamin A include dark green leafy vegetables, carrots, broccoli, tomatoes, and egg yolks.

b Vitamin A is also known as retinol because it plays a vital role in helping the retina of your eye detect light.

c The vitamin A molecule is mainly composed of carbon and hydrogen, making it nonpolar.

TEACHING TIP

Classifying Vitamins   Point out that vitamins are divided into two categories according to solubility. Water-soluble vitamins include B_1 (thiamine), B_2 (riboflavin), B_6 (pyridoxine), B_{12}, niacin, pantothenic acid, folic acid, biotin, and vitamin C. Oil-soluble vitamins are A, D, E, and K.

💡 DID YOU KNOW?

Many vitamins, especially the water-soluble vitamins, act as coenzymes or are precursors to coenzymes. These molecules must be present and bind with an enzyme and substrate for the enzyme-catalyzed reaction to take place. Usually, the coenzymes are changed in the reaction and then enter a biochemical cycle that returns the coenzyme to its original form. Coenzymes might better be called co-substrates.

Variation

Do this demonstration in Petri dishes on an overhead projector. View the coloration on the screen. Slight stirring may be necessary. Try dissolving I_2 in a little cyclohexane, C_6H_{12}, to see a violet solution.

Safety

Wear goggles and a lab apron. Students should remain 10 ft from the demonstration.

Disposal

Slowly add 1 M sodium thiosulfate solution to the iodine solution while stirring until the mixture is colorless. Pour the mixture down the drain.

ANSWERS

SECTION REVIEW

Total recall

1. Solubility of a gas in a liquid depends on the partial pressure of the gas in contact with the liquid. When the pressure is reduced by opening the bottle, CO_2 comes out of the aqueous solution.

2. Answers may vary and may include temperature, polarity of solvent, polarity of solute, and pressure.

3. Answers will vary. Accept all plausible answers. Examples include using a nonpolar solvent to remove an oil stain, chromatography, production of carbonated beverages, and separating soluble materials from insoluble impurities.

4. Gases increase in solubility with decreasing temperature. Therefore, the cold soda retains more dissolved CO_2.

5. Nitrogen in air dissolves in the blood and can form bubbles in the bloodstream and tissues when a diver rises. Helium is much less soluble than nitrogen.

Critical thinking

6. The CO_2 molecule is linear and therefore the two C=O bond dipoles cancel each other.

7. Because PCBs concentrate in fat, they are likely to be soluble in nonpolar solvents.

The body's use of vitamins follows solubility principles

Vitamin A is nonpolar and is therefore soluble in fat. Excess vitamin A is stored in the fat of the liver. It can be released to your tissues when you are not getting enough from your diet. However, this vitamin's excellent solubility in fat means that it is not soluble in water or in the watery blood serum. Other fat-soluble vitamins are vitamin D and vitamin E.

When vitamin A is secreted from the liver, it is packaged with a molecule of retinol-binding protein. The retinol-binding protein makes a nonpolar substance mix with water. This large, globular, water-soluble molecule carries the water-insoluble vitamin A molecule through the blood to the tissues where it is needed.

Because vitamin A is present in food only in small amounts, it is usually impossible to consume too much. But sometimes people become enthusiastic about improving their diet and start taking large quantities of vitamin supplements. Large doses of vitamin A, taken for many weeks, can overload the storage capacity of the liver and raise the concentration of the vitamin throughout the body to toxic levels. Toxicity symptoms include dry, rough skin, cracked lips, hair loss, headaches, muscle and joint pain. Among pregnant women, vitamin A toxicity can lead to babies with birth defects.

Why is it possible to overdose on vitamin A but not on vitamin C? Vitamin A is fat-soluble; vitamin C is water-soluble. The kidneys remove chemicals that are toxic or too concentrated from the blood. You would expect, therefore, that the kidneys would remove excesses of both vitamin A and vitamin C. But while the kidneys do a thorough job of regulating small water-soluble molecules, they are far less effective in processing large molecules, including many proteins. This means that vitamin A is only gradually metabolized, or broken down by chemical reactions within the cells.

SECTION REVIEW

Total recall

1. Why do bubbles escape from a soda that has just been opened?

2. Name two factors that affect solubility.

3. Describe one practical example of solubility principles.

4. Why does cold soda taste less flat than warm soda?

5. Why is an oxygen-helium mixture favored over compressed air in a diver's air tanks?

Critical thinking

6. Explain why CO_2 is a nonpolar molecule even though it possesses two dipolar bonds.

7. **Story Clue** Based on the fact that PCBs have been found in the fat tissue of polar bears, what can you predict about the solubility of PCBs?

DEMONSTRATION 7

Conductance of Solutions

Approximate time: 10 minutes

This demonstration will help clarify the conditions that produce conductance.

1. Write the formulas CH_3COOH, HCl, NaCl, and H_2O on the board. Ask students what kind of bonding exists in each of the compounds, and ask them to predict the conductivity of each of these substances in solution.

2. Half-fill four equal-size beakers with 1 M acetic acid, 1 M hydrochloric acid, 0.5 M sodium chloride solution, and distilled water, and label the beakers.

3. Use a battery-powered conductivity tester to examine the conductivity of each solution. Compare the results with students' predictions and with Figure 13-14, on page 488.

SECTION 13-3

What causes conductivity in solutions?

OBJECTIVES
▶ **Identify** substances that are good, intermediate, and poor conductors of electricity.

▶ **Discuss** nonelectrolytes, weak electrolytes, and strong electrolytes.

▶ **Describe** the enthalpy and entropy changes that accompany the dissolution of an ionic solid.

Electrical conduction

In Chapter 5 you learned that some substances can conduct electricity and some cannot. Two requirements must be satisfied for a substance to behave as an electrical conductor. First, the substance must contain particles with positive charges and others with negative charges. Second, the charged particles must be able to move about within the substance. Solid sodium chloride, NaCl, meets the first requirement but not the second one. NaCl is made of nothing but Na^+ and Cl^- ions, but they cannot move. Conversely, pure water meets the second requirement but not the first. Ions are able to move about in water, but there are virtually none present in pure water.

Separately, neither NaCl nor H_2O can conduct electricity, but when combined in an aqueous solution, they form a conductor. The ions are provided by the solute; the opportunity to move is provided by the fluidity of the solvent.

Electrical conductivities span a wide range

A material's ability to conduct electricity is referred to as its **conductivity.** Conductivity can be measured by suitable electrical equipment. Generally speaking, aqueous ionic solutions are much better conductors than water and much worse conductors than metals.

The apparatus shown in **Figure 13-13** assesses the conductivity of aqueous solutions. The device uses electricity to power a light bulb, except that there is a gap in the circuit between the two electrode rods. These rods dip into the beaker containing the test solution. If the solution has a high conductivity, there is electrical continuity between the rods and the bulb lights up. The brightness of the light is a measure of the solution's conductivity. The brighter the light is, the greater the conductivity.

conductivity
the ability to conduct an electric current

FIGURE 13-13 ▼

The presence of ions in a solution being tested provides the conductivity to light the bulb.

SOLUTIONS   **487**

Sucrose solution   Sodium chloride solution   Acetic acid solution   Hydrochloric acid solution

▲ FIGURE 13-14

For solutions at the same concentration, the brightness of the bulb is an indication of the conductivity.

electrolyte

a substance that, when dissolved in a solvent, increases the solvent's conductivity

Figure 13-14 shows four different aqueous solutions being tested. The brightest light occurs when hydrogen chloride, HCl, is the solute. The light from the aqueous NaCl solution is also bright, whereas the acetic acid solution, CH_3COOH, barely allows the bulb to glow. No light at all comes from the bulb when sucrose (table sugar), $C_{12}H_{22}O_{11}$, is the solute. Three of the solutions conduct electricity, although one does so poorly. The fourth has no greater conductivity than pure water has.

Electrolytes provide a liquid with ions

Any substance that, when dissolved in a liquid solvent, increases that solvent's conductivity is called an **electrolyte.** This classification is based not on any feature of the substance itself but on how the substance behaves when dissolved in water or some other liquid. Thus, an electrolyte may be a solid, a liquid, or a gas, and it may be ionically or covalently bonded. Electrolytes are further classified as *strong electrolytes* or *weak electrolytes*. As you might expect, strong electrolytes provide a high conductivity, whereas weak electrolytes dissolve to produce a solution that is only mildly conducting.

Acetic acid is considered a weak electrolyte because its solutions exhibit low conductivity, lighting the bulb only dimly in Figure 13-14. Sodium chloride and hydrogen chloride are classified as strong electrolytes because their aqueous solutions have high conductivities, lighting the bulb brightly. When a solution does not contain charged

DEMONSTRATION 8

Conductance of Tap Water

Approximate time: 5 minutes

This demonstration shows the presence of electrolytes in tap water.

1. Fill one beaker with tap water and another with distilled water. If you use de-ionized water instead of distilled water, check its conductivity before the demonstration.

2. Use a battery-powered ohmmeter and the probes discussed in the Teaching Tip on

page 488 to measure each solution's resistance. The tap water should show much less resistance than the distilled water.

Safety

Safety goggles and a lab apron must be worn. Students must remain 10 ft from the demonstration.

particles, there is nothing to transport the electricity between the electrodes, and the bulb will not light. Any solute in this type of solution is called a **nonelectrolyte.** An example is sucrose. When dissolved in water, sucrose, $C_{12}H_{22}O_{11}$, produces no measurable conductivity change even in an apparatus much more sensitive than the one shown in Figure 13-13 on page 487.

Strong electrolytes confer conductivity because they introduce a large quantity of ions into the solution. Sodium chloride is already wholly ionic as a solute. Dissolving it merely separates the ions from each other.

$$NaCl(s) \xrightarrow{\text{H}_2\text{O}} Na^+(aq) + Cl^-(aq)$$

In the case of hydrogen chloride, which is a gaseous covalent solute, a chemical reaction occurs in addition to a dissolution.

$$HCl(g) + H_2O(l) \longrightarrow H_3O^+(aq) + Cl^-(aq)$$

One mole of solute produces 1 mol of chloride ions and 1 mol of cations. You would expect the conductivity of these solutions to increase proportionally to their concentration, and this is exactly what happens.

Acetic acid is a weak electrolyte. Dissolving acetic acid in water forms a solution that contains acetic acid molecules, water molecules, acetate ions, and **hydronium ions.** The reaction that takes place is shown as a chemical equation with models in **Figure 13-15.** The double arrows are used to show that both reactants and products exist in the solution because the conversion to ions is not complete. In fact, as much as 99% of the acetic acid may remain as molecules. Because of its low percentage of ionization, a weak electrolyte solution's conductivity is not directly proportional to its concentration. Acids and bases are discussed further in Chapter 15.

Keep in mind that the use of the term *strong* as related to electrolytes has nothing to do with their concentration in a solution. Likewise the term *weak* has nothing to do with dilute solutions. For example, HCl is a strong electrolyte in solution, whether the solution is very concentrated (10 M) or very dilute (0.000 001 M). A very dilute solution, however, has low conductivity. Similarly, CH_3COOH is a weak electrolyte in solution is, no matter how concentrated or dilute the solution is.

nonelectrolyte

a substance that, when dissolved in a solvent, does not enhance that solvent's conductivity

hydronium ion

a hydrogen ion covalently bonded to a water molecule, written as H_3O^+

TEACHING TIP

Electrolyte Strength Point out that the strength of a molecular electrolyte, such as HCl and CH_3COOH, depends on the extent to which it dissociates into ions in aqueous solution, not on its concentration. Also note that electrolyte strength is independent of molecular complexity. Compounds with polyatomic ions, such as HNO_3, H_2SO_4, and H_3PO_4, can be either weak or strong electrolytes, depending on the degree to which they dissociate in water.

DID YOU KNOW?

The H^+ ion from the ionization of an acid is hydrated by water molecules. The formula H_3O^+ is used to represent the hydrated state. However, experimental evidence indicates that the proton is more likely to be hydrated by three or four water molecules, giving it a formula of $H_7O_3^+$ or $H_9O_4^+$. In all but advanced applications, the actual formula is unimportant as long as students recognize that H^+ does not exist in an unhydrated form in water. Writing the hydronium ion, H_3O^+, is convenient to remind students that the acidic proton ionizes in a way that ties up water molecules.

$H_2O(l)$ + $CH_3COOH(aq)$ $\rightleftharpoons$ $H_3O^+(aq)$ + $CH_3COO^-(aq)$

Water   Acetic acid   Hydronium ion   Acetate ion

FIGURE 13-15 ◄

When acetic acid dissolves in water, most of the acid remains as un-ionized molecules in equilibrium with ions.

Disposal
Pour water down the sink.

ADDITIONAL APPLICATION

In newer buildings, electrical outlets near water supplies, such as in bathrooms, kitchens, and laundry areas, are being wired with *ground-fault interrupters*. These devices minimize the hazard of electrocution. The center prong of a three-prong outlet provides a path to ground for any current that leaks from a faulty electrical device, but it provides no protection against electrocution from dropping an appliance in water. A ground-fault interrupter constantly checks to see if current is flowing to ground by whatever path and breaks the circuit completely within a few thousandths of a second when this occurs—in time to prevent electrocution. Most older buildings are being fitted with these devices whenever the wiring is upgraded. They are also required in the electrical codes of many localities.

TEACHING TIP

Dipoles in Solution Have students take note of the orientations of the hydrating water molecules in Figure 13-17 on page 491 and give a reason for the difference. *(The δ^+ end of the water molecule turns toward the negative chloride ion. The δ^- end turns toward the positive sodium ion.)*

ANSWERS

CONCEPT CHECK

1. a. nonconductor
   b. nonconductor
   c. conductor
   d. nonconductor

2. HCl, acetic acid, sucrose

3. The water in the swimming pool contains electrolytes from both the water source and added substances.

Places never to set your electric eel

▲ **FIGURE 13-16**

A person can suffer severe electric shock when electricity comes in contact with water.

Tap water conducts electricity

The instructions included with a hair dryer warn of the danger of dropping it into a tub or sink full of water. When using extension cords outdoors, you are cautioned to keep them away from water. Electricity and water are a hazardous combination that, at times, can prove fatal. **Figure 13-16** provides a reminder of this danger.

Have you ever wondered why you should avoid water when you are using electricity? The contents of the water, rather than the water itself, create the danger. You have already learned that water is a good solvent. Unlike distilled water, which does not conduct enough electricity to light the bulb in the conductivity apparatus, tap water contains various ions from dissolved minerals. Depending on where your water supply comes from, your tap water may contain various dissolved salts and other solutes. Because ground water, such as well water, comes in contact with so many mineral deposits, it may have a greater concentration of salts than does surface water, such as lakes and rivers. These salts generally do not give tap water high conductivity, but the dilute solution may nevertheless conduct the small quantity of electricity needed to cause a painful or lethal electric shock. That is why you have to be careful when using electricity near water. If you are swiming in a pool, a lake, or the ocean and a thunderstorm comes into the area, keep in mind that chlorinated water, ground water, and salt water are conductors of electricity. Get out of the water during a thunderstorm. Also remember not to seek shelter under a tree. Electrolytes in the sap of trees make them conductors, so lightning frequently finds a path to the ground through the trunk of a tree.

CONCEPT CHECK

1. Identify the following as conductors or nonconductors of electricity.
   a. solid NaCl   **c.** copper wire
   b. pure water   **d.** oxygen gas

2. Arrange the following substances according to their performance as an electrolyte, listing the strongest electrolyte first:
   a. sucrose   **b.** hydrogen chloride   **c.** acetic acid

3. Explain why swimming in a pool during a thunderstorm is dangerous.

DEMONSTRATION 9

Saturation

Approximate time: 40 minutes

This demonstration can be set up at the beginning of class and allowed to run during class.

1. To four separate test tubes, add 10 mL of distilled H_2O and one of the following: 3 g, 4 g, 5 g, and 6 g of NH_4Cl. Mark each test tube with the amount of ammonium chloride it contains.

2. Place the test tubes in a water bath using a 600 mL beaker. The water should come just above the solution level in the test tubes. If you will be using a burner, place the beaker on a wire gauze mounted on an iron tripod or on a large ring on a ring stand.

3. Heat the beaker with a hot plate or a burner until the NH_4Cl in the four tubes completely dissolves.

The dissolving process

What happens when table salt, sodium chloride, dissolves in a polar solvent, such as water? And why does it dissolve? You know that NaCl has an ionic lattice and that strong bonds hold it together as a solid. Energy needs to be provided to overcome the powerful attraction between the neighboring ions in the **dissociation** process shown in the equation below.

$$NaCl(s) \xrightarrow{\text{H}_2\text{O}} Na^+(aq) + Cl^-(aq)$$

Though dissociation is energetically disfavored, the entropy factor favors the creation of separated ions. It is clear that without the water the enthalpy factor wins out in the solid state— otherwise sodium chloride would spontaneously vaporize. What is different when the dissociation occurs in an aqueous solution?

There are several factors involved. One is that the force of attraction between two ions is diminished when the space between them is filled by a liquid. Another very important factor is **hydration.** Remember from Chapter 6 that water is a dipole; its molecule has a positive end and a negative end. The positive end of a water molecule is attracted to an anion, while its negative end is similarly attracted to a cation. Accordingly, water molecules like to cluster around ions of either charge, as depicted in **Figure 13-17.**

Enthalpy and entropy affect the solubility of salts

You would expect the hydration process to be exothermic, and indeed it is. Moreover, you would expect the energy release to be greater the smaller the ion and the larger its charge. These predictions are confirmed in practice. On the other hand, small ionic size and large ionic charge are precisely the factors that contribute to making the lattice energy of the crystal large. So the two energy terms shown in Figure 13-17 are both large, and either may dominate.

The situation is similar with entropy. The drive toward increasing entropy favors the dissociation process, but hydration decreases the solution's entropy because the water molecules become more ordered

dissociation

a process in which a compound separates into fragments, such as simpler molecules, atoms, radicals, or ions

hydration

the process by which water molecules surround each ion as it moves into solution

FIGURE 13-17 ▼

Individual ions are separated from the solid lattice by absorbed energy before they are hydrated by water molecules. Energy is released when hydrated ions are released from the lattice.

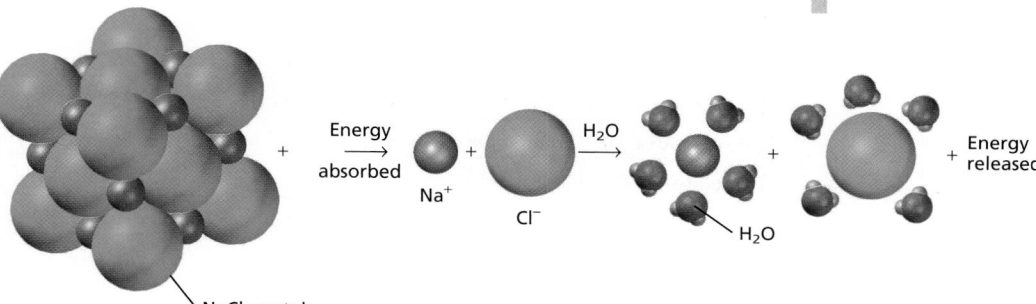

NaCl crystal

Energy absorbed

Na$^+$

Cl$^-$

H$_2$O

H$_2$O

Energy released

4. Remove the heat source, and place a non-mercury thermometer in each test tube. After one minute, remove the tubes and their thermometers from the bath and place them side by side in a test-tube rack.

5. Have students watch the tubes. When they notice crystallization occurring in a tube, have them read the temperature of the crystallizing solution. Record the tube contents and temperature on the board. You may wish to graph the solubility curve at the end of class.

Safety
Wear goggles and a lab apron; tie back hair and loose clothing. Students should remain 10 ft from the demonstration.

Disposal
Combine all liquids and solids from the tubes in an Erlenmeyer flask. Allow the water to evaporate, and save the NH$_4$Cl for future use.

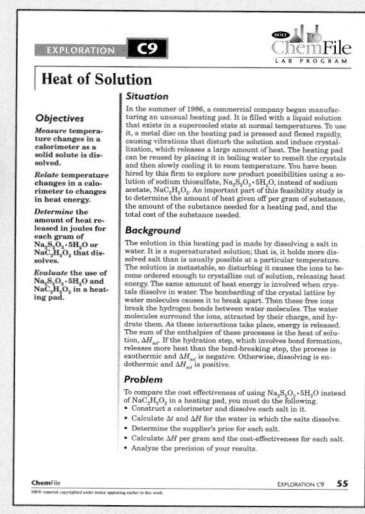

Chemists and technicians who prepare solutions know that certain substances dissolve in a highly exothermic way. Sometimes this release of heat is helpful, as in the dissolving of crystalline NaOH. Solutions of NaOH are often required in laboratory work. Usually, the NaOH to be dissolved is placed in a relatively small amount of water. The solution becomes hot as the NaOH dissolves, which helps the remaining NaOH dissolve rapidly. The small volume of solution produced is easy to cool, after which it can be diluted to the desired final concentration.

In other cases, the release of heat is hazardous. The ionization and hydration of H_2SO_4 presents a hazard because the heat released can cause the solution to boil and spatter, especially when water is poured into the concentrated acid. For this reason, H_2SO_4 solutions are always made by adding the acid slowly to water while stirring. In this way the whole volume of water is already present and acts as a heat sink. The solution may get very hot but usually does not reach its boiling temperature if monitored carefully.

when they become localized around an ion. The result is that it is no easier to predict the solubility of salts in water than it is to predict other solubilities.

Solubilities of ionic compounds

Though difficult to predict, the solubilities of ionically bonded electrolytes, mostly solid salts, are quite easy to measure. A qualitative classification into *soluble* and *insoluble* is sometimes useful, and **Table 13-2** provides a classification that is helpful in predicting the solubility of many ionic compounds.

Technically, all salts dissolve to some, possibly minute, extent and most have a solubility limit beyond which no more will dissolve. Solubilities of ionic compounds, too, depend on temperature. Unlike the solubility of gases, the solubility of most ionic compounds increases as the temperature increases.

TABLE 13-2 Solubility of Common Ionic Compounds

Compounds containing these ions are soluble in water:

Acetates, $CH_3CO_2^-$, *except* that of Fe^{3+}

Alkali metal (Group 1) compounds *except* LiF

Ammonium, NH_4^+, compounds

Bromides, Br^-, *except* those of Ag^+, Hg_2^{2+}, and Pb^{2+}

Chlorates, ClO_3^-

Chlorides, Cl^-, *except* those of Ag^+ and Hg_2^{2+}

Iodides, I^-, *except* those of Ag^+, Hg_2^{2+}, and Pb^{2+}

Nitrates, NO_3^-

Perchlorates, ClO_4^-

Sulfates, SO_4^{2-}, *except* those of Ca^{2+}, Ba^{2+}, Pb^{2+}, Sr^{2+}, and Hg_2^{2+}

Compounds containing these ions are insoluble in water:

Carbonates, CO_3^{2-}, *except* those of Group 1 and NH_4^+

Chromates, CrO_4^{2-}, *except* those of Group 1 and NH_4^+

Hydroxides, OH^-, *except* those of Group 1, Ca^{2+}, Sr^{2+}, and Ba^{2+}

Oxalates, $C_2O_4^{2-}$, *except* those of Group 1 and NH_4^+

Oxides, O^{2-}, *except* those of Group 1, Ca^{2+}, Sr^{2+}, and Ba^{2+} (which form hydroxides)

Phosphates, PO_4^{3-}, *except* those of Group 1 and NH_4^+

Sulfides, S^{2-}, *except* those of Group 1, Group 2, and NH_4^+

DEMONSTRATION 10

Supersaturation

Approximate time: 30 minutes

1. Pour crystalline sodium thiosulfate pentahydrate, $Na_2S_2O_3 \cdot 5H_2O$, into a very clean large demonstration test tube (25 mm × 200 mm) until it is two-thirds full.

2. Clamp the tube to a ring stand, and heat it gently with a burner. The crystals will appear to melt, but in a sense, they are forming a solution in their own water of hydration.

3. When only liquid remains in the tube, remove the burner, and place a small watch glass over the mouth of the tube to prevent dust from entering.

4. After the tube cools, it will contain a supersaturated solution. Drop a small seed crystal of sodium thiosulfate into the liquid. The tube will become warm as the crystals "crash" out of solution.

Solubility can be exceeded

In a saturated solution, some excess solute remains, and the mass that dissolves is equal to the solubility value for that temperature. Supersaturated liquid-solid solutions also exist, and some show very interesting behavior. Supersaturated solutions are able to contain more than the solubility as long as there is no excess undissolved solute remaining. Refer to the photos of the hand warmer Heat Solution™ shown in **Figure 13-18** as you read the following description. Inside the plastic pack, 60 g of sodium acetate, $NaCH_3COO$, has been combined with 100 mL of water. When the $NaCH_3COO$ solution is heated to 100°C, all of the $NaCH_3COO$ completely dissolves. **Figure 13-18a** confirms that the solution is unsaturated, and no undissolved salt remains. When the solution is allowed to cool to 20°C, crystals of solute *should* start to form. **Figure 13-18b** shows that they do not. Instead, the solution becomes increasingly supersaturated. However, if you disturb the cooled solution by clicking the disk in the center of the pack, crystallization immediately occurs, as shown in **Figure 13-18c**. Sodium acetate is an electrolyte with a highly endothermic enthalpy of solution. The heat required to dissolve the crystals is regenerated when recrystallization of the cold solution occurs.

TEACHING TIP

Supersaturation in Hand Warmers
Demonstrate reusable hand warmers of the type shown in Figure 13-18 to show the cycle from supersaturated solution to saturated and back to supersaturated. These warmers can be purchased at ski shops and camp supply stores.

FIGURE 13-18 ▼

On a cold day it can be comforting to use a hand warmer.

Cooling

Unsaturated

a At 100°C, 60 g of $NaCH_3COO$ will dissolve completely in the 100 mL of water contained in a Heat Solution pack.

b When the solution is cooled to 20°C, $NaCH_3COO$ does not crystallize unless the solution is disturbed.

Supersaturated

Crystallization

Heat to re-use

Saturated

c Clicking the disk in the center of the pack triggers rapid exothermic crystallization. The hand warmer can be reused if it is heated above the saturation point again.

SOLUTIONS 493

Safety
Wear goggles and a lab apron; tie back hair and loose clothing. Students should remain 10 ft from the demonstration.

Disposal
Pour the solution down the drain, or save for reuse.

CONSUMER FOCUS

Abnormal concentrations of electrolytes in the blood often point to disease. An excess of potassium ions is generally caused by kidney failure. Some gastrointestinal conditions cause a deficiency of potassium ions. An abnormal concentration of sodium ions indicates a water imbalance between blood and tissue cells.

TEACHING TIP

Ion Pumps Never Stop Point out that the ion pumps in cells work constantly and that the body is always striving to maintain equilibrium.

ADDITIONAL APPLICATION

The medical community has noted that backyard athletes do not normally need electrolyte drinks because they do not lose enough salt during exercise. In their case, the biggest need of the body is water replenishment.

ANSWERS

SECTION REVIEW

Total recall

1. The substance must contain positive and negative particles, and charges must be able to move.

2. Tap water contains ions in solution from dissolved minerals.

3. The solution of a solid in a liquid usually involves an increase in entropy (with some exceptions in which the hydration is especially strong). If the solution process is also exothermic, the solid will dissolve. The solid will dissolve even if the process is endothermic if the entropy increase is sufficient.

4. Solubility of salts usually increases with temperature.

CONSUMER FOCUS

SPORTS DRINKS

Replacing lost electrolytes

Whenever you perform hard physical labor or participate in sports activities, you sweat. When you sweat, you need to drink water to replace the lost fluids containing electrolytes.

The next time you shop for sports drinks, look at labels. Check the labels for electrolytes, such as **potassium** ions, K^+; **sodium** ions, Na^+; and **calcium** ions, Ca^{2+}. The electrolytes serve important roles in various physiological functions, including nerve-impulse conduction and muscle contraction.

Ion pumps

At rest, a nerve cell uses "ion pumps" to maintain a high concentration of Na^+ ions outside the cell and of K^+ ions inside the cell. These ions do not diffuse through the membrane when the nerve cell is at rest. However, when the cell is stimulated, ions pass through the cell membrane, moving Na^+ ions inside the nerve cell and K^+ ions outside the nerve cell. When the cell re-

turns to its resting state, Na^+ ions are again pumped out and the K^+ ions diffuse in to compensate, readying the cell for the next stimulus.

Muscle contractions also depend on the movement of ions. When muscle cells are stimulated, Ca^{2+} ions go into the cells and cause protein fibers to slide together, resulting in a muscle contraction. When Ca^{2+} ions move back outside the cells, the muscle relaxes.

internet**connect**

*SC*LINKS™ NSTA

TOPIC: Sports drinks
GO TO: www.scilinks.org
KEYWORD: HW133

Cell membrane

Na^+

K^+

At rest   Stimulated

SECTION REVIEW

Total recall

1. What two conditions must a substance meet in order to behave as an electrical conductor?

2. Why does tap water conduct electricity?

3. What usually happens to the entropy of a system as a salt dissolves? What usually happens to the enthalpy?

4. Does the solubility of most ionic compounds increase or decrease with temperature?

Critical thinking

5. Explain how a soluble salt with a highly exothermic enthalpy of solution could also be used in a hand warmer. Would this hand warmer be reusable?

6. Identify the ions that are produced when the following compounds dissociate in water:
   a. HNO_3 **c.** KOH
   b. NH_4CH_3COO **d.** CH_3COOH

Critical thinking

5. Water and a salt are in separated sealed pouches inside the hand warmer. Breaking the seal allows them to mix, and heat is given off as the salt dissolves. These hand warmers are not reusable because once the seal is broken, it is not possible to recrystallize the salt and separate it from the water again.

6. **a.** H_3O^+, NO_3^-
   b. NH_4^+, CH_3COO^-
   c. K^+, OH^-
   d. H_3O^+, CH_3COO^-

How are a liquid's properties changed by solutes?

OBJECTIVES

▶ **Define** colligative properties.

▶ **Explain** why a liquid's boiling point is elevated but its freezing point is depressed when a solute dissolves.

▶ **Describe** how the magnitude of a colligative property depends on the amount of solute and on the chemistry of the dissolution process.

▶ **Compare** and contrast the roles of emulsifiers and surfactants.

▶ **Explain** what hard water is and why its occurrence makes detergents superior to soaps.

LESSON WARM-UP

Group Strategy Ask students why salt is spread on icy roads and used in making homemade ice cream. Most will say that it melts the ice. Respond by asking how it melts the ice. Ask them why calcium chloride is better than salt for melting ice. Return to these questions after students have studied the next three pages.

COMMON MISCONCEPTION

Be sure students understand that the amount of salt put in water to cook pasta or vegetables raises the boiling point only *very slightly*. Raising the boiling point of 2 L of water just 2°C requires about 240 g, or more than 0.5 lb, of salt.

Colligative properties

Dissolving a solute in a liquid can produce new chemical properties in the resulting solution. Adding sodium hydroxide to water, for example, creates a solution with many chemical properties that the water did not previously possess. But the *physical* properties of water are also changed when substances dissolve in it. So too are its *solvent* properties, such as how well the water mixes with other compounds.

When you cook pasta or vegetables in boiling water, you may find that the recipe calls for the addition of salt to the water. Though its purpose is to enhance the food's flavor, the salt has a slight effect on the boiling process. Adding salt to the water *elevates* its boiling point. Salted water boils at a slightly higher temperature. The **boiling-point elevation** is 0.51 K for every mole of solute particles added to 1 kg of water.

The converse effect is found during freezing; a solute *depresses* the freezing point. This change is called **freezing-point depression.** Dilute aqueous solutions invariably freeze at lower temperatures. When homemade ice cream is being prepared, as in **Figure 13-20** on the next page, salt is mixed into the water-ice bath to reduce the temperature of the ice-salt mixture. Preparation temperatures below 0°C make better ice cream.

boiling-point elevation

the difference between the boiling point of a solution and that of the pure solvent

freezing-point depression

the difference between the freezing point of a pure solvent and that of a solution

FIGURE 13-19 ◀

If you add 58.44 g (1 mol) of NaCl to 1000 g of water, the boiling point increases by 1 K.

RESOURCE LINK

IN-TEXT LAB

Skills Development

Have students do Exploration 13B on page 768 to improve their understanding of the effect of molar mass on boiling-point elevation.

ChemFile Mini-Guide to Problem Solving

Assign Chapter 16: *Colligative Properties* for additional practice.

CHAPTER 16
Colligative Properties

Colligative properties of solutions are properties that depend solely on the number of particles of solute in solution. In other words, these properties depend only on the concentration of solute particles, not on the identity of those particles. Colligative properties result from the interference of solute particles with the motion of solvent molecules.

Solute molecules can be either electrolytes or nonelectrolytes. When a nonelectrolyte dissolves, the molecule remains whole in the solution. Glucose and glycerol are examples of nonelectrolyte solutes.

Ionic solutes are electrolytes. When they dissolve, they dissociate into multiple particles, or ions. When magnesium chloride dissolves in water, it dissociates as follows.

$$MgCl_2(s) \xrightarrow{H_2O} Mg^{2+}(aq) + 2Cl^-(aq)$$

As you can see, when a mole of $MgCl_2$ completely dissociates in solution, it produces 1 mol of Mg^{2+} ions and 2 mol of Cl^- ions for a total of 3 mol of solute particles. Because colligative properties depend on the number of particles in solution, 1 mol of $MgCl_2$ in solution should have three times the effect of 1 mol of a nonelectrolyte solute, such as glucose.

Two important colligative properties are freezing-point depression and boiling-point elevation. A dissolved solute lowers the freezing point of the solution. The freezing point of a solution differs from that of the pure solvent according to the following equation, in which Δt_f is the change in freezing point.

$$\Delta t_f = K_f m$$

K_f is a constant that differs for each solvent. Because the freezing point of the solution is lower than that of the solvent alone, K_f is a negative number. The symbol m represents the molality (moles of solute per kilogram of solvent) of the solution.

Boiling-point elevation works in the same way. The equation to determine the change in boiling point is as follows.

$$\Delta t_b = K_b m$$

Like K_f, K_b is a constant that differs for each solvent. But unlike K_f, K_b is a positive number because the boiling point of the solution is higher than that of the solvent alone.

184 Chapter 16

TEACHING TIP

Particle Interactions Students should develop the idea that freezing-point depression and boiling-point elevation depend only on the number of solute particles present relative to solvent molecules. The kind of particles present is irrelevant because the effects are caused by mechanical interference of solute particles with the organization of solvent molecules (freezing-point depression) and the ability of solvent molecules to leave the liquid phase and go into the vapor phase.

RESOURCE LINK

ChemFile Lab C

Skills Development
Have students do Exploration 16: *Freezing-Point Depression—Testing De-Icing Chemicals.*

Self-Directed Inquiry
Have students do Investigation 16: *Freezing-Point Depression—Making Ice Cream.*

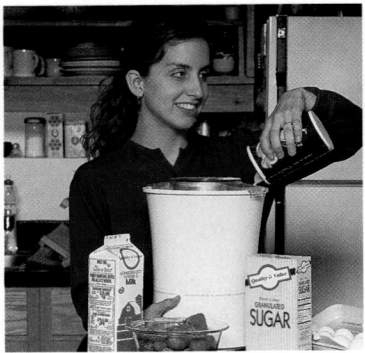

▲ **FIGURE 13-20**

An ice cream maker uses an ice-salt-water mixture to provide a temperature that is colder than that of ice and water alone.

colligative property

a physical property that is dependent on the number of solute particles present rather than on the identity of those particles

▶ **FIGURE 13-21**

This is a modified phase diagram for pure water (red lines) and for an aqueous solution (blue lines). The addition of a solute has the effect of extending the range of the liquid phase.

The identity of the solute is unimportant

Each of these properties of solutions—boiling-point elevation and freezing-point depression—is an example of a **colligative property.** Colligative properties depend only on the concentration of the solute particles rather than on the solute's identity. If there are several solutes present, the effect is additive; the total number of solute moles in a given quantity of solvent determines the magnitude of the effect.

Both of these colligative properties arise because the vapor pressure of an aqueous solution is less than that of pure water at the same temperature. Vapor-pressure lowering is also a colligative property. The vapor pressure decreases because the presence of solute particles lowers the concentration of solvent molecules at the liquid's surface. How does this lowering of vapor pressure affect the solvent's boiling and freezing points?

Figure 13-21 illustrates the difference between water's boiling point and freezing point and those of an aqueous solution. Recall that the boiling point of a liquid is the temperature at which the liquid's vapor pressure reaches atmospheric pressure. Because the vapor pressure of water is lowered by the addition of a nonvolatile solute, the solution must be heated to a higher temperature in order for its vapor pressure to reach atmospheric pressure, at which point the solution boils. Figure 13–21 illustrates how the boiling point is increased by the lowering of the vapor pressure curve. On the other hand, the freezing point of a substance is the temperature at which the liquid and solid phases are

Solute Effects on the Vapor Pressure
of a Pure Solvent

in equilibrium, which means that their vapor pressures must be equal. Because the addition of a solute to water lowers the vapor pressure of water, the vapor pressures of water and ice can only be equal at a temperature lower than the freezing point of pure water. Therefore, the addition of a solute lowers the freezing point of water.

The concentration of the solute affects freezing- and boiling-point changes

Any solute, whether an electrolyte or a nonelectrolyte, contributes to the colligative property of the solution. The intensity of the effect depends on the number of solute particles (molecules and ions) in a certain mass of solvent. The more particles there are, the greater the freezing-point depression and the boiling-point elevation are. Based on the number of moles of solute particles produced, 1 mol of sodium chloride is expected to be twice as effective dissolved in water as 1 mol of sucrose, $C_{12}H_{22}O_{11}$. In practice, however, due to interionic attractions, the effect is slightly less than twofold. Likewise, 1 mol of calcium chloride, $CaCl_2$, is predicted to be three times as effective, for reasons that **Figure 13-22** illustrates. The following equations show how 1 mol, 2 mol, and 3 mol of solute particles arise when 1 mol each of sucrose, sodium chloride, and calcium chloride are dissolved in water.

$$C_{12}H_{22}O_{11}(s) \xrightarrow{H_2O} C_{12}H_{22}O_{11}(aq)$$

$$NaCl(s) \xrightarrow{H_2O} Na^+(aq) + Cl^-(aq)$$

$$CaCl_2(s) \xrightarrow{H_2O} Ca^{2+}(aq) + 2Cl^-(aq)$$

FIGURE 13-22 ▼

Colligative properties depend on the number of particles formed by the solute in the solution. Sugar, table salt, and calcium chloride form aqueous solutions with differing colligative properties.

Sucrose solution   Sodium chloride solution   Calcium chloride solution

COMMON MISCONCEPTION

Students may wonder why a change in vapor pressure has anything to do with changing the freezing point of a solution. In this case, the solute particles interfere with the aggregation of solute molecules to form crystals in the same way that they interfered with vaporization. For this reason, the temperature must be lowered to enable the solvent molecules to become arranged in a crystal lattice. Therefore, the lowering of freezing point is a function of change in vapor pressure, just as the increase in boiling point is.

CONTENT STRATEGY

In this textbook, students do not use *molality, m*. Molality is listed in Table 13-1 on page 471. If you cover molar mass determinations, you will have to introduce molality.

RESOURCE LINK

ChemFile Lab A
Skills Development
Have students do Experiment 11: *Ice-Nucleating Bacteria*.

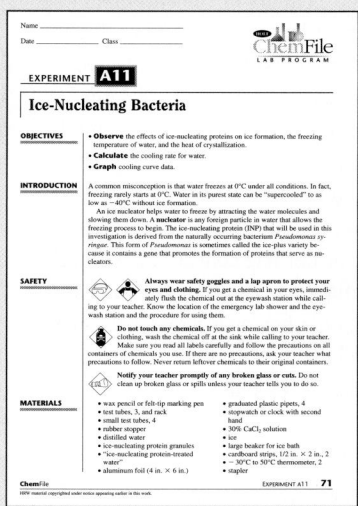

internetconnect

SC/LINKS
NSTA
TOPIC: Emulsions
GO TO: www.scilinks.org
KEYWORD: HW134

emulsion
colloidal-sized droplets (about 100 nm in diameter) of one liquid suspended in another liquid

▼ **FIGURE 13-23**

Oil and vinegar will mix if shaken vigorously. However, the particles of oil and vinegar do not make a homogeneous solution.

Emulsions

You have probably heard the saying that oil and water do not mix. It is true. They are immiscible liquids. You can demonstrate it the next time you prepare an oil-and-vinegar salad dressing.

Place about 60 mL of olive oil in a small bottle or carafe. Add about half as much vinegar, which is a solution of acetic acid and water. You will see the vinegar sink through the oil and collect at the bottom, as shown in **Figure 13-23**. This observation indicates two things—that vinegar is denser than olive oil, and that the two liquids are immiscible. If you cap the container and shake it well, you will see a turbulent mixture of oil and vinegar. What you cannot see are millions of microscopic droplets of vinegar surrounded by oil. This mixture is called an **emulsion.** The droplets formed in an emulsion are colloidal particles, discussed in Section 13-1. They are smaller than the particles in a suspension but larger than the particles in a solution.

This salad-dressing emulsion is temporary. As soon as you stop shaking the container, the droplets of vinegar begin to come together and sink, the oil rises, and the layers of each eventually reappear. Clearly, the olive oil and vinegar are immiscible. This is expected because olive oil is almost nonpolar, while the aqueous vinegar solution is polar.

Water
Acetic acid
Components of vinegar

Typical oil molecule
Oleic acid triglyceride

498 CHAPTER 13

DEMONSTRATION 11

Forming an Emulsion

Approximate time: 10 minutes

1. Place 25 mL of H_2O and 25 mL of vegetable oil in a 250 mL Erlenmeyer flask.

2. Stopper the flask, and shake it vigorously. Note that the oil and water separate after standing a short time.

3. Add a few squirts of liquid soap, and shake the flask again. The mixture should remain in an emulsified state instead of separating into layers.

Safety
Wear safety goggles and a lab apron.

Disposal
Pour the contents of the flask down the drain.

Acetic acid

Lecithin

Nonpolar branches dissolve in oil

Oil

Water

Polar branch dissolves in water

FIGURE 13-24 ◀

An oil-and-vinegar emulsion can be stabilized by adding an emulsifier, such as lecithin. The emulsifier acts as a bridge between the oil and the aqueous vinegar, preventing the droplets within each component from coming together.

Emulsions can be stabilized

The next time you are at the grocery store, look at the commercial oil-and-vinegar salad dressings. You will see two types. The traditional type has distinct layers, just like the dressing shown in Figure 13-23. The newer type, shown in **Figure 13-24,** has no layers because the oil and vinegar have been mixed with another ingredient, an **emulsifier,** that ensures the layers stay mixed.

Lecithins, found in all living organisms, are a family of several similar molecules that stabilize emulsions. Lecithins are obtained commercially by extraction from soybeans. Eggs are also rich in lecithins. You may decide to convert your oil-and-vinegar dressing into mayonnaise, which you can do by beating in an egg yolk. The egg yolk serves as an emulsifier. As you can see in Figure 13-24, lecithin molecules have three major branches. The two longer branches are nonpolar, but the shorter third branch is polar.

The role of lecithins is to dissolve in both oil and water when these solvents are present together. Each molecule of lecithin dissolves partly in the oil and partly in the water, linking two immiscible liquids. Lecithins stabilize emulsions, preventing separation. They modify the properties of water and aqueous solutions, making them accommodate nonpolar molecules.

It is often said that emulsifiers make oil and water mix. A better description is to say that they coat the tiny globules of oil and stabilize the emulsion, keeping the oil and water mixed. The next time you eat a candy bar, read its label. You will often find lecithin listed.

emulsifier

a substance that stabilizes an emulsion by forming a molecular layer between two immiscible liquids

CONCEPT CHECK

1. Explain how you can get oil and water to "mix."
2. Are emulsions temporary mixtures or stable mixtures?
3. What is the role of a lecithin in forming a mixture?

ADDITIONAL APPLICATION

Other common emulsions include floor and car waxes, paints, milk, certain cosmetics, and skin creams.

💡 DID YOU KNOW?

Commercial lecithin is obtained as a byproduct of the production of soybean oil. It is used in margarine, mayonnaise, chocolate candy, lubricant sprays for cooking pans, baked goods, animal feeds, printing inks, paints, soaps, and cosmetics. It is also used as a mold-release agent for plastics, as a blending agent in oils and resins, as a component in rubber processing, and as a fiber lubricant in textiles. Its structure is similar to the triglyceride fat shown in Figure 13-23 on the previous page. Instead of being bonded to the third fatty acid, the third carbon is bonded to the group $-O_3P-O^--CH_2CH_2N^+(CH_3)_3$, which is ionic and soluble in water.

ANSWERS

CONCEPT CHECK

1. You must use a third substance whose molecules have an attraction for both oil and water molecules, such as a soap, a detergent, or an emulsifying agent.

2. In general, emulsions are stable mixtures.

3. Part of the lecithin molecule is soluble in oils, and another part is soluble in water. This property gives lecithin the ability to cause oil and water to emulsify.

soap

a sodium or potassium salt of a long-chain fatty acid

micelle

a spherical arrangement formed by molecules of fat or fatlike substances in an aqueous environment

surfactant

a class of salts, valued for their cleansing properties, whose anions possess a negatively charged "head" and a long nonpolar "tail"

Surfactants

Have you ever gotten dirty from working outside and tried to clean your hands with water alone? You would have been only partly successful because much of the dirt would have remained on your hands. To get your hands really clean, plain water is not enough. You have to use small amounts of a surfactant, such as **soap,** with the water. The reason again relates to emulsions.

Perspiration is a mixture of water and oils. Water cools your body by evaporation; oils keep your skin soft. However, over a period of time, the oils accumulate and coat your skin with an oily layer in which flakes of old skin, dirt, and bacteria become embedded.

Oil and water are immiscible, so the water may never remove the oil and dirt on your skin. To remove all of the dirt, you must first emulsify the oil by scrubbing, then stabilize it with an emulsifier such as soap. Only then can the soap-and-oily-dirt emulsion be rinsed away from your skin by more water.

Though chemically dissimilar in other ways, a soap ion and a lecithin molecule both have a polar end and a nonpolar end. When you wash your hands with soap, as shown in **Figure 13-25,** one end of the soap ion dissolves in the oil, forming a tiny sphere called a **micelle,** while the other end—on the outside of the micelle—dissolves in the surrounding water. The oil droplet stays suspended in the water and can be easily washed away.

The characteristic property of a **surfactant** is its ability to form a layer between two dissimilar phases. Soap shows this property in forming micelles and in its ability to form bubbles. In a soap bubble, a thin film of water is coated on both surfaces by soap molecules. The nonpolar end of these micelles is able to be next not only to oils but also to another nonpolar fluid, air.

▶ **FIGURE 13-25**

When you wash with soap, you create an emulsion of oil droplets dispersed in water and stabilized by soap.

Polar head

Oil in micelle interior

Aqueous phase

Nonpolar tail

Hard water destroys soap's surfactant abilities

Though soap's texture is very different from most other salts, soap is a salt. Potassium palmitate is a typical soap; it dissolves in water to form the potassium ion, $K^+(aq)$, and the palmitate anion, $C_{15}H_{31}COO^-(aq)$. It is the $C_{15}H_{31}$ part of the anion that forms a long zigzag "tail," shown in Figure 13-25, which constitutes the nonpolar section of the surfactant. The COO^- part is polar and has a strong affinity for water.

Soaps are not ideal cleaning agents because some palmitate salts are insoluble in water. If the water in your home comes from an underground source, it may be hard water, which contains calcium or magnesium ions. These cations combine with the palmitate anion to form insoluble salts, such as the one shown in the following equation.

$$Ca^{2+}(aq) + 2C_{15}H_{31}COO^-(aq) \longrightarrow Ca(C_{15}H_{31}COO)_2(s)$$

You may have seen this salt in the form of a scum or bathtub ring. If you use soap and hard water in the washing machine, this salt forms a scum that clings to fabric and makes the clothes look dingy.

Detergents outperform soaps in hard water

In the 1930s, chemists developed soap substitutes called **detergents.** Detergents can be used in hard water without forming insoluble salts. Today, almost all laundry products are detergents.

To replace soap, synthetic chemists kept the long zigzag hydrocarbon tail of the soap but substituted a different anionic head group, such as that shown in **Figure 13-26.** Like soaps, these ions are surfactants; they have one end that is charged and soluble in water and another end that is nonpolar. Unlike soaps, however, their calcium and magnesium salts are soluble.

detergent
a surfactant other than a soap

FIGURE 13-26 ▼
Sodium dodecylbenzene sulfonate is an anionic surfactant. This ionic compound does not make an insoluble scum with calcium or magnesium ions.

SECTION REVIEW

Total recall

1. What is the only aspect of a solute that is important in conferring a colligative property to a solution?

2. How are the behaviors of emulsifiers and surfactants in solution similar?

3. How are soaps and detergents different?

4. What is the purpose of adding salt to cooking water?

Critical thinking

5. Why does 1 mol of table salt lower water's freezing point to a greater extent than does 1 mol of table sugar added to an equal mass of water?

6. Why is a substance that contains only ionic bonds not a good emulsifier?

7. How does an emulsion differ from a homogeneous mixture?

Critical thinking

5. The 1 mol of NaCl dissociates into 2 mol of particles. Sugar neither dissociates nor ionizes.

6. Such a compound will not be soluble in fats and oils.

7. A homogeneous mixture (solution) consists of two or more substances mixed to the molecular level. An emulsion contains suspended micelles of many molecules of oil suspended in an aqueous material by an emulsifying agent that is soluble in both the oil and the aqueous material.

TEACHING TIP

Soluble Salts in Detergents Point out to students that calcium and magnesium salts of detergents remain soluble because the attraction between water molecules and the sulfonate ion is much stronger than water's attraction for the palmitate (or other fatty acid) ion in soaps.

Comparing Soaps and Detergents Consider demonstrating the action of soaps and detergents in hard water by adding a few small crystals of $CaCl_2$ and $MgCl_2$ to each of two flasks or jars. Place 250 mL of distilled water in each and another 250 mL in a third container. Add a small amount of soap to one jar and a similar quantity of detergent to the other. Add a little soap to the jar having only distilled water. Stopper or cap the containers securely, and have student volunteers shake them vigorously for about a minute. Allow the containers to stand for another minute. Examine the results carefully, and look for insoluble soap salts around the side of the jar, just above the water line.

ANSWERS

SECTION REVIEW

Total recall

1. the number (concentration) of particles of solute present

2. Both have the ability to dissolve in oil and water simultaneously.

3. Detergents are generally sulfonate salts that do not form insoluble salts of calcium and magnesium. Soaps are salts of fatty acids.

4. only to flavor the food

At the beginning of this chapter you followed Dr. Malcolm Ramsay as he examined a polar bear and took samples of its fat tissue to determine the PCB content. So far, the concentration of PCBs found in the bear has caused it no apparent harm, but scientists are still concerned about the polar bears. The way PCBs dissolve in fat makes it possible for the concentration of PCBs to increase in the bears even if the amount of PCBs in the environment does not change. Now that you have completed the chapter, you should be able to answer the questions about PCBs and polar bears.

LOOKING BACK

Why would you not expect to find PCBs dissolved in Hudson Bay or any other body of water?

PCBs and water are chemically dissimilar substances. PCBs are nonpolar molecules, while water is a polar molecule. Water will form hydrogen bonds with itself but not with PCB molecules. All these things would lead you to expect not to find PCBs dissolved in any body of water to an appreciable extent.

In fact, the concentration of PCBs in Hudson Bay's water is very small, about 5×10^{-14} mol/L, or one PCB molecule for every 1×10^{15} water molecules. However, this is enough to worry Professor Ramsay. He and his colleagues know that this concentration will become magnified enormously as the PCB molecules make their way up the food chain.

Why were the PCBs not removed from the polar bear's system by the kidneys?

The kidneys are good at regulating the amount of water-soluble substances in the body by excreting them as waste. However, PCBs are not water-soluble and therefore would not be removed from the animal's body by the kidneys.

How did PCBs end up in the bear's fat?

When a seal eats a fish, the oil-soluble PCBs end up in the seal's oily blubber in concentrations that are even higher than those in fish. Because polar bears prey on seals, PCBs become concentrated in polar bears' fat. The animals that are the most likely to have PCBs concentrated in their fatty tissues are polar bears. They are at the top of the food chain and live for a long time.

CHAPTER 13

HIGHLIGHTS

KEY TERMS

13-1
aqueous
chromatography
colloid
concentration
distillation
molarity
solute
solvent
suspension

13-2
Henry's law
immiscible
insoluble
miscible
saturated
solubility
soluble
supersaturated

13-3
conductivity
dissociation
electrolyte
hydration
hydronium ion
nonelectrolyte

13-4
boiling-point elevation
colligative property
detergent
emulsifier
emulsion
freezing-point depression
micelle
soap
surfactant

KEY CONCEPTS

13-1 What is a solution?

▶ A solution is a homogeneous mixture in which the particles remain dissolved.

▶ A solution is made by dissolving a solute in a solvent; water is the solvent in aqueous solutions.

▶ Many methods can be used to separate the components in a mixture.

▶ Concentration can be expressed in various ways; a common concentration measure in chemistry is molarity.

13-2 Does A dissolve in B?

▶ The solubility of a substance can depend on the chemical nature of the solute and solvent, the pressure, the temperature, hydrogen bonding, enthalpy, and entropy.

▶ Because of the many factors that can affect solubility, predicting solubilities is very difficult.

▶ Solubility principles have many applications, including dry-cleaning and vitamin storage in the body.

13-3 What causes conductivity in solutions?

▶ Substances that do not dissociate in solution are nonelectrolytes; those that dissociate to a slight extent are weak electrolytes; those that dissociate completely are strong electrolytes.

▶ The ions provided by dissolved electrolytes give electrical conductivity to solutions.

▶ The solubility of salts in water depends on enthalpy and entropy.

▶ A solution is supersaturated when it contains more than the amount of solute specified by the solubility at a given temperature.

13-4 How are a liquid's properties changed by solutes?

▶ Colligative properties depend solely on the concentration of the solute in solution.

▶ Colligative properties include freezing-point depression and boiling-point elevation.

▶ Emulsifiers and surfactants enable two immiscible substances to mix.

▶ Detergents are more effective than soaps in hard water.

KEY SKILLS

How To Prepare 1.000 L of a 0.5000 M solution (p. 472)

Sample Problem 13A Calculating molarity (p. 473)

Sample Problem 13B Determining the mass of solute (p. 473)

Sample Problem 13C Using solution stoichiometry (p. 474)

READING STRATEGY

Assimilating Knowledge

Have students return to their lists of things they want to know about the nature of solutions, the solubility of substances, the nature of electrolyte solutions, and the way solutes change a solution's properties that they created on page 466. Have them place check marks next to the questions that they are now able to answer. Students should finish by making a list of what they have learned. Have students identify unanswered questions as well as new questions they may have. These questions could be used as the basis for a research project.

REVIEW & ASSESS ASSIGNMENT GUIDE

Term Review

Assign after Section 13-4.

Concept and Skills Review

Section 13-1
▶ Items 1–18

Section 13-2
▶ Items 19–20, 22

Section 13-3
▶ Items 21, 23–26

Section 13-4
▶ Items 27–37

Linking Chapters

Assign after Section 13-4.

Alternative Assessments

Assign after Section 13-4.

Test Prep

Assign prior to the chapter test.

Complete worked-out solutions for these problems can be found on the teacher's interleaved pages at the end of this chapter.

TERM REVIEW

1. suspension
2. electrolyte
3. molarity
4. micelle
5. polar
6. strong electrolyte
7. supersaturated
8. solute
9. hydration
10. weak electrolyte

CONCEPT & SKILLS REVIEW

1. a. A solution is a stable homogeneous mixture.
   b. The solvent is the substance that dissolves the solute. The solute is the substance dissolved in the solvent.
   c. Answers will vary but could include air, an alloy, sea water, and soda.

2. a. The particles of a suspension are larger than those of a colloid and will settle out upon standing. The particles of a colloid are also suspended, but they are small enough to remain suspended over time.
   b. Answers will vary but could include muddy water and oil shaken with water.
   c. Answers will vary but could include mayonnaise, creamy salad dressings, liquid antacid medicines, and hand cream.

3. Sea water is boiled, and the water vapor is removed and allowed to cool and condense.

4. As the solution travels through a chromatography medium, such as paper, components with less affinity for the solvent lag behind and those with greater affinity move with the solvent to different degrees.

TERM REVIEW

1. A mixture in which the particles are uniformly dispersed but later settle at the bottom of the container is called a _____.
   (suspension, colloid, solution)

2. A substance that, when added to a liquid, allows the fluid to conduct an electric current is a(n) _____.
   (electrolyte, surfactant, micelle)

3. The number of moles of solute dissolved per liter of solution is known as the _____.
   (solubility, molarity)

4. The spherical arrangement formed by a group of lipid molecules in an aqueous environment is known as a(n) _____.
   (micelle, emulsion)

5. A molecule that has an uneven distribution of charge is said to be _____.
   (immiscible, polar)

6. _____ is the term that is used to describe NaCl when it dissolves in water.
   (Emulsifier, Strong electrolyte)

7. A solution that contains more than the amount of solute specified by the solubility at a given temperature is said to be _____.
   (supersaturated, immiscible, aqueous)

8. The material dissolved in a solution is the _____.
   (solvent, solute)

9. The process by which water molecules surround ions in solution is called _____.
   (hydration, dissociation, conductivity)

10. A compound that experiences only a small degree of dissociation in an aqueous solution is said to be a _____.
    (nonelectrolyte, weak electrolyte, strong electrolyte)

CONCEPT & SKILLS REVIEW

SOLUTIONS, SUSPENSIONS, COLLOIDS

1. a. What is a solution?
   b. Identify and define the two components of a solution.
   c. Give two examples of common solutions.

2. a. How does a suspension differ from a colloid?
   b. Give two examples of common suspensions.
   c. Give two examples of common colloids.

3. Explain how distillation can be used to obtain drinking water from sea water.

4. Explain how chromatography separates the components in a solution.

5. List these mixtures in order of increasing particle size: muddy water (settles after a few hours), sugar water, ketchup (settles after an extended period of time), sand in water (settles rapidly), salt water.

CONCENTRATION AND MOLARITY

6. Describe in detail how you would make 250.0 mL of a 0.500 M solution of NaCl with equipment found in your chemistry lab.

7. You have 500 mL of a 0.5 M NaOH solution. For an experiment, you need 0.1 M NaOH. Describe how you would make 100 mL of a 0.1 M NaOH solution from the 0.5 M NaOH.

Practice Problems

8. Determine the molarity of each of the following solutions. (Hint: See Sample Problem 13A.)
   a. 0.250 mol of $FeCl_3$ in 2.00 L of solution
   b. 0.015 mol of $KMnO_4$ in 350 mL of solution
   c. 3.5×10^{-4} mol of $NaCH_3COO$ in 25.0 mL of solution

9. Determine the molarity of each of the following solutions. (**Hint: See Sample Problem 13A.**)
  a. 20.0 g of NaOH in enough H_2O to make 2.00 L of solution
  b. 14.0 g of NH_4Br in enough H_2O to make 150.0 mL of solution
  c. 65.0 g of $CuCl_2$ in enough H_2O to make 300.0 mL of solution

10. How many moles of each solute would be required to prepare each of the following solutions? (**Hint: See Sample Problem 13B.**)
  a. 1.0 L of a 4.0 M $AgNO_3$ solution
  b. 2.50 L of a 0.500 M HCl solution
  c. 400.0 mL of a 0.250 M HNO_3 solution

11. How many moles of each solute would be required to prepare each of the following solutions? (**Hint: See Sample Problem 13B.**)
  a. 30.0 mL of a 0.0100 M H_3PO_4 solution
  b. 5 mL of an 18 M H_2SO_4 solution
  c. 250.0 mL of a 1.00×10^{-4} M CH_3OH solution

12. What mass of solid $Ca_3(PO_4)_2$ results if 750.0 mL of 6.00 M H_3PO_4 react with an excess of $Ca(OH)_2$ according to the following equation? (**Hint: See Sample Problem 13C.**)

$$2H_3PO_4(aq) + 3Ca(OH)_2(aq) \longrightarrow$$
$$Ca_3(PO_4)_2(s) + 6H_2O(l)$$

13. A yellow pigment in some artists' oil paints is cadmium sulfide. What mass of cadmium sulfide would be made if 350.0 mL of 2.00 M $(NH_4)_2S$ reacted with 400.0 mL of 1.50 M $Cd(NO_3)_2$ according to the following equation? (**Hint: See Sample Problem 13C.**)

$$(NH_4)_2S(aq) + Cd(NO_3)_2(aq) \longrightarrow$$
$$2NH_4NO_3(aq) + CdS(s)$$

14. You are determining the concentration of a solution of salt water by evaporating different samples and measuring the mass of salt that remains. Your data are shown below. Calculate the molar concentration of the original solution.

Sample volume (mL)	Mass of NaCl (g)
25	2.9
50.0	5.6
75	8.5
100.0	11.3

15. The actual molarity of the solution in item 14 is determined to be 2.00 M. Calculate the percent error in the calculated concentration of the salt water.

16. The owner's manual for an outboard motor gives the proportion for mixing gasoline and oil as 100:1. You have 2.5 L of gasoline. According to the manual, how much oil do you need to mix with this much gasoline?

17. A shipment of shark meat was destroyed after it was found to contain 1.76 ppm methyl mercury, $[HgCH_3]^+$, which is higher than the legal limit of 1.00 ppm.
  a. If the shark meat had a mass of 12.5 kg, what mass of methyl mercury was present in the shark meat?
  b. What is the maximum number of grams of methyl mercury the shark meat could contain and still be considered safe according to the legal limit?

18. Prolonged exposure to lead or lead salts is toxic. To prevent lead poisoning, the current standard for lead in paint is 600.0 ppm, though some older paints had a concentration of 5.00×10^4 ppm. On average, a bucket of paint has a mass of 900.0 g.
  a. Calculate the maximum mass of lead in a bucket of new paint of average mass.
  b. Calculate the mass of lead in a bucket of old paint, based on the concentration and mass given.

SOLUBILITY AND POLARITY

19. Use **Table 13-2** to determine whether the following compounds are soluble in water:
  a. copper(II) sulfate
  b. copper(II) sulfide
  c. iron(III) chloride
  d. aluminum acetate

20. Explain what is meant by the chemist's expression, "like dissolves like."

21. If you mix silver nitrate with water, will it dissolve? If you mix potassium chloride with water, will it dissolve? If you mix the contents of these two combinations, will anything settle to the bottom? If so, what will settle?

SOLUTIONS 505

Complete worked-out solutions for these problems can be found on the teacher's interleaved pages at the end of this chapter.

5. salt water, sugar water, ketchup, muddy water, sand in water

6. A typical procedure would be as follows: weigh out 7.305 g of NaCl in a clean beaker; transfer it to a 250.0 mL volumetric flask; wash all residue from the beaker and funnel used in the transfer; pour in about 100 mL of distilled H_2O and swirl the flask until the solid is dissolved; fill the flask to the mark with additional distilled water; stopper, swirl, and invert the flask several times to ensure thorough mixing.

7. You need a total of 0.01 mol of NaOH (0.10 L $\times$ 0.1 mol NaOH/L). This amount would be contained in 20 mL of the 0.5 M solution (0.02 L $\times$ 0.5 mol NaOH/L = 0.01 mol). Measure out 20 mL of the 0.5 M solution, pour it into a 250 mL flask, and add 80 mL of water.

8-18. *See page 509A.*

19. a. soluble
   b. insoluble
   c. soluble
   d. soluble

20. The substances that are soluble in a solvent are those whose molecular structure and polarity are most like the solvent itself.

21. Both silver nitrate and potassium chloride are soluble in water. However, when aqueous solutions of silver nitrate and potassium chloride are mixed, a precipitate of silver chloride will form and settle to the bottom of the container.

Complete worked-out solutions
for these problems can be found
on the teacher's interleaved
pages at the end of this chapter.

22.

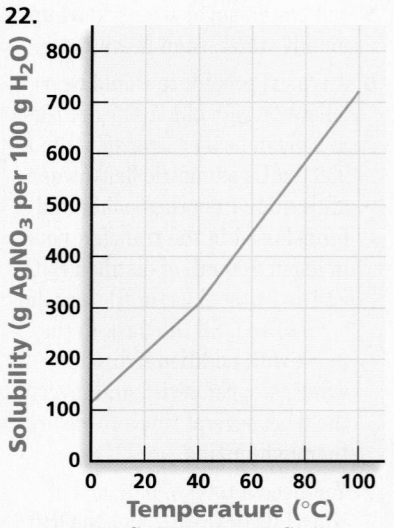

a. at 30°C, 270 g; at 55°C, 410 g;
at 75°C, 550 g
b. about 33°C
c. unsaturated

23. a. supersaturated
b. saturated
c. unsaturated

24. a. All electrolytes produce ions in
solution.
b. Use a battery-powered ohmmeter to check the conductance
of the solution. A solution containing ions will conduct an
electric current to some degree.

25. a. most conductive
b. moderately conductive
c. least conductive

26. The liquids in the blood and cells
contain ions, making them
conductive.

27. Vitamin A is an oil-soluble vitamin. It would not be soluble in
fruit juices.

28. The chemicals do not dissolve but
are separated into micelles small
enough to remain suspended in an
aqueous medium.

29. Detergents do not form insoluble
salts with Ca^{2+} and Mg^{2+}, the
typical ions in hard water,
whereas soaps do.

22. Plot a solubility graph for $AgNO_3$ with the
data below. Plot grams of solute (in increments of 50 g) per 100 g of H_2O on the vertical axis and the temperature in degrees
Celsius on the horizontal axis.
   a. Estimate the solubility of $AgNO_3$ at 30°C,
   55°C, and 75°C.
   b. At what temperature would the solubility
   of $AgNO_3$ be 275 g per 100 g of H_2O?
   c. If 98.5 g of $AgNO_3$ were added to 100 g of
   H_2O at 10°C, would the resulting solution
   be saturated or unsaturated?

Grams of solute per 100 g of H_2O	Temperature (°C)
122	0.0
216	20.0
311	40.0
440	60.0
585	80.0
733	100.0

AQUEOUS SOLUTIONS

23. In each of the diagrams shown below, 5.0 g of
sodium acetate has been added to different concentrations of sodium acetate solutions, leading
to the results noted. Indicate whether each of
the original solutions was unsaturated, saturated, or supersaturated.
   a.

   Rapid recrystallization of more
   than the added amount
   b.

   Added amount
   remains undissolved

c.

Most of the added
amount dissolves

24. a. What property is common to all
electrolytes?
   b. How could you safely determine whether or
   not an unknown aqueous solution contains
   ions?

25. Rate the solutions below from most conductive
to least conductive.
   a. 1.0 M KOH solution
   b. 10.0 M ammonia solution
   c. 2.0 M glucose solution

26. When you touch an appliance that has a short
circuit, an electric current travels through your
body, giving you a shock. What feature of the
human body allows the electric current to
travel through it?

APPLICATIONS OF SOLUBILITY

27. Foods and beverages are often fortified with
vitamins. For instance, many fruit juices contain vitamin C. Why do fruit juices not contain vitamin A?

28. Explain why it is inaccurate to say that
emulsifiers actually make insoluble chemicals
dissolve. What really happens to the insoluble
chemicals?

29. Explain why detergents are better emulsifiers
than soaps in hard water, which contains calcium and magnesium ions.

30. Butter is an emulsion containing about 80%
oily butterfat and 16% water. During the
process of making butter, it is churned, or
stirred very quickly, for a long period of time.
Explain why the churning step is necessary in
converting cream to butter.

31. What are the chemical characteristics of a
good dry-cleaning solvent? How do they differ
from the chemical characteristics of a good
emulsifier?

32. The table below lists the solubility of three gases in grams of solute per 100 g of water at various temperatures. Use the data to plot a solubility versus temperature graph for each gas listed, with grams of solute per 100 g of H_2O on the vertical axis and temperature in degrees Celsius on the horizontal axis. Then answer the questions that follow.

Gas	20°C	30°C	40°C	50°C	60°C
CO_2	0.169	0.126	0.097	0.076	0.058
H_2S	0.38	0.30	0.24	0.19	0.15
Cl_2	0.73	0.57	0.46	0.39	0.33

a. Estimate the solubility of each gas at 45°C.
b. At what temperature would the solubility of Cl_2 be 0.50 g per 100 g of H_2O?
c. If a solution contains 0.100 g of CO_2 in 100 g of H_2O at 35°C, is it unsaturated, saturated, or supersaturated?
d. Assuming that other gases follow the pattern of these three gases, should you heat or cool water if you are trying to dissolve a gas in it?

33. Explain the role of solubility in accounting for the fact that you are more likely to overdose on vitamin A than on vitamin C.

34. Crayon companies recommend treating wax stains on clothes by spraying them with WD-40 lubricant, applying dishwashing liquid, and then washing them. Explain why.

35. To produce ice cubes that are clear instead of cloudy, should hot or cold water be used? Explain your answer.

Practice Problems

36. Ascorbic acid, vitamin C, has the formula $C_6H_8O_6$. What is the molarity of a solution of ascorbic acid if the concentration is 5.0 mg/L? **(Hint: See Sample Problem 13A.)**

37. A cup (250 mL) of whole milk contains about 0.4 mg of riboflavin, $C_{17}H_{20}N_4O_6$. What is the molarity of riboflavin in the milk? **(Hint: See Sample Problem 13A.)**

LINKING CHAPTERS

1. Precipitation reactions
Use **Table 13-2** to predict whether any precipitate will form when the following solutions are mixed. If a precipitate does form, what would you expect it to be?
a. $KOH(aq)$ and $NaNO_3(aq)$
b. $CaCl_2(aq)$ and $H_2CO_3(aq)$
c. $Na_2S(aq)$ and $FeBr_3(aq)$

2. Endothermic and exothermic processes
Enthalpy of solution refers to the total enthalpy change that accompanies the addition of 1 mol of solute to a large volume of solvent. The table below shows the enthalpy of solution for various solutes dissolved in water. Use it to answer the following questions:
a. Which solutes have endothermic enthalpies of solution?
b. Which solutes would increase the temperature of the solution?
c. Which solutes would dissolve better in hot water? Cite reasons for your answer.

Solute	Enthalpy of solution (kJ/mol)
Hydrogen chloride, $HCl(g)$	−74.84
Potassium chloride, $KCl(s)$	+17.22
Potassium hydroxide, $KOH(s)$	−57.61
Potassium nitrate, $KNO_3(s)$	+34.89
Silver nitrate, $AgNO_3(s)$	+22.59
Sodium chloride, $NaCl(s)$	+3.88
Sodium hydroxide, $NaOH(s)$	−44.51
Sodium nitrate, $NaNO_3(s)$	+20.50

Complete worked-out solutions for these problems can be found on the teacher's interleaved pages at the end of this chapter.

30. The cream from which butter is churned is already an emulsion, and the churning process destabilizes the emulsion and causes it to reverse from an oil-in-water emulsion to a colloid of water in solid fat called a solid emulsion.

31. A good solvent should be nonpolar so that it can dissolve oils. It should also evaporate cleanly. An emulsifier must have both polar and nonpolar regions.

32.

a. solubilities at 45°C: CO_2, 0.086 g/100 g H_2O; H_2S, 0.22 g/100 g H_2O; Cl_2, 0.42 g/100 g H_2O
b. 36°C
c. unsaturated
d. Cool the water, because gases are more soluble at lower temperatures.

33. Vitamin C is water soluble, so excess quantities can be eliminated by the kidneys, which regulate the concentrations of water-soluble materials. Vitamin A is fat soluble and must be processed by the liver at a much slower rate.

CHAPTER 13
Review Answers

Complete worked-out solutions for these problems can be found on the teacher's interleaved pages at the end of this chapter.

34. WD-40 consists of oils dissolved in nonpolar solvent. This mixture dissolves crayon wax, which is also nonpolar. Washing in soap will emulsify the oils and dissolved wax so that they can be rinsed down the drain.

35. You would use hot water because it usually contains much less dissolved air than cold water.

36-37. *See page 509A.*

LINKING CHAPTERS

1. a. no precipitate
   b. $CaCO_3$ precipitates
   c. Fe_2S_3 precipitates

2. a. KCl, KNO_3, $AgNO_3$, NaCl, $NaNO_3$
   b. HCl, KOH, NaOH
   c. Solutes that dissolve endothermically—the list in part (a)—would dissolve faster in hot water.

3. a. The fact that the enthalpy of solution for KCl is more endothermic than for NaCl indicates that a solution of RbCl is even more endothermic than a solution of KCl.
   b. Following the pattern for chlorides, the order should be: LiBr, NaBr, KBr, RbBr.

Answers continue on page 509A.

3. Classification and trends
   Use the table from item 2 for these questions.
   a. The enthalpy of solution for rubidium chloride, RbCl, is not given in the table. Predict how its enthalpy of solution compares with that of potassium chloride, KCl. (Hint: Examine the chart closely, looking for patterns, and examine a periodic table.)
   b. Arrange the following compounds in order of their enthalpies of solution, beginning with the most exothermic: NaBr, LiBr, RbBr, KBr.

ALTERNATIVE ASSESSMENTS

Performance assessment

1. Design a solubility experiment to identify an unknown substance that is CsCl, RbCl, LiCl, NH_4Cl, KCl, or NaCl. (Hint: You will need a solubility versus temperature graph for each of the salts.) If your instructor approves your design, get a sample from the instructor, and perform your experiment.

2. The more concentrated an aqueous solution of ethylene glycol is, the more dense it is. Mechanics keep this in mind when they check the antifreeze in a car's radiator. Using the data for ethylene glycol solutions shown below, graph the density versus the concentration. Then determine the concentration of a solution with a density of 1.030 g/mL. What density would you predict for a 2.50 M solution?

Concentration (M)	Density (g/mL)
0.65	1.003
1.30	1.008
3.30	1.024
7.50	1.057

3. Computer spreadsheet
   Many reagent chemicals used in the lab are sold in the form of concentrated aqueous solutions, as shown in the table below. Different volumes are diluted to 1.00 L to make less-concentrated solutions. Create a spreadsheet that will calculate the volume of concentrated reagent needed to make 1.00 L solutions of any molar concentration that you enter.

Reagent	Concentration (M)
H_2SO_4	18
HCl	12.1
HNO_3	16
H_3PO_4	14.8
CH_3COOH	17.4
NH_3	15

Portfolio projects

1. Chemistry and you
   For 1 week, record instances in which you use a mixture of some type. Identify whether each mixture is a solution, a suspension, an emulsion, or a heterogeneous mixture. If possible, identify the different components of each mixture.

2. Research and communication
   Emergency-response teams working with oil spills use chemical and physical properties of oil and water along with solubility principles to control and clean up spills. Research the techniques used, and explain why they work. Present your findings to the class.

3. Chemistry and you
   Read the labels of three different over-the-counter vitamin supplements. Write down the amount of vitamin A supplied in one tablet of each supplement. What dosage of each supplement could cause vitamin A toxicity (which is determined to be >15 000 µg/day)? (Hint: To convert IUs to µg, multiply by 0.025.)

4. internet**connect**

SC*L*INKS NSTA

TOPIC: Vitamin supplements
GO TO: www.scilinks.org
KEYWORD: HW135

Research and communication
Research the many arguments for and against the use of vitamin supplements. What is the role of the U.S. Food and Drug Administration in the regulation of vitamin supplements? Prepare an argument for or against the increased regulation of vitamin supplements, and debate the issue in class.

1. Two immiscible liquids can be mixed by the addition of a(n) _____.
   a. weak electrolyte
   b. emulsifier
   c. colloid
   d. hydronium ion

2. _____ of NaOH must be used to prepare 2.5 L of a 0.010 M solution.
   a. 0.01 g
   b. 1.0 g
   c. 2.5 g
   d. 0.4 g

3. The molarity of 300.0 mL of a sodium carbonate solution that contains 22.5 g of Na_2CO_3 is _____.
   a. 0.700 M
   b. 0.210 M
   c. 0.100 M
   d. 1.210 M

4. Water is an excellent solvent because _____.
   a. it is a covalent compound
   b. of its polarity
   c. it does not form any electrolytes in aqueous solution
   d. of its colligative properties

5. Two liquids are likely to be immiscible if _____.
   a. both have nonpolar molecules
   b. both have polar molecules
   c. one has nonpolar molecules and the other has polar molecules
   d. one is water and the other is another polar solvent

6. A(n) _____ would increase the solubility of a gas in a liquid.
   a. decrease in temperature
   b. decrease in atmospheric pressure
   c. increase in temperature
   d. agitation of the solution

7. Acetic acid is considered a weak electrolyte because it _____.
   a. is immiscible in water
   b. forms both hydronium ions and hydroxide ions in aqueous solution
   c. lowers the boiling point of water
   d. does not fully ionize in aqueous solution

8. Which of the following molecules is a dipole?
   a.
   b.
   c.
   d.

9. The boiling-point elevation is _____.
   a. 0.51 K for every mole of solute particles present in 1 kg of water
   b. 0.51 K for every mole of solute particles present in 1 mol of water
   c. 1 K for every mole of solute particles present in 1 mol of water
   d. 1 K for every mole of solute particles present in 1 kg of water

10. Because vitamin A is fat-soluble, it _____.
    a. does not mix well with nonpolar substances
    b. is stored in the liver
    c. passes out of the body in the urine
    d. cannot accumulate in the body

SOLUTIONS 509

1. b
2. b
3. a
4. b
5. c
6. a
7. d
8. b
9. a
10. b

Answers from page 505

8. a. $[FeCl_3] = \dfrac{0.250 \text{ mol}}{2.00 \text{ L}} = 0.125 \text{ M}$

b. $[KMnO_4] = \dfrac{0.015 \text{ mol}}{0.350 \text{ L}} = 0.043 \text{ M}$

c. $[NaCH_3COO] = \dfrac{3.5 \times 10^{-4} \text{ mol}}{0.025 \text{ L}} = 0.014 \text{ M}$

9. a. $[NaOH] = \dfrac{20.0 \text{ g} \times \dfrac{1 \text{ mol NaOH}}{40.00 \text{ g}}}{2.00 \text{ L}} = 0.250 \text{ M}$

b. $[NH_4Br] = \dfrac{14.0 \text{ g} \times \dfrac{1 \text{ mol } NH_4Br}{97.95 \text{ g}}}{0.150 \text{ L}} = 0.953 \text{ M}$

c. $[CuCl_2] = \dfrac{65.0 \text{ g} \times \dfrac{1 \text{ mol } CuCl_2}{134.45 \text{ g}}}{0.300 \text{ L}} = 1.61 \text{ M}$

10. a. $4.0 \text{ M } AgNO_3 \times 1.0 \text{ L} = 4.0 \text{ mol } AgNO_3$
b. $0.500 \text{ M HCl} \times 2.50 \text{ L} = 1.25 \text{ mol HCl}$
c. $0.250 \text{ M } HNO_3 \times 0.400 \text{ L} = 0.100 \text{ mol } HNO_3$

11. a. $0.0100 \text{ M } H_3PO_4 \times 0.0300 \text{ L} = 3.00 \times 10^{-4} \text{ mol } H_3PO_4$
b. $18 \text{ M } H_2SO_4 \times 0.005 \text{ L} = 0.09 \text{ mol } H_2SO_4$
c. $1.00 \times 10^{-4} \text{ M } CH_3OH \times 0.2500 \text{ L} = 2.5 \times 10^{-5} \text{ mol } CH_3OH$

12. $0.7500 \text{ L} \times 6.00 \text{ M } H_3PO_4 \times \dfrac{1 \text{ mol } Ca_3(PO_4)_2}{2 \text{ mol } H_3PO_4} \times \dfrac{310.18 \text{ g}}{\text{mol } Ca_3(PO_4)_2} =$

$698 \text{ g } Ca_3(PO_4)_2$

13. $2.00 \text{ M } (NH_4)_2S \times 0.3500 \text{ L} = 0.700 \text{ mol } (NH_4)_2S$
$1.50 \text{ M } Cd(NO_3)_2 \times 0.4000 \text{ L} = 0.600 \text{ mol } Cd(NO_3)_2$; $Cd(NO_3)_2$ is the limiting reagent.

$0.600 \text{ mol } Cd(NO_3)_2 \times \dfrac{1 \text{ mol CdS}}{1 \text{ mol } Cd(NO_3)_2} \times \dfrac{144.48 \text{ g}}{\text{mol CdS}} = 86.7 \text{ g CdS}$

14. Averaging data points:
$\dfrac{1}{4}\left(\dfrac{2.9 \text{ g}}{0.025 \text{ L}} + \dfrac{5.6 \text{ g}}{0.0500 \text{ L}} + \dfrac{8.5 \text{ g}}{0.075 \text{ L}} + \dfrac{11.3 \text{ g}}{0.1000 \text{ L}}\right) \times \dfrac{1 \text{ mol NaCl}}{58.44 \text{ g}} = 1.9 \text{ M NaCl}$

15. $\dfrac{2.00 - 1.9}{2.00} \times 100\% = 5\%$

16. $2.5 \text{ L gasoline} \times \dfrac{1 \text{ L oil}}{100 \text{ L gasoline}} = 0.025 \text{ L oil}$

17. a. $\dfrac{1.76 \text{ g } [HgCH_3]^+}{10^6 \text{ g shark}} \times (1.25 \times 10^4 \text{ g shark}) = 0.0220 \text{ g } [HgCH_3]^+$

b. $1.25 \times 10^4 \text{ g shark} \times \dfrac{1.00 \text{ g } [HgCH_3]^+}{10^6 \text{ g shark}} = 0.0125 \text{ g } [HgCH_3]^+$

18. a. $\dfrac{600.0 \text{ g Pb}}{10^6 \text{ g paint}} \times 900.0 \text{ g paint} = 0.540 \text{ g Pb}$

b. $\dfrac{5.00 \times 10^4 \text{ g Pb}}{10^6 \text{ g paint}} \times 900.0 \text{ g paint} = 45.0 \text{ g Pb}$

Answers from page 508

36. $5.0 \text{ mg/L } C_6H_8O_6 \times \dfrac{1 \text{ mol } C_6H_8O_6}{176.14 \text{ g}} \times \dfrac{1 \text{ g}}{1000 \text{ mg}} = 2.8 \times 10^{-5} \text{ M } C_6H_8O_6$

37. $\dfrac{0.4 \text{ mg } C_{17}H_{20}N_4O_6}{0.25 \text{ L}} \times \dfrac{1 \text{ mol}}{376.41 \text{ g}} \times \dfrac{1 \text{ g}}{1000 \text{ mg}} = 4 \times 10^{-6} \text{ M riboflavin}$

ALTERNATIVE ASSESSMENTS

Performance assessment

1. Experimental designs will vary but should include a method for determining the mass of solute needed to form a saturated solution at a certain temperature.

2. 1.030 g/mL is equivalent to 4.06 M; 2.50 M is equivalent to 1.018 g/mL.

3. If all solutions are to be 1.00 L in volume, the program should calculate the volume of stock solution to use in liters as $V_{stock} = M_{solution}/M_{stock}$. To calculate the volume in milliliters, the expression is $V_{stock} = 1000(M_{solution}/M_{stock})$. The volume to use cannot have more significant figures than the given molarity of the concentration reagents. Students cannot expect to know what volume to use to make, for example, a 0.8150 M solution. Solutions of such accurate concentrations would have to be made roughly and then titrated against a standard.

Portfolio projects

1. Lists will vary and are apt to be long if students are able to recognize all of the mixtures they encounter during a week. Check to be sure that they have not included any pure substances.

2. Research should include both biological and mechanical means of cleaning up spills as well as chemical methods.

3. Students could include an examination of the popular use of beta-carotene as a "safe" version of vitamin A. This substance is a biological precursor to the vitamin. It has about twice the IU activity of the same mass of vitamin A. Many supplements will contain beta-carotene instead of vitamin A.

4. Some students may want to research the biochemical roles of the various vitamins.

Chemical Equilibrium

CLASSROOM RESOURCES

SECTIONS	TEACHER'S DEMONSTRATIONS	PROBLEM SOLVING ■ *Text* ◆ *ChemFile Mini-Guide*	LABORATORIES ■ *Text* ◆ *ChemFile Manuals: A, B, C, D*
14-1 **What is an equilibrium system?** Section Review, p. 521	**Demo 1** Completion Reactions, p. 512 **Demo 2** Reversible Reactions, p. 514 **Demo 3** Temperature Effects on Gas Production, p. 516 **Demo 4** Complex Ion Equilibria, p. 520	◆ **Chapter 20** Equilibrium	◆ **B19** Equilibrium
14-2 **How is equilibrium measured?** Section Review, p. 533	**Demo 5** Kinetics Simulation, p. 524 **Demo 6** Common Ion Effect, p. 532	■ **Sample Problem 14A** Calculating K_{eq} for a system at equilibrium ■ **Sample Problem 14B** Calculating concentrations using the equilibrium constant ■ **Sample Problem 14C** Calculating K_{sp} from solubility ■ **Sample Problem 14D** Calculating concentrations using K_{sp} ◆ **Chapter 22** Equilibrium of Salts, K_{sp}	■ **QuickLab** Finding Equilibrium, p. 524 ◆ **A19** The Solubility Product Constant of NaCl ◆ **Exp. C15** Solubility Product Constant ◆ **Inv. C15** Solubility Product Constant— Algae Blooms

SECTIONS	VIDEOS/VIDEODISC *Holt Chemistry Videodisc* CNN PRESENTS *Science in the NEWS*	CHEMFILE CD-ROMS ● *Teaching Resources* ◆ *Interactive Tutor*	OVERHEADS ● *Color Transparencies* ◆ *Transparency Masters*
14-1	Reversible Reaction: Cobalt Complexes Equilibrium: Nitrogen Dioxide Synthesis Iron Thiocyanate Equilibrium Common Ion Effect	◆ **Module 7:** Equilibrium **Topic:** Equilibrium	● **99** Temperature Changes Affect an Equilibrium System ● **100** Particle Model for the Common Ion Effect ◆ **98A** Reaction Rate over Time for an Equilibrium System
14-2	Equilibrium: Sparingly Soluble Salt Solubility Equilibrium and Lead(II) Iodide	● Supplemental Reading: *The Same and Not the Same*, Ch. 33 "Fritz Haber" ◆ **Module 7:** Equilibrium **Topic:** Shifting Equilibrium	◆ **101A** Equilibrium Calculations

ASSESSMENT RESOURCES

ALTERNATIVE ASSESSMENTS	CHAPTER TESTING	SCORING RUBRICS *Holt ChemFile Teaching Resources CD-ROM*
Student Text Performance assessments, p. 538 Portfolio projects 1–2, p. 538 **Study Guide** Sections 14-1 to 14-2	**Student Text** Test Preparation, p. 539 **Holt Chemistry: Visualizing Matter Chapter 14 Test** (blackline masters) **Holt ChemFile Test Generator for Macintosh and Windows**	**Lab Work** Student-Designed Experiments Rubric Performance-Tasks Scoring Rubric Assessment for Structured Inquiry Assessment for Open-Ended Inquiry **Portfolio Projects** Evaluating Concept Maps Assessing Portfolios Portfolio Assignment Student Evaluation Form

CHAPTER 14

Chemical Equilibrium

FERTILIZERS, EXPLOSIVES, AND WORLD WAR I

On July 28, 1914, Austria-Hungary declared war on Serbia. Six days later, Germany, an ally of Austria-Hungary, declared war on France. German troops stormed through Belgium and a short time later invaded France. The German army expected a quick victory, but the French and British forces resisted, and the battle escalated into World War I, four years of grueling trench warfare.

The Allies quickly set up a blockade in the Atlantic Ocean to prevent supplies from reaching Germany. The Germans especially needed sodium nitrate imported from Chile. They needed this mineral to make nitric acid, some of which was used to make fertilizers that were needed to increase food production in the relatively small country. But the bulk of the nitric acid was used to make explosives, such as trinitrotoluene (TNT) and nitroglycerin. If access to Chilean sodium nitrate had been cut off, the German armies would have run out of explosives in a fairly short time and the war would have ground to a halt.

In a remarkable coincidence, in 1913 the German chemist Carl Bosch commercialized a chemical procedure for synthesizing am-

monia. Ammonia could be used as the basis for the production of nitric acid. He started with a process developed by Fritz Haber in 1904 that combined nitrogen and hydrogen according to the following equation.

$$N_2(g) + 3H_2(g) \longrightarrow 2NH_3(g)$$

Even before World War I, chemists realized that they needed to discover a process similar to the one used by nitrogen-fixing bacteria to fix atmospheric nitrogen into other useful chemical compounds. As early as the 1890s, chemists had shown that small amounts of ammonia could be synthesized at high temperatures and at atmospheric pressure from elemental hydrogen and nitrogen.

Bosch improved the yield of ammonia by properly choosing the pressure and temperature of the reaction system. By 1913, Germany was producing ammonia in industrial quantities. The German army had a continuous supply of explosives, and the war dragged on until November 1918.

CHAPTER LINKS

How would increasing the pressure of the reaction to produce ammonia affect the ammonia yield?

How would increasing the reaction temperature affect the amount of ammonia produced in this exothermic reaction?

Nitrogen compounds have been used in making explosives for about a thousand years. The first explosive, black powder, contained potassium nitrate and is believed to have been invented in China in the tenth century.

The discovery of large deposits of sodium nitrate in Chile in the 1850s was important to the production of several forms of explosives. In addition to being a source for nitric acid, the starting material for such explosives as dynamite and nitroglycerin, sodium nitrate can also be reacted with potassium chloride to make potassium nitrate.

Module 7: Equilibrium
Topic: Equilibrium

CONCEPT PREVIEW

Section 14-1
Equilibrium reactions
▶ comparing reversible and completion reactions
▶ dynamic equilibrium

Factors that affect equilibria
▶ pressure in gaseous systems
▶ effect of temperature
▶ Le Châtelier's principle
▶ effect of concentration changes

Complex ion equilibria
▶ nature of complex ions
▶ ligands
▶ color changes

Section 14-2
Measuring equilibria
▶ the meaning of the equilibrium constant, K_{eq}
▶ determining K_{eq}
▶ using K_{eq} in calculations

Solubility equilibria
▶ the solubility constant, K_{sp}
▶ calculating K_{sp}
▶ common ion effect

What is an equilibrium system?

OBJECTIVES

▶ ***Distinguish*** between reactions that go to completion and those that do not.

▶ ***Determine*** whether the forward or reverse reaction is favored when a stress is applied to an equilibrium system using Le Châtelier's principle.

▶ ***Describe*** complex-ion behavior in aqueous equilibrium.

▶ ***Discuss*** examples of equilibrium systems.

Reversible and completion reactions

When you look at the components of a chemical reaction, you are looking at how compounds and elements react to form products. In studying reactions, you may have observed changes such as the formation of a precipitate or the evolution of a gas. Reactions that produce these types of changes often proceed very nearly to completion. **Figure 14-1** shows a reaction that produces a precipitate. Two examples of reactions that go to completion or very nearly to completion are shown in the following equations.

$$NaHCO_3(aq) + CH_3COOH(aq) \longrightarrow NaCH_3COO(aq) + CO_2(g) + H_2O(l)$$
Formation of a gas

$$NaCl(aq) + AgNO_3(aq) \longrightarrow AgCl(s) + Na^+(aq) + NO_3^-(aq)$$
Formation of a precipitate

▶ **FIGURE 14-1**

When a clear sodium chloride solution is mixed with a clear solution of silver nitrate, an insoluble white precipitate of silver chloride is formed.

DEMONSTRATION 1

Completion Reactions

Approximate time: 5 minutes

1. Place 15 mL of 0.1 M $AgNO_3$ solution in a test tube.

2. Add 15 mL of 0.2 M NaCl solution. A white AgCl precipitate forms. Note that NaCl is in excess.

3. Wet a filter paper, and use a small funnel to filter the solution into another test tube.

4. Add 5 mL more of 0.2 M NaCl solution to show that the reaction is complete and that no more $AgNO_3$ is present.

5. Add 1 drop of $AgNO_3$ to show what happens when Ag^+ is present.

6. Allow the filter paper with the AgCl to stand in the light. After several minutes

Reversible reactions reach equilibrium

Some reactions do not proceed to completion. Instead, the reaction ceases before the reactants are fully consumed. If the reactants and products of such a reaction are kept in a closed system, where nothing can escape, the reaction may proceed in either direction. Recall that a system consists of all the components that are being studied at a given time.

A reversible reaction that you might encounter is the recharging of an automobile battery. The interior of the battery has lead plates, lead(IV) oxide plates, and a sulfuric acid solution, H_2SO_4. The reversible reaction that takes place within a car battery is represented by the following equation. Notice that the arrows in the equation point in both directions, indicating a reversible reaction.

$$Pb(s) + PbO_2(s) + 2H_2SO_4(aq) \rightleftarrows 2PbSO_4(s) + 2H_2O(l) + energy$$

When the battery is used for power, the forward reaction occurs, releasing energy in the form of electricity. If you leave your car lights on, the forward reaction (discharge) will continue until most of the PbO_2 is used up, and the battery "dies." The reverse reaction occurs when electricity from an outside source is fed into the circuit. You must force the reverse reaction (charge) by passing a direct current through the battery in the opposite direction, as happens when someone gives your dead battery a jump-start.

Reversible reactions lead to an equilibrium system when the forward and reverse reactions occur at equal rates and the conditions remain the same. At equilibrium, the total amount of particles remains constant. Because our model of a system at equilibrium has constant concentrations, we can use this information to determine the completeness of the reaction and to make predictions.

Consider the following equation, which represents the reaction of acetic acid with 3-methyl-1-butanol, $C_5H_{11}OH$, to form the ester 3-methylbutyl acetate, $C_7H_{14}O_2$, and water. Recall from Chapter 7 that esters are organic compounds that can be used as flavoring agents. The ester formed in this reaction is commonly known as banana oil or pear oil. It is often used to add flavor to syrups and mineral waters.

$$CH_3-\overset{O}{\underset{OH}{C}} + \underset{CH_3}{\overset{CH_3}{CH}}-CH_2-\overset{OH}{\underset{H}{C}}-H \Longleftrightarrow \underset{CH_3}{\overset{CH_3}{CH}}-CH_2-CH_2-O-\overset{O}{C}-CH_3 + H_2O$$

acetic acid   3-methyl-1-butanol   3-methylbutyl acetate (banana oil)   water

CHEMICAL EQUILIBRIUM   513

TEACHING TIP

Reversible Processes Students should understand that reversible processes, both physical and chemical, are a necessary characteristic of equilibrium systems.

COMMON MISCONCEPTION

Students think of equilibrium as referring to a point or position of balance, and there is a temptation to equate equilibrium with equal masses on a double-pan balance. An equilibrium does have two equal "sides," but it is the rates of change that are equal. Equal masses on a balance represent a static equilibrium because nothing is happening.

A chemical equilibrium, on the other hand, is a dynamic equilibrium in which opposite processes are occurring at equal rates. When we look at a system in chemical equilibrium, we may see no evidence of reactions taking place. Students should understand, though, that the chemical processes are quite active at the molecular level.

READING STRATEGY

Peer Teaching

Have each student read the section on reversible and completion reactions and study the figures. After reading, students should pair up and take turns asking and answering the following questions:

▶ Under what conditions do reactions go to completion?

▶ Contrast reversible reactions and completion reactions in terms of the behavior of reactants and products.

▶ What is taking place when a reaction reaches equilibrium?

▶ What happens to the rate of the forward reaction after reactants are combined? Why does the rate not drop to zero?

---

students may notice that the photoreactive AgCl turns gray. Point out that silver halides (usually AgBr and AgI) are commonly used in photographic film and paper.

Safety

Wear safety goggles and a lab apron. Students must be 10 ft or more from the demonstration.

Disposal

Add a few drops of NaCl solution to any leftover AgNO₃ solution until all of the silver ions precipitate. Decant the liquid from the AgCl crystals, and evaporate the liquid. Put the AgCl in a bottle labeled "AgCl(s)," and keep it for future display. Do not dispose of AgCl in a landfill.

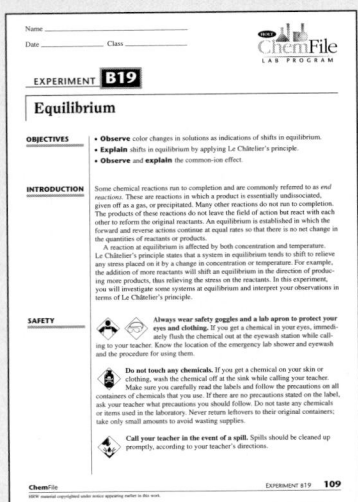
► **FIGURE 14-3**

The rate of the forward and reverse reactions for the equilibrium system of the banana-oil reaction can be shown graphically.

Rate Comparison for the Equilibrium System
$$CH_3COOH + C_5H_{11}OH \rightleftharpoons CH_3COOC_5H_{11} + H_2O$$

Opposing reaction rates are equal at equilibrium

Figure 14-3 shows a graph of what happens as the reaction that produces banana oil attains equilibrium. Initially, the concentration of each product, water and 3-methylbutyl acetate, is zero, and the rate of the reverse reaction is zero. At the same time, the concentration of each reactant, acetic acid and 3-methyl-1-butanol, is at a maximum, and the rate of the forward reaction is the maximum rate. The rate of the forward reaction decreases as reactants are used up, and the rate of the reverse reaction increases until finally, at time t_1, the rates become equal and the equilibrium condition begins.

At equilibrium, the individual concentrations of the reactants and the products undergo no further changes as long as conditions remain the same. However, chemical reactions continue to occur even after equilibrium is reached. Although the macroscopic properties no longer change (the system appears unchanging), the forward and reverse reactions are still occurring. In other words, the reactions do not stop at equilibrium but maintain constant concentrations of reactants and products. The reactants continue forming products, and the reverse reaction continues at the same rate, with the products re-forming reactants. That is why any chemical equilibrium system is really a dynamic situation, not a static one.

To understand the difference between a dynamic situation and a static situation, imagine that you and a friend are each standing on a treadmill, similar to those shown in **Figure 14-4**. If you stand still on the treadmill and do not move at all, your situation can be described as static; there is no change in your position, and you and the equipment are at rest. If your friend runs at a steady pace on the treadmill, the situation is described as being in dynamic equilibrium because your friend and the treadmill are moving at a constant rate but your friend's position does not change.

▲ **FIGURE 14-4**

Two people on different treadmills, one standing still and one running, illustrate static and dynamic situations.

514   CHAPTER 14

DEMONSTRATION 2

Reversible Reactions

Approximate time: 5 minutes

The demonstration shows the reversibility of the following reaction (In represents the indicator phenolphthalein).

$$H_2In(aq) + 2OH^-(aq) \rightleftharpoons In^{2-}(aq) + 2H_2O(l)$$

1. Place 2 drops of phenolphthalein in a test tube half-filled with distilled water.

2. Dilute 1 mL of 0.1 M NaOH with 100 mL of distilled water. Add the resulting solution to the test tube dropwise until the solution turns light pink.

3. Add 2 drops of 0.1 M NaOH to the solution. It should become magenta.

4. Add 2 more drops of phenolphthalein (reactant) to the test tube. The magenta of the solution should become darker.

Equilibrium systems and stress

Equilibrium is established in a reversible reaction when the forward and reverse reactions occur at the same rate and when the amounts of the reactants and products are constant. One example of a reversible reaction involves oxides of nitrogen, as represented by the following equation.

$$2NO_2(g) \rightleftarrows N_2O_4(g)$$

Brown   Colorless

internet connect

SC LINKS
NSTA

TOPIC: Factors affecting equilibrium
GO TO: www.scilinks.org
KEYWORD: HW141

Pressure changes may alter gaseous equilibrium systems

According to the balanced equation above, 2 mol of nitrogen dioxide, NO_2, reacts to produce 1 mol of dinitrogen tetroxide, N_2O_4. When the system reaches equilibrium, there will be no change in the amounts of reactants and products until something alters the system. The factors that can alter an equilibrium system are called stresses. Suppose the NO_2/N_2O_4 equilibrium mixture is subjected to an increase in pressure caused by decreasing the volume of the container, as shown in **Figure 14-5**. Let us explore the system's response to an increase in pressure. Remember that the pressure of a gas in a container is caused by collisions of molecules against the walls of the container. The system can

a Low pressure   **b** Higher pressure   **c** New equilibrium

SECTION 14-1

TEACHING TIP

Equal Rates, Not Equal Amounts
Remind students that equilibrium does not mean that the amounts of reactants and products are equal. It means that the rates of conversion (the number of reactions per unit of time) are equal. Only when $K_{eq} = 1$ does the reaction reach equilibrium with equal concentrations of reactants and products.

ANSWERS

CONCEPT CHECK

1. gases and precipitates

2. by using both a forward arrow and a backward arrow

3. The forward reaction decreases from its initial rate. The reverse reaction increases in rate from zero. At equilibrium, the rates become equal.

4. In a static equilibrium, nothing is happening. In a dynamic equilibrium, processes take place, but forward and reverse processes are in balance.

FIGURE 14-5 ◄

A decrease in volume increases the pressure and the concentrations of both NO_2 and N_2O_4, disturbing the equilibrium and temporarily making the mixture darker. The color fades as more N_2O_4 is formed to reduce the pressure and restore equilibrium.

CHEMICAL EQUILIBRIUM 515

RESOURCE LINK

ChemFile Mini-Guide to Problem Solving
Assign Chapter 20: *Equilibrium* for additional practice.

CHAPTER 20
Equilibrium

Not all processes in nature proceed to completion. In fact, most changes hover somewhere between the initial state and what would ideally be the final state. Compare a light switch and a dimmer. If the mechanical switch is working properly, it can be stable in only two positions: on or off. Either current flows or it doesn't. With a dimmer you can regulate the flow of current so that it stays somewhere between fully on and fully off. If you've used mechanical balances, you know that to weigh an object accurately you must adjust the masses so that the pointer hovers in the middle of its range. The balance is in a state of equilibrium.

Most chemical reactions also reach a state of equilibrium between no reaction at all and the complete reaction to form products. Equilibrium states occur when reactions are reversible, that is, when products react to re-form the original reactants. When the products re-form reactants at the same rate as the reactants form the products, then the equilibrium point of the reaction has been reached.

The progress of a reaction is gauged by measuring the concentrations in moles per liter of reactants and products. At the equilibrium point, these concentrations stop changing.

$$A + 2B \rightleftarrows 2C$$

The equation above represents a reaction in which 1 mol of A reacts with 2 mol of B to produce 2 mol of C. As C is formed, it breaks down to re-form reactants. The extent of the reaction at equilibrium is indicated by the equilibrium constant, K.

$$K = \frac{[C]^2}{[A][B]^2}$$

As you can see, the concentration of each reaction component is raised to the power of its coefficient in the balanced equation. These concentration terms are arranged in a fraction with products in the numerator and reactants in the denominator. Pure substances (substances that appear in the chemical equation as solids or pure liquids) are not included in the equilibrium expressions because their concentrations are meaningless.

Problems involving chemical equilibrium will ask you to solve for either the equilibrium constant, K, given the concentrations of all of the reaction components, or the concentration of one of the reaction components, given K.

Equilibrium **233**

Figure 14-6 Point out that the equilibrium of this system can also be affected by the concentrations of the components. If you could introduce either gas into the bottle without losing any of the gas already contained in the bottle, the equilibrium position would shift toward the gas with the lower concentration.

ADDITIONAL APPLICATION

The dissolving of carbon dioxide in water is another reversible reaction that demonstrates Le Châtelier's principle. A physical equilibrium exists between gaseous and dissolved CO_2.

$$CO_2(g) \rightleftarrows CO_2(aq)$$

A chemical equilibrium exists between dissolved CO_2 and H_2CO_3.

$$CO_2(aq) + H_2O(l) \rightleftarrows H_2CO_3(aq)$$

Students should recall the relationship between pressure and gas solubility. When CO_2 is added to water under higher pressure, the solution equilibrium is pushed to the right, increasing the concentration of $CO_2(aq)$. This increase pushes the second equilibrium to the right. When a bottle of soda is opened, the CO_2 pressure drops, the whole equilibrium system moves to the left, and CO_2 bubbles out of solution.

Write the equilibrium equations on the board, and ask students what happens when carbonated water is made. Then open a bottle of club soda and ask students to explain what they see.

Module 7: Equilibrium
Topic: Shifting Equilibrium

relieve the stress by favoring the reaction that produces fewer gas molecules. Fewer gas molecules will exert less pressure. If the forward reaction is favored, two molecules of NO_2 will form one molecule of N_2O_4, decreasing the total number of molecules in the system and therefore moderating the increase in pressure. Observations show that an increase in pressure caused by a decrease in volume actually does favor the forward reaction, forming more N_2O_4 molecules.

You can follow the changes in concentrations of the two gases by observing the changes in the color of the gas mixture. In Figure 14-5a, a medium brown equilibrium mixture of NO_2 and N_2O_4 is contained in the syringe. When pressure is applied to the gas inside the syringe, the equilibrium is disturbed, as shown in Figure 14-5b. The volume decreases, altering the concentrations of the two gases and temporarily changing the color to dark brown. To restore the equilibrium position, the forward reaction is favored, as shown in Figure 14-5c, forming more colorless N_2O_4 molecules and giving the gas mixture a lighter color.

Temperature affects equilibrium systems

You have seen how changing the pressure affected the equilibrium between $NO_2(g)$ and $N_2O_4(g)$. Now consider what happens when the temperature is changed. The NO_2/N_2O_4 equilibrium system is shown at three different temperatures in **Figure 14-6.** At 25°C, the system at equilibrium is a medium shade of brown. When cooled to 0°C, the color of the mixture of gases in the flask is lighter. We can see that some of the dark brown NO_2 is no longer present and that more of the colorless N_2O_4 has formed. At 100°C, the contents of the flask are darker. We observe that more of the brown NO_2 has formed at the higher temperature.

The NO_2/N_2O_4 system discussed exemplifies an important principle developed by the French chemist Henri Louis Le Châtelier. This principle enables us to predict how changes imposed on a system at equilibrium will affect the status of the system. **Le Châtelier's principle** tells us how a system at equilibrium reacts to an applied stress. Le Châtelier defined *stress* as a change in the temperature or pressure of the system or a change in the concentration of a component.

Le Châtelier's principle
if a system at equilibrium is disturbed by applying stress, the system attains a new equilibrium position to accommodate the change and tends to relieve the stress

▶ **FIGURE 14-6**

Temperature changes put stress on equilibrium systems, causing either the forward or reverse reaction to be favored.

0°C	25°C	100°C
Very light brown	Medium brown	Dark brown

DEMONSTRATION 3

Temperature Effects on Gas Production

Approximate time: 25 minutes

This demonstration should help students understand how a system's equilibrium depends on temperature. Perform steps 1–3 a day before the demonstration, and perform step 4 in time to have the flasks at the different temperatures.

1. Inflate and stretch three identical balloons several times.

2. Stretch the opening of each balloon over the mouth of a 250 mL Erlenmeyer flask to be sure the balloons fit.

3. Place 10 g of sodium carbonate, Na_2CO_3, in each uninflated balloon.

4. Place 50 mL of 1 M HCl and a thermometer in each flask. Loosely cover the mouth of each flask with plastic wrap to hinder

Consider the following exothermic reaction.

$$2NO_2(g) \xrightleftharpoons{25°C} N_2O_4(g) + 57.2 \text{ kJ}$$

Le Châtelier's principle states that a system at equilibrium will react to relieve any stress placed on it. In the preceding reaction, heat energy is one of the products. Therefore, by lowering the reaction temperature, one of the products (heat) is being removed. As the temperature drops, the system reacts in a way that relieves this stress. To accomplish this, more NO_2 is converted to N_2O_4, causing the gas to become lighter in color. When the rate of the forward reaction is greater than the rate of the reverse reaction, the forward arrow can be shown as longer than the reverse arrow, and the equation is written as follows.

$$\begin{array}{cc} \text{Brown} & \text{Colorless} \\ 2NO_2(g) & \xrightleftharpoons[\text{}]{\text{during cooling}} N_2O_4(g) + 57.2 \text{ kJ} \end{array}$$

Forward reaction favored

The system reaches a new equilibrium state with constant macroscopic properties at the new temperature of 0°C. As long as this temperature is maintained, the gas in the flask will remain a light brown. The rates of the forward and reverse reactions are again equal.

On the other hand, by increasing the temperature to 100°C, more heat energy is added to the system. The system reacts to relieve the stress and absorbs some of the heat. The reverse reaction is favored, so more brown NO_2 is formed as equilibrium is reestablished.

$$\begin{array}{cc} \text{Brown} & \text{Colorless} \\ 2NO_2(g) & \xleftrightharpoons[\text{}]{\text{during heating}} N_2O_4(g) + 57.2 \text{ kJ} \end{array}$$

Reverse reaction favored

Another example of the effect of temperature on a system at equilibrium is shown in **Figure 14-8.** A solution of cobalt(II) chloride at room temperature is pink. The forward reaction, forming the blue solution, is an endothermic reaction. The reversible reaction is shown in the following equation.

$$\underset{\text{Pink}}{Co(H_2O)_6^{2+}(aq)} + 4Cl^-(aq) \xrightleftharpoons{\text{heat}} \underset{\text{Blue}}{CoCl_4^{2-}(aq)} + 6H_2O(l)$$

FIGURE 14-7 ▲

Henri Le Châtelier (1850–1936) was particularly interested in the relationship between science and industry and in how the maximum yield can be obtained from any chemical reaction.

FIGURE 14-8 ◄

Depending on whether heat energy is removed or added, the reverse or forward reaction will be favored, forming a pink solution or a blue solution, respectively.

CHEMICAL EQUILIBRIUM **517**

COMMON MISCONCEPTION

Students sometimes mistakenly interpret Le Châtelier's principle to mean that an equilibrium system somehow "knows" what to do when a stress is placed upon it. Emphasize that this principle, like all scientific laws, simply describes a phenomenon that occurs unfailingly in nature. Nothing in nature happens *because* of a law.

TEACHING TIP

Reaching a New Equilibrium
Emphasize that the equations shown with arrows of unequal length represent only how the reaction proceeds as it is establishing a new equilibrium position. Once equilibrium is reached, the forward and reverse reactions proceed at equal rates once again.

evaporation. Place one flask in the refrigerator at about 4°C, the second at room temperature (usually 24–25°C), and the third in a warm place at about 50°C.

5. When the proper temperatures are reached, twist each balloon so that it can be placed onto a flask without any sodium carbonate falling into the flask. Working rapidly to minimize temperature change, place the balloons over the mouths of the three flasks.

6. Clamp the three flasks to separate ring stands, making sure that no sodium carbonate falls out of the balloons and into the flasks.

7. Have three student volunteers release the sodium carbonate into the flasks at the same time. All volunteers must then stand back. The balloons should inflate at different rates.

CONTINUED ON PAGE 518

When French chemist Henri Louis Le Châtelier (1850–1936) proposed his principle in 1888, he was translating a work by American physicist Josiah Willard Gibbs (1839–1903). As it turned out, Gibbs's theories of thermodynamics explained Le Châtelier's principle quite well.

Removing heat from the equilibrium system favors the reverse reaction and the formation of more of the pink ion. If the cold solution is allowed to warm, adding heat back into the system, the forward reaction will be favored and more of the blue ion will be produced.

Changes in concentration alter equilibrium systems

One way to affect which reaction will be favored in an equilibrium system is to change a concentration in a reaction mixture. This can be done by removing a product or adding a reactant. Suppose you remove a product from an equilibrium reaction system. The system will react to the stress of removing a product by favoring the reaction that will produce more of that product. On the other hand, if you were to add a reactant to an equilibrium reaction system, the system would react to the stress by favoring the reaction that would consume the additional reactant. Consider the following example and its illustration in **Figure 14-9.**

Aspirin can cause damage to the walls of the stomach. Aspirin, acetylsalicylic acid, can exist in both its ionized form and nonpolar molecular form in the stomach. When aspirin combines with water, as when you swallow a tablet, some of the aspirin forms ions, shown by the forward reaction represented in the following equation.

$$H_2O + Aspirin \rightleftharpoons Aspirin^- + H_3O^+$$

Stomach lining

Interior of the stomach

▶ **FIGURE 14-9**

Aspirin molecules re-form in the reverse reaction of the equilibrium system inside a human stomach. Once the molecules pass through the stomach lining to the cells of the stomach, they are converted back to ions by the forward reaction.

DEMONSTRATION 3   *CONTINUED*

Safety
Safety goggles and a lab apron must be worn by the three volunteers. Students must be 10 ft or more from the demonstration. In case of an acid spill, dilute the spill with water and, while wearing gloves, soak up the spill with cloth or paper towels. Rinse the towels, neutralize the rinsings with 1 M NaOH, and flush down the drain.

Disposal
Combine all liquids. If the solution is alkaline, pour it down the drain. If the solution is still acidic, neutralize it with 1 M NaOH and then pour it down the drain.

In the ionized (acetylsalicylate) form, aspirin cannot pass through the stomach's protective lining. When acetylsalicylate ions remain in the stomach, they come into contact with a high concentration of H_3O^+ ions. The large number of H_3O^+ ions puts a stress on the equilibrium system, increasing the rate of the reverse reaction represented in the equation on the previous page. In the reverse reaction, nonpolar aspirin molecules are formed. These molecules then pass through the protective lining of the stomach and into the cells of the stomach itself. Once in the stomach cells, the H_3O^+ ion concentration is low, causing the forward reaction that produces the acetylsalicylate ions to be favored. These ions cannot pass back into the interior of the stomach, so they are trapped in the stomach cells, where they can cause damage.

One way to reduce the irritating effect of aspirin is to take buffered aspirin, in which aspirin is combined with an added ingredient, such as calcium carbonate. The carbonate ion reduces the amount of H_3O^+ ions within the contents of the stomach by reacting with them to form the bicarbonate ion, HCO_3^-, which reacts with additional H_3O^+ ions to form carbonic acid, H_2CO_3. These reactions are shown by the following equations.

$$H_3O^+(aq) + CO_3^{2-}(aq) \rightleftarrows HCO_3^-(aq) + H_2O(l)$$
$$H_3O^+(aq) + HCO_3^-(aq) \rightleftarrows H_2CO_3(aq) + H_2O(l)$$

Lowering the H_3O^+ ion concentration in the stomach favors the formation of acetylsalicylate ions, which cannot pass through the lining of the stomach. These acetylsalicylate ions pass into the intestines. They are then absorbed through the intestinal walls, limiting their irritating effect on the stomach.

CONCEPT CHECK

1. Name two factors that can disturb an equilibrium system.
2. Why does a pressure increase on a gaseous system at equilibrium favor the reaction that produces fewer gas molecules?
3. Why is removing a product from an equilibrium system as it forms a way to help produce maximum yield of that product?

Complex ion equilibria

Complex ions are composed of a central metal ion bonded to a specific number of other ions or polar molecules. For example, $[Cu(NH_3)_4]^{2+}$, shown in **Figure 14-10,** is a complex ion. Each ammonia molecule, NH_3, furnishes a pair of electrons to form what is called a *coordinate covalent bond* with the central copper ion. The formation of a complex ion generally involves a reversible reaction that reaches equilibrium. Many complex ions have color, and their reactions can be tracked by color changes.

complex ion

an ion having a structure in which a central atom or ion is bonded by coordinate covalent bonds to other ions or molecules

FIGURE 14-10 ▼

In this complex ion, $[Cu(NH_3)_4]^{2+}$, the ammonia molecules are bonded to the central copper ion.

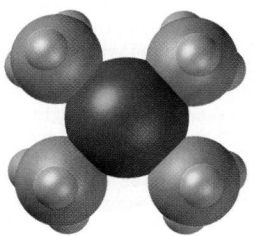

Another approach that has been used to reduce the activity of aspirin in the stomach is *enteric coating*. Each aspirin tablet is coated with a mixture of substances, such as proteins, carbohydrates, or other polymers. This coating is designed to break down in the small intestine but not in the stomach.

ANSWERS

CONCEPT CHECK

1. Answers will vary. Possibilities are change in pressure, change in temperature, or change in concentration (including removal of a product and addition of a reactant).

2. The pressure of a gas depends partly on the number of molecules that are present. The reaction that produces fewer molecules relieves the stress of increased pressure.

3. Removing a product decreases the concentration of that product. The equilibrium then shifts toward the production of more products. Therefore, removing a product causes a greater proportion of the reactants to form products.

GRAPHIC ORGANIZER

Effect of Stress Factors on Equilibrium Reactions

Type of reaction	Temperature ↑	Pressure ↑	Reactant concentration ↑	Removing a product
Gaseous	Favors endothermic	Favors reaction that produces fewest moles of gas	Favors products	Favors products
Solution	Favors endothermic	No effect unless a solute is in equilibrium with its gas phase	Favors products	Favors products
Mixed phases	Favors endothermic	Favors reaction that produces lower volume	Favors products	Favors products

TABLE 14-1	Examples of Complex Ions
Complex ion	**Color**
$[Co(NH_3)_5Cl]^{2+}$	violet
$[Co(NH_3)_5H_2O]^{3+}$	red
$[Co(NH_3)_6]^{3+}$	yellow-orange
$[Co(CN)_6]^{3-}$	pale yellow
$[Ni(NH_3)_6]^{2+}$	blue-violet
$[Cu(NH_3)_4]^{2+}$	blue-purple
$[Cu(H_2O)_4]^{2+}$	light blue
$[Fe(CN)_6]^{4-}$	yellow
$[Fe(CN)_6]^{3-}$	red
$[Fe(SCN)(H_2O)_5]^{2+}$	deep red
$[Zn(NH_3)_4]^{2+}$	colorless

ligand

a molecule or ion that is bonded to the central atom of a complex ion

In this section, you will see how changing a concentration in a complex-ion equilibrium system also illustrates Le Châtelier's principle.

Complex ion behavior is affected by stresses

In our example, copper is the central metal ion that is bonded to four ammonia molecules. The molecules (or ions) that are bonded to the central metal atom are often referred to as **ligands**. Some common ligands are ions such as Cl^-, F^-, and CN^- and polar molecules such as NH_3 and H_2O. Examples of complex ions are listed in **Table 14-1**.

Figure 14-11 shows two solutions containing complex ions of copper. As the equation beneath the figure shows, the complex ion in the beaker on the left consists of a Cu^{2+} ion bonded to four water molecules. This complex ion produces a light blue color in the solution. When an excess of ammonia solution is added to this light-blue solution, a deep blue-purple color forms, as shown in the beaker on the right. This blue-purple color is characteristic of the $[Cu(NH_3)_4]^{2+}$ complex ion. Ammonia molecules have replaced the water molecules bonded to the copper ion, as shown by the equation.

Complex ions containing transition metals usually have a distinct color that helps to identify which ion is present in higher concentration in the solution. Exceptions are complex ions containing Ag^+, Zn^{2+}, Cd^{2+}, and Hg^{2+}, which are usually colorless. Table 14-1 lists the characteristic colors of some transition metal-complex ions. The reaction that forms complex ions is reversible and eventually reaches equilibrium. However, either the forward or the reverse reaction can be favored, depending on the stress applied. For example, if more NH_3 is added to the light blue solution, the stress causes the forward reaction, which consumes NH_3, to be favored. Thus, the color of the system will change to blue-purple.

▶ **FIGURE 14-11**

The color of the solution makes it easy to see which complex ion is favored. The reaction on the right can be reversed by adding more water to the copper ammonia complex ion.

$$[Cu(H_2O)_4]^{2+} + 4NH_3 \rightleftharpoons [Cu(NH_3)_4]^{2+} + 4H_2O$$

DEMONSTRATION 4

Complex Ion Equilibria

Approximate time: 5 minutes

This demonstration shows a shift in equilibrium for a complex ion solution.

1. Half-fill a test tube with a 1 M $CuSO_4$ solution. The blue color is characteristic of the $[Cu(H_2O)_4]^{2+}$ ions.

2. Add NaCl crystals, and stir the solution. Continue to add salt until the solution turns deep green. The new color indicates the replacement of the water ligands with chloride ions to form $[CuCl_4]^{2-}$ ions.

3. Add more water to reduce the Cl^- ion concentration. You should see a shift to the blue color. Note that the water concentration changes very little.

Some other chemical equations representing aqueous equilibrium reactions involving complex ions are shown below.

$$[Zn(H_2O)_4]^{2+} + 4NH_3 \rightleftharpoons [Zn(NH_3)_4]^{2+} + 4H_2O$$
Colorless   Colorless

$$[Ni(H_2O)_6]^{2+}(aq) + 6NH_3(aq) \rightleftharpoons [Ni(NH_3)_6]^{2+}(aq) + 6H_2O(l)$$
Green   Blue-violet

Practical use of Le Châtelier's principle and complex ions

Have you ever seen a weather indicator that appears blue when the weather is supposed to stay dry and turns pink when it is supposed to rain? This simple little item involves some interesting chemistry. The color changes are shown in **Figure 14-12**. The weather indicator contains a piece of fabric or paper that has absorbed a solution of cobalt(II) chloride, $CoCl_2$. The equation for the reaction involved follows.

$$[CoCl_4]^{2-} + 6H_2O \rightleftharpoons [Co(H_2O)_6]^{2+} + 4Cl^-$$
Blue   Pink

Le Châtelier's principle explains these color changes. When the humidity is high, the $[CoCl_4]^{2-}$ reacts with water vapor in the air and forms the pink complex ion that has six water molecules bonded to cobalt, $[Co(H_2O)_6]^{2+}$. When the moisture in the air is low, the reverse reaction is favored, and the blue $[CoCl_4]^{2-}$ forms.

FIGURE 14-12 ▲

The treated cloth for a simple weather indicator is light blue in dry conditions and turns more reddish in high humidity.

SECTION REVIEW

Total recall

1. Name one reversible reaction you may encounter in your everyday life.

2. In a complex ion, what type of chemical bond is formed between the ligands and the central metal atom?

3. Name one characteristic of complex-ion chemistry that makes some reactions easy to monitor.

Critical thinking

4. When antacid tablets are added to water, a chemical reaction occurs, as evidenced by the production of bubbles. Is this a reaction that goes to completion or one that reaches an equilibrium? Explain your answer.

5. Using the equations for complex ions found on pages 520 and 521, develop a hypothesis about how each system would change under the following conditions.
   a. NH_3 is added to the copper complex-ion system.
   b. $[CoCl_4]^{2-}$ is removed from the cobalt complex-ion system.
   c. Water is added to the zinc complex-ion system.

6. **Story Clue** How would the removal of ammonia as it is made in the Haber process affect the equilibrium?

4. Write a list of the species involved in this reaction, and ask students to write an equilibrium equation.

$$[Cu(H_2O)_4]^{2+}(aq) + 4Cl^-(aq) \rightleftharpoons$$
$$[CuCl_4]^{2-}(aq) + 4H_2O(l)$$

Safety
Safety goggles and a lab apron must be worn. Students must be 10 ft or more from the demonstration.

Disposal
Add an excess of 1 M NaOH to precipitate the copper as $Cu(OH)_2$. Filter the precipitate and wash it with water. Neutralize the combined filtrate and washings with 1 M HCl, and pour down the drain. Wrap the wet $Cu(OH)_2$ crystals in newspaper, and place them in the trash.

TEACHING TIP

Weather Indicators Demonstrate one of the weather indicators discussed here. If you have two, enclose one in a beaker with a bit of damp filter paper. Enclose the other in a beaker containing a small amount of desiccant, such as Drierite™ (anhydrous $CaSO_4$), anhydrous calcium chloride, or silica gel.

New Bonding Concept All of the complexes studied here involve coordinate covalent bonding, in which one atom or molecule bonds to another by "using" an unshared pair of electrons available on the second atom or molecule.

ANSWERS

SECTION REVIEW

Total recall
1. Answers will vary. One example given in the text is the recharging of an automobile battery.

2. coordinate covalent bonds

3. Many complex ions have distinctive colors.

Critical thinking
4. The reaction goes to completion because one of the products, CO_2, is lost as a gas.

5. **a.** Adding ammonia shifts the equilibrium toward the formation of more $[Cu(NH_3)_4]^{2+}$.
   b. More $[CoCl_4]^{2-}$ will be formed and the concentration of $[Co(H_2O)_6]^{2+}$ will decrease.
   c. More $[Zn(H_2O)_4]^{2+}$ will be formed and the concentration of $[Zn(NH_3)_4]^{2+}$ will decrease.

6. Removal of ammonia causes the equilibrium to shift toward the production of more ammonia.

Did You Know?

We see many old houses painted white today, but white houses were relatively uncommon before the 1940s.

Until the development of the bright white pigment titanium(IV) oxide, TiO_2, the only acceptable white pigment was "white lead," whose formula is $Pb(OH)_2 \cdot PbCO_3$. Besides being poisonous, white lead reacts with sulfur compounds in the air to produce black lead(II) sulfide, PbS. In the past, sulfur compounds were prevalent in the air, especially in areas where a great deal of coal was burned by industries. A person who wanted a white house would have to repaint it often because the paint soon turned dirty gray.

The original owners of many nineteenth-century houses would be shocked to see their houses painted white today. In their time, houses were painted in colors such as cream, tan, green, blue, and rusty red, and very colorful combinations were often used on the same house.

82
Pb
Lead
207.2
$[Xe]4f^{14}5d^{10}6s^26p^2$

Lead inside the human body interferes with the production of red blood cells and can cause damage to the kidneys, liver, brain, and other organs.

Where is it?

Earth's Crust
<0.01% by mass

internet connect

SCiLINKS
NSTA
TOPIC: Lead
GO TO: www.scilinks.org
KEYWORD: HW142

A Brief History

Get the lead out

Humans have known for many centuries that lead is toxic, but lead is still used in many common materials. High levels of lead were used in paints until the 1940s. Since then, the lead compounds in paints have gradually been replaced with less toxic titanium compounds. However, many older buildings still have significant amounts of lead paint, and many also have lead solder in their water pipes.

Lead poisoning is caused by the absorption of lead through the digestive tract, lungs, or skin. Children living in older homes are especially susceptible to lead poisoning. Paint chips that contain lead have a sweet taste that young children like to chew on.

The hazards of lead poisoning can be greatly reduced through programs that increase public awareness, the removal of lead-containing paint from old buildings, and the screening of children for lead exposure.

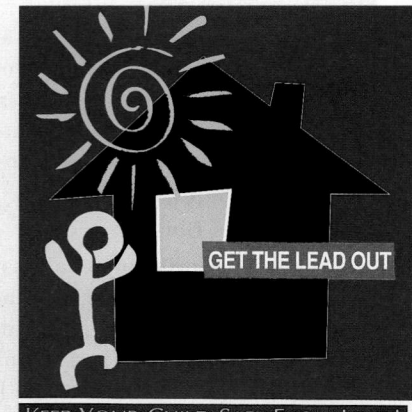

GET THE LEAD OUT
KEEP YOUR CHILD SAFE FROM LEAD!

Posters such as this one are part of public-awareness programs to reduce the hazards of lead poisoning.

Industrial Uses

▶ The largest industrial use of lead is in the manufacture of storage batteries.

▶ Solder used for joining metals is often an alloy of lead and tin.

▶ Other lead alloys are used to make bearings for gasoline and diesel engines, type metal for printing, corrosion-resistant cable coverings, and ammunition.

▶ Lead sheets and lead bricks are used to shield workers and sensitive objects from X rays.

1977: U.S. government restricts lead content in paint.

3000 B.C.   1000 B.C.   A.D. 1   A.D. 1000

3000 B.C.: Egyptians refine and use lead to make art figurines.

600 B.C.: Lead ore deposits are discovered near Athens; they are mined until the second century A.D.

60 B.C.: Romans begin making lead pipes, lead sheets for waterproofing roofs, and lead crystal.

How is equilibrium measured?

OBJECTIVES

▶ **Write** K_{eq} expressions for reactions in equilibrium.

▶ **Calculate** concentrations of reactants or products in an equilibrium system using K_{eq} values.

▶ **Write** K_{sp} expressions for the solubility of slightly soluble salts.

▶ **Determine** concentrations using K_{sp} expressions.

The equilibrium constant, K_{eq}

Consider the following reaction again.

$$2NO_2(g) \rightleftharpoons N_2O_4(g)$$

When the NO_2 is first placed in a container, no N_2O_4 is present. The rate of the reverse reaction is zero. After this first instant, the NO_2 will immediately begin to form N_2O_4. As this reaction proceeds, there is less NO_2 present, and therefore the rate of the forward reaction gradually decreases. As more N_2O_4 is formed, the collisions between these molecules increase. These collisions can cause NO_2 to re-form. The rate of the reverse reaction increases. Eventually the rates of the forward and reverse reactions are equal, and equilibrium is reached.

In systems at equilibrium, the reactants continue to form the products, and the products react to re-form the reactants at the same rate. Consequently, the equilibrium concentrations of reactants and products remain constant.

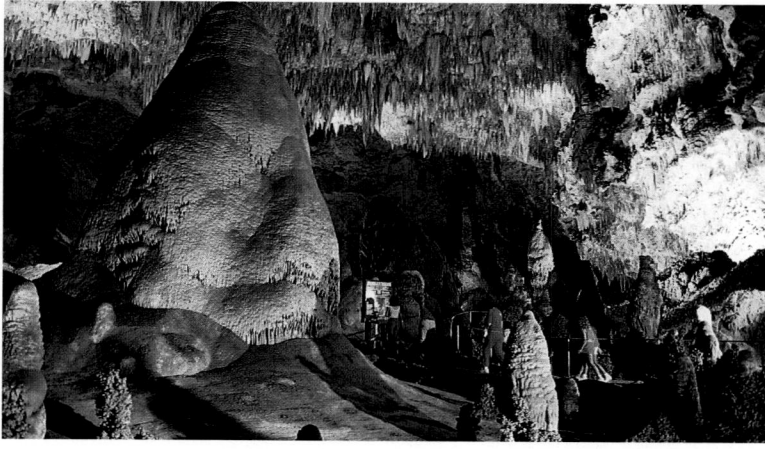

FIGURE 14-13 ◄

The creation of stalactites and stalagmites is a result of a reversible chemical reaction.

LESSON WARM-UP

Discussion Strategy Write the equilibrium equation from the following Visual Strategy on the board, and ask students to explain the formation of stalactites and stalagmites as you describe the changes in CO_2 concentration.

VISUAL STRATEGY

Figure 14-13 Caves having stalactites and stalagmites occur in regions where there are large deposits of limestone, calcium carbonate, $CaCO_3$. Rainwater that runs down into limestone formations contains dissolved CO_2 from the air and can dissolve limestone by the following equilibrium process:

$$CaCO_3(aq) + CO_2(aq) + H_2O(l) \rightleftharpoons$$
$$Ca^{2+}(aq) + 2HCO_3^-(aq)$$

When the resulting solution seeps through the roof of a cave, the air in the cave often has a lower CO_2 concentration than the outside air. As a result, the solution loses CO_2 as it drips from the ceiling. This loss pushes the equilibrium to the left, and a very small quantity of insoluble $CaCO_3$ precipitates.

In time, a stalactite made of crystalline $CaCO_3$ develops. As the solution drops to the floor, more CO_2 is lost and more $CaCO_3$ is deposited, leading to a stalagmite. After many thousands of years, the two deposits meet, forming a solid column.

QUICKLAB

You may want to tint the water with food coloring to make the levels more visible. For a more accurate simulation of a reaction coming to equilibrium, have the "products" student start by dipping the measure once for every fourth dip of the "reactants" student. After some time, increase the frequency to one for every three, then one for every two, and finally one for one, which represents equal rates. The time intervals between increases will determine whether the equilibrium favors products or reactants.

Analysis

1. Yes. The system should come to equilibrium in favor of reactants as soon as the depth of water in the products aquarium allows the student to fill the cup measure.

2. Increase the frequency at which cupfuls of water are returned to the reactants aquarium.

RESOURCE LINK

ChemFile Teaching Resources CD-ROM
Supplemental Reading Projects
Assign the guided reading worksheets for Essay 33 of *The Same and Not the Same*, "Fritz Haber," for cross-curricular connections to language arts.

equilibrium constant

for a reversible reaction in equilibrium, an expression that relates the concentrations of the reactants and products at a specific temperature to a constant

K_{eq} quantitatively describes the equilibrium state

When working with equilibrium systems, you can make calculations involving the concentrations of the products and the reactants. When a system has reached equilibrium, the relationship between the concentrations of reactants and products can be expressed mathematically. The mathematical product of the concentrations of the products, raised to an appropriate power, divided by the mathematical product of the concentrations of the reactants, raised to an appropriate power, is a constant called the **equilibrium constant, K_{eq}.** For the NO_2/N_2O_4 equilibrium system, the equilibrium-constant expression is written as follows.

$$K_{eq} = \frac{[N_2O_4]}{[NO_2]^2}$$

Each formula in brackets represents the concentration of that substance in mol/L at equilibrium. Each concentration is raised to a power equal to its coefficient in the balanced chemical equation for that reaction. In the example shown, the concentration of NO_2 is squared because the coefficient of NO_2 is 2 in the balanced equation.

Now consider the following equilibrium expressions for the condensation of water vapor and the decomposition of calcium carbonate.

$$H_2O(g) \rightleftharpoons H_2O(l)$$
$$CaCO_3(s) \rightleftharpoons CaO(s) + CO_2(g)$$

The first equation contains a pure liquid, $H_2O(l)$, and the second contains two pure solids, $CaCO_3(s)$ and $CaO(s)$. Because the concentrations of pure liquids and solids do not change to any measurable extent, they can be considered constant. As constants, the concentrations of pure liquids and solids are not included in equilibrium-constant expressions. The K_{eq} expressions for the two equations shown above are written as follows.

$$K_{eq} = 1/[H_2O(g)]$$
$$K_{eq} = [CO_2(g)]$$

QUICKLAB

CONSUMER ACTIVITY

Finding Equilibrium

Equilibrium reactions do not start out at equilibrium. Instead, they begin with more reactants than products and eventually reach a state of equilibrium, where the amount of products and reactants remains constant. In this activity, you will see firsthand how a process reaches equilibrium and how changing conditions will affect the forward and reverse reactions.

Materials   2 (5 gal) aquariums, water, 2 sets of measuring cups

Procedure   Label one aquarium "Products" and the other one "Reactants." Fill the reactants aquarium full of water, but leave the products aquarium empty for now. One student should be in charge of reactants and one in charge of products. Give each student a 1-cup measuring cup. They should begin to dip into their aquarium and pour the contents into the other's aquarium. Make sure they dip and pour at the same rate. What happens to the amount of reactants? What happens to the amount of products? Revise the procedure to favor the forward reaction.

Analysis   1. Does the system reach a state of equilibrium?
2. Which variables could you change to favor the reverse reaction?

DEMONSTRATION 5

Kinetics Simulation

Approximate time: 15 minutes

1. Half-fill a shallow container with water to which food coloring has been added. Submerge a 60 cm piece of clear plastic (or rubber) tubing in the water.

2. Place 450 mL of colored water (using the same food coloring as before) into a 600 mL beaker. Set the beaker on a raised, stable support about 5 cm high.

3. Place a second 600 mL beaker next to and 4 cm below the first beaker.

4. Place a finger over each end of the tubing, put one end of the tubing into the beaker filled with colored water, and remove the finger at that end. Place the other end into the empty beaker, and let the water flow.

Determining K_{eq} for reactions at equilibrium

The actual value for a particular K_{eq} must be determined experimentally. Once the system has reached equilibrium, the chemist must sample the reactants and products, analyze them, and calculate the concentrations of all substances involved in the reaction. When determining the K_{eq} value for a particular reaction, the temperature under which the concentrations are measured must be specified. The value of the equilibrium constant for a specific reaction is dependent on the temperature of that system. **Table 14-2** lists values for equilibrium constants for some representative reactions. You can see that the same reaction has different K_{eq} values at different temperatures. As temperature increases, K_{eq} increases for endothermic reactions and decreases for exothermic reactions.

The equilibrium constant can be calculated when all the concentrations of reactants and products are known. Just as with all mathematical expressions, the equilibrium-constant expression can be used to solve for an unknown quantity. Specifically, an unknown concentration can be calculated if the K_{eq} and all but one of the concentration values are known. Do not assume that pure solids and pure liquids are not important to equilibrium systems because they do not appear in the equilibrium expression. These substances are just as essential to establishing equilibrium as the other substances in the reaction, but you do not need to know their concentrations when calculating K_{eq}.

TABLE 14-2	Equilibrium Constants	

Equation	K_{eq} value	Temperature (°C)
$2NO_2(g) \rightleftharpoons N_2O_4(g)$	1250	0
	165	25
	22.6	55
	2.0	100
$CO_2(g) + H_2(g) \rightleftharpoons CO(g) + H_2O(g)$	2.2	1400
	4.6	2000
$N_2(g) + O_2(g) \rightleftharpoons 2NO(g)$	4.5×10^{-31}	25
	6.7×10^{-10}	627
	1.65×10^{-3}	2027
$H_2(g) + I_2(g) \rightleftharpoons 2HI(g)$	113	250
	57	427
	18	1127
$N_2(g) + 3H_2(g) \rightleftharpoons 2NH_3(g)$	3.3×10^8	25
	1.7×10^2	227
	4.2	327
	0.29	427
	3.8×10^{-2}	527

TEACHING TIP

Temperature Dependence of Equilibrium Constant The distribution of products and reactants of a reaction at equilibrium is quantified in the equilibrium constant, K_{eq}, for that reaction. Students should be made aware that an equilibrium constant is specific for only one reaction at a certain temperature. If the temperature changes, the reaction will have a different K_{eq}.

CONTENT STRATEGY

The point of the last paragraph on this page can be stated in another way. The word *concentration* is taken to apply only to substances in dispersed phases. *Dispersed* refers to matter that is spread out throughout a volume of space, such as a gas or a solute in a solution. Other dispersed phases are possible, such as when particles of a solid are suspended in a gas, but here only solutions and gases are considered. Concentrations are usually measured in moles per liter (of space).

5. Discuss with students when and where the flow will stop.

6. Raise or lower one of the beakers to demonstrate the system's reversibility. Shift the water back and forth between the beakers several times.

7. Remove water from the lower beaker to show that water will flow into it again.

Safety

Safety goggles must be worn. Students must be 10 ft or more from the demonstration.

Disposal

Pour water down the sink.

ADDITIONAL EXAMPLES

SAMPLE PROBLEM 14A

Calculate K_{eq} for the following reactions from the data given:

a. $COCl_2(g) \rightleftarrows CO(g) + Cl_2(g)$
At equilibrium $[CO] = 0.0178$ mol/L, $[Cl_2] = 0.0178$ mol/L, and $[COCl_2] = 0.00740$ mol/L.

Ans. $K_{eq} = 0.0428$

b. $2NO(g) + O_2(g) \rightleftarrows 2NO_2(g)$
$[NO_2] = 0.388$ mol/L, $[NO] = 0.0290$ mol/L, and $[O_2] = 0.0107$ mol/L.

Ans. 1.67×10^4

ANSWERS

PRACTICE PROBLEMS

1. $K_{eq} = \dfrac{[CO][H_2O]}{[CO_2][H_2]} = \dfrac{(0.019)^2}{(0.012)(0.014)} = 2.1$

2. $K_{eq} = \dfrac{[N_2O_4]}{[NO_2]^2} = \dfrac{4.0 \times 10^{-2}}{(1.4 \times 10^{-1})^2} = 2.0$

3. $K_{eq} = \dfrac{[SO_3]^2}{[SO_2]^2[O_2]} =$
$\dfrac{(1.01 \times 10^{-2})^2}{(3.61 \times 10^{-3})^2(6.11 \times 10^{-4})} = 1.28 \times 10^4$

TEACHING TIP

Using Exponents in Calculating
K_{eq} Be sure students can calculate K_{eq} in Additional Example (b) above. If they have trouble, it is likely that they are not squaring the concentrations of NO_2 and NO. Use this problem as an example to reinforce the correct way to set up an equilibrium expression.

SAMPLE PROBLEM 14A   Calculating K_{eq} from equilibrium concentrations

At a temperature of 25°C, the following concentrations (in mol/L) of the reactants and products for the reaction involving carbonic acid and water are present.

$[H_2CO_3] = 3.3 \times 10^{-2}$ M, $[H_3O^+] = 1.19 \times 10^{-4}$ M, and $[HCO_3^-] = 1.19 \times 10^{-4}$ M

What is the K_{eq} value for the following reaction at equilibrium in a dilute aqueous solution?

$$H_2CO_3(aq) + H_2O(l) \rightleftarrows H_3O^+(aq) + HCO_3^-(aq)$$

1   **List what you know**
- $[H_2CO_3] = 3.3 \times 10^{-2}$ M
- $[H_3O^+] = 1.19 \times 10^{-4}$ M
- $[HCO_3^-] = 1.19 \times 10^{-4}$ M
- The $[H_2O]$ will not be included in the calculation because it is considered to be constant in this dilute solution.
- $K_{eq} = ?$

2   **Set up the problem**
- Write the K_{eq} expression for this reaction.

$$K_{eq} = \frac{[H_3O^+][HCO_3^-]}{[H_2CO_3]}$$

- Substitute the given values into the expression.

$$K_{eq} = \frac{(1.19 \times 10^{-4})^2}{(3.3 \times 10^{-2})}$$

3   **Calculate**

$$K_{eq} = \frac{(1.19 \times 10^{-4})^2}{(3.3 \times 10^{-2})} = 4.3 \times 10^{-7}$$

PRACTICE PROBLEMS

1. For the following reaction, equilibrium is established at a certain temperature when the following concentrations (in mol/L) are present: $[CO_2] = 0.012$ M, $[H_2] = 0.014$ M, $[CO] = 0.019$ M, and $[H_2O] = 0.019$ M. Calculate the K_{eq} value for this reaction. Note that the $[H_2O]$ must be included because it is a gas in this reaction.

$$CO_2(g) + H_2(g) \rightleftarrows CO(g) + H_2O(g)$$

2. For the system involving N_2O_4 and NO_2 at equilibrium at a temperature of 100°C, the concentration of N_2O_4 is 4.0×10^{-2} mol/L, and the concentration of NO_2 is 1.4×10^{-1} mol/L. What is the K_{eq} value for the reaction to form N_2O_4?

3. An equilibrium mixture at 852 K is found to contain 3.61×10^{-3} mol/L of SO_2, 6.11×10^{-4} mol/L of O_2, and 1.01×10^{-2} mol/L of SO_3. Calculate the equilibrium constant, K_{eq}, for the following reaction.

$$2SO_2(g) + O_2(g) \rightleftarrows 2SO_3(g)$$

Ammonia gas is soluble in water. An aqueous solution of ammonia is known as ammonium hydroxide. The equilibrium existing in this solution can be represented by the following equation.

$$NH_3(aq) + H_2O(l) \rightleftarrows NH_4^+(aq) + OH^-(aq)$$

K_{eq} for this reaction equals 1.8×10^{-5} at a temperature of 298 K. The equilibrium concentration of NH_3 is 6.82×10^{-3} M, and the equation shows that the equilibrium concentration of NH_4^+ equals the equilibrium concentration of OH^-. Calculate the concentration of the ammonium ion at equilibrium.

1 List what you know

▸ $K_{eq} = 1.8 \times 10^{-5}$
▸ $[NH_3] = 6.82 \times 10^{-3}$ M
▸ The $[H_2O]$ is not included in the K_{eq} expression because as a pure liquid, it is considered to be constant.
▸ $[NH_4^+] = [OH^-] = ?$ M

2 Set up the problem

▸ Write the K_{eq} expression for this reaction.

$$K_{eq} = \frac{[NH_4^+][OH^-]}{[NH_3]}$$

▸ Substitute the known values into the expression.

$$1.8 \times 10^{-5} = \frac{[NH_4^+][OH^-]}{(6.82 \times 10^{-3})}$$

▸ Solve for $[NH_4^+][OH^-]$.

$$[NH_4^+][OH^-] = (1.8 \times 10^{-5})(6.82 \times 10^{-3})$$

3 Calculate

$$[NH_4^+][OH^-] = (1.8 \times 10^{-5})(6.82 \times 10^{-3}) = 1.2 \times 10^{-7} \text{ M}^2$$

▸ Because $[NH_4^+] = [OH^-]$, you can think of this calculation as $(x)(x) = x^2$.
▸ The concentration of the ammonium ion, $[NH_4^+]$, is found by taking the square root of 1.2×10^{-7} M^2.

$$[NH_4^+]^2 = 1.2 \times 10^{-7} \text{ M}$$

$$[NH_4^+] = 3.5 \times 10^{-4} \text{ M}$$

PRACTICE PROBLEMS

1. In the presence of a catalyst, methanol, CH_3OH, can be prepared by the reaction of H_2 and CO at high temperatures according to the following equation.

$$CO(g) + 2H_2(g) \rightleftarrows CH_3OH(g)$$

What is the concentration of $CH_3OH(g)$ in mol/L if $[H_2] = 0.080$ M, [CO] = 0.025 M, and $K_{eq} = 290$ at 700 K?

TEACHING TIP

A Unitless Quantity Students have probably noticed by now that values of K_{eq} include no units. Units are not used because they would vary depending on the powers to which the concentrations are raised. In some cases all units would cancel. Remind students to be careful to assign the correct units to concentrations calculated by using equilibrium constants.

ADDITIONAL EXAMPLES

SAMPLE PROBLEM 14B

a. Determine the concentrations of H_3O^+ and HCO_3^- in a solution of carbonic acid at 25°C in which the concentration of H_2CO_3 is 0.027 M. See Sample Problem 14A for the equation and K_{eq}.

Ans. 1.1×10^{-4} M (Students should assume that $[H_3O^+] = [HCO_3^-]$.)

b. Use K_{eq} and the equilibrium equation for the manufacture of methanol in Practice Problem 1 to determine the concentration of hydrogen remaining at 700 K when $[CH_3OH] = 0.25$ mol/L and [CO] = 0.0098 mol/L.

Ans. 0.094 mol/L

ANSWERS

PRACTICE PROBLEMS

1. $K_{eq} = 290 = \dfrac{[CH_3OH]}{[CO][H_2]^2}$; $[CH_3OH] = (290)(0.025)(0.080)^2 = 0.046$ mol/L

2. $K_{eq} = 1.65 \times 10^{-3} = \dfrac{[NO]^2}{[N_2][O_2]}$; $[NO]^2 = 1.65 \times 10^{-3}(1.8 \times 10^{-3})(4.2 \times 10^{-4})$; $[NO] = 3.5 \times 10^{-5}$ mol/L

3. $K_{eq} = 4.32 = \dfrac{[SO_3]^2}{[SO_2]^2[O_2]}$; $[SO_2]^2 = \dfrac{(0.260)^2}{(4.32)(0.045)}$; $[SO_2] = 0.59$ mol/L

ANSWERS

CONCEPT CHECK

1. The equilibrium constant relates the concentration of products to the concentration of reactants in a system at equilibrium. Its value relates to how far the reaction has proceeded toward products. If a reaction has a large K_{eq}, the formation of products is favored. If K_{eq} is small, very little of the reactants is converted to products.

2. K_{eq} depends on the temperature of the equilibrium system.

3. A reaction has different values of K_{eq} at different temperatures.

4. There is no way to determine mathematically how a particular K_{eq} will change with temperature. Therefore K_{eq} must be experimentally determined for each temperature of interest.

5. A formula in brackets represents the concentration of that substance or ion in moles per liter.

2. Using a K_{eq} value of 1.65×10^{-3} at 2027°C for the reaction below, what is the equilibrium concentration of nitrogen monoxide, NO, when the concentrations of nitrogen and oxygen at equilibrium are 1.8×10^{-3} mol/L and 4.2×10^{-4} mol/L, respectively?

$$N_2(g) + O_2(g) \rightleftarrows 2NO(g)$$

3. The following equation shows the equilibrium reaction between sulfur dioxide and oxygen.

$$2SO_2(g) + O_2(g) \rightleftarrows 2SO_3(g)$$

At 600°C, the K_{eq} for this reaction is 4.32 when $[SO_3] = 0.260$ mol/L and $[O_2] = 0.045$ mol/L. Calculate the equilibrium concentration for SO_2.

The value of K_{eq} can be used to make predictions about equilibrium systems

Now that you know how to calculate K_{eq}, what kind of information does that value provide? If K_{eq} has a value close to 1, the products of the concentrations (raised to the appropriate power) in the numerator and the denominator are approximately equal. Therefore, if K_{eq} is approximately equal to 1, there are roughly equal concentrations of reactants and products at equilibrium.

In reactions that have a K_{eq} value much larger than 1, the original reactants are largely converted to products, and the concentration at equilibrium of products will be greater than the concentration of reactants. For reactions that have a K_{eq} value much smaller than 1, the forward reaction occurs only to a very small extent before equilibrium is established. The reverse reaction is favored, resulting in a larger concentration of reactants than products at equilibrium. By knowing the value of K_{eq} for a specific reaction, you can estimate whether reactants or products will be more abundant at equilibrium. In addition, by using known values of K_{eq}, you can make calculations and predictions about equilibrium systems, as you saw in the previous practice problems.

CONCEPT CHECK

1. What does K_{eq}, the equilibrium constant, tell you about a system at equilibrium?
2. Is the value of K_{eq} dependent on the temperature or the pressure of the system at equilibrium?
3. Can the same reaction have different K_{eq} values? Why or why not?
4. Why is the value of K_{eq} for a particular reaction calculated using concentrations from experimental data?
5. What does a chemical formula in brackets, such as $[N_2O_4]$, represent?

The solubility product constant, K_{sp}

K_{sp} is a special equilibrium constant for very slightly soluble ionic substances

Recall from Chapter 13 that solubility refers to the maximum amount of a solute that will dissolve per unit volume of a solvent to produce a saturated solution. In Chapter 13, solubility was expressed in units of grams of solute per 100 g of water. Solubility can also be expressed as concentration in moles of solute per liter of solution (mol/L). As you will see in this section, solubility is related to the equilibrium-constant expression for the process of dissolution.

In Section 14-1 you learned about reactions going to completion. There are two ways of looking at these reactions. Consider the following reaction, also shown in Figure 14-1, on page 512.

$$Na^+(aq) + Cl^-(aq) + Ag^+(aq) + NO_3^-(aq) \longrightarrow AgCl(s) + Na^+(aq) + NO_3^-(aq)$$

The precipitation of AgCl goes nearly to completion, but virtually no reaction goes entirely to completion. In the reaction represented above, a very low concentration of Ag^+ and Cl^- ions still exists in the solution. This concentration of ions in solution represents the solubility of AgCl at the given temperature. AgCl is considered an insoluble salt. Actually, most salts described as insoluble will dissolve to some extent in water and are more accurately described as being *very slightly soluble*. In such cases, an extremely small concentration of the salt saturates the solution, usually less than 0.01 M.

An example of a slightly soluble salt is barium sulfate, $BaSO_4$. The equation representing the dissociation of this salt in aqueous equilibrium follows.

$$BaSO_4(s) \rightleftharpoons Ba^{2+}(aq) + SO_4^{2-}(aq)$$

The concentration of $BaSO_4$ in the solid state is a constant and does not need to be included in the equilibrium expression. The K_{eq} expression for this reaction is written as follows.

$$K_{eq} = [Ba^{2+}][SO_4^{2-}]$$

The equilibrium expression above can also be thought of as governing the solubility of $BaSO_4(s)$ in water. When dealing with solubilities of slightly soluble salts, a new constant called the **solubility product constant, K_{sp},** is used. The K_{sp} expression for the dissociation of $BaSO_4$ follows.

$$K_{sp} = [Ba^{2+}][SO_4^{2-}]$$

The solubility product constant of a salt is the product of the equilibrium concentrations of its ions, each raised to a power equal to its coefficient in the balanced chemical equation.

Recall that the concentration of any pure solid or liquid substance is a constant.

solubility product constant

the equilibrium constant for a slightly soluble ionic solid in equilibrium with its ions in a saturated solution

FIGURE 14-14 ▼

Seashells are made mostly of calcium carbonate, which is considered to be insoluble in sea water. The shells' composition keeps them from dissolving noticeably in water.

SECTION 14-2

TEACHING TIP

K_{sp} Is an Equilibrium Constant
Students should understand that solubility product constants are simply equilibrium constants that represent the reversible process taking place in a saturated solution in contact with undissolved solute.

READING STRATEGY

Peer Teaching Have each student read the section on the solubility product constant and look over the problem setups in Sample Problems 14C and 14D. After reading, students should pair up and take turns asking and answering the following questions:

▸ Why is the word *insoluble* an inexact term when applied to real solutions?
▸ Describe the dynamic equilibrium that occurs in a saturated solution.
▸ Why is the concentration of undissolved substance not included in the equilibrium expression?
▸ Why do K_{sp} values depend on temperature?

RESOURCE LINK

ChemFile Lab C
Skills Development
Have students do Exploration 15: *Solubility Product Constant.*

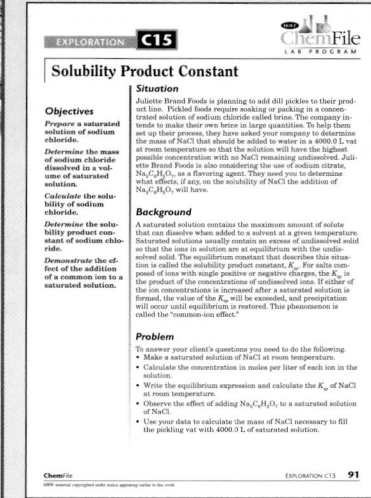

If students learn to interpret reaction and solubility equilibria correctly and understand that K_{eq} can be calculated for any equilibrium process, they will find the concepts of K_w, pH, K_a, and K_b in Chapter 15 easy to grasp.

VISUAL STRATEGY

Table 14-3 Ask students to study the table and determine which listed substance has the lowest solubility. Many will choose Ag_2S because of its extremely small K_{sp}. Explain that this compound is *not* the least soluble.

Direct students' attention to the compounds $Ca_3(PO_4)_2$ and $Fe(OH)_3$, and ask them to write K_{sp} expressions for these substances as well as for Ag_2S. Have them explain why you cannot judge solubility from K_{sp} values alone. The powers of 2 and 3 to which the concentrations are raised contribute to the very small K_{sp} values.

The least soluble compound on the list is CuS with Cu^{2+} and S^{2-} concentrations of 1.14×10^{-18} mol/L. By contrast, the concentration of Ag^+ ions in a saturated solution of Ag_2S is 6.0×10^{-17} mol/L, roughly five times that of Cu^{2+} ions in a solution of CuS.

DID YOU KNOW?

Note that the K_{sp} of CuS is 1.3×10^{-36}. This value means that each ion in a saturated solution would have a concentration of $(1.3 \times 10^{-36})^{1/2}$ M = 1.14×10^{-18} M, or only about 690 000 ions per liter.

Therefore, a solubility-product-constant expression contains only concentrations of ions formed during the solution process. Only substances that can change concentration, such as gases or substances in solution (solutes), are included in equilibrium expressions.

Each ion concentration is raised to the power equal to its coefficient in the balanced chemical equation

Just as in writing equilibrium constants, the concentration of each ion in a K_{sp} expression is raised to the power corresponding to its coefficient in the balanced chemical equation. Here are some examples.

$$Fe(OH)_3(s) \rightleftharpoons Fe^{3+}(aq) + 3OH^-(aq)$$
$$K_{sp} = [Fe^{3+}][OH^-]^3$$
$$Ca_3(PO_4)_2(s) \rightleftharpoons 3Ca^{2+}(aq) + 2PO_4^{3-}(aq)$$
$$K_{sp} = [Ca^{2+}]^3[PO_4^{3-}]^2$$

Table 14-3 gives K_{sp} values for several slightly soluble salts at 25°C. These K_{sp} values apply only in dilute solutions. When the concentration of any ion (whether involved in the equilibrium reaction or not) is greater than about 0.1 M, the electrical attractions between positive and negative ions disturb the equilibrium, and the K_{sp} values for these systems do not apply. That is one reason why K_{sp} values are seldom given to more than two significant figures.

TABLE 14-3 Solubility Product Constants at 25°C

Salt	K_{sp}	Salt	K_{sp}
Ag_2CO_3	8.4×10^{-12}	CuS	1.3×10^{-36}
Ag_2CrO_4	1.1×10^{-12}	$Fe(OH)_3$	2.6×10^{-39}
Ag_2S	1.1×10^{-49}	FeS	1.6×10^{-19}
AgBr	5.4×10^{-13}	$MgCO_3$	6.8×10^{-6}
AgCl	1.8×10^{-10}	$MnCO_3$	2.2×10^{-11}
AgI	8.5×10^{-17}	PbS	9.0×10^{-29}
$Al(OH)_3$	2.0×10^{-31}	$PbSO_4$	1.8×10^{-8}
$BaSO_4$	1.1×10^{-10}	$SrSO_4$	3.4×10^{-7}
$Ca_3(PO_4)_2$	2.1×10^{-33}	$ZnCO_3$	1.2×10^{-10}
$CaSO_4$	7.1×10^{-5}	ZnS	2.9×10^{-25}

SAMPLE PROBLEM 14C — Calculating K_{sp} from solubility

Consider the dissociation of the salt CaF_2 in water.

$$CaF_2(s) \rightleftharpoons Ca^{2+}(aq) + 2F^-(aq)$$

Most parts of the oceans are nearly saturated with CaF_2. In a region where evaporation raises the concentration of dissolved materials, the mineral fluorite, CaF_2, may precipitate. A saturated solution of CaF_2 at 25°C is 3.4×10^{-4} M. Calculate the solubility product constant for CaF_2.

1 List what you know
- Saturated CaF_2 is 3.4×10^{-4} M.
- The balanced chemical equation is $CaF_2(s) \rightleftharpoons Ca^{2+}(aq) + 2F^-(aq)$
- $K_{sp} = ?$

ADDITIONAL EXAMPLES

SAMPLE PROBLEM 14C

a. Calculate the solubility product constant of HgI_2 if the Hg^{2+} concentration in a saturated solution is 1.9×10^{-10} M.

Ans. $K_{sp} = 2.7 \times 10^{-29}$

b. Calculate the solubility product constant of $Fe(OH)_2$ if the OH^- concentration in a saturated solution is 4.6×10^{-6} M.

Ans. $K_{sp} = 4.9 \times 10^{-17}$

c. The K_{sp} of CdF_2 is 6.4×10^{-3}. Calculate the concentration of the ions in a saturated solution of CdF_2.

Ans. $[Cd^{2+}] = 0.12$ M, $[F^-] = 0.24$ M

d. The K_{sp} of $MgCO_3$ is 6.8×10^{-6}. The concentration of CO_3^{2-} ions in a solution containing both $MgCO_3$ and Na_2CO_3 is 4.0×10^{-2} M. What is the concentration of magnesium ions if the solution is saturated with respect to $MgCO_3$?

Ans. $[Mg^{2+}] = 1.7 \times 10^{-4}$ M

2 Set up the problem

▶ Write the K_{sp} expression for the reaction.

$$K_{sp} = [Ca^{2+}][F^-]^2$$

▶ 3.4×10^{-4} mol of CaF_2 dissolves in each liter of solution. Using the mole ratio from the balanced chemical equation, you know that each liter of the solution contains 3.4×10^{-4} mol of Ca^{2+} and $2(3.4 \times 10^{-4})$, or 6.8×10^{-4}, mol of F^-.

▶ Substitute these concentration values raised to the correct power in the K_{sp} expression.

$$K_{sp} = (3.4 \times 10^{-4})(6.8 \times 10^{-4})^2$$

3 Calculate

▶ Solve the expression for K_{sp}.

$$K_{sp} = (3.4 \times 10^{-4})(6.8 \times 10^{-4})^2 = 1.57216 \times 10^{-10}$$

▶ Round to two significant figures.

$$K_{sp} = 1.6 \times 10^{-10}$$

SAMPLE PROBLEM 14D **Calculating concentrations using K_{sp}**

At a temperature of 298 K, the concentration of Ca^{2+} in a given saturated solution of CaF_2 is 2.2×10^{-4} M and the K_{sp} for CaF_2 is 1.6×10^{-10}. Calculate the concentration of F^- in the solution.

1 List what you know

▶ $[Ca^{2+}] = 2.2 \times 10^{-4}$ M
▶ $K_{sp} = 1.6 \times 10^{-10}$
▶ $[F^-] = ?$ M

2 Set up the problem

▶ Write the K_{sp} expression for the dissociation process.

$$K_{sp} = [Ca^{2+}][F^-]^2$$

▶ Substitute the known values into this expression.

$$1.6 \times 10^{-10} = (2.2 \times 10^{-4})[F^-]^2$$

▶ Rearrange to solve for $[F^-]^2$.

$$[F^-]^2 = \frac{1.6 \times 10^{-10}}{(2.2 \times 10^{-4})} = 7.27 \times 10^{-7} \text{ M}^2$$

3 Calculate

▶ Solve for $[F^-]$ by determining the square root of the above result on your calculator.

$$[F^-] = \sqrt{7.27 \times 10^{-7} \text{ M}^2} = 8.5264295 \times 10^{-4} \text{ M (calculator answer)}$$

▶ Round the final calculator answer to two significant figures.

$$[F^-] = 8.5 \times 10^{-4} \text{ M}$$

ADDITIONAL EXAMPLES

SAMPLE PROBLEM 14D

a. Calculate the concentration of Ba^{2+} ion in a saturated solution of $BaSO_4$ both before and after the SO_4^{2-} concentration has been boosted to 0.010 M by the addition of Na_2SO_4. The K_{sp} of $BaSO_4$ is 1.1×10^{-10}. By what factor is the Ba^{2+} concentration decreased?

Ans. Before: 1.0×10^{-5} M; after: 1.1×10^{-8} M. The Ba^{2+} concentration is reduced to approximately 0.001 of its original concentration.

b. A chemist wishes to reduce the silver ion concentration in saturated AgCl solution to 2.0×10^{-6} M. What concentration of Cl^- would achieve this goal?

Ans. $[Cl^-] = 9.0 \times 10^{-5}$ M

ANSWERS

PRACTICE PROBLEMS

1. $K_{sp} = [Ca^{2+}]^3[PO_4^{3-}]^2 = (3.42 \times 10^{-7})^3(2.28 \times 10^{-7})^2 = 2.08 \times 10^{-33}$

2. $K_{sp} = 8.4 \times 10^{-12} = [Ag^+]^2(1.28 \times 10^{-4})$; $[Ag^+] = 2.6 \times 10^{-4}$ M

3. $K_{sp} = [Cu^+][Br^-] = (7.9 \times 10^{-5})^2 = 6.2 \times 10^{-9}$

4. $K_{sp} = 1.17 \times 10^{-5} = [Pb^{2+}](2.86 \times 10^{-2})^2$; $[Pb^{2+}] = 1.43 \times 10^{-2}$ M

5. $K_{sp} = 1.8 \times 10^{-10} = [Ag^+][Cl^-]$; $[Ag^+] = 1.34 \times 10^{-5}$; $(2.0 \text{ L})[Ag^+](107.87 \text{ g/mol}) = 2.9 \times 10^{-3}$ g Ag^+

6. $K_{sp} = 1.72 \times 10^{-7} = [Cu^+][Cl^-]$; $[Cu^+] = 4.15 \times 10^{-4}$ M

PRACTICE PROBLEMS

1. What is the K_{sp} value for $Ca_3(PO_4)_2$ at 298 K if the concentrations in an aqueous solution at equilibrium with excess solid are determined to be 3.42×10^{-7} M for Ca^{2+} ions and 2.28×10^{-7} M for PO_4^{3-} ions?

2. The K_{sp} value for silver carbonate is 8.4×10^{-12} at 298 K. The concentration of carbonate ions in a saturated solution is 1.28×10^{-4} M. What is the concentration of silver ions?

3. Copper(I) bromide is dissolved in water to saturation at 25°C. The concentration of Cu^+ ions in solution is 7.9×10^{-5} mol/L. Calculate the K_{sp} for copper(I) bromide at this temperature.

4. Calculate the concentration of Pb^{2+} ions in solution when $PbCl_2$ is dissolved in water. The concentration of Cl^- ions in this solution is found to be 2.86×10^{-2} mol/L. At 25°C, the K_{sp} of $PbCl_2$ is 1.17×10^{-5}.

5. What mass of Ag^+ ions will be present in 2.0 L of a saturated solution of AgCl at 25°C? (Hint: Using Table 14-3 on page 530, first calculate the concentration of Ag^+ ions that will be present in this solution.)

6. What is the concentration of Cu^+ ions in a saturated solution of copper(I) chloride, given that the K_{sp} of CuCl is 1.72×10^{-7} at 25°C?

▼ **FIGURE 14-15**

The light areas on this X ray of the digestive tract show the insoluble barium sulfate.

Common ion effect
Practical uses of equilibrium constants and the common ion effect

Barium sulfate, $BaSO_4$, is usually called an insoluble salt, which means that only an extremely small portion of it will dissolve in water. Doctors use $BaSO_4$ as an X-ray contrast medium. (The heavy barium atom absorbs X rays more readily than other atoms present.) The patient ingests solid $BaSO_4$ powder that is suspended in water. The $BaSO_4$ will appear as light areas on the X-ray film. By studying these light areas, like those shown in **Figure 14-15,** doctors can diagnose problems in the patient's digestive tract. Doctors must make sure that almost no Ba^{2+} ions are present to dissolve in the patient's body fluids because Ba^{2+} ions are poisonous. To ensure that the concentration of Ba^{2+} ions will not exceed the safety level, a soluble salt, such as Na_2SO_4, which also contributes SO_4^{2-} ions in solution, is added to increase the SO_4^{2-} ion concentration and to reduce the Ba^{2+} ion concentration.

Na_2SO_4 dissociates, as shown by the following equation.

$$Na_2SO_4(s) \longrightarrow 2Na^+(aq) + SO_4^{2-}(aq)$$

Dissolving the Na_2SO_4 increases the concentration of SO_4^{2-} ions in the solution. These SO_4^{2-} ions affect the chemical reaction involving the dissociation of $BaSO_4$. Consider the following equation.

$$BaSO_4(s) \rightleftarrows Ba^{2+}(aq) + SO_4^{2-}(aq)$$

DEMONSTRATION 6

Common Ion Effect

Approximate time: 5 minutes

This demonstration shows how an excess of ammonium ions, NH_4^+, reduces the concentration of hydroxide ions, OH^-.

1. Place half a Petri dish on an overhead projector and half-fill it with 1 M $NH_3(aq)$ (sometimes labeled as NH_4OH).

2. Add 2 drops of phenolphthalein. The solution should be magenta. If it is too pale,

add more indicator. Write the equilibrium equation for the ionization of NH_3 on the board. Point out that the presence of OH^- ions causes the indicator to be magenta. Ask students to predict what will happen when the NH_4^+ ion concentration is increased.

As $[SO_4^{2-}]$ increases, $[Ba^{2+}]$ must decrease in order to keep the K_{sp} constant. Some Ba^{2+} reacts with some of the added SO_4^{2-}, re-forming solid $BaSO_4$. This precipitation of some $BaSO_4$ causes a lower concentration of Ba^{2+} ions in the solution. Adding the Na_2SO_4 has the effect of reducing the concentration of Ba^{2+} ions in the solution. Because SO_4^{2-} ions are present in both $BaSO_4$ and Na_2SO_4, sulfate is referred to as the **common ion.**

The displacement of an ionic equilibrium caused by the presence of more than one source for a reactant or product ion is called the **common ion effect.** Remember from Le Châtelier's principle that changing the concentration of any of the ions involved in the reaction can have an effect on the equilibrium of the system. When Na_2SO_4 is added to the saturated solution of $BaSO_4$, a stress is put on the system. The increase in the concentration of SO_4^{2-} ions in the solution disturbs the equilibrium and favors the reverse reaction. Less $BaSO_4$ dissolves in the presence of the common ion, thereby causing a decrease in the Ba^{2+} ion concentration in the solution.

common ion

an ion that is present in two or more substances involved in an ionic chemical equilibrium

common ion effect

the reduction in the solubility of an ionic compound by the addition of a soluble compound that provides an ion in common with it

ANSWERS

SECTION REVIEW

Total recall

1. The equilibrium constant relates the concentration of products to the concentration of reactants in a system at equilibrium. Its value relates to how far the reaction has proceeded toward products. If a reaction has a large K_{eq}, the formation of products is favored. If K_{eq} is small, very little of the reactants is converted to products. It is also useful in calculating the concentrations of reactants or products at equilibrium.

2. Their concentrations remain the same throughout an equilibrium process.

Critical thinking

3. a. $K_{eq} = [Ag^+][Cl^-]$

   b. $K_{eq} = [Ag^+]^2[CrO_4^{2-}]$

   c. $K_{eq} = [Ca^{2+}]^3[PO_4^{3-}]^2$

4. $K_{sp} = [Al^{3+}][OH^-]^3$

5. The concentrations of Ca^{2+} and PO_4^{3-} ions are cubed and squared, respectively. Since equilibrium concentrations are much less than 1 M, cubing and squaring greatly diminishes the K_{sp} value. The K_{sp} for PbS is also very low numerically, but it is equal to just the product of the concentrations of Pb^{2+} and S^{2-}, so these concentrations must be very low.

SECTION REVIEW

Total recall

1. What information does the K_{eq} value for a reaction provide?

2. Why are pure liquids and pure solids not included in equilibrium-constant expressions?

Critical thinking

3. Write the K_{eq} expression for each of the following reactions:
   a. silver chloride in an aqueous solution
   b. silver chromate in an aqueous solution
   c. calcium phosphate in an aqueous solution

4. Write the solubility product expression for the slightly soluble compound aluminum hydroxide, $Al(OH)_3$.

5. The K_{sp} of PbS is 9.0×10^{-29}; that of $Ca_3(PO_4)_2$ is smaller, 2.1×10^{-33}. Yet PbS is much less soluble. Explain why this is not a contradiction.

Practice problems

6. Given that the K_{sp} value of CuS is 1.3×10^{-36}, what is the concentration of Cu^{2+} ions in a saturated solution?

7. For the reaction $H_2(g) + I_2(g) \rightleftarrows 2HI(g)$ at 425°C, calculate [HI], given $[H_2] = [I_2] = 4.79 \times 10^{-4}$ M and $K_{eq} = 54.3$.

8. Carbon reacts with carbon dioxide to produce carbon monoxide and reaches equilibrium, as shown by the following equation.

$$C(s) + CO_2(g) \rightleftarrows 2\,CO(g)$$

At equilibrium, a 2.0 L reaction vessel is found to contain 0.40 mol C, 0.20 mol CO_2, and 0.10 mol CO. Determine the K_{eq} for this reaction. Be sure to express the concentrations as mol/L.

Practice problems

6. $K_{sp} = 1.3 \times 10^{-36} = [Cu^{2+}][S^{2-}]$;
   $[Cu^{2+}] = 1.1 \times 10^{-18}$ M

7. $K_{eq} = 54.3 = \dfrac{[HI]^2}{[H_2][I_2]}$;
   $[HI]^2 = (54.3)(4.79 \times 10^{-4})^2$;
   $[HI] = 3.53 \times 10^{-3}$ M

8. $K_{eq} = \dfrac{[CO]^2}{[CO_2]} = \dfrac{\left(\dfrac{0.10}{2.0}\right)^2}{\left(\dfrac{0.20}{2.0}\right)} = 2.5 \times 10^{-2}$

3. Stir a little solid NH_4Cl into the solution. The magenta color should disappear. The added NH_4^+ ions suppress the ionization of the aqueous ammonia.

Safety

Safety goggles, a lab apron, and rubber gloves must be worn. (NH_4Cl is toxic.) Students must be 10 ft or more from the demonstration.

Disposal

Rinse all of the liquid from the Petri dish into a beaker, and add an excess of 1 M NaOH to convert the NH_4Cl into $NH_3(aq)$. In an operating fume hood, warm the solution to expel the NH_3. Neutralize the remaining liquid with 1 M HCl, and pour it down the drain.

At the beginning of this chapter you learned that before World War I, nitric acid was made by a reaction involving sodium nitrate. Nitric acid was the principal ingredient in the reaction that produces explosives. By 1913, the work of Fritz Haber and Carl Bosch made it possible to produce ammonia on an industrial scale. The ammonia could then be used in the production of nitric acid for use in fertilizer and explosives.

Today ammonia is produced on an industrial scale in plants like this one.

LOOKING BACK

How would increasing the pressure of the reaction to produce ammonia affect the ammonia yield?

Before Germany could produce enough nitric acid to fulfill its needs, much research had to be done. First, Haber learned that the mixing of nitrogen and hydrogen to yield ammonia had to be done under high pressure. An increase in pressure would favor the reaction that produces the fewest number of gas molecules, in this case the forward reaction and the product ammonia. For commercial production today, the reaction is carried out at pressures ranging from 200 to 400 atm.

$$N_2(g) + 3H_2(g) \longrightarrow 2NH_3(g)$$

How would increasing the reaction temperature affect the amount of ammonia produced in this exothermic reaction?

Haber discovered that the reaction temperature had to be high in order for the reaction to progress at a reasonable speed. However, the production of ammonia is exothermic, so raising the temperature favors the reverse reaction, decreasing the ammonia yield. More experiments were needed to find the minimum temperature that would give a speedy reaction and produce sufficient amounts of ammonia.

Bosch discovered that a catalyst containing a mixture of iron(II) and iron(III) oxide called magnetic iron oxide, Fe_3O_4, enabled the reaction to be carried out at a lower temperature than would otherwise be practical, at temperatures ranging from 400°C to 650°C. Removing the ammonia from the batch as soon as it is formed is another way of manipulating the equilibrium system to favor the forward reaction.

In 1918, Fritz Haber received a Nobel Prize in chemistry for his invention of the process for synthesizing ammonia, a discovery that increased food production but also prolonged the war. The Nobel Prizes were established through a will set up by Alfred Nobel, a Swedish chemist who had become wealthy from his discovery of dynamite. Nobel later developed strong misgivings about the possible uses of his discovery, and the Nobel Prizes were his contribution to the welfare of mankind.

$\mathscr{H}$IGHLIGHTS

KEY TERMS

14-1
complex ion
Le Châtelier's principle
ligand

14-2
common ion
common ion effect
equilibrium constant
solubility product
  constant

KEY CONCEPTS

14-1 **What is an equilibrium system?**

▶ Reactions that go to completion or nearly to completion include those whose products include such substances as a precipitate or a gas.

▶ Reactions that are reversible can re-form the reactants. When the forward and reverse reactions occur at equal rates, the reaction is at equilibrium.

▶ A system stays at equilibrium until conditions change. Le Châtelier's principle describes how stress—changes in temperature, pressure, and concentration—can favor the forward or reverse reaction of the equilibrium system.

▶ At equilibrium, the individual concentrations of the reactants and products undergo no further changes as long as all reaction conditions remain the same.

▶ A chemical equilibrium system is a dynamic system, not a static one.

▶ The formation of a complex ion generally involves a reversible reaction. Many complex ions containing transition metals form colorful compounds.

14-2 **How is equilibrium measured?**

▶ The equilibrium constant, K_{eq}, is a value that expresses the relationship between the concentrations of substances present at equilibrium in a reversible reaction at a given temperature.

▶ The solubility product constant, K_{sp}, is the equilibrium constant for a slightly soluble solid in equilibrium with its ions in a saturated solution.

▶ Adding a common ion to a solution displaces the ionic equilibrium of the system and can cause the forward or reverse reaction to be favored.

▶ The concentrations of pure liquids and solids do not change and therefore can be considered constant. As constants, these concentrations are not included in equilibrium constant expressions.

▶ The value of K_{eq} for a given equilibrium system can be used to determine whether the formation of products or reactants will be favored.

▶ K_{sp} values apply only in dilute solutions. When the concentration of any ion is greater than approximately 0.1 M, the attraction between positive and negative ions disturbs the equilibrium.

KEY SKILLS

Review the following models before your exam. Be sure you can solve these types of problems.

Sample Problem 14A: Calculating K_{eq} from equilibrium concentrations (p. 526)

Sample Problem 14B: Calculating concentrations using the equilibrium constant (p. 527)

Sample Problem 14C: Calculating K_{sp} from solubility (p. 530)

Sample Problem 14D: Calculating concentrations using K_{sp} (p. 531)

READING STRATEGY

Assimilating Knowledge
Have students return to their list of things they want to know about equilibrium processes, which they created on page 510. Have them place check marks next to the questions that they are now able to answer. Students should finish by making a list of what they have learned. Have students identify unanswered questions as well as new questions they may have. These questions could be used as the basis for a research project.

REVIEW & ASSESS ASSIGNMENT GUIDE

Term Review
Assign after Section 14-2.

Concept & Skills Review
Section 14-1
▶ Items 1–6
Section 14-2
▶ Items 7–26

Linking Chapters
Assign after Section 14-2.

Alternative Assessment
Assign after Section 14-2.

Test Prep
Assign prior to the chapter test.

TERM REVIEW

1. one
2. ligands
3. common ion
4. solubility product constant
5. an increase in pressure
6. dynamic

CONCEPT & SKILLS REVIEW

1. a. The rate of formation of H_2O is increasing.
   b. The forward rate is greatest when the reaction begins.

2. Drawings should show a dynamic process at the microscopic level, with forward and reverse reactions taking place. The macro level should appear static, with no apparent change occurring.

3. a. fluoride ions, F^-
   b. cyanide ions, CN^-

4. No. Although the sugar appears to have stopped dissolving, sugar molecules are dissolving and recrystallizing at equal rates.

5. a. $CH_3COOH(l) + C_2H_5OH(l) \rightleftharpoons CH_3COOC_2H_5(l) + H_2O(l)$
   b. Add more of the reactants or remove either of the products.
   c. Removal of the ethyl acetate shifts the equilibrium toward additional products.

6. A shift to the right could be caused by removing CO_2 as it formed, by adding more H_2CO_3, or by increasing the temperature of the system.

7. K_{eq} is constant for a given reaction at a given temperature but is not constant over a range of temperatures.

8. a. The concentration of products will be greater than that of the reactant.
   b. The concentration of products will be less than that of the reactant.
   c. The concentration of products and reactant will be about equal.

TERM REVIEW

1. At equilibrium, when there are roughly equal concentrations of reactants and products, K_{eq} will be close to ———.
   (one, zero)

2. Ions or molecules that are bonded to a central metal atom are referred to as ———.
   (ligands, common ions)

3. The sulfate ion, SO_4^{2-}, present in a solution of $BaSO_4$ and Na_2SO_4 is called the ———.
   (complex ion, common ion)

4. The mathematical representation of the solubility of a compound in solution is the ———.
   (solubility product constant, equilibrium constant)

5. One example of a stress on an equilibrium system as defined by Le Châtelier is ———.
   (an increase in pressure, an increase in solubility)

6. The cruise control on a car is an example of a ——— process.
   (dynamic, static)

CONCEPT & SKILLS REVIEW

SOLUTIONS IN EQUILIBRIUM

1. Use **Figure 14-3** to answer the following questions:
   a. What is happening to the rate of formation of H_2O before the system reaches equilibrium?
   b. When is the rate of the forward reaction the greatest?

2. Draw two diagrams that depict the difference between the microscopic and macroscopic events that occur when a reaction is at equilibrium.

---

3. Identify the ligands in the following complex ions:

   a.   b.

4. A home economics teacher instructs students to add several teaspoons of sugar to their homemade lemonade and then stir until the sugar stops dissolving. Is this instruction chemically correct? Explain.

5. Ethyl acetate, $CH_3COOC_2H_5(l)$, is used to make artificial silk and is prepared by reacting acetic acid, $CH_3COOH(l)$, and ethanol, $C_2H_5OH(l)$. Water is also produced in this reaction.
   a. Write the balanced equation for this reaction.
   b. If the production of ethyl acetate is not sufficient, what would increase the yield?
   c. Why is it a good idea to remove ethyl acetate as it forms?

6. Carbonated beverages contain carbonic acid in solution. The reaction that occurs upon opening the bottle is represented by the following equation:

$$H_2CO_3(aq) \rightleftharpoons H_2O(l) + CO_2(g)$$

What changes in conditions would cause the forward reaction to be favored?

EQUILIBRIUM CONSTANTS

7. Although the K_{eq} value is known as the equilibrium constant, **Table 14-2** shows that one reaction can have several different K_{eq} values. Why is it still called a constant?

8. Predict the approximate relative concentration(s) of the reactant and the products in the decomposition reaction of phosphorus pentachloride if K_{eq} is ———.
   a. much larger than 1   c. equal to 1
   b. much smaller than 1

$$PCl_5(g) \rightleftharpoons PCl_3(g) + Cl_2(g)$$

9. Use **Table 14-2** to determine whether the following equations favor the forward or the reverse reaction at the given temperature:
   a. $2HI(g) \rightleftharpoons H_2(g) + I_2(g)$ at 250°C
   b. $N_2(g) + O_2(g) \rightleftharpoons 2NO(g)$ at 25°C
   c. $N_2(g) + 3H_2(g) \rightleftharpoons 2NH_3(g)$ at 25°C
   d. $N_2(g) + 3H_2(g) \rightleftharpoons 2NH_3(g)$ at 527°C
   e. $N_2O_4(g) \rightleftharpoons 2NO_2(g)$ at 55°C

10. Write equilibrium constant expressions for the following reactions:
    a. $2NO_2(g) \rightleftharpoons N_2O_4(g)$
    b. $CO(g) + Cl_2(g) \rightleftharpoons COCl_2(g)$
    c. $AgCl(s) \rightleftharpoons Ag^+(aq) + Cl^-(aq)$
    d. $CH_3COOH(aq) + H_2O(l) \rightleftharpoons H_3O^+(aq) + CH_3COO^-(aq)$

11. Relate Le Châtelier's principle to the common ion effect.

Practice Problems

12. Vinegar—a solution of acetic acid, CH_3COOH, and water—is used in varying concentrations for different household tasks.

    $$CH_3COOH(aq) + H_2O(l) \rightleftharpoons H_3O^+(aq) + CH_3COO^-(aq)$$

    If the concentration of the acetic acid solution at equilibrium is 3.00 M and the $[H_3O^+] = [CH_3COO^-] = 7.22 \times 10^{-3}$ M, what is the K_{eq} value for acetic acid? **(Hint: See Sample Problem 14A.)**

13. Aniline, $C_6H_5NH_2$, is a weak base. If the concentration of aniline is 0.0600 M at equilibrium and the $[C_6H_5NH_3^+] = [OH^-] = 5.08 \times 10^{-6}$ M, what is the K_{eq} value for aniline? **(Hint: See Sample Problem 14A.)**

    $$C_6H_5NH_2(l) + H_2O(l) \rightleftharpoons C_6H_5NH_3^+(aq) + OH^-(aq)$$

14. Phenol, C_6H_5OH, is used as a disinfectant in many household cleaning solutions. If the equilibrium concentration of phenol is 1.61×10^{-3} M, what are the concentrations of H_3O^+ and $C_6H_5O^-$? K_{eq} for phenol is 1.60×10^{-10} at 25°C. **(Hint: See Sample Problem 14B.)**

15. Benzoic acid, C_6H_5COOH, is a slightly soluble acid used in food preservation. K_{eq} for benzoic acid is 6.30×10^{-5} at 25°C. For a solution of benzoic acid that has an equilibrium concentration of 0.0200 M, what are the concentrations of H_3O^+ and $C_6H_5COO^-$? **(Hint: See Sample Problem 14B.)**

16. The solubility of cobalt(II) sulfide, CoS, is 1.7×10^{-13} M. Calculate the solubility product constant for CoS. **(Hint: See Sample Problem 14C.)**

17. What is the solubility product constant for copper(I) sulfide, Cu_2S, given that its solubility is 8.5×10^{-17} M? **(Hint: See Sample Problem 14C.)**

18. Aluminum hydroxide, $Al(OH)_3$, is used to waterproof fabrics. If the OH^- concentration is 2.8×10^{-8} M, what is the concentration of Al^{3+}? See Table 14-3 for the K_{sp} of $Al(OH)_3$. **(Hint: See Sample Problem 14D.)**

19. Silver sulfide, Ag_2S, is an ingredient used to make ceramics. If the Ag_2S in your dog's ceramic water dish dissolves in the water, giving an Ag^+ concentration of 4.93×10^{-17} M, what concentration of S^{2-} will be in your dog's water? See Table 14-3 for the K_{sp} of Ag_2S. **(Hint: See Sample Problem 14D.)**

20. What is the concentration of F^- ions in a saturated solution that is 0.10 M in Ca^{2+}? The K_{sp} of CaF_2 is 1.6×10^{-10}.

21. Silver bromide, AgBr, is used to make photographic black-and-white film. Calculate the concentration of Ag^+ and Br^- ions in a saturated solution at 25°C.

22. Write K_{eq} expressions for the following reactions:
    a. $4H_3O^+(aq) + 2Cl^-(aq) + MnO_2(s) \rightleftharpoons Mn^{2+}(aq) + 6H_2O(l) + Cl_2(g)$
    b. $As_4O_6(s) + 6H_2O(l) \rightleftharpoons 4H_3AsO_3(aq)$

9. a. reverse
   b. reverse
   c. forward
   d. reverse
   e. reverse

10. a. $K_{eq} = \dfrac{[N_2O_4]}{[NO_2]^2}$

    b. $K_{eq} = \dfrac{[COCl_2]}{[CO][Cl_2]}$

    c. $K_{sp} = [Ag^+][Cl^-]$

    d. $K_{eq} = \dfrac{[H_3O^+][CH_3COO^-]}{[CH_3COOH]}$

11. When added to a solution, a common ion becomes more concentrated, placing a stress on the equilibrium that exists between a solid substance and its dissolved ions in a saturated solution. The equilibrium shifts, relieving the stress by removing some of the common ion by precipitation. Thus, the concentration of the other ion in the equilibrium is also reduced.

Practice problems

12. $K_{eq} = \dfrac{(7.22 \times 10^{-3})^2}{3.00} = 1.74 \times 10^{-5}$

13. $K_{eq} = \dfrac{(5.08 \times 10^{-6})^2}{0.0600} = 4.30 \times 10^{-10}$

14. $6.30 \times 10^{-5} = \dfrac{x^2}{0.0200}$; $x = [H_3O^+] = [C_6H_5COO^-] = 1.12 \times 10^{-3}$ M

15. $1.60 \times 10^{-10} = \dfrac{x^2}{1.61 \times 10^{-3}}$;
    $x = [H_3O^+] = [C_6H_5O^-] = 5.08 \times 10^{-7}$ M

16. $K_{sp} = [Co^{2+}][S^{2-}] = (1.7 \times 10^{-13})^2 = 2.9 \times 10^{-26}$

17. $K_{sp} = [Cu^{2+}]^2[S^{2-}] = \left(2(8.5 \times 10^{-17})\right)^2 (8.5 \times 10^{-17}) = 2.5 \times 10^{-48}$

18. $K_{sp} = 2.0 \times 10^{-31} = [Al^{3+}](2.8 \times 10^{-8})^3$; $[Al^{3+}] = 9.1 \times 10^{-9}$ M

19. $K_{sp} = 1.1 \times 10^{-49} = (4.93 \times 10^{-17})^2[S^{2-}]$; $[S^{2-}] = 4.5 \times 10^{-17}$ M

20. $K_{sp} = 1.6 \times 10^{-10} = (0.10)[F^-]^2$; $[F^-] = 4.0 \times 10^{-5}$ M

21. $K_{sp} = 5.4 \times 10^{-13} = x^2$;
$x = [Ag^+] = [Br^-] = 7.3 \times 10^{-7}$ M

22. a. $K_{eq} = \dfrac{[Mn^{2+}][Cl_2]}{[H_3O^+]^4[Cl^-]^2}$

b. $K_{eq} = [H_3AsO_4]^4$

23. $K_{eq} = \dfrac{[H_2O][CO]}{[H_2][CO_2]} = $

$$\dfrac{\left(\dfrac{0.2296}{2.0}\right)^2}{\left(\dfrac{0.4693}{2.0}\right)\left(\dfrac{0.0715}{2.0}\right)} = 1.57$$

24. $K_{eq} = \dfrac{[N_2O_4]}{[NO_2]^2}$, $K_{eq} = \dfrac{[CO][H_2O]}{[CO_2][H_2]}$,

$K_{eq} = \dfrac{[NO]^2}{[N_2][O_2]}$, $K_{eq} = \dfrac{[HI]^2}{[H_2][I_2]}$,

$K_{eq} = \dfrac{[NH_3]^2}{[N_2][H_2]^3}$

25. a. 1 mol KOH is completely soluble in 1 L of water.

b. No. A very small amount of AgCl dissolves as equilibrium is established. $Ba(OH)_2$ is likewise slightly soluble in water (more so than AgCl) and establishes an equilibrium between dissolved ions and solid $Ba(OH)_2$.

26. $K_{sp} = 1.6 \times 10^{-10} = (0.10)[F^-]^2$;
$[F^-] = 4.0 \times 10^{-5}$ M. It is assumed here that F^- ions are added in a way that does not significantly change the concentration of Ca^{2+} ions.

LINKING CHAPTERS

1. Percentage yield can be increased by removing a product as it forms, adding more reactants, or changing the conditions of temperature and pressure (depending on the nature of the reaction).

2. a. No. If the process reaches a dynamic equilibrium, it is still taking place, but the rates of the forward and reverse directions are equal.

b. Yes. If the reaction reaches equilibrium, reactants are forming from products at the same rate that products are forming from reactants.

Continued on page 539.

---

23. The following equation shows an equilibrium reaction between hydrogen and carbon dioxide.

$$H_2(g) + CO_2(g) \rightleftarrows H_2O(g) + CO(g)$$

At 986°C, the following data were obtained at equilibrium in a 2.0 L reaction vessel.

Substance	Number of moles
H_2	0.4693
CO_2	0.0715
H_2O	0.2296
CO	0.2296

Calculate the K_{eq} for this reaction.

24. Write an equilibrium-constant expression for each reaction listed in **Table 14-2.**

25. The figure below shows the results of adding three different chemicals to distilled water and stirring well.

a. Which substance(s) is completely soluble in water?

b. Is it correct to say that AgCl is completely insoluble? Explain your answer. Is $Ba(OH)_2$ completely insoluble?

AgCl   NaBr $Ba(OH)_2$

26. A solution has $[Ca^{2+}] = 0.10$ M. As F^- ion is added, a precipitate of $CaF_2(s)$ will eventually form. What is the concentration of F^- ions when the precipitate just begins to form? (Hint: The solution will be saturated, and $K_{sp} = 1.6 \times 10^{-10}$ will apply.)

LINKING CHAPTERS

1. Percent yield
Using Le Châtelier's principle, devise one way to increase the percent yield of product from a reversible chemical reaction.

---

2. Theme: Equilibrium and change

a. If a process is in equilibrium, does that mean nothing is changing?

b. If a reversible reaction favors the formation of the products, are any reactants still present?

3. Electron configuration
Complex ions of Ag^+, Zn^{2+}, Cd^{2+}, and Hg^{2+} are usually colorless. What electron configuration do these ions have in common?

ALTERNATIVE ASSESSMENTS

Performance assessment

1. Your instructor will give you an index card with a specific equilibrium reaction on it. Describe how you would alter the reaction to produce either more of the products or more of the reactants. Show your method to your instructor. If your method is approved, obtain the necessary materials from your instructor and perform the experiment.

Portfolio projects

1. Models in science
Develop a model that demonstrates the concept of a chemical equilibrium. Be sure that your model includes the impact of Le Châtelier's principle on equilibrium and the common ion effect.

2. internet**connect**

SCI**LINKS**
NSTA

TOPIC: Separating ions
GO TO: www.scilinks.org
KEYWORD: HW144

Research and communication
Many different pollutants are in the form of ions dissolved in water. Industries must remove these ions from their waste water to avoid exposing the environment to harmful chemicals. Research the use of solubility principles and equilibrium to remove the ions listed below. Write a report about the effect that these chemicals have on our environment.

a. Pb^{2+} **c.** Cl^- **e.** PO_4^{3-}
b. Ba^{2+} **d.** SO_4^{2-}

1. _____ will *not* affect the equilibrium of a reaction.
   a. A change in temperature
   b. The addition of a catalyst
   c. Increasing the concentration of the reactants
   d. Decreasing the concentration of the products

2. Examine the following equation for an equilibrium system.

$$NaF(s) + 0.90 \text{ kJ} \rightleftarrows Na^+(aq) + F^-(aq)$$

   The reverse reaction would be favored by _____.
   a. increasing the temperature
   b. increasing the pressure
   c. adding $KF(s)$ to the reaction
   d. adding more $NaF(s)$

3. If the K_{eq} value is larger than one, then _____.
   a. the concentrations of the products equal those of the reactants
   b. a catalyst must have been added to the reaction
   c. the reaction must be endothermic
   d. the forward reaction is favored

4. NaCl does not have a K_{sp} value because this salt _____.
   a. cannot participate in an equilibrium reaction
   b. does not form aqueous solutions
   c. is very soluble in water
   d. retains its crystal lattice structure in aqueous solution

5. Consider the following equation for an equilibrium system:

$$2PbS(s) + 3O_2(g) + C(s) \rightleftarrows$$
$$2Pb(l) + CO_2(g) + 2SO_2(g)$$

   The concentration(s) that would be included in the denominator of the equilibrium-constant expression are _____.
   a. $Pb(l)$, $CO_2(g)$, $SO_2(g)$
   b. $PbS(s)$, $O_2(g)$, $C(s)$
   c. $O_2(g)$, $Pb(l)$, $CO_2(g)$, $SO_2(g)$
   d. $O_2(g)$

6. A reaction that has reached equilibrium is a reaction in which _____.
   a. the concentration of the reactants equals the concentration of the products
   b. the rate of the reverse reaction equals the rate of the forward reaction
   c. all conditions are static
   d. products are no longer being formed

7. If an exothermic reaction has reached equilibrium, then increasing the temperature will _____.
   a. favor the forward reaction
   b. favor the reverse reaction
   c. favor both the forward and reverse reaction
   d. have no effect on the equilibrium

8. The K_{eq} value for a reaction must specify the temperature at which the concentrations are measured because the K_{eq} value _____.
   a. is a constant
   b. does not have any units
   c. will change if the temperature changes
   d. may or may not be larger than 1

9. Consider the following reaction:

$$COBr_2(g) \rightleftarrows CO(g) + Br_2(g)$$

   At 73°C, the K_{eq} value for this reaction is 0.190. This K_{eq} value indicates that _____.
   a. the reverse reaction is favored
   b. the forward reaction is favored
   c. the reaction has reached equilibrium
   d. the concentrations of $CO(g)$ and $Br_2(g)$ are greater than the concentration of $Br_2(g)$

CHEMICAL EQUILIBRIUM 539

1. b	4. c	7. b
2. c	5. d	8. c
3. d	6. b	9. a

Continued from page 538.

3. The outer energy level of each of these ions contains only a full set of *d* orbitals.

ALTERNATIVE ASSESSMENTS

Performance assessment

1. Methods chosen by students will vary. Many of the equilibrium reactions cited in text cannot be used because of the temperature and pressure conditions needed. In other reactions, it is difficult to demonstrate changes in equilibrium. Consider using the colored complex ions and extending the assessment into Chapter 15 using indicators, pH meters, and buffers to demonstrate changes in ionization equilibria.

Portfolio projects

1. Student models will vary. Consider operational physical models as well as analogies and conceptual models that are effectively illustrated in an innovative way. Models should demonstrate both dynamic equilibrium and the effects of two or more kinds of stress.

2. Student reports will vary. Each of these ions can be precipitated by adding a solution containing an ion that forms an insoluble product with it. The common ion effect is especially used to enhance the precipitation of heavy-metal ions and reduce their concentration in effluents. Adding chelating agents (ligands) that scavenge metal ions is another practical method. Students should also consider means used by industry to remove substances that are in particulate form.

CHAPTER 15 PLANNING GUIDE

Acids and Bases

CLASSROOM RESOURCES

SECTIONS	TEACHER'S DEMONSTRATIONS	PROBLEM SOLVING ■ *Text* ◆ *ChemFile Mini-Guide*	LABORATORIES ■ *Text* ◆ *ChemFile Manuals: A, B, C, D*
15-1 **What are acids and bases?** Section Review, p. 549	**Demo 1** Ionization in Aqueous Acids, p. 542	■ **Sample Problem 15A** Determining $[OH^-]$ using K_w, p. 549	■ **EXP. 15A** Drip-Drop Acid-Base Experiment, p. 772
15-2 **Can the strengths of acids and bases be quantified?** Section Review, p. 558		■ **Sample Problem 15B** Calculating K_a of a weak acid, p. 557	◆ **D14** Acids and Bases: Lemon Cheese ◆ **D18** Shampoo Chemistry
15-3 **How are acidity and pH related?** Section Review, p. 567	**Demo 2** pH, p. 560 **Demo 3** Effects of pH on Chlorophyll Stability, p. 562 **Demo 4** Buffers in Solution, p. 566	■ **How To** Use logarithms in pH calculations, p. 561 ■ **Sample Problem 15C** Calculating the pH of an acidic solution, p. 561 ■ **Sample Problem 15D** Calculating the pH of a basic solution, p. 562 ◆ **Chapter 17** pH	■ **QUICKLAB** An Acid Among Us, p. 564 ■ **EXP. 15C** Measuring the pH of Household Products, p. 782 ◆ **A12** $[H_3O^+]$ and pH ◆ **A20** Buffering Capacity ◆ **B15** $[H_3O^+]$ and pH ◆ **INV. C17** Measuring pH—Home Test Kit ◆ **D15** How Effective Is an Antacid?
15-4 **What is a titration?** Section Review, p. 577	**Demo 5** Indicators, p. 572	■ **How To** Carry out a titration, p. 574 ■ **Sample Problem 15E** Calculating concentration from titration data, p. 576 ◆ **Chapter 18** Titrations	■ **EXP. 15B** Acid-Base Titration of an Eggshell, p. 775 ■ **INV. 15B** Acid-Base Titration—Industrial Spill, p. 780 ◆ **A13** Titration of an Acid with a Base ◆ **B16** Titration of an Acid with a Base ◆ **B17** Percentage of Acetic Acid in Vinegar ◆ **INV. C18** Measuring pH—Acid Precipitation Testing ◆ **INV. C19** Acid-Base Titration—Vinegar Tampering Investigation ◆ **D16** Titration of Aspirin ◆ **D17** Household Indicators

SECTIONS	VIDEOS/VIDEODISC *Holt Chemistry Videodisc* CNN PRESENTS *Science in the NEWS*	CHEMFILE CD-ROMS ● *Teaching Resources* ◆ *Interactive Tutor*	OVERHEADS ● *Color Transparencies* ◆ *Transparency Masters*
15-1	Acid Strength: Acetic Acid, Weak Acid Strength: Hydrochloric Acid, Strong Ammonia–Water Reaction Antacid Reaction Phenolphthalein in Acid and Base Uses of Sulfuric Acid CNN PRESENTS Segment 26 Acids in the Environment	● Occupational Application: Pool Technician	● **87** Self-Ionization of Water ◆ **70A** Names of Acids and Bases ● **71A** Common Aqueous Acids and Bases
15-2		● Supplemental Reading: "Chemistry and Physics in the Kitchen"	● **84** Monoprotic and Diprotic Acids ● **85** Oxyacids of Chlorine ◆ **72A** Relative Strengths of Acids and Bases ◆ **73A** Acid-Base Definitions
15-3	Buffer Preparation Bufferless Solution: pH Changes Buffered Solution: pH Stays the Same	◆ **Module 8:** Strong and Weakly Ionized Species, pH, and Titrations **Topic:** pH	● **88** pH Scale Relationships ● **89** Color Ranges of Indicators ● **101** Equilibrium and pH Calculations ● **102** Buffered vs. Nonbuffered Solutions ◆ *See also* **74A, 76A.**
15-4	Calcium Carbonate—Hydrochloric Acid Reaction	● Occupational Application: Baker ◆ **Module 8:** Strong and Weakly Ionized Species, pH, and Titrations **Topic:** Titrations	● **86** Neutralization Reaction ● **90** Titration Curve for a Strong Acid and a Strong Base ● **91** Titration Curve for a Weak Acid and a Strong Base ◆ *See also* **99A, 100A.**

ASSESSMENT RESOURCES

ALTERNATIVE ASSESSMENTS	CHAPTER TESTING	SCORING RUBRICS *Holt ChemFile Teaching Resources CD-ROM*
Student Text Performance assessments, p. 584 Portfolio projects 1–2, p. 584 **Teacher's Edition** Depicting Acidic and Basic Solutions, p. 557 Presenting a Titration, p. 574 **Study Guide** Sections 15-1 to 15-4	**Student Text** Test Preparation, p. 585 **Holt Chemistry: Visualizing Matter Chapter 15 Test** (blackline masters) **Holt ChemFile Test Generator for Macintosh and Windows**	**Lab Work** Student-Designed Experiments Rubric Performance-Tasks Scoring Rubric Assessment for Structured Inquiry Assessment for Open-Ended Inquiry **Portfolio Projects** Assessing Portfolios Portfolio Assignment Student Evaluation Form

Acids and Bases

Establishing Prior Knowledge

Make sure students understand the following concepts.

▸ Chapter 8: measuring amounts in moles
▸ Chapter 9: balancing chemical equations
▸ Chapter 10: stoichiometric calculations
▸ Chapter 13: the nature of solutions, ionization, expressing solution concentration

READING STRATEGY

Assimilating Knowledge

Before reading this chapter, have students write a short list of all the things they already know or think they know about acids and bases in aqueous solution, strengths of acids and bases, pH, and titrations. When students have finished their list, ask them to contribute their entries to a group list on the board or on an overhead projector. Then have students list the things they might want to know about the chemistry of acids and bases. If students have trouble coming up with questions, offer the following suggestions to get them on track:

▸ What are some properties that acids and bases in aqueous solution have in common?
▸ What ions exist in acid solution?
▸ How do weak acids and strong acids differ?
▸ What are typical pH values of acids and bases?
▸ What is formed when an acid reacts with a base?

ABOUT THE ILLUSTRATION

Oranges, like other citrus fruits, contain citric acid and ascorbic acid, two important organic acids.

 internet **connect**

Holt Chemistry: Visualizing Matter
On-Line Resources
go.hrw.com
Visit the HRW Web site for a variety of resources related to this chapter. Just type in the keyword HW0 Chapt15.

SCi**LINKS**℠
NSTA

National Science Teachers Association
On-Line Resources: www.scilinks.org
The following Scilinks Internet resources can be found in the student text for this chapter:

Page 543
TOPIC: Acids
KEYWORD: HW151

Page 546
TOPIC: Bases
KEYWORD: HW152

Page 568
TOPIC: Antacids
KEYWORD: HW153

Page 569
TOPIC: Titration/Indicators
KEYWORD: HW154

Page 565
TOPIC: Buffers
KEYWORD: HW155

Page 584
TOPIC: Baking soda/Baking powder
KEYWORD: HW156

CHEMICAL FOES DO BATTLE

Nestled in the New England uplands, the lake is a beautiful sight. Glacier-smoothed rocks fringe its southern shore, while to the north stately pines and leafless maples cloak the hills that crowd the Canadian border. Now, in the cold light of an early February evening, the lake is covered by a thick layer of ice. But the tranquillity is suddenly shattered by a noisy convoy of dump trucks driving onto the frozen surface. They disperse and unload piles of gray rock over the ice. What is going on? Why is this mechanical invasion taking place?

Formerly, the lake was a favorite haunt of fishers, both human and feathered. But as the fish population has declined in recent years, the anglers have departed and the ospreys have died or gone elsewhere in search of food. What is responsible for the death of this lake? Acid precipitation is to blame. Prevailing wind patterns carry polluting gases from the Midwest to Canada and the Northeast. The gases originate in the power plants, refineries, and smelters of America's industrial heartland, a region whose commercial products are consumed throughout the country. Some factories, such as steel-producing plants, burn fossil fuels, as do automobiles. The fuels contain sulfur, nitrogen, and other contaminants that become gaseous pollutants when the fuel is burned. These gases dissolve in atmospheric water to form acids, which are then washed from the air by summer rains and winter snows. Regions such as this one, where there is a large snowpack in winter, are especially vulnerable because the spring melt releases a sudden rush of acidic water. Acids have accumulated in the lake, killing much of the plant and animal life that once flourished in it.

A group of environmentalists have chartered the fleet of trucks to deposit limestone from a quarry hundreds of miles away onto the frozen lake. They plan to combat the polluting, not to mention deadly, acidity by introducing a base into the lake. They hope to rehabilitate the lake's ecology and restore the lake to its former state. In this chapter, you will learn that bases counteract the effects of acids. As you read through the chapter, consider the following questions.

CHAPTER LINKS

How are the industrial gases responsible for acid rain?

Why did environmentalists transport limestone into the region instead of using local rock?

Why was the operation carried out during the winter?

In addition to affecting lakes, acid precipitation has caused extensive damage to the landscape. In many cities, statues and gargoyles have been eroded dramatically. Acid precipitation has also caused forest degradation in areas such as the Appalachian Mountains, where spruce forests have suffered from defoliation, increased susceptibility to injury in winter, and growth reduction. The effects are visible on landmarks such as Mount Mitchell, in North Carolina, where there has been significant destruction of pine trees.

CNN. Science in the News

PRESENTS Feature story 26
Acids in the Environment   See the Science in the News video guide for more details.

CONCEPT PREVIEW

Section 15-1
Ionization of acids in water
▸ hydronium ions
▸ acids as electrolytes
▸ organic acids

Bases in aqueous solution
▸ hydroxide ions
▸ organic amines as bases

Reaction of an acid and base
▸ neutralization
▸ self-ionization of water

Section 15-2
Strengths of acids and bases
▸ acids as proton donors
▸ polyprotic acids
▸ conjugate acids and bases
▸ K_a, an index of acid strength

Section 15-3
The meaning of pH
▸ calculating pH from $[H_3O^+]$
▸ relating pH to K_w and K_a

▸ measuring pH
▸ buffer solutions

Section 15-4
Using neutralization reactions
▸ neutralization in ionic and quantitative terms
▸ methods of detecting equivalence points
▸ how to perform a titration
▸ titration calculations

SECTION 15-1

What are acids and bases?

▶ **Describe** the distinctive properties of acids and bases.

▶ **Distinguish** between the terms *strong* and *weak* as they apply to acids and bases.

▶ **Explain** the unusually high electrical conductivities of acidic solutions.

▶ **Use** K_w to calculate a solution's hydronium ion or hydroxide ion concentration.

▶ **Name** and describe the functional groups that characterize organic acids and bases.

LESSON WARM-UP

Discussion Strategy It is likely that students have studied acids and bases every year since elementary school and have studied pH at least once. To help them recall some of what they have already learned, exhibit a bottle of vinegar, a bottle of household ammonia, and an equal volume of both 1 M HCl and 1 M NaOH. Each solution should be in a small beaker, and both beakers should be labeled. Two other labeled beakers should contain samples of the vinegar (5% CH_3COOH, approximately 0.8 M) and ammonia, $NH_3(aq)$. Place a watch glass over the beaker containing the ammonia.

Ask students to identify the acids and bases in the group. Ask them which solutions will conduct electricity and how well; what ions are in each solution; and how each solution will react with other substances.

During this discussion, conduct the following tests with a minimum of comment. Dip strips of blue and red litmus paper in each solution, and display the pairs on a white porcelain or plastic background. Test the conductivity of each solution with a battery-powered conductivity tester or an ohmmeter. Test the pH with a pH meter or pH paper. Drop a 1 cm strip of Mg ribbon in each beaker, and observe the reactivity. Do the same with a marble chip. When you have completed the tests, summarize the results in a table, identifying each solution as a strong or weak acid or base.

Acids

How would you describe the tastes of the beverages and fruits shown in **Figure 15-1**? Some are sweet, but all have a quality to their taste that people describe as sour, tart, or acidic. Is there anything that these sour-tasting substances have in common? Indeed there is. They all contain chemicals known as acids.

Acids are hydronium ion generators

When the term *acid* is used, chemists usually think of the definition proposed by Swedish chemist Svante Arrhenius. In a modern version of this definition, an acid is a substance that, when dissolved in water, increases the hydronium ion, H_3O^+, concentration of the water.

Both **strong acids** and **weak acids** exist. These adjectives, *strong* and *weak,* have the same meanings that they did in Chapter 13, where

strong acid

an acid that ionizes completely in aqueous solution

weak acid

an acid that is a weak electrolyte

▼ **FIGURE 15-1**

Fruits and fruit juices contain citric and ascorbic acids, carbonated beverages contain carbonic acid, and vinegar contains acetic acid.

Carbonic acid

Acetic acid

Citric acid

Ascorbic acid

DEMONSTRATION 1

Ionization in Aqueous Acids

Approximate time: 10 minutes

1. Pour 150 mL of distilled water into each of four beakers. Use a battery-powered conductivity tester to demonstrate to students that the water is nonconductive.

2. Write the formulas $C_{12}H_{22}O_{11}$, CH_3COOH, HCl, and NaCl on the board. Ask students to describe the type of bonding in each substance.

3. Add 2 g of sucrose to beaker 1, 10 mL of 1 M CH_3COOH to beaker 2, 10 mL of 1 M HCl to beaker 3, and 2 g of NaCl to beaker 4. Stir all solutions.

4. Test each solution with a battery-powered conductivity tester. Ask students why the solution of HCl conducts. Also ask them why acetic acid and HCl are conductors even though they are covalent compounds.

TABLE 15-1 Some Strong and Weak Acids

Strong acids	Weak acids
Chloric acid, $HClO_3$	Acetic acid, CH_3COOH
Hydrobromic acid, HBr	Boric acid, H_3BO_3
Hydrochloric acid, HCl	Hydrocyanic acid, HCN
Hydriodic acid, HI	Hydrofluoric acid, HF
Nitric acid, HNO_3	Hydrosulfuric acid, H_2S
Perchloric acid, $HClO_4$	Hypochlorous acid, $HClO$
Periodic acid, HIO_4	Nitrous acid, HNO_2
Permanganic acid, $HMnO_4$	Phosphoric acid, H_3PO_4
Sulfuric acid, H_2SO_4	Sulfurous acid, H_2SO_3

internet**connect**

SCI**LINKS**
NSTA
TOPIC: Acids
GO TO: www.scilinks.org
KEYWORD: HW151

strong and weak electrolytes were discussed. A *strong acid* is an acid that ionizes completely in aqueous solution to form ions, one of which is the hydronium ion. Nitric acid, HNO_3, is an example of a strong acid. The following equation represents its reaction with water.

$$HNO_3(l) + H_2O(l) \longrightarrow H_3O^+(aq) + NO_3^-(aq)$$

When a *weak acid* dissolves in water, only a small fraction of its molecules ionize. An example of a weak acid is hypochlorous acid, $HClO$. Its reaction with water is represented by the following equation.

$$HClO(aq) + H_2O(l) \rightleftharpoons H_3O^+(aq) + ClO^-(aq)$$

Recall from Chapter 14 that the double arrows in this equation indicate equilibrium. Hypochlorite ions, ClO^-, are reacting with hydronium ions to form $HClO$ at the same rate that $HClO$ molecules are reacting with water to form ions. **Table 15-1** lists the names and formulas of several strong and weak acids.

Acid solutions are good conductors of electricity

In addition to their sour taste, aqueous acid solutions share the ability to conduct electricity, as illustrated in **Figure 15-2**. This is because acids, like other electrolytes, produce ions when dissolved in solution. Strong acids are particularly good conductors of electricity because the hydronium ion can move faster than other ions, and electricity is conducted by this ion movement. Why is that?

When an ion—for example, a sodium ion, Na^+—moves through water, it has to push the water molecules out of its way. The H_3O^+ ion, however, does not. Instead of pushing the water molecule aside, like other ions do, the hydronium ion transfers a proton to the impeding H_2O molecule. This proton transfer converts the water molecule to a hydronium ion, and the former hydronium ion reverts to a water

FIGURE 15-2 ▼

Hydrochloric acid solution is a good conductor of electricity. It ionizes completely in water, causing the bulb to be brightly lit.

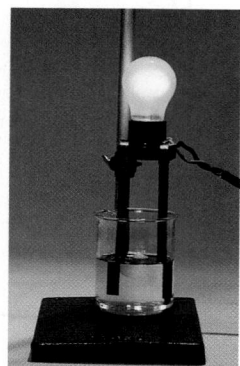

ACIDS AND BASES **543**

SECTION 15-1

ADDITIONAL APPLICATION

Hydrochloric acid is sold at hardware and building-supply stores as *muriatic acid*. It is used for cleaning mortar stains from bricks and tile, and lime deposits (resulting from hard water) from tile, porcelain, and some metals. The name *muriatic acid* is considered obsolete in chemistry.

VISUAL STRATEGY

Figure 15-2 Remind students that the brightness of the bulb depends on the concentration of ions in solution. HCl ionizes nearly 100% in dilute solution and therefore is a strong electrolyte.

CONTENT STRATEGY

Many students will already be familiar with acids and bases as discussed in this section. This is the Arrhenius model, in which acids form H^+ (as H_3O^+) in solution and bases form OH^- in solution. In Section 13-2, the Arrhenius model is compared with the Brønsted-Lowry model.

Challenge students to account for the difference in conductivity between acetic acid and HCl. Have them recall what they learned about molecular electrolytes in Chapter 13.

Safety
Wear safety goggles and a lab apron. Students should remain 10 ft from the demonstration.

Disposal
Combine the acid solutions, and neutralize them with 1 M NaOH. Pour all the solutions down the drain.

RESOURCE LINK

IN-TEXT LAB
Skills Development
Have students do Exploration 15A on page 772 for an introduction to acids and bases in the laboratory.

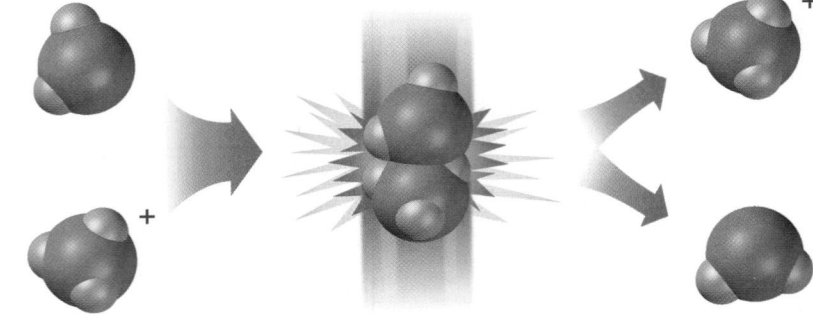

a Successive transfers of protons from H_3O^+ to H_2O make the hydronium ion appear to move through a solution much faster than an ion can actually move.

b The movement of a proton through an acid solution resembles the movement of a pail of water along a bucket brigade.

▲ **FIGURE 15-4**

The hydronium ions formed by hydrochloric acid in aqueous solution react with zinc to produce hydrogen gas.

molecule. In turn, the new hydronium ion passes a proton to a third water molecule. The process of proton transfer in an acid solution is illustrated in **Figure 15-3**.

Hydronium ions react with some metals

Another property shared by many acids is the ability to react with metals above hydrogen in the activity series to produce hydrogen gas. This reaction is actually a property of the hydronium ion and not of the acid itself. An example is the reaction of hydrochloric acid and zinc, which is illustrated in **Figure 15-4** and represented by the following net ionic equation. Notice that even though hydrochloric acid has the formula HCl, only the H_3O^+ ions produced by the acid appear in the equation.

$$2H_3O^+(aq) + Zn(s) \longrightarrow 2H_2O(l) + Zn^{2+}(aq) + H_2(g)$$

Not all acids react with zinc as readily as hydrochloric acid does. Reactions involving acids and metals depend on the amount of hydronium ion present, which in turn depends on the strength and concentration of the acid. The *strength* of an acid is a measure of how much it ionizes in solution. The strength of an acid has nothing to do with its *concentration*, which is the amount of dissolved acid per liter of solution.

Organic acids are carboxylic acids

You learned in Chapter 7 that molecules of most organic acids have the characteristic carboxyl group, —COOH. These compounds are called **carboxylic acids.** When a carboxylic acid ionizes in aqueous solution, the result is a hydronium ion and an anion with the following group.

$$\overset{O}{\underset{}{\overset{\|}{-C}}-O^-}$$

Although the negative charge is shown as being located on one oxygen atom of the carboxyl group, experiments show that the oxygen atoms share the negative charge equally.

carboxylic acid

an organic compound that contains the carboxyl functional group

CONCEPT CHECK

1. Why is nitric acid classified as a strong acid whereas hypochlorous acid is considered a weak acid?

2. Describe the movement of the hydronium ion through an aqueous solution.

3. What products are formed when a metal reacts with a strong acid?

4. Why is the carboxyl group considered to be acidic?

Bases

According to Arrhenius, a base is a substance that increases the concentration of hydroxide ions, OH⁻, when dissolved in water. Unlike acids, which are usually liquids or gases, many bases are solids. Solutions of bases are slippery to the touch. **Figure 15-5** shows some bases with which you may be familiar. A base that dissolves easily in water is called an *alkali,* and the resulting solution is said to be *alkaline.* Many cleaning agents are classified as alkaline because of their high concentration of hydroxide ions. These ions interact with oil and grease by a process that you learned about in Section 13-4.

Even though acids taste sour and bases feel slippery, *it is not safe* to use these properties to identify substances. Solutions of acids or bases can cause serious burns to living tissue.

Bases are hydroxide ion generators

Sodium hydroxide, NaOH, is an example of a *strong base.* It is an ionic compound, and it is very soluble in water. Sodium hydroxide is classified as a strong base because it fully dissociates in solution, as shown by the following equation.

$$NaOH(s) \xrightarrow{H_2O} Na^+(aq) + OH^-(aq)$$

FIGURE 15-5 ▼

Many household products contain bases, such as sodium hydroxide, NaOH(s), and ammonia, NH₃(aq).

TEACHING TIP

Organic Acids You may wish to explain to students why the carboxyl group can ionize in water. The carboxyl group is acidic because the oxygen atoms, being strongly electronegative, attract electrons to themselves. These electrons include bonding electrons. The hydrogen atom is thereby "deprived" of its electron, and the proton alone can easily transfer to another atom that offers an unshared pair of electrons.

ANSWERS

CONCEPT CHECK

1. Nitric acid ionizes nearly 100% when dissolved in water, whereas hypochlorous acid ionizes only to a small degree.

2. The hydronium ion moves more rapidly through a solution than most other ions because it regenerates itself by transferring its proton to a nearby water molecule, which then becomes the hydronium ion.

3. a salt and hydrogen gas

4. The carboxyl group can ionize in aqueous solution to form hydronium ions.

DID YOU KNOW?

Alkalis react not only with skin oils but also with the proteins in the skin by hydrolyzing peptide bonds. This reaction also contributes to the slippery feeling of bases.

TABLE 15-2 **Some Strong and Weak Bases**

Strong bases	Weak bases
Barium hydroxide, $Ba(OH)_2$	Ammonia, NH_3
Calcium hydroxide, $Ca(OH)_2$	Aniline, $C_6H_5NH_2$
Potassium hydroxide, KOH	Potassium carbonate, K_2CO_3
Sodium hydroxide, NaOH	Sodium carbonate, Na_2CO_3
Sodium phosphate, Na_3PO_4	Trimethylamine, $(CH_3)_3N$

TEACHING TIP

Producing Hydroxide Ions Stress that the criterion by which a substance is classified as an Arrhenius base is that it must produce hydroxide ions in solution. These ions are produced by two principal methods. One method is to dissolve an ionic metal hydroxide in water. The other method is to dissolve a substance that removes a proton from a water molecule, leaving a hydroxide ion. This method is illustrated by the equilibrium equation shown on this page.

Students may wonder why carbonates and phosphates qualify as bases. These ions acquire protons from water and set up equilibria that have hydroxide ions as products, as shown by the following equations.

$$CO_3^{2-}(aq) + H_2O(l) \rightleftharpoons$$
$$HCO_3^-(aq) + OH^-(aq)$$
$$PO_4^{3-}(aq) + H_2O(l) \rightleftharpoons$$
$$HPO_4^{2-}(aq) + OH^-(aq)$$
$$HPO_4^{2-}(aq) + H_2O(l) \rightleftharpoons$$
$$H_2PO_4^-(aq) + OH^-(aq)$$

CONTENT STRATEGY

The introduction of nonhydroxide bases on this page sets the stage for the introduction of the Brønsted-Lowry acid-base theory in Section 15-2.

internetconnect

SCiLINKS

NSTA

TOPIC: Bases
GO TO: www.scilinks.org
KEYWORD: HW152

Some examples of strong and weak bases are listed in **Table 15-2,** and one of each is shown in **Figure 15-6.**

As you can see from Table 15-2, several of the strong bases are the hydroxides of metals in Groups 1 and 2 of the periodic table. This is why Group 1 elements are called alkali metals and Group 2 elements are called alkaline earth metals. It is easy to see how these compounds produce OH^- ions in solution because the solid bases already contain hydroxide ions. However, some strong bases and most weak bases are not hydroxide compounds. How, then, can these substances produce hydroxide ions in solution? To find out, look at what happens when ammonia, a typical weak base, dissolves in water.

Ammonia, a gas at room temperature, dissolves readily in water. Most of the ammonia molecules do not react with water to form ions, so ammonia is classified as a *weak base.*

$$NH_3(aq) + H_2O(l) \rightleftharpoons NH_4^+(aq) + OH^-(aq)$$

▼ **FIGURE 15-6**

a Ammonia only slightly ionizes in aqueous solution. Therefore, most of the ammonia remains as neutral molecules in solution.

Ammonium ion, NH_4^+

Water molecule, H_2O

Ammonia molecule, NH_3

Hydroxide ion, OH^-

b Sodium hydroxide is a strong base. There are no sodium hydroxide molecules left in solution.

Sodium ion, Na^+

Water molecule, H_2O

Hydroxide ion, OH^-

Because bases produce ions in solution, solutions of bases, like solutions of acids, are electrical conductors.

Organic bases contain nitrogen

All important organic bases can be viewed as derivatives of ammonia, NH_3. Recall from Chapter 6 that ammonia is not a flat molecule. Instead, the three hydrogen atoms and the unshared pair of electrons form the four corners of a tetrahedron, as shown in **Figure 15-7.** This unshared pair of electrons gives ammonia the character of a base.

Organic compounds in which one or more organic groups replace the hydrogen atoms in ammonia are called **amines.** Amines, like ammonia, are weak bases that ionize slightly in water. The replacement of one hydrogen atom in ammonia by an organic group does not eliminate ammonia's ability to accept a proton. In fact, an amine can still act as a base even if two (or all three) of ammonia's hydrogen atoms are replaced by organic groups.

Just as ammonia forms the ammonium cation, methylamine forms the methylammonium ion, $CH_3NH_3^+$, and pyridine forms the pyridinium ion, $C_5H_5NH^+$.

$$CH_3NH_2(aq) + H_2O(l) \rightleftharpoons CH_3NH_3^+(aq) + OH^-(aq)$$

Compounds such as pyridine, C_5H_5N, in which the nitrogen atom is incorporated into a ring structure, also act as bases, as indicated by the equation below.

Amines that have only one organic group, such as CH_3NH_2, are called *primary amines*. Similarly, amines that have two hydrogen atoms replaced by two organic groups are called *secondary* amines. Finally, *tertiary* amines contain a nitrogen atom that is bonded to three organic groups. Pyridine is an example of a tertiary amine.

CONCEPT CHECK

1. Write an equation for the dissociation of the strong base $Ca(OH)_2$.
2. Write an equation showing how aniline, $C_6H_5NH_2$, acts as a weak base when dissolved in water.
3. Does ammonia still act like a weak base even when its hydrogen atoms are replaced by organic groups? Explain.

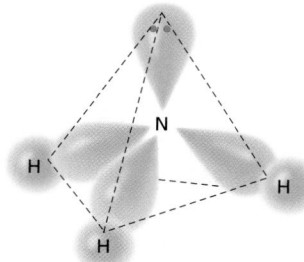

FIGURE 15-7 ▲

Ammonia and organic amines are classified as bases because the nitrogen atom has an unshared pair of electrons that can accept a hydrogen ion from an acid.

amine

an organic compound that contains a nitrogen atom and that can be considered a derivative of ammonia

TEACHING TIP

Nonbonding Electrons Draw a Lewis dot diagram of ammonia on the board. One by one, replace the hydrogens with small hydrocarbon chains. Point out that nitrogen retains its nonbonding pair of electrons, giving it the ability to accept a proton regardless of the hydrocarbon substitutions.

COMMON MISCONCEPTION

Reagent bottles of aqueous ammonia solution are sometimes labeled "NH_4OH" or "ammonium hydroxide." These labels are now considered to be misleading because ammonia ionizes only to a slight extent in water to form NH_4^+ and OH^- ions. The bulk of the NH_3 in solution remains in the molecular form. Newer reagent bottles are labeled "$NH_3(aq)$" or "aqueous ammonia." If you have older bottles in the laboratory, remind students of the true nature of the solution inside.

ANSWERS

CONCEPT CHECK

1. $Ca(OH)_2(s) \longrightarrow$
$$Ca^{2+}(aq) + 2OH^-(aq)$$

2. $C_6H_5NH_2(l) + H_2O(l) \rightleftharpoons$
$$C_6H_5NH_3^+(aq) + OH^-(aq)$$

3. Yes, it still acts as a weak base because the nitrogen atom has an unshared pair of electrons and can accept a proton from water.

When acids and bases meet

Dissolving a base in water increases the OH^- ion concentration; dissolving an acid in water increases the H_3O^+ ion concentration. But what happens if a base *and* an acid are added to water? The hydronium ions and hydroxide ions react with each other to form water, as shown by the following equation.

$$H_3O^+(aq) + OH^-(aq) \longrightarrow 2H_2O(l)$$

neutralization reaction

a reaction in which hydronium ions from an acid and hydroxide ions from a base react to produce water molecules

This reaction is called a **neutralization reaction.**

The self-ionization of water

Recall from Chapter 14 that even pure water has a small concentration of hydronium ions. This is a result of the *self-ionization* of water. The self-ionization of water is an equilibrium system; it is modeled in **Figure 15-8** and in the following chemical equation.

$$2H_2O(l) \rightleftharpoons H_3O^+(aq) + OH^-(aq)$$

You can see from the reaction equation that the self-ionization of pure water produces equal amounts of H_3O^+ ions and OH^- ions. Therefore, the concentrations of these ions in pure water must be equal.

$$[OH^-] = [H_3O^+]$$

Experiments show that in pure water at 25°C, the concentrations of H_3O^+ ions and OH^- ions are equal to 1.00×10^{-7} mol/L.

Recall from Chapter 14 that an equilibrium constant, K_{eq}, can be calculated for a reaction that reaches equilibrium. Because the self-ionization of water is an equilibrium reaction, the equilibrium constant for this reaction, called K_w, can be calculated as follows.

$$K_w = [H_3O^+][OH^-] = (1.00 \times 10^{-7})(1.00 \times 10^{-7})$$
$$K_w = 1.00 \times 10^{-14}$$

This new constant, K_w, is called the ionic product constant of water or the *autoionization constant* for water. Note that K_w has no unit.

In dilute solutions of acids and bases at 25°C, the product of $[H_3O^+]$ and $[OH^-]$ must equal 1.00×10^{-14}. Because K_w is a constant, once you know the concentration of either the H_3O^+ ions or the OH^- ions in a solution, you can easily find the concentration of the other.

▼ **FIGURE 15-8**

Two water molecules can react to produce a hydronium ion and a hydroxide ion.

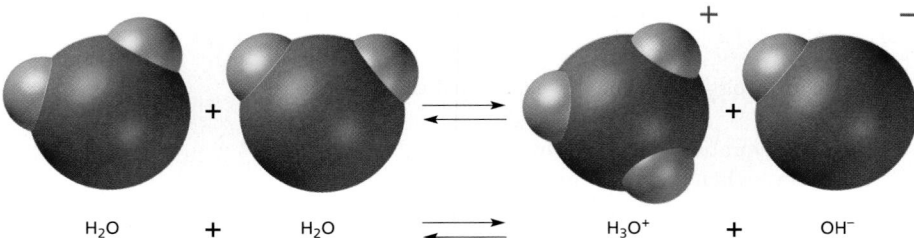

Water molecule		Water molecule		Hydronium ion		Hydroxide ion
H_2O	+	H_2O		H_3O^+	+	OH^-

SAMPLE PROBLEM 15A Determining [OH⁻] using K_w

What is [OH⁻] in a 3.00×10^{-5} M solution of HCl?

1 List what you know
- Concentration of HCl solution = 3.00×10^{-5} M
- [OH⁻] = ? M

2 Set up the problem
- Because HCl is a strong acid, 1 mol of HCl produces 1 mol of H_3O^+.

$$[H_3O^+] = 3.00 \times 10^{-5} \text{ M}$$

- Use the ion product of water to calculate the concentration of OH⁻ ions.

$$K_w = [H_3O^+][OH^-] = 1.00 \times 10^{-14}$$

3 Calculate
- Rearrange the K_w expression and calculate [OH⁻].

$$[OH^-] = \frac{K_w}{[H_3O^+]} = \frac{1.00 \times 10^{-14}}{3.00 \times 10^{-5}} = 3.33 \times 10^{-10} \text{ M}$$

SAMPLE PROBLEM 15A

ADDITIONAL EXAMPLES

a. Determine the hydroxide ion concentration in a 0.00725 M solution of nitric acid, HNO_3.

Ans. 1.38×10^{-12} M

b. What is the hydronium ion concentration in a 5.0×10^{-4} M solution of NaOH?

Ans. 2.0×10^{-11} M

c. The hydronium ion concentration in a solution is determined to be 3.84×10^{-9} M. What is the hydroxide ion concentration of the solution?

Ans. 2.60×10^{-6} M

ANSWERS

SECTION REVIEW

Total recall

1. **a.** weak base
   b. strong base
   c. strong acid
   d. weak acid

2. In aqueous solutions, water is in an ionization equilibrium with hydronium and hydroxide ions. The equilibrium constant is 1×10^{-14}, so if the OH⁻ concentration increases, the H_3O^+ concentration decreases to maintain the equilibrium.

3. Two water molecules react to form H_3O^+ and OH⁻ ions.

Critical thinking

4. It is weak because the acid ionizes only to a slight extent.

SECTION REVIEW

Total recall

1. **Interpreting Tables** Classify the following as either a strong acid, a strong base, a weak acid, or a weak base.
   a. sodium carbonate
   b. potassium hydroxide
   c. hydrobromic acid
   d. hydrofluoric acid

2. Why does the hydronium ion concentration of an aqueous solution decrease when the hydroxide ion concentration increases?

3. Describe the self-ionization of water.

Critical thinking

4. Explain how an acid can be considered weak, even in a concentrated solution.

5. How does [OH⁻] in an aqueous solution of sodium carbonate compare with [OH⁻] in a sodium hydroxide solution of similar concentration?

6. Can you neutralize a strong acid solution by adding an equal volume of a weak base having the same molarity as the acid? Support your position.

Practice problems

7. An aqueous solution is prepared by dissolving 86.5 g of the strong acid HNO_3 in water to make 2.3 L of solution at 298 K. What is [OH⁻] in this solution?

8. At normal body temperature (310 K, 37°C), the ion product of water is 2.50×10^{-14}. What are the concentrations of hydronium ions and hydroxide ions in water at this temperature?

ACIDS AND BASES **549**

5. The [OH⁻] will be less in the solution of Na_2CO_3 because sodium carbonate is a weak base and NaOH is a strong base.

6. Yes. The ionization of the weak base will continue to produce OH⁻ ions as others are used up. This will continue until practically all of the OH⁻ has reacted with H_3O^+.

7. $[H_3O^+] = \dfrac{86.5 \text{ g}}{2.3 \text{ L}} \times \dfrac{1 \text{ mol}}{63.02 \text{ g}} = 0.60 \text{ M}$;

$[OH^-] = \dfrac{K_w}{[H_3O^+]} = 1.7 \times 10^{-14}$ M

8. $[H_3O^+] = [OH^-] = \sqrt{2.50 \times 10^{-14}} = 1.58 \times 10^{-7}$ M

Section 15-2

LESSON WARM-UP

Discussion Strategy When students come into class, have stoppered 250 mL reagent bottles or stoppered flasks of concentrated aqueous ammonia solution and concentrated HCl a few inches apart. Draw students' attention to the bottles and their contents. Remove the stoppers from both bottles simultaneously, and leave them open for no more than 10 seconds. Students should see a white cloud of NH_4Cl form.

Inform the students that they have witnessed a reaction between an acid and a base but that no H_3O^+ ions or OH^- ions were involved. Write the chemical equation on the board, and point out that HCl acts as a proton donor to NH_3, the proton acceptor.

Wear goggles, gloves, and a lab apron during the demonstration. Use a working fume hood when preparing the bottles or flasks.

VISUAL STRATEGY

Figure 15-9 Ask students to interpret the ionization of HCl in water in Brønsted-Lowry terms. Ask them to identify the proton acceptor (H_2O), which acts as a base.

TEACHING TIP

Introducing Brønsted-Lowry Bases Students encounter the Brønsted-Lowry definition of a base on page 552, but you may wish to introduce it here because the donation of a proton requires that the proton be accepted by another species, a Brønsted-Lowry base.

Can the strengths of acids and bases be quantified?

OBJECTIVES

▶ *State* the Brønsted-Lowry definitions of an acid and a base.

▶ *Differentiate* between monoprotic, diprotic, and triprotic acids.

▶ *Write* chemical equations showing how an amphoteric species can behave as both an acid and a base.

▶ *Identify* conjugate acid-base pairs.

▶ *Calculate* K_a from the hydronium ion concentration of a weak acid solution.

Brønsted-Lowry classification

The definition of an acid that was given on page 542 is a modern version of the one proposed by Arrhenius in the late nineteenth century. The Arrhenius definition of acids has several drawbacks, one of which is that it applies only to aqueous solutions. HCl is an acid whether it is in the form of a pure gas or in a water solution. Another drawback is that the Arrhenius definition cannot clearly classify species that can increase or decrease $[H_3O^+]$, depending on the conditions.

Acids donate protons

In 1923, a broader definition of *acid* was independently proposed by the Danish chemist Johannes Brønsted and the British scientist Thomas Lowry. A **Brønsted-Lowry acid** is any molecule or ion that can transfer a *proton*—a hydrogen atom nucleus—to another species. The transfer of a proton from an acid to water is shown in **Figure 15-9**.

Because all of the Arrhenius acids you have studied so far donate a proton (hydrogen ion) to a water molecule to form a hydronium ion, they are included in the Brønsted-Lowry definition of an acid. Sulfuric acid, H_2SO_4, is one example.

$$H_2SO_4(l) + H_2O(l) \longrightarrow H_3O^+(aq) + HSO_4^-(aq)$$

Brønsted-Lowry acid

any ion or molecule that can donate a proton to another species

▶ **FIGURE 15-9**

The ionization of an HCl molecule in water illustrates the transfer of a proton from HCl to H_2O to form a hydronium ion, H_3O^+.

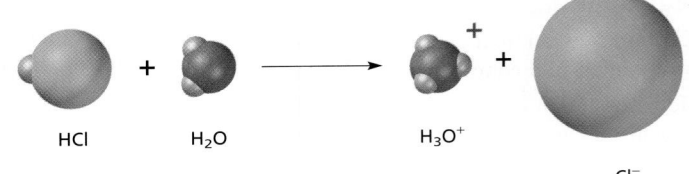

HCl H_2O H_3O^+ Cl^-

GRAPHIC ORGANIZER

Distinguishing Brønsted-Lowry Acids and Bases

Brønsted-Lowry acids and bases

B-L acids — *donate a proton* — to water → forming $H_3O^+(aq)$ (Arrhenius acid)

to a base (not H_2O) → conjugate base

B-L bases — *accept a proton* — from an acid (not H_2O) → conjugate acid

from water → leaving OH^- (aq) (Arrhenius base)

This diagram considers only molecular substances. It does not include ionic hydroxides.

The hydrogen sulfate ion, HSO_4^-, is also a Brønsted-Lowry acid because it too can donate a proton to a water molecule.

$$HSO_4^-(aq) + H_2O(l) \rightleftharpoons H_3O^+(aq) + SO_4^{2-}(aq)$$

Note that a Brønsted-Lowry acid is simply a proton donor. Nothing requires that the proton be transferred to water. The following reaction between HSO_4^- and CO_3^{2-} equally establishes hydrogen sulfate's role as a proton donor and therefore an acid.

$$HSO_4^-(aq) + CO_3^{2-}(aq) \rightleftharpoons HCO_3^-(aq) + SO_4^{2-}(aq)$$

Some acids can donate more than one proton

Many common acids donate only *one* proton per molecule. For this reason, such acids are called **monoprotic acids.** Nitric acid, shown in **Figure 15-10a,** is a typical monoprotic acid; it reacts with water according to the following equation.

$$HNO_3(l) + H_2O(l) \longrightarrow H_3O^+(aq) + NO_3^-(aq)$$

Acids that donate more than one proton per molecule are called *polyprotic acids.* For example, each molecule of sulfuric acid, H_2SO_4, shown in **Figure 15-10b,** has two ionizable hydrogen atoms and can donate *two* protons. Therefore, H_2SO_4 is a **diprotic acid.** In the reaction between H_2SO_4 and water, the two hydronium ions produced are formed in two distinct steps. The first step generates one hydronium ion and a hydrogen sulfate ion, HSO_4^-.

$$H_2SO_4(l) + H_2O(l) \longrightarrow H_3O^+(aq) + HSO_4^-(aq)$$

In the second step, the hydrogen sulfate anion donates a proton to form a second hydronium ion and a sulfate ion, SO_4^{2-}.

$$HSO_4^-(aq) + H_2O(l) \rightleftharpoons H_3O^+(aq) + SO_4^{2-}(aq)$$

Similarly, phosphoric acid, H_3PO_4, shown in **Figure 15-10c,** is a **triprotic acid,** an acid molecule that can donate *three* protons.

monoprotic acid

an acid that can donate one hydrogen ion per molecule

diprotic acid

an acid that can donate two hydrogen ions per molecule

triprotic acid

an acid that can donate three hydrogen ions per molecule

TEACHING TIP

Vocabulary Strategy Help students link *-protic* in the words *polyprotic, monoprotic,* and similar words to the word *proton.* Help them understand that the words indicate the number of protons an acid can donate to a base.

COMMON MISCONCEPTION

Students may wonder how H_2SO_4 qualifies as a strong acid if its ionization in water is an equilibrium process like that of CH_3COOH. Help students understand that the first ionization of H_2SO_4 proceeds nearly 100%, like that of HCl, and that H_2SO_4 is therefore a strong acid. The resulting HSO_4^- ion acts as a weak acid because it ionizes only partially to H_3O^+ and SO_4^{2-} ions. Stress to students that the product of each ionization of a polyprotic acid is considered to be a new acid if it can donate another proton.

FIGURE 15-10 ▼

a Nitric acid is a monoprotic acid. It has only one ionizable hydrogen atom per molecule.

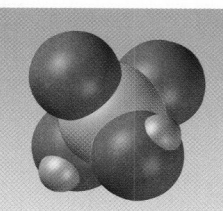

b Sulfuric acid is a diprotic acid. Each of its molecules can form two hydronium ions when dissolved in water.

c Both sulfuric and phosphoric acids are polyprotic. Phosphoric acid is triprotic. It has three ionizable hydrogen atoms.

ACIDS AND BASES 551

RESOURCE LINK

ChemFile Lab D
Consumer Lab
Have students do Experiment 14: *Acids and Bases: Lemon Cheese.*

TEACHING TIP

Demonstration If you did not do the short demonstration described in the Lesson Warm-up on page 550, you may wish to present it now as an introduction to Brønsted-Lowry bases.

DISCUSSION STRATEGY

Write the full equation for the neutralization reaction HCl + NaOH $\longrightarrow$ NaCl + H$_2$O. Have students rewrite the equation in ionic form and reduce it to the net ionic equation, H$_3$O$^+$ + OH$^-$ $\longrightarrow$ 2H$_2$O. Ask students to analyze the equation and identify the acid (H$_3$O$^+$) and base (OH$^-$) in Brønsted-Lowry terms as proton donor and acceptor. Compare students' responses with the original equation in order to stress the idea that in an aqueous neutralization reaction, the acid is H$_3$O$^+$ and the base is OH$^-$ regardless of the substances that produced the ions.

▲ FIGURE 15-11

Although acetic acid has four hydrogen atoms, only the one shown in red ionizes in water.

Brønsted-Lowry base

any atom, ion, or molecule that can accept a proton from another species

It would be easy to assume that the number of protons an acid molecule can donate equals the number of hydrogen atoms that it contains. However, this is not always the case. For example, acetic acid has four hydrogen atoms, but it is monoprotic. Only the hydrogen atom that is part of the carboxyl group is ionized in water.

Bases accept protons

As you might expect, a **Brønsted-Lowry base** is any atom, ion, or molecule that receives a proton from another species. Chemists say that acids *donate* protons and bases *accept* them. Ammonia is a typical base. It ionizes in aqueous solution by accepting a proton from water, as shown by the following equation.

$$NH_3(aq) + H_2O(l) \rightleftharpoons NH_4^+(aq) + OH^-(aq)$$

Again, notice that the Brønsted-Lowry definition of a base, unlike that of Arrhenius, does not mention water. For example, ammonia does not have to react in aqueous solution to qualify as a Brønsted-Lowry base. Even in the gas phase ammonia accepts a proton from hydrogen chloride, as shown in **Figure 15-12**. This reaction produces the ionic compound NH$_4$Cl, which is composed of NH$_4^+$ and Cl$^-$ ions.

$$HCl(g) + NH_3(g) \longrightarrow NH_4Cl(s)$$

► FIGURE 15-12

HCl(*g*) and NH$_3$(*g*) that have each escaped from aqueous solution combine to form a cloud of solid ammonium chloride.

																		18 8A
1 1A			Basic oxide															
	2 2A		Acidic oxide							13 3A	14 4A	15 5A	16 6A	17 7A		
Li_2O	BeO		Amphoteric oxide								B_2O_3	CO_2	N_2O_5		OF_2	
Na_2O	MgO	3 3B	4 4B	5 5B	6 6B	7 7B	8	9 —8B—	10	11 1B	12 2B	Al_2O_3	SiO_2	P_4O_{10}	SO_3	Cl_2O_7
K_2O	CaO											Ga_2O_3	GeO_2	As_2O_5	SeO_3	Br_2O_7
Rb_2O	SrO											In_2O_3	SnO_2	Sb_2O_5	TeO_3	I_2O_7
Cs_2O	BaO											Tl_2O_3	PbO_2	Bi_2O_5	PoO_3	At_2O_7

FIGURE 15-13 ▲

Periodic trends determine whether an element will form a basic, acidic, or amphoteric oxide.

Some species are both acids and bases

Is water an acid or a base? Water can act as an acid by donating a proton, and it can act as a base by accepting a proton.

$$H_2O(l) + H_2O(l) \rightleftharpoons OH^-(aq) + H_3O^+(aq)$$

Therefore, water is both an acid and a base.

A species that can act as either an acid or a base is described as **amphoteric.** The hydrogen carbonate ion is an example of an amphoteric species. It behaves as an acid when it reacts with a hydroxide ion, as shown by the following equation.

$$HCO_3^-(aq) + OH^-(aq) \rightleftharpoons CO_3^{2-}(aq) + H_2O(l)$$

But it behaves as a base in the presence of an acid such as formic acid, HCOOH.

$$HCOOH(aq) + HCO_3^-(aq) \rightleftharpoons HCOO^-(aq) + H_2CO_3(aq)$$

Each base has a conjugate acid, and each acid has a conjugate base

Look again at the equation for the reversible reaction of ammonia, NH_3, with water.

$$\underset{\text{base}}{NH_3(aq)} + \underset{\text{acid}}{H_2O(l)} \rightleftharpoons NH_4^+(aq) + OH^-(aq)$$

Water donates a proton to ammonia; it is an acid. Ammonia accepts a proton from water; it is a base. The ammonium ion is what forms when NH_3 has accepted a proton, and the hydroxide ion is what forms when water has lost a proton. Note that this reaction is reversible. It can be written as follows.

$$\underset{\text{acid}}{NH_4^+(aq)} + \underset{\text{base}}{OH^-(aq)} \rightleftharpoons NH_3(aq) + H_2O(l)$$

amphoteric

any molecule or ion that can act as either an acid or a base

Figure 15-13 Students should note that oxides of the alkali metals and of the alkaline earth metals are basic anhydrides because they form ionic hydroxides when hydrated, as in the following equation.

$$K_2O + H_2O \longrightarrow 2KOH$$

Nonmetallic elements form a wide range of oxides that, when hydrated, generally form acids. Sulfurous acid is formed when sulfur dioxide is hydrated, as shown in the following equation.

$$SO_2 + H_2O \longrightarrow H_2SO_3$$

Oxides of borderline elements, such as aluminum, antimony, and zinc, tend to be amphoteric, acting as acids in the presence of strong bases and as bases in the presence of strong acids.

TEACHING TIP

Discussion Strategy The concept of conjugate acids and bases is often confusing to students. Students should note that in Table 15-3 each acid-base pair differs by one proton. Help students understand that if a molecule or ion can donate a proton *to* another species, the resulting molecule or ion can also accept a proton *from* another species to form the original molecule or ion. As an example, write the equation for the ionization equilibrium of HCN on the board. HCN ionizes weakly in water to form hydronium ions and CN^- ions.

$$HCN + H_2O \rightleftharpoons H_3O^+ + CN^-$$

By looking at the left side of the equation, students can see that HCN acts as an acid by donating a proton to H_2O to form H_3O^+. However, the reaction is in equilibrium, and the back-reaction readily occurs. If students look at the right side of the equilibrium, they can see that CN^- acts as a base by accepting a proton from H_3O^+ to re-form HCN.

ANSWERS

CONCEPT CHECK

1. a. forward reaction: acid, H_2O;
base, CH_3NH_2
reverse reaction: acid, $CH_3NH_3^+$;
base, OH^-

b. forward reaction: acid, HSO_4^-;
base, H_2O
reverse reaction: acid, H_3O^+;
base, SO_4^{2-}

2. a. base
b. acid

3. $H_3PO_4 + H_2O \longrightarrow H_3O^+ + H_2PO_4^-$
$H_2PO_4^- + H_2O \longrightarrow H_3O^+ + HPO_4^{2-}$
$HPO_4^{2-} + H_2O \longrightarrow H_3O^+ + PO_4^{3-}$

4. Only the hydrogen in the carboxyl group can ionize to form hydronium ions.

TABLE 15-3		Acids and Their Conjugate Bases	
Acid name	**Acid formula**	**Conjugate base name**	**Conjugate base formula**
Ammonium ion	NH_4^+	ammonia	NH_3
Hydrochloric acid	HCl	chloride ion	Cl^-
Hydrocyanic acid	HCN	cyanide ion	CN^-
Hydrofluoric acid	HF	fluoride ion	F^-
Hydronium ion	H_3O^+	water	H_2O
Nitric acid	HNO_3	nitrate ion	NO_3^-
Nitrous acid	HNO_2	nitrite ion	NO_2^-
Phosphoric acid	H_3PO_4	dihydrogen phosphate ion	$H_2PO_4^-$
Sulfuric acid	H_2SO_4	hydrogen sulfate ion	HSO_4^-

conjugate acid

the acid formed when a base accepts a proton

conjugate base

the base formed when an acid donates a proton

In this reaction, the ammonium ion donates a proton to the hydroxide ion. NH_4^+ is an acid, and OH^- is a base. The ammonium ion is called the **conjugate acid** of the base, ammonia. The hydroxide ion is called the **conjugate base** of the acid, water.

$$NH_3(aq) + H_2O(l) \rightleftharpoons NH_4^+(aq) + OH^-(aq)$$
$$\text{base} \qquad \text{acid} \qquad \text{conjugate acid} \quad \text{conjugate base}$$

By convention, the term *conjugate* is used for the acid and base on the right side of the equation. Every Brønsted-Lowry acid has a conjugate base. **Table 15-3** gives you more examples of acids and their conjugate bases.

CONCEPT CHECK

1. In the following equations, identify which reactant is the Brønsted acid and which reactant is the Brønsted base.
   a. $CH_3NH_2(aq) + H_2O(l) \rightleftharpoons CH_3NH_3^+(aq) + OH^-(aq)$
   b. $HSO_4^-(aq) + H_2O(l) \rightleftharpoons H_3O^+(aq) + SO_4^{2-}(aq)$
2. In the following reactions, identify whether H_2O behaves as a Brønsted acid or a Brønsted base.
   a. $HClO_4(aq) + H_2O(l) \longrightarrow H_3O^+(aq) + ClO_4^-(aq)$
   b. $H_2O(l) + SO_3^{2-}(aq) \rightleftharpoons HSO_3^-(aq) + OH^-(aq)$
3. Phosphoric acid, H_3PO_4, can donate three hydrogen ions in three distinct steps. Write an equation for each of these three ionization steps.
4. Acetic acid, CH_3COOH, is a weak monoprotic acid. Why is it classified as a monoprotic acid even though it contains four hydrogen atoms?

Weak acids and bases

Consider the reaction represented by the following equation, in which one arrow is longer than the other.

$$A(aq) + B(aq) \rightleftharpoons C(aq) + D(aq)$$

Recall from Chapter 14 that chemists say the forward reaction in this example is *favored*. When the reaction reaches equilibrium, the products C and D will be abundant and at least one reactant will be scarce.

Some acids are better proton donors than others

Reconsider the reaction of formic acid, HCOOH, with the hydrogen carbonate ion. The forward reaction is favored.

$$\underset{\text{acid}}{HCOOH(aq)} + HCO_3^-(aq) \rightleftharpoons HCOO^-(aq) + \underset{\text{acid}}{H_2CO_3(aq)}$$

If you mix equal amounts of all four of the species in this equation—formic acid, hydrogen carbonate ion, formate ion, and carbonic acid—you will find that after mixing, the concentrations of $HCOO^-$ and H_2CO_3 will increase at the expense of HCOOH and HCO_3^-. Because HCOOH is more likely to lose a hydrogen atom than H_2CO_3 is, HCOOH, shown in **Figure 15-14,** is the stronger acid.

Some bases accept protons more readily than others

Now look at the same reaction from the standpoint of the bases.

$$HCOOH(aq) + \underset{\text{base}}{HCO_3^-(aq)} \rightleftharpoons \underset{\text{base}}{HCOO^-(aq)} + H_2CO_3(aq)$$

Both HCO_3^- and $HCOO^-$ are weak bases; therefore, both can accept a proton. But when all four species are mixed in equal concentrations, it

FIGURE 15-14 ▼

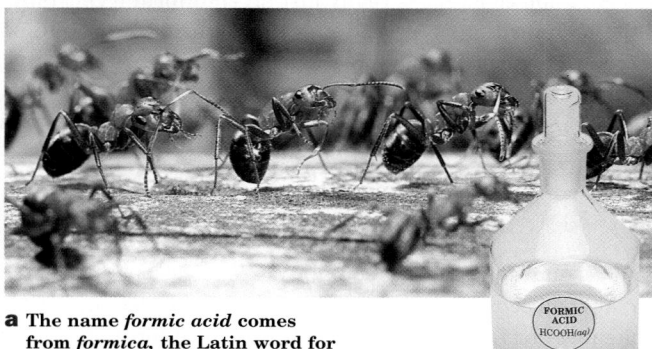

a The name *formic acid* comes from *formica*, the Latin word for "ant." Some species of ants produce this acid and inject it into their victims when they bite.

FORMIC ACID
HCOOH(aq)

b Formic acid was first isolated by distillation from ants in 1670.

c If you are bitten by ants, your body will eventually neutralize the acidity of the formic acid with bases, mainly the hydrogen carbonate ion, HCO_3^-, in your blood. A model of formic acid is shown.

ACIDS AND BASES 555

RESOURCE LINK

ChemFile Lab D
Consumer Lab
Have students do Experiment 16: *Titration of Aspirin.*

ChemFile Teaching Resources CD-ROM
Supplemental Reading Projects
Assign the guided reading worksheets for the article "Chemistry and Physics in the Kitchen" for cross-curricular connections to language arts.

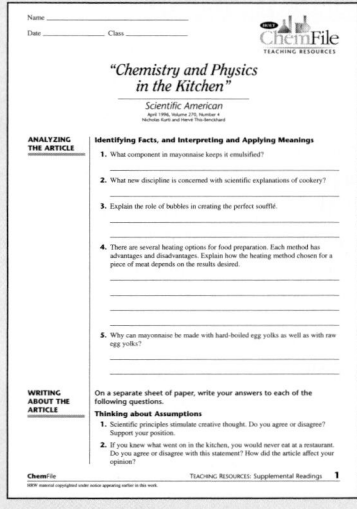

Vinegar consists of about a 5% solution of acetic acid. This gives vinegar its sour taste.

Water, H₂O

Acetate ion, CH₃COO⁻

Acetic acid, CH₃COOH

Hydronium ion, H₃O⁺

TEACHING TIP

Discussion Strategy Help students understand the italicized statement by providing extra examples, such as nitric acid and potassium hydroxide. First look at the ionization of HNO₃. Recall that H_2O can act as both a proton donor (acid) and a proton acceptor (base). In this case it acts as a base.

$$\underset{\text{strong acid}}{HNO_3} + \underset{\text{weak acid/base}}{H_2O} \longrightarrow$$

$$\underset{\text{strong acid}}{H_3O^+} + \underset{\text{weak base}}{NO_3^-}$$

The conjugate base of HNO₃ is NO_3^-. Nitric acid is strong because it loses a proton readily, even to a weak base like H_2O. Therefore, the conjugate base of nitric acid, the nitrate ion, has very little tendency to regain (accept) a proton, and thus NO_3^- is a very weak base.

What happens when the nitric acid solution is combined with a KOH solution, which consists of K^+, OH^-, and H_2O?

$$\underset{\text{strong acid}}{H_3O^+} + \underset{\text{weak base}}{NO_3^-} + K^+ + \underset{\text{strong base}}{OH^-} \longrightarrow$$

$$2H_2O + K^+ + NO_3^-$$

In this mixture, OH^- is a much better proton acceptor (stronger base) than NO_3^-, so it reacts with H_3O^+, leaving NO_3^- as a spectator ion. Note that H_2O is the weak conjugate acid of the strong base OH^- and the weak conjugate base of the strong acid H_3O^+.

VISUAL STRATEGY

Table 15-4 Students should note that the strong acids HCl, HClO₃, HBr, H₂SO₄, and HNO₃ are not included in the table because they ionize almost completely in water (true for only the first ionization of H₂SO₄). Their acid form in aqueous solution is H_3O^+, which is the strongest acid species that can exist in aqueous solution. If a stronger acid is added, it will simply protonate more water molecules, forming more H_3O^+.

is the hydrogen carbonate ion, HCO_3^-, that accepts the proton more readily. The formate ion, $HCOO^-$, is a weaker base and therefore cannot compete with HCO_3^-.

The formate ion, $HCOO^-$, is the conjugate base of formic acid, and carbonic acid, H_2CO_3, is the conjugate acid of the hydrogen carbonate ion. You know that of the two acids, formic acid is the stronger acid. You also know that the hydrogen carbonate ion is the stronger of the two bases. This leads to a very important conclusion. *In an acid/base reaction, the conjugate base of the stronger acid is the weaker base, and the conjugate acid of the stronger base is the weaker acid.*

K_a is the acid-ionization constant

It is possible not only to compare the strengths of acids and bases qualitatively, as you have seen, but also to express these strengths quantitatively. The equilibrium constant of the ionization of a weak acid in water is known as the **acid-ionization constant** and is symbolized by K_a. The acid-ionization constant is really just an equilibrium constant, K_{eq}, applied to the ionization of an acid in water. Consider the equilibrium established when acetic acid is dissolved in water, as in the vinegar shown in **Figure 15-15**.

$$CH_3COOH(aq) + H_2O(l) \rightleftharpoons H_3O^+(aq) + CH_3COO^-(aq)$$

The equilibrium expression for this reaction is written as follows.

$$K_a = \frac{[H_3O^+][CH_3COO^-]}{[CH_3COOH]} = 1.75 \times 10^{-5}$$

Recall that only solutes appear in equilibrium expressions; solvents, such as water, are omitted. Also remember that K_a is a unitless quantity.

Physical chemists have carefully measured the acid-ionization constants of hundreds of acids. Values for a few of these are reproduced in **Table 15-4**. The arrows on this table illustrate that the conjugate of a stronger acid or base is a weaker base or acid, respectively.

acid-ionization constant

the equilibrium constant for a reaction in which an acid donates a proton to water

TABLE 15-4 Relative Strengths of Acids and Bases

Conjugate acid	Formula	K_a	Conjugate base	Formula
Hydronium ion	H_3O^+	5.53×10^1	water	H_2O
Sulfurous acid	H_2SO_3	1.23×10^{-2}	hydrogen sulfite ion	HSO_3^-
Hydrogen sulfate ion	HSO_4^-	1.02×10^{-2}	sulfate ion	SO_4^{2-}
Phosphoric acid	H_3PO_4	7.08×10^{-3}	dihydrogen phosphate ion	$H_2PO_4^-$
Nitrous acid	HNO_2	6.76×10^{-4}	nitrite ion	NO_2^-
Formic acid	$HCOOH$	1.82×10^{-4}	formate ion	$HCOO^-$
Benzoic acid	C_6H_5COOH	6.31×10^{-5}	benzoate ion	$C_6H_5COO^-$
Acetic acid	CH_3COOH	1.75×10^{-5}	acetate ion	CH_3COO^-
Carbonic acid	H_2CO_3	4.47×10^{-7}	hydrogen carbonate ion	HCO_3^-
Hydrogen sulfite ion	HSO_3^-	6.61×10^{-8}	sulfite ion	SO_3^{2-}
Dihydrogen phosphate ion	$H_2PO_4^-$	6.31×10^{-8}	monohydrogen phosphate ion	HPO_4^{2-}
Hypochlorous acid	$HClO$	2.95×10^{-9}	hypochlorite ion	ClO^-
Ammonium ion	NH_4^+	5.75×10^{-10}	ammonia	NH_3
Hydrogen carbonate ion	HCO_3^-	4.68×10^{-11}	carbonate ion	CO_3^{2-}
Monohydrogen phosphate ion	HPO_4^{2-}	4.47×10^{-13}	phosphate ion	PO_4^{3-}
Water	H_2O	1.81×10^{-16}	hydroxide ion	OH^-

Increasing acid strength (downward arrow on left)

Increasing base strength (downward arrow on right)

SAMPLE PROBLEM 15B   Calculating K_a of a weak acid

A vinegar sample is found to be 0.837 M acetic acid. Its hydronium ion concentration is measured as 3.86×10^{-3} mol/L. Calculate K_a for CH_3COOH.

1 List what you know

- $[CH_3COOH] = 0.837$ M
- $[H_3O^+] = 3.86 \times 10^{-3}$ mol/L
- $K_a = ?$

ACIDS AND BASES   557

ALTERNATIVE ASSESSMENT

Depicting Acidic and Basic Solutions

Have students make drawings to model aqueous solutions of HCl, a strong acid, and HF, a weak acid. Make sure water molecules and hydronium ions are shown correctly and in proportions that contrast the strengths of the two acids.

When the drawings are reasonably accurate, have students write a paragraph contrasting the composition of the two solutions.

Repeat the exercise using KOH, a strong base, and NH_3, a weak base.

ANSWERS

SECTION REVIEW

Total recall

1. a. acid: H_3PO_4; conj. base: $H_2PO_4^-$
base: NO_2^-; conj. acid: HNO_2

b. base: CN^-; conj. acid: HCN
acid: HCO_3^-; conj base: CO_3^{2-}

c. acid: HCN; conj. base: CN^-
base: SO_3^{2-}; conj. acid: HSO_3^-

2. A polyprotic acid is one that has more than one ionizable hydrogen atom and thus can donate more than one proton.

3. Water can act as both an acid and a base, depending on other substances present.

4. HCl can donate a proton in the gas phase to an acceptor, such as NH_3, also in the gas phase.

Critical thinking

5. The reverse reaction is favored because H_3O^+ is a much stronger acid than H_2CO_3.

6. $K_a = \dfrac{[H_3O^+][H_2PO_4^-]}{[H_3PO_4]}$

$K_a = \dfrac{[H_3O^+][HPO_4^{2-}]}{[H_2PO_4^-]}$

$K_a = \dfrac{[H_3O^+][PO_4^{3-}]}{[HPO_4^{2-}]}$

The third expression will have the smallest value.

7. a. If an acid is strong, its conjugate base is weak.

b. If a base is strong, its conjugate acid is weak.

8. 3.52×10^{-3} M H_3O^+

9. $K_a = 1.57 \times 10^{-5}$

---

2 **Set up the problem**

▶ CH_3COOH is monoprotic, so one H_3O^+ is formed for every CH_3COOH that ionizes, and $[CH_3COO^-] = [H_3O^+]$.

▶ Also, $[CH_3COOH]_{final} = [CH_3COOH]_{initial} - [CH_3COO^-]$.

▶ Write the equilibrium expression for K_a.

$$K_a = \frac{[H_3O^+][CH_3COO^-]}{[CH_3COOH]_{final}}$$

3 **Calculate and verify**

▶ Substitute the concentration of each component into the equilibrium expression, and compute K_a.

$$[CH_3COO^-] = [H_3O^+] = 3.86 \times 10^{-3}$$

$$[CH_3COOH]_{final} = 0.837 - 0.00386 = 0.833$$

$$K_a = \frac{[H_3O^+][CH_3COO^-]}{[CH_3COOH]_{final}} = \frac{(3.86 \times 10^{-3})^2}{0.833} = 1.79 \times 10^{-5}$$

▶ The calculated value, $K_a = 1.79 \times 10^{-5}$, is very near the literature value of 1.75×10^{-5} found in Table 15-4. Therefore, the answer is reasonable.

SECTION REVIEW

Total recall

1. In the following reactions, identify and label the conjugate acid-base pairs.

a. $H_3PO_4(aq) + NO_2^-(aq) \rightleftarrows$
$HNO_2(aq) + H_2PO_4^-(aq)$

b. $CN^-(aq) + HCO_3^-(aq) \rightleftarrows$
$HCN(aq) + CO_3^{2-}(aq)$

c. $HCN(aq) + SO_3^{2-}(aq) \rightleftarrows$
$HSO_3^-(aq) + CN^-(aq)$

2. What is meant by *polyprotic acid*?

3. Why is water considered amphoteric?

4. How does Arrhenius's definition fail to classify $HCl(g)$ as an acid?

Critical thinking

5. **Interpreting Tables** Use Table 15-4 to determine which direction is favored in the following reaction.

$$H_2CO_3 + H_2O \rightleftarrows HCO_3^- + H_3O^+$$

6. Write all three K_a expressions for H_3PO_4. Which will have the smallest value?

7. a. What is the relationship between the strength of an acid and the strength of its conjugate base?

b. What is the relationship between the strength of a base and the strength of its conjugate acid?

8. Benzoic acid ionizes to form benzoate ions and hydronium ions. The K_a of benzoic acid is 6.30×10^{-5}. Use the following equation to calculate $[H_3O^+]$ in a 0.200 M solution of benzoic acid.

$$H_2O(l) + C_6H_5COOH(aq) \rightleftarrows$$
$$C_6H_5COO^-(aq) + H_3O^+(aq)$$

9. Butanoic acid, C_3H_7COOH, ionizes in water to form $C_3H_7COO^-$ ions and H_3O^+ ions. When 0.20 mol of the acid is dissolved in 500.0 mL of water, $[H_3O^+]$ of this solution is 2.50×10^{-3} M. Calculate K_a for butanoic acid.

How are acidity and pH related?

OBJECTIVES

▶ **State** the definition of pH, and explain the relationship between pH and H_3O^+ ion concentration.

▶ **Perform** calculations using pH, $[H_3O^+]$, $[OH^-]$, and quanti-

tative descriptions of aqueous solutions.

▶ **Describe** two methods of measuring pH.

▶ **Describe** how a buffer solution is able to resist changes in pH.

Determining pH

You have probably seen commercials in which products such as cosmetics, soaps, or shampoos are described as "pH balanced." In fact, you probably use one of these products every day, just like the student seen in **Figure 15-16.** Maybe you even know that pH has something to do with how acidic or basic a material is and that the pH of pure water is 7.

What do pH values mean?

You know from Sections 15-1 and 15-2 that a solution's hydronium ion concentration measures how acidic or basic the solution is. To better

FIGURE 15-16 ◀

Soap manufacturers sometimes make claims about the pH of their products. The pH value is a measure of how acidic or basic a material is.

ACIDS AND BASES **559**

LESSON WARM-UP

Discussing pH Nearly all students will have heard of pH and are likely to have encountered it in previous science courses. Before starting the section, conduct a short inquiry to gauge students' understanding of the pH concept by asking the following questions: What pH values are typical of acids and bases? What pH is considered neutral? What is the pH of pure water? Have students review the concept of the self-ionization of water, discussed on page 548, to find out why the pH of water is 7.

VISUAL STRATEGY

Figure 15-16 Ask students to find products at home that make pH claims and to bring them in the next day. Make a display of the contributions from all classes.

RESOURCE LINK

ChemFile Lab A
Skills Development
Have students do Experiment 12: *Hydronium Ion Concentration and pH*.

HISTORICAL CONNECTION

Sørensen, a biochemist, introduced the concept of pH in 1909 as a tool to simplify his studies of the effects of hydronium concentration on the activity of enzymes. He refined the idea and presented it in 1923 in his research on dyes that can act as acidity indicators. Chemists did not generally accept the use of the pH scale until the mid-1930s, partly because many older physical, analytical, and inorganic chemists looked with suspicion and disdain on any idea that originated in the realm of biological science or biochemistry.

neutral

describes a solution that contains equal concentrations of hydronium ions and hydroxide ions

pH

the negative logarithm of the hydronium ion concentration in a solution

TABLE 15-5	pH Values at Specified [H₃O⁺]		

Sample	Solution	$[H_3O^+]$(M)	pH
1	0.100 mol HCl in 1.00 L of H_2O	1.00×10^{-1}	1.00
2	0.100 mol NaCl in 1.00 L of H_2O	1.00×10^{-7}	7.00
3	0.100 mol NaOH in 1.00 L of H_2O	1.00×10^{-13}	13.00

understand this relationship between acidity and hydronium ion concentration, consider the three solutions found in **Table 15-5.**

Solution 2 is described as **neutral** because it has equal concentrations of hydronium ions and hydroxide ions. Solution 3 is *basic* because it has a lower concentration of H_3O^+ ions than OH^- ions. Solution 1 is *acidic* because it has a higher concentration of H_3O^+ ions than OH^- ions.

Notice that these three solutions span an immense range of hydronium ion concentrations: the concentration in Solution 1 is a million times more than the concentration in Solution 2 and a trillion times more than that in Solution 3. As you can see, working with hydronium ion concentrations can involve negative exponents or long chains of zeros. To simplify these expressions, chemists have adopted a system devised in 1909 by the Danish chemist Søren Peter Sørensen. Sørensen focused his attention on the magnitude of the power of 10 that results when hydronium ion concentration is expressed in scientific notation. He proposed using the negative of the power of 10 (the negative logarithm) and calling it the **pH** (the letters *p* and *H* come from *power of hydrogen*) of the solution. Using Sørensen's definition for the three solutions previously discussed results in the pH values listed in Table 15-5.

How can you calculate pH from [H₃O⁺]?

Based on Sørensen's definition, the relationship between $[H_3O^+]$ and pH is given by the following mathematical equation.

$$pH = -\log[H_3O^+] = \log(1/[H_3O^+])$$

This equation can be used to determine either the pH or the $[H_3O^+]$, depending on the information given. You can see in Table 15-5 that as the hydronium ion concentration *increases,* the pH *decreases.* The pH decreases because the negative logarithm of a number is the same as the logarithm of the reciprocal of the number, and as a number increases, its reciprocal decreases. For example, a tenfold increase in $[H_3O^+]$ decreases the pH by 1.00, and a thousandfold decrease in $[H_3O^+]$ increases the pH by 3.00.

STUDY SKILLS

USING MNEMONICS

Mnemonic devices are effective tools to aid you in learning chemical concepts. To help you remember which end of the pH range is acidic and which is basic, use the following mnemonic device: the first letter of the alphabet, A (for acid), corresponds to the first number, 0.

DEMONSTRATION 2

pH

Approximate time: 10 minutes

Prepare small samples of the following for pH testing with pH paper: 1 M NaOH in a dropper bottle, household ammonia, milk of magnesia, lake water, 1 M sodium hydrogen carbonate solution, distilled water, milk, rainwater, apple juice, orange juice, vinegar, lemon juice, and 1 M HCl in a dropper bottle. Have students note the range of pH represented by these materials.

Safety
Wear safety goggles and a lab apron.

Disposal
Combine all liquids, and neutralize with 1 M acid or base as appropriate. Pour the neutralized solution down the drain.

HOW TO — Use logarithms in pH calculations

It is easy to find the pH or the $[H_3O^+]$ of a solution by using a scientific calculator. Because calculators differ, check your manual to find out exactly which keys are used for log and antilog functions.

1 Calculate pH from $[H_3O^+]$
- **Key in the value of $[H_3O^+]$.**
  You can but do not have to use scientific notation. To enter the value in scientific notation, key in the first part of the number, then press the exponent key and key in the exponent. If your exponent is negative, you will need to press the sign-change key before you key in the value of the exponent.
- **Press $\boxed{\text{LOG}}$ (the base-10 logarithm key).**
- **Press the sign-change key, which is usually labeled $\boxed{+/-}$.**

2 Calculate $[H_3O^+]$ from pH
- **Key in the pH value.**
- **Change its sign by pressing $\boxed{+/-}$.**
- **Press $\boxed{10^x}$.**
  This key raises 10 to the power of the number displayed on your calculator. With –pH displayed, it gives 10^{-pH}, which equals $[H_3O^+]$.

SAMPLE PROBLEM 15C — Calculating the pH of an acidic solution

What is the pH of a 0.00010 M solution of HCl, a strong acid?

1 List what you know
- Concentration of HCl = 0.00010 M
- pH = ?

2 Set up the problem
- Because HCl is a strong acid, the hydronium ion concentration equals the concentration of the solution.

$$[H_3O^+] = 0.00010 \text{ M} = 1.0 \times 10^{-4} \text{ M}$$

- Write the equation for pH.

$$pH = -\log(1.0 \times 10^{-4})$$

3 Calculate
- Use your calculator to determine the log of 1.0×10^{-4}. A special rule is applied for reporting the log using the correct number of significant figures. Only digits to the right of the decimal count as significant figures. Here, your given value has two significant figures. Therefore, your answer should have two digits to the right of the decimal.

$$pH = -(-4.00) = 4.00$$

ACIDS AND BASES 561

TEACHING TIP

Reviewing Logarithms A short review of logarithms may be useful for students. Point out that the logarithm of a number is the power to which 10 must be raised in order to equal the number.

$$100 = 10^2, \text{ so } \log 100 = 2$$
$$1000 = 10^3, \text{ so } \log 1000 = 3$$
$$0.01 = 10^{-2}, \text{ so } \log 0.01 = -2$$

Ask students to determine the logarithms of 10 000, 100 000, 0.1, 0.001, and 0.000 001.

Logarithms of other numbers are between integers. Show students how the logarithm of 200 is determined. Writing numbers in scientific notation will help students understand the process.

$$200 = 2 \times 10^2$$
$$\log 200 = \log 2 + \log 10^2$$
$$\log 10^2 = 2, \text{ so}$$
$$\log 200 = \log 2 + 2$$
The log of 2 is 0.301, so
$$\log 200 = 0.301 + 2 = 2.301.$$

Point out that 200 is between 100 and 1000, so you would expect log 200 to be between 2 and 3. Ask students to determine the logarithms of 2000, 20 000, 0.2, and 0.002.

HOW TO

ADDITIONAL EXAMPLES

Have students estimate the magnitude of each of the following examples before using a calculator:

a. Determine the logarithm of 3.5×10^{-8}.

Ans. –7.46

b. Determine the logarithm of 0.000644.

Ans. –3.191

c. Determine the antilog of –10.415.

Ans. 3.846×10^{-11}

d. Determine the antilog of –0.499.

Ans. 0.317

ADDITIONAL EXAMPLES

a. What is the pH of a 0.0825 M solution of HBr?

Ans. 1.084

b. Determine the pH of a solution made by diluting 25.00 mL of 1.429 M HCl to 500.00 mL in a volumetric flask.

Ans. 1.1460

c. Determine the H_3O^+ concentration in a solution of pH 8.83.

Ans. 1.48×10^{-9} M

ANSWERS

PRACTICE PROBLEM 15C

1. a. $pH = -\log 0.010 = 2.00$

 b. $pH = -\log (4.7 \times 10^{-2}) = 1.33$

 c. $pH = -\log (3.8 \times 10^{-3}) = 2.41$

 d. $pH = -\log (5.5 \times 10^{-4}) = 3.26$

2. $10^{-2.50} = 0.0032$ M HNO_3

3. $[H_3O^+] = \dfrac{10.0 \text{ mL} \times 2.00 \text{ M}}{500.0 \text{ mL}} =$

 0.0400 M; $pH = -\log 0.0400 = 1.398$

HISTORICAL CONNECTION

Sørensen's decision in 1909 to use the negative logarithm of the H_3O^+ concentration was arbitrary but practical. He was a biochemist dealing with solutions similar to those occurring in and around living things. The H_3O^+ concentration in nearly all such solutions is less than 1 M. Because log 1 = 0, the pH of a 1 M H_3O^+ solution is zero. Consequently, log $[H_3O^+]$ is negative for most natural solutions. To avoid having to write negative numbers, Sørensen decided to make pH the *negative* logarithm of $[H_3O^+]$, thus turning common pH values into positive numbers.

1. Calculate the pH of each of the following solutions.

 a. 0.010 M HNO_3

 b. 4.7×10^{-2} M HBr

 c. 3.85×10^{-3} M HI

 d. 5.5×10^{-4} M HCl

2. What is the concentration of a nitric acid solution with a pH of 2.50?

3. What is the pH of a solution made by diluting 10.0 mL of 2.00 M HCl to 500.0 mL with water?

How does pH relate to K_a and K_w?

You have now calculated the pH of strong acid solutions, but what about the pH of solutions of weak acids? In order to calculate pH information for weak acids, you must find the hydronium ion concentration using the equilibrium expression and the acid-ionization constant. Examine the following example, which uses the weak acid benzoic acid.

$$C_6H_5COOH(aq) + H_2O(l) \rightleftarrows C_6H_5COO^-(aq) + H_3O^+(aq)$$

$$K_a = \frac{[C_6H_5COO^-][H_3O^+]}{[C_6H_5COOH]} = 6.31 \times 10^{-5}$$

By rearranging the above equation, and given the appropriate concentration data, you can solve for $[H_3O^+]$ and determine the pH of the solution.

To find the pH of basic solutions, first think of the relationship between the hydronium ion concentration and the hydroxide ion concentration in any solution.

$$K_w = [H_3O^+][OH^-] = 1.00 \times 10^{-14}$$

By rearranging the above expression, you can use the ionic product constant of water to relate pH to $[OH^-]$.

What is the pH of a 0.0136 M solution of $Ba(OH)_2$, a strong base?

1 List what you know

 ▶ Concentration of $Ba(OH)_2$ = 0.0136 M

 ▶ pH = ?

2 Set up the problem

 ▶ Use the given data to determine the concentration of hydroxide ions. Recognize that 1 mol of $Ba(OH)_2$ produces 2 mol of OH^- ions.

 concentration of OH^- = 2 × concentration of $Ba(OH)_2$

 ▶ Use the ionic product of water to calculate $[H_3O^+]$.

 $$K_w = [H_3O^+][OH^-] = 1.00 \times 10^{-14}$$

 ▶ Use the definition of pH to calculate its value.

 $$pH = -\log[H_3O^+]$$

DEMONSTRATION 3

Effects of pH on Chlorophyll Stability

Approximate time: 20 minutes

Add approximately 300 mL of tap water to two 600 mL beakers marked *A* and *B* and heat with Bunsen burners until boiling. Check the pH of each beaker's boiling water.

Slowly add baking soda to the boiling water in beaker B. Evolution of gas may occur rapidly upon addition. Make sure that all baking soda has dissolved completely. Check

the pH of the solution in beaker B. It should be approximately pH 8.

Slowly add frozen green peas to each beaker. After 10 minutes, check the pH of each beaker's water. The tap water in beaker A will be at about pH 6 because of the acids that are liberated from the frozen green peas upon heating. The pH of the solution in

3 Calculate

▶ Calculate [OH⁻].

$$[OH^-] = 2 \times (0.0136) = 0.0272 \text{ M}$$

▶ Solve the K_w equation for $[H_3O^+]$, substitute data into the equation, and calculate $[H_3O^+]$.

$$[H_3O^+] = \frac{K_w}{[OH^-]} = \frac{1.00 \times 10^{-14}}{0.0272} = 3.68 \times 10^{-13} \text{ M}$$

▶ Determine pH, and round your answer to the correct number of significant figures.

$$pH = -\log(3.68 \times 10^{-13})$$
$$pH = -(-12.435) = 12.435$$

PRACTICE PROBLEMS

1. What is the pH of a 0.00256 M KOH solution?

2. Calculate the pH of a 1.00 L solution made by dissolving 1.40 g of NaOH in water.

3. Determine the pH of human blood in which [OH⁻] is 2.60×10^{-7} M.

How is pH measured?

There are two ways to measure pH. The first method is quick and convenient but not particularly accurate. The second is accurate but more complicated and more expensive than the first.

The first method relies on the fact that certain dyes, called **indicators,** have different colors in solutions of different pH. Thymol blue is an example of an indicator. It is yellow in solutions with a pH between 3 and 8 and blue in solutions with a pH of 10 and above. In solutions with a pH between 8 and 10, thymol blue exhibits shades of green. **Figure 15-17** shows the structures of the yellow and blue forms of this dye. The yellow form is a weak acid with an acid-ionization constant around 1.0×10^{-9}, and the blue form is its conjugate base.

indicator

dye that changes to different colors in solutions of different pH

FIGURE 15-17 ▼

The indicator thymol blue is yellow in neutral and acidic solutions. As the OH⁻ concentration of the solution increases, the indicator turns blue.

SAMPLE PROBLEM 15D

ADDITIONAL EXAMPLES

a. What is the pH of a 0.0050 M NaOH solution?

   Ans. 11.70

b. Determine the H_3O^+ concentration of a 0.0208 M solution of $Ca(OH)_2$.

   Ans. 2.404×10^{-13} M

c. What is the OH⁻ concentration of a solution of pH 10.480?

   Ans. 3.02×10^{-4} M

ANSWERS

PRACTICE PROBLEM 15D

1. $pH = -\log\left(\dfrac{1.00 \times 10^{-14}}{0.00256}\right) = 11.408$

2. $[OH^-] = \dfrac{1.40 \text{ g}}{1.00 \text{ L}} \times \dfrac{1 \text{ mol}}{40.00 \text{ g}} = 0.0350$ M;

   $pH = -\log\left(\dfrac{K_w}{0.0350}\right) = 12.544$

3. $pH = -\log\left(\dfrac{1.00 \times 10^{-14}}{2.60 \times 10^{-7}}\right) = 7.415$

TEACHING TIP

Indicators Are Acids and Bases
Inform students that color indicators themselves are acids and bases. Generally, each indicator has a protonated acid form and a deprotonated basic form. Some require pH values as low as 2 or 3 to remain in the acid form. These indicators provide color changes at low pH values. Others change color at very high pH values of 12 or 13. The color change occurs because these molecules change in electron arrangement when protonated or deprotonated. As little indicator as possible is used in a titration because the indicator itself must be titrated. Therefore, it should be present in insignificant amounts if possible. In very exact work, a correction is made to account for the indicator present.

---

beaker B should remain at about pH 8 because an excess of baking soda was added. Point out to students that the water in beaker A is about 100 times more acidic than the solution in beaker B due to the logarithmic nature of the pH scale.

Carefully place the cooked peas on two white paper plates that have been labeled *A* and *B* for their respective beakers. The peas from beaker B should be much greener than those from beaker A because chlorophyll, the

pigment in most green vegetables, decomposes readily in an acidic environment.

DID YOU KNOW?

Note that the pH of stomach acid (HCl) is about 2. Indigestion can cause a burning sensation when acid from the stomach enters the esophagus, whose lining is not resistant to acid as the lining of the stomach is. When this occurs occasionally, we generally refer to it as heartburn because the resulting pain appears to come from the location of the heart. The action of the acid as a result of continued indigestion or bulimia can permanently damage the tongue, throat, and esophagus. In addition, the acid can damage teeth by dissolving the enamel.

TEACHING TIP

pH Is Logarithmic Stress that the pH scale is a logarithmic scale, so an increase in OH^- ion concentration by a factor of 10 (10^1) results in a pH increase of 1 unit. Likewise, an increase in H_3O^+ concentration by a factor of 10 results in a pH decrease of 1 unit.

QUICKLAB

Analysis

1. Red cabbage juice varies in color from light red at pH 2, through purple at pH 7, and on to green and yellow as pH values increase from about 9 through 14.

2. Results will vary. In general, cleaning products are basic because alkaline solutions are good at removing grease. Products meant to remove water deposits are likely to be acidic.

3. Food products are more likely to be somewhat acidic. Plants and fruits tend to be naturally acidic, and processed products are generally acidic because keeping the pH low retards growth of bacteria. Another factor is that the taste of basic materials is disagreeable to most people.

▶ **FIGURE 15-18**

The pH of these substances is easily determined by comparing the color the substance turns a strip of pH paper with the color scale on the pH-paper dispenser.

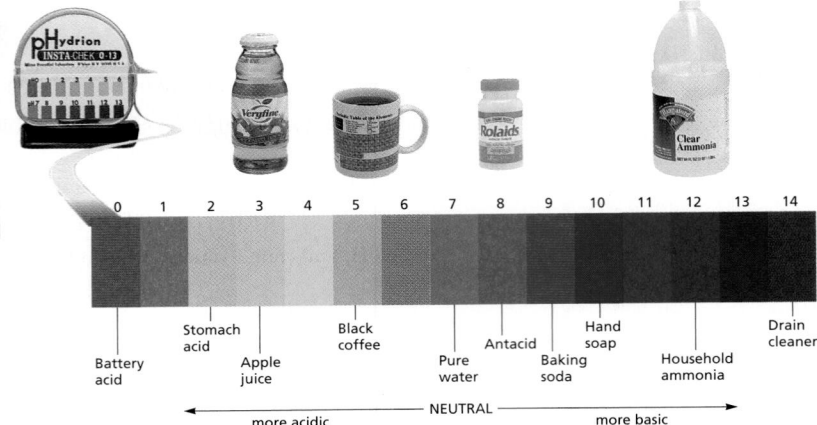

0 1 2 3 4 5 6 7 8 9 10 11 12 13 14

Battery acid · Stomach acid · Apple juice · Black coffee · Pure water · Antacid · Baking soda · Hand soap · Household ammonia · Drain cleaner

◄— more acidic — NEUTRAL — more basic —►

pH meter

an electronic device that measures pH

In addition to thymol blue, many other indicators exist. Every indicator changes color over a certain pH range. Some change at acidic (low) pH values, while others change at basic pH values even greater than 10. Because many different indicators exist, it is possible to prepare mixtures that can give a continuous gradation of color through a wide pH range. The color of a strip of pH paper, as depicted in **Figure 15-18,** can be matched against a standard color chart to easily measure the pH of a solution.

pH meters are more accurate than indicators

The second way to measure pH is to use a **pH meter,** which measures pH by determining the voltage between two electrodes. A pH meter provides a direct digital reading of the pH of the solution into which the electrodes are dipped. Careful experiments using a pH meter can yield accurate pH readings with a precision of ±0.01. This is a much more exact result than can be obtained by judging the color change of an indicator in solution.

QUICKLAB   **CONSUMER ACTIVITY**

An Acid Among Us

You know that taste and feel are not safe ways to determine whether a substance is an acid or a base, so how can you figure out which household products are acids and which are bases?

Materials red cabbage (cut up), blender, strainer, 500 mL beaker, water, assorted household cleaners and food products, small beakers, spatula

Procedure Use the blender to grind the red cabbage with water. Strain the liquid into the large beaker, and dilute. You now have an indicator. Using your indicator, test the household products. Start with an item that you know is an acid and one that you know is a base.

Analysis
1. What color is the indicator in acidic solution? in basic solution?
2. Are cleaning products more likely to be acidic or basic?
3. Are food products more likely to be acidic or basic?

564 CHAPTER 15

internetconnect

SCiLINKS.
NSTA
TOPIC: Buffers
GO TO: www.scilinks.org
KEYWORD: HW155

CONCEPT CHECK

1. Explain why pH meters provide a more accurate reading of pH values than do indicators.

2. How can pH paper indicate such a wide range of pH values?

3. What color would a solution of thymol blue be if it had a high concentration of hydroxide ions?

SECTION 15-3

ANSWERS

CONCEPT CHECK

1. Some pH meters have a precision of ±0.01 pH units.

2. pH paper contains several indicators that change color at various pH values from low to high.

3. blue

Buffer solutions

You can see in **Table 15-6** that the pH of blood is 7.4. Keeping your blood pH within the very narrow range of 7.35 to 7.45 is crucial to your health. If your pH gets outside the range of 7.35 to 7.45, you will become ill. At a blood pH lower than 7.35, you suffer acidosis. At a blood pH higher than 7.45, you suffer alkalosis. How does your body control the pH of blood within such narrow bounds? It relies on the properties of **buffer solutions**—solutions that resist changes in pH due to the addition of acids or bases. These solutions are said to be *buffered* against changes in pH.

buffer solution

a solution that resists changes in pH

CHEMISTRY INTERACTIVE TUTOR

Module 8: Strong and Weakly Ionized Species, pH, and Titrations
Topic: pH
This engaging tutorial reviews and reinforces the concept of pH through modeling and guided practice.

A buffer has two ingredients

A buffer solution, often simply called a *buffer,* is a solution of a weak acid and its conjugate base in approximately equal amounts. For example, consider a solution made by dissolving 1 mol each of acetic acid, CH_3COOH, and sodium acetate, $NaCH_3COO$, in water. Sodium acetate is a strong electrolyte that ionizes completely in aqueous solution, as shown by the following equation.

$$NaCH_3COO(s) \xrightarrow{\text{H}_2\text{O}} Na^+(aq) + CH_3COO^-(aq)$$

On the other hand, acetic acid is a weak acid that is scarcely ionized at all in water. The ionization of acetic acid, shown by the following equation, reaches equilibrium by forming only very small amounts of H_3O^+ ions and CH_3COO^- ions.

$$CH_3COOH(aq) + H_2O(l) \rightleftharpoons H_3O^+(aq) + CH_3COO^-(aq)$$

Buffered Aspirin
EXTRA STRENGTH
40 Coated Buffered Aspirin Caplets
500 mg each

RESOURCE LINK

IN-TEXT LAB
Skills Development
Have students do Exploration 15C on page 782 to familiarize themselves with acids and bases commonly found at home.

ChemFile Mini-Guide to Problem Solving
Assign Chapter 17: *pH* for additional practice.

FIGURE 15-19 ▲

Many medications are buffered to protect your body from changes in pH that can be harmful.

| TABLE 15-6 | Typical pH Values of Human Body Fluids | | |

Solution	pH	Solution	pH
Gastric juice	1.5	Blood	7.4
Urine	6.0	Tears	7.4
Saliva	6.5	Pancreatic juice	7.9
Milk	6.6	Bile	8.2

ACIDS AND BASES **565**

CHAPTER 17
pH

In 1909, Danish biochemist S. P. L. Sørensen introduced a system in which acidity was expressed as the negative logarithm of the H^+ concentration. In this way, the acidity of a solution having H^+ concentration of 10^{-5} M would have a value of 5. Because the *power* of 10 was now a part of the number, the system was called *pH*, meaning *power of hydrogen*.

Taking the negative logarithm of the hydronium ion concentration will give you a solution's pH as given by the following equation.

$$pH = -log[H_3O^+]$$

Likewise, the value pOH equals the negative logarithm of the hydroxide ion concentration.

$$pOH = -log[OH^-]$$

Water molecules interact with each other and ionize. At the same time, the ions in solution reform molecules of water. This process is represented by the following reversible equation.

$$H_2O(l) + H_2O(l) \rightleftharpoons H_3O^+(aq) + OH^-(aq)$$

In pure water the concentrations of hydroxide ions and hydronium ions will always be equal. These two quantities are related by a term called the *ion product constant for water, K_w.*

$$K_w = [H_3O^+][OH^-]$$

The ion product constant for water can be used to convert from pOH to pH. The following equations derive a simple formula for this conversion. Pure water has a pH of 7. Rearranging the equation for pH, you can solve for the hydronium ion concentration of pure water, which is equal to the hydroxide ion concentration. These values can be used to obtain a numerical value for K_w.

$$K_w = [H_3O^+][OH^-] = [1 \times 10^{-7}][1 \times 10^{-7}] = 1 \times 10^{-14}$$

Rearrange the K_w expression to solve for $[OH^-]$.

$$[OH^-] = \frac{K_w}{[H_3O^+]}$$

Substitute this value into the equation for pOH.

$$pOH = -log\frac{K_w}{[H_3O^+]}$$

pH **197**

FIGURE 15-20

The left-hand beaker in each photo contains a neutral solution. The right-hand beaker contains a solution to which hydrochloric acid has been added.

a When a small amount of HCl is added to a buffered solution, the pH of the solution does not change dramatically.

b When HCl is added to an unbuffered solution, the solution's pH drops significantly. This drop can be seen on the pH meter or in the color change of an indicator.

When additional acetate ions from $NaCH_3COO$ appear in this weak acid solution, the reverse reaction is favored even more strongly, and more acetic acid forms.

$$CH_3COOH(aq) + H_2O(l) \xrightleftharpoons{} H_3O^+(aq) + CH_3COO^-(aq)$$

This change in equilibrium is in accordance with Le Châtelier's principle, which was discussed in Chapter 14. In that chapter you also learned about the *common-ion effect,* of which this is also an example. The acetate ion is the common ion in this case, and almost all of the acetate ions in the solution are supplied by the sodium acetate because sodium acetate ionizes much more completely than acetic acid does. As a result of the change in equilibrium, the concentration of $CH_3COO^-(aq)$ is practically equal to the concentration of dissolved $NaCH_3COO$. Likewise, the amount of $CH_3COOH(aq)$ will be very close to the amount of CH_3COOH that was originally dissolved.

How does a buffer control pH?

Why is it that a buffered solution resists changes in pH? Look at what happens to the acetic acid–sodium acetate solution when a small amount of strong acid is added. Remember that H_3O^+ ions and CH_3COO^- ions can combine to form CH_3COOH, shifting the equilibrium further to the left.

$$CH_3COOH(aq) + H_2O(l) \xrightleftharpoons{} H_3O^+(aq) + CH_3COO^-(aq)$$

As a result, the added H_3O^+ ions are "used up," and the pH changes very little.

Conversely, when a small amount of a strong base is added to the buffer solution, the OH^- ions react with CH_3COOH to produce more acetate ions, shifting the equilibrium to the right. Consequently, the added OH^- ions raise the pH very little.

$$OH^-(aq) + CH_3COOH(aq) \xrightleftharpoons{} H_2O(l) + CH_3COO^-(aq)$$

DEMONSTRATION 4

Buffers in Solution

Approximate time: 10 minutes

1. Make a pH 7 buffer solution by dissolving 6.8 g of KH_2PO_4 in water. Add 295 mL of a 0.1 M KOH solution, and dilute to 1 L.

2. Pour 50 mL of distilled water into a 250 mL beaker, and pour 50 mL of the buffer solution into another beaker. Place the beakers on the overhead projector.

3. Add 3 drops of phenolphthalein indicator to each beaker, and mix well. Using a dropper, add 0.1 M KOH dropwise to both solutions, swirling the beaker after adding each drop. The water solution should change after a few drops, but the buffer solution will require more than 7 mL of the base before a color change occurs.

A solution containing a weak acid and its conjugate base in nearly equal concentrations can absorb added H_3O^+ ions and OH^- ions, thus minimizing pH changes. Now you can understand that when manufacturers of shampoos and antacids boast that their products are buffered, they mean that the products contain substances in solution that can absorb small amounts of acids or bases with a result of little or no change in pH.

The liquid portion of blood is an example of a buffer solution. This buffering system helps keep the pH of blood between 7.35 and 7.45. The buffering system in blood is the weak acid H_2CO_3 (carbon dioxide combined with water) and its conjugate base, the hydrogen carbonate ion, HCO_3^-.

$$H_2CO_3(aq) + H_2O(l) \rightleftarrows H_3O^+(aq) + HCO_3^-(aq)$$

The equilibrium of the buffering system in blood is important to maintaining good health. Many medical conditions can disrupt the equilibrium of this system, resulting in either acidosis or alkalosis, both of which can be serious and even fatal. Uncontrolled diabetes and intoxication are common causes of acidosis and alkalosis, respectively.

SECTION REVIEW

Total recall

1. Explain what is meant by the pH of a solution.

2. Name the two methods of measuring pH.

Critical thinking

3. Explain the relationship between the self-ionization of water and the pH of a neutral solution.

4. Explain what a buffer does. What two ingredients does a buffer contain?

5. The phosphate buffer system consists of the dihydrogen phosphate ion, $H_2PO_4^-$, and the monohydrogen phosphate ion, HPO_4^{2-}. Describe how this system reacts to maintain a constant pH when OH^- ions are added.

6. **Interpreting Graphics** Describe how a benzoic acid–sodium benzoate buffer reacts

with both H_3O^+ and OH^- ions. (Hint: See the formula for benzoic acid on page 562.)

Practice problems

7. One aqueous solution of a base has a pH of 8. A second has a pH of 11. Which solution has the larger concentration of OH^- ions? How many times larger? Which solution has the larger concentration of H_3O^+ ions? How many times larger?

8. An aqueous solution has a pH of 3.10. Determine $[H_3O^+]$ and $[OH^-]$ of this solution.

9. **Interpreting Tables** Refer to Table 15-6 on page 565. Calculate $[H_3O^+]$ and $[OH^-]$ in human saliva.

10. The $[OH^-]$ of apple juice is 3.2×10^{-11} M. Determine its pH.

ANSWERS

SECTION REVIEW

Total recall

1. The pH is the negative logarithm of the H_3O^+ concentration. Strongly acidic solutions have low pH values in the range of 0–2; strongly basic solutions have high pH values in the range of 12–14.

2. Use a pH meter or pH paper.

Critical thinking

3. Pure water self-ionizes to produce a 1×10^{-7} M concentration of H_3O^+ ions. Thus, the pH of pure water is 7, the negative log of 10^{-7}.

4. A buffer resists changes in pH by absorbing added H_3O^+ or OH^- ions. It contains a weak acid and its conjugate base.

5. The OH^- ions react as in the following equation:

$$H_2PO_4^- + OH^- \longrightarrow HPO_4^{2-} + H_2O$$

6. $C_6H_5COOH + OH^- \longrightarrow$
$$C_6H_5COO^- + H_2O$$
$C_6H_5COO^- + H_3O^+ \longrightarrow$
$$C_6H_5COOH + H_2O$$

Practice problems

7. Solution 1: pH = 8; $[OH^-] = 10^{-6}$ M; $[H_3O^+] = 10^{-8}$ M
Solution 2: pH = 11; $[OH^-] = 10^{-3}$ M; $[H_3O^+] = 10^{-11}$ M

The solution of pH 11 has 1000 times the concentration of OH^- ions that the pH 8 solution has. The solution of pH 8 has 1000 times the concentration of H_3O^+ ions that the pH 11 solution has.

8. pH = 3.10; $[H_3O^+] = 10^{-3.10} =$
7.9×10^{-4} M; $[OH^-] = \dfrac{K_w}{[H_3O^+]} =$
1.3×10^{-11} M

9. pH = 6.5; $[H_3O^+] = 10^{-6.5} =$
3×10^{-7} M; $[OH^-] = \dfrac{K_w}{[H_3O^+]} =$
3×10^{-8} M

10. pH $= -\log\left(\dfrac{1.00 \times 10^{-14}}{3.2 \times 10^{-11}}\right) = 3.51$

4. Repeat the demonstration using methyl orange or bromcresol green as the indicator, and add 0.1 M HCl dropwise. Again only a few drops are needed in the water, but several milliliters are needed to change the color in the buffer solution.

Safety
Wear safety goggles and a lab apron.
Students should remain back at least 10 ft.

Disposal
Combine all solutions, and neutralize the mixture with 1 M HCl or 1 M NaOH as appropriate. Pour the neutralized solution down the drain.

The medical term for heartburn is *gastroesophageal reflux.* Its cause is momentary relaxation of the lower esophageal sphincter muscle, which lies at the junction of the esophagus and the stomach. Normally, this muscle keeps the esophagus closed off from the stomach except during swallowing. Occasional heartburn is not unusual, but if the problem occurs continually, it should not be ignored because it can be a symptom of a hiatal hernia, an ulcer, stomach or esophageal cancer, or a neurological disorder.

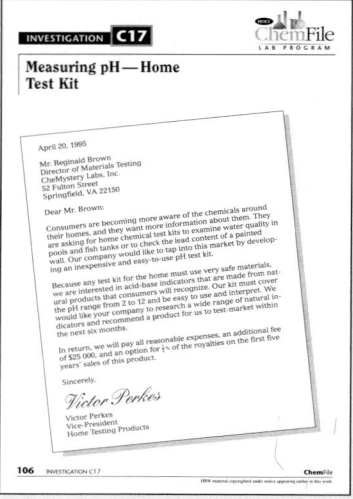

CONSUMER FOCUS

ANTACIDS

Stomach acids and antacids

According to Table 15-6, the pH of gastric juice in the human stomach is 1.5. This strongly acidic environment is essential to activate digestive enzymes that work in the stomach, such as pepsin. Acidity is provided by approximately 0.03 M concentration of hydrochloric acid, HCl(*aq*). Sometimes a person's stomach generates too much acid. This causes the discomfort known as heartburn that results when the acid solution is forced into the esophagus. Heartburn can be temporarily relieved by taking an **antacid** to neutralize the excess stomach acid.

Although antacids contain a variety of ingredients, they all contain a base that counteracts stomach acid. The base is either sodium hydrogen carbonate, $NaHCO_3$, calcium carbonate, $CaCO_3$, aluminum hydroxide, $Al(OH)_3$, or magnesium hydroxide, $Mg(OH)_2$.

Dangers of excess metals from antacids

In any antacid, the carbonate, hydrogen carbonate, or hydroxide ion is the base that neutralizes the excess stomach acid. However, the metal in the antacid is also important. Antacids containing $NaHCO_3$ work fastest because $NaHCO_3$ is much more soluble than other antacid substances. Overuse of these antacids, however, can raise the level of sodium ions in the body, just as salt does. Overuse can also seriously disrupt the acid-base balance in your blood.

Because of the risks associated with an excess of sodium, some antacid manufacturers have substituted calcium carbonate, $CaCO_3$, for $NaHCO_3$. But if taken in large amounts, calcium can promote kidney stones. Too much aluminum

ingested from antacid products, such as $Al(OH)_3$, can interfere with the body's absorption of important minerals, such as phosphorus, which is needed to maintain healthy bones. Also, some people believe there is a connection between the ingestion of aluminum ions and Alzheimer's disease. This belief may be misguided because it is not yet known whether aluminum plays a role in the onset of Alzheimer's disease. Excess magnesium from antacids with $Mg(OH)_2$ may pose problems for people with kidney trouble.

You should know the active ingredient in any antacid product before you ingest it, and you should never use an antacid product for more than a few days without consulting a doctor. It is best to avoid the need for an antacid in the first place. You can minimize the production of excess stomach acid by following a healthy diet, avoiding stress, and limiting your consumption of coffee, fatty foods, and chocolate.

What is a titration?

OBJECTIVES

▶ **Write** an ionic equation for a neutralization reaction, and identify its reactants and products.

▶ **Describe** the conditions at the equivalence point in a titration.

▶ **Tell** how a buret is used in a titration.

▶ **Discuss** two methods used to detect the equivalence point in a titration.

▶ **Calculate** the unknown concentration of an acid or base using titration data.

▶ **Explain** how you would select an indicator for an acid-base titration.

Neutralization

The solution of a strong acid, shown in the beaker on the left in **Figure 15-21,** contains a high concentration of hydronium ions—high enough to react with metals such as zinc. The solution of a strong base, shown in the beaker on the right, contains a high concentration of hydroxide ions—high enough to free a grease-clogged drain. But if you mix these two solutions in the correct proportions, you get an aqueous solution that has neither of these properties—it will not react with metals and it cannot unclog a drain. How can you account for this significant change in properties?

The change occurs because large concentrations of $H_3O^+(aq)$ ions and $OH^-(aq)$ ions cannot exist together in the same solution. Upon mixing of

> **internet connect**
>
> **SCiLINKS**
> **NSTA**
> TOPIC: Titration/Indicators
> GO TO: www.scilinks.org
> KEYWORD: HW154

a This beaker contains a solution of nitric acid, a strong acid. It turns pH paper red.

c The reaction produces a sodium nitrate solution, which has a neutral pH of 7.

b This beaker contains a solution of sodium hy-droxide, a strong base. It turns pH paper blue.

LESSON WARM-UP

Discussion Strategy Ask students to answer the question posed at the end of the first paragraph. To help them analyze the question, ask what is in the acid solution that reacts with metals (H_3O^+). Ask what is in the base solution that reacts with grease (OH^-). Finally, ask what happens to these ions when the solutions are combined. *(They react to form water.)*

VISUAL STRATEGY

Figure 15-21 Help students avoid a misconception by informing them that this neutralization of a strong acid, HNO_3, with a strong base, NaOH, is complete at pH 7 but that not all acid-base reactions reach completion at pH 7.

RESOURCE LINK

ChemFile Lab A
Skills Development
Have students do Experiment 13: *Titration with an Acid and a Base.*

Chloride ion, Cl^- · Hydronium ion, H_3O^+ · Water molecule, H_2O · Hydroxide ion, OH^- · Sodium ion, Na^+

▲ **FIGURE 15-22**

When HCl(*aq*) reacts with NaOH(*aq*), the reaction produces NaCl(*aq*). When the water is evaporated, pure sodium chloride salt is left.

the solutions, most of the hydronium ions from the acid solution and most of the hydroxide ions present in the base solution combine to form water in a neutralization reaction.

$$H_3O^+(aq) + OH^-(aq) \longrightarrow 2H_2O(l)$$

All strong acid–strong base neutralizations are the same reaction

When strong acid and strong base solutions having equal amounts of H_3O^+ and OH^- ions are mixed, as in the third beaker in **Figure 15-22**, virtually all of the hydronium and hydroxide ions react to form water. The H_3O^+ and OH^- ions remaining have concentrations of 1×10^{-7} M each, as they do in pure water. The pH of the solution will be 7.

The resulting solution contains only spectator ions. For example, suppose that the strong acid is nitric acid, HNO_3, which in aqueous solution consists of hydronium ions and nitrate ions, NO_3^-, and that the base is sodium hydroxide, which in aqueous solution consists of hydroxide ions and sodium ions, Na^+. After the contents of the two beakers are combined, the resulting solution will contain water, NO_3^- ions, and Na^+ ions. This is just an aqueous solution of sodium nitrate. You can prepare the same solution by dissolving the *salt* sodium nitrate, $NaNO_3$, in water. As you can see, the neutralization of an Arrhenius acid by an Arrhenius base in aqueous solution produces a salt and water.

$$acid + base \longrightarrow salt + water$$

No matter which strong acid and strong base are used, every neutralization reaction in aqueous solution is the same—the ionic reaction between H_3O^+ ions and OH^- ions to form water. Only the spectator ions differ.

Principles of titrations

The point at which a neutralization reaction is complete is known as the **equivalence point.** When a strong base is used to neutralize a strong acid, the equivalence point is the point at which the amount of added hydroxide ions exactly equals the amount of hydronium ions originally in solution. At a temperature of 25°C, H_3O^+ and OH^- ions have concentrations of 1.00×10^{-7} M each at the equivalence point, the same concentrations that they have in pure water.

The operation of gradually adding one solution to another to reach an equivalence point is known as a **titration.** The How To feature on pages 574–575 of this section will show you how to use burets to carry out a titration. If an acid is to be titrated with a base, one buret may be used to measure the volume of the acid into the titration flask, and a second buret may be used to deliver and measure the volume of **titrant** needed as shown in **Figure 15-23.** In this case, the titrant is the base solution. Titrations can just as well be carried out the other way around, delivering an acid into a base solution. However, you cannot determine the concentration of one solution unless the concentration of the other is known accurately. A **standard solution** is one whose concentration is accurately known, normally because it has previously been used to titrate a precisely weighed mass of a solid acid or base. A standard solution is usually used as the titrant.

equivalence point

the point in a titration when the amount of added base or acid exactly equals the amount of acid or base originally in solution

titration

the operation of gradually adding one solution to another to reach an equivalence point

titrant

the solution added to another solution in a titration

standard solution

a solution whose concentration is accurately known

FIGURE 15-23 ▼

a The How To feature on pages 574–575 of this section will show you how to use burets like those shown here to carry out a titration.

b When reading the liquid level in a buret, you must read the level at the bottom of the meniscus.

ACIDS AND BASES 571

Figure 15-24 Remind students that this curve represents a titration of a strong acid with a strong base. Challenge them to explain why the pH rises so rapidly at the equivalence point. The solution consists of Na^+ ions, NO_3^- ions, and H_2O molecules as well as concentrations of H_3O^+ and OH^- ions of 1×10^{-7} mol/L. The concentration of OH^- in the base being used in the titration is huge compared with the concentration in water. Therefore, a drop or two of base raises the pH by several units.

TEACHING TIP

Changes in Concentration Ask students to describe the composition of the titration mixture represented by the graph at pH 1 and at pH 7.

Strong Acid Titrated with Strong Base

▲ **FIGURE 15-24**

When 100.0 mL of this nitric acid solution is titrated with a 1.000 M NaOH solution, the equivalence point occurs after the addition of 38.6 mL of the base.

transition range
the pH range through which an indicator changes color

Detecting the equivalence point

A titration is accurate only if it ends at the equivalence point, but how will you know when that point arrives? Several methods are available for detecting the equivalence point. As the two most common techniques are explained, assume that a strong acid is being titrated with a strong base, which means that the acid is in the flask and the base is the titrant being added from the buret.

One method of detecting the equivalence point is to use a pH meter, which you read about in Section 15-3. A pH meter can be used to monitor changes in H_3O^+ concentration. The pH values obtained during a titration can be used to generate a titration curve such as the one shown in **Figure 15-24**. Notice in the graph that the equivalence point, the place of most rapid change, corresponds to pH 7, the point of neutralization for a strong acid–strong base reaction.

The oldest method of detecting the equivalence point is to use an indicator. An indicator exhibits one color at low pH values and another color at high pH values. You read about indicators in Section 15-3.

Table 15-7 lists a few of the indicators that chemists have evaluated. All indicators have a **transition range,** often about 2 pH units wide. At pH values within its transition range, an indicator exists partially in its acid form and partially in its base form. As a result, its color is intermediate

| TABLE 15-7 | Transition Ranges of Some Indicators |

Indicator name	Acid color	Transition range (pH)	Base color
Thymol blue	red	1.2–2.8	yellow
Methyl orange	red	3.1–4.4	orange
Litmus	red	5.0–8.0	blue
Bromthymol blue	yellow	6.0–7.6	blue
Thymol blue	yellow	8.0–9.6	blue
Phenolphthalein	colorless	8.0–9.6	red
Alizarin yellow	yellow	10.1–12.0	red

DEMONSTRATION 5

Indicators

Approximate time: 5 minutes

It is advisable to do a trial run of this demonstration to see how deep the resulting color is. If it is too pale, increase the phenolphthalein concentration.

1. The day before class, mix 10 drops of phenolphthalein indicator with 20 mL of distilled water.

2. Make a sign with a saying of your choice on a large piece of white paper using the

indicator-water mixture, and allow the paper to dry.

3. Hang the paper on the wall or chalkboard, and have a bottle of ammonia-based window cleaner on the desktop.

4. Pick up the cleaner and spray the sign. The message should appear in pink letters. Ask students to explain why this

| pH 5 | pH 7 | pH 9 |
| Bromthymol blue | | |

| pH 7 | pH 9 | pH 11 |
| Phenolphthalein | | |

between the acid and base colors. Notice that thymol blue can exist in three different colored forms; therefore, it has two transition ranges.

Which indicator do I choose?

Choosing an indicator for a titration of a strong acid with a strong base is easy. Because the equivalence point occurs at pH 7, you would choose an indicator that has a transition range around this value. The point at which the indicator changes color is the **end point** of a titration. If you choose the right indicator, the end point and the equivalence point will be the same.

Not all titrations have equivalence points at pH = 7.0. When a weak acid is titrated with a strong base, the equivalence point is at a pH greater than 7.0. If a strong acid is titrated with a weak base, the equivalence point is at a pH lower than 7.0. **Figure 15-25** shows how different indicators are effective for different types of titrations.

> **FIGURE 15-25** ▲
>
> **Bromthymol blue changes color between a pH of 6.0 and 7.6. It is ideal for a titration involving a strong acid and a strong base. Phenolphthalein changes color between a pH of 8.0 and 9.6. It is suitable for the titration of a weak acid with a strong base.**

end point

the point in a titration at which the indicator changes color

CONCEPT CHECK

1. What indicators could you use if a solution of HCl, a strong acid, is titrated with a solution of Na_2CO_3, a weak base?
2. Why should an indicator be chosen so that the equivalence point and the end point coincide during a titration?
3. How is the concentration of a standard solution of an acid or a base usually determined?
4. Write the ionic equations for the neutralization reaction that occurs between the following.
   a. HNO_3 and $Ca(OH)_2$
   b. KOH and H_2SO_4
5. If a titration between a weak acid and a strong base has an equivalence point at a pH of 9.5, which indicators could be used to detect the equivalence point of the titration?

💡 DID YOU KNOW?

Because of the large pH change at the equivalence point of a strong acid–strong base titration, the choice of indicator is not as critical as in titrations involving weak acids or bases. Bromthymol blue, thymol blue, and phenolphthalein can all be used.

TEACHING TIP

Explaining Terms Stress to students that the term *end point* is a descriptive, qualitative term pertaining to the color change of an indicator. The term *equivalence point* is quantitative, referring to stoichiometric equivalence between acid and base. The key to an accurate titration is choosing an indicator such that the end point and equivalence point are the same.

ANSWERS

CONCEPT CHECK

1. thymol blue or methyl orange

2. This allows the equivalence point to be determined accurately.

3. by titration with a precisely weighed solid

4. **a.** $2H_3O^+(aq) + 2NO_3^-(aq) + Ca^{2+}(aq) + 2OH^-(aq) \longrightarrow 4H_2O(l) + 2NO_3^-(aq) + Ca^{2+}(aq)$

   b. $K^+(aq) + OH^-(aq) + H_3O^+(aq) + HSO_4^-(aq) \longrightarrow K^+(aq) + HSO_4^-(aq) + 2H_2O(l)$ (first proton)

   $K^+(aq) + OH^-(aq) + H_3O^+(aq) + SO_4^{2-}(aq) \longrightarrow K^+(aq) + SO_4^{2-}(aq) + 2H_2O(l)$ (second proton)

5. Thymol blue and phenolphthalein would be suitable.

Module 8: Strong and Weakly Ionized Species, pH, and Titrations
Topic: Titrations
This engaging tutorial reviews and reinforces titration methods through modeling and guided practice.

happened. Other indicators can be used to add other colors to the sign.

Safety
Wear safety goggles and a lab apron.
Students should remain back at least 10 ft.
Spray cleaner away from students.

Disposal
Throw the sign into the trash.

TEACHING TIP

Reading the Meniscus The meniscus in a buret can sometimes be hard to read, partly because it tends to reflect and refract room lights. To solve this problem, place a piece of nonreflective black tape across the center of a small white card (the size of a business card), leaving part of the white card exposed on both sides of the tape. The tape should be no more than 1 cm in width. A black marker could also be used.

When reading the buret, students should hold the card behind the buret with the black tape running horizontally. The card should be tilted back at about a 45° angle. By moving the card up and down, students can find a position where the image of the black line is reflected by the meniscus, making it appear black against the white background of the card. When this position is found, the bottom of the meniscus and its position against the volume scale can be seen quite clearly.

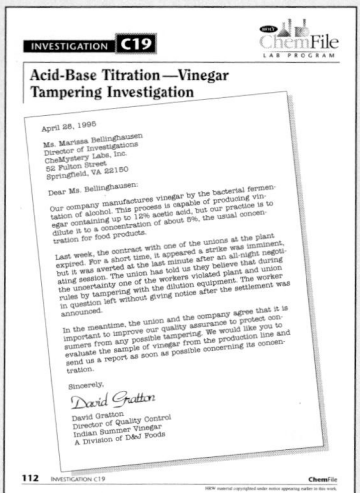
HOW TO   Carry out a titration

This procedure would be used to determine the unknown concentration of an acid by titrating it with a standardized base solution. Decide which of the burets will be used for the acid and which will be used for the base. Label each buret to avoid confusion. Rinse the acid buret three times with the acid to be used in the titration. Use the base solution to rinse the other buret in the same manner.

2 Fill the acid buret with the acid solution to a point above the 0 mL mark.

3 Release some acid to remove any air bubbles and to lower the volume into the calibrated portion of the buret.

4 Record the exact volume of the acid in the buret to the nearest 0.01 mL as your starting point.

5 Release a volume of acid (determined by your lab procedure) into a clean, dry Erlenmeyer flask.

6 Record the new volume reading, and subtract the starting volume from it to find the volume of acid added.

7 Add three drops of an appropriate indicator (phenolphthalein in this case) to the flask.

ALTERNATIVE ASSESSMENT

Presenting a Titration

If your laboratory is not equipped to allow all students to run titrations, have a group of students conduct a demonstration titration similar to the one shown here. They should write all chemical equations and data on the board for the class to share. Students should narrate during the titration, describing each solution and what is being done at each step.

If you have a pH meter, students could run a titration and read the pH meter at approximately 1 mL intervals, recording the volume and pH data in a table on the board. When pH begins to show signs of changing more rapidly, immediately reduce the readings to 0.1 mL intervals or even smaller intervals until the equivalence point has passed and the pH begins to change more slowly again. Take a few more readings after this point. Have the class plot the data to obtain

Fill the other buret with standardized base solution to a point above the 0 mL mark. The concentration of the standardized base solution is known because it was previously used to titrate a precisely weighed mass of a solid acid.

8

9

Release some base from the buret so that the volume is in the calibrated portion of the buret.

10

Record the exact volume of the base to the nearest 0.01 mL as your starting point.

11

Place the flask containing the acid under the base buret. Notice that the tip of the buret extends into the mouth of the flask.

12

Slowly release base from the buret into the flask while *constantly* swirling the flask. The pink color should fade with swirling.

13

Near the end point, add base drop by drop.

14

The end point is reached when a very light pink color remains after 30 seconds of swirling.

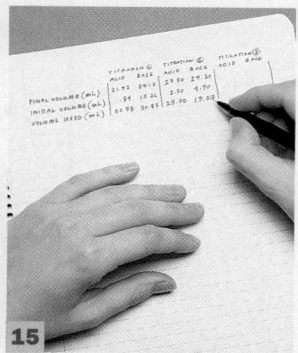

15

Record the new volume, and determine the volume of base added.

ACIDS AND BASES   575

COMMON MISCONCEPTION

Remind students that a buret should be read to the nearest 0.01 mL by mentally breaking the space between 0.1 mL markings into 10 equal spaces.

TEACHING TIP

Using a Buret   Right-handed people generally find it easier to swirl the flask with the right hand and control the stopcock with the left. However, students should experiment to find the most comfortable position. The buret can be turned around if necessary, but the student will not be able to glance at the delivered volume during the titration. The flask contents should always be viewed against a white background in a well-lighted area. Use white sheets of paper if necessary.

RESOURCE LINK

IN-TEXT LAB
Self-Directed Inquiry
Have students do Investigation 15B on page 780 to design an experiment dealing with an industrial spill.

ChemFile Teaching Resources CD-ROM
Career Extension
Assign Occupational Applications Worksheet 10: *Baker* to emphasize relevant applications of text concepts.

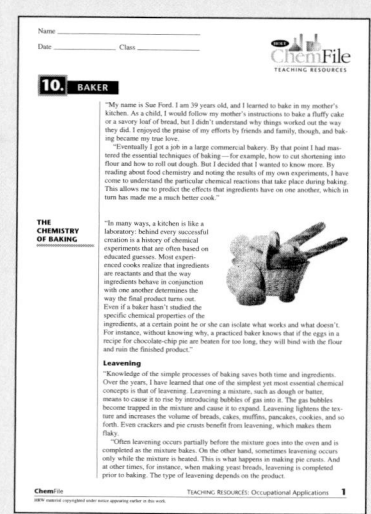

a graph similar to the one shown in Figure 15-24, on page 572.

An advantage of doing a titration with a pH meter is that usually the end point is not determined during the titration but by recording data carefully and locating the end point on the graph (or by mathematical data analysis). If you have a pH meter that interfaces with a computer or graphing calculator, use these along with manual data recording.

ADDITIONAL EXAMPLES

a. A volume of 20.00 mL of a solution of HNO_3 having an unknown titration is titrated with 34.37 mL of a 0.8220 M solution of NaOH. What is the concentration of the HNO_3 solution?

Ans. 1.413 M HNO_3

b. A lab worker makes up 1000.00 mL of a KOH solution but has forgotten to record the mass of KOH dissolved. When a 42.82 mL sample of the solution is titrated with a 1.209 M solution of HCl, 28.35 mL of the acid solution is required to reach the equivalence point. What is the concentration of the KOH solution, and what mass of KOH was dissolved?

Ans. 0.8004 M KOH; 44.91 g KOH was dissolved

c. What volume of a 1.366 M solution of NaOH would be required to titrate 47.22 mL of a 2.075 M solution of H_2SO_4?

Ans. 143.5 mL. Note that two protons must be titrated.

Titration calculations

No matter what method you use to detect the equivalence point in a titration, the next step is always the same. Remember that the goal of a titration is to determine the amount of a substance, such as the amount of nitric acid in the sample being titrated.

Volumes of solution are measured

At the equivalence point in a titration of a strong acid with a strong base, the amount of hydroxide ions added equals the initial amount of hydronium ions. Recall from Chapter 13 that molarity multiplied by volume yields amount. At the equivalence point, the amount of added base equals the amount of acid originally present in solution. This relationship is often expressed symbolically by the following equation, where c_{OH^-} and $c_{H_3O^+}$ are concentrations of OH^- and H_3O^+, respectively, and V_{OH^-} and $V_{H_3O^+}$ are volumes of OH^- and H_3O^+, respectively.

$$c_{OH^-} \times V_{OH^-} = c_{H_3O^+} \times V_{H_3O^+}$$

SAMPLE PROBLEM 15E   **Calculating concentration from titration data**

A student titrates 40.00 mL of an HCl solution of unknown concentration with a 0.5500 M NaOH solution. The volume of base solution needed to reach the equivalence point is 24.64 mL. What is the molarity of the HCl solution?

1 List what you know

▶ Volume of HCl solution titrated = 40.00 mL
▶ Concentration of NaOH titrant = 0.5500 M
▶ Volume of NaOH titrant = 24.64 mL
▶ Concentration of HCl solution = ? M

2 Set up the problem

▶ Write out the titration reaction.

$$HCl(aq) + NaOH(aq) \longrightarrow NaCl(aq) + H_2O(l)$$

▶ Use the net ionic equation for a strong acid–strong base titration.

$$H_3O^+(aq) + OH^-(aq) \longrightarrow 2H_2O(l)$$

▶ Relate the concentrations of acid and base to the concentrations of H_3O^+ and OH^- ions, respectively. NaOH is a strong base that ionizes to produce 1 mol of OH^- ions per 1 mol of NaOH dissolved. HCl is a monoprotic strong acid that ionizes to give 1 mol of H_3O^+ ions per 1 mol of HCl dissolved.

$$c_{OH^-} = 0.5500 \text{ M}$$

$$c_{H_3O^+} = ?$$

▶ Use the concentration-volume relationship to calculate $c_{H_3O^+}$.

$$c_{OH^-} \times V_{OH^-} = c_{H_3O^+} \times V_{H_3O^+}$$

3 Calculate and verify

▶ Solve the concentration-volume equation for $c_{H_3O^+}$, substitute data values, and calculate.

$$c_{H_3O^+} = \frac{c_{OH^-} \times V_{OH^-}}{V_{H_3O^+}} = \frac{0.5500 \text{ mol/L} \times 0.02464 \text{ L}}{0.04000 \text{ L}} = 0.3388 \text{ mol/L}$$

Concentration of HCl = 0.3388 M

▶ The NaOH concentration was 0.5500 M. The volume of NaOH solution required ($\approx$ 25 mL) was a bit more than half the volume ($\approx$ 40 mL) of HCl titrated. Therefore, the concentration of the acid must be a bit more than half the concentration of the base, so $\approx$ 0.34 M is a reasonable result.

SECTION REVIEW

Total recall

1. What two products are formed in a neutralization reaction?

2. What is the determining factor in selecting an indicator to use in a titration?

3. What is the equivalence point of a titration? Describe the two methods that are used to detect the equivalence point in a titration.

Critical thinking

4. Why is a buret rather than a graduated cylinder used in a titration?

5. **Interpreting Tables** Refer to Table 15-7 on page 572. Explain why methyl orange is not a good choice when titrating a strong acid with a strong base.

6. Explain the difference between end point and equivalence point. Why is it important that both occur at approximately the same pH in a titration?

7. Assume that the equivalence point is reached when 0.0103 M CH_3COOH is titrated with 0.0117 M KOH. Predict what the pH of the resulting solution will be. What pH will result by titrating 0.00203 M HNO_3 with 0.00404 NaOH until the equivalence point is reached?

8. Explain why the titration of a strong acid with a weak base ends at a pH lower than 7. Use chemical equations to explain what happens.

Practice problems

9. If 20.6 mL of 0.010 M aqueous HCl are required to titrate 30.0 mL of an aqueous solution of NaOH to the equivalence point, what is the molarity of the NaOH solution?

10. In the titration of 35.0 mL of liquid drain cleaner containing NaOH, 50.08 mL of 0.409 M HCl must be added to reach the equivalence point. What is the concentration of the base in the cleaner?

11. Calculate the volume of 0.256 M $Ba(OH)_2$ that must be added to titrate 46.0 mL of 0.407 M $HClO_4$. (Hint: Write the equation for the reaction and note the mole ratios.)

12. Potassium hydrogen phthalate is a monoprotic acid with a molar mass of 204.23 g/mol that is often used to standardize basic solutions. If a 2.00 g sample of potassium hydrogen phthalate is titrated with 34.7 mL of an NaOH solution, what is the molarity of the NaOH solution?

Practice problems

9. $\dfrac{20.6 \text{ mL} \times 0.010 \text{ M HCl}}{30.0 \text{ mL}} = 0.0069 \text{ M NaOH}$

10. $\dfrac{50.08 \text{ mL} \times 0.409 \text{ M HCl}}{35.0 \text{ mL}} = 0.585 \text{ M NaOH}$

11. $\dfrac{46.0 \text{ mL} \times 0.407 \text{ M HClO}_4}{0.256 \text{ M Ba(OH)}_2} \times \dfrac{1 \text{ mol Ba(OH)}_2}{2 \text{ mol HClO}_4} = 36.6 \text{ mL}$

12. $\dfrac{2.00 \text{ g} \times \dfrac{1 \text{ mol}}{204.23 \text{ g}}}{0.0347 \text{ L}} = 0.282 \text{ M}$

ANSWERS

SECTION REVIEW

Total recall

1. water and a salt

2. the pH at the equivalence point

3. The equivalence point in the titration of a strong acid with a strong base is the point at which the added OH^- equals the amount of H_3O^+ originally in solution. Indicators and pH meters may be used.

Critical thinking

4. A buret can be read to greater precision than a graduated cylinder. Also, the buret has a mechanism for delivering solution and adjusting the rate of its delivery.

5. The equivalence point in the titration of a strong acid with a strong base comes at or very near pH 7. The transition range of methyl orange is pH 3.1 to pH 4.4.

6. The end point is the point at which an indicator changes color. An equivalence point (in a strong acid–strong base titration) is the point at which stoichiometrically equal amounts of H_3O^+ and OH^- have been combined. The two should occur at about the same pH so that the titration will be concluded at the equivalence point.

7. The pH will be about 9. The equivalence point of the NaOH–HNO_3 combination would be at pH 7.

8. The solution at the equivalence point is the same as dissolving the resulting salt in water. An example of a weak base–strong acid salt is NH_4Cl. This dissociates in water as follows:

$$NH_4Cl(s) \longrightarrow NH_4^+(aq) + Cl^-(aq)$$

However, the ammonium ion enters into an equilibrium with water.

$$NH_4^+(aq) + H_2O(l) \rightleftarrows NH_3(aq) + H_3O^+(aq)$$

Thus, the reaction increases the hydronium ion concentration of the solution, lowering the pH.

At the beginning of this chapter, you read about the acidification of a New England lake and the efforts to restore the lake's ecological health. Now that you know more about acids and bases, let us reconsider the questions that were posed.

LOOKING BACK

How are the industrial gases responsible for acid rain?

The industrial gases responsible for acid rain are oxides of nitrogen and sulfur, such as $NO_2(g)$ and $SO_2(g)$. These gases dissolve in rainwater and in snow by reactions such as the following.

$$2NO_2(g) + 3H_2O(l) \longrightarrow$$
$$2H_3O^+(aq) + NO_2^-(aq) + NO_3^-(aq)$$

The hydronium ions produced by such reactions are evidenced by a lowering of the rain's pH. Rain-fed streams convey the acidity to the lake, and the accumulation of H_3O^+ ions leads to detrimental biological effects.

Why did environmentalists transport limestone into the region instead of using local rock?

Not all rock exhibits basic properties, and evidently the rock basin in which the lake is nestled is made of an inactive mineral, such as granite. If the rock basin were made of limestone, the lake would have been naturally protected against acidification.

Limestone consists mainly of the base calcium carbonate, which reacts with hydronium ions by the following reaction.

$$CaCO_3(s) + H_3O^+(aq) \longrightarrow$$
$$Ca^{2+}(aq) + HCO_3^-(aq) + H_2O(l)$$

As the acidity is neutralized, the lake's ecological health is restored. Because limestone is insoluble in acid-free water, there is no fear of dangerously high pH levels that could occur if bases such as NaOH(s) were used to combat lake acidity.

Why was this operation carried out during the winter?

The most convenient way to distribute the limestone evenly is to spread the rock on the ice and allow the rock to drop to the lake bed during the spring thaw. Other methods can be expensive and may destroy the fragile shoreline.

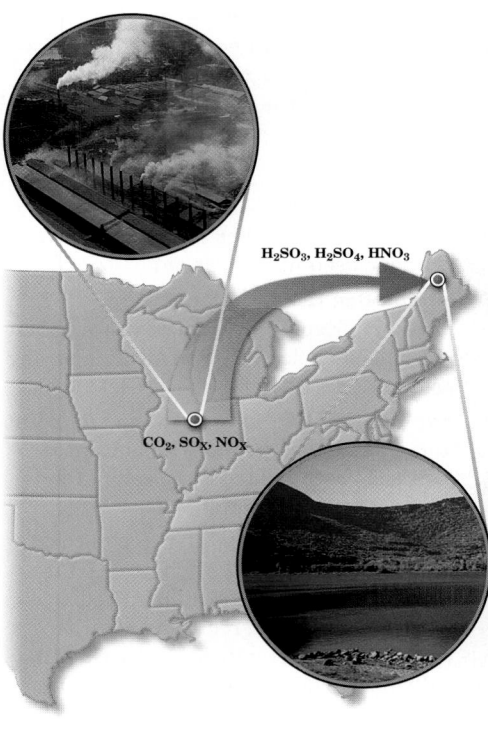

H_2SO_3, H_2SO_4, HNO_3

CO_2, SO_X, NO_X

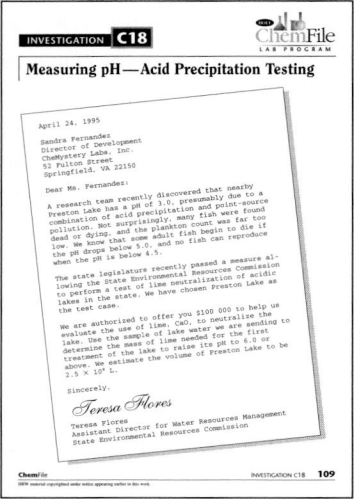

KEY TERMS

15-1
amine
carboxylic acid
neutralization reaction
strong acid
weak acid

15-2
acid-ionization constant
amphoteric
Brønsted-Lowry acid
Brønsted-Lowry base
conjugate acid
conjugate base
diprotic acid
monoprotic acid
triprotic acid

15-3
buffer solution
indicator
neutral
pH
pH meter

15-4
end point
equivalence point
standard solution
titrant
titration
transition range

READING STRATEGY

Assimilating Knowledge
Have students return to the list of things they want to know about the chemistry of acids and bases, which they created on page 540. Have them place check marks next to the questions that they are now able to answer. Students should finish by making a list of what they have learned. Have students identify unanswered questions as well as new questions they may have. These questions could be used as the basis for a research project.

KEY CONCEPTS

15-1 What are acids and bases?

▶ Acids generate hydronium ions in aqueous solution; bases generate hydroxide ions in aqueous solution.

▶ Strong acids and strong bases ionize completely in aqueous solution and are good electrical conductors. Weak acids and bases ionize only partially.

▶ Given either the hydronium ion or hydroxide ion concentration, the K_w can be used to calculate the concentration of the other ion in aqueous solution.

15-2 Can the strengths of acids and bases be quantified?

▶ A Brønsted-Lowry acid is a proton donor, and a Brønsted-Lowry base is a proton acceptor. Some compounds, such as water, can function as both and are considered amphoteric.

▶ A conjugate acid forms when a Brønsted-Lowry base accepts a proton. A conjugate base forms when a Brønsted-Lowry acid releases a proton.

▶ Acids and bases are ranked according to their strengths on the basis of their ionization constants, K_a, or on those of their conjugate acids.

15-3 How are acidity and pH related?

▶ The pH is the negative logarithm of the hydronium ion concentration in a solution.

▶ The pH can be measured with the use of an indicator or a pH meter.

▶ A buffer consists of a weak acid and its conjugate base and resists changes in the pH of a solution.

15-4 What is a titration?

▶ When mixed in the proper stoichiometric ratios, acids and bases neutralize each other.

▶ The concentration of an acidic or basic solution can be determined through a titration.

▶ The equivalence point of a strong acid–strong base titration occurs when the amount of H_3O^+ or OH^- added equals the amount of OH^- or H_3O^+ that was originally present.

REVIEW & ASSESS ASSIGNMENT GUIDE

Term Review
Assign after Section 15-4.

Concept and Skills Review
Section 15-1
Items 1–7, 21–27

Section 15-2
Items 8–20, 28–30

Section 15-3
Items 31–51

Section 15-4
Items 52–72

Linking Chapters
Assign after Section 15-4.

Alternative Assessment
Assign after Section 15-4.

Test Prep
Assign prior to the chapter test.

KEY SKILLS

Review the following models before your exam. Be sure you can solve these types of problems.

How To Use logarithms in pH calculations (p. 561)

How To Carry out a titration (p. 574)

Sample Problem 15A Determining [OH⁻] using K_w (p. 549)

Sample Problem 15B Calculating K_a of a weak acid (p. 557)

Sample Problem 15C Calculating the pH of an acidic solution (p. 561)

Sample Problem 15D Calculating the pH of a basic solution (p. 562)

Sample Problem 15E Calculating concentration from titration data (p. 576)

Complete worked-out solutions for these problems can be found on the teacher's interleaved pages at the end of this chapter.

TERM REVIEW

1. neutralization
2. weak base
3. conjugate base
4. amphoteric
5. K_a
6. antacid
7. hydronium ion
8. pH meter
9. weak acid
10. standard solution
11. equivalence point
12. —COOH

CONCEPT & SKILLS REVIEW

1. Acids are electrolytes that have a sour taste and react with metals. Bases are electrolytes that have a bitter taste and a slippery feel.

2. $Mg(s) + 2HCl(aq) \longrightarrow MgCl_2(aq) + H_2(g)$

3. Water self-ionizes to produce concentrations of H_3O^+ and OH^- ions equal to 10^{-7} M each. K_w is the ion product of water, equal to the product of $[H_3O^+][OH^-] = 10^{-7} \times 10^{-7} = 10^{-14}$.

4. because they ionize only slightly, producing low concentrations of ions in solution

5. The strength of an acid is the degree to which it ionizes in solution. Its concentration is how much of it is dissolved per liter of solution.

6. The concentration of water does not change appreciably as a result of ionization.

7. moles per liter

8. The bulb will glow dimly (if at all) because boric acid is a very weak acid.

9. The hydronium ion can participate in proton transfer to move through a solution faster than other cations.

TERM REVIEW

1. The process by which hydronium ions react with hydroxide ions to produce water is known as ——.
(titration, neutralization)

2. Ammonia is an example of a ——.
(weak base, weak acid)

3. The substance formed when an acid donates a proton to another species is known as a ——.
(conjugate acid, conjugate base)

4. A substance that can act as either an acid or a base is said to be ——.
(amphoteric, diprotic)

5. Because of its small ——, the hydrogen carbonate ion, HCO_3^-, is considered a weak conjugate acid.
(K_a, K_w)

6. A basic material that can be used to neutralize excess stomach acidity is a(n) ——.
(buffer solution, antacid)

7. The pH of a solution is directly related to its —— concentration.
(hydronium ion, hydroxide ion)

8. To measure the pH of a solution as accurately as possible, a(n) —— is used.
(pH meter, indicator)

9. The two ingredients in a buffer include a —— and its conjugate base.
(weak acid, diprotic acid)

10. The solution in a titration whose concentration is accurately known is the ——.
(titrant, standard solution)

11. When the H_3O^+ concentration equals the OH^- concentration in a strong acid–strong base titration, then the —— has been reached.
(end point, equivalence point)

12. A carboxylic acid contains the functional group ——.
(—COOH, —COO)

CONCEPT & SKILLS REVIEW

ACIDS AND BASES

1. Compare the properties of an acid with those of a base.

2. Write the equation that shows the reaction between magnesium metal and hydrochloric acid.

3. Explain the relationship between the self-ionization of water and K_w.

4. Why are weak acids and weak bases poor conductors of electricity?

5. What is the difference between the strength of an acid and its concentration?

6. Water is not included in the equilibrium expression to show what happens in the self-ionization of water. Why not?

7. What unit is implied by brackets placed around the formula of an acid or a base?

8. Explain how the bulb in **Figure 15-2** on page 543 will glow if the solution is replaced with boric acid ($K_a = 5.8 \times 10^{-10}$).

9. Explain what the hydronium ion can do in solution that no other cation can do.

10. Why is rainwater normally slightly acidic?

11. What is neutralization?

12. Write an equation for the reaction between hydrocyanic acid, HCN, and water. Label the acid, base, conjugate acid, and conjugate base in the reaction.

13. Explain how the hydrogen carbonate ion, HCO_3^-, acts as an amphoteric ion.

14. Explain how the acetate ion formed as a product in the following forward reaction acts as a base in the reverse reaction.

$CH_3COOH(aq) + H_2O(l) \rightleftharpoons CH_3COO^-(aq) + H_3O^+(aq)$

Acid	Formula	Value of K_a
Arsenic	H_3AsO_4	5.62×10^{-3}
Acetic	CH_3COOH	1.76×10^{-5}
Benzoic	C_6H_5COOH	6.5×10^{-5}
Cyanic	$HCNO$	7.4×10^{-4}
Phosphoric	H_3PO_4	7.5×10^{-3}
Hydrofluoric	HF	6.8×10^{-4}
Carbonic	H_2CO_3	4.3×10^{-7}

15. Use the table above to answer the following questions:
 a. Which is the strongest acid? Why?
 b. Which acid ionizes the least? Why?

16. Write an equilibrium expression for the ionization of phenol, a weak monoprotic acid whose formula is C_6H_5OH.

17. Place the following acids in order of increasing strength:
 a. valeric acid $K_a = 1.5 \times 10^{-5}$
 b. glutaric acid $K_a = 3.4 \times 10^{-4}$
 c. hypobromous acid $K_a = 2.5 \times 10^{-9}$
 d. acetylsalicylic acid $K_a = 3.3 \times 10^{-4}$

18. Classify sulfurous acid, H_2SO_3, based on what it does in an aqueous solution.

19. Explain why sodium hydroxide, $NaOH$, is used in oil refining to remove acids.

20. Identify each of the following as an acid or a base according to the Brønsted-Lowry classification. For each species, write the formula and the name of its conjugate.
 a. CH_3COO^-
 b. HCN
 c. $H_2C_2O_4$
 d. $C_6H_5NH_3^+$

Practice Problems

21. Calculate the hydroxide ion concentration in a 0.010 M HCl solution at 298 K. **(Hint: See Sample Problem 15A.)**

22. At 60°C, the value of K_w is 1.0×10^{-13}. Calculate the concentrations of hydronium ions and hydroxide ions in water at this temperature.

23. The value of K_w at 0°C is 1.14×10^{-15}. Calculate the concentrations of hydronium ions and hydroxide ions in pure water at 0°C. How do these concentrations compare with the concentrations of hydronium and hydroxide ions in pure water at 25°C?

24. Propanoic acid is used in the production of plastics. K_a for propanoic acid is 1.4×10^{-5}. If 0.600 g of this acid is dissolved in water to make 250.0 mL of solution, what would be the hydronium ion concentration of the solution? The following equation shows the ionization of propanoic acid in water:

$$H_2O(l) + C_2H_5COOH(aq) \rightleftharpoons C_2H_5COO^-(aq) + H_3O^+(aq)$$

25. An alkaline solution is prepared by dissolving 12 g of NaOH in 2.5 L of water. What is the hydroxide ion concentration in this solution? the hydronium ion concentration?

26. Aqueous hypoiodous acid, HIO, exists in the following equilibrium:

$$HIO(aq) + H_2O(l) \rightleftharpoons H_3O^+(aq) + IO^-(aq)$$

The hypoiodite ion, IO^-, has a concentration of 2.14×10^{-6} M in a 0.200 M aqueous solution of HIO. What is the acid-ionization constant of hypoiodous acid?

27. If the hydronium ion concentration of sea water at 298 K is 5.0×10^{-9} M, what is the hydroxide ion concentration in this sea water? **(Hint: See Sample Problem 15A.)**

28. Lactic acid gives sour milk its taste. Lactic acid is a weak acid that dissociates as shown in the following equation:

$$CH_3CHOHCOOH(aq) \rightleftharpoons CH_3CHOHCOO^-(aq) + H_3O^+(aq)$$

Assume that the concentration of lactic acid in sour milk is 0.100 M and that the concentration of hydronium ions is 3.72×10^{-3} M. Calculate the K_a for lactic acid. **(Hint: See Sample Problem 15B.)**

29. The hydroxide ion concentration of human blood at 25°C is 2.6×10^{-7} M. What is the hydronium ion concentration of human blood?

Complete worked-out solutions for these problems can be found on the teacher's interleaved pages at the end of this chapter.

10. Rainwater contains dissolved CO_2, which dissociates into H_3O^+ and HCO_3^- ions.

11. Neutralization is the reaction of H_3O^+ ions from an acid with OH^- ions from a base.

12. $HCN + H_2O \rightleftharpoons H_3O^+ + CN^-$. CN^- is the conjugate base of HCN. H_3O^+ is the conjugate acid of H_2O.

13. The HCO_3^- ion can react with H_3O^+ to form H_2CO_3, and it can react with OH^- to form CO_3^{2-} ions.

14. The acetate ion can act as a base by accepting a proton to form molecular CH_3COOH.

15. a. Phosphoric acid is the strongest. Its K_a has the highest value, indicating that it is the most ionized.
 b. Carbonic acid is the weakest. Its K_a is the lowest, indicating that it is the least ionized.

16. $C_6H_5OH + H_2O \rightleftharpoons C_6H_5O^- + H_3O^+$

17. hypobromous acid, valeric acid, acetylsalicylic acid, glutaric acid

18. The first ionization of H_2SO_3 is fairly strong, with a K_a of 1.23×10^{-2}, but not strong enough to be classified as a strong acid. The second ionization is weak. Therefore, it is classified as a weak acid.

19. NaOH is a strong base.

20. a. base, CH_3COOH
 b. acid, CN^-
 c. acid (oxalic), $HC_2O_4^-$ ($HOOCCOO^-$)
 d. acid, $C_6H_5NH_2$

21–30. *See page 585A.*

581

Complete worked-out solutions for these problems can be found on the teacher's interleaved pages at the end of this chapter.

31. Enough H_3O^+ ions have reacted with OH^- ions to reduce the H_3O^+ concentration from 0.1 M to 0.066 M. Approximately 0.034 mol/L of OH^- ions has been added. We cannot know the precise amounts because we do not know the volumes involved.

32. For example, at pH 4, the $[H_3O^+]$ is 0.0001 M. If pH decreases to 2, $[H_3O^+]$ has increased to 0.01 M, 100 times the concentration at pH 4.

33. The blood is buffered by the presence of HCO_3^- ions, which can react with either H_3O^+ or OH^-.

34. Acetic acid is a weak acid and ionizes only slightly, regardless of concentration.

35. It will have a low pH value because HCl ionizes almost completely.

36. A solution of a strong acid can have a negative pH if $[H_3O^+]$ is greater than 1 M (10^0 M). For example, a 6 M HCl would have a pH of −0.78 if HCl is completely ionized.

37. The second and, if applicable, third ionizations are very weak, so the first ionization is by far the greatest contributor to the H_3O^+ concentration.

38. The solution would have a pH of 7 because NaCl is a salt of a strong acid and a strong base. Neither ion has a tendency to accept a proton from water.

39. The stronger an acid is, the lower the pH of its aqueous solution because the acid donates protons to H_2O to form H_3O^+ more readily.

40. The K_a of an acid is a measure of its tendency to ionize in water. Weaker acids have lower K_a values and thus lower $[H_3O^+]$ and higher pH.

41–51. *See page 585A.*

30. A solution is prepared by dissolving 0.56 g of benzoic acid in enough water to make 1.0 L of solution. Benzoic acid ionizes in aqueous solution, as shown in the following equation:

$$C_6H_5COOH(aq) \rightleftharpoons C_6H_5COO^-(aq) + H_3O^+(aq)$$

The K_a of benzoic acid is 6.4×10^{-5}. Calculate the hydronium ion concentration in this solution, assuming that a negligible amount of benzoic acid ionizes.

PH

31. A solution of HCl has a pH of 1.00. You add NaOH to the solution, and the pH rises to 1.18. What happened? What does this have to do with the relationship of acids to bases along the pH scale? Can you estimate what amounts of HCl and NaOH might have been used?

32. Use two arbitrary pH values to show mathematically how the concentration of H_3O^+ increases as pH decreases.

33. How does the pH of human blood remain extremely constant?

34. Explain why a 1.00 M acetic acid solution does not have a low pH.

35. Explain why a 0.10 M hydrochloric acid solution has a low pH.

36. How can a pH be negative?

37. Why is the pH of a polyprotic acid primarily determined by its first dissociation?

38. What would be the pH of a 2.0 M NaCl solution? Explain your answer.

39. How does the strength of an acid relate to the pH of its solutions?

40. How does the K_a value of an acid relate to the pH of its solutions?

Practice Problems

41. What is the pH of a 0.025 M NaOH solution?

42. Determine the pH of a 8.75×10^{-4} M HCl solution. **(Hint: See Sample Problem 15C.)**

43. The pH of the precipitation in an area near a power plant is 3.45. What is the OH^- ion concentration in this precipitation?

44. The pH of a glass of soda water is 4.3. What is the $[H_3O^+]$?

45. What is the pH of a 2.5×10^{-5} M KOH solution?

46. What is the pH of an ammonia solution that has a hydroxide ion concentration of 10^{-3} M? **(Hint: See Sample Problem 15D.)**

47. A solution of 5% acetic acid has a concentration of 0.83 M and a K_a of 1.8×10^{-5}. What is the pH of the solution?

48. What are the concentrations of all of the components of a benzoic acid solution if K_a is 6.5×10^{-5}, pH is 2.96, and C_6H_5COOH is 0.020 M?

49. The pH of a solution is 3.9. Calculate the hydroxide ion concentration of this solution.

50. What is the OH^- concentration of a solution of HNO_3 with a pH value of 2.89?

51. The pH of one sample of fruit juice is 2.80. Determine both the hydronium and hydroxide ion concentrations in this juice sample.

TITRATION

52. Write the complete molecular and net ionic equations for the neutralization of sulfuric acid with potassium hydroxide.

53. Describe the role of an indicator in the titration of an unknown acid against a standardized base.

54. Why is the transition range of an indicator critically important when performing different titrations?

55. How is the color change of an indicator related to pH?

56. For the following titrations, select the best indicator from these choices: bromphenol blue, bromthymol blue, phenol red.
a. formic acid, HCOOH, with NaOH
b. perchloric acid with LiOH
c. sulfuric acid with potassium hydroxide
d. ammonia with hydrochloric acid

Indicator	Acid color	pH range of color	Base color
Thymol blue	red	1.2–2.8	yellow
Bromphenol blue	yellow	3.0–4.6	blue
Bromcresol green	yellow	2.0–5.6	blue
Bromthymol blue	yellow	6.0–7.6	blue
Phenol red	yellow	6.6–8.0	red
Alizarin yellow	yellow	10.1–12.0	red

57. Refer to the table above to answer the following questions:
   a. Which indicator would be the best choice for a titration with an end point at a pH of 4.0?
   b. Which indicators would work best for a titration of a weak base with a strong acid?

58. Why is a different indicator used for a strong acid–strong base titration than for a weak acid–strong base titration?

59. Why does an indicator need to be a weak acid or a weak base?

60. How is the transition range of an indicator related to the end point of a titration?

61. A 50 mL solution of CH_3COOH is titrated with a 1.000 M NaOH solution. Describe what species (molecules and ions) are present in the titration flask at the following points in the titration:
   a. pH 6
   b. pH 9
   c. pH 11

62. In the titration of a weak acid with a strong base, the pH of the equivalence point is higher than 7. Use the concept of conjugate acids and bases to explain why the pH is in the basic range.

63. A student passes an end point in a titration. Is it possible to add an additional measured amount of the unknown and continue the titration? Explain how this process might work. How would the answer for the calculation of the molarity of the unknown differ from the answer the student would have gotten if the titration had been run properly?

Practice Problems

64. You wish to determine the molarity of a lactic acid solution. A 150.0 mL sample of lactic acid, $CH_3CHOHCOOH$, is titrated with 125 mL of 0.750 M NaOH. What is the molarity of the acid sample? **(Hint: See Sample Problem 15E.)**

65. Formic acid is used in the production of leather. Residue from leather production is tested to determine the concentration of formic acid. A 50.0 mL sample of formic acid, HCOOH, is neutralized by 35.0 mL of 0.250 M NaOH. What is the molarity of the formic acid solution?

66. If 35.40 mL of 1.000 M HCl is neutralized by 67.3 mL of NaOH, what is the molarity of the NaOH solution?

67. If 50.00 mL of 1.000 M H_2SO_4 is neutralized by 35.4 mL of KOH, what is the molarity of the KOH solution?

68. If 18.5 mL of a 0.350 M H_2SO_4 solution neutralizes 12.5 mL of aqueous LiOH, how many grams of LiOH was used to make 1.00 L of the LiOH solution?

69. An HCl solution has a pH of 2.40. Calculate the amount of hydronium ions in 125.5 mL of this solution.

70. An NaOH solution has a pH of 10.50. What volume of this solution would contain 8.0×10^{-5} mol of OH^- ions? What volume of 0.010 M HCl would be required to titrate this solution to the equivalence point?

71. An HNO_3 solution has a pH of 3.06. What amount of 0.015 M NaOH will be required to

Complete worked-out solutions for these problems can be found on the teacher's interleaved pages at the end of this chapter.

52. $H_2SO_4(aq) + 2KOH(aq) \longrightarrow$
$\qquad K_2SO_4(aq) + 2H_2O(l)$
$H_3O^+(aq) + OH^-(aq) \longrightarrow 2H_2O(l)$

53. When properly chosen, the indicator changes color at the equivalence point.

54. The transition range must include the pH at the equivalence point of the titration.

55. Indicators are weak acids and weak bases that change color when they change to the corresponding conjugate base or conjugate acid.

56. a. phenol red
   b. bromthymol blue
   c. phenol red (The titration of the second proton is like the titration of a weak acid.)
   d. bromphenol blue

57. a. bromphenol blue
   b. Thymol blue, bromphenol blue, or bromcresol green would be chosen depending on the pH of the equivalence point, which would be in the acid pH range.

58. The equivalence point of a strong acid–strong base titration occurs near pH 7, so the chosen indicator must change color near this pH. The equivalence point of a weak acid–strong base titration would occur at a basic pH, usually 10–12, so the chosen indicator must change color in that range and not at pH 7.

59. The indicator must respond to increasing or decreasing acidity by being titrated itself.

60. The end-point color change occurs within the transition range of the indicator.

61. The following species are present at all pH levels of the titration, but they vary in relative concentration: Na^+, OH^-, CH_3COOH, CH_3COO^-, H_3O^+.

Complete worked-out solutions for these problems can be found on the teacher's interleaved pages at the end of this chapter.

62. When the equivalence point is reached, the conjugate base (A^-) of the weak acid (HA) is still in equilibrium with the molecular acid as in $A^-(aq) + H_2O(l) \longrightarrow HA(aq) + OH^-(aq)$. Thus, the OH^- concentration at the equivalence point is significantly higher than at pH 7, resulting in a higher pH.

63. Additional unknown can be added as long as its volume is known with the same precision as the original sample. The student would continue titrating to the new end point. The concentration of unknown is not affected because the second sample is of the same concentration as the first.

64–71. *See page 585A.*

72. The anions of those weak acids are conjugate bases that can react with excess H_3O^+ ions. Because the acids are weak, the molecular form is in equilibrium with the conjugate base. The molecular form can react with excess OH^- ions.

Answers continue on page 585A.

titrate 65.0 mL of the HNO_3 solution to reach the equivalence point?

72. Explain how weak acids in the body can help maintain the buffering capacity of a living system.

LINKING CHAPTERS

1. Applying scientific laws
How do nitrous acid, HNO_2, and nitric acid, HNO_3, demonstrate the law of multiple proportions?

2. Stoichiometry
An excess of zinc reacts with 250.0 mL of 6.00 M sulfuric acid.
a. What mass of $ZnSO_4$ is produced?
b. What volume of $H_2(g)$ is produced at STP?

3. Stoichiometry
A seashell (mostly $CaCO_3$) is placed in a solution of HCl. From the reaction, 1.50 L of CO_2 is produced at 25°C and 100 kPa.
a. What mass of $CaCO_3$ was consumed in the reaction?
b. If the HCl solution was 2.00 M, what volume was used in this reaction?

4. Balancing equations
Write balanced equations for each of the following reactions between acids and metal oxides:
a. $MgO(s) + H_2SO_4(aq) \longrightarrow$
b. $CaO(s) + HCl(aq) \longrightarrow$
c. $Al_2O_3(s) + HNO_3(aq) \longrightarrow$
d. $ZnO(s) + H_3PO_4(aq) \longrightarrow$

5. Balancing equations
Write balanced equations for each of the following reactions between acids and carbonates:
a. $BaCO_3(s) + HCl(aq) \longrightarrow$
b. $MgCO_3(s) + HNO_3(aq) \longrightarrow$
c. $Na_2CO_3(s) + H_2SO_4(aq) \longrightarrow$
d. $CaCO_3(s) + H_3PO_4(aq) \longrightarrow$

ALTERNATIVE ASSESSMENTS

Performance assessment

1. Design an experiment to measure the pH of four types of hair shampoo: baby shampoo, shampoo for extra body, shampoo for oily hair, and shampoo with conditioner. Chart any patterns you detect. Also compare and contrast two brands of "pH balanced" shampoo.

2. Your teacher will give you a solution to test for pH. Describe exactly how you would test the solution. If your teacher approves your plan, complete the test.

3. Design an experiment to test the neutralization effectiveness of various brands of antacid. Show your procedure, including all safety procedures and cautions, to your teacher for approval. Write an advertisement for the antacid you judge to be the most effective. Cite data from your experiments as part of your advertising claims.

Portfolio projects

1. Chemistry and you
Collect data on the acidity of rain in your area over the last 10 years. Graph the data, and make a prediction concerning acid-rain damage in your area by the year 2010. Provide evidence to support your prediction.

2. internet**connect**

SC**LINKS**
NSTA

TOPIC: Baking soda/Baking powder
GO TO: www.scilinks.org
KEYWORD: HW156

Research and communication
A reaction between baking soda, $NaHCO_3$, and a baking batter that contains acidic ingredients produces carbon dioxide gas. The reaction results in a fluffier cake. Some recipes rely on baking powder instead of baking soda. Research the ingredients of regular baking powder and double-acting baking powder to discover how they differ from baking soda. Which is more likely to be used in creating a light, fluffy cake? How does the pH affect the final product?

1. Which of the following aqueous solutions would have the highest concentration of hydronium ions?
   a. nitrous acid
   b. acetic acid
   c. potassium carbonate
   d. periodic acid

2. When an acid reacts with a metal, ——.
   a. the hydronium ion concentration increases
   b. the metal forms anions
   c. water is produced
   d. the K_w value is changed

3. The K_w value can be affected by ——.
   a. dissolving a salt in the solution
   b. changes in temperature
   c. changes in the hydroxide ion concentration
   d. the presence of a strong acid

4. Which of the following is a strong diprotic acid?
   a. H_2O
   b. H_3PO_4
   c. H_2SO_4
   d. H_2O_2

5. The stronger an acid is, ——.
   a. the smaller its K_a value
   b. the stronger its conjugate base
   c. the more hydronium ions produced in aqueous solution
   d. the more hydroxide ions produced in aqueous solution

6. Identify the species that is considered a base according to Brønsted-Lowry but not according to Arrhenius.
   a. H_2SO_4
   b. $NH_3(g)$
   c. KOH
   d. $Ca(OH)_2$

7. Which of the following solutions would have a pH value greater than 7?
   a. $[OH^-] = 2.4 \times 10^{-2}$ M
   b. $[H_3O^+] = 1.53 \times 10^{-2}$ M
   c. 0.0001 M HCl
   d. $[OH^-] = 4.4 \times 10^{-9}$ M

8. If the pH of a solution of a strong base is known, the —— of the solution can be calculated.
   a. molarity
   b. $[OH^-]$
   c. $[H_3O^+]$
   d. All of the above

9. A neutral aqueous solution ——.
   a. has a 7 M H_3O^+ concentration
   b. contains neither hydronium ions nor hydroxide ions
   c. has an equal number of hydronium ions and hydroxide ions
   d. contains buffers that resist changes in pH

10. Which of the following indicators is the best choice to use when titrating a strong base with a weak acid?
    a. thymol blue
    b. alizarin yellow
    c. methyl orange
    d. bromthymol blue

11. Identify the salt that is produced when a solution of H_2SO_4 is titrated with a solution of $Ca(OH)_2$.
    a. calcium sulfate
    b. calcium hydroxide
    c. calcium oxide
    d. calcium phosphate

12. In functioning as a base, an amine molecule with its unshared pair of electrons can accept a(n) ——.
    a. hydroxide ion
    b. carboxyl group
    c. proton
    d. amino group

1. d
2. c
3. b
4. c
5. c
6. b
7. a
8. d
9. c
10. b
11. a
12. c

ACIDS AND BASES 585

21. $[OH^-] = \dfrac{K_w}{[H_3O^+]} = \dfrac{1.0 \times 10^{-14}}{0.010} = 1.0 \times 10^{-12}$ M

22. $[H_3O^+] = [OH^-] = \sqrt{1.0 \times 10^{-13}} = 3.2 \times 10^{-7}$ M

23. $[H_3O^+] = [OH^-] = \sqrt{1.14 \times 10^{-15}} = 3.38 \times 10^{-8}$; about $\frac{1}{3}$ as much

24. $[C_2H_5COOH] = \dfrac{0.600 \text{ g}}{0.2500 \text{ L}} \times \dfrac{1 \text{ mol}}{74.09 \text{ g}} = 0.0324$ M;

$K_a = 1.4 \times 10^{-5} = \dfrac{[C_2H_5COO^-][H_3O^+]}{0.0324}$; $[H_3O^+] = \sqrt{4.535 \times 10^{-7}} = 6.7 \times 10^{-4}$ M

25. $[OH^-] = \dfrac{12 \text{ g} \times \dfrac{1 \text{ mol}}{40.0 \text{ g}}}{2.5 \text{ L}} = 0.12$ M; $[H_3O^+] = \dfrac{K_w}{[OH^-]} = 8.3 \times 10^{-14}$ M

26. $K_a = \dfrac{[H_3O^+][IO^-]}{[HIO]} = \dfrac{(2.14 \times 10^{-6})^2}{0.200} = 2.29 \times 10^{-11}$

27. $[OH^-] = \dfrac{1.0 \times 10^{-14}}{5.0 \times 10^{-9}} = 2.0 \times 10^{-6}$ M

28. $K_a = \dfrac{[CH_3CHOHCOO^-][H_3O^+]}{[CH_3CHOHCOOH]} = \dfrac{(3.72 \times 10^{-3})^2}{0.100 - 0.00372} = 1.44 \times 10^{-4}$

29. $[H_3O^+] = \dfrac{1.0 \times 10^{-14}}{2.6 \times 10^{-7}} = 3.8 \times 10^{-8}$ M

30. $[C_6H_5COOH] = \dfrac{0.56 \text{ g}}{1.0 \text{ L}} \times \dfrac{1 \text{ mol}}{122.13 \text{ g}} = 4.59 \times 10^{-3}$;

$K_a = 6.4 \times 10^{-5} = \dfrac{[C_6H_5COO^-][H_3O^+]}{4.59 \times 10^{-3}}$; $[H_3O^+] = \sqrt{2.94 \times 10^{-7}} = 5.4 \times 10^{-4}$ M

41. $[H_3O^+] = \dfrac{K_w}{[OH^-]} = \dfrac{1.0 \times 10^{-14}}{0.025} = 4.0 \times 10^{-13}$; pH = 12.40

42. pH = $-\log[H_3O^+] = -\log(8.75 \times 10^{-4}) = 3.058$

43. $[OH^-] = \dfrac{1.0 \times 10^{-14}}{10^{-3.45}} = 2.8 \times 10^{-11}$ M

44. $[H_3O^+] = 10^{-4.3} = 5 \times 10^{-5}$ M

45. $[H_3O^+] = \dfrac{1.0 \times 10^{-14}}{2.5 \times 10^{-5}} = 4.0 \times 10^{-10}$; pH = $-\log[H_3O^+] = 9.40$

46. $[OH^-] = 10^{-3}$; $[H_3O^+] = 10^{-11}$; pH = 11

47. $K_a = \dfrac{[H_3O^+][CH_3COO^-]}{0.83} = 1.8 \times 10^{-5}$; $[H_3O^+] = 0.0039$; pH = 2.41

48. pH = 2.96; $[H_3O^+] = 1.1 \times 10^{-3}$; $K_a = 6.5 \times 10^{-5} = \dfrac{(1.1 \times 10^{-3}) - [C_6H_5COO^-]}{0.020 - [C_6H_5COO^-]}$; $[C_6H_5COO^-] = \dfrac{1.3 \times 10^{-6}}{1.16 \times 10^{-3}} = 1.1 \times 10^{-3}$; $[C_6H_5COOH] = 0.019$

49. $[OH^-] = \dfrac{1.0 \times 10^{-14}}{10^{-3.9}} = 8 \times 10^{-11}$ M

50. $[OH^-] = \dfrac{1.0 \times 10^{-14}}{10^{-2.89}} = 7.8 \times 10^{-12}$ M

51. $[H_3O^+] = 10^{-2.80} = 0.016$ M; $[OH^-] = \dfrac{K_w}{[H_3O^+]} = 6.3 \times 10^{-12}$ M

64. $125(0.75) = 150 \, c_{acid}$; $c_{acid} = 0.625$ M

65. $35.0(0.250) = 50.0 \, c_{acid}$; $c_{acid} = 0.175$ M

66. $35.40(1.000) = 67.3 \, c_{NaOH}$; $c_{NaOH} = 0.526$ M

67. $50.00(1.000)(2) = 35.4 \, c_{KOH}$; $c_{KOH} = 2.82$ M

68. 0.0185 L $H_2SO_4 \times 0.350$ mol/L $H_2SO_4 \times \dfrac{2 \text{ mol LiOH}}{\text{mol } H_2SO_4} \times \dfrac{23.95 \text{ g}}{\text{mol LiOH}}$

$\times \dfrac{1}{0.0125 \text{ L LiOH}} = 24.8$ g/L LiOH

69. $10^{-2.40}$ M $H_3O^+ \times 0.1255$ L $= 5.0 \times 10^{-4}$ mol H_3O^+

70. $\dfrac{\text{mol } OH^-}{[OH^-]} = \dfrac{8.0 \times 10^{-5}}{\dfrac{K_w}{10^{-10.50}}} = 0.25$ L NaOH; $\dfrac{8.0 \times 10^{-5}}{0.010 \text{ M}} = 8.0$ mL HCl

71. $\dfrac{(10^{-3.06} \text{ M})(0.0650 \text{ L})}{0.015 \text{ M}} = 3.8$ mL NaOH

LINKING CHAPTERS

1. Both have the same kinds of atoms in their formulas, but the atoms occur in different proportions by count and by mass. In 1 mol of HNO_2, 32.00 g of oxygen is combined with 15.02 g of hydrogen and nitrogen. In 1 mol of HNO_3, 48.00 g of oxygen is combined with 15.02 g of hydrogen and nitrogen. So oxygen occurs in a 2:3 ratio in the two compounds.

2. a. 242 g $ZnSO_4$ is produced
b. 33.6 L H_2 is produced at STP

3. a. 6.70 g $CaCO_3$
b. 67.0 mL HCl

4. a. $MgO(s) + H_2SO_4(aq) \longrightarrow MgSO_4(aq) + H_2O(l)$
b. $CaO(s) + 2HCl(aq) \longrightarrow CaCl_2(aq) + H_2O(l)$
c. $Al_2O_3(s) + 6HNO_3(aq) \longrightarrow 2Al(NO_3)_3(aq) + 3H_2O(l)$
d. $3ZnO(s) + 2H_3PO_4(aq) \longrightarrow Zn_3(PO_4)_2(s) + 3H_2O(l)$

5. a. $BaCO_3(s) + 2HCl(aq) \longrightarrow BaCl_2(aq) + H_2O(l) + CO_2(g)$
b. $MgCO_3(s) + 2HNO_3(aq) \longrightarrow Mg(NO_3)_2(aq) + H_2O(l) + CO_2(g)$
c. $Na_2CO_3(s) + H_2SO_4(aq) \longrightarrow Na_2SO_4(aq) + H_2O(l) + CO_2(g)$
d. $3CaCO_3(s) + 2H_3PO_4(aq) \longrightarrow Ca_3(PO_4)_2(s) + 3H_2O(l) + 3CO_2(g)$

Performance assessment

1. Answers will vary depending on the shampoos selected. Shampoos may have to be diluted with distilled water (the same volume in each sample) in order to get a reliable pH reading.

2. Plans will vary but should include the use of a pH meter or pH test paper. Be sure students follow all lab safety precautions.

3. Answers should involve titrations with standardized acid solution. Students should consider what to do with insoluble antacids, such as $Mg(OH)_2$. One technique is to react them completely with excess standard acid to form soluble products and then back-titrate with a base to the equivalence point.

Portfolio projects

1. Baking powder contains a solid, acid-forming substance, while baking soda is only $NaHCO_3$. Using soda alone requires that an acidic material such as buttermilk be added to the batter. Double-acting baking powder contains another ingredient that produces more CO_2 when the batter is baked.

2. Answers will vary depending on the geographic area.

Reaction Rates

CLASSROOM RESOURCES			
SECTIONS	TEACHER'S DEMONSTRATIONS	PROBLEM SOLVING ■ *Text* ◆ *ChemFile Mini-Guide*	LABORATORIES ■ *Text* ◆ *ChemFile Manuals: A, B, C, D*
16-1 **What is a reaction rate?** Section Review, p. 598	**Demo 1** Calculating the Rate of a Reaction, p. 590 **Demo 2** Change in Rate over Time, p. 592 **Demo 3** Oxidizing Iron, p. 594	■ **Sample Problem 16A:** Determining a rate law, p. 595	■ **QuickLab** Measuring Reaction Rate, p. 590 ■ **Exp. 16A** Reaction Rates, p. 784 ◆ **B18** Clock Reactions ◆ **D19** Rust Race
16-2 **How can reaction rates be explained?** Section Review, p. 603	**Demo 4** Lycopodium Powder, p. 600		
16-3 **How do catalysts change the rates of chemical reactions?** Section Review, p. 609	**Demo 5** Three Kinds of Catalysts, p. 604		◆ **Exp. C20** Catalysts ◆ **Inv. C20** Catalysts—Peroxide Disposal

SECTIONS	VIDEOS/VIDEODISC *Holt Chemistry Videodisc* CNN PRESENTS *Science in the NEWS*	CHEMFILE CD-ROMs ● *Teaching Resources* ◆ *Interactive Tutor*	OVERHEADS ● *Color Transparencies* ◆ *Transparency Masters*
16-1	Collisions and Reaction Mechanisms Magnesium and Hydrochloric Acid, Different Concentrations CNN PRESENTS Segment 27 Synthetic Soil	● Supplemental Reading: *Heads* ● Math Skills: Logarithms	● **96** Reaction Pathways for Ineffective and Effective Collisions ● **97** Possible Collision Orientations for the Reaction of H_2 and I_2 ● **98** Concentration vs. Possible Collisions ◆ **95A** Activation Energy Differences in Exothermic and Endothermic Reactions ◆ **98A** Reaction Rate Over Time for an Equilibrium System
16-2	Bleaching Dye in Hot and Cold Water Reaction Rate: Lycopodium Explosion Methanol Combustion	● Math Skills: Geometry: Surface Area and Volume	
16-3	Catalyst and Hydrogen Peroxide Decomposition CNN PRESENTS Segment 28 Ozone-Eater Radiator		◆ **97A** Comparing Reaction Pathways for H_2O_2 Decomposition by Various Catalysts

ASSESSMENT RESOURCES

ALTERNATIVE ASSESSMENTS	CHAPTER TESTING	SCORING RUBRICS *Holt ChemFile Teaching Resources CD-ROM*
Student Text Performance assessments, p. 616 Portfolio projects 1, p. 616 **Teacher's Edition** Group Strategy, p. 602 Catalysis, p. 606 **Study Guide** Sections 16-1 to 16-3	**Student Text** Test Preparation, p. 617 **Holt Chemistry: Visualizing Matter Chapter 16 Test** (blackline masters) **Holt ChemFile Test Generator for Macintosh and Windows**	**Lab Work** Student-Designed Experiments Rubric Performance-Tasks Scoring Rubric Assessment for Structured Inquiry Assessment for Open-Ended Inquiry **Portfolio Projects** Assessing Portfolios Portfolio Assignment Student Evaluation Form

CHAPTER
16

Establishing Prior Knowledge

Make certain students understand the following concepts.

▶ Chapter 10: stoichiometry
▶ Chapter 11: energy changes in chemical reactions
▶ Chapter 13: concentration of solutions

 READING STRATEGY

Assimilating Knowledge

Before reading this chapter, have students each write a short list of all the things they already know (or think they know) about the meaning of *rate* and how rates can be measured. When students have finished their list, ask them to contribute their entries to a group list on the board or on an overhead projector. Then have students list the things they want to know about rates.

If students have trouble coming up with questions, ask the following to get them on track:

▶ How do you describe the rate of motion of a car?
▶ If two different reactions give off hydrogen gas, how could you compare the rate of one with the rate of the other?
▶ How could you make a reaction go faster?

ABOUT THE ILLUSTRATION

Reaction rates are time dependent. Rate is determined by measuring a change and dividing that measurement by the time elapsed for the change to occur.

CHAPTER
16 Reaction Rates

 internet connect

Holt Chemistry: Visualizing Matter
On-Line Resources
go.hrw.com
Visit the HRW Web site for a variety of resources related to this chapter. Just type in the keyword HW0 Chapt16.

SCLINKS
NSTA

National Science Teachers Association
On-Line Resources: www.scilinks.org
The following Scilinks Internet resources can be found in the student text for this chapter:

Page 593
TOPIC: Magnesium
KEYWORD: HW161

Page 599
TOPIC: Factors affecting rate
KEYWORD: HW162

Page 607
TOPIC: Enzymes
KEYWORD: HW163

Page 608
TOPIC: Inhibitors
KEYWORD: HW164

Page 616
TOPIC: Biochemical processes
KEYWORD: HW165

MORE RED TIDES IN OUR FUTURE?

In 1987, large numbers of fish along the North Carolina and Maryland coasts began to die. Scientists soon discovered that a hidden algae was to blame.

The variety of algae that caused these fish to die is called *Pfiesteria piscicida* (derived from the Latin term for "fish killer"). A short-term warming of the water in that area of the Atlantic Ocean caused a huge increase in the algae population. This warming was caused by the Gulf Stream, a warm-water current that flows up the eastern coast of North America and across the ocean to Europe. In 1987, the Gulf Stream swept in closer to shore than usual.

The algae produce chemicals that are toxic not only to marine life but also to humans. The algae give off a neurotoxin called domoic acid, which paralyzes fish so that they cannot breath. Shellfish, such as oysters and clams, are not themselves harmed by the domoic acid, but they store it in their bodies. Humans who consume these shellfish can become seriously ill. Domoic acid has been found to cause irritation of the eyes and throat, severe headaches, and short-term memory loss.

Gymnodinium breve is another algae that produces toxins. In addition to poisons, they produce red pigments that can be seen in the water where the algae grow. When the pigment is visible, it is called a *red tide*. Red tides occur when these algae *bloom*. An algal bloom is a rapid increase in population.

Algal blooms occur seasonally and are an important part of marine life cycles. The Red Sea probably got its name from seasonal red tides. In the central Pacific Ocean, an event called El Niño triggers a warming of water every few years. During El Niño periods, such as the one that occurred in 1997 and 1998, unusually large red tides can be observed around Pacific islands. These algal blooms, like the bloom off the North Carolina and Maryland coasts, can cause large numbers of fish to die.

Domoic acid

CHAPTER LINKS

How does temperature affect reaction rate?

How does the warming of coastal waters disturb the ecological balance of an area?

Why might eating oysters and other shellfish harvested in the summer months be more of a risk than eating shellfish harvested in the winter months?

The algae that produce red tides generally belong to a group of organisms called *dinoflagellates*, which have two flagella oriented at right angles to each other. When the flagella beat, the organisms spin. The name *dinoflagellate* derives from the Greek word *dinos*, which means "rotation." Except during algal blooms, these organisms are a natural part of the phytoplankton that populates the oceans.

ChemFile Teaching Resources CD-ROM
Supplemental Reading Projects
Assign the guided reading worksheets for George Bear's *Heads* for cross-curricular connections to language arts.

CONCEPT PREVIEW

Section 16-1
Reaction rate
▸ expressing reaction rates
▸ measuring disappearance of reactants or appearance of products

Rate law equations
▸ effect of concentration changes

▸ writing rate law equations
▸ reaction mechanisms

Section 16-2
Factors that affect reaction rates
▸ nature of reactants
▸ surface area
▸ temperature
▸ concentration

Energy changes in reactions
▸ activation energy
▸ collision theory

Section 16-3
The effects of catalysts on reaction rates
▸ homogeneous catalysts
▸ heterogeneous catalysts
▸ enzymes

SECTION 16-1

What is a reaction rate?

OBJECTIVES

▶ ***Calculate*** the rate of a reaction in terms of the disappearance of a reactant or appearance of a product.

▶ ***Determine*** the effects of changing concentrations on a rate given a rate law expression.

Rate is a ratio

How could you make the following statements more informative? *The level on the gas gauge went down. The car sped down the highway. Hydrogen gas bubbled from the solution.* Although these statements identify the changes taking place, they would be more informative if they were expressed in terms of numbers: *The level on the gas gauge fell at a rate of one-fourth of a tank per 35 minutes. The car was traveling 88 km/h (55 mi/h). One-half liter of hydrogen gas was generated in 14 minutes.* Each of the measurable changes is expressed as a function of time. These values are called rates. The car travels at a rate of 88 km/h. Hydrogen gas was evolved at a rate of 0.5 L per 14 minutes.

Rates usually change over the period of time they are measured. For example, suppose you're traveling on an interstate highway. At 2:15 P.M. you pass mile marker 92. At 4:30 P.M. you pass mile marker 227. Your travel speed (rate) is the distance you traveled divided by the elapsed time. But this reflects your average speed. You may have been slowed down by a car in front of you, or you may have sped up to pass another car. You also may have stopped to get gas. Your speed changed. As you

▶ **FIGURE 16-1**

The winner of the race is the car that travels at the highest average rate.

GRAPHIC ORGANIZER

For the reaction
A + 2B ⟶ 2C + D
reaction rate is . . .

either the rate of disappearance of reactants, given by . . .

the change in concentration of reactants per unit time, which is equal to . . .

either $\text{rate} = \dfrac{-1}{2} \times \dfrac{\Delta[B]}{\Delta t}$

or $\text{rate} = \dfrac{-1}{1} \times \dfrac{\Delta[A]}{\Delta t}$

or the rate of appearance of products, given by . . .

the change in concentration of products per unit time, which is equal to . . .

either $\text{rate} = \dfrac{1}{2} \times \dfrac{\Delta[C]}{\Delta t}$

or $\text{rate} = \dfrac{1}{1} \times \dfrac{\Delta[D]}{\Delta t}$

were slowing down to pull up to the gas pump, your speed decreased steadily. By looking at your speedometer, you can determine your rate of travel at any given time. This instantaneous rate of travel is equal to a very short distance traveled divided by a very small time interval.

Just as you can determine average and instantaneous rates for a car traveling on a highway, you can determine average and instantaneous rates for any change. When the change under consideration is a chemical reaction, the rate is called a **reaction rate. Chemical kinetics** is the study of reaction rates and the factors that affect them.

Reaction rate is an experimental quantity

A reaction rate tells how fast a chemical change takes place. It is an experimental quantity found by measuring the disappearance of a reactant or the appearance of a product over a period of time. Expressing a rate requires the ability to accurately measure a change in some variable, such as volume, temperature, color, mass, concentration, or acidity. Study **Figure 16-2.** Magnesium metal has been added to hydrochloric acid. The ionic equation for this reaction is written as follows.

$$Mg(s) + 2H_3O^+(aq) + 2Cl^-(aq) \longrightarrow Mg^{2+}(aq) + 2Cl^-(aq) + H_2(g) + 2H_2O(l)$$

reaction rate

the decrease in reactant concentration or increase in product concentration per unit of time as a reaction proceeds

chemical kinetics

the branch of chemistry concerned with reaction rates and how reactions occur

VISUAL STRATEGY

Figure 16-2 Ask students to examine the diagrams to identify the particles that undergo change in the reaction and those that do not. Create a link to the previous chapter on acid-base chemistry by asking students which test tubes have the largest concentration of hydronium ions and which have the smallest. Ask them to also state what happens to the magnesium atoms that seem to disappear.

CHAPTER CONNECTION

The reaction between Mg(s) and HCl(aq) is an oxidation-reduction reaction in which electrons are transferred from Mg atoms to H_3O^+ ions. Students will encounter redox reactions in Chapter 17.

▼ **FIGURE 16-2**

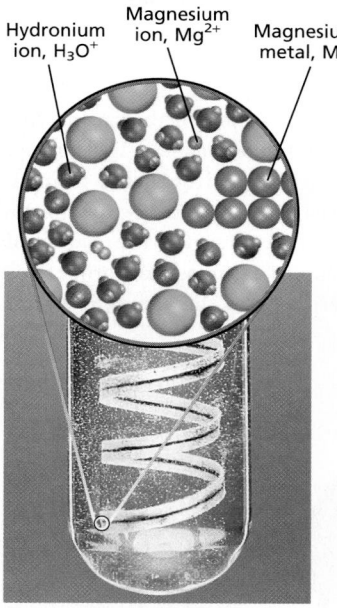
Hydronium ion, H_3O^+ · Magnesium ion, Mg^{2+} · Magnesium metal, Mg

Chloride ion, Cl^- · Water molecule, H_2O

a When Mg is added to aqueous HCl, H_2 and H_2O are formed as two H_3O^+ ions react. The decrease in $[H_3O^+]$ means an increase in pH.

b The Mg piece becomes smaller as its atoms become Mg^{2+} ions. The rate at which H_2 is made decreases as the Mg is used up.

c The reaction continues until the Mg piece disappears, because it is the limiting reagent.

REACTION RATES 589

QUICKLAB

Try to use water that is below room temperature (about 10°C) to keep the reaction rate slower. This will produce more-consistent results.

Analysis

1. Students' answers will vary. Rates should be given in grams per second (or minute).

2. Accept all plausible answers. Students could suggest collecting the gas given off and measuring its volume. Removing the tablet, drying it, and determining its mass is probably not appropriate. Ask students to explain why. *(Water is not a reactant in the reaction of effervescent tablets. It only serves as a solvent for the dry ingredients that react in solution. Therefore, the tablet will continue reacting until it is thoroughly dried.)*

3. Calculated rates should be significantly higher at higher temperatures.

TEACHING TIP

Average Rate Only the *average* rate of a reaction can be determined by taking one measurement at the beginning and another at the end. In order to examine the progress of a reaction in more detail, a chemist must conduct an experiment in which the reaction is sampled at several time intervals. Graphing these concentrations over time will produce a rate curve that allows the chemist to determine the reaction rate at any given instant.

QUICKLAB

CONSUMER ACTIVITY

Measuring Reaction Rate

The reaction rate involved in the dissolution of an effervescent tablet in water is easy to measure. You can determine the average rate of reaction in terms of the disappearance of the tablet.

Materials cup, water, effervescent tablet, balance, stopwatch

Problem How can you determine the rate of reaction when an effervescent tablet dissolves in water? Use the balance to measure the mass of the tablet. Use the stopwatch to measure the time elapsed as the tablet dissolves.

Analysis

1. Determine the average rate of the reaction in terms of the disappearance of the effervescent tablet. What units do you use?

2. Can you think of another method for determining the rate of this reaction? What other change in the materials do you observe?

3. Repeat the procedure using warm water. How does the rate change with the temperature of the water?

average rate

the change in a measured property (usually concentration) divided by the total time elapsed

▶ **FIGURE 16-3**

Average rate can be determined by monitoring a reaction and measuring the total time elapsed. For the reaction of Mg and HCl, you can monitor the disappearance of Mg.

What observations indicate that a reaction is taking place? Bubbles are coming off the piece of metal because H_2 gas is being produced. The metal piece is getting smaller and finally disappears. A pH meter can be used to tell that the concentration of H_3O^+ ions is decreasing during the reaction.

How can rate be measured? The rate of this reaction can be expressed as the rate of disappearance of Mg or H_3O^+ or by the rate of appearance of H_2 or Mg^{2+}. In practice, the rate of appearance of Mg^{2+} is difficult to determine because the ions remain in aqueous solution, making their concentrations difficult to measure. Therefore, the appearance of Mg^{2+} will almost never be used to determine the rate of this reaction.

You can determine the rate using one of the measurable properties of this reaction: the decrease in mass of Mg, the decrease in hydronium ion concentration (or acidity), or the volume of hydrogen gas formed. Any one of the three observable properties permits you to express the change from initial to final conditions that occurs over the course of the reaction. Dividing the change in each of the measured properties by the total time elapsed during the reaction gives the **average rate** for the reaction.

DEMONSTRATION 1

Calculating the Rate of a Reaction
Approximate time: 5 minutes

1. Cut two 4 cm pieces of Mg ribbon.

2. Tie a 10 cm length of thread around each ribbon. Tape the free ends of thread just outside the mouths of two 50 mL eudiometer tubes (burets turned upside down can be substituted for the eudiometer tubes).

3. With the Mg pieces outside the tube, pour 15 mL of 1 M HCl solution into each of the tubes.

4. Fill one tube with tap water that has come to room temperature. Pour the water slowly down the side of the tube at first to prevent too much water from mixing with the HCl. Repeat the procedure with the second eudiometer, but this time use ice water. Record the temperature of each tube.

| TABLE 16-1 | Reaction Rate Data and Calculations for the Reaction of Mg in Aqueous HCl |

Property	Initial quantity	Final quantity	Change in quantity	Change in quantity (mol)	Time elapsed (s)	Average rate = $\dfrac{\text{change}}{\text{time elapsed}}$
Mass of Mg	0.376 g	0.000 g	−0.376 g	−0.0155	32	rate = $\dfrac{0.0155 \text{ mol Mg}}{32 \text{ s}}$ = 0.00048 mol/s
Volume of H_2	0.0 mL	418 mL	418 mL	0.0154*	32	rate = $\dfrac{0.0154 \text{ mol } H_2}{32 \text{ s}}$ = 0.00048 mol/s
$[H_3O^+]$**	0.500 M	0.293 M	−0.207 M	−0.0310	32	rate = $\dfrac{0.0310 \text{ mol } H_3O^+}{32 \text{ s}}$ = 0.00097 mol/s

* determined using the ideal gas law equation at 40°C and 0.947 atm
** determined from the pH of the 150 mL solution

Rate can be noted from the disappearance of a reactant or the appearance of a product

Table 16-1 summarizes the calculation of the average reaction rate using data obtained by each of the methods for measuring change in the reaction between magnesium and hydrochloric acid. At the end of the reaction, you have no magnesium left; consequently, subtracting the initial mass of magnesium from the final mass of magnesium yields a negative number. By convention, reaction rates are always written as positive values. Therefore, when rate is determined in terms of the disappearance of a reactant, the change is multiplied by −1 to give a positive value for the rate.

How do the three values in the rate column of Table 16-1 compare? The reaction rate calculated in terms of the mass of magnesium is equal to that calculated in terms of the hydrogen gas. The reaction rate calculated in terms of the hydronium ion concentration, however, is twice as large as that determined in terms of either Mg or H_2. This difference suggests that hydronium ions are disappearing twice as fast as magnesium atoms are and that hydronium ions are also disappearing twice as fast as hydrogen gas is appearing. How can you account for this difference? Look again at the balanced equation for the overall reaction.

$$Mg(s) + 2H_3O^+(aq) \longrightarrow Mg^{2+}(aq) + H_2(g) + 2H_2O(l)$$

Consider the coefficients for Mg, H_3O^+, and H_2. Both Mg and H_2 have coefficients of 1. So H_2 is formed as rapidly as Mg disappears. The mole ratio between H_3O^+ and Mg, however, is 2:1. This means that 2 mol of H_3O^+ must be used for every 1 mol of Mg consumed. The ratio indicates that the rate for the disappearance of H_3O^+ is twice as fast as that for the disappearance of Mg. The mole ratio between H_3O^+ and H_2 is also 2:1. To compensate for this effect of stoichiometry on reaction rate, chemists divide the rate of change for each reactant or product by

Table 16-1 Before students read this page, ask them to inspect the rate calculations in the right column of the table and determine the relationship of the rate calculated for the disappearance of H_3O^+ with the rates calculated for production of H_2 and the disappearance of Mg. Ask students to account for this difference. If they have trouble doing so, refer them to the ionic equation on the previous page, and recommend that they examine the equation's stoichiometry.

5. Fill a 600 mL beaker almost full with tap water, and set the beaker in a pan to catch any overflow.

6. Place the ribbon inside the eudiometer with the ice water, and plug the mouth with a one-hole stopper. Immediately invert the eudiometer tube while submerging the stoppered end in the water in the beaker.

7. Every 15 seconds, record the total volume of gas that has been produced until the reaction stops. Calculate the reaction rate.

8. Repeat steps 6 and 7 for the eudiometer tube filled with room-temperature water.

Safety
Wear safety goggles and a laboratory apron. Use a nonmercury thermometer.

Disposal
Rinse any unreacted Mg, and put it in the trash. Combine the rinsings with the liquid from the eudiometers and beakers, neutralize with 0.1 M NaOH until the pH is between 6 and 8, and flush the rinsings down the drain.

RESOURCE LINK

IN-TEXT LAB
Skills Development
Have students do Exploration 16A, on page 784, to develop their skills working with reaction rates.

TEACHING TIP

Units for Rate Point out the advantage of expressing reaction rate as the change in concentration per unit of time. Concentration is expressed as the amount of a substance per unit of volume. Therefore, the concentration term is independent of the total volume of a reaction or the total mass of a reactant or product. The rate calculated for a reaction done at test-tube scale will theoretically be the same as the reaction taking place in 1000 kL as long as other conditions remain the same.

ANSWERS

CONCEPT CHECK

1. It is a reactant because its concentration decreases during the reaction.

   2.0 M/40 min = 0.05 M/min

2. relative to N_2, rate = 0.02 M/s
   relative to H_2, rate = 0.06 M/s

3. $rate = \dfrac{-1}{6} \times \dfrac{\Delta[HCl]}{\Delta t}$

   $rate = \dfrac{-1}{1} \times \dfrac{\Delta[KClO_3]}{\Delta t}$

   $rate = \dfrac{1}{3} \times \dfrac{\Delta[Cl_2]}{\Delta t}$

   $rate = \dfrac{1}{1} \times \dfrac{\Delta[KCl]}{\Delta t}$

   Rate as a function of $[H_2O]$ is not usually written for a reaction in aqueous solution.

its coefficient in the balanced chemical equation. Thus, for the reaction between Mg and aqueous HCl, the reaction rate is expressed as follows.

$$rate = \frac{-1}{1} \times \frac{\Delta(\text{mol Mg})}{\Delta t} = \frac{1}{1} \times \frac{\Delta(\text{mol } H_2)}{\Delta t} = \frac{-1}{2} \times \frac{\Delta(\text{mol } H_3O^+)}{\Delta t}$$

The units for a reaction rate must always be expressed. The units for the rate in the above equation are moles per second. However, reaction rates are usually stated as $\dfrac{\text{concentration}}{\text{time}}$. When concentration units are moles of a substance per liter of solution (M), the general equation for rate is written as follows.

$$rate = \frac{-1}{a} \times \frac{\Delta[\text{reactant}]}{\Delta t} = \frac{1}{b} \times \frac{\Delta[\text{product}]}{\Delta t}$$

The minus sign makes the decrease in reactant concentration a positive number. The a is the coefficient of the reactant in the balanced chemical equation; b is the coefficient of the product. For example, sodium hypochlorite is prepared according to the following equation.

$$Cl_2(aq) + 2NaOH(aq) \longrightarrow NaOCl(aq) + NaCl(aq) + H_2O(l)$$

The rate can be expressed as follows. The change in H_2O is ignored because a slight addition to the solvent is difficult to measure.

$$rate = \frac{-1}{1} \times \frac{\Delta[Cl_2]}{\Delta t} = \frac{-1}{2} \times \frac{\Delta[NaOH]}{\Delta t} = \frac{1}{1} \times \frac{\Delta[NaOCl]}{\Delta t} = \frac{1}{1} \times \frac{\Delta[NaCl]}{\Delta t}$$

Very few chemical reactions proceed at a constant rate throughout the entire process. Most reactions are fast at the beginning, when all of the reactant concentrations are high, and slow down as the reactants are consumed. In some reactions, the rate becomes constant when the reaction reaches equilibrium. In other reactions, the rate decreases to zero when the reaction nears completion.

CONCEPT CHECK

1. The concentration of a substance involved in a reaction changes from 4.0 M to 2.0 M in 40 minutes. Is the substance a reactant or a product? Explain how you know. Express the average rate of this reaction in M/min.

2. Ammonia is formed from its elements according to the equation below.

   $$N_2(g) + 3H_2(g) \longrightarrow 2NH_3(g)$$

   One mole of N_2 is mixed with 1 mol of H_2 in a 1 L container. After 5 seconds, the reaction is stopped and the gases are remeasured. There are 0.9 mol of N_2, and 0.7 mol of H_2. Calculate the average reaction rate in terms of each reactant.

3. Given the following chemical equation, write expressions for the rate in terms of each reactant and product.

   $$KClO_3(aq) + 6HCl(aq) \longrightarrow 3Cl_2(g) + 3H_2O(l) + KCl(aq)$$

DEMONSTRATION 2

Change in Rate over Time

Approximate time: 15 minutes

1. Cut four 20.0 cm pieces of clean magnesium ribbon. Check masses to be sure the pieces are within 0.002 g of each other. Tie a 15 cm piece of thread to each.

2. Write the mass of 20.0 cm of Mg ribbon on the board to the nearest 0.001 g. This is the mass at time 0.

3. Tie the other end of the thread to each of four glass or plastic stirring rods, keeping

about 1 cm of thread between the rod and the Mg strip.

4. Place 150 mL of 0.1 M HCl solution in each of four 250 mL beakers. Have a 400 mL beaker of water available.

5. Place one of the Mg pieces in the first beaker. After 1 minute, remove and rinse it in the beaker of water.

ELEMENT SPOTLIGHT

Mg

Magnesium

12

24.3050

[Ne]3s²

Magnesium, an unlimited resource

Extracting magnesium from sea water is an efficient and economical process. Sea water is mixed with lime, CaO, from oyster shells to form insoluble magnesium hydroxide, $Mg(OH)_2$, which can be easily filtered out. Hydrochloric acid is added to the solid to form magnesium chloride, which undergoes electrolysis to produce pure magnesium metal.

Industrial Uses

▶ Magnesium oxide, MgO, is used in paper manufacturing, as well as in fertilizers, pharmaceuticals, and household cleaners.

▶ Magnesium hydroxide, $Mg(OH)_2$, suspended in aqueous solution is known as *milk of magnesia* and is used as an antacid.

▶ Magnesium is an important component in the production of dry-cell batteries and fireworks.

▶ Magnesium is the lightest metal used in industrial construction; its density is less than two-thirds that of aluminum.

▶ Magnesium alloys are used in aircraft fuselages, engine parts, missiles, luggage, optical and photo equipment, lawn mowers, and portable tools.

ELEMENT SPOTLIGHT

In addition to its low density and strength, magnesium burns brightly in air. Because of this property, it is used in some types of emergency flares and fireworks.

If 90 million metric tons of Mg were extracted per year for 1 million years, the Mg content of the oceans would drop by 0.01%.

WHERE IS IT?

Earth's Crust
2.5% by mass

eighth most abundant element

Sea Water
0.13% by mass

internet**connect**

SCI*LINKS*
NSTA

TOPIC: Magnesium
GO TO: www.scilinks.org
KEYWORD: HW161

Spinach is a good source of dietary magnesium. Magnesium is the central atom in the green plant pigment chlorophyll.

Chlorophyll-a

A BRIEF HISTORY

1833: Michael Faraday makes magnesium metal through the electrolysis of molten magnesium chloride.

1852: Robert Bunsen designs an electrolytic cell that allows molten Mg to be collected without burning when it makes contact with the air.

1800

1900

1828: A.A.B. Bussy obtains the first pure magnesium metal.

1808: Humphry Davy discovers that the compound *magnesia alba* is the oxide of a new metal.

1944: L. M. Pidgeon discovers how to extract magnesium from its ore, dolomite.

REACTION RATES 593

---

6. Dry the piece, remove the thread, and measure the mass of the Mg to the nearest 0.001 g.

7. Repeat steps **5** and **6** with the other three pieces of Mg ribbon, leaving the pieces in the acid for 2, 3, and 4 minutes, respectively.

8. Plot the four masses on the *y*-axis of a graph, plot the time on the *x*-axis, and draw a smooth curve through the data points.

Safety

Wear safety goggles and a laboratory apron. Keep students at least 10 ft away from the demonstration.

Disposal

Rinse the unreacted Mg, and put it in the trash. Combine the rinsings with the liquid from the beakers, neutralize the liquid with 0.1 M NaOH, and flush it down the drain.

► **FIGURE 16-4**

Pieces of magnesium ribbon react more rapidly with HCl in the beaker at right because it is more concentrated than the HCl in the beaker at left.

 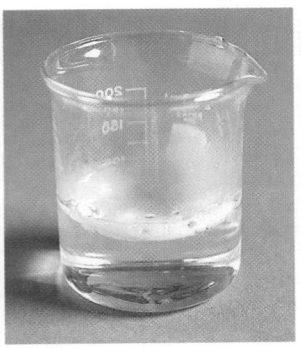

▲ **FIGURE 16-5**

The colorless gas HI decomposes at an observable rate, as can be seen by the production of violet iodine gas.

rate law

an expression for the rate of a reaction as a function of the concentration of one or more reactants

order

the exponent on the concentration for a specified reactant in a rate law expression

The effect of concentration on rate

Examine the two photographs in **Figure 16-4.** The reaction on the right is more vigorous than the reaction on the left. Both beakers contain aqueous hydrochloric acid and magnesium, but the solution on the right has a higher concentration of HCl than the solution on the left.

With some reactions, doubling the concentration doubles the rate. But with other reactions, doubling the concentration causes a fourfold increase in the reaction rate. This is true for the decomposition of HI to form H_2 and I_2, shown in **Figure 16-5.** In this type of reaction, the rate is proportional to the square of the reactant concentration. There are even reactions for which increasing the concentration has no effect on the reaction rate. How can that be true? It was all a mystery until chemists began to look at reaction *mechanisms* and *rate laws.*

Determining a general rate law equation

Experiments show that reaction rate is directly proportional to reactant concentration raised to some power, n. This proportionality is made an equality by the inclusion of k, the experimentally determined rate constant.

$$\text{rate} = k[\text{A}]^n$$

This equation is a general **rate law.** The exponent, n, is called the **order** with respect to substance A and *must be determined from experimental data.*

It is possible for a reaction to have a rate that is independent of a particular reactant concentration. In this case, the reaction is of zero order with respect to that reactant. Look again at the rate law equation. A reaction that is first order with respect to A has a value of 1 for n. With an exponent of 1, the reaction rate will be proportional to the concentration of A. If the data show that doubling the concentration of reactant A causes the rate to double, you know the rate law must be first order. Sample Problem 16A gives an example of a reaction that is not first order. It is still possible to determine the rate law equation.

594   CHAPTER 16

DEMONSTRATION 3

Oxidizing Iron

Approximate time: 10 minutes

1. Pour about 25 mL of fresh 3% H_2O_2 into a heavy glass bottle of about 250 mL capacity, and add about a gram of MnO_2 powder. The mixture will bubble as the MnO_2 catalyzes the decomposition of H_2O_2 to H_2O and O_2 gas.

2. Lay a glass plate over the mouth of the bottle so that the O_2 will not diffuse out.

3. Hold a small loose tuft of fine steel wool with crucible tongs, and thrust the steel wool into the flame of a laboratory burner. Have students note that it stops burning soon after it is withdrawn from the flame.

4. Light the tuft again, and while it is glowing, thrust it into the bottle of oxygen. It will burn brightly as the iron oxidizes.

SAMPLE PROBLEM 16A   Determining a rate law

Determine the rate law equation for the following reaction, given the experimental data shown.

$$3A \longrightarrow C$$

Concentration of A	Reaction rate
0.2 M	1.0 M/s
0.4 M	4.0 M/s

1 List what you know

▶ When the concentration of A is 0.2 M, the reaction rate is 1.0 M/s.
▶ When the concentration of A is 0.4 M, the reaction rate is 4.0 M/s.
▶ When the concentration of A doubles, the rate quadruples.

2 Set up the problem

▶ Write rate law equations for the data given using rate $= k[A]^n$.

$$\text{rate}_1 = 1.0 \text{ M/s} = k[0.2 \text{ M}]^n$$
$$\text{rate}_2 = 4.0 \text{ M/s} = k[0.4 \text{ M}]^n$$

3 Calculate

▶ Divide the two rate equations and solve for n.

$$\frac{4.0 \text{ M/s}}{1.0 \text{ M/s}} = \frac{k[0.4 \text{ M}]^n}{k[0.2 \text{ M}]^n}$$

$$4.0 = 2^n$$

For this simple problem, you can see that $n = 2$.

$$4 = 2^2$$

Logarithmic solution

▶ For more complex equations, logarithms can be used to solve for n. Take the logarithm of both sides of the equation.

$$\log(4.0) = \log(2)^n$$

You have an equation in which the variable you want to solve for is an exponent. To rearrange the equation so that the variable is no longer an exponent, use the following law of logarithms.

$$\log(2)^n = n\log(2)$$

Substitute and solve.

$$\log(4.0) = n\log(2)$$
$$0.602 = n(0.301)$$
$$n = 2$$

▶ Write the rate law for the chemical equation.

$$\text{rate} = k[A]^2$$

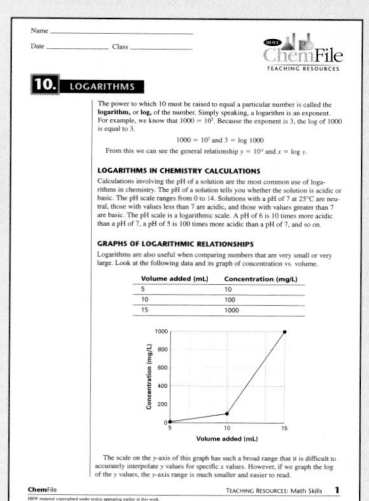

---

5. Ask students to account for the difference in the way the iron burned in air and in nearly pure oxygen. Air is about 20% O_2, while the gas in the bottle was much more concentrated—near 100% O_2.

Safety
Wear a lab apron, gloves, and goggles during this demonstration. Keep students at least 10 ft away from the demonstration.

Disposal
Filter off the solids, and rinse them with tap water. Pour the liquid down the drain, provided your school drains are connected to a sanitary sewer system with a treatment plant. Dispose of the solids in the trash.

ANSWERS

PRACTICE PROBLEMS 16A

1. $rate_1 = 3.3 \times 10^{-2}$ M/s
   $= k[0.020 \text{ M}]^n$
   $rate_2 = 8.2 \times 10^{-3}$ M/s
   $= k[0.010 \text{ M}]^n$

   $$\frac{3.3 \times 10^{-2} \text{ M/s}}{8.2 \times 10^{-3} \text{ M/s}} = \frac{k[0.020 \text{ M}]^n}{k[0.010 \text{ M}]^n}$$

   $4.0 = 2.0^n$
   $n = 2$
   $rate = k[\text{HI}]^2$

2. **a.** $rate = k[x]^0$
   $k[2x]^0 = 2^0 k[x]^0 = 1k[x]^0$
   $= 1 \times rate$

   b. $rate = k[x]^3$
   $k[2x]^3 = 2^3 k[x]^3 = 8k[x]^3$
   $= 8 \times rate$

   c. $rate = k[x]^4$
   $k[2x]^4 = 2^4 k[x]^4 = 16k[x]^4$
   $= 16 \times rate$

ADDITIONAL EXAMPLES

SAMPLE PROBLEM 16A

1. Determine the rate laws of the following reactions from the data given:

   a. $A \longrightarrow 2B + C$

[A]	Reaction rate
0.30 M	0.19 M/s
0.60 M	0.38 M/s

   Ans. $rate = k[A]$

   b. $A \longrightarrow B + 3C$

[A]	Reaction rate
0.072 M	0.0013 M/s
0.144 M	0.0104 M/s

   Ans. $rate = k[A]^3$

2. The reaction $X \longrightarrow 2Y + 2Z$ is a second-order reaction with respect to [X]. How will the reaction rate change if [X] is doubled? How will the rate change if [X] is reduced by half?

   Ans. The reaction rate is increased to four times its original rate if [X] is doubled. The reaction rate is decreased to one-fourth its original rate if [X] is reduced by half.

1. Look again at the reaction for the decomposition of hydrogen iodide.

   $$2\text{HI}(g) \longrightarrow \text{H}_2(g) + \text{I}_2(g)$$

   The rate of this reaction changes with the concentration of HI according to the following experimental data.

[HI]	0.010	0.020	0.040
Rate	8.2×10^{-3} M/s	3.3×10^{-2} M/s	0.13 M/s

   Determine the rate law equation for this reaction.

2. By what factor will the rate of a reaction increase if a reactant's concentration is doubled? Use the following values as the order with respect to that reactant.

   a. 0   **b.** 3   **c.** 4

Rate laws for reactions with more than one reactant

The rate law equations you have looked at so far have been for reactions involving only one reactant. But what about cases in which there are two or more reactants?

If more than one reactant is found to contribute to the rate of the reaction, then all contributing reactants must appear in the rate law. The general rate law equation for a reaction in which two components, A and B, affect the rate is written as follows.

$$rate = k[A]^n[B]^m$$

overall reaction order

the sum of all the exponents in a rate law expression

The value of n is the order with respect to reactant A. The value of m is the order with respect to reactant B. The **overall reaction order** is equal to the sum of m and n. Again, these exponents can be determined only by experimentation.

If you double the concentration of A and find that the rate doubles, you know that the reaction is first order with respect to A. This would be the same as it would be if A were the only reactant. To find the reaction order with respect to B, you must run the reaction again, this time holding [A] constant but changing the concentration of B. If [B] is doubled and the reaction rate quadruples, the reaction is second order with respect to B. This is the same result as in Sample Problem 16A. For the reaction of A and B in this example, the rate law would be written as follows.

$$rate = k[A][B]^2$$

The overall order of this reaction is third order.

Rate laws cannot be derived from a chemical equation

Do not confuse the exponents in the rate law with those in an equilibrium expression. Exponents in equilibrium expressions are coefficients in the balanced chemical equation; *exponents in the rate law must be derived from experimental data.* The equilibrium expression for the decomposition of N_2O_5 is derived from its balanced chemical equation.

$$2N_2O_5 \rightleftharpoons 4NO_2 + O_2$$

$$K_{eq} = \frac{[NO_2]^4[O_2]}{[N_2O_5]^2}$$

N_2O_5 has an exponent of 2 because its coefficient in the balanced chemical equation is 2. However, the experimentally determined rate law expression for this same reaction is the following.

$$\text{rate} = k[N_2O_5]^1$$

The difference between the exponents in a rate law and those in an equilibrium equation comes from the difference between a balanced chemical equation and a reaction *mechanism*.

A cartoonist named Rube Goldberg drew images of imaginary machines that performed a seemingly simple task using many steps. An example of one of his machines is shown in **Figure 16-6.** Like this machine, most chemical reactions proceed through a series of steps called a pathway, or **mechanism.** The slowest step in the pathway determines the reaction rate and is called the **rate-determining step.**

Each reaction step is called an **elementary step.** The rate law is determined by the rate-determining step, so there may be substances in the elementary steps that do not appear in the rate law. Also, many substances may be made and used during the course of the reaction. These **intermediates** do not appear in the rate law expression.

It is very important to keep in mind that a balanced chemical equation and a reaction mechanism are two different expressions. A rate law can be written from a mechanism, never from a balanced chemical equation. Because many reaction pathways occur very rapidly, it can be difficult to determine mechanisms. In fact, mechanisms are commonly disproved and newer ones are proposed.

mechanism

a proposed sequence of steps that describes how reactants are changed into products

rate-determining step

the slowest elementary step in a reaction mechanism

elementary step

a single step in the mechanism of a reaction

intermediate

a structure formed in one elementary step but consumed in a later step of a mechanism

Bottle opener

Elephant (A) eats peanuts (B)—as bag gets lighter weight (C) drops and spike (D) punctures balloon (E)—explosion scares monkey (F)—his hat (G) flies off and releases hook (H), causing spring (I) to pull string (J) which tilts tennis racket (K)—racket hits ball (L), making it spin around on attached string, thereby screwing corkscrew into cork (M)—ball hits sleeping dog (N) who jumps and pulls cork out of bottle with string (O)—my how simple!

FIGURE 16-6 ◄

Some mechanisms are easier to figure out than others. Try to determine the rate-determining step in this mechanism.

ANSWERS

SECTION REVIEW

Total recall

1. The concentration of reactants is highest at the beginning of a reaction, so the rate is fastest then.

Critical thinking

2. A rate law is a mathematical equation that expresses the rate of a reaction as a function of the concentration of one or more reactants. A chemical equation gives little or no indication of the reaction mechanism from which the rate law is determined.

3. **a.** $\text{rate} = \dfrac{-1}{2} \times \dfrac{\Delta[H_2O_2]}{\Delta t} = \dfrac{\Delta[O_2]}{\Delta t}$

   b. $\text{rate} = \dfrac{-1}{1} \times \dfrac{\Delta[Cl_2]}{\Delta t} = \dfrac{\Delta[OCl^-]}{\Delta t}$

   c. $\text{rate} = \dfrac{-1}{2} \times \dfrac{\Delta[NH_3]}{\Delta t} = \dfrac{1}{3} \times \dfrac{\Delta[Cl_2]}{\Delta t}$

   d. $\text{rate} = \dfrac{-1}{1} \times \dfrac{\Delta[NH_4NO_3]}{\Delta t} =$

   $\dfrac{\Delta[N_2O]}{\Delta t}$

4. Change in concentration has no effect on reaction rate.

5. 5.0 M/s

6. The growth rate of the algae depends on the availability of nutrients in the same way that a reaction rate depends on the availability of a limiting reactant. Once a critical nutrient is used up, the algae stop growing.

Practice problems

7. **a.** $\text{rate} = \dfrac{-1}{4} \times \dfrac{\Delta[PH_3]}{\Delta t} = \dfrac{\Delta[P_4]}{\Delta t} =$

   $\dfrac{1}{6} \times \dfrac{\Delta[H_2]}{\Delta t}$

   b. $\text{rate} = \dfrac{-1}{1} \times \dfrac{\Delta[S^{2-}]}{\Delta t} = \dfrac{-1}{1} \times \dfrac{\Delta[I_3^-]}{\Delta t} =$

   $\dfrac{\Delta[S]}{\Delta t} = \dfrac{1}{3} \times \dfrac{\Delta[I^-]}{\Delta t}$

Rates can be manipulated

For most chemical reactions, the reaction rate is highest at the beginning, when reactant concentrations are highest, and decreases as reactants are used up and products are formed. Other than concentration, what affects the rate of a chemical reaction? The next section identifies four of the five factors that affect reaction rates and explains why or how the rate is affected. The fifth factor will be discussed in Section 16-3.

SECTION REVIEW

Total recall

1. Explain why the rate of a simple reaction is likely to be fastest at the beginning of the reaction.

Critical thinking

2. What is meant by a rate law for a chemical reaction? Why can a rate law not be written from a balanced chemical equation?

3. For each of the following reactions, write one expression for the reaction rate that uses a reactant and one expression that uses a product.
   a. $2H_2O_2(aq) \longrightarrow 2H_2O(l) + O_2(g)$
   b. $Cl_2(aq) + 2OH^-(aq) \longrightarrow$
   $OCl^-(aq) + Cl^-(aq) + H_2O(l)$
   c. $2NH_3(aq) + 6OCl^-(aq) \longrightarrow$
   $3Cl_2(g) + N_2(g) + 6OH^-(aq)$
   d. $NH_4NO_3(aq) \longrightarrow N_2O(g) + 2H_2O(l)$

4. How does a reactant with an order of zero in the rate law affect the reaction rate?

5. Dinitrogen pentoxide decomposes into nitrogen dioxide and oxygen according to the following equation.

   $2N_2O_5(g) \longrightarrow 4NO_2(g) + O_2(g)$

   If the change in O_2 concentration was found to be 2.5 M/s, what is the reaction rate in terms of N_2O_5?

6. **Story Clue** Compare the limiting of algae growth by a shortage of nutrients with the limiting reagent in a chemical reaction.

Practice problems

7. Express the reaction rate in terms of the rate of change of each reactant and each product in the following reactions:
   a. $4PH_3(g) \longrightarrow P_4(s) + 6H_2(g)$
   b. $S^{2-}(aq) + I_3^-(aq) \longrightarrow S(s) + 3I^-(aq)$
   c. $C_2H_4(g) + Br_2(g) \longrightarrow C_2H_4Br_2(g)$

8. Ammonia, NH_3, reacts with O_2 to form NO and H_2O as follows:

   $4NH_3(g) + 5O_2(g) \longrightarrow 4NO(g) + 6H_2O(g)$

   a. At the instant when NH_3 is reacting at a rate of 0.80 M/min, what is the rate at which O_2 is disappearing?
   b. At what rate is each product being formed?

9. The observed rate law for the reaction of NO with Cl_2 is written as follows:

   $$\text{rate} = k[NO]^2[Cl_2]$$

   What is the order of reaction with respect to NO? with respect to Cl_2? for the overall reaction?

10. If the rate of a reaction is expressed by $k[B]^2$, how would the rate change if the concentration of B were increased by a factor of 1.41? if it were decreased by a factor of 0.5?

---

c. $\text{rate} = \dfrac{-1}{1} \times \dfrac{\Delta[C_2H_4]}{\Delta t} = \dfrac{-1}{1} \times \dfrac{\Delta[Br_2]}{\Delta t} = \dfrac{\Delta[C_2H_4Br_2]}{\Delta t}$

8. **a.** $\text{rate}_{O_2} = \dfrac{5}{4}\text{rate}_{NH_3} = \dfrac{5}{4}(0.80 \text{ M/min}) = 1.0 \text{ M/min}$

   b. $\text{rate}_{NO} = \text{rate}_{NH_3} = 8.0 \text{ M/min}$

   $\text{rate}_{H_2O} = \dfrac{6}{4}\text{rate}_{NH_3} = \dfrac{6}{4}(0.80 \text{ M/min}) = 1.2 \text{ M/min}$

9. with respect to NO: second order; with respect to Cl_2: first order; overall: third order

10. $\text{rate} = k[B]^2$

   $k[1.41 \times B]^2 = 1.41^2 k[B]^2 = 1.99k[B]^2 \approx 2 \times \text{rate}$

   $k[0.5 \times B]^2 = 0.5^2 k[B]^2 = 0.25k[B]^2 = \dfrac{1}{4} \times \text{rate}$

How can reaction rates be explained?

OBJECTIVES ▶ **List** four major factors that affect the rate of a reaction, and describe how changes in each factor affect the rate.

▶ **Discuss** how collision theory explains reaction rates.

The factors that influence rate of reaction

You are already familiar with one of the factors that influence rates of chemical reactions. You learned in Section 16-1 that concentration can have an effect on reaction rates.

The identity of the substances involved in a reaction is even more important to the rate than the reactant concentrations, as shown in **Figure 16-7.** When you build a campfire, you do not use rocks; you use wood. If the tiniest spark is introduced into a mixture of H_2 and O_2, a violent explosion can occur as the reaction proceeds very quickly. If the same spark is introduced into a mixture of H_2 and N_2, nothing happens.

If you have ever tried to start a campfire, you also know that you do not start with logs. You start with small twigs or crumpled newspapers. The more finely divided a solid is, the easier it is to cause it to react. This illustrates the third factor in determining reaction rates—surface area.

The fourth factor is temperature. Sugar dissolves faster in hot tea than it does in iced tea. An increase in temperature speeds up a reaction. The remainder of this section will discuss the factors that influence the rates of chemical reactions in more detail.

internet connect

SCi LINKS.
NSTA
TOPIC: Factors affecting rate
GO TO: www.scilinks.org
KEYWORD: HW162

FIGURE 16-7 ◀

Potassium reacts very rapidly with water. Iron also reacts with water, but the reaction is much slower.

REACTION RATES 599

LESSON WARM-UP

Discussion Strategy Before beginning this section, point out to students that chemical reactions occur when reactant particles collide with each other with sufficient energy to cause a reaction. Ask them to suggest ways that you could increase the frequency of collisions, the energy of the collisions, or both to increase the reaction rate. Lead students to realize that increasing concentration, temperature, or surface area will increase the reaction rate. Ask students to explain how each of these changes would affect the frequency or energy of the collisions.

ADDITIONAL APPLICATION

The study of reaction rates is very important to chemical engineers, who often must design processes to produce substances on an industrial scale. These engineers are always concerned with getting the best possible yield of a product without producing large amounts of impurities or products of side reactions. After studying the kinetics of a reaction, an engineer designs ways to regulate temperatures, pressures, rates of flow of reactants, rates of removal of products, and other factors to produce the substance in an efficient and economical way.

READING STRATEGY

Organizing Concepts Build the following table as you proceed through this section.

Factor increased	Effect on particles	Effect on collisions	Effect on reaction rate
Concentration	increases number of particles in the same space	increases frequency of collisions	increases rate
Temperature	increases average velocity of particle motion	increases both frequency and average energy of collisions	increases rate
Surface area	increases number of particles exposed	increases frequency of collisions	increases rate

The nature of the reactants affects reaction rate

Reactions involve the making and breaking of bonds. The rate at which bonds break and re-form depends on the type of bond and the nature of the molecules in which the bonds are found. Some processes, like the potassium and water reaction, take place very rapidly, while others, like the oxidation of lead by oxygen dissolved in water, take place very slowly if at all. The nature of a reactant is not a variable that can be adjusted to improve reaction rate.

Surface area affects rate of reaction

If you have ever tried to sweeten tea with sugar cubes, you know that it is much easier to dissolve the sugar if the cubes are crushed. Crushing the cube increases its surface area. The larger surface area allows more sugar molecules to contact the solution. Sugar dissolving in tea is a physical process, not a chemical one, but the explanation for this observation also applies to chemical reactions.

Reactions in which the reactants are all gases or liquids can happen quickly because the fluid particles are free to mix and collide. Particles in a solid, however, are in relatively fixed positions; only particles at the surface of the solid come into contact with other reactants. Therefore, if the surface area of the solid is increased, the number of particles available for reaction increases as well, and the reaction rate increases.

When wood burns, a reaction occurs between the wood and the oxygen in the air. The larger the area where oxygen can contact the wood, the more rapidly the wood will burn. **Figure 16-8** illustrates this point by showing that it is easier to ignite tiny twigs than it is to ignite a large piece of wood.

▼ FIGURE 16-8

a Division of a solid makes the exposed surface of the solid larger.

b More divisions mean more exposed surface.

c Hence, more surface is available for other reactant molecules to come together.

600   CHAPTER 16

DEMONSTRATION 4

Lycopodium Powder

Approximate time: 10 minutes

1. Place a small pile of lycopodium powder in an evaporating dish or watch glass, and play the flame of a laboratory burner over it. Students will note that the powder will scorch but not burn.

2. Next set the burner on the table. Toss a small pinch of the powder into the flame. A dramatic fireball will occur as the separated particles burn more rapidly.

Safety

Wear safety goggles and a lab apron. Practice this before exhibiting it to the class so that you know how much lycopodium to use. Remove all flammable material within 3 ft of the burner, and do not wear long sleeves during this demonstration. Keep students at least 10 ft away from the demonstration.

Temperature influences reaction rate

What do you do if you have a group of people coming for dinner and your food is not cooking fast enough? The best way to speed up the cooking process is to raise the temperature of your stove or oven. The cooking of food, like any chemical reaction, will generally occur faster at higher temperatures. Likewise, wood can lie around for centuries and not oxidize very much. But put a hot flame to it, and it oxidizes rapidly.

CONCEPT CHECK

1. For each of the following pairs, choose the substance or process that you would expect to react more rapidly.
   a. 5 cm of thick copper wire or 5 cm of thin copper wire
   b. dissolving granulated sugar or sugar cubes
   c. zinc in HCl(*aq*) at 20°C or zinc in HCl(*aq*) at 35°C
   d. hydrogen reacting with iodine at 300°C or at 500°C

2. Identify the factor that affects a reaction rate but cannot itself be adjusted.

3. A reaction occurs in 30 seconds as evidenced by a color change. The same color change occurs when the reaction is run at a lower temperature, but this time it takes 60 seconds. Is the rate of the second trial greater or less than the first?

Modeling how reactions proceed

If two molecules approach each other, the outer electrons on each molecule repel the electrons on the other molecule. Ordinarily the molecules just bounce off each other. If these molecules are going to react chemically, they must collide with enough energy to cause the outer electrons to merge with each other to some extent. This merging of electrons leads to the formation of new bonds. Only the very high energy molecules have enough energy to bump and merge electrons.

The activation-energy diagram models a reaction's progress

Many reactions double or triple in rate when the temperature increases by as little as 10°C. This is an enormous effect. How can this rate increase be explained?

As you have already learned, molecules are in constant motion and have kinetic energy. At higher temperatures, molecules move faster and have greater kinetic energies. In Chapter 12 you learned that the average molar kinetic energy of a molecule is proportional to the absolute temperature, *R*, the ideal gas constant being the proportionality factor.

$$\text{average molar kinetic energy} = \tfrac{3}{2}RT$$

ANSWERS

CONCEPT CHECK

1. a. 5 cm of thick wire (surface area)
   b. granulated sugar (surface area)
   c. zinc in HCl at 35°C (temperature)
   d. hydrogen reacting with iodine at 500°C (temperature)

2. the nature of the reactants

3. slower, because more time is required for the same change

TEACHING TIP

Designing a Model Model the effect of increasing concentration on reaction rate by using a CD case and metal BBs. Remove the plastic insert that holds the CD in the case. This will give you a clear-plastic, shallow, lidded box. Place 25 to 50 BBs in the case, and place the case on an overhead projector. Swirl and jerk the case at random so that students can note the frequency of collisions between the BBs. Next double the number of BBs in the box. This is equivalent to doubling the concentration because the BBs are confined to the same space. Swirl the box again; students should be able to see the increase in the frequency of collisions. You may want to cover the outer 3/4 in. of all sides of the box so that students will not be distracted by the BBs hitting and clumping against the sides of the box.

FIGURE 16-9 ▲

A lizard gathers radiant energy from sunlight to warm its body. This increase in body temperature allows the lizard to move faster by increasing the rate of its metabolic reactions.

Figure 16-10 The two graphs indicate that the height of the peak of the curves for the two reactions is nearly equal relative to zero. Ask students to interpret the graphs and to explain why it is possible that the HBr reaction has a lower activation energy than the HI reaction, even though the peaks are approximately the same height. The activation energy of a reaction is measured relative to the normal energy state of the reactants. HBr molecules require less added energy to react than do HI molecules.

activation energy

the least amount of energy needed to permit a particular chemical reaction

activated complex

a temporary combination of high-energy reactant atoms or molecules that decomposes into products; also called a transition state

▼ **FIGURE 16-10**

The peak of each curve represents the energy of an activated complex.

For any chemical reaction to occur, the reactant molecules must have a certain energy. This energy is called the **activation energy,** E_a. The activation energy is much greater than the average energy of reactant molecules. The shaded region of Figure 12-4 page, 426, shows that a temperature increase of 10° roughly doubles or triples the number of molecules with energies equal to or greater than the activation energy. This explains the drastic effect of temperature changes on reaction rates. The activation energy is like a hill the reactants must climb in order to reach the products. At higher temperatures, more molecules have sufficient energy to climb the hill.

When molecules collide successfully, they form an **activated complex.** **Figure 16-10** shows how the activated complex is formed when the molecules collide with enough energy to equal the activation energy. The left side of each curve represents the energy of the reactant molecules. The right side of each curve represents the energy of the products. Note that the energy of the products in each reaction is less than the energy of the reactants. Both of the reactions shown in Figure 16-10 are exothermic processes.

The activation energy in Figure 16-10b is lower than that in 16-10a. A lower activation energy means that the molecules do not need as much energy to react. Reactions with lower activation energies occur at greater rates than reactions with higher activation energies.

Colliding particles need the right orientation to react

If molecules have enough energy to equal E_a, will they react? They may or may not. As shown in Figure 16-10, a possible activated complex for the decomposition of HI has the two H atoms together and the two I

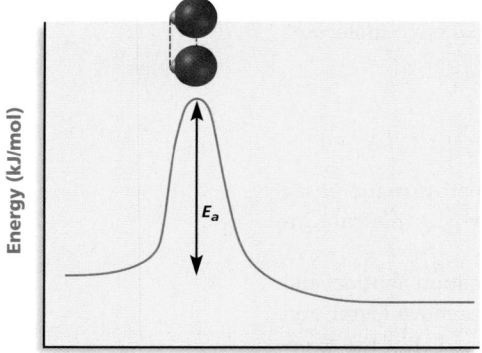

Activation Energies for the Decomposition of HI and HBr

a The difference in energy between the bottom of this curve and the peak is the energy of activation for the decomposition of HI.

b The decomposition of HBr occurs at a faster rate than the decomposition of HI because this reaction has a lower activation energy.

Group Strategy

Collisions and Reactions The text on this page stresses that the likelihood of a reaction between particles depends on the energy and orientation of the collisions between the particles. Having learned this fact, students usually understand how increasing temperature speeds up a reaction because the kinetic energy of the particles increases. However, they sometimes find it hard to explain how an increase in concentration or surface area relates to collision energy.

Divide the class into groups of six, and ask each group to write an explanation of the effect of increasing temperature on the reaction rate. Have a member of one group read the group's explanation. Compare explanations until students have established that particles move faster, colliding more often and with more energy.

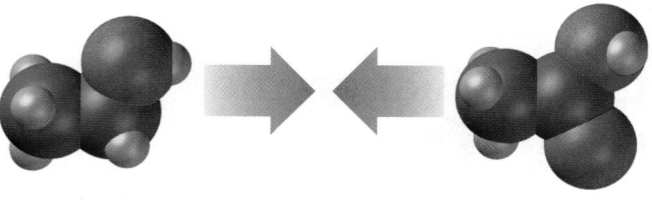

Ethanol   Acetic acid

FIGURE 16-11 ◄

Ethanol and acetic acid can collide in many orientations but will seldom be oriented suitably for a reaction.

atoms together. The molecules must collide in this orientation to react. The chance of randomly moving particles colliding with the correct orientation is fairly low, especially among complicated molecules.

Figure 16-11 illustrates how unlikely it is for complex molecules such as ethanol and acetic acid to collide with the one orientation that will allow them to react. Can you imagine how seldom these molecules meet so that they are positioned in the orientation necessary for them to react?

SECTION REVIEW

Total recall

1. When will a collision lead to chemical reaction?

2. Compare and contrast activation energy and activated complex.

Critical thinking

3. **Interpreting Graphics** Arrange the three energy curves below in order of increasing E_a values. If each curve represents a separate reaction, which reaction would you predict to be the slowest?

4. Using what you know about the kinetic energy of molecules, explain why reaction rates vary greatly when temperature changes.

5. Compare the potential energies of the following stages of an endothermic reaction: reactants, activated complex, and products.

6. **Story Clue** Predict how the concentration of domoic acid along the North Carolina and Maryland coasts might change over the course of a year.

Reaction progress
a

Reaction progress
b

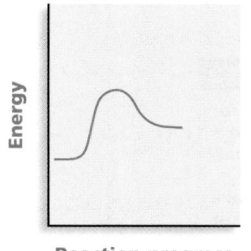

Reaction progress
c

ANSWERS

SECTION REVIEW

Total recall

1. when the energy of the collision equals or exceeds the activation energy and the molecules collide in the correct orientation

2. Activation energy is the minimum amount of energy with which particles must collide in order to react. An activated complex is the short-lived grouping of ions, molecules, or atoms that forms when particles collide with the necessary activation energy.

Critical thinking

3. The order of increasing E_a is b, c, a. The graph, a, represents the reaction with the highest E_a; thus it has the slowest rate.

4. Increasing temperature increases the average kinetic energy of the particles in the system. As a result, collisions will occur more frequently and more of those collisions will occur with an energy equal to or above the activation energy.

5. The energy of the reactants is less than that of the activated complex and that of the products. The products have less energy than the activated complex but more than the reactants because the reaction is endothermic.

6. The concentration of domoic acid should be very low in the cold months of January and February. It should begin increasing in spring, reach a peak in July or August, then decrease again through December.

Next ask them to explain the effects of increasing concentration and surface area. Proceed as you did with the temperature question. Guide students to understand that neither of these factors affects the energy of the collisions. However, by increasing the overall frequency of collisions, these factors also increase the frequency of collisions that occur with the needed activation energy and orientation.

SECTION 16-3

How do catalysts change the rates of chemical reactions?

OBJECTIVES

▶ *Describe* how catalysts affect E_a and the rate of a reaction.

▶ *Explain* the mechanism of enzyme action in terms of chemical bonds and energy.

▶ *Give* an example of an inhibitor used to prevent chain reactions from occurring.

Pathways are modified by catalysts

catalyst
a substance added to a chemical reaction to increase the rate that is not itself changed in the reaction

catalysis
the process by which reaction rates are increased by the addition of a catalyst

The energy diagram for a reaction indicates that if the height of the energy hill—or activation energy—is increased, the rate decreases. If the height of the hill is reduced, the rate increases. Lowering the activation energy means changing to a new reaction mechanism. A **catalyst** lowers the energy barrier by forming an activated complex of lower energy. In short, it provides the reactant molecules with a more favorable, lower energy pathway to the products. This process is called **catalysis.**

Hydrogen peroxide, H_2O_2, decomposes slowly over time, as represented by the following reaction.

$$2H_2O_2(aq) \longrightarrow 2H_2O(l) + O_2(g)$$

Comparison of Pathways for the Decomposition of H_2O_2

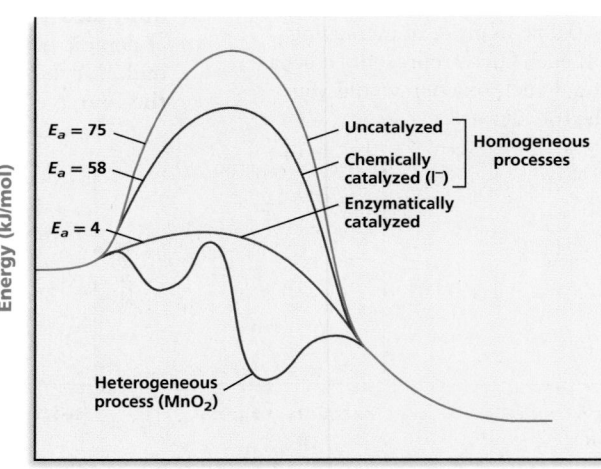

▶ **FIGURE 16-12**

Activation energy for a reaction can be reduced by adding a catalyst to the system. Some catalysts work better than others. For example, MnO_2 is a better catalyst for the decomposition of H_2O_2 than I^-.

DEMONSTRATION 5

Three Kinds of Catalysts

Approximate time: 15 minutes

In this demonstration students can compare the actions of three kinds of catalysts.

1. Place three Petri dishes on an overhead projector. Hold one back if all three do not fit.

2. Pour 10 mL of 3% H_2O_2 (ordinary hydrogen peroxide) into each Petri dish.

3. To the first dish, add 3 drops of 1 M KI solution (homogeneous catalyst).

4. To the second dish, add juice from a crushed turnip (the enzyme catalase).

5. Allow students to compare the activities in the first two dishes. Next drop a very small amount of powdered MnO_2 (heterogeneous catalyst) from the end of a small spatula into the third dish. CAUTION: The activity may be vigorous.

A 30% solution of H_2O_2 will decompose at a rate of about 0.5% per year at room temperature. This rate corresponds to the uncatalyzed curve in the energy diagram for the decomposition of H_2O_2 shown in **Figure 16-12**. If iodide ions, I^-, from potassium iodide, KI, are added to the peroxide solution, the activation energy is lowered from 75 kJ/mol to 58 kJ/mol. The I^- ions form a reaction intermediate, IO^-, when they react with H_2O_2 molecules. The IO^- ions then react with other H_2O_2 molecules to regenerate iodide ions as products are formed. The I^- ions are a catalyst for the decomposition of H_2O_2 because they are added to the reaction to increase the reaction rate but are not actually used up in the overall reaction. The iodide ion is an example of a **homogeneous catalyst** for the decomposition of hydrogen peroxide because KI and H_2O_2 are both in aqueous solution. Catalysts sometimes appear above the arrow in chemical equations.

$$2H_2O_2(aq) \xrightarrow{KI} 2H_2O(l) + O_2(g)$$

Catalase and manganese dioxide also catalyze the decomposition of H_2O_2 by lowering the E_a for the reaction to 4 kJ/mol or less. Note that although a catalyst changes the value for E_a of a reaction, the value of ΔH for the reaction is left unchanged. If a reaction is exothermic without a catalyst, the same amount of energy is released when the reaction is carried out with a catalyst. Likewise, an endothermic reaction absorbs the same quantity of energy with or without a catalyst.

The lowest energy pathway shown on Figure 16-12 is an example of a **heterogeneous catalyst.** The catalyst, manganese dioxide, is a solid, whereas the hydrogen peroxide is in solution. Catalysts in heterogeneous systems have the advantage of being more easily separated from the reaction products. A comparison of the catalyzed and uncatalyzed decomposition of H_2O_2 appears in **Figure 16-13**. Note that no observable changes are taking place in the uncatalyzed reaction, but the hydrogen peroxide decomposes rather vigorously in the presence of MnO_2.

homogeneous catalyst

a catalyst that is in the same phase as all of the reactants and products in a system

heterogeneous catalyst

a catalyst whose phase is different from the reactants'

FIGURE 16-13 ▼

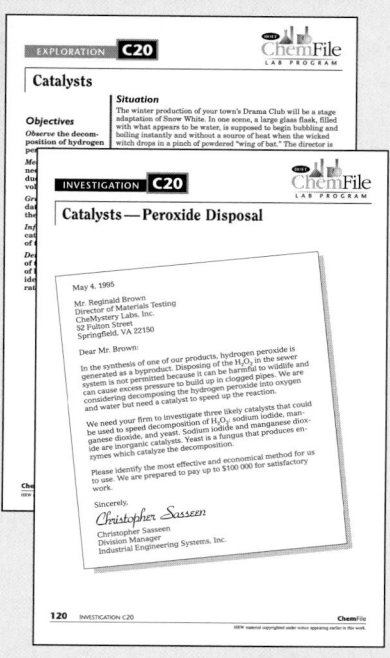

a The decomposition of H_2O_2 is such a slow process without a catalyst that no reaction is observed.

b In contrast, a very rapid decomposition of H_2O_2 occurs in the presence of MnO_2.

6. Ask students to compare their observations with the graph in Figure 16-12 and explain any observed differences in activity.

Safety
Wear safety goggles and a laboratory apron.

Disposal
Filter off any remaining solids, and rinse with tap water. Combine solutions. When bubbling stops, flush the liquid down the drain. Dispose of the solids in the trash.

▲ FIGURE 16-14

An enzyme speeds up the reaction that produces the dark pigment in this cat's fur at cooler temperatures. That is why the cooler regions of the cat's body have the darker fur.

enzyme

a large protein molecule that catalyzes chemical reactions in living things

substrate

the molecule or molecules with which an enzyme interacts

Enzymes are nature's catalysts

Reactions of organic compounds are generally slow. If living things had to depend on uncatalyzed reactions, life as we know it could not exist. Catalysts found in biological systems are called **enzymes.** Most enzymes are large protein molecules. Like all catalysts, enzymes are not used up in a reaction, so only small amounts are needed. However, unlike most catalysts, enzymes catalyze a particular type of reaction because the enzyme molecule has a specific three-dimensional conformation. That is, a specific location on the enzyme is shaped to receive a specific reactant, just as a specific lock is shaped to accept a specific key. Look at the interaction between the enzyme and **substrate** shown in **Figure 16-15.**

The substrate must have the correct structure to bind to the enzyme's active site. The active site of the enzyme molecule is where catalysis takes place. During the catalytic process, the enzyme's active site distorts the bonds in the substrate. This distortion strains the substrate's bonds and weakens them. The reaction progresses more rapidly because the already weakened bonds need less energy to get to the activated complex, making the E_a value lower than that for the uncatalyzed reaction. When the substrate is positioned within the active site, the activated complex at the top of the energy hill is formed. After this point, the product is made and it leaves the active site. The overall ΔH for the reaction does not change, but the activation energy is lowered.

Enzyme supplements reduce the effects of lactose intolerance

The human body has hundreds of highly specialized enzymes that control growth, reproduction, and other processes. Enzymes in the body speed up the chemical processes that sustain life. Most reactions in the body are so complex that if they were not catalyzed, they would require extremely high temperatures to occur at rates fast enough for life to exist. Fortunately, enzymes alter reaction pathways so that the

▼ FIGURE 16-15

a The enzyme reacts with the substrate in a fast, reversible reaction.

b The substrate-enzyme-activated complex can either revert to the reactants or . . .

c . . . proceed in a slow reaction to the products.

Lactose

complex reactions of metabolism occur at 37.0°C (98.6°F) at a rate several million times faster than they would without a catalyst.

Lactose is a sugar found in many dairy products. Lactase is a digestive enzyme that breaks down lactose into its constituent sugars, glucose and galactose. Some people lack the ability to produce lactase. These people have what is known as lactose intolerance. Undigested lactose molecules collect in the intestine and attract water. As a result, a person with lactose intolerance can experience painful cramps or diarrhea after ingesting foods with lactose. Enzyme supplements can be added to or taken with dairy products to break down the lactose.

Enzymatic cleaners reduce protein buildup on contact lenses

Modern contact lenses are made of plastics that absorb a great deal of water. Most lenses are gas permeable to enable sensitive corneas to receive the oxygen they require. However, the protein matter in tears can clog the pores in contact lenses, making both lenses and eyes susceptible to bacterial growth and potentially serious damage. Protein buildup is removed from the lenses by special enzymatic cleaners. These enzymes are known as proteases because they break down proteins into amino acids, which can be easily washed away, leaving the contact lenses clear and clean.

FIGURE 16-16 ▲

The complex sugar lactose causes problems for some people in digesting milk, ice cream, cheese, and other dairy products.

internetconnect

SCILINKS
NSTA
TOPIC: Enzymes
GO TO: www.scilinks.org
KEYWORD: HW163

CONCEPT CHECK

1. What effect does a catalyst have on ΔH for a reaction?
2. A reaction occurs without the addition of a catalyst. A chemist determines its rate law. The rate law for the same reaction is determined after a catalyst has been added. Will the two rate laws be the same? Explain your answer.
3. What is a catalyst? Explain the effect of a catalyst on the rate of chemical reactions. How does a catalyst influence the activation energy required by a particular reaction?

607

TEACHING TIP

Discussion Strategy Ask students to use their knowledge of enzymes to explain why ectothermic, or cold-blooded, animals become slow or dormant when the temperature drops. Reinforce the idea that most activities of a living thing involve enzymes and that these enzymes function efficiently only within a narrow range of temperatures. At low temperatures, enzyme activity may slow down drastically, slowing down the organism.

DID YOU KNOW?

Uncooked pineapple cannot be used in gelatin desserts or salads because the enzymes in the pineapple break down the protein chains of the gelatin and keep it in the liquid state. The principal enzyme responsible is bromelain. Cooking the pineapple destroys these enzymes, so cooked pineapple may be used in gelatin. Bromelain is also used to break down proteins in the tenderizing of meats.

ANSWERS

CONCEPT CHECK

1. ΔH for a reaction is unchanged when a catalyst is used.
2. The use of a catalyst changes a reaction's mechanism. The rate law is determined by the mechanism. Therefore, the rate law for an uncatalyzed reaction will differ from that for the same reaction performed with a catalyst.
3. A catalyst is a substance that increases the rate of a reaction but is not changed or used up in the reaction. It speeds up a reaction by lowering the activation energy of the reaction.

Figure 16-17 Point out that compound *b* is the so-called *octane* by which the antiknock properties of gasoline are measured. The octane rating of a gasoline is the percentage of 2,2,4-trimethylpentane (in a mixture with heptane, compound *a*) that has the same antiknock properties as the gasoline being tested. For example, a gasoline that is rated at 90 octane will run an engine exactly the same way as a mixture of 10% heptane and 90% 2,2,4-trimethylpentane.

HISTORICAL CONNECTION

The demand for gasoline increased rapidly in the early part of the twentieth century as automobiles and trucks replaced other forms of transportation. Only a certain amount of gasoline (called straight-run gasoline) can be obtained from the fractional distillation of raw petroleum—not nearly enough to meet demand. In 1912, large-scale "cracking" first began in the United States. In cracking, larger molecules, for which there is less commercial demand, are broken down into smaller molecules suitable for blending into gasoline. Initially, distillation at high temperatures was used to crack molecules. Catalytic cracking was developed in 1936, just in time to supply sufficient gasoline to the Allies in World War II.

Science in the News

PRESENTS Feature story 28
Ozone-Eater Radiator See the Science in the News video guide for more details.

antioxidant

a substance that can prevent chain reactions involving O_2 and O_3

inhibitor

a substance added to a chemical reaction to slow the reaction down

Chain reactions and inhibitors

Many reactions occur by mechanisms consisting of repeated elementary steps in which one reaction initiates the next reaction. These are called chain reactions. In Chapter 10 you encountered one that is involved in the destruction of the ozone layer. Chlorofluorocarbons diffuse into the stratosphere, where ultraviolet light disintegrates them, forming chlorine atoms with an unpaired electron. These atoms then initiate the destructive chain reaction shown below.

$$Cl\cdot + O_3 \longrightarrow ClO\cdot + O_2$$
$$ClO\cdot + O\cdot \longrightarrow Cl\cdot + O_2$$

The Cl atom, with its unpaired electron, is a free radical. One Cl radical can destroy thousands of O_3 molecules and O radicals (which are the precursors of ozone). This continues until the Cl atoms diffuse down into the troposphere.

The decomposition of hydrogen peroxide solution involves free radicals in the mechanism. Hydrogen peroxide solutions usually contain an **antioxidant.** The antioxidant preserves the hydrogen peroxide by destroying free radicals. It acts as an **inhibitor,** interrupting chain reactions. Many reactions of O_2 and O_3 involve free radicals. Ordinary rubber is attacked by atmospheric oxygen and even by traces of ozone, and it degrades rather rapidly. Most rubber products, especially tires, contain antioxidants that remove free radicals and slow down the reaction. Reactions of oxygen in the body form free radicals. Many people believe that free radicals are harmful in the body. Some dietary supplements contain antioxidants, such as vitamin C and selenium. The effectiveness of these supplements has not been proven.

Inhibitors and catalysts work together

If combustion in an automobile engine were 100% efficient, the engine would convert gasoline into only carbon dioxide and water. Unfortunately, significant amounts of nitrogen oxides, carbon monoxide, and unburned hydrocarbons are discharged out of the car's tailpipe and into the air. For this reason, modern cars are equipped with catalytic converters to reduce pollution. Catalytic converters consist mainly of active platinum and

▼ **FIGURE 16-17**

a Gasoline is a mixture of hydrocarbons. Some are straight, like heptane, . . .

b and others are branched, like 2, 2, 4-trimethylpentane (isooctane).

palladium metals that catalyze the conversion of carbon monoxide, hydrocarbons, and nitrogen oxides to carbon dioxide, water, and nitrogen.

Gasoline is a mixture of hydrocarbons obtained from the fractional distillation of petroleum. Two of the many components of gasoline are shown in **Figure 16-17.** Some of the hydrocarbon chains in gasoline are straight, and some are branched. The branched chains burn more slowly and smoothly than the straight chains do. Therefore, the higher the percentage of branched chains in the gasoline mixture, the more efficiently it burns. If the gas burns too quickly inside the cylinder, it causes engine knock.

To inhibit the fast combustion that causes knocking, tetraethyl lead was once added to gasoline. At the time, tetraethyl lead was an attractive choice because it mixed readily with gasoline, was inexpensive, and did its job well. However, scientists did not realize how much lead would be dumped into the atmosphere or how serious the effects of lead poisoning would be. Lead itself is a relatively inert metal, but its compounds are toxic to most biological systems because they inhibit the actions of enzymes.

Cars equipped with catalytic converters must use unleaded gasoline. Lead ruins the platinum catalyst in the catalytic converters by covering it with a layer of lead that renders the active sites useless. Other antiknock agents, such as ethanol, t-butyl methyl ether, and aromatic compounds, are now used.

SECTION REVIEW

Total recall

1. **Interpreting Graphics** Sketch an energy diagram for a simple reaction, and label E_a. On the same plot, sketch how the diagram might look if the reaction went through catalysis.

2. How does catalysis speed up a chemical reaction?

Critical thinking

3. A particular reaction is found to have the following rate law.

$$\text{rate} = k[A][B]^2$$

How is the rate affected by each of the following changes?

  a. the concentration of A is cut in half
  b. the concentration of B is tripled
  c. a catalyst is added
  d. the temperature is increased
  e. the concentration of A is doubled, and the concentration of B is cut in half

4. For enzyme-catalyzed reactions, the rate of reaction no longer increases after the substrate concentration reaches a certain level. Suggest a reason for this observation.

5. Predict how a catalyst would affect a reaction that reaches equilibrium.

6. Explain why there must be many different enzymes to catalyze all of the reactions in the body.

ANSWERS

SECTION REVIEW

Total recall

1.

2. Catalysis lowers the activation energy of the reaction. This causes the reaction rate to increase.

Critical thinking

3. **a.** The rate is cut in half.
  b. The rate increases to nine times the original rate.
  c. The rate increases.
  d. The rate increases
  e. The rate is cut in half.

4. The enzyme is saturated with substrate. In other words, all of the available enzyme-active sites are in use at any given moment.

5. A catalyst speeds up the rate at which the reaction reaches equilibrium, but it has no effect on the equilibrium itself.

6. In general, each enzyme can bind with only a specific substrate, just as a particular key can fit only a specific lock. Therefore, many kinds of enzymes are needed to accommodate the many different biomolecules used in the reactions in the body.

STORY CONCLUSION

Even though the causes of shellfish poisoning are known, many people still go by an old folk rule that advises eating oysters only during months with an *R* in their name. You may want to ask students what months these are and how this rule might relate to the story of red tides.

LOOKING BACK

How does temperature affect reaction rate?

Reactant molecules are more likely to have higher kinetic energies at higher temperatures. This translates into a greater number of molecules with energies above the activation energy. These molecules are then capable of colliding with adequate energy to cause a reaction. With more molecules able to react, the rate of a reaction increases. Metabolic reactions involved in growth and reproduction also experience an increased rate at increased temperature. This is why the rate of algae growth increases with the warming of their environment.

How does the warming of coastal waters disturb the ecological balance of an area?

As long as environmental conditions remain fairly constant, an ecological system in any region will reach a steady state. However, when a change is made in the environment, the balance shifts. This shift functions just as a shift in the equilibrium of a chemical reaction does. Any change disrupts the balance of the entire system.

Pfiesteria piscicida are naturally occurring organisms in the ocean that normally feed off fish. However, the increase in water temperature shifts the balance between the fish and the algae in favor of *Pfiesteria piscicida*. As you have learned, an increase in temperature increases the rate of chemical reactions, including those involved in the growth of organisms such as algae. But all reactions are

The Gulf Stream is a warm water current that flows up the eastern coast of the United States.

not equally accelerated, which means that some organisms will be favored by an increase in temperature. *Pfiesteria piscicida* is one such organism. For this reason, large algal blooms are more likely to occur in warmer water, killing unusually large numbers of fish.

Why might eating oysters and other shellfish harvested in the summer months be more of a risk than eating shellfish harvested in the winter months?

During the colder months, the rate of growth of algae such as *Pfiesteria piscicida* and *Gymnodinium breve* slows as the rates of their metabolic reactions slow. The organisms can remain fairly dormant; they do not emit toxins into coastal waters. In warmer months, the toxic algae populations develop faster due to the increased water temperatures. Shellfish harvested during these warmer periods have a higher likelihood of being contaminated with domoic acid. For this reason the oyster harvest season has traditionally occurred in the fall and winter.

KEY TERMS

16-1
average rate
chemical kinetics
elementary step
intermediate
mechanism
order
overall reaction order

rate-determining step
rate law
reaction rate

16-2
activated complex
activation energy

16-3
antioxidant
catalysis
catalyst
enzyme

heterogeneous catalyst
homogeneous catalyst
inhibitor
substrate

KEY CONCEPTS

16-1 What is a reaction rate?

▶ The average reaction rate is expressed as the ratio of a measured change, usually with concentration units, to the time interval during which the change takes place.

▶ Reaction rates generally decrease as the reaction progresses.

▶ The reaction rate is proportional to the concentration of each reactant raised to some power. This exponent must be determined experimentally for each reaction.

▶ The mechanism of a reaction usually involves a step-by-step sequence. The slowest step determines the overall rate and is called the rate-determining step.

16-2 How can reaction rates be explained?

▶ Factors affecting the reaction rate include the nature of the reactants as well as their concentration, temperature, and surface area.

▶ Increasing the concentration, temperature, or surface area of the reactants increases the reaction rate because the number of effective collisions between reactants increases.

▶ Not all molecular collisions result in a reaction. Molecules must have the proper orientation and sufficient kinetic energy to bring reactants together in such a way that new bonds can form.

16-3 How do catalysts change the rates of chemical reactions?

▶ Catalysts increase the reaction rate by lowering the energy barrier for the reaction. Catalysts can be recovered unchanged after the reaction is complete.

▶ Enzymes are catalysts found in biological systems. They bind substrates in their active site to form an activated complex. The shape of the substrate is altered, weakening its bonds until it decomposes and the reaction products are released from the enzyme.

▶ Inhibitors, such as antioxidants, can decrease the rate of a chain reaction.

KEY SKILLS

Review the following model before your exam. Be sure you can solve this type of problem.

Sample Problem 16A: Determining a rate law (p. 595)

READING STRATEGY

Assimilating Knowledge

Have students return to their list of things they want to know about rates, which they created on page 586. Have them place a check mark next to each question that they are now able to answer. Students should finish by making a list of what they've learned. Have students identify unanswered questions as well as new questions they may have. These questions could be used as the basis for a research project.

REVIEW & ASSESS ASSIGNMENT GUIDE

Term Review

Assign after Section 16-3.

Concept & Skills Review

Section 16-1
▶ Items 1–13, 16–25

Section 16-2
▶ Items 14, 15, 26–35

Section 16-3
▶ Items 36–41

Linking Chapters

Section 16-1
▶ Items 1–3, 5

Section 16-2
▶ Item 4

Alternative Assessments

Assign after Section 16-3.

Test Prep

Assign prior to the chapter test.

Complete worked-out solutions for these problems can be found on the teacher's interleaved pages at the end of this chapter.

TERM REVIEW

1. intermediate
2. overall reaction order
3. inhibitors
4. catalysis
5. elementary step
6. activation energy
7. rate-determining step
8. rate law

CONCEPT & SKILLS REVIEW

1. Answers may vary.
   a. volume collected per unit time: L/h or gal/h
   b. km/h or mi/h
   c. rotations per unit time
   d. milliliters per unit time

2. a. Answers will vary. Possibilities include changes in mass of a reactant, in mass of a product, in pH, in characteristic color, in volume, in pressure, and in temperature.
   b. Students should select appropriate instruments for their answer to part (a). Possibilities include a balance, pH meter, colorimeter, eudiometer to measure the volume of gas evolved, pressure gauge or manometer, calorimeter, and thermometer.

3. The change in concentration of a reactant during a reaction is negative. Thus, the factor −1 is used when measuring the loss of a reactant in order to express rate as a positive number.

4. All of the substances are colorless gases, and no change in pressure occurs because the amount of product is equal to the amount of reactant. It would be difficult to measure the concentration of each gas in the reaction mixture.

5. *See page 617A.*

6. *See page 617A.*

TERM REVIEW

1. During a chemical reaction a(n) ——— may be formed but disappears.
   (catalyst, intermediate, substrate)

2. Summing the exponents in a rate law expression yields the ———.
   (elementary step, overall reaction order)

3. Antioxidants serve as ——— to prevent some harmful reactions in the body.
   (catalysts, inhibitors, free radicals)

4. If a reaction is too slow to be practical, you could try ——— to speed it up.
   (catalysis, activation energy, average rate)

5. A reaction mechanism may have one ——— or many.
   (rate-determining step, elementary step)

6. If a reaction has a very high ———, it will likely be a slow reaction.
   (order, activation energy, reaction rate)

7. For a reaction mechanism that has three steps, if the first two steps are fast, then the third step must be the ———.
   (rate-determining step, elementary step)

8. The ——— of a reaction can be determined from the reaction's mechanism. It cannot be determined from a balanced chemical equation.
   (reaction rate, rate law, average rate)

CONCEPT & SKILLS REVIEW

CLOCKING CHEMICAL REACTIONS

1. Give the appropriate units for expressing the rates of the following processes:
   a. water dripping from a leaky faucet
   b. a person's walking speed on an exercise path
   c. a fan blade rotating
   d. water evaporating from a 1 L container

2. a. List four physical properties or observations that can be measured during a chemical reaction to determine the reaction rate.
   b. For each of the four variables that you listed in (a), what equipment would be necessary for making measurements?

3. Why does a minus sign appear in some reaction rate expressions?

4. Why might measuring the rate of the following reaction be difficult?

$$H_2(g) + CO_2(g) \longrightarrow H_2O(g) + CO(g)$$

Practice Problems

5. Write an expression for the rate of the decomposition of acetoacetic acid into acetone and CO_2.

$$\underset{\substack{\| \\ O}}{H_3C-C}-CH_2\underset{\substack{\| \\ O}}{C}OH(l) \longrightarrow$$

$$H_3C-\underset{\substack{\| \\ O}}{C}-CH_3(l) + CO_2(g)$$

6. The reaction between methanol and hydrochloric acid to form methyl chloride and water is written as follows:

$$CH_3OH(aq) + H_3O^+(aq) + Cl^-(aq) \longrightarrow$$
$$CH_3Cl(aq) + H_2O(l)$$

The concentration of H_3O^+ was measured at various times, as shown in the following table:

Time	$[H_3O^+]$
0 min	1.83 M
79 min	1.67 M
158 min	1.52 M
316 min	1.30 M
632 min	1.00 M

a. Prepare a graph of H_3O^+ concentration versus time. Determine the average rate of the reaction for each of the four time intervals.
b. Is the rate constant throughout the reaction? Explain your answer.

7. Ethene, also called ethylene, reacts with chlorine gas to form 1,2-dichloroethane, as shown in the following equation:

$$CH_2{=}CH_2(g) + Cl_2(g) \longrightarrow Cl{-}CH_2{-}CH_2{-}Cl(l)$$

Two moles of chlorine gas are mixed with 3.3 mol of ethene in a 500 mL flask. After 10 minutes, the reaction is stopped and the amounts of the gases are measured again. There are 1.3 mol of Cl_2 and 2.6 mol of $CH_2{=}CH_2$. Calculate the average reaction rate.

8. Calculate the average rate of the following reaction:

$$H_2S(aq) + Cl_2(g) \longrightarrow S(s) + 2HCl(aq)$$

Time	Concentration of H_2S (mol/L)
1:30	2.30
1:42	0.57

9. Many solutions to environmental problems involve changing a soluble toxic substance into a solid that can be filtered out. If mercury(II) chloride, a highly toxic substance in aqueous solution, is treated with sodium oxalate, mercury precipitates from the solution as mercury(I) chloride, and carbon dioxide is released as a gas.

$$2HgCl_2(aq) + Na_2C_2O_4(aq) \longrightarrow$$
$$2NaCl(aq) + 2CO_2(g) + Hg_2Cl_2(s)$$

a. Write a rate expression with respect to $HgCl_2$.

b. Would it be easier to monitor the formation of Hg_2Cl_2 than the formation of the other two products?

c. Examine the data in the table below. Is 30 minutes sufficient time to treat 0.050 M $HgCl_2$ with 0.40 M $Na_2C_2O_4$? Would 1 hour suffice? Why or why not?

Trial	Initial concentration of $HgCl_2$ (M)	Initial concentration of $Na_2C_2O_4$ (M)	Initial concentration of NaCl (M)	Δt (min)	Final concentration of NaCl (M)
1	0.050	0.10	0.00	30	0.0010
2	0.050	0.20	0.00	30	0.0042
3	0.050	0.40	0.00	30	0.0168

10. A mixture of nitric acid and hydrochloric acid, called aqua regia, is used to dissolve gold and platinum. Nitrosyl chloride, NOCl, is present in the solution. A 0.95 M NOCl solution slowly decomposes into nitrogen monoxide and chlorine, causing the color of the aqua regia to change from reddish brown to light green.

$$2NOCl(soln) \longrightarrow 2NO(g) + Cl_2(g)$$

a. Use the following graph to determine the average rate of decrease in NOCl concentration during the first 90 days and between days 360 and 450.

b. Propose a reason why the rates for days 1–90 and days 360–450 differ.

REPRESENTING REACTION RATES

11. How is the order of reaction with respect to a reactant determined from experimental data?

Complete worked-out solutions for these problems can be found on the teacher's interleaved pages at the end of this chapter.

7. rate = 0.1 M/min

8. rate = 0.14 M/min

9. a. rate = $\dfrac{-1}{2} \times \dfrac{\Delta[HgCl_2]}{\Delta t}$

b. yes, because Hg_2Cl_2 is a precipitate that can be filtered off, dried, and weighed

c. No; when all of the 0.050 M $HgCl_2$ has reacted, the concentration of NaCl will be 0.050 M. In 30 minutes, the concentration of NaCl is only 0.0168 M. One hour would not be sufficient, even if the rate were to remain constant, which it probably would not.

10. a. 1.9×10^{-3} M/day
1.4×10^{-4} M/day

b. The reaction rate during the first 90 days is higher because the concentration of the reactant NOCl is significantly higher than it is during days 360–450.

11. An experiment is done in which the reaction rate is measured at several different reactant concentrations. A relationship between the concentration and the rate is determined.

12. A chemical equation tells what substances react and in what proportions they react. The equation tells nothing about the mechanism of the reaction. The rate law depends on the mechanism of reaction.

13. a. first order
b. third order
c. second order

14. The activated complex occurs at the peak of the energy diagram for a reaction. Therefore, the energy of the activated complex is greater than either the energy of the reactants or the energy of the products.

Complete worked-out solutions for these problems can be found on the teacher's interleaved pages at the end of this chapter.

15. Both an intermediate and an activated complex are made and destroyed during a reaction. An intermediate is the product of an elementary step in a reaction mechanism. It may be a stable compound. An activated complex is a high-energy arrangement of atoms or molecules that forms as a result of a collision. It is not stable, and it decomposes into products or back into reactants.

16. If [A] triples, the reaction rate increases to nine times the original rate. If [A] is halved, the rate is divided by four.

17. Measure the reaction rate while varying the [A] and holding [B] constant. Next do the same thing, but vary [B] while holding [A] constant. Finally, determine the order by which the concentration of each reactant affects the rate, and write the rate law equation.

18. If [A] is halved, the rate is halved. If [B] is halved, the rate decreases to one-fourth the original rate.

19. The rate of release of O_2 is very fast compared with that of CO. If enough binding sites are occupied by CO at a given time, a victim can die of oxygen starvation before enough sites become free.

20. The reaction rate would slow because the OH^- ions in the base would react with the H_3O^+ ions, reducing their concentration.

21. You cannot determine the order of a reaction by the coefficients in a balanced equation.

22. rate $= k[Mn_2O_7]^2$

23. 27

24. a. rate $= k[NO_2]^2$
 b. second order in $[NO_2]$
  zero order in [CO]

25. a. rate is quadrupled
 b. rate is multiplied by 16
 c. rate is multiplied by 16

12. Why aren't the coefficients in a balanced equation used to write the rate law expression?

13. Determine the overall reaction order for each of the following rate law expressions:
 a. rate $= k[N_2O_5]$
 b. rate $= k[CH_3OH]^2[(C_6H_5)_3CCl]$
 c. rate $= k[O_3][NO]$

14. How does the energy of the activated complex compare with the energies of reactants and products?

15. Compare an intermediate with an activated complex.

16. If the rate law expression for a reaction is determined to be rate $= k[A]^2$ and the concentration of A is tripled, what happens to the rate? What happens to the rate if the concentration of A is halved?

17. Describe how you would carry out a typical experiment with two reactants that would determine a rate law expression.

18. If the rate law expression for a reaction is determined to be rate $= k[A][B]^2$ and the concentration of A is halved, what happens to the rate? What happens to the rate if the concentration of B is halved?

19. Carbon monoxide and oxygen bind to the hemoglobin molecule. The time it takes for the oxygen to be released to the tissues is measured in seconds. The release of CO from hemoglobin takes from five to eight hours. Both reactions are first order with respect to the oxygen and carbon monoxide complexes with hemoglobin. Compare the kinetics of these reactions, and explain why carbon monoxide poisoning occurs.

20. The hydrolysis of thioacetamide is described by the following chemical equation:

$$CH_3CSNH_2(aq) + H_2O(l) \longrightarrow$$
$$H_2S(aq) + CH_3CONH_2(aq)$$

The rate law is determined to be rate $= k[H_3O^+][CH_3CSNH_2]$. How does adding some 0.1 M NaOH to a solution that is 0.10 M in both hydronium ion and thioacetamide affect the rate?

21. If you were told that the rate law expression for the following reaction is second order with respect to H_2O because the coefficient is 2, how would you respond?

$$CaC_2(s) + 2H_2O(l) \longrightarrow C_2H_2(g) + Ca(OH)_2(s)$$

Practice Problems

22. Given the following data, write a rate law expression for the decomposition of manganese oxide. **(Hint: See Sample Problem 16A.)**

$$2Mn_2O_7(aq) \longrightarrow 4Mn(s) + 7O_2(g)$$

Mn_2O_7 (M)	Rate (M/s)
7.5×10^{-5}	1.2×10^{-4}
1.5×10^{-4}	4.8×10^{-4}

23. The rate law for a reaction is found to be rate $= k[X]^3$. By what factor does the rate increase if [X] is tripled?

24. Given the following reaction:

$$NO_2(g) + CO(g) \longrightarrow CO_2(g) + NO(g)$$

If the CO concentration is held constant and the NO_2 concentration is doubled, the rate of formation of CO_2 quadruples. However, doubling the concentration of CO has no effect on the rate of CO_2 being formed.
 a. Write a rate law expression for this reaction.
 b. Determine the order of the reaction with respect to NO_2 and with respect to CO.

25. Determine the factor by which the rate changes for the reaction with the rate law rate $= k[A]^n[B]^m$ if both [A] and [B] are doubled, given the following values of n and m:
 a. $n = 0, m = 2$
 b. $n = 2, m = 2$
 c. $n = 1, m = 3$

CAUSES FOR VARIOUS REACTION RATES

26. If the temperature of the reactants is raised, are all of the reactant particles likely to have enough energy to form products? Why?

27. Why does grinding a solid cause an increase in the reaction rate of the material?

28. The conversion of cyclopropane to propene is shown below. The first-order rate constant, k, is $6.1 \times 10^{-2} \text{ s}^{-1}$ at 500°C.

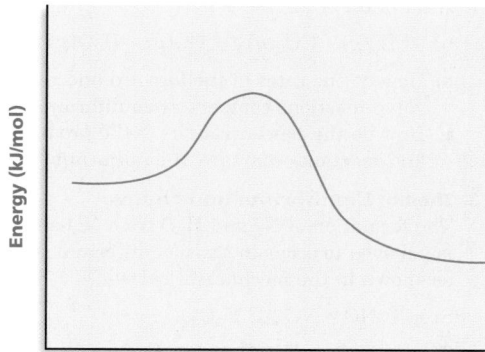

a. Write the rate law expression for this reaction.

b. Determine the actual rate if the concentration of cyclopropane is 0.015 M.

c. The rate constant is $5.70 \times 10^{-4} \text{s}^{-1}$ at 25°C. How do you account for the difference in rate at the two temperatures?

29. Why is the basic chemical nature of a substance important when studying chemical kinetics?

30. Why does a change in the concentration of reactants usually change the reaction rate?

31. Use graphs to illustrate the following situations:
a. an exothermic reaction with a relatively large E_a value
b. an exothermic reaction with a relatively small E_a value

32. At normal body temperature (37°C), the body can survive for only 5 minutes without oxygen. When the body temperature is lowered to a state of hypothermia (28–30°C), the body can survive almost 30 minutes without damage to tissues. Why?

33. Iron nails will corrode slowly when placed in sulfuric acid. If iron filings are substituted, the corrosion will occur more rapidly. Why?

34. White phosphorus will ignite and burn spontaneously around 34°C according to the following equation:

$$P_4(s) + 5O_2(g) \longrightarrow P_4O_{10}(s)$$

a. Do you think that E_a is large or small? Explain.
b. Draw an energy diagram for this reaction.
c. On the graph, label the following: x and y axes, reactants, products, activated complex, and E_a.
d. Propose two ways that white phosphorus could be stored to prevent a reaction with oxygen.

35. Explosions sometimes occur in factories where wheat is ground into flour. Would a factory containing processed flour be more likely to sustain an explosion than a factory containing whole grains of wheat? Why? What is the difference?

ACTIVITY OF ENZYMES AND INHIBITORS

36. In the diagram below, the energy pathway for a reaction is represented by the curved line. Draw another line representing the possible energy pathway that might result if an enzyme were present. Is the reaction exothermic or endothermic? Does ΔH change when the catalyst is present?

Reaction progress

(Energy (kJ/mol))

37. Briefly describe the process involved in the enzyme-catalyzed conversion of a substrate to a product.

38. What is the difference between a homogeneous catalyst and a heterogeneous catalyst?

39. Explain the effect of an inhibitor on the rate of a free-radical reaction.

40. A certain nerve gas, soman, inhibits the enzyme cholinesterase. Antidotes to poisoning by this nerve gas are cholinesterase reactivators. Suggest what can happen to a body's nervous system when it is inhibited by this nerve gas.

41. Look up the formula for t-butyl methyl ether. Compare its formula with that of 2,2,4-trimethylpentane. Why do you think it is a good antiknock agent?

> Complete worked-out solutions for these problems can be found on the teacher's interleaved pages at the end of this chapter.

26. Raising the temperature raises the average kinetic energy of particles. More but not all particles will have enough energy to collide successfully.

27. Grinding increases the surface area of the solid, exposing more particles to collisions.

28. a. rate = $6.1 \times 10^{-2} \text{ s}^{-1} [C_3H_6]$
b. rate = 9.2×10^{-4} M/s
c. You would expect the rate of the reaction to be considerably faster at 500°C than at 25°C. A change in temperature does not change the reaction mechanism, but it does cause more molecules to collide successfully. Therefore, the rate constant will be larger, but the reaction order will stay the same.

29. The overall reactive nature of a substance is one factor that affects reaction rate.

30. Increasing concentration increases the number of particles in a given space. Particles will collide more often at a higher concentration, increasing the reaction rate.

31. *See page 617B.*

32. Oxygen is required for reactions in the body. If these reactions are slowed, less oxygen is required in a given time interval.

33. The iron filings will have a much larger surface area than iron in the form of a nail. Therefore, iron filings will react, or corrode, more quickly.

34. *See page 617B.*

35. An explosion is more likely with flour because flour is finely ground, with much more exposed surface area than whole grains.

36. *See page 617B.*

Complete worked-out solutions for these problems can be found on the teacher's interleaved pages at the end of this chapter.

37. One or more substrates bind to the active site of the enzyme. The site is specific to the structure of the substrate involved. Binding to the active site distorts the bonds of the substrate, thereby weakening the bonds. This weakening of bonds makes the activation energy of the reaction lower, and the substrate proceeds to react by breaking apart or by combining with another molecule.

38. A homogeneous catalyst is in the same phase as the reactants, usually in solution. A heterogeneous catalyst is in a different phase from the reactants and can easily be separated from the reaction mixture.

39. Inhibitors destroy free radicals, thus reducing their concentration and slowing down the reaction of the radicals with the material being protected.

40. Cholinesterase is an enzyme. Soman might bind to the enzyme at the active site, preventing the enzyme from binding to its substrate. Soman might also bind to the enzyme but not at the active site. This could cause a distortion in the cholinesterase so that the substrate would no longer fit in the active site. Reactions that would usually allow the nervous system to function normally would be too slow or would not occur at all.

41. *See page 617B.*

LINKING CHAPTERS

1. 0.75 M

2. a. At equilibrium the forward and backward rates are equal.

b. Because the equilibrium constant is less than one, the total concentration of reactants will be greater than the total concentration of products.

Answers continue on page 617B.

LINKING CHAPTERS

1. Molarity
H_2O_2 is stored in dark bottles because light increases the rate of decomposition.

$$2H_2O_2(l) \longrightarrow 2H_2O(l) + O_2(g)$$

A 500 mL bottle of 1.50 M H_2O_2 decomposes at an average rate of 0.25 M/h in a clear bottle and at a rate of 0.013 M/y in a dark bottle. What is the difference in H_2O_2 concentration in the two bottles after three hours?

2. Theme: Equilibrium and change
The following reaction has an equilibrium constant of 0.771 at 750°C.

$$H_2(g) + CO_2(g) \rightleftharpoons CO(g) + H_2O(g)$$

a. How do the rates of the forward and reverse reactions compare at equilibrium?

b. How do the concentrations of the products and reactants compare at equilibrium?

3. Theme: Equilibrium and change
The formation of N_2 and H_2O from NO and H_2 is believed to occur in three equilibrium steps, as shown in the mechanism below.

Step 1: $NO + NO \rightleftharpoons N_2O_2$

Step 2: $N_2O_2 + H_2 \rightleftharpoons N_2O + H_2O$

Step 3: $N_2O + H_2 \rightleftharpoons N_2 + H_2O$

When the elementary steps are added together, the K_{eq} of the overall reaction is equal to the product of K_{eq} for all the steps.

a. Write K_{eq} expressions for each step and for the overall reaction.

b. Why do concentration terms for the intermediates not appear in the K_{eq} expressions for the overall equation?

4. Theme: Systems and interactions
Iodine monochloride, ICl, a substance used to determine the degree of unsaturation of fats and oils, is a gas above 97°C. ICl reacts with hydrogen gas to form I_2 gas and HCl gas.

$$2\ ICl(g) + H_2(g) \longrightarrow I_2(g) + 2HCl(g)$$

The rate law for this reaction is rate = $k[ICl][H_2]$. At 230°C, k has a value of 0.163 $M^{-1}s^{-1}$. At 240°C k increases to 0.348 $M^{-1}s^{-1}$.

a. If [ICl] and [H_2] are both 0.020 M, compare the rates at 230°C and 240°C.

b. Compare the rates at 230°C for reactant concentrations of 0.010 M and 0.020 M, respectively.

c. Which has a greater effect on the reaction rate, a 10°C increase in temperature or a doubling of a concentration?

5. Stoichiometry
Given the following reaction, write expressions for the rate of the reaction in terms of each product and reactant.

$$5Sb^{3+}(aq) + 2MnO_4^-(aq) + 36H_2O(l) \longrightarrow$$
$$5SbO_4^{3-}(aq) + 2Mn^{2+}(aq) + 24H_3O^+(aq)$$

ALTERNATIVE ASSESSMENTS

Performance assessment

1. Boilers are used to heat large buildings. Deposits of $CaCO_3$, $MgCO_3$, and $FeCO_3$ can hinder the boiler operation. Aqueous solutions of hydrochloric acid are commonly used to remove these deposits. The general equation for the reaction is written as follows:

$$MCO_3(s) + 2H_3O^+(aq) \longrightarrow$$
$$M^{2+}(aq) + 3H_2O(l) + CO_2(g)$$

M stands for Ca, Mg, or Fe. Design an experiment to determine the effect of various HCl concentrations on the rates of this reaction. Present your design to a panel group.

Portfolio project

1. internet**connect**

SC**LINKS**
NSTA

TOPIC: Biochemical processes
GO TO: www.scilinks.org
KEYWORD: HW165

Research and communication
Many of the chemical reactions that take place in living organisms are catalyzed by specific enzymes. Choose a biochemical process, such as respiration, photosynthesis, vision, or muscular contraction. Prepare a diagram of this process, and detail all of the chemical reactions that occur, noting the enzymes associated with each reaction.

1. The sequence of steps that occurs in a reaction process is called the _____.
   a. heterogeneous reaction
   b. rate law
   c. overall reaction
   d. reaction mechanism

2. In order to be effective, a collision requires _____.
   a. enough energy only
   b. favorable orientation only
   c. enough energy and a favorable orientation
   d. a reaction mechanism

3. In an endothermic reaction, _____.
   a. energy of products < activation energy < energy of reactants
   b. energy of reactants < activation energy < energy of products
   c. energy of products < energy of reactants < activation energy
   d. energy of reactants < energy of products < activation energy

4. How does the energy of the activated complex compare with the energies of the reactants and products?
   a. It is lower than the energy of the reactants and the energy of the products.
   b. It is lower than the energy of the reactants but higher than the energy of the products.
   c. It is higher than the energy of the reactants but lower than the energy of the products.
   d. It is higher than the energy of the reactants and the energy of the products.

5. If a collision between molecules is very gentle, the molecules are _____.
   a. more likely to be orientated favorably
   b. less likely to be orientated favorably
   c. likely to react
   d. likely to rebound without reacting

6. Reaction rate is proportional to the change in _____.
   a. reactant concentration per degree Celsius
   b. reactant concentration per unit time
   c. temperature per unit time
   d. time per reactant concentration

7. Which of the following may affect reaction rate?
   a. nature of reactants
   b. surface area
   c. temperature
   d. all of the above

8. A substance that slows down a reaction process is called a(n) _____.
   a. inhibitor   c. catalyst
   b. reactant   d. activated complex

9. A rate law relates _____.
   a. reaction rate and temperature
   b. reaction rate and concentration
   c. temperature and concentration
   d. energy and concentration

10. The human body uses _____ to speed up reactions that are necessary for life.
    a. reactants   c. collisions
    b. enzymes   d. temperature

11. In an energy-profile graph, the activated complex is represented at the _____.
    a. left end of the curve
    b. right end of the curve
    c. bottom of the curve
    d. peak of the curve

12. Raising temperature _____.
    a. increases average molecular motion
    b. decreases average molecular motion
    c. has no effect on average molecular motion
    d. does not allow collision theory to operate

Answers from page 612

5. Students should write an expression containing any one of the following terms:

$$\text{rate} = \frac{-1}{1} \times \frac{\Delta[CH_3\overset{O}{\overset{\|}{C}}CH_2\overset{O}{\overset{\|}{C}}OH]}{\Delta t} = \frac{\Delta[CH_3\overset{O}{\overset{\|}{C}}CH_3]}{\Delta t} = \frac{\Delta[CO_2]}{\Delta t}$$

6. a.

$$\text{rate}_{79\ \text{min}} = -\frac{[1.67\ \text{M}] - [1.83\ \text{M}]}{79\ \text{min} - 0\ \text{min}} = 2.0 \times 10^{-3}\ \text{M/min}$$

$$\text{rate}_{158\ \text{min}} = -\frac{[1.52\ \text{M}] - [1.67\ \text{M}]}{158\ \text{min} - 79\ \text{min}} = 1.9 \times 10^{-3}\ \text{M/min}$$

$$\text{rate}_{316\ \text{min}} = -\frac{[1.30\ \text{M}] - [1.52\ \text{M}]}{316\ \text{min} - 158\ \text{min}} = 1.4 \times 10^{-3}\ \text{M/min}$$

$$\text{rate}_{632\ \text{min}} = -\frac{[1.00\ \text{M}] - [1.30\ \text{M}]}{632\ \text{min} - 316\ \text{min}} = 9.5 \times 10^{-4}\ \text{M/min}$$

b. The rate changes, becoming slower over time.

Answers from page 613

7. $\text{rate} = \frac{-1}{1} \times \frac{\Delta[CH_2{=}CH_2]}{\Delta t} = \frac{-1}{1} \times \frac{\Delta[Cl_2]}{\Delta t}$

$$\Delta[Cl_2] = [Cl_2]_f - [Cl_2]_i = \frac{1.3\ \text{mol}}{0.5\ \text{L}} - \frac{2.0\ \text{mol}}{0.5\ \text{L}} = -1.4\ \text{M}$$

$\Delta t = 10\ \text{min}$

$$\text{rate} = \frac{-1}{1} \times \frac{[-1.4\ \text{M}]}{10\ \text{min}} = 0.1\ \text{M/min}$$

8. $\text{rate} = \frac{-1}{1} \times \frac{\Delta[H_2S]}{\Delta t}$

$\Delta t = 1{:}42 - 1{:}30 = 12\ \text{min}$

$$\text{rate} = -\frac{[0.57\ \text{M}] - [2.30\ \text{M}]}{12\ \text{min}} = 0.14\ \text{M/min}$$

10. a. Rate in first 90 days:

$$\text{rate} = \frac{-1}{2} \times \frac{\Delta[NOCl]}{\Delta t} = \frac{-1}{2} \times \frac{[0.60\ \text{M}] - [0.95\ \text{M}]}{90\ \text{days}} = 1.9 \times 10^{-3}\ \text{M/day}$$

b. Rate for days 360 to 450:

$$\text{rate} = \frac{-1}{2} \times \frac{\Delta[NOCl]}{\Delta t} = \frac{-1}{2} \times \frac{[0.225\ \text{M}] - [0.25\ \text{M}]}{90\ \text{days}} = 1.4 \times 10^{-4}\ \text{M/day}$$

Answers from page 614

13. order = sum of exponents from rate law

a. first order

b. order = $2 + 1 = 3$

c. order = $1 + 1 = 2$

16. rate = $k[A]^2$

$$k[3A]^2 = (3)^2 k[A]^2 = 9k[A]^2 = 9 \times \text{rate}$$

$$k\left[\frac{1}{2}A\right]^2 = \left(\frac{1}{2}\right)^2 k[A]^2 = \frac{1}{4}k[A]^2 = \frac{1}{4} \times \text{rate}$$

18. rate = $k[A][B]^2$

$$k\left[\frac{1}{2}A\right][B]^2 = \frac{1}{2}k[A][B]^2 = \frac{1}{2} \times \text{rate}$$

$$k[A]\left[\frac{1}{2}B\right]^2 = \left(\frac{1}{2}\right)^2 k[A][B]^2 = \frac{1}{4}k[A][B]^2 = \frac{1}{4} \times \text{rate}$$

22. rate = $k[Mn_2O_7]^n$

$$\frac{1.2 \times 10^{-4}\ \text{M/s}}{4.8 \times 10^{-4}\ \text{M/s}} = \frac{k[7.5 \times 10^{-5}]^n}{k[1.5 \times 10^{-4}]^n}$$

$$\frac{1}{4} = \left[\frac{1}{2}\right]^n$$

$$\log\left(\frac{1}{4}\right) = n\ \log\left[\frac{1}{2}\right]$$

$$-0.602 = n[-0.301]$$

$$n = 2$$

rate = $k[Mn_2O_7]^2$

23. rate = $k[X]^3$

$$k[3X]^3 = 3^3 k[X]^3 = 27k[X]^3 = 27 \times \text{rate}$$

24. a. $\dfrac{\text{rate}}{4 \times \text{rate}} = \dfrac{k[CO]^n[NO_2]^m}{k[CO]^n[2NO_2]^m}$

$$\frac{1}{4} = \left[\frac{1}{2}\right]^m$$

$$m = 2$$

$$\frac{\text{rate}}{\text{rate}} = \frac{k[CO]^n[NO_2]^m}{k[2CO]^n[NO_2]^m}$$

$$1 = \left[\frac{1}{2}\right]^n$$

$$n = 0$$

rate = $k[NO_2]^2$

25. a. $k[2A]^0[2B]^2 = (2)^0(2)^2 k[A]^0[B]^2 = 4k[A]^0[B]^2 = 4 \times \text{rate}$

b. $k[2A]^2[2B]^2 = (2)^2(2)^2 k[A]^2[B]^2 = 16k[A]^0[B]^2 = 16 \times \text{rate}$

c. $k[2A][2B]^3 = 2(2)^3 k[A][B]^3 = 16k[A][B]^3 = 16 \times \text{rate}$

Answers from page 615

28. a. rate = $k[C_3H_6]$

rate = $6.1 \times 10^{-2}\ \text{s}^{-1}[C_3H_6]$

b. rate = $0.061\ \text{s}^{-1} \times [0.015\ \text{M}] = 9.2 \times 10^{-4}\ \text{M/s}$

31. a.

b.

34. a. E_a is probably small because the reaction proceeds easily and rapidly.

b.

c. See the graph in part (b).

d. It must be stored surrounded by a substance it cannot react with, such as a noble gas, pure N_2, or in a vacuum.

36.

The reaction is exothermic. ΔH does not change, even though a catalyst is present.

41.

$$CH_3-\underset{\underset{CH_3}{|}}{\overset{\overset{CH_3}{|}}{C}}-O-CH_3 \quad \textit{t}\text{-butyl methyl ether (2-methyl 2-methoxypropane)}$$

$$CH_3-\underset{\underset{CH_3}{|}}{\overset{\overset{CH_3}{|}}{C}}-CH_2-\underset{\underset{CH_3}{|}}{CH}-CH_3 \quad 2,2,4\text{-trimethylpentane}$$

These are good antiknock agents because they are branched.

LINKING CHAPTERS

1. clear bottle: (0.25 M/h)(3 h) = 0.75 M lost

              1.50 M – 0.75 M = 0.75 M remaining

dark bottle: $\left(\dfrac{0.013\ M}{y} \times \dfrac{1\ y}{365\ days} \times \dfrac{1\ day}{24\ h}\right)$(3 h) $= 4.5 \times 10^{-6}$ M lost

              1.50 M – 4.5×10^{-6} M = 1.50 M remaining

the difference between the two bottles: 1.50 M – 0.75 M = 0.75 M

3. a. step 1: $K_{eq} = \dfrac{[N_2O_2]}{[NO]^2}$

    step 2: $K_{eq} = \dfrac{[N_2O]}{[N_2O_2][H_2]}$

    step 3: $K_{eq} = \dfrac{[N_2]}{[N_2O][H_2]}$

$$K_{eq} = \dfrac{[N_2O_2]}{[NO]^2} \times \dfrac{[N_2O]}{[N_2O_2][H_2]} \times \dfrac{[N_2]}{[N_2O][H_2]} = \dfrac{[N_2]}{[NO]^2[H_2]^2}$$

b. The terms representing concentrations of intermediates cancel out in the overall equilibrium equation.

4. a. $rate_{230°C} = 0.163\ M^{-1}/s^{-1}[ICl][H_2] = 0.163\ M^{-1}/s^{-1}[0.020\ M][0.020\ M]$
            $= 6.5 \times 10^{-5}$ M/s

    $rate_{240°C} = 0.348\ M^{-1}/s^{-1}[ICl][H_2] = 0.348\ M^{-1}/s^{-1}[0.020\ M][0.020\ M]$
            $= 1.4 \times 10^{-4}$ M/s

    $rate_{240°C} \approx 2 \times rate_{230°C}$

b. $rate_{0.020\ M} = 0.163\ M^{-1}/s^{-1}[ICl][H_2] = 0.163\ M^{-1}/s^{-1}[0.020\ M][0.020\ M]$
            $= 6.5 \times 10^{-5}$ M/s

    $rate_{0.010\ M} = 0.163\ M^{-1}/s^{-1}[ICl][H_2] = 0.163\ M^{-1}/s^{-1}[0.010\ M][0.010\ M]$
            $= 1.6 \times 10^{-5}$ M/s

    $rate_{0.020\ M} \approx 4 \times rate_{0.010\ M}$

c. doubling the concentration

5. $rate = \dfrac{-1}{5} \times \dfrac{\Delta[Sb^{3+}]}{\Delta t} = \dfrac{-1}{2} \times \dfrac{\Delta[MnO_4^-]}{\Delta t} = \dfrac{1}{5} \times \dfrac{\Delta[SbO_4^{3-}]}{\Delta t} =$

$$\dfrac{1}{2} \times \dfrac{\Delta[Mn^{2+}]}{\Delta t} = \dfrac{1}{24} \times \dfrac{\Delta[H_3O^+]}{\Delta t}$$

ALTERNATIVE ASSESSMENTS

Performance assessment

1. It is unlikely that only one carbonate will be present in the boiler scale, so the plan should include mixed carbonates.

Portfolio project

1. Many biochemical processes involve a complex series of reactions and repeating sets of reactions (cycles). After students decide on a process and learn more about it, they may want to concentrate on only a portion of it. For example, tracing the entire Krebs cycle would probably be too complicated.

Electrochemistry

CLASSROOM RESOURCES

SECTIONS	TEACHER'S DEMONSTRATIONS	PROBLEM SOLVING ■ *Text* ◆ *ChemFile Mini-Guide*	LABORATORIES ■ *Text* ◆ *ChemFile Manuals: A, B, C, D*
17-1 **What is electro-chemistry all about?** Section Review, p. 627	**Demo 1** Electric Current, p. 620 **Demo 2** An Oxidation-Reduction Reaction, p. 622 **Demo 3** Three Oxidation States of Manganese, p. 624	■ **Sample Problem 17A** Calculating electric charge used in an electrolytic cell, p. 625	■ **EXP. 17A** Redox Titration, p. 788 ◆ **A21** Oxidation-Reduction Reactions ◆ **B20** Oxidation-Reduction Reactions ◆ **EXP. C22** Voltaic Cells ◆ **D22** Electric Charge
17-2 **How are electrolytic cells used?** Section Review, p. 633	**Demo 4** The Electrolysis of KI, p. 628	■ **Sample Problem 17B** Calculating energy needed for electrolysis, p. 631	■ **INV. 17A** Redox Titration—Mining Feasibility Study, p. 792
17-3 **How do batteries work?** Section Review, p. 641	**Demo 5** Making a Six-Cell Fruit Battery, p. 636	■ **Sample Problem 17C** Calculating the mass of products of galvanic cell reactions, p. 639	■ **QuickLab** Listen Up, p. 637 ◆ **A22** Cathodic Protection: Factors Affecting the Corrosion of Iron ◆ **B21** Cathodic Protection: Factors that Affect the Corrosion of Iron ◆ **EXP. C21** Electroplating for Corrosion Protection ◆ **INV. C22** Voltaic Cells—Designing Batteries
17-4 **What can be learned from an equilibrium cell?** Section Review, p. 648	**Demo 6** Predicting Reactions, p. 646	■ **Sample Problem 17D** Predicting the direction of electrochemical reactions, p. 647 ◆ **Chapter 24** Electrochemistry	

SECTIONS	VIDEOS/VIDEODISC *Holt Chemistry Videodisc* CNN *Science in the NEWS*	CHEMFILE CD-ROMs ● *Teaching Resources* ◆ *Interactive Tutor*	OVERHEADS ● *Color Transparencies* ◆ *Transparency Masters*
17-1	Copper/Nitric Acid Redox Reaction Copper/Silver Nitrate Redox Reaction Permanganate/Iron Redox Reaction Electrochemical Cell CNN PRESENTS Segment 29 Electric Car	◆ **Module 10:** Electrochemistry **Topic:** Electricity **Topic:** Electrochemical Cells	● **104** Particle Model for a Redox Reaction ● **105** Ion Movement Through a Porous Barrier ● **106** Electron Pathway in an Electrochemical Cell ● **107** Particle Models for Redox Reactions in Electrochemical Cells ● **108** Comparison of Voltaic and Electrolytic Cells
17-2	Sodium/Chlorine Redox Reaction Iron(III) Chloride Synthesized	● Occupational Application: Water-Quality Manager	
17-3	Battery: Dry Cell CNN PRESENTS Segment 30 Battery Technology	● Occupational Application: Photo-Lab Technician	● **109** Model of a Zinc-Carbon Dry Cell ● **110** Model of an Alkaline Dry Cell ● **111** Model of a Mercury Cell ● **112** Model of a Lead-Acid Storage Battery
17-4	Cell Potentials: Cu and Zn Cell Potentials: Zn and Ag Cell Potentials: Cu and Ag		● **113** Comparing Reduction Potentials of Various Metals ◆ **103A** Standard Reduction Potentials

ASSESSMENT RESOURCES

ALTERNATIVE ASSESSMENTS	CHAPTER TESTING	SCORING RUBRICS *Holt ChemFile Teaching Resources CD-ROM*
Student Text Performance assessments, p. 654 Portfolio projects 1–4, p. 654 **Teacher's Edition** Group Strategy, p. 632 **Study Guide** Sections 17-1 to 17-4	**Student Text** Test Preparation, p. 655 **Holt Chemistry: Visualizing Matter Chapter 17 Test** (blackline masters) **Holt ChemFile Test Generator for Macintosh and Windows**	**Lab Work** Student-Designed Experiments Rubric Performance-Tasks Scoring Rubric Assessment for Structured Inquiry Assessment for Open-Ended Inquiry **Portfolio Projects** Evaluating Concept Maps Assessing Portfolios Portfolio Assignment Student Evaluation Form

CHAPTER

17

Establishing Prior
Knowledge

Make sure students understand
the following concepts.
▸ Chapter 6: electronegativity
▸ Chapter 8: the mole
▸ Chapter 9: balancing equations,
  the activity series
▸ Chapter 13: the nature of solu-
  tions, ionization
▸ Chapter 14: chemical equilibrium

READING STRATEGY

Assimilating Knowledge

Before reading this chapter, have students write a short list of all the
things they already know or think
they know about electrochemistry.
When students have finished their
list, ask them to contribute their
entries to a group list on the board or
on an overhead projector. Then have
students list the things they might
want to know about electrochemistry.
If students have trouble coming up
with questions, offer the following:

▸ What are the components of various
  types of batteries?
▸ How is electrical energy used to
  electroplate metals onto jewelry
  and flatware?
▸ What happens when iron corrodes?

ABOUT THE
ILLUSTRATION

Lightning is an electric spark caused
by a separation of charge. The spark
can strike between two clouds or
between a cloud and the ground.
Lightning strikes generate peak
currents of about 20 000 A.

Electrochemistry

internet connect

Holt Chemistry:
Visualizing Matter
On-Line Resources
go.hrw.com
Visit the HRW Web site for a
variety of resources related
to this chapter. Just type in
the keyword HW0 Chapt17.

SCLINKS
NSTA

National Science Teachers Association
On-Line Resources: www.scilinks.org
The following Scilinks Internet resources can
be found in the student text for this chapter:

Page 621
TOPIC: Electrical energy
KEYWORD: HW171

Page 623
TOPIC: Electroplating
KEYWORD: HW172

Page 625
TOPIC: Electrochemical
cells
KEYWORD: HW173

Page 634
TOPIC: Chlorine
KEYWORD: HW174

Page 642
TOPIC: Fuel cells
KEYWORD: HW175

Page 654
TOPIC: Redox reactions
KEYWORD: HW176

FARADAY'S FISH

Michael Faraday was an outstanding physicist and chemist who lived from 1791 to 1867. He was one of the world's most versatile experimentalists. Although Faraday was both a brilliant chemist and a brilliant physicist, he never performed experiments in the field of biology. So why would this scientist keep a fish in his laboratory?

Faraday made many important chemical discoveries in his laboratory in London's Royal Institution. He was the first to make benzene and liquid chlorine. He made breakthroughs in many fields of physics, but he is perhaps best remembered for his invention of the electric motor, which converts electrical energy into mechanical energy. He also invented the *dynamo,* which converts mechanical energy into electrical energy. His passion for chemistry and electricity led him to found the field of electrochemistry, the branch of science that is the subject of this chapter.

The fish in Faraday's lab was a *torpedo ray.* You are probably familiar with the word *torpedo* in the context of a naval weapon. It is from this fish that the weapon derives its name. Faraday's interest in the torpedo ray arose because, like his dynamo, it could gen-erate electricity. In fact, many fish produce pulses of electricity. Most electric fish use the reflection of these pulses as a navigation and hunting aid in much the same way that bats use sonar. This ability allows electric fish to navigate and find food in very murky water. A few species, notably the electric eel, the torpedo ray, and the electric catfish, use their ability to generate electricity as a weapon. These fish can produce enough voltage to stun or even kill their prey. Large electric eels have even been known to produce enough electricity to kill adult humans.

As you read this chapter, you will learn about electrochemical cells that generate electricity. Electricity is a movement of charge. You have already learned about two types of charged particles, electrons and ions. Electricity is generated by the movement of one or both of these two types of charged particles. Electrochemical cells, such as batteries, generate electricity as a flow of electrons and ions. Electric fish, such as the torpedo ray, generate electricity as a flow of ions.

CHAPTER LINKS

How does the torpedo ray generate electricity in its electric-organ cells?

Would you expect electric organs to be more useful to fish that swim in salt water or fresh water? in clear water or murky water?

How is it possible for large voltages, as great as 600 V in some electric eels, to be produced?

ELECTROCHEMISTRY 619

CONCEPT PREVIEW

What is electrochemistry all about?

OBJECTIVES

▶ **Convert** voltage and charge to electrical energy.

▶ **Explain** the significance of Faraday's constant.

▶ **Distinguish** between anodic and cathodic reactions.

▶ **Define,** with examples, the terms *electrode, cathode,* and *anode.*

▶ **Explain** the distinctions between electrolytic, galvanic, and equilibrium cells.

Introduction to electricity

Electrochemistry is the union of electricity and chemistry. You probably know more about chemistry than you do about electricity, so this chapter will start with some of the fundamentals of electricity.

Figure 17-1 shows the components of a typical flashlight. There are two *cells,* or *batteries.* Each cell has a metal *terminal* at each end. Near the top terminal you will find a *positive* symbol, either + or ⊕. The *negative* terminal, at the bottom of the cell, might have a – or ⊖. Both terminals are made of metal, and both contain electrons, but there is a greater electron density at the negative terminal. Think of the greater density as being caused by "electrical pressure" inside the battery pushing electrons away from the positive terminal and into the negative terminal.

Volts measure "electrical pressure"

This "electrical pressure" is called **voltage,** or *electric potential,* and is measured in **volts** (V). The cells that power your flashlight are likely labeled "1.5 V." When the batteries are placed *in series,* as in Figure 17-1, the voltages add up, giving a total potential of 3.0 V.

voltage

an electric potential difference

volt

the SI unit of voltage

▶ **FIGURE 17-1**

When the switch of a flashlight is closed, electrons driven by the "pressure" of the battery are forced through the thin tungsten filament of the bulb. This flow of electrons makes the filament so hot that light is emitted.

620 CHAPTER 17

DEMONSTRATION 1

Electric Current

Approximate time: 10 minutes

1. Set up an electric circuit with one battery and a light bulb, but do not complete the circuit. Arrange a compass so the needle points north on the numbered scale (this scale is in degrees). Arrange the wires so that one wire lies on top of the compass in the same direction as the needle.

2. Have students watch the compass needle as the circuit is completed. Read the angle where the compass needle finally settles. Tap the compass to make sure the needle is not stuck.

3. Add a second battery to the circuit. Again, watch the compass as you make the final connection.

When you turn on the flashlight, you create a continuous path for the electrons to flow through. The electrons at the negative terminal respond to their higher "pressure" and flow through the metal circuit to the positive terminal. While they are flowing from negative to positive, the electrons pass through the tungsten filament in the light bulb, heating the filament and causing it to glow. When you turn off the flashlight, you break the metallic path, and electron flow is prevented.

Electrical energy is easy to calculate

A **coulomb** is the unit used to measure electric charge. You already encountered it in Chapter 3, where you learned that the charge on a single electron is negative, with a magnitude of $1.602\,177 \times 10^{-19}$ C. Therefore, -1 C is to the charge on $6.241\,508 \times 10^{18}$ electrons.

If you examine the bulb in an ordinary flashlight, you might find that it has "0.5 A" inscribed on the base. What does this mean? The letter A is the abbreviation for **ampere,** the unit of electric current. Current is the flow of charge per unit of time. One ampere is defined as 1 C/s. Every second, 0.5 C, or about 3×10^{18} electrons, pass through the flashlight bulb. It's no wonder the filament gets hot! The units have been defined so that it is easy to relate electricity to energy. One joule of energy is used when 1 C moves across a potential of 1 V.

$$\text{energy (J)} = \text{potential (V)} \times \text{charge (C)}$$

Electricity can be measured by the mole

Chemists generally measure amounts in terms of mole units. You know how much electric charge there is in one electron, so how much electric charge is there in 1 mol of electrons? Avogadro's constant tells you that there are $6.022\,137 \times 10^{23}$ electrons in 1 mol of electrons. As mentioned above, the charge on one electron has the magnitude of $1.602\,177 \times 10^{-19}$ C. Multiplying these constants together gives $96\,485.309$ C/mol, which is represented by the symbol F. This is called Faraday's constant in honor of Michael Faraday, the father of electrochemistry.

internetconnect

SCiLINKS
NSTA
TOPIC: Electrical energy
GO TO: www.scilinks.org
KEYWORD: HW171

coulomb

the SI unit of electric charge

ampere

the SI unit of electric current; equal to 1 C/s

> ### FIGURE 17-2 ▲
>
> The words *electrode, anode, cathode, ion, anion,* and *cation* were all introduced by Michael Faraday.

CONCEPT CHECK

1. A typical lightning bolt has about 10.0 C of charge. How many electrons are in a typical lightning bolt?
2. A charge of 9.0 mC passes through a length of thin wire in 3.5 seconds.
   a. What is the current in the wire?
   b. How many electrons would pass through the section of wire in 10.0 seconds?
   c. If a voltage of 4.5 V is applied to the wire, how much energy is dissipated in 5.0 minutes using the current from item (a)?

TEACHING TIP

Vocabulary Strategy The term *coulomb* honors Charles Augustin de Coulomb (1736–1806), a French physicist whose research resulted in Coulomb's law. This law is an inverse-square law that describes the relationship of the force between two charged objects and the distance between them.

The *ampere* honors the French mathematician and physicist André Marie Ampère (1775–1836), who discovered another inverse-square law relating the force between two current-carrying conductors and the distance between them.

ANSWERS

CONCEPT CHECK

1. 6.24×10^{19} electrons
2. **a.** 2.6×10^{-3} A
   b. 1.6×10^{17} electrons
   c. 3.5 J

CHEMISTRY INTERACTIVE TUTOR

Module 10: Electrochemistry
Topic: Electricity
This engaging tutorial reviews the basic laws of electricity.

---

4. Have students observe the evidence indicating that more current flows with two batteries. *(The bulb burns brighter, and the compass needle is deflected at a greater angle.)*

5. Ask students to calculate the voltage of the circuit with one battery and with two batteries, given the individual battery voltages.

Vocabulary Strategy The idea of reduction relates to the fact that when an ion or atom gains electrons, its oxidation state is reduced to a lower value—in the case of copper, from +2 to 0. The opposite process, oxidation, relates to the fact that elements lose electrons in the same way they do when combining with oxygen, taking on higher oxidation states. This terminology goes back to before Mendeleev's time, when the combining abilities of elements were studied by examining and comparing the proportions in their various oxides.

Mnemonic Devices An easy mnemonic device for associating oxidation and reduction with electron transfer is **OIL RIG: O**xidation **I**s the **L**oss of electrons, **R**eduction **I**s the **G**ain of electrons. Students may prefer **LEO** says **GER: L**oss of **E**lectrons is **O**xidation, **G**ain of **E**lectrons is **R**eduction.

Another helpful mnemonic device is that reduction occurs at the cathode, and *cathode* and *reduction* both start with consonants. Oxidation occurs at the anode, and *oxidation* and *anode* both start with vowels.

Figures 17-3 and 17-4 Be sure students realize that each of these figures represents half an electrochemical cell. In Figure 17-3, electrons for the reduction of Cu^{2+} to Cu come from the oxidation of Zn to Zn^{2+}. In Figure 17-4, the electrons lost by the oxidation of Zn to Zn^{2+} are gained by copper ions as they are reduced from Cu^{2+} to Cu. Use these figures to reinforce the idea that an oxidation process never occurs without a simultaneous reduction process.

Electrodes

electrode

> the junction between a metallic conductor and an ionic conductor, often an electrolyte solution

cathode

> the electrode at which reduction takes place

reduction

> a chemical reaction in which the reactant gains electrons

electroplating

> an electrochemical process in which a metal ion is reduced and solid metal is deposited on a surface

In Chapter 4 you learned that metals are good conductors of electricity. They conduct by electron motion. In Chapter 13 you found that electrolyte solutions conduct electricity by the motion of ions, not electrons. All conductors can be classified into two groups: those that conduct by *electron* motion and those that conduct by *ion* motion.

What happens when a substance that conducts by electron motion is placed in contact with a material that conducts by the motion of ions? This junction between an electronic conductor and an ionic conductor is called an **electrode.** Electronic conduction can transfer electricity through the metal and up to the junction. Likewise, ionic conduction can transfer electricity through the solution and up to the junction. But without something special happening, the electricity cannot cross the junction itself. The "something special" that must occur is called an *electrode reaction.*

If electrons are consumed, the reaction is cathodic

Electrode reactions involve the transfer of electrons. If the electronic conductor gives up electrons to the ionic conductor in the electrode reaction, then the electrode is said to be a **cathode** and the reaction is *cathodic.* The flow of electrons and ions at a cathode is shown in **Figure 17-3.** The copper strip is the electronic conductor that gives up electrons to the ionic conductor, the copper(II) sulfate solution.

The chemistry that occurs at a cathode is described as **reduction.** The conversion of copper(II) ions to copper metal shown in Figure 17-3 is a reduction reaction.

$$Cu^{2+}(aq) + 2e^- \longrightarrow Cu(s)$$

You can see in Figure 17-3 that during reduction, copper is deposited on the metal strip. Solid metal appears as the product. This process of depositing a metal on a conductive surface is used in the **electroplating** of silver onto jewelry and flatware.

Neutral species can also undergo reduction at a cathode. For example, chlorine is reduced to chloride ions according to the following equation.

$$Cl_2(aq) + 2e^- \longrightarrow 2Cl^-(aq)$$

Another example of a cathodic reaction is one in which the solvent itself is reduced. This reaction occurs at the cathode during the *electrolysis* of water.

$$2H_2O(l) + 2e^- \longrightarrow H_2(g) + 2OH^-(aq)$$

▼ **FIGURE 17-3**

Copper(II) ions are reduced as they gain electrons at the cathode.

Copper(II) ion, Cu^{2+}

Copper atoms, Cu

Copper metal

Sulfate ion, SO_4^{2-}

Copper(II) sulfate, $CuSO_4$, solution

Cathodic reaction:
$Cu^{2+}(aq) + 2e^- \longrightarrow Cu(s)$

DEMONSTRATION 2

An Oxidation-Reduction Reaction
Approximate time: 10 minutes

Be sure students understand that this simple redox demonstration is not a Cu/Zn galvanic cell.

1. Half-fill a Petri dish with a 0.5 M $CuSO_4$ solution.

2. Place the dish on an overhead projector.

3. Add to the Petri dish a few pieces of mossy zinc or some 1 cm² pieces of zinc sheet.

4. Copper metal should form on the zinc as the blue color of the solution fades, indicating the removal of Cu^{2+} ions from solution.

5. Allow students to view the dish under room light so that they can see the reddish color of the copper metal formed. Discuss the process in terms of electron transfer, oxidation, reduction, and the ions present in solution both before and after the reaction.

If electrons are released, an anodic reaction has occurred

An **anode** is an electrode at which electrons are generated, as shown in **Figure 17-4.** The anode shown in the figure involves the reaction of zinc atoms to form zinc ions according to the following equation.

$$Zn(s) \longrightarrow Zn^{2+}(aq) + 2e^-$$

A reaction occurring at an anode is an *anodic* reaction, and the resulting chemical change is called **oxidation.** Electrons are evolved at the anode during the electrolysis of water.

$$6H_2O(l) \longrightarrow 4e^- + O_2(g) + 4H_3O^+(aq)$$

The rusting of iron is another example of an oxidation reaction. Iron metal in the presence of water forms iron(III) oxide, also known as rust.

$$2Fe(s) + 11H_2O(l) \longrightarrow$$
$$Fe_2O_3 \cdot 2H_2O(s) + 6H_3O^+(aq) + 6e^-$$

Notice that the beakers in Figures 17-3 and 17-4 appear to be cut in half. Each beaker shows only part of a complete picture. These electrode reactions appear to occur on their own, but that never actually happens. Reduction reactions always occur with oxidation reactions. The electrons used in reduction must come from an oxidation reaction. The overall reaction is an oxidation-reduction reaction, or **redox reaction.** Although electrons cancel out of redox equations, when the reaction occurs electrochemically, the electrons are often indicated above the arrow, as shown in the following equation that combines the cathodic and anodic reactions from Figures 17-3 and 17-4.

$$Zn(s) + Cu^{2+}(aq) \xrightarrow{2e^-} Zn^{2+}(aq) + Cu(s)$$

Zinc metal

Sulfate ion, SO_4^{2-}

Zinc(II) ion, Zn^{2+}

Zinc sulfate, $ZnSO_4$, solution

Anodic reaction:
$$Zn(s) \longrightarrow Zn^{2+}(aq) + 2e^-$$

FIGURE 17-4 ▲

Zinc atoms are oxidized as they lose electrons at the anode. The metal strip dissolves as the reaction proceeds.

 internetconnect

SCI**LINKS**
NSTA

TOPIC: Electroplating
GO TO: www.scilinks.org
KEYWORD: HW172

anode

the electrode at which oxidation takes place

oxidation

a chemical reaction in which the reactant loses electrons

redox reaction

any chemical process in which both oxidation and reduction occur

---

CONCEPT CHECK

1. Identify the following reactions as oxidation or reduction reactions.
   a. $Na \longrightarrow Na^+ + e^-$
   b. $Cr_2O_7^{2-} + 14H^+ + 6e^- \longrightarrow 2Cr^{3+} + 7H_2O$
   c. $2Cl^- \longrightarrow Cl_2 + 2e^-$
   d. $Br_2 + 2e^- \longrightarrow 2Br^-$

2. Identify which of the following reactions is an anodic reaction and which is a cathodic reaction. Write the balanced overall ionic equation for the redox reaction between these two.

$$Cd(s) \longrightarrow Cd^{2+}(aq) + 2e^-$$
$$I_3^-(aq) + 2e^- \longrightarrow 3I^-(aq)$$

ANSWERS

CONCEPT CHECK

1. a. oxidation
   b. reduction
   c. oxidation
   d. reduction

2. anodic: $Cd(s) \longrightarrow Cd^{2+}(aq) + 2e^-$
   cathodic: $I_3^-(aq) + 2e^- \longrightarrow 3I^-(aq)$

$$Cd(s) + I_3^-(aq) \xrightarrow{2e^-}$$
$$Cd^{2+}(aq) + 3I^-(aq)$$

RESOURCE LINK

IN-TEXT LAB

Skills Development
Have students do Exploration 17A on page 788 to develop their skills working with redox titrations.

ChemFile Lab A
Skills Development
Have students do Experiment 21: *Oxidation-Reduction Reactions.*

ChemFile Lab B
Microscale Lab
Have students do Experiment 20: *Oxidation-Reduction Reactions.*

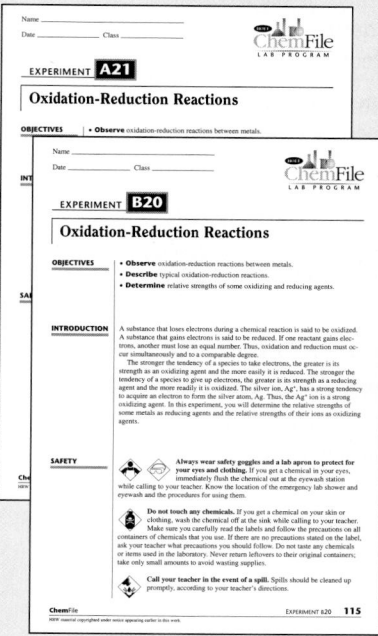

ELECTROCHEMISTRY 623

Safety

Wear safety goggles and a lab apron. Keep students at least 10 ft away from the demonstration.

Disposal

Separate the solids from the supernatant liquid, and rinse the solids with water. Throw the solids in the trash. Combine the rinsings with the supernatant. Slowly with stirring add 1 M sulfuric acid solution until the pH is between 5 and 6. Scour six 6d iron nails with steel wool until they are bright and shiny.

Immerse the nails in the acidified solution. Let the nails remain immersed overnight until all the copper has precipitated. Remove the nails, and filter the solution. Heat the nails and any precipitate obtained from filtration sufficiently to convert the copper precipitate and the copper on the nails to copper oxide. Let them cool, and put the copper oxide and the nails in the trash. Treat the filtrate with sufficient 1 M NaOH to bring the pH to between 8 and 10. Filter. Let the precipitate dry, and put it in the trash. Pour the filtrate down the drain.

Lead a discussion on the function of the porous barrier and why it is needed in order to get usable energy from a galvanic cell. Help students by asking them to discuss what would happen if the barrier were removed. *(Copper ions would be able to reach the zinc strip and would be reduced in a direct exchange of electrons with zinc rather than causing the electrons to pass through the external circuit.)* Students should understand that a cell can generate an electric current only if the oxidation and reduction halves of an overall redox reaction are isolated from each other. This way the electrons being lost at the anode pass through an external wire, reaching the cathode, where reduction takes place.

READING STRATEGY

Organizing Concepts You may want to have students organize information about anodic and cathodic processes in a table like this one. Tell students that the information is valid for both galvanic and electrolytic cells.

Electrode	anode	cathode
Process	oxidation	reduction
Change in electrons	loss	gain
Species becomes	more positive	more negative

Module 10: Electrochemistry
Topic: Electrochemical Cells
This engaging tutorial reviews the components and reactions of electrochemical cells.

▼ FIGURE 17-5

A porous partition allows the two electrodes to be bathed by different solutions.

Electrodes   Porous barrier

electrochemical cell

an apparatus through which electricity can flow that includes at least two electrodes and at least one electrolyte solution

▼ FIGURE 17-6

Copper is refined in an electrolytic cell.

Electrochemical cells

Electrons produced by an anode must be consumed by a cathodic reaction. Therefore, an anode must be paired with a cathode. The two electrodes combine in an **electrochemical cell.** The simplest electrochemical cell consists of two pieces of metal in an electrolyte solution. **Figure 17-5** shows a common type of electrochemical cell in which a porous barrier divides the cell into two compartments. Ions are allowed to pass through this barrier so that electricity can flow between the compartments.

An *electrode* was defined as a surface: the junction between an electronic conductor and an ionic conductor. That definition is technically correct, but be aware that the words *electrode, anode,* and *cathode* are also used to refer to the pieces of metal. The words *anode* and *cathode* are often incorrectly interchanged with *positive* and *negative* electrodes. An anode may be the positive *or* the negative electrode of a cell; the anode is wherever oxidation occurs. The cathode may be the positive *or* negative electrode; it is wherever reduction occurs.

There are three kinds of electrochemical cells. The cell depicted in Figure 17-5 has wires that are not attached to anything. What those wires are attached to determines whether the cell is an electrolytic cell, a galvanic cell, or an equilibrium cell.

Electrolytic cells are used to refine metals

The cell shown in **Figure 17-6** illustrates a copper-refining plant. A power source drives electricity through the cell. The anode is impure copper containing zinc, gold, and silver. The electrolyte is an acidified $CuSO_4$ solution. The following chemical equation shows that copper metal is oxidized to copper(II) ions that go into solution at the anode.

$$Cu(s) \longrightarrow 2e^- + Cu^{2+}(aq)$$

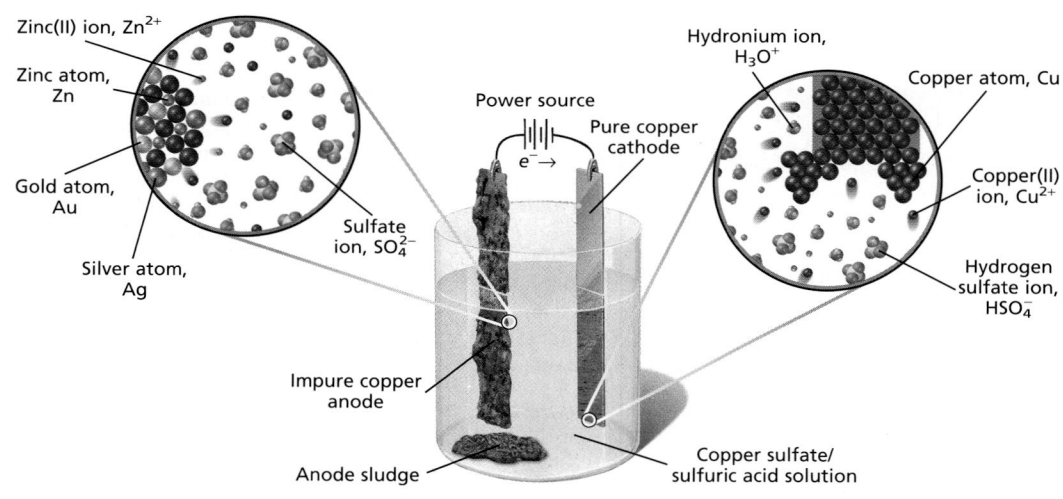

Zinc(II) ion, Zn^{2+}
Zinc atom, Zn
Gold atom, Au
Silver atom, Ag
Sulfate ion, SO_4^{2-}
Power source
Pure copper cathode
Hydronium ion, H_3O^+
Copper atom, Cu
Copper(II) ion, Cu^{2+}
Hydrogen sulfate ion, HSO_4^-
Impure copper anode
Anode sludge
Copper sulfate/ sulfuric acid solution

DEMONSTRATION 3

Three Oxidation States of Manganese

Approximate time: 10 minutes

1. Pour 0.05 M $KMnO_4$ solution into a Petri dish until the dish is one-fourth full. Point out to students that manganese is in the +7 oxidation state.

2. Place the dish on the overhead projector.

3. Add 1 mL of 0.1 M NaOH to the solution.

4. Gently add one drop of acetaldehyde, which acts as a reducing agent.

5. Let the acetaldehyde remain undisturbed on the surface. Three separate colored rings should appear, corresponding to three oxidation states of Mn: brown, +4; green, +6; and purple, +7.

Exactly the opposite reaction occurs at the cathode, which is a strip of pure copper.

$$Cu^{2+}(aq) + 2e^- \longrightarrow Cu(s)$$

The solid copper dissolves from the impure anode. The copper ions then move through the solution toward the cathode, where they are deposited as pure metal. The impurities include active metals, such as zinc, which also oxidize and dissolve from the anode.

$$Zn(s) \longrightarrow 2e^- + Zn^{2+}(aq)$$

Unlike the copper ions, these impurities are not reduced at the cathode, so they remain in solution. Inactive impurities, such as platinum, silver, and gold, fall to the bottom of the vessel as *anode sludge*. The sludge is such a valuable source of these expensive elements that their recovery more than justifies the cost of the copper-refining process.

The cell used to refine impure copper uses an external power source to drive a chemical reaction. It is an example of an **electrolytic cell.** Electrolytic cells convert electrical energy into chemical energy. **Galvanic cells** do the opposite; they convert chemical energy into electrical energy.

internet**connect**

SC*i*LINKS
NSTA
TOPIC: Electrochemical cells
GO TO: www.scilinks.org
KEYWORD: HW173

electrolytic cell

an electrochemical cell in which electrical energy is used to drive two electrode reactions and bring about desired chemical changes

galvanic cell

an electrochemical cell in which two electrode reactions occur spontaneously and produce electrical energy

SAMPLE PROBLEM 17A

ADDITIONAL EXAMPLES

1. What is the charge required to reduce 0.725 mol of Cu^{2+} ions to copper metal?

   Ans. 1.40×10^5 C

2. How much mass will a zinc anode lose when zinc is oxidized to Zn^{2+} by a current of 3.80 A flowing for 2.50 hours?

   Ans. 11.6 g Zn

3. What current would be necessary in an electrolytic cell in order to plate out 2.85 g of silver from Ag^+ ions in 45.0 minutes?

   Ans. 0.944 A

SAMPLE PROBLEM 17A | Calculating electric charge used in an electrolytic cell

How much electric charge is used in refining 1.0000 kg of copper?

1 List what you know

▶ Mass of Cu = 1.0000 kg = 1000.0 g
▶ Charge = ? C

2 Set up the problem

▶ Write the chemical equation for the reaction involved in refining copper.

$$Cu^{2+}(aq) + 2e^- \longrightarrow Cu(s)$$

From this equation you see that 2 mol of electrons is required to reduce 1 mol of Cu^{2+} to 1 mol of Cu.

▶ In order to calculate the amount of electricity required for the process, you must convert the mass of copper to the amount of copper in moles. To do this, you need to know the molar mass of copper.

$$1 \text{ mol Cu} = 63.55 \text{ g}$$

▶ Set up your equation. Remember that you must first convert the 1000.0 g Cu to the amount of Cu in moles. Because 1 mol of Cu is produced by 2 mol of electrons, you must next include a factor to determine the amount of electrons involved in refining the given mass of copper. Then you must use Faraday's constant to determine the amount of electricity needed.

$$1000.0 \text{ g Cu} \times \frac{1 \text{ mol Cu}}{63.55 \text{ g Cu}} \times \frac{2 \text{ mol } e^-}{1 \text{ mol Cu}} \times \frac{96\,485 \text{ C}}{\text{mol } e^-} = ? \text{ C}$$

ELECTROCHEMISTRY   625

Safety
Wear safety goggles and a lab apron. Keep students at least 10 ft away from the demonstration.

Disposal
While stirring, add 1.0 M $Na_2S_2O_3$ until the mixture is brown. Adjust the pH to between 5 and 9, dilute tenfold, and pour down the drain.

PRACTICE PROBLEMS 17A

1. energy = potential × charge
   energy = $(0.25 \text{ V})(3.037 \times 10^6 \text{ C})$
   $= 7.6 \times 10^5 \text{ J}$

2. $30.0 \text{ min} \times \dfrac{1.50 \text{ C}}{1 \text{ s}} \times \dfrac{60 \text{ s}}{1 \text{ min}} \times$

   $\dfrac{1 \text{ mol } e^-}{96\,485 \text{ C}} \times \dfrac{1 \text{ mol Ag}}{1 \text{ mol } e^-} \times \dfrac{107.87 \text{ g Ag}}{1 \text{ mol Ag}} =$

   $\qquad\qquad\qquad\qquad\qquad 3.02 \text{ g Ag}$

TEACHING TIP

Designing a Model Have students model the electrochemical cell in Figure 17-7 using objects that can be manipulated to show electron and ion movement. For example, students could cut electron and ion models out of poster board and attach magnets to the back of them. The models could be moved around on a magnetic board on which the basic cell is drawn.

3 Calculate and verify

▶ Calculate and round off correctly.

$$1000.0 \text{ g Cu} \times \frac{1 \text{ mol Cu}}{63.55 \text{ g Cu}} \times \frac{2 \text{ mol } e^-}{1 \text{ mol Cu}} \times \frac{96\,485 \text{ C}}{\text{mol } e^-} = 3.037 \times 10^6 \text{ C}$$

▶ Check your answer by estimating with round figures.

$$\frac{(10^3)(2)(1 \times 10^5)}{60} \approx 3 \times 10^6$$

PRACTICE PROBLEMS

1. The copper refining cell requires only a small voltage, typically 0.25 V. How much energy is required to refine 1.0 kg of copper? (Hint: Use the result from Sample Problem 17A.)

2. Ag^+ ions are reduced at a cathode to produce silver metal. Calculate how much silver metal is produced at the cathode in 30.0 minutes if a current of 1.50 A flows through a solution containing Ag^+.

Galvanic cells produce electrical energy

A Daniell cell is illustrated in **Figure 17-7**. Galvanic cells like this one were used as power sources in the early days of electrical research. The zinc anode is dissolving as zinc ions enter the solution. The cathodic and anodic reactions are as follows. Note that the same number of elec-

▼ **FIGURE 17-7**

A Daniell cell produces the electrical energy used to illuminate the light bulb as electrons move through the filament from the anode to the cathode.

Zinc atoms losing two electrons to become ions

Zinc atom, Zn   Zinc ion, Zn^{2+}

Water molecule, H_2O

Sulfate ion, SO_4^{2-}

Zinc strip   Copper strip

Porous barrier

Copper(II) sulfate, $CuSO_4$, solution

Zinc sulfate, $ZnSO_4$, solution   Anode   Cathode

Copper ion, Cu^{2+} Copper atom, Cu

Copper(II) ions gaining two electrons to become atoms

trons are given up in oxidation at the anode as are used in reduction at the cathode.

$$\text{oxidation: } Zn(s) \longrightarrow 2e^- + Zn^{2+}(aq)$$
$$\text{reduction: } Cu^{2+}(aq) + 2e^- \longrightarrow Cu(s)$$

Figure 17-7 also shows the movement of ions through the porous barrier. Solid copper is depositing at the cathode. In which direction are the electrons moving through the light bulb of this Daniell cell?

Equilibrium cells are cells without reactions

Look at the cell in Figure 17-5, on page 624. The electrodes in this cell are not joined to complete a circuit, so no electricity flows and no reactions occur. This cell is still an electrochemical cell. Cells through which *no* electricity flows are called **equilibrium cells.** Equilibrium cells are used to determine thermodynamic data and other useful information. For example, the pH meter in Chapter 15 contains a probe that is an equilibrium cell. Notice that because there are no electrode reactions taking place, an equilibrium cell does not have an anode or a cathode. Those labels apply only to electrolytic and galvanic cells.

equilibrium cell

an electrochemical cell in which no electric current flows

SECTION REVIEW

Total recall

1. Explain how the flow of electrons in a flashlight produces light.

2. How does an equilibrium cell differ from an electrolytic cell and a galvanic cell? How is it similar to the two?

Critical thinking

3. Why must reduction always be accompanied by oxidation, and vice versa?

4. Correct the following statement: Oxidation is a reaction in which a chemical species gains electrons at the cathode.

Practice problems

5. Calculate how much electric charge is present in 2.5 mol of electrons.

6. A car battery operates at 12.0 V and is rated at 100 ampere-hours, which means that the battery can deliver 5.0 A of current for 20.0 hours. How much energy can this battery generate in 1.0 minute when operating at these conditions?

7. Write balanced equations to represent the following electrode reactions.
   a. reduction of Pt^{2+} to Pt
   b. oxidation of Fe^{2+} to Fe^{3+}
   c. reduction of S to S^{2-}
   d. reduction of Br_2 to Br^-
   e. oxidation of Au to Au^{3+}

8. **Story Clue** An electric fish can produce exactly 300 discharges per second. Each discharge has a potential of 100.0 mV and a current of 1.00 A. How much energy is released with each discharge?

9. **Story Clue** An electric eel can produce a discharge of 600.0 V. It does this by combining the voltages of individual *electroplates.* If each electroplate produces 150.0 mV, how many plates are required to give off the total discharge?

SECTION 17-2

How are electrolytic cells used?

OBJECTIVES

▶ **Explain** how nonspontaneous chemical reactions can be driven by electrolytic cells.

▶ **Describe** briefly the following electrolytic processes: sodium production, water electrolysis, and electrowinning of Al.

▶ **Calculate** the electricity and energy requirements of an electrolytic cell.

Electrosynthesis of sodium

Pure sodium metal does not occur in nature. By mass, about 2.7% of sea water can be considered to be sodium chloride, NaCl. Sodium is also found in nature as nitrate, carbonate, and sulfate salts, and in more complex minerals. A lot of sodium exists in the form of the cation, Na^+, but getting it into the form of the element $Na(s)$ is not easy.

You learned in Chapter 4 that sodium metal is very reactive. This means that the synthesis of Na is very endothermic.

$$NaCl(s) \longrightarrow Na(s) + 1/2Cl_2(g) \ \Delta H = 411 \text{ kJ}$$

Such reactions are almost always nonspontaneous.

In Chapter 11 you learned about one trick to get an endothermic reaction to occur. If the process has a positive entropy change, it will be spontaneous at a sufficiently high temperature. The decomposition of sodium chloride changes a solid into a solid and a gas; the entropy of this system increases.

$$NaCl(s) \longrightarrow Na(s) + 1/2Cl_2(g) \ \Delta S = 90.6 \text{ J/K}$$

▶ **FIGURE 17-8**

Most of the salt in the oceans is the product of rain rinsing salts from rocks and minerals into the sea.

DEMONSTRATION 4

The Electrolysis of KI

Approximate time: 15 minutes

1. Place a Petri dish on an overhead projector. Add 20 mL of 0.1 M KI solution.

2. Add a few drops of phenolphthalein and a few drops of starch solution to the KI solution.

3. Using insulated leads, attach two electrodes to a 9 V transistor-radio battery.

4. Hold the electrodes in the KI solution. I_2 can be detected at the anode by the characteristic blue-black color of starch in the presence of I_2. H_2 bubbles can be detected at the cathode. OH^- ions can be detected near the cathode by the pink color of phenolphthalein.

How high must the temperature be to make the decomposition of NaCl spontaneous? This temperature can be determined by the following calculation.

$$\Delta G = \Delta H - T\Delta S < 0$$

$$T > \frac{\Delta H}{\Delta S} = \frac{411 \text{ kJ}}{0.0906 \text{ kJ/K}} = 4540 \text{ K}$$

Such a high temperature (which is only a little less than the temperature at the sun's surface) is not practical in manufacturing.

Electrochemistry makes sodium production possible

Sodium is manufactured by the electrolysis of molten sodium chloride. This method is named the Downs process and is carried out industrially in a **Downs cell,** as shown in **Figure 17-9.** The cell reaction is given by the following equation.

$$Na^+(l) + Cl^-(l) \xrightarrow{e^-} Na(l) + 1/2Cl_2(g)$$

Notice that this is virtually the same equation for a nonspontaneous decomposition on the previous page; this is because NaCl is ionic.

This redox reaction can be divided into two reactions. Cl^- is oxidized at the anode, and Na^+ is reduced at the cathode.

anode: $Cl^-(l) \longrightarrow e^- + 1/2Cl_2(g)$
cathode: $Na^+(l) + e^- \longrightarrow Na(l)$

How is it possible for each of these half-reactions to occur when the overall process is nonspontaneous? Remember that voltage is analogous to electron pressure. The cathode in a Downs cell is at a negative voltage, which means it has a high pressure of electrons. The high pressure

Downs cell

an electrolytic cell that uses a graphite anode and an iron cathode to produce sodium metal

FIGURE 17-9 ◄

In a Downs cell the electrolysis of molten NaCl produces elemental sodium and chlorine.

HISTORICAL CONNECTION

The Downs cell was first used to produce sodium by the DuPont Company in 1921. Because of its great consumption of electricity, the cell was located at Niagara Falls to take advantage of the hydroelectric station located there.

ADDITIONAL APPLICATION

Much metallic sodium was once used in the production of tetraethyl lead, used as an antiknock agent in gasoline. Today, not much sodium is produced for that purpose because of environmental concerns about lead pollution. As a result, the production of sodium has declined in recent years. Metallic sodium is used in the industrial synthesis of some organic compounds. Sodium is also used in the molten state as a cooling liquid in nuclear reactors.

---

5. Students can use the above evidence to write the electrode reactions that took place.
   Anode: $2I^- \longrightarrow I_2 + 2e^-$
   Cathode: $2H_2O + 2e^- \longrightarrow H_2 + 2OH^-$

6. Discuss the fact that the reaction did not proceed until the electrodes and battery were added. When students realize that this is a nonspontaneous reaction, have them trace the path of the electrons. Electrons are pumped from the anode, where I^- ions are oxidized, and forced through the external circuit to the cathode, where H^+ ions from the water are reduced to H_2.

Safety
Wear safety goggles and a lab apron.

Disposal
Add sufficient 1.0 M $Na_2S_2O_3$ while stirring to convert all iodine to iodide. Adjust the pH to between 5 and 9, and pour down the drain.

CONCEPT CHECK

1. The electron pressure (negative voltage) at the cathode of a Downs cell forces electrons onto Na^+ ions, reducing them to Na metal. The low electron pressure (positive voltage) at the anode pulls electrons away from the chloride ions, forcing a nonspontaneous, endothermic reaction to proceed.

2. 1830 K or 1560°C; the process is impractical because of the high temperatures involved.

TEACHING TIP

Discussion Strategy Students should note that H_2O is both reduced at the cathode and oxidized at the anode during electrolysis. Have them take note of the products at each electrode. Ask why the electrodes in water electrolysis must be isolated in separate housings, while those in copper refining are not. *(Both products are gases, so this arrangement must be used to keep them separate.)* Ask what happens to the nongaseous products produced in the reactions. *(They combine to form water.)*

electrosynthesis

a synthesis reaction that is carried out in an electrochemical cell using an electric current

electrolysis

the decomposition of a substance by an electric current

In order for the electrolysis of water to work, an electrolyte must be added to the water to make it an effective conductor.

forces electrons onto the sodium ions. Think of the anode as an electron vacuum. It has a voltage that is positive enough to pull electrons away from the chloride ions.

Pure NaCl melts at 1074 K, but some $CaCl_2$ is added to lower the melting point. (Remember from Chapter 13 the colligative property of freezing point depression.) This allows the cell to operate at about 860 K.

The Downs process demonstrates a typical electrolytic cell. Electrical energy drives a nonspontaneous process. In many respects, the operation of electrolytic cells is similar to photosynthesis; nonchemical energy is used to cause a nonspontaneous chemical process. Photosynthesis uses light energy, and **electrosynthesis** uses electrical energy.

CONCEPT CHECK

1. Use the concept of electron pressure to explain how electrochemistry makes sodium production possible.

2. Calculate the temperature at which the following reaction would become spontaneous. Is this a practical way to produce hydrogen industrially?

$$Cu(s) + H_2O(l) \rightarrow CuO(s) + H_2(g)$$
$$\Delta H = 128.6 \text{ kJ}$$
$$\Delta S = 70.2 \text{ J/K}$$

Electrolysis of water

If cars like the hydrogen car described in Chapter 11 ever become practical, a reliable supply of low-cost hydrogen will be needed to fuel them. Some hydrogen is currently available as a byproduct of petroleum refining. Hydrogen can also be made by passing steam over hot iron, but any large demand for H_2 will more likely be met by the **electrolysis** of water.

Figure 17-10 shows the laboratory equipment used in the electrolysis of water. The following reactions occur at the anode and cathode.

anode: $6H_2O(l) \longrightarrow 4e^- + O_2(g) + 4H_3O^+(aq)$
cathode: $4H_2O(l) + 4e^- \longrightarrow 2H_2(g) + 4OH^-(aq)$

The overall reaction occurs when the applied voltage is at least 1.23 V, but for the cell to be practical, about 2.0 V is required.

What if two different cell reactions are possible?

Sodium chloride is often used as the electrolyte in the electrolysis of water. The solution contains the same ions that are present in a Downs cell. Why then are the electrode reactions in the electrolysis of water different from those in the Downs process? When two electrode reactions are possible, the one that occurs at a lower voltage is favored.

SAMPLE PROBLEM 17B   Calculating energy needed for electrolysis

How much electrical energy is required to generate 1.000 L of H_2 at 25°C and 1.00 atm pressure by the electrolysis of water?

1   List what you know

- $V = 1.000$ L
- $T = 25°C = 298$ K
- $P = 1.00$ atm $= 101$ kPa
- Electrical energy = ? J

2   Set up the problem

- You are given the volume of hydrogen, so you must use the ideal gas law to determine the amount of H_2.

$$PV = nRT$$

$$n = \frac{PV}{RT} = \frac{101 \text{ kPa} \times 1.000 \text{ L}}{8.314 \text{ kPa} \cdot \text{L/K} \cdot \text{mol} \times 298 \text{ K}}$$

- Write the chemical equation involved in the electrolysis of water.

$$4H_2O(l) + 4e^- \longrightarrow 2H_2(g) + 4OH^-(aq)$$

For every 2 mol of H_2 made, 4 mol of e^- are used.

- Use Faraday's law to calculate the charge. First determine the amount of electrons required to produce the amount of H_2 calculated above.

$$\text{charge} = n \times \frac{4 \text{ mol } e^-}{2 \text{ mol } H_2} \times \frac{96\,485 \text{ C}}{\text{mol } e^-}$$

- You have learned that the cell used in the electrolysis of water operates at a voltage of 2.0 V. Use this voltage and the charge calculated above to calculate the electrical energy.

$$\text{electrical energy} = \text{voltage} \times \text{charge} = 2.0 \text{ V} \times ? \text{ C}$$

3   Calculate

- Calculate and round off correctly.

$$n = \frac{PV}{RT} = \frac{101 \text{ kPa} \times 1.000 \text{ L}}{8.314 \text{ kPa} \cdot \text{L/K} \cdot \text{mol} \times 298 \text{ K}} = 0.0408 \text{ mol}$$

$$\text{charge} = 0.0408 \text{ mol } H_2 \times \frac{4 \text{ mol } e^-}{2 \text{ mol } H_2} \times \frac{96\,485 \text{ C}}{\text{mol } e^-} = 7.87 \times 10^3 \text{ C}$$

$$\text{electrical energy} = 2.0 \text{ V} \times 7.87 \times 10^3 \text{ C} = 1.6 \times 10^4 \text{ J} = 16 \text{ kJ}$$

PRACTICE PROBLEMS

1. Calculate how much electrical energy is required to generate 1.000 L of oxygen by the electrolysis of water under the same conditions.

2. How many moles of chlorine gas would be produced in 1.0 hour in a Downs cell that is operated at a current of 3.0×10^4 A?

ANSWERS

PRACTICE PROBLEMS 17B

1. $n = \dfrac{PV}{RT} =$

$$\frac{(101 \text{ kPa})(1.000 \text{ L})}{(8.314 \text{ kPa} \cdot \text{L/K} \cdot \text{mol})(298 \text{ K})} = 4.08 \times 10^{-2} \text{ mol } O_2$$

$$6H_2O(l) \longrightarrow$$
$$4e^- + O_2(g) + 4H_3O^+(aq)$$

charge $= 4.08 \times 10^{-2}$ mol $O_2 \times$

$$\frac{4 \text{ mol } e^-}{1 \text{ mol } O_2} \times \frac{96\,485 \text{ C}}{1 \text{ mol } e^-} = 1.57 \times 10^4 \text{ C}$$

energy $= (2.0 \text{ V})(1.57 \times 10^4 \text{ C})$
$= 3.1 \times 10^4$ J

2. 1.0 H $\times \dfrac{60 \text{ min}}{1 \text{ h}} \times \dfrac{60 \text{ s}}{1 \text{ min}} \times$

$$\frac{3.0 \times 10^4 \text{ C}}{1 \text{ s}} \times \frac{1 \text{ mol } e^-}{96\,485 \text{ C}} \times$$

$$\frac{1 \text{ mol } Cl_2}{2 \text{ mol } e^-} = 560 \text{ mol } Cl_2$$

SAMPLE PROBLEM 17B

ADDITIONAL EXAMPLES

1. What volume of hydrogen and oxygen gases, measured at 1.00 atm and 273 K, would be produced by 2.40×10^4 coulombs of charge passing through an electrolysis apparatus?

   Ans. 2.79 L H_2 and 1.39 L O_2

2. What mass of sodium metal would be produced by passing a current of 8550 A through a Downs cell for 12.0 hours?

   Ans. 88.0 kg of Na

3. What current would be necessary to generate 1.00×10^3 mol of hydrogen gas in a 24.0 hour period by electrolysis of water?

   Ans. 2230 A

The electrowinning of aluminum

Metallurgists describe getting a metal from its ore as *winning* the metal. Aluminum is won from its ore, bauxite, by the electrochemical Hall-Héroult process, illustrated in **Figure 17-11.** This process is the largest single user of electricity in the United States, consuming nearly 5% of the total electrical power generated. This electrical energy consumption makes the electrowinning of aluminum a very expensive process.

Bauxite is impure alumina, Al_2O_3. The alumina is first purified from the ore and then dissolved in molten cryolite, Na_3AlF_6, at a temperature of about 970°C. Huge carbon-lined iron tanks hold this molten mixture. At the high temperature at which the cell is operated, the aluminum metal is a liquid and is more dense than the molten mixture, so it falls to the floor of the tank. The liquid aluminum on the tank floor is in contact with the carbon-lined tank, and it serves as the cathode. Reduction occurs at the cathode to produce more molten aluminum metal.

Carbon rods dip into the molten cryolite solution and function as anodes. Carbon is the species oxidized at the anode to produce gaseous carbon dioxide. Therefore, the carbon rods are eaten away by this reaction and must be replaced periodically.

The process has been used for more than a century, but the chemistry that goes on during the dissolution and the electrochemical reactions are not well understood. Although scientists still debate exactly how the Hall-Héroult process works, they do agree that 12 electrons are transferred in the overall reaction shown below.

$$2Al_2O_3(s) + 3C(s) \xrightarrow{12e^-} 4Al(l) + 3CO_2(g)$$

▼ **FIGURE 17-11**

The Hall-Héroult process is used to manufacture aluminum by the electrolysis of dissolved alumina, Al_2O_3.

Carbon anode

Solution of alumina, Al_2O_3, in cryolite, Na_3AlF_6

Molten aluminum, Al

Carbon cathode

Power source

6.2 V

ALTERNATIVE ASSESSMENT

Group Strategy

Aluminum and its alloys have many uses. Consider having groups of students do visual presentations on the uses of aluminum and how those uses relate to aluminum's chemical and physical properties. Each group should focus on a particular application. One group could prepare a video presentation demonstrating the overall properties of aluminum. Consider some of the following lines of inquiry:

▶ Why does aluminum make up 90% of overhead power lines though it is only about 60% as effective a conductor as copper?

▶ Aluminum is called a self-protecting metal. What does this mean, and what applications of aluminum are related to this property?

▶ What other elements are alloyed with aluminum, and what properties does each confer on the alloy?

▶ Why is aluminum used in the aerospace industry, and what alloys are suitable for such uses?

Electrical energy is an expensive raw material

Why does aluminum production use so much electricity? Look at the last equation. Twelve electrons produce four aluminum atoms. So each mole of Al needs the following amount of electricity.

$$\frac{12 \text{ mol } e^-}{4 \text{ mol Al}} \times \frac{96\,485 \text{ C}}{\text{mol } e^-} = \frac{2.8946 \times 10^5 \text{ C}}{\text{mol Al}}$$

The Hall-Héroult cell operates at an average voltage of 6.2 V. The amount of energy needed to produce 1 mol (27 g) of aluminum can be calculated as follows.

$$6.2 \text{ V} \times 2.8946 \times 10^5 \text{ C} = 1.8 \times 10^6 \text{ J}$$

This much energy is needed to drive the electrochemical reactions. Additional energy is needed to keep the cell at a temperature that is high enough to melt the cryolyte.

A standard aluminum soft-drink can has a mass of about 27 g. The next time you open a can of soda, consider this: The beverage contains only about 600 J of *food* energy, but 3000 times that amount of energy was required to produce the can. Recycling aluminum metal is very important because it takes so much energy to manufacture it. Without recycling, we remove aluminum from the ground as bauxite, spend a lot of energy and money to process it, and then return it to the ground as landfill. What a waste!

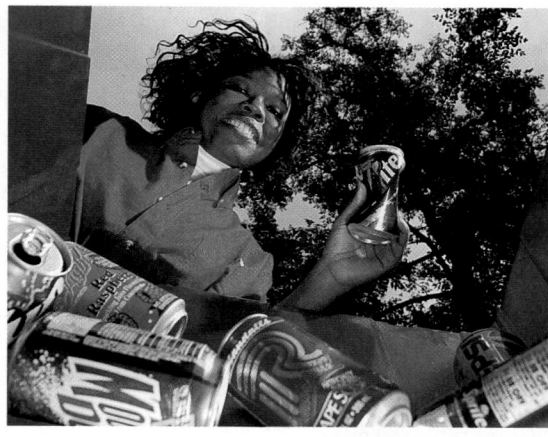

FIGURE 17-12 ▲

Producing aluminum from bauxite ore requires up to 95% more energy than is required to obtain aluminum by recycling.

SECTION REVIEW

Total recall

1. What form of energy is used to drive an electrolytic cell?
2. List three commercial products made by using electrolytic cells.
3. Write the equation for the cathodic reaction that occurs in an electrolytic cell that is used to make sodium.

Critical thinking

4. Explain why raising the temperature to decompose sodium chloride into sodium metal is not a good way to extract the sodium from the salt.
5. Why is it so important to recycle aluminum products rather than to simply discard them?

Practice problems

6. Calculate the energy needed to produce 100.0 g of aluminum in the Hall-Héroult cell.

TEACHING TIP

Recycling Inform students that the cost of refining aluminum from recycled materials is between 5% and 10% of the cost of producing the same amount of aluminum from ore. As a result, aluminum scrap has considerable value, and aluminum recycling has been highly successful.

ANSWERS

SECTION REVIEW

Total recall

1. electrical energy, the energy of flowing electrons
2. Answers may vary and may include sodium metal, aluminum, chlorine gas, and hydrogen gas.
3. $Na^+ (l) + e^- \longrightarrow Na(l)$

Critical thinking

4. The temperature at which the reaction proceeds spontaneously is about 4540 K, an impractically high temperature that is almost as high as the temperature at the surface of the sun.
5. The production of aluminum from ore requires much more energy than is needed to process recycled aluminum. Aluminum production also depletes natural ore reserves.

Practice problems

6. $100.0 \text{ g Al} \times \dfrac{1 \text{ mol Al}}{26.98 \text{ g Al}} \times \dfrac{12 \text{ mol } e^-}{4 \text{ mol Al}} \times$

$\dfrac{96\,485 \text{ C}}{1 \text{ mol } e^-} = 1.07 \times 10^6 \text{ C}$

$\text{energy} = (6.2 \text{ V})(1.07 \times 10^6 \text{ C})$
$= 6.7 \times 10^6 \text{ J}$

ELEMENT SPOTLIGHT

All halogens kill bacteria and other microorganisms. Chlorine is the only halogen that is safe enough and readily available for large-scale treatment of public water supplies.

When chlorine is added to water, the following reaction produces HCl and hypochlorous acid.

$$Cl_2(g) + H_2O(l) \longrightarrow HCl(aq) + HOCl(aq)$$

Hypochlorous acid is a weak acid that ionizes to give hydronium ions and hypochlorite ions, OCl^-.

$$HOCl(aq) + 2H_2O(l) \longrightarrow$$
$$H_3O^+(aq) + OCl^-(aq)$$

The OCl^- ions are strong oxidizing agents that can destroy microorganisms.

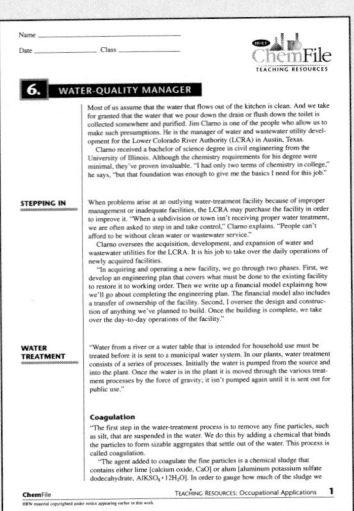
ELEMENT SPOTLIGHT

C1 ¹⁷
Chlorine
35.4527
$[Ne]3s^2 2p^5$

Many Third World regions have outbreaks of deadly diseases, such as cholera and typhoid fever, that could easily be prevented by disinfecting water supplies with chlorine.

WHERE IS IT?

Earth's Crust
0.045% by mass

Oceans
30.61% of dissolved materials; 1.9% by mass

internetconnect

SCiLINKS
NSTA

TOPIC: Chlorine
GO TO: www.scilinks.org
KEYWORD: HW174

Chlorine gives us clean drinking water

The practice of chlorinating drinking water to disinfect it began in the early twentieth century. Chlorinating water greatly reduced the number of infectious diseases. No other method of disinfecting drinking water is as inexpensive and reliable as chlorination. Today, chlorine is used as a disinfectant in almost every drinking-water treatment plant in the United States and Canada. This method will probably continue to be used well into the twenty-first century.

Industrial Uses

◗ Chlorine is a strong oxidizing agent. It is used as a bleaching agent for paper, pulp, and textiles.

◗ Chlorine gas is used as a germicide for drinking water.

◗ Chlorine gas is used in the production of bromine compounds for use as a fire retardant.

◗ Sodium chloride, which is table salt, is one of the most important chlorine-containing compounds.

◗ Plastics, such as the vinyl used in automobile upholstery and sporting goods, contain chlorine.

◗ Many pharmaceuticals, including antibiotics and allergy medications, require chlorine for their manufacture.

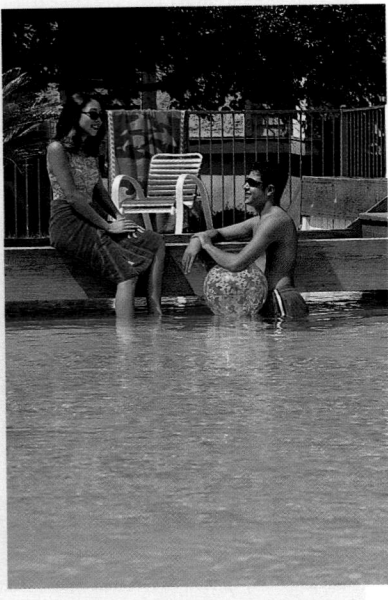

Chlorine gas and chlorine compounds are used to purify swimming pools.

A BRIEF HISTORY

1648: J. R. Glauber prepares concentrated hydrochloric acid.

1774: C. W. Scheele isolates chlorine gas, then called dephlogisticated marine acid air.

1801: W. Cruickshank recommends the use of Cl_2 as a disinfectant.

1810: Henry Davy proves that chlorine is a new element and names it.

1902: J. C. Downs patents the Downs cell for the production of $Cl_2(g)$ and $Na(s)$.

1908: P. Sommerfeld shows that HCl is present in the gastric juices of animals.

1600   1700   1800   1900

634   CHAPTER 17

How do batteries work?

OBJECTIVES

▶ **Explain** the difference between primary and secondary galvanic cells.

▶ **Describe** briefly the electrochemistry used in fuel cells, Leclanché cells, and lead-acid batteries.

▶ **Calculate** the electricity output of a galvanic cell and the changes in the amounts of reactants in the cell.

▶ **Describe** conditions that lead to corrosion and things that can be done to prevent it.

Galvanic cells

The last section described electrolytic cells. Galvanic cells work in the opposite direction as electrolytic cells. Galvanic cells convert chemical energy into electrical energy.

Electrochemical power sources can be divided into **primary cells** and **secondary cells.** Primary cells function only as galvanic cells. A primary cell can be either a *fuel cell* or a *battery*. A primary battery is thrown away when its active materials are used up. Primary fuel cells are never used up because the reactants are supplied from outside the cell. Secondary cells can operate electrolytically as well as galvanically. Secondary cells include *storage cells, accumulators,* or *rechargeable batteries.*

Fuel cells could revolutionize power production

In concept, **fuel cells** are very simple. **Figure 17-13** shows that the fuel and oxidizer are supplied to the two electrodes from outside the cell. The two electrodes are separated by a thin layer of electrolyte.

primary cell

a galvanic cell converting chemical energy to electrical energy; it cannot be recharged

secondary cell

an electrochemical cell that can act as a galvanic cell or, on recharge, as an electrolytic cell

fuel cell

a galvanic cell in which electricity is produced using reactants supplied from outside the cell

LESSON WARM-UP

Discussion Strategy Students should understand that the difference between a primary cell and a secondary cell is that the secondary cell can be recharged by being connected to an outside source of electric current. When a secondary cell is being recharged, it acts as an electrolytic cell. Primary cells cannot be recharged, and they often have printed warnings against attempts to recharge them.

Excess $H_2(g)$ + $H_2O(g)$ Excess $O_2(g)$ + $H_2O(g)$

$H_2(g)$ →   ↑e   e↓   ← $O_2(g)$

K^+

OH^-

Porous graphite anode

Porous graphite cathode

Electrolyte solution

FIGURE 17-13 ◀

The electrode reactions in a fuel cell take place where the graphite electrodes, solution, and gas all meet.

RESOURCE LINK

ChemFile Lab C
Self-Directed Inquiry
Have students do Investigation 22:
Voltaic Cells—Designing Batteries.

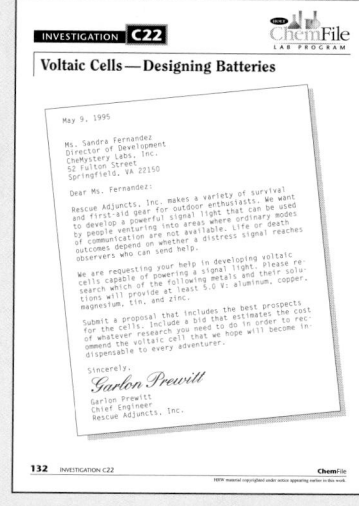

ELECTROCHEMISTRY   635

In conventional power plants, the chemical energy in the fuel is turned first into heat then into mechanical energy and finally into electricity. This is an inefficient process. The fuel cell *directly* converts chemical energy into electrical energy. This direct conversion is simpler, and it avoids the problem that only a fraction of heat energy can ever be converted into another energy form. Perfectly efficient energy conversion is theoretically possible with fuel cells. Fuel-cell design is an active area of electrochemical research, and a few experimental power plants using fuel cells are already in operation.

CONCEPT CHECK

1. Explain the difference between primary and secondary cells.
2. Explain why fuel cells theoretically could produce electrical energy in a perfectly efficient way.
3. List two other names for secondary cells.

battery

self-contained galvanic cells that convert chemical energy into electrical energy

Portable energy—the battery

Batteries supply energy to a variety of devices, from small wristwatches to the starters on diesel-truck engines. There are many types of batteries, and each has its own chemistry. Most batteries use a metal as the active material of the negative electrode. The battery *positive* is usually made up of metal oxides in higher-than-normal valence states, as shown in **Table 17-1**. These oxides are usually poor conductors of electricity, so their conductivity must be improved by mixing the oxide with graphite or by putting the oxide on a metal grid. A porous barrier is included so that the electrodes do not touch each other. The electrolyte solutions are concentrated to improve conductivity and to decrease the amount of liquid inside the battery.

▲ **FIGURE 17-14**

How many different types of batteries can you find around your home?

TABLE 17-1 **Common batteries**

Battery type	Negative	Positive	Voltage
Leclanché	$Zn \longrightarrow Zn(II)$	$Mn(IV) \longrightarrow Mn(III)$	1.5 V
Silver oxide	$Zn \longrightarrow Zn(II)$	$Ag(I) \longrightarrow Ag$	1.5 V
Lithium	$Li \longrightarrow Li(I)$	various	up to 4 V
NiCad	$Cd \rightleftarrows Cd(II)$	$Ni(III) \rightleftarrows Ni(II)$	1.4 V
Lead-acid	$Pb \rightleftarrows Pb(II)$	$Pb(IV) \rightleftarrows Pb(II)$	12.00 V

DEMONSTRATION 5

Making a Six-Cell Fruit Battery

Approximate time: 10 minutes

You can perform this demonstration with six whole lemons (or other fruit), or six wedges if you prefer. Using six wedges is more economical.

1. Obtain a lemon, grapefruit, or apple, and slice it into six sections.

2. Cut six Cu and six Zn strips, each 1 cm × 10 cm, and clean them with steel wool.

3. Insert one Cu strip through the skin and into the flesh of each section of fruit. Also insert one Zn strip at least 1 cm from the Cu strip.

4. Lay the fruit sections side by side. Using paper clips or wires with alligator clips at each end, attach the Cu strip in one fruit section to the Zn strip in a second section.

Dry cells aren't dry

The common zinc-carbon battery was invented over a century ago by the French chemist Georges Leclanché. **Figure 17-15a** shows a model of a Leclanché cell. A carbon rod, the battery's positive terminal, contacts a wet paste of carbon; ammonium chloride, NH_4Cl; manganese(IV) oxide, MnO_2; starch; and water. The reaction in this paste is as follows.

$$2MnO_2(s) + 2NH_4^+(aq) + 2e^- \longrightarrow$$
$$Mn_2O_3(s) + 2NH_3(aq) + H_2O(l)$$

The zinc case constitutes the negative of the cell. It dissolves in the following oxidation reaction.

$$Zn(s) \longrightarrow 2e^- + Zn^{2+}(aq)$$

The zinc ions combine with the ammonia made at the positive to form $Zn(NH_3)_4^{2+}$, the chloride salt of which is the white material you see on old corroded batteries.

The $NH_4^+(aq)$ ions cause the electrolytic paste to be acidic. That is why this cell is called *acidic*. The *alkaline cell*, shown in **Figure 17-15b,** is a newer, better version of the Leclanché cell. It is gradually replacing the acidic version. If you look at the batteries in electronic devices around your home, you will probably find many alkaline cells. They are similar to the acidic version, but the ammonium chloride is replaced by

Listen Up

In 1786, Luigi Galvani believed that he had discovered "animal electricity" because his experiments showed that dead frogs convulsed when they were part of electric circuits that contained dissimilar metals. In the 1800s, Volta proved the current was due to the metals rather than the frogs. In this activity, you will construct a potato cell and collect evidence of current flow.

Materials

raw potato, Cu strip, Zn strip, earphone, 2 alligator clips or electrical tape

Problem

1. Press the Cu and Zn strips into the potato about 0.5 cm apart. Do not allow the metals to touch one another.
2. Touch the wires from the earphone to both metals at the same time. What do you hear?
3. Touch the wires from the earphone to one metal only. What do you hear?

Analysis

1. Compare the results from step 2 with the results from step 3. Suggest an explanation for any similarities or differences.
2. Suggest an explanation for the sound.

TEACHING TIP

Dry-Cell Batteries If you have access to a machine shop, have a qualified person use a band saw or other kind of fine-toothed saw to cut an ordinary carbon-zinc dry cell battery in half lengthwise. Try to preserve the carbon rod whole in one of the halves rather than slicing it in half. **Be sure the battery is a zinc-carbon cell and not an alkaline battery. Do not cut open any other kind of battery.** Be sure the person who cuts the cell cleans off the saw blade afterward because of the corrosive nature of the battery materials on metal. Place sheets of plastic wrap over the cut faces to help retain moisture, and exhibit them to students. Do not let students touch the battery contents. Wear a lab apron and goggles, and wash your hands thoroughly after handling the cut battery.

QUICKLAB

The metal strips should be about 1 cm wide and 5 cm long. If you have a very small speaker, like those in very small portable radios, try it as a demonstration of the lab.

Analysis

1. When the wires from the earphone are touched to both strips, the earphone makes a crackling noise. Touching the wire to only one strip produces no sound. A complete circuit exists only when the wires are connected to separate strips.

2. The potato "battery" is producing an electric current that passes through the earphone, causing it to produce a crackling sound.

FIGURE 17-15 ▼

a The familiar flashlight battery has two versions. The *acidic* version is illustrated here.

Carbon rod (cathode)
Porous separator
Zinc shell (anode)
Moist paste of C, MnO_2 and NH_4Cl

b Unlike the acidic version, the *alkaline* Leclanché cell does not have a central carbon rod.

Steel jacket
graphite-MnO_2 cathode mix
Zn-KOH anode paste
Porous separator
KOH electrolyte
Brass current collector

ELECTROCHEMISTRY 637

Continue this process until all six sections are connected.

5. Connect the free copper strip to one end of a light-emitting diode (LED) and the free zinc strip to the other end. Dim the lights; students should see the LED glowing brightly. If it does not glow, reverse your connections. An LED conducts only in one direction.

6. Attach a voltmeter to measure the voltage of the battery.

Safety
Do not eat the fruit. Wear goggles and a lab apron.

Disposal
Mark the fruit "Unfit for food use," and throw it in the trash. Save the metal strips for the next time.

Fifty years ago, a large amount of lead was used to manufacture paint pigments and tetraethyl lead, $Pb(C_2H_5)_4$, which was used as an antiknock agent in gasoline. Today lead compounds in gasoline have been replaced by other substances in most developed countries. The use of lead-based pigments in paints has been reduced significantly in recent years because exposure to lead-based paints has been found to be a health hazard. Lead is still used in primers for iron and steel structures, such as bridges. Today, more lead is used in storage batteries than in any other application. Lead-acid batteries should always be recycled for both economic and health-related reasons.

potassium hydroxide. The presence of a strong base gives the alkaline cell its name. The electrode reactions are shown below.

$$positive: 2MnO_2(s) + H_2O(aq) + 2e^- \longrightarrow Mn_2O_3(s) + 2OH^-(aq)$$
$$negative: Zn(s) + 2OH^-(aq) \longrightarrow 2e^- + Zn(OH)_2(s)$$

A steel outer shell is needed to prevent the caustic contents from leaking out of the battery. Because of this extra packaging cost, alkaline cells are slightly more expensive than their acidic counterpart.

The automobile battery

The standard automobile battery is a lead-acid storage battery. The lead-acid battery has six cells mounted side by side in a single case, as illustrated in **Figure 17-16.** The cells are coupled together so that each 2.0 V cell adds to the 12.0 V overall battery. Lead-acid batteries are very heavy, but lighter alternatives have never become popular because the lead-acid battery is able to deliver the large surges of electricity needed to start cold automobile engines.

A fully charged lead-acid cell is made up of a stack of alternating lead, Pb, and lead(IV) oxide, PbO_2, plates isolated from each other by layers of porous separators. All of these parts sit in a concentrated solution of sulfuric acid. Intercell connectors link the positive of one cell to the negative of the next cell, so the six cells are in series. When the cell discharges, it acts as a galvanic cell. The following reactions occur.

$$negative: Pb(s) + HSO_4^-(aq) + H_2O(l) \longrightarrow 2e^- + PbSO_4(s) + H_3O^+(aq)$$
$$positive: PbO_2(s) + HSO_4^-(aq) + 3H_3O^+(aq) + 2e^- \longrightarrow PbSO_4(s) + 5H_2O(l)$$

Notice that lead sulfate, $PbSO_4$, is produced at *both* electrodes. Also note that two electrons are transferred in the overall cell reaction.

These reactions are reversed during the recharging cycle. During this cycle, the automobile battery functions as an electrolytic cell. The energy to drive the recharging of the cell comes from an external source, such as the alternator of a car's engine.

▼ **FIGURE 17-16**

A lead-acid battery is housed in a thick plastic or rubber case. This prevents leakage of the corrosive sulfuric acid.

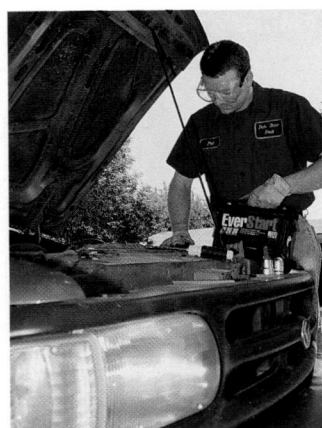

Intercell connector

Pb plates

$H_2SO_4(aq)$

PbO_2 plates

Cell spacers

SAMPLE PROBLEM 17C — Calculating the mass of products of galvanic cell reactions

If you allow a 12 V car battery to completely run down so that its 1.6 MJ of energy is spent, what mass of lead sulfate is created?

1. List what you know

- Electrical energy = 1.6 MJ = 1.6×10^6 J
- Battery voltage = 12 V
- Mass of $PbSO_4$ = ? g

2. Set up the problem

- Use the energy and voltage to determine the charge.

$$\text{energy} = \text{voltage} \times \text{charge}$$

$$\text{charge} = \frac{\text{energy}}{\text{voltage}} = \frac{1.6 \times 10^6 \text{ J}}{12 \text{ V}} = ? \text{ C}$$

Recall the chemical equations on page 638; 2 mol of electrons flows when 2 mol of $PbSO_4$ is produced. That is a mole ratio of 1:1. Use the charge calculated above along with Faraday's constant to determine the amount of lead(II) sulfate produced.

$$\text{amount of } PbSO_4 = \text{charge} \times \frac{\text{mol } e^-}{96\,485 \text{ C}} \times \frac{1 \text{ mol } PbSO_4}{1 \text{ mol } e^-} = ? \text{ mol}$$

- Convert amount to mass by using the molar mass of $PbSO_4$.

$$\text{molar mass of } PbSO_4 = 303.3 \text{ g/mol}$$

3. Calculate and verify

- Calculate the answer, and round correctly.

$$\text{charge} = \frac{1.6 \times 10^6 \text{ J}}{12 \text{ V}} = 1.33 \times 10^5 \text{ C}$$

$$\text{amount of } PbSO_4 = 1.33 \times 10^5 \, \cancel{C} \times \frac{\cancel{\text{mol } e^-}}{96\,485 \, \cancel{C}} \times \frac{1 \text{ mol } PbSO_4}{1 \, \cancel{\text{mol } e^-}} = 1.38 \text{ mol } PbSO_4$$

$$\text{mass of } PbSO_4 = 1.38 \, \cancel{\text{mol}} \times 303.3 \text{ g/} \cancel{\text{mol}} = 420 \text{ g } PbSO_4$$

- The battery voltage and energy spent have two significant figures each. Therefore, the answer is correctly rounded to two significant figures.
- Verify your answer by working the problem backward.

$$\frac{(420 \text{ g})(96\,485 \text{ C/mol})(12 \text{ V})}{303.3 \text{ g/mol}} = 1.6 \times 10^6 \text{ J}$$

PRACTICE PROBLEMS

1. Calculate the mass of lead that was used up as the 12 V car battery in Sample Problem 17C ran down.

2. An alkaline Leclanché cell has a voltage of 1.54 V. The anodic reaction involves the oxidation of zinc as shown in the following equation.

$$Zn(s) + 2OH^- (aq) \longrightarrow Zn(OH)_2(s) + H_2O(l) + 2e^-$$

What mass of $Zn(OH)_2$ is produced after the battery has delivered 1.3 kJ of energy?

ELECTROCHEMISTRY   639

SAMPLE PROBLEM 17C

ADDITIONAL EXAMPLES

1. The equation for the overall redox process that takes place in a mercury (actually Hg-Zn) battery is as follows.

$$Zn + HgO \xrightarrow{2e^-} ZnO + Hg$$

The battery operates at 1.35 V. What mass of mercury is produced when the battery delivers 0.280 kJ of energy?

Ans. 0.216 g Hg

2. The redox reaction of one type of lithium battery follows.

$$4Li + 2SOCl_2 \xrightarrow{4e^-}$$
$$4LiCl + S + SO_2$$

What mass of lithium will be oxidized as the battery supplies 0.177 mA of current at 2.67 V to a heart pacemaker for 500.0 days? How much energy in kilojoules is generated in this time?

Ans. 0.550 g Li, 20.4 kJ

3. If a lead-acid battery operating at 11.85 V delivers 2.50 MJ of energy, what mass of lead is oxidized?

Ans. 227 g Pb

ANSWERS

PRACTICE PROBLEMS 17C

1. 1.33×10^5 C $\times \dfrac{1 \text{ mol } e^-}{96\,485 \text{ C}} \times \dfrac{1 \text{ mol Pb}}{2 \text{ mol } e^-} \times \dfrac{207.2 \text{ g}}{1 \text{ mol Pb}} = 140$ g Pb

2. charge $= \dfrac{\text{energy}}{\text{potential}} = \dfrac{1300 \text{ J}}{1.54 \text{ V}} = 844$ C

   844 C $\times \dfrac{1 \text{ mol } e^-}{96\,485 \text{ C}} \times \dfrac{1 \text{ mol } Zn(OH)_2}{2 \text{ mol } e^-} \times \dfrac{99.41 \text{ g } Zn(OH)_2}{1 \text{ mol } Zn(OH)_2} = 0.43$ g $Zn(OH)_2$

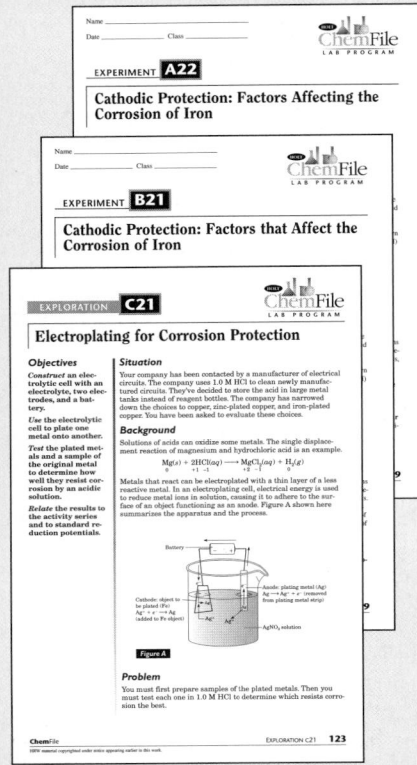

Corrosion cells

Oxygen is so reactive that any metal except gold can spontaneously oxidize in air. Fortunately for our civilization, many of these metal oxidation reactions are very slow. The disintegration of metals through oxidation is called **corrosion.** The general equation for the corrosion of metal, M, by oxygen is as follows.

corrosion

the deterioration of metals due to oxidation reactions with their environment

$$2M(s) + (n/2)O_2(g) \longrightarrow M_2O_n(s)$$

Agents other than O_2 can cause corrosion. Some metals can also corrode when placed in contact with water or an acidic aqueous solution. Take iron, for example, which can be oxidized to iron(III) ions according to the following equation.

$$2Fe(s) + 11H_2O(l) \longrightarrow Fe_2O_3 \cdot 2H_2O(s) + 6H_3O^+(aq) + 6e^-$$

You know that oxidation reactions must always be accompanied by reduction reactions. If a metal corrodes, or oxidizes, then the oxygen, water, or hydronium ion must be reduced. As you have seen with other galvanic cells, oxidation and reduction do not have to occur at the same site. **Figure 17-17** illustrates how oxidation can occur at an *anodic site,* while reduction occurs simultaneously at a *cathodic site.* This system looks very similar to the galvanic cells you have already studied.

Corrosive conditions are all around us

The corrosion of metals generally requires three ingredients: oxygen, water, and ions. These three ingredients are very easy to find together. Even pure rainwater contains a few H_3O^+ and HCO_3^- ions from dissolved carbon dioxide. This means that all exposed metalwork is a potential target for corrosion. Corrosion problems are even worse in areas where ion concentrations are high, such as in marine environments and where salts are spread on icy roads.

▼ **FIGURE 17-17**

This cathodic reaction occurs where the O_2 concentration is relatively high. The anodic reaction occurs in a region where the O_2 concentration is rather low, such as in a pit in the metal.

Where two different metals are in contact with one another, corrosion is more likely. This is because the more-active metal provides the anodic region and the less-active metal provides the cathodic region. Corrosion is often the cause of plumbing leaks where steel and copper water pipes are joined.

How to curb corrosion

Corrosion is a major economic problem. Approximately 20% of all iron and steel produced replaces corroded structures. That is why corrosion prevention is a major focus of electrochemical research. An obvious response to corrosion is to paint the metal or to coat it with some other material that will not corrode. However, once a crack occurs in the coating, a corrosion cell forms.

Ironically, it is better to coat steel with another metal, one that *does* corrode. Trash cans, for example, are made of zinc-coated steel. The coating does not stop corrosion; in fact, it promotes it. But, it is the zinc that corrodes first, making the steel underneath last much longer than it would without the protective zinc layer. This is the principle behind equipping ships and pipelines with **sacrificial anodes.** The sacrificial anode makes use of the fact that when two different metals are in contact with one another, corrosion is likely. The sacrificial anode, which is not necessary to the structure, dissolves anodically, but in doing so it protects the ship or pipeline from corrosion. Therefore, it protects the more important structural metal. This process is called *cathodic protection.*

FIGURE 17-18 ▲

The Alaskan oil pipeline is *cathodically protected* by a parallel zinc cable.

sacrificial anode

metal attached to a metallic structure that serves as an anode, preventing the corrosion of the structural metal

SECTION REVIEW

Total recall

1. What advantages do fuel cells have over standard power plants?
2. Explain what is meant by the term *secondary cell.*
3. List three conditions that foster corrosion.

Critical thinking

4. How is a fuel cell similar to a battery? How is it different?
5. Why is the name *dry cell* a misnomer?
6. Why does a car rust quickly at a place where the paint has been chipped?
7. Explain why a small piece of zinc is usually attached to a boat's propeller shaft.

TEACHING TIP

Interpreting Tables Have students look ahead to Table 17-2, on page 646. Theoretically, any metal near the top of the list should be able to act as a sacrificial anode and protect any metal lower on the table. However, Li, K, Ca, and Na are too reactive to use under most conditions. Magnesium is less reactive and makes an excellent sacrificial material. Zinc is also widely used.

ANSWERS

SECTION REVIEW

Total recall

1. Fuel cells can potentially convert chemical energy into electrical energy with perfect efficiency.
2. A secondary cell is one that can operate as an electrolytic cell by an input of energy. Therefore, the cell can be recharged.
3. a metal, oxygen, and an ionic solution

Critical thinking

4. A fuel cell operates much like a battery in that it produces an electric current by means of an oxidation-reduction reaction. However, the fuel cell oxidizes a fuel supplied from outside the cell, while batteries are self-contained.
5. A dry cell actually contains a moist electrolyte paste.
6. The chipped spot provides a place where a corrosion cell can begin.
7. The zinc acts as a sacrificial anode and undergoes corrosion, protecting the steel shaft.

SCIENCE & TECHNOLOGY

The space shuttles use three fuel-cell power plants to generate the 28 V direct current required to run their electrical systems. Before launch, electrical energy is provided to the systems by power supplies on the ground. When the launch countdown reaches T minus 3 minutes 30 seconds, the onboard fuel cells take over.

SCIENCE & TECHNOLOGY

FUEL CELLS

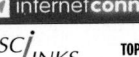
internet**connect**

SC*LINKS*
NSTA

TOPIC: Fuel cells
GO TO: www.scilinks.org
KEYWORD: HW175

Historical Perspective

In 1839, Sir William Robert Grove, a British lawyer and physicist, built the first fuel cell. More than 100 years later, this fuel cell finally found a practical application.

The United States Space Program Finds Uses for Fuel Cells

During the middle part of the twentieth century, the space race was on. The United States was rushing to turn a lunar landing from science fiction into reality. Space capsules required electrical energy to keep the astronauts warm and to power electrical systems. During

During the 1960s and 1970s, fuel cells provided on-board electricity and drinking water for the Apollo and Gemini space capsules.

the Mercury project—the first six missions into space—the flights were very short. Batteries were sufficient to power the capsules. But later programs needed electrical power for much longer periods of time; fuel cells became the best solution for the problem. Today, fuel cells are critical to the space shuttle missions and to future missions on the international space station.

In 1970, fuel cells played a critical role in the *Apollo 13* mission. A short circuit in a fuel cell caused an explosion in an oxygen tank. This damaged the spacecraft and caused a loss of oxygen needed for breathing and for generating electricity. For this reason, *Apollo 13* never made it to the moon as planned.

Fuel Cells Have Many Uses

Electrical Power Systems   There are many problems with conventional power stations that burn fossil fuels to generate electricity. These stations first produce heat energy, which is converted to mechanical energy, which is then converted to electrical energy. They are only about 40% efficient. Standard power plants give off pollutants that lead to acid rain and other environmental problems. Fuel-cell power stations currently being tested can operate at up to 80% efficiency. They also give off 80% less pollution than fossil-fuel-burning stations. The maximum theoretical efficiency of fuel cells is 100%.

Blood Alcohol Testing   Blood alcohol testing is very important to traffic-law enforcement. Police officers need quick and simple ways to determine a suspect's blood alcohol level in the field. If the suspect is carried back to the station or to a medical facility for a blood or urine test, so much time may elapse that their blood alcohol content (BAC) will no longer indicate impairment. Fuel cells, such as the one shown on the right, provide a quick and accurate way to measure BAC from a breath sample. The alcohol and oxygen in a person's breath are the two reactants in this electrochemical cell.

Ethanol is oxidized to acetic acid at the anode. At the cathode, gaseous oxygen is reduced and combined with hydrogen ions (released from the anode) to form water. The reactions generate an electric current. The magnitude of the current generated is related to the BAC.

A small pump ensures that a precise sample size is delivered into the fuel cell inside this device.

CAREER APPLICATION

What would it be like to . . .
▶ design ways to reduce pollution?
▶ work with high-tech materials?
▶ develop renewable fuel sources?

Science/Math Career Preparation	
High School	**College**
Mathematics	Mathematics
Chemistry	Chemistry
Physics	Physics
	Engineering

Chemical Engineer

Chemical engineers do much of the ongoing fuel-cell research. These scientists combine knowledge of chemistry, physics, and mathematics to link laboratory chemistry with its industrial applications. As with any scientist, they must be good problem solvers as well.

There are many types of careers open to chemical engineers. They can find alternative, renewable fuel sources, such as fuel cells and diesel fuels made from sewage sludge. They design new recyclable materials and devise new ways of recycling materials that are already in existence. Chemical engineers clean up and prevent much of the pollution in the environment.

Chemical engineers use lab techniques that you may be familiar with from your own chemistry laboratory. These include distillation, evaporation, absorption, separation, and mixing. A chemical engineer can move these techniques from the laboratory to the large

scale required by industry. Many of the synthetic fibers in your clothing were developed by chemical engineers. Although you may have seen nylon made in your chemistry laboratory, it would be difficult to make enough nylon using this method to satisfy the demand for nylon clothing and other items. Chemical engineers find ways to optimize chemical processes, as with the production of nylon, and make them industrially practical.

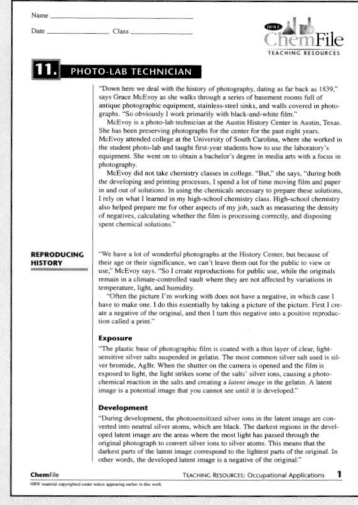

What can be learned from an equilibrium cell?

OBJECTIVES	▶ **Explain** the meaning of the voltage produced by an equilibrium cell.	▶ **Predict** the direction of cell reactions, and **explain** the reactions in terms of electron transfers using a table of standard electrode potentials.

Equilibrium cell voltages

A voltmeter can measure cell voltage without allowing any appreciable current to flow through the electrochemical cell. The cell is neither producing nor using electrical energy. It is neither an electrolytic cell nor a galvanic cell. It is an equilibrium cell, and the voltage measured by the voltmeter is the **equilibrium voltage,** ΔE.

Electrochemical equilibrium will become clearer after you study **Figure 17-19.** This figure shows three cells, each attached to an adjustable power source. If the applied voltage differs from the equilibrium voltage even a little bit, current flows in one direction or the other. No cur-

equilibrium voltage

the voltage of a cell as measured by a voltmeter when no current is flowing

▼ **FIGURE 17-19**

Zinc strip
Adjustable power source
Copper strip
+1.09 V
e^-
Zinc sulfate, $ZnSO_4$, solution
Copper sulfate, $CuSO_4$, solution
+1.11 V
e^-
+1.10 V

a An electrochemical cell will function galvanically if the voltage applied is less than the equilibrium voltage, . . .

b . . . electrolytically if the voltage applied is greater than the equilibrium voltage, . . .

c . . . and as an equilibrium cell if the applied voltage equals the equilibrium voltage.

GRAPHIC ORGANIZER

Electrochemical cells

Electrolytic cells
• Copper-refining cell
• Downs cell
• Electrolysis of water
• Electrowinning of aluminum

Equilibrium cells
• pH meter

Galvanic cells
Primary cells
• Fuel cells
• Zinc-carbon dry cell
• Alkaline dry cell

Secondary cells
• NiCad battery
• Lead-acid storage cell

rent flows when the applied voltage exactly matches the equilibrium voltage. The state of the cell shown in Figure 17-19c is exactly the same as that in Figure 17-5 on page 624—both are equilibrium cells.

Cell potentials are measured using the standard hydrogen electrode

There are so many combinations of electrode reactions that it would be nearly impossible to measure the cell voltages for all of them. It is much easier to choose one electrode as a standard and to pair it with all the others. The one that has been chosen for this purpose is the **standard hydrogen electrode** (SHE).

The SHE is made up of an aqueous solution of a strong acid in which the effective H_3O^+ concentration is 1.000 M. A platinum electrode is dipped into this solution, and a stream of hydrogen gas at a pressure of 1.0 atm bubbles in, as shown in **Figure 17-20.**

Of course, the voltage of a single electrode cannot be measured because voltage is a difference in "electron pressure." The SHE is conventionally assigned an electrode potential of 0.00 V. Therefore, if you connect a copper electrode to a SHE with a voltmeter, the reading on the voltmeter indicates only the voltage coming from the copper electrode. This means that the **standard electrode potential** of any electrode is defined as the voltmeter reading when the electrode is coupled to a SHE in the way shown in **Figure 17-21.** The standard electrode potential is sometimes called the *standard reduction potential* because the electrode reactions are usually written as reduction reactions.

standard hydrogen electrode

an electrode used as a reference for measuring other electrode potentials; it is arbitrarily assigned an electrode potential of 0.00 V

standard electrode potential

the measured voltage when an electrode, under standard conditions of temperature, pressure, and concentration, is paired with a standard hydrogen electrode in an equilibrium cell

FIGURE 17-21 ▼

When an electrode is paired with a SHE, its *standard electrode potential* is given by the voltmeter reading.

Voltmeter

-0.40 V

Cadmium strip

1.0 M cadmium sulfate, $CdSO_4$, solution

💡 DID YOU KNOW?

In addition to 1.000 M H_3O^+ concentration at 1 atm pressure of H_2, the standard hydrogen electrode must also be at 25°C. The standard potentials of other electrodes given in Table 17-2 also assume that these electrodes are operating at 25°C and a 1.000 M concentration of the ions involved in the electrode reaction.

TEACHING TIP

Reduction Potentials Show students the following electrode reaction that occurs at the SHE.

$$2H_3O^+(aq) + 2e^- \longrightarrow H_2(g) + 2H_2O(l)$$

By convention, the equation is written in the reduction direction, as are all of the equations in Table 17-2. Point out that this reaction can proceed in either direction, depending on the electrode with which it is paired. All electrodes, except those at the very top and very bottom of Table 17-2, can proceed in either direction.

VISUAL STRATEGY

Table 17-2 Refer students to the activity series shown in Table 9-8, on page 327, and ask them to compare its arrangement with that of Table 17-2. The two do not contain the exact same set of elements, but students can see that the elements common to the two tables are in the same order. Ask students to scan the text relating to Table 9-8 and summarize its points while you record the summary on the board. The summary should include the following:

▶ The table shows the relative chemical activity of elements. Those higher on the list can replace lower ones from their salts in single replacement reactions.
▶ Those above H_2 on the list will replace hydrogen in acids.
▶ The more active a metal is, the more stable its compounds are.
▶ Pairs of elements that are far apart in the table react more vigorously in single-displacement reactions.

Help students reinterpret the activity series in light of what they have learned in this chapter. They should realize that a single-displacement reaction is also an oxidation-reduction reaction. The higher an element is in the series, the more likely it is to be oxidized by losing electrons to the cation of an element lower in the table. This includes the replacement of hydrogen from acids, which is the reduction reaction of the SHE.

Reaction pairs that are farther apart on the table of electrode potentials have greater voltages in the galvanic cell involving that pair. This correlates to the observation that reaction pairs farther apart on the activity series react more vigorously.

electrochemical series

a table in which the elements are listed in order of increasing standard electrode potential

▼ FIGURE 17-22

It would be difficult to measure every possible combination of electrodes using the technique shown here. This is why the SHE is used as a reference for all other electrodes.

For example, the measurement shown in Figure 17-21 indicates that −0.40 V is the standard electrode potential for the following reaction.

$$Cd^{2+} + 2e^- \longrightarrow Cd$$

Remember, this value is not the *actual* voltage of a single electrode. True electrode potentials cannot be measured; electrodes must always be paired. **Table 17-2** includes a number of standard electrode potentials that have been determined by pairing each electrode with a standard hydrogen electrode. In each case, ion concentrations are 1.00 M and gases are at 1.0 atm.

This table is the **electrochemical series** of the elements. Notice that the elements are in the same order as they are in the activity series, which was introduced in Chapter 9. The higher the element is in the electrochemical series, the more likely it is to be oxidized.

You have already seen that a chemical reaction such as the following can be thought of as two electrode reactions occurring together.

$$Cu^{2+}(aq) + Zn(s) \longrightarrow Cu(s) + Zn^{2+}(aq)$$

You can use the electrochemical series to determine the direction of an electron-transfer reaction. The above reaction occurs in the direction shown by the arrow because zinc is higher in the series than copper is, thus zinc is more likely to be oxidized than copper.

Table 17-3 gives even more electrode potentials. Tables 17-2 and 17-3 may be used

TABLE 17-2 — Standard electrode potentials for some elements

Electrode reaction	E^0(V)	Electrode reaction	E^0(V)
$Li^+(aq) + e^- \longrightarrow Li(s)$	−3.0401	$Pb^{2+}(aq) + 2e^- \longrightarrow Pb(s)$	−0.1262
$K^+(aq) + e^- \longrightarrow K(s)$	−2.931	$Fe^{3+}(aq) + 3e^- \longrightarrow Fe(s)$	−0.037
$Ca^{2+}(aq) + 2e^- \longrightarrow Ca(s)$	−2.868	$Cu^{2+}(aq) + 2e^- \longrightarrow Cu(s)$	+0.3419
$Na^+(aq) + e^- \longrightarrow Na(s)$	−2.71	$I_2(s) + 2e^- \longrightarrow 2I^-(aq)$	+0.5355
$Mg^{2+}(aq) + 2e^- \longrightarrow Mg(s)$	−2.372	$Hg_2^{2+}(aq) + 2e^- \longrightarrow 2Hg(l)$	+0.7973
$Al^{3+}(aq) + 3e^- \longrightarrow Al(s)$	−1.662	$Ag^+(aq) + e^- \longrightarrow Ag(s)$	+0.7996
$Zn^{2+}(aq) + 2e^- \longrightarrow Zn(s)$	−0.7618	$Br_2(l) + 2e^- \longrightarrow 2Br^-(aq)$	+1.066
$Fe^{2+}(aq) + 2e^- \longrightarrow Fe(s)$	−0.447	$Cl_2(g) + 2e^- \longrightarrow 2Cl^-(aq)$	+1.358
$Cd^{2+}(aq) + 2e^- \longrightarrow Cd(s)$	−0.4030	$F_2(g) + 2e^- \longrightarrow 2F^-(aq)$	+2.866

DEMONSTRATION 6

Predicting Reactions

Approximate time: 10 minutes

1. Half-fill one Petri dish with 0.1 M $AgNO_3$ solution and another with 0.1 M $Zn(NO_3)_2$ solution. Place both dishes on an overhead projector.

2. Write the contents of each dish on the board. Display two polished copper strips about 0.5 cm × 2 cm in size, and ask students to predict what will happen when the strips are placed in the dishes.

3. Place one strip in each dish, and observe the results. Silver should form on the copper strip placed in the $AgNO_3$ solution. No reaction will take place in the other dish.

4. Allow students to observe the dishes in room light to see the silver crystals that form on the copper.

5. Ask students to explain the difference in the results.

TABLE 17-3 More standard electrode potentials

Electrode reaction	E^0 (V)
$Zn(OH)_2(s) + 2e^- \longrightarrow Zn(s) + 2OH^-(aq)$	-1.249
$2H_2O(l) + 2e^- \longrightarrow H_2(g) + 2OH^-(aq)$	-0.828
$PbSO_4(s) + H_3O^+(aq) + 2e^- \longrightarrow Pb(s) + HSO_4^-(aq) + H_2O(l)$	-0.42
$2H_3O^+(aq) + 2e^- \longrightarrow H_2(g) + 2H_2O(l)$	0.000
$AgCl(s) + e^- \longrightarrow Ag(s) + Cl^-(aq)$	$+0.222$
$O_2(g) + 2H_2O(l) + 4e^- \longrightarrow 4OH^-(aq)$	$+0.401$
$I_3^-(aq) + 2e^- \longrightarrow 3I^-(aq)$	$+0.536$
$Fe^{3+}(aq) + e^- \longrightarrow Fe^{2+}(aq)$	$+0.771$
$MnO_2(s) + 4H_3O^+(aq) + 2e^- \longrightarrow Mn^{2+}(aq) + 6H_2O(l)$	$+1.224$
$O_2(g) + 4H_3O^+(aq) + 4e^- \longrightarrow 6H_2O$	$+1.229$
$Cr_2O_7^{2-}(aq) + 14H_3O^+(aq) + 6e^- \longrightarrow 2Cr^{3+}(aq) + 21H_2O(l)$	$+1.232$
$PbO_2(s) + 4H_3O^+(aq) + 2e^- \longrightarrow Pb^{2+}(aq) + 6H_2O(l)$	$+1.455$
$MnO_4^-(aq) + 8H_3O^+(aq) + 5e^- \longrightarrow Mn^{2+}(aq) + 12H_2O(l)$	$+1.507$
$PbO_2(s) + HSO_4^-(aq) + 3H_3O^+(aq) + 2e^- \longrightarrow PbSO_4(s) + 5H_2O(l)$	$+1.691$
$Ce^{4+}(aq) + e^- \longrightarrow Ce^{3+}(aq)$	$+1.72$
$Ag_2O_2(s) + 4H^+(aq) + e^- \longrightarrow 2Ag(s) + 2H_2O(l)$	$+1.802$

VISUAL STRATEGY

Table 17-3 Point out that these electrode reactions could have been included in Table 17-2, but they are listed separately as examples of possible electrode reactions that involve something other than the simple reduction of an element or its ion. Separating these makes it easier for students to draw comparisons between the activity series in Chapter 9 and Table 17-2. Note also that many of these reactions require the presence of H_3O^+ or OH^- in order to take place.

to predict the direction of cell reactions and redox reactions. Think of E^0 as a measure of the tendency of the electrode to consume electrons. In other words, a more positive standard electrode potential means the electrode is more likely to be a cathode and the reaction is more likely to proceed in the direction shown in the tables. For example, Ce^{4+}/Ce^{3+}, with an E^0 of +1.72 V, can overpower Fe^{3+}/Fe^{2+}, with an E^0 of only +0.771 V, so that the following reaction occurs spontaneously.

$$Ce^{4+}(aq) + Fe^{2+}(aq) \xrightarrow{e^-} Ce^{3+}(aq) + Fe^{3+}(aq)$$

SAMPLE PROBLEM 17D Predicting the direction of electrochemical reactions

Write the equation for the cell reaction that will occur spontaneously in a cell that contains a mercury, Hg_2^{2+}/Hg, electrode and a cadmium, Cd^{2+}/Cd, electrode.

1 List what you know

▸ Electrodes: Hg_2^{2+}/Hg and Cd^{2+}/Cd

RESOURCE LINK

ChemFile Mini-Guide to Problem Solving
Assign Chapter 24: *Electrochemistry* for additional practice.

CHAPTER 24
Electrochemistry

The potential in volts has been measured for many different reduction half-reactions. The potential value is measured against the standard hydrogen electrode, which is assigned a value of zero. For consistency, these half-reactions are always written in the direction of the reduction. A half-reaction that has a positive reduction potential proceeds in the direction of the reduction when it is coupled with a hydrogen electrode. A reaction that has a negative reduction potential proceeds in the oxidation direction when it is coupled with a hydrogen electrode. Table 24-1 gives some common standard reduction potentials.

TABLE 24-1

Electrochemistry 277

Safety

Wear safety goggles and a lab apron. Keep students at least 10 ft away from the demonstration.

Disposal

Remove the Cu strip coated with Ag, and scour off the Ag with emery paper. Put the emery paper in a labeled container for future use; do not discard. Remove the other Cu strip. Save both Cu strips for future use. Save left-over $AgNO_3$ and $Zn(NO_3)_2$ solutions for reuse, or treat with an excess of 1.0 M NaOH while stirring to precipitate all of the silver and zinc as oxides. Filter. Adjust the pH of the solutions to be between 8 to 10 with 0.5 M HCl, and pour down the drain. After the solids have dried, wrap them in newspaper, and put them in the trash.

SAMPLE PROBLEM 17D

ADDITIONAL EXAMPLES

1. Write the electrochemical equation for the spontaneous reaction of a cell involving Mg^{2+}/Mg and Pb^{2+}/Pb electrodes.

Ans. $Mg(s) + Pb^{2+}(aq) \xrightarrow{2e^-} Mg^{2+}(aq) + Pb(s)$

2. Write the electrochemical equation for the spontaneous reaction of a zinc-oxygen alkaline cell involving the reduction of O_2 in alkaline solution to OH^- ions.

Ans. $2Zn(s) + O_2(g) + 2H_2O(l) \xrightarrow{4e^-} 2Zn^{2+}(aq) + 4OH^-(aq)$

ANSWERS

SECTION REVIEW

Total recall

1. a galvanic cell

2. standard hydrogen electrode, 0.000 V

3. A voltmeter is a device that measures cell voltage without allowing any appreciable current to flow through the cell.

Critical thinking

4. This is the voltage produced by a Zn^{2+}/Zn electrode when measured against a SHE. The negative value indicates that zinc will undergo oxidation to Zn^{2+} when coupled with the SHE.

5. No current is passing through an equilibrium cell. A galvanic cell is generating an electric current, and an electrolytic cell is being supplied with current from an outside source.

---

2 **Set up the problem**

▸ Find the two electrode reactions in the tables of standard electrode potentials. Compare the values of their standard electrode potentials.

$$Hg_2^{2+}(aq) + 2e^- \longrightarrow 2Hg(l)\ E^0 = +0.7973\ V$$
$$Cd^{2+}(aq) + 2e^- \longrightarrow Cd(s)\ E^0 = -0.4030\ V$$

3 **Calculate**

▸ The standard electrode potential for mercury is greater than that for cadmium. Therefore, mercury has a greater tendency to be reduced. Cadmium will be oxidized, so the cadmium reaction shown above will be reversed. Note that two electrons are transferred in each reaction. If the number of electrons transferred were not the same, coefficients would have to be added to one or both reactions to balance the electrons.

$$Hg_2^{2+}(aq) + Cd(s) \xrightarrow{2e^-} 2Hg(l) + Cd^{2+}(aq)$$

SECTION REVIEW

Total recall

1. A voltage source is attached to an electrochemical cell. The cell has an equilibrium voltage of 0.57 V. The voltage source is set at 0.44 V. Is the electrochemical cell acting as a galvanic or an electrolytic cell?

2. What does SHE represent? What electrode potential value is assigned to SHE?

3. What is a voltmeter?

Critical thinking

4. The standard electrode potential for the reduction of $Zn^{2+}(aq)$ to $Zn(s)$ is -0.762 V. What does this value indicate?

5. How is an equilibrium cell different from both a galvanic cell and an electrolytic cell?

Practice problems

6. Explain why the following reaction will not occur spontaneously.

$$Mg^{2+}(aq) + Pb(s) \longrightarrow Mg(s) + Pb^{2+}(aq)$$

7. Write an equation for the electrochemical reaction that occurs spontaneously between the following two electrodes.

$$AgCl(s) + e^- \longrightarrow Ag(s) + Cl^-(aq)$$
$$Ce^{4+}(aq) + e^- \longrightarrow Ce^{3+}(aq)$$

8. Would the following electrochemical reaction be spontaneous as written?

$$PbSO_4(s) + H_3O^+(aq) + Ca(s) \longrightarrow$$
$$Pb(s) + HSO_4^-(aq) + Ca^{2+}(aq) + H_2O(l)$$

9. Write the equation for the reaction that occurs between the following two electrodes.

$$I_2(s) + 2e^- \longrightarrow 2I^-(aq)$$
$$Pb^{2+}(aq) + 2e^- \longrightarrow Pb(s)$$

10. Write the equation for the reaction that occurs between the following two electrodes.

$$Fe^{3+}(aq) + 3e^- \longrightarrow Fe(s)$$
$$2H_2O(l) + 2e^- \longrightarrow H_2(g) + 2OH^-(aq)$$

Practice problems

6. $Mg^{2+}(aq) + 2e^- \longrightarrow Mg(s)\ E^0 = -2.372\ V$
$Pb^{2+}(aq) + 2e^- \longrightarrow Pb(s)\ E^0 = +0.1262\ V$
Magnesium has a greater tendency to give up electrons than does lead. Therefore, only the reverse reaction will occur spontaneously.

7. $AgCl(s) + e^- \longrightarrow Ag(s) + Cl^-(aq)\ E^0 = +0.222\ V$
$Ce^{4+}(aq) + e^- \longrightarrow Ce^{3+}(aq)\ E^0 = +1.72\ V$
$Ce^{4+}(aq) + Ag(s) + Cl^-(aq) \longrightarrow Ce^{3+}(aq) + AgCl(s)$

8. $PbSO_4(s) + H_3O^+(aq) + 2e^- \longrightarrow$
$Pb(s) + HSO_4^-(aq) + H_2O(l)\ E^0 = -0.42\ V$

$Ca^{2+}(aq) + 2e^- \longrightarrow Ca(s)\ E^0 = -2.868\ V$
Calcium has a greater tendency to give up electrons than does lead sulfate. Therefore, the reaction will occur as written.

9. $I_2(s) + 2e^- \longrightarrow 2I^-(aq)\ E^0 = +0.5355$
$Pb^{2+}(aq) + 2e^- \longrightarrow Pb(s)\ E^0 = -0.1262$
$I_2(s) + Pb(s) \longrightarrow 2I^-(aq) + Pb^{2+}(aq)$

10. $Fe^{3+}(aq) + 3e^- \longrightarrow Fe(s)\ E^0 = -0.037$
$2H_2O(l) + 2e^- \longrightarrow H_2(g) + 2OH^-(aq)\ E^0 = -0.828$
$2Fe^{3+}(aq) + 3H_2(g) + 6OH^-(aq) \longrightarrow 2Fe(s) + 6H_2O(l)$

At the beginning of this chapter, you read about Michael Faraday's interest in electric fish. You were asked to consider several questions.

LOOKING BACK

How does the torpedo ray generate electricity in its electric-organ cells?

The method used by the electric fish is similar to that used by nerve cells, from which the electric organs of fish have probably evolved. The electric-organ cells have a semipermeable membrane that allows potassium ions, K^+, to enter the cell but does not allow sodium ions, Na^+, to enter the cell. A pump system removes sodium ions from the interior of the cell, causing potassium ions to diffuse from outside the cell into the cell's interior. This *sodium ion pump* creates a concentration difference between the exterior and interior of the cell. This concentration gradient produces a potential difference of about 0.08 V. When the fish needs to create an electric pulse, a sodium ion *gate* on the outside of the cell wall opens, allowing Na^+ ions to flood out of the cell's interior. This sets up the potential difference between the interior and exterior of the cell.

Would you expect electric organs to be more useful to fish that swim in salt water or fresh water? in clear water or murky water?

Pure, or fresh, water is a very poor conductor of electricity. Sea water is a much better conductor of electricity because of its high concentration of dissolved salts. This means that you might expect ocean, but not freshwater, fish to use electric organs. Many freshwater rivers, however, also contain enough ions to allow fish to use electric organs. The electric catfish found in the Nile River is one example.

In fairly clear water, fish can easily navigate and hunt without the use of electric organs. In murky water, their sense of sight is of limited value. Fish need another method of finding their way. It is under these conditions that the electric organ finds use as a "sixth sense" for navigation and prey detection.

How is it possible for large voltages, as great as 600 V in some electric eels, to be produced?

Most small flashlights require a voltage of 3.0 V. A standard flashlight battery has a voltage of only 1.5 V. In order to generate the necessary voltage, two batteries are placed *in series*, one behind the other. Using the same principle, a large torpedo ray can have up to a half-million electric plates in a stack, or *in series*, producing a lethal voltage.

The cells used by electric fish to generate electricity begin as muscle cells but lose that function as they develop, changing into cells called electroplaques. They are connected in series, in stacks of several thousand, to produce a high voltage. The cells from torpedo rays have been used extensively in research on nerve function.

CHAPTER 17
Highlights

READING STRATEGY

Assimilating Knowledge

Have students return to the list of things they want to know about electrochemistry, which they created on page 618. Have them place check marks next to the questions that they are now able to answer. Students should finish by making a list of what they've learned. Have students identify unanswered questions as well as new questions they may have. These questions could be used as the basis for a research project.

REVIEW & ASSESS ASSIGNMENT GUIDE

Term Review

Assign after Section 17-4.

Concept & Skills Review

Section 17-1
▶ Items 1–15

Section 17-2
▶ Items 16–27

Section 17-3
▶ Items 28–37

Section 17-4
▶ Items 38–46

Linking Chapters

Section 17-1
▶ Items 1, 3

Section 17-4
▶ Item 2

Alternative Assessments

Assign after Section 17-4.

Test Prep

Assign prior to the chapter test.

KEY TERMS

17-1
ampere
anode
cathode
coulomb
electrochemical cell
electrode
electrolytic cell
electroplating
equilibrium cell

galvanic cell
oxidation
redox reaction
reduction
volt
voltage

17-2
Downs cell
electrolysis
electrosynthesis

17-3
battery
corrosion
fuel cell
primary cell
sacrificial anode
secondary cell

17-4
electrochemical series
equilibrium voltage
standard electrode
  potential
standard hydrogen
  electrode

KEY CONCEPTS

17-1 What is electrochemistry all about?

▶ The relationship between electricity and chemistry is known as electrochemistry.

▶ Electric potential is measured in volts (V), electric current is measured in amperes (A), and electric charge is measured in coulombs (C).

▶ Electrical energy equals electric potential multiplied by electric charge ($J = V \times C$).

▶ Cathodic reactions involve reduction in which electrons are consumed, while anodic reactions involve oxidation in which electrons are created.

▶ Electrode reactions occur in electrochemical cells.

17-2 How are electrolytic cells used?

▶ An electrolytic cell uses electrical energy to drive a nonspontaneous redox reaction.

▶ A Downs cell is an electrolytic cell used to produce sodium metal and chlorine gas.

▶ An electrolytic cell can be used to decompose water into hydrogen gas and oxygen gas.

▶ Aluminum is commercially prepared by the electrolysis of Al_2O_3 obtained from bauxite ore.

17-3 How do batteries work?

▶ Galvanic cells, which include batteries and fuel cells, use cell reactions to convert chemical energy into electrical energy.

▶ Corrosion occurs because of electrode reactions usually involving metals and oxygen.

▶ Corrosion can be curbed by coating a metal with paint or another metal, or by attaching a sacrificial anode.

17-4 What can be learned from an equilibrium cell?

▶ An equilibrium cell can be used to measure the equilibrium voltage.

▶ The standard electrode potential of an electrode is determined by coupling it with a standard hydrogen electrode (SHE), which is assigned an electrode potential of 0.00 V.

▶ An element with a positive electrode potential is likely to be reduced, while an element with a negative electrode potential is likely to be oxidized.

KEY SKILLS

Review the following models before your exam. Be sure you can solve these types of problems.

Sample Problem 17A: Calculating electric charge used in an electrolytic cell (p. 625)

Sample Problem 17B: Calculating energy needed for electrolysis (p. 631)

Sample Problem 17C: Calculating the mass of products of galvanic cell reactions (p. 639)

Sample Problem 17D: Predicting the direction of electrochemical reactions (p. 647)

TERM REVIEW

1. Oxidation takes place at the ———.
   (cathode, anode)

2. A ——— could be used to produce electricity with nearly perfect efficiency.
   (Downs cell, standard hydrogen electrode, fuel cell)

3. The outcome of oxidation-reduction reactions can be determined using the ———.
   (electrochemical series, fuel cell)

4. The rusting of iron is an example of ———.
   (sacrificial anodes, corrosion)

5. No current flows in a(n) ———.
   (Downs cell, primary cell, equilibrium cell)

6. ——— corrode faster than the structural metal they protect.
   (Electrodes, Sacrificial anodes)

7. ——— can be used to produce sodium metal.
   (Electroplating, Electrosynthesis)

8. A(n) ——— converts electrical energy into chemical energy.
   (galvanic cell, electrolytic cell)

CONCEPT & SKILLS REVIEW

ELECTROCHEMISTRY

1. What is an electrochemical cell?

2. What is a redox reaction?

3. Use Figure 17-7, on page 626, to answer the following questions:
   a. Explain what will happen to the zinc and copper strips over time.
   b. Explain what would happen if the porous barrier were removed.
   c. In what direction do electrons flow through the wire?

4. Identify the following reactions as either reduction or oxidation. Indicate whether they occur at the cathode or anode.
   a. $Ra(s) \longrightarrow Ra^{2+}(aq) + 2e^-$
   b. $Hg_2^{2+}(aq) + 2e^- \longrightarrow 2Hg(l)$
   c. $Pb(s) + SO_4^{2-}(aq) \longrightarrow PbSO_4(s) + 2e^-$
   d. $O_2(g) + 2H_2O(l) + 4e^- \longrightarrow 4OH^-(aq)$

5. The process of oxidation may or may not involve oxygen. Explain this statement.

6. What is the Faraday constant? How is this constant used?

7. Complete the following table.

	Oxidation/ reduction	Loss or gain of electrons	Change in charge of reactant
Cathode			
Anode			

8. Describe the difference between an electrolytic cell and a galvanic cell.

9. Explain how a metallic object is electroplated.

10. Refer to the diagram below to answer the following questions:

CuCl₂ solution — Zn — Cu

   a. What macroscopic observations suggest that a chemical reaction has taken place?
   b. Write an equation to show what happened to the Zn metal.
   c. Explain where the Cu metal came from that collected at the bottom of the beaker.
   d. Write an equation to show how the Cu metal was formed.

TERM REVIEW

1. anode
2. fuel cell
3. electrochemical series
4. corrosion
5. equilibrium cell
6. Sacrificial anodes
7. Electrosynthesis
8. electrolytic cell

CONCEPT & SKILLS REVIEW

1. an apparatus that contains two electrodes and an electrolyte medium through which current can flow

2. a reaction in which one species is oxidized (loses electrons) while another species is reduced (accepts electrons)

3. a. Zinc will oxidize, so the zinc strip will slowly dissolve. The copper strip will have copper from the reduction of copper ions added to it until the copper ions are depleted.
   b. If the porous barrier were removed, the solutions would mix, the redox reaction would occur in the solution, and the cell would stop producing current.
   c. Electrons flow from the zinc electrode to the copper electrode.

4. a. oxidation, anode
   b. reduction, cathode
   c. oxidation, anode
   d. reduction, cathode

5. When substances react with oxygen, they usually do so by losing electrons to oxygen atoms. Substances may lose electrons to species other than oxygen, but the process is still called oxidation.

6. 96 485 C/mol. It is used to relate quantity of charge in coulombs to amount of electrons in moles.

Complete worked-out solutions for these problems can be found on the teacher's interleaved pages at the end of this chapter.

7. See page 655A.

8. In an electrolytic cell, an outside power supply pumps electric current through the cell to cause a chemical change. A galvanic cell produces electric current by converting chemical energy to electrical energy.

9. The object to be plated is placed in the cell as the cathode. The electrolyte solution contains ions of the metal that is to be plated. The anode is usually made of the metal to be plated. Voltage is applied, causing the anode to dissolve and the plating metal to deposit at the cathode.

10. a. Copper metal has precipitated in the beaker, and the zinc appears eaten away.
   b. $Zn(s) \longrightarrow Zn^{2+}(aq) + 2e^-$
   c. The Cu came from the reduction of Cu^{2+} ions that were in solution.
   d. $Cu^{2+}(aq) + 2e^- \longrightarrow Cu(s)$

11. 120 V

12. Aluminum is the anode and gold is the cathode.
$Al \longrightarrow Al^{3+} + 3e^-$; $Au^+ + e^- \longrightarrow Au$

13. 3.8 cents

14. 2.8×10^5 J

15. 0.18 J

16. An electrolytic cell uses an outside source of current to carry out an oxidation-reduction reaction. They may be used to plate, or refine metals, or electrolyze salts.

17. because the cell requires an outside current source to drive an otherwise nonspontaneous redox reaction

18. The reduction of water occurs at a lower voltage than the reduction of sodium ions.

19. The products would be Na metal and Br_2.

20. $6H_2O(l) \longrightarrow O_2(g) + 4H_3O^+(aq) + 4e^-$

21. Anode: $2I^-(l) \longrightarrow I_2(g) + 2e^-$
Cathode: $Na^+(l) + e^- \longrightarrow Na(s)$

---

11. What voltage is needed to generate 9.6 kJ of electrical energy that carries a charge of 80.0 C?

12. Label the cathode and anode in the diagram below. Write the equations for the redox reactions that are taking place in this electrochemical cell.

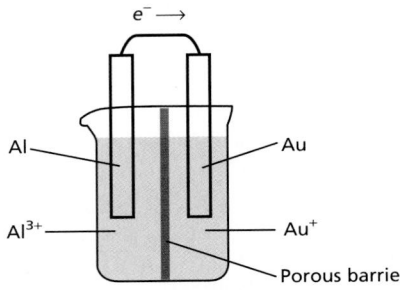

13. An ordinary 60 W light bulb (120 V) is designed for a current of 0.50 A. If your utility company sells electricity at 2.2¢/MJ, how much money do you waste by leaving a light on during an 8 hour night?

14. Batteries are sometimes listed with their "cranking power." This is the amount of current the battery can produce for a period of 30 seconds. If a battery has a cranking power of 1300 A at a voltage of 7.2 V, how much energy is supplied by the battery in 30.0 seconds?

15. Remote controls for TVs and VCRs usually require two AAA batteries. Each battery generates 1.5 V and a total electric current of 60.0 mA. Calculate how much electrical energy is expended each time a button on the remote control is pressed. Assume that each use takes 1.0 second.

ELECTROLYTIC CELLS

16. What does an electrolytic cell do?

17. Why is a battery or some other energy source connected to an electrolytic cell?

18. Tap water contains salts, such as NaCl. Why doesn't sodium metal form during the electrolysis of tap water?

---

19. What products would be made if a Downs cell operated with NaBr(l) instead of NaCl(l)?

20. What is the oxidation reaction that occurs during the electrolysis of water?

21. Write equations to show what happens at the anode and cathode when molten NaI is placed in an electrolytic cell.

22. How is photosynthesis different from electrosynthesis? How is it similar?

23. How much electric charge is needed to produce 1.000 kg of Na metal from the Na^+ ions in NaCl? **(Hint: See Sample Problem 17A.)**

24. A current of 2.50 A is passed through a solution containing Cu^{2+} ions for 4.00 hours. Calculate the mass of Cu atoms that form at the cathode. **(Hint: See Sample Problem 17A.)**

25. The Hall-Héroult process requires 5.4×10^4 kJ to produce 1.0 kg of aluminum. The enthalpy of fusion for aluminum is 10.7 kJ/mol. Prove mathematically that recycling aluminum saves energy.

26. What volume of F_2 gas is produced when molten KF is electrolyzed by a current of 20.0 A for 2.00 hours? Assume that the gas is collected at 1.00 atm and 298 K. **(Hint: See Sample Problem 17B.)**

27. Hydrogen is being tested as a possible fuel. Hydrogen gas can be produced at the cathode during the electrolysis of sulfuric acid. The cathodic reaction is written as follows.

$$2H_3O^+(aq) + 2e^- \longrightarrow H_2(g) + 2H_2O(l)$$

Calculate how much electrical energy must be supplied to produce 1.00 L of hydrogen at 1.00 atm and 298 K if the electrolytic cell operates at 1.23 V. **(Hint: See Sample Problem 17B.)**

GALVANIC CELLS

28. What are the differences between an alkaline dry cell and a zinc-carbon dry cell?

29. Explain how cathodic protection works to prevent corrosion.

30. Stainless steel contains chromium, which reacts with oxygen. Why might this metal be added to iron to make the stainless steel? The standard electrode potential of Cr^{3+}/Cr is -0.744.

31. Write the oxidation reaction showing what happens to iron ship hulls when they corrode in ocean water.

32. Explain why the terms *cathode* and *anode* cause confusion when they are used to refer to a rechargeable battery.

33. Identify the reactants that are supplied to a fuel cell aboard the space shuttle.

34. Explain why a rechargeable battery is considered a combination galvanic/electrolytic cell.

35. How does painting a metal protect it against corrosion?

Practice Problems

36. The cathodic reaction that occurs in an alkaline battery is shown by the following equation.

$$2MnO_2(s) + H_2O(l) + 2e^- \longrightarrow$$
$$Mn_2O_3(s) + 2OH^-(aq)$$

Calculate the mass of $MnO_2(s)$ that must be added to this 1.54 V battery to produce a total of 22.8 kJ of energy. **(Hint: See Sample Problem 17C.)**

37. What mass of water will be produced after a 12 V car battery has completely run down and delivered its 1.6 MJ of energy? **(Hint: See Sample Problem 17C.)**

EQUILIBRIUM CELLS

38. How can you tell from Table 17-2, on page 646, that $Cl_2(g)$ is likely to be reduced?

39. Explain why the voltage of a single electrode cannot be determined.

40. Explain how the voltages in Table 17-3 were determined.

41. Examine the following reaction.

$$Cu(s) + Fe^{2+}(aq) \rightarrow Cu^{2+}(aq) + Fe(s)$$

Predict whether this reaction will take place spontaneously in a galvanic cell. Explain your answer.

42. Compare the standard reduction potential for a metal with the reactivity of that metal.

Practice Problems

43. Write an equation for the electrochemical reaction that would occur in a galvanic cell in which one electrode is made of zinc metal in an aqueous solution of zinc ions and the other electrode contains liquid bromine. **(Hint: See Sample Problem 17D.)**

44. Write an equation for the electrochemical reaction that would spontaneously occur between potassium metal in aqueous potassium ions and solid zinc hydroxide with zinc metal in a hydroxide solution.

45. If a galvanic cell were made with a magnesium electrode and a cadmium electrode in which each electrode is bathed by a solution of its ions, which metal would be the cathode and which would be the anode?

46. Predict whether each of the following reactions will occur spontaneously as written. Write a balanced overall equation for each reaction that does occur.
a. $K + Al^{3+} \longrightarrow$
b. $Li^+ + Zn \longrightarrow$
c. $Cu + Cl_2 \longrightarrow$
d. $AgCl + Ca^{2+} \longrightarrow$
e. $Ce^{3+} + I_3^- \longrightarrow$

Complete worked-out solutions for these problems can be found on the teacher's interleaved pages at the end of this chapter.

22. Both photosynthesis and electrosynthesis convert nonchemical energy to chemical energy. In photosynthesis, light is the outside energy source. In electrosynthesis, electric current is the outside energy source.

23. 4.197×10^6 C

24. 11.9 g Cu

25. To melt 1.0 kg of Al at its melting point requires 4.0×10^2 kJ, compared with 5.4×10^4 kJ to produce the same 1.0 kg by electrolysis.

26. 18.3 L F_2 gas

27. 9.70 kJ

28. Alkaline and zinc-carbon dry cells both oxidize Zn to Zn^{2+} and reduce MnO_2 to Mn_2O_3. The difference is the environment in which the reactions occur. The Zn electrode in an alkaline cell is in a paste containing OH^- (which is basic or alkaline). The Zn electrode in a zinc-carbon cell is not. The MnO_2 in a zinc-carbon is in a paste containing NH_4^+ (which is acidic). The MnO_2 in an alkaline cell is in water.

29. Cathodic protection occurs when a metal to be protected is attached to a sacrificial anode made of a metal that is oxidized more readily than the other metal. In this way, the protected metal is maintained as the cathode of a cell, so it stays in the reduced state.

30. Cr is more likely to be oxidized than Fe, so it serves as a sacrificial anode in stainless steel.

31. *See page 655A.*

32. When a battery is recharged, the flow of current is opposite the direction of the current when the battery is producing current. Therefore, the electrodes switch identity when the cell switches from galvanic to electrolytic.

Complete worked-out solutions for these problems can be found on the teacher's interleaved pages at the end of this chapter.

33. H_2, hydrogen gas, and O_2, oxygen gas

34. When it is delivering electric current, it acts as a galvanic cell. When it is being recharged, it acts as an electrolytic cell.

35. Painting a metal prevents the metal from becoming an anode, or corroding, by keeping oxygen and water away from it.

36. 13.3 g MnO_2

37. 62 g H_2O

38. Cl_2 has a relatively high, positive reduction potential, so it is likely to be reduced.

39. A single electrode cannot exist on its own. Another electrode must be present to have a potential difference.

40. The voltages were determined by pairing each electrode with a standard hydrogen electrode.

41. The reaction is not spontaneous because copper has a greater reduction potential than iron. Copper is more likely to be reduced. So the reverse reaction will be spontaneous.

42. The order of decreasing reactivity of metals matches the order of increasing reduction potentials.

43. $Zn(s) + Br_2(l) \xrightarrow{2e^-} Zn^{2+}(aq) + 2Br^-(aq)$

44. $2K(s) + Zn(OH)_2(s) \xrightarrow{2e^-} 2K^+(aq) + Zn(s) + 2OH^-(aq)$

45. Magnesium will be the anode, and cadmium will be the cathode.

46. a. $3K + Al^{3+} \longrightarrow 3K^+ + Al$
  b. no reaction
  c. $Cu + Cl_2 \longrightarrow Cu^{2+} + 2Cl^-$
  d. no reaction
  e. no reaction

Answers continue on page 655A.

LINKING CHAPTERS

1. Theme: Conservation
In a balanced redox reaction, what is being conserved?

2. Energy and ions
In Chapter 5, you learned that iron can form either of two ions, Fe^{3+} or Fe^{2+}. Use the reactions and E^0 values in Table 17-2 to determine which oxidation state is preferred. Explain your reasoning.

3. Gibbs Free energy
  a. What would you expect the ΔG value to be for a galvanic cell?
  b. What is the ΔG value of the cell reaction in an electrolytic cell?
  c. What is the ΔG value of a dead dry cell?
  d. Electrical energy is Gibbs free energy, ΔG, and in theory, it is all available for work. Use the following equation to calculate the amount of electrical work generated per gram of water produced in a fuel cell that operates at 60% efficiency.

$$2H_2(g) + O_2(g) \longrightarrow 2H_2O(l)$$

ALTERNATIVE ASSESSMENTS

Performance assessment

1. Your teacher will assign you a known metal with an unknown reduction potential. Devise a method to determine the E^0 value of the metal from a list of metals with known E^0 values. Present your method to your teacher.

2. Investigate the development and operation of the sodium-sulfur battery being proposed to run electric cars. Choose a stand for or against its use, and present your findings in a persuasive speech to your classmates.

Portfolio projects

1. Chemistry and you
For one week, keep a record of how many times you use devices powered by batteries. Record what kind of device you used and the number and type of batteries it contained. Your teacher will provide you with various batteries and a balance. Record the mass of each type of battery you used during the week. Assuming that your battery usage is typical of everyone in the country, estimate the mass of waste material produced by battery usage in one year. Write a short report offering ways to reduce the amount of waste.

2. Cooperative group project
In small groups, research the environmental effects of different types of batteries. Analyze both the production and waste costs. Share your research with the other groups in the class.

3. Chemistry and you
Consumer use of rechargeable batteries is growing. Many people either own devices using rechargeable batteries or have access to them. Nickel-cadmium batteries, a common type of rechargeable battery, are used in cellular phones, electric shavers, and portable video-game systems. Make a list of the items that you come into contact with that use nickel-cadmium batteries or other rechargeable batteries. Write a short essay about technology that was not and could not have been available before the development of the nickel-cadmium battery.

4. internet**connect**

SC**LINKS**
NSTA

TOPIC: Redox reactions
GO TO: www.scilinks.org
KEYWORD: HW176

Research and communication
Redox reactions are not limited to electrochemical cells and batteries. Research common occurrences of redox reactions, and identify the chemical that is oxidized and the chemical that is reduced.

1. In the following reaction, which species is being reduced?

$$2K + Br_2 \longrightarrow 2K^+ + 2Br^-$$

a. K only
b. Br_2 only
c. both K and Br_2
d. neither K nor Br_2

2. The electrode at which reduction occurs is _____.
a. always the anode
b. always the cathode
c. either the anode or the cathode
d. always the half-cell

3. In an galvanic cell, the anode _____.
a. can be either positive or negative
b. is positive
c. is not charged
d. is negative

4. In a cell with Zn/Zn^{2+} and Cu/Cu^{2+} electrodes, _____.
a. Cu is oxidized and Zn^{2+} is reduced
b. Cu is reduced and Zn^{2+} is oxidized
c. Cu^{2+} is oxidized and Zn is reduced
d. Cu^{2+} is reduced and Zn is oxidized

5. When water is electrolyzed, oxygen gas is formed at _____.
a. the anode only
b. the cathode only
c. the midpoint between the anode and cathode
d. both the anode and the cathode

6. Sulfuric acid, H_2SO_4, or a similar substance is added to water that is to be electrolyzed in order to _____.
a. react with the water
b. keep the electrode clean
c. provide adequate conductivity
d. supply energy

7. In a Downs cell, which of the following is produced at the anode?
a. H_2
b. Na
c. Cl_2
d. O_2

8. When a rechargeable cell is being recharged, the cell acts as a(n) _____.
a. fuel cell
b. electrolytic cell
c. galvanic cell
d. equilibrium cell

9. When silver is electroplated onto an object, Ag^+ is _____.
a. oxidized at the anode
b. reduced at the anode
c. oxidized at the cathode
d. reduced at the cathode

10. The standard automobile battery consists of six _____.
a. lead(IV) oxide-lead-sulfuric acid cells
b. copper(II) oxide-copper-sulfuric acid cells
c. zinc oxide-zinc-sulfuric acid cells
d. iron(III) oxide-iron-sulfuric acid cells

11. A battery that can be recharged is an example of a(n) _____.
a. primary cell
b. equilibrium cell
c. secondary cell
d. Downs cell

12. The equilibrium voltage of a cell is measured when _____.
a. the cell is operating as a galvanic cell
b. the cell is operating as an electrolytic cell
c. the temperature of the cell is 25°C
d. no current is flowing through the cell

1. b
2. b
3. d
4. d
5. a
6. c
7. c
8. b
9. d
10. a
11. c
12. d

Answers from page 651

7.

	Oxidation/ Reduction	Loss or gain of electrons	Change in charge of reactant
Cathode	reduction	gain of electrons	charge goes down
Anode	oxidation	loss of electrons	charge goes up

Answers from page 652

11. $voltage = \dfrac{energy}{charge} = \dfrac{9.6 \times 10^3 \text{ J}}{80.0 \text{ C}} = 120 \text{ V}$

13. $\dfrac{0.50 \text{ C}}{s} \times \dfrac{60 \text{ s}}{min} \times \dfrac{60 \text{ min}}{h} \times 8 \text{ h} = 1.44 \times 10^4 \text{ C}$

$energy = (1.44 \times 10^4 \text{ C})(120 \text{ V}) = 1.73 \times 10^6 \text{ J} = 1.73 \text{ MJ}$

$1.73 \text{ MJ} \times \dfrac{2.2\cancel{c}}{MJ} = 3.8\cancel{c}$

14. $30.0 \text{ s} \times \dfrac{1300 \text{ C}}{s} \times 7.2 \text{ V} = 2.8 \times 10^5 \text{ J}$

15. $60.0 \text{ mA} \times \dfrac{1 \text{ A}}{1000 \text{ mA}} = 6.00 \times 10^{-2} \text{ A} = 6.00 \times 10^{-2} \text{ C/s}$

$1.0 \text{ s} \times \dfrac{6.00 \times 10^{-2} \text{ C}}{s} \times (1.5 \text{ V} + 1.5 \text{ V}) = 0.18 \text{ J}$

23. $1.00 \text{ kg Na} \times \dfrac{1000 \text{ g}}{kg} \times \dfrac{1 \text{ mol Na}}{22.99 \text{ g Na}} \times \dfrac{1 \text{ mol } e^-}{1 \text{ mol Na}} \times \dfrac{96\,485 \text{ C}}{1 \text{ mol } e^-} = 4.197 \times 10^6 \text{ C}$

24. $4.00 \text{ h} \times \dfrac{60 \text{ min}}{h} \times \dfrac{60 \text{ s}}{min} \times \dfrac{2.50 \text{ C}}{s} \times \dfrac{1 \text{ mol } e^-}{96\,485 \text{ C}} \times \dfrac{1 \text{ mol Cu}}{2 \text{ mol } e^-} \times \dfrac{63.55 \text{ g Cu}}{1 \text{ mol Cu}} =$

11.9 g Cu

25. $1.0 \text{ kg Al} \times \dfrac{1000 \text{ g}}{kg} \times \dfrac{1 \text{ mol Al}}{26.98 \text{ g Al}} \times \dfrac{10.7 \text{ kJ}}{mol} = 4.0 \times 10^2 \text{ kJ}$

26. $2.00 \text{ h} \times \dfrac{60 \text{ min}}{1 \text{ h}} \times \dfrac{60 \text{ s}}{1 \text{ min}} \times \dfrac{20.0 \text{ C}}{s} \times \dfrac{1 \text{ mol } e^-}{96\,485 \text{ C}} \times \dfrac{1 \text{ mol F}_2}{2 \text{ mol } e^-} = 0.746 \text{ mol F}_2$

$PV = nRT$

$V = \dfrac{nRT}{P} = \dfrac{(0.746 \text{ mol F}_2)(0.0821 \text{ L} \cdot \text{atm/mol} \cdot \text{K})(298 \text{ K})}{1.00 \text{ atm}} = 18.3 \text{ L}$

27. $PV = nRT$

$n = \dfrac{PV}{RT} = \dfrac{(1.00 \text{ atm})(1.00 \text{ L})}{(0.0821 \text{ L} \cdot \text{atm/mol} \cdot \text{K})(298 \text{ K})} = 4.09 \times 10^{-2} \text{ mol H}_2$

$energy = 4.09 \times 10^{-2} \text{ mol H}_2 \times \dfrac{2 \text{ mol } e^-}{1 \text{ mol H}_2} \times \dfrac{96\,485 \text{ C}}{1 \text{ mol } e^-} \times 1.23 \text{ V}$

$= 9.70 \times 10^3 \text{ J} = 9.70 \text{ kJ}$

Answers from page 653

31. $2Fe(s) + 11H_2O(l) \longrightarrow Fe_2O_3 \cdot 2H_2O(s) + 6H_3O^+(aq) + 6e^-$

36. $charge = \dfrac{22.8 \times 10^3 \text{ J}}{1.54 \text{ V}} = 1.48 \times 10^4 \text{ C}$

$1.48 \times 10^4 \text{ C} \times \dfrac{1 \text{ mol } e^-}{96\,485 \text{ C}} \times \dfrac{2 \text{ mol MnO}_2}{2 \text{ mol } e^-} \times \dfrac{86.94 \text{ g MnO}_2}{1 \text{ mol MnO}_2} = 13.3 \text{ g MnO}_2$

37. $charge = \dfrac{1.6 \times 10^6 \text{ J}}{12 \text{ V}} = 1.33 \times 10^5 \text{ C}$

$1.33 \times 10^5 \text{ C} \times \dfrac{1 \text{ mol } e^-}{96\,485 \text{ C}} \times \dfrac{5 \text{ mol H}_2O}{2 \text{ mol } e^-} \times \dfrac{18.02 \text{ g H}_2O}{1 \text{ mol H}_2O} = 62 \text{ g H}_2O$

Answers from page 654

LINKING CHAPTERS

1. As in any chemical reaction, mass, energy, and charge are conserved.

2. The preferred oxidation state for iron is 2+. Fe^{2+} ions are more difficult to reduce to Fe than Fe^{3+} is to reduce to Fe^{2+}.

3. a. negative

b. positive

c. zero

d. Thermodynamic data can be found in Table A-13.

$\Delta H = 2\Delta H^0_{f_{H_2O}} - (2\Delta H^0_{f_{H_2}} + \Delta H^0_{f_{O_2}}) = 2 \times -285.8 \text{ kJ/mol} - (0 \text{ kJ/mol} +$
$0 \text{ kJ/mol}) = -571.6 \text{ kJ/mol}$

$\Delta S = 2\Delta S_{H_2O} - (2\Delta S_{H_2} + \Delta S_{O_2}) = 2 \times 70.0 \text{ J/mol} \cdot \text{K} -$
$[(2 \times 130.7 \text{ J/mol} \cdot \text{K}) + 205.1 \text{ J/mol} \cdot \text{K}] = -326 \text{ J/mol} \cdot \text{K}$

$\Delta G = \Delta H - T\Delta S = -571.6 \text{ kJ/mol} - (298 \text{ K})(-0.326 \text{ kJ/mol} \cdot \text{K})$
$= -474.5 \text{ kJ/mol at 100\% efficiency}$

$\Delta G = -284.7 \text{ kJ/mol at 60\% efficiency}$

$\Delta G = \dfrac{-284.7 \text{ kJ}}{2 \text{ mol H}_2O} \times \dfrac{1 \text{ mol H}_2O}{18.02 \text{ g H}_2O} = -7.899 \text{ kJ/g}$

ALTERNATIVE ASSESSMENTS

Performance assessment

1. Answers will vary. Plans should involve making the metal an electrode in a cell along with a second electrode of known ΔE^0. The resulting cell voltage and the direction of current flow are the needed data. Students should note that electrode potentials must be compared at 25°C and at a 1.000 M concentration of the respective ions.

2. Student presentations should clearly show the electrode reactions, the products given off, and the nature of the starting materials. The sodium must be in the liquid state, so operating temperatures are around 200°C. Students should explain why such a cell cannot work in an aqueous medium.

Portfolio projects

1. Answers will vary. Students should consider several factors, including the various types of batteries used and their typical lifetime in each application.

2. Answers will vary. Students should consider how the materials to make the battery are obtained as well as the problems of disposal. They should research the recommended disposal methods for each type of battery and note that some types are recyclable.

3. Answers will vary. Students should note that many devices that use rechargeable batteries would be too expensive to use with non-rechargeable batteries or that the user would have to stay near an electrical outlet. Video camcorders are a good example of devices dependent on rechargeable batteries.

4. Answers will vary. Students may want to search the textbook for examples of redox reactions that were previously termed single-replacement reactions.

Nuclear Chemistry

CLASSROOM RESOURCES			
SECTIONS	TEACHER'S DEMONSTRATIONS	PROBLEM SOLVING ■ *Text* ◆ *ChemFile Mini-Guide*	LABORATORIES ■ *Text* ◆ *ChemFile Manuals: A, B, C, D*
18-1 **Which atomic are nuclei stable?** Section Review, p. 663	**Demo 1** Electric Forces, p. 658		
18-2 **What kinds of nuclear change occur?** Section Review, p. 673	**Demo 2** Detecting and measuring radiation, p. 664		◆ **A26** Radioactivity
18-3 **How is nuclear chemistry used?** Section Review, p. 681			◆ **A27** Detecting Radioactivity

TECHNOLOGY RESOURCES

See page 656 for a listing of Internet resources.

SECTIONS	VIDEOS/VIDEODISC *Holt Chemistry Videodisc* **CNN** *Science in the NEWS*	CHEMFILE CD-ROMS ● *Teaching Resources* ◆ *Interactive Tutor*	OVERHEADS ● *Color Transparencies* ◆ *Transparency Masters*
18-1	Transmutation	● Supplemental Reading Project: Chapter 7 of Linus Pauling's *In His Own Words,* "Atomic Politics"	● **130** Binding Energy per Nucleon Title ● **131** Band of Stability
18-2	Potassium-40 Half-Life Comparison Radioactive Isotope Decay Radiation Separation into Types **CNN** Segment 31 Nuclear Waste Segment 32 Radioisotopes in Medicine		● **132** Uranium-238 Decay Series ● **133** Potassium-40 Half-Life Comparison ● **134** Nuclear Chain Reaction ◆ **125A** Radioactive Nuclide Emissions ◆ **126A** Rate of Decay
18-3	Nuclear Fusion	● Occupational Application: Archaeologist	

ASSESSMENT RESOURCES

ALTERNATIVE ASSESSMENTS	CHAPTER TESTING	SCORING RUBRICS *Holt ChemFile Teaching Resources CD-ROM*
Student Text Performance assessment, p. 686 Portfolio projects 1–4, p. 686 **Teacher's Edition** Writing nuclear equations, p. 667 Group Strategy, p. 676, p. 680 Half-life, p. 678 **Study Guide** Sections 18-1 to 18-3	**Student Text** Test Preparation, p. 687 **Holt Chemistry: Visualizing Matter Chapter 18 Test** (blackline masters) **Holt ChemFile Test Generator for Macintosh and Windows**	**Lab Work** Student-Designed Experiments Rubric Performance-Tasks Scoring Rubric Assessment for Structured Inquiry Assessment for Open-Ended Inquiry **Portfolio Projects** Evaluating Concept Maps Assessing Portfolios Portfolio Assignment Student Evaluation Form

CHAPTER

18

Establishing Prior Knowledge

Make certain students understand the following concepts:
▶ Chapter 2: energy, mass-energy relationship
▶ Chapter 3: subatomic particles, atomic number, atomic mass number, isotopes
▶ Chapter 4: periodic table

 READING STRATEGY

Assimilating Knowledge

Before reading this chapter, have each student write a short list of all the things he or she knows about the forces that hold an atom's nucleus together, the role of neutrons in nuclear stability, the nature of radioactivity, the relationship between nuclear changes and radioactivity, nuclear fission and nuclear fusion, and applications of nuclear changes. When students have finished their list, ask them to contribute their entries to a group list on the board. Then have students list the things they want to know about nuclear changes.

If students have trouble coming up with questions, offer these suggestions to get them on track:

▶ How do nuclear changes differ from chemical changes?
▶ Considering that all charged particles in a nucleus are positive, what effect must they have on one another?
▶ What keeps an atom's nucleus from flying apart as a result of electrostatic repulsion?

ABOUT THE ILLUSTRATION

Cloud chamber photographs allow nuclear chemists to view the tracks made by ionized particles.

---

internet connect

Holt Chemistry: Visualizing Matter
On-Line Resources
go.hrw.com
Visit the HRW Web site for a variety of resources related to this chapter. Just type in the keyword HW0 Chapt18.

SCLINKS
NSTA

National Science Teachers Association
On-Line Resources: www.scilinks.org
The following Scilinks Internet resources can be found in the student text for this chapter:

Page 664
TOPIC: Radioactive emissions
KEYWORD: HW181

Page 669
TOPIC: Fission
KEYWORD: HW182

Page 671
TOPIC: Fusion
KEYWORD: HW183

Page 674
TOPIC: Radioactive dating
KEYWORD: HW184

Page 686
TOPIC: Radiation effects on humans
KEYWORD: HW185

Page 686
TOPIC: Nuclear Power
KEYWORD: HW186

THE ICEMAN MEETS NUCLEAR CHEMISTRY

While hiking through the Alps near the border between Austria and Italy, in September 1991, Helmut and Erika Simon noticed something protruding from the ice. At first the Simons thought they had stumbled across a discarded doll covered with ice.

But on closer inspection, the Simons realized they were looking at the frozen body of a man. Sticking out of the ice were the head and shoulders of a prehistoric man, now known throughout the world as the Iceman.

For four days following the discovery, workers struggled to free the Iceman's body. They hacked away at the ice using axes and ski poles, unaware of the importance of what they were uncovering. The Iceman's left hip was broken with a jackhammer, and much of his clothing was destroyed. But when the figure was finally freed, the workers were astonished by what they saw.

The body was amazingly well preserved. The Iceman stood 5 ft 2 in. tall and appeared to be somewhere between 25 and 40. He had wavy, medium-length, dark hair and a beard. He wore clothes made of animal skins and boots stuffed with grass to keep his feet warm. His skin bore markings in various spots, including stripes on his right ankle and a cross behind his left knee.

The Iceman had been carrying a stone knife, a wooden backpack, a small bag containing a flint lighter and some kindling, a bow and a quiver containing 14 arrows, and a copper ax. Shortly after the Iceman's body was freed from the ice, an archaeologist examined the ax. The age of the ax indicated that the Iceman lived about 4000 years ago.

If the Iceman is indeed that old, then his body is the oldest ever retrieved from an Alpine glacier. And at over 10 000 feet, the site where the Iceman was found is the highest point at which any prehistoric human has ever been found in Europe. Moreover, the Iceman is one of the best-preserved early humans ever found.

Scientists immediately arranged to have the body placed in a freezer, where the temperature would be maintained at a constant −6°C and the humidity at a constant 98%. These conditions would replicate those of the ice in which the body was preserved for so long.

CHAPTER LINKS

Exactly when did the Iceman die?

How did scientists determine what the Iceman looked like when he was alive?

How did the Iceman die?

STORY BACKGROUND

Of the Iceman's possessions, the most revealing is his copper-bladed ax. It was at first mistaken for bronze, an alloy of copper and tin that was common from 2200 B.C. to 1000 B.C. (the Bronze Age). Bronze is harder than copper, and because copper's melting point is lowered when mixed with a metal that has a low melting point, bronze is easier to cast. Because of this mistake, anthropologists at first underestimated the Iceman's age.

The Iceman lived in a time when people were first making tools from metal instead of stone. Elemental copper, along with copper ore, occurs naturally on the Earth's surface, but its high melting point makes removing it from its ore challenging. The copper–copper ore mixture was put in a clay crucible while several workers blew through clay or wooden tubes onto the hot coals. The additional oxygen made the coals heat to a temperature above 1083°C, copper's melting point.

RESOURCE LINK

Supplemental Reading Projects
Guided reading worksheets for Chapter 7 of Linus Pauling's *In His Own Words,* "Atomic Politics," can be found on the Holt ChemFile Teaching Resources CD-ROM.

CONCEPT PREVIEW

Section 18-1

Forces in the nucleus
- the strong nuclear force
- mass defect
- nuclear binding energy

Stability of the nucleus
- binding energy per nucleon
- factors that influence nuclear stability

Section 18-2

Changes in unstable nuclei
- radioactivity
- beta emission
- electron capture
- positron emission
- alpha emission
- balancing nuclear equations

Causing nuclear changes
- requirements for nuclear fission

- nuclear fusion and containment
- transmutation by particle bombardment

Section 18-3

Using radioactivity
- half-life
- radioactive dating
- smoke detectors
- monitoring exposure to radioactivity

Which atomic nuclei are stable?

OBJECTIVES

▶ **Describe** how the strong nuclear force acts among nucleons.

▶ **Discuss** the nature and origin of binding energy.

▶ **Account** for the increase in nuclear stability of the smaller nuclei followed by the decrease in stability of the larger nuclei as atomic number increases.

Nuclear stability

You learned in Chapter 3 of Ernest Rutherford's famous gold-foil experiment, which solved a basic riddle about the distribution of charge and mass in an atom. Rutherford's results showed that all of the atom's positive charge and almost all of its mass are contained in an extremely small nucleus. This discovery led to another mystery about the nucleus. Protons are positively charged, and when packed together in a nucleus they exert a tremendous force of electrostatic repulsion on each other. So why doesn't the nucleus fly apart?

Nuclei are composed of both protons and neutrons. The number of protons is the *atomic number, Z,* and the total number of protons and neutrons is the *mass number, A*. The symbol for the nucleus of an atom of element *X* is shown in **Figure 18-1.**

The protons and neutrons in a nucleus are collectively known as **nucleons.** A **nuclide** is any combination of these protons and neutrons. You already know that *isotopes* are atoms that have the same atomic number but different mass numbers. In other words, isotopes are nuclides that have the same number of protons but different numbers of neutrons. The following nuclei are stable isotopes of tellurium.

$$^{122}_{52}\text{Te} \qquad ^{124}_{52}\text{Te} \qquad ^{128}_{52}\text{Te}$$

A related term is *isobar,* which refers to atoms that have the same mass number but different atomic numbers. The following stable nuclei are isobars.

$$^{124}_{54}\text{Xe} \qquad ^{124}_{52}\text{Te} \qquad ^{124}_{50}\text{Sn}$$

Notice they have different numbers of protons, Z, but the same mass number, A.

nucleons

the protons and neutrons that make up the nucleus of an atom

nuclide

any combination of protons and neutrons in a nucleus

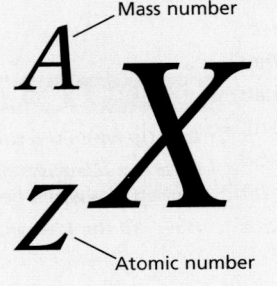

▶ **FIGURE 18-1**

X represents the element, *Z* is the element's atomic number, and *A* is the element's mass number.

Mass number

Atomic number

DEMONSTRATION 1

Electric Forces

Approximate time: 5 minutes

1. Obtain two pith balls or plastic-foam balls, and attach a 20 cm length of thread to each ball with a small piece of cellophane tape.

2. Hang the balls about 1 cm apart on an iron ring attached to a ring stand.

3. Stroke an ebonite rod with fur or wool, and touch each ball with the rod. The balls

should repel each other because both have a negative charge.

4. Touch each ball with your finger to remove the charge. Now move the balls 3 cm apart on the iron ring.

5. Stroke the ebonite rod with the fur as before, and touch one ball with the rod.

FIGURE 18-2 ▼

In this nucleus, the strong nuclear force acts only over a distance of only a few nucleon diameters. Attractions occur between protons A and B, neutrons D and E and the more distant proton C and neutron F, but not as strongly.

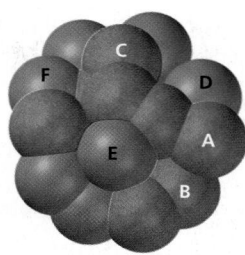

The strong force holds the nucleus together

Electrostatic repulsion occurs between the protons of a nucleus. In 1935, the Japanese physicist Hideki Yukawa proposed the theory that some other force overwhelms the electrostatic repulsion among protons. This force is called the **strong nuclear force** and is exerted by nucleons on one another when they are very close to each other. Forces that hold nucleons together are generally called *binding forces*.

Although the strong nuclear binding force is much stronger than the electrical force, it acts only over very *short* distances. Look at the nucleus illustrated in **Figure 18-2.** The nucleons are close enough together for each nucleon to attract all of the other nucleons by the strong nuclear force. In larger nuclei the strong nuclear force does not reach far enough to allow each nucleon to attract all others. However, the much weaker electrostatic repulsion between protons does act over large distances. When there is an imbalance between the strong nuclear force and electrostatic repulsion, the nucleus decays. You will learn more about nuclear decay in section 18-2.

Binding energy comes from loss of mass

Because the strong nuclear force of attraction holds the nuclear particles together, the nucleus is at a lower energy state than are its separated nucleons. A system becomes more stable when it moves to a lower energy state. When protons and neutrons that are far apart come together to form a nucleus, energy is given off because of the increased stability of the nucleus. This stabilization reaction can be written as follows.

$$\text{separated nucleons} \longrightarrow \text{nucleus} + \text{energy}$$

The energy produced in the above reaction is enormous compared with the energy changes that take place in ordinary chemical reactions. Nuclear energy is produced at the expense of mass, implying that the mass of the nucleus is less than the combined masses of the separated nucleons. This difference in mass is known as the **mass defect.** For helium, $_2^4\text{He}$, the mass of the nucleus is about 0.75% less than the total mass of two protons and two neutrons. This energy released, *E,* and decrease in mass, *m,* are related according to Einstein's mass-energy equation.

$$E = mc^2$$

strong nuclear force

the force of attraction among the particles of a nucleus that overcomes electrostatic repulsion and holds the nucleus together

mass defect

the mass lost by conversion to energy when a nucleus forms from separated nucleons

NUCLEAR CHEMISTRY 659

nuclear binding energy

the energy emitted when nucleons come together to form a nucleus; also the energy needed to break a nucleus into individual, separated nucleons

The constant c, 3.00×10^8 m/s, is the speed of light. Notice that if mass, m, is expressed in kilograms, and c^2 in m^2/s^2, the product mc^2 will have the units kg•m^2/s^2 so that E will be calculated directly in joules, the *SI* unit of energy.

The energy emitted when nucleons come together is the **nuclear binding energy.** You could also say that the nuclear binding energy is the energy required to separate a nucleus into its components.

Binding energy is easily calculated

Consider the stable oxygen isotope, $^{16}_{8}$O, with a mass number of 16. One atom of this isotope contains eight protons and eight neutrons, as well as eight electrons in two energy levels. The total mass of all its separate particles is equivalent to eight hydrogen atoms, each with a mass of 1.007 825 amu, combined with eight neutrons, each with a mass of 1.008 665 amu. In **Figure 18-3,** you can see how the total mass of these particles compares with the actual mass of a $^{16}_{8}$O atom. The mass defect for one atom of $^{16}_{8}$O is 0.137 005 amu, as shown in Figure 18-3. Einstein's mass-energy equation can be used to calculate the binding energy. Remember to convert amu per atom to grams per mole when calculating binding energy.

Binding energy is one indicator of nuclear stability

The binding energy, 1.23×10^{13} J, results from the formation of a mere 16 g of oxygen nuclei. That is roughly the amount of energy required to heat 4.6 million liters of liquid water from 0°C to 100°C and boil it away completely.

As you know, the more energy released in a process, the more stable are the products of that process. The binding energy of a selenium, $^{80}_{34}$Se, nucleus is much greater than that of a $^{16}_{8}$O nucleus. Does this difference

▶ **FIGURE 18-3**

The mass defect is the difference between the mass of the nucleus and the sum of the masses of its protons, neutrons and electrons.

Mass defect

Oxygen nucleus

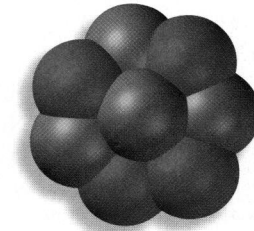

$^{16}_{8}$O isotope = 8(1.007 825 amu) + 8(1.008 665 amu)

= 8.062 600 amu + 8.069 320 amu

= 16.131 920 amu

m = (total mass of separate nucleons) − (mass of nucleus)

= 16.131 920 − 15.994 915

= 0.137 005 amu per isotope of $^{16}_{8}$O

Relative Stability of Nuclei

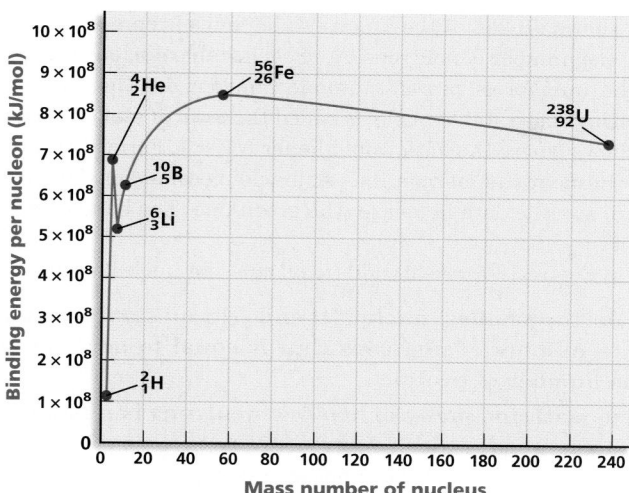

FIGURE 18-4 ◀

The plot of average binding energy per nucleon versus mass number indicates the relative stability of nuclei. Isotopes that have a high binding energy per nucleon are more stable. $^{56}_{26}$Fe is the most stable nucleus.

in energy mean that the $^{80}_{34}$Se nucleus is more stable than the $^{16}_{8}$O nucleus? Not necessarily. After all, $^{80}_{34}$Se contains many more nucleons than $^{16}_{8}$O does. To make a fair comparison you must look at the binding energy *per nucleon.* Look at the graph of these energies versus mass number in **Figure 18-4.** Notice that the binding energy per nucleon rises rapidly among the lighter nuclei. The higher the binding energy per nucleon, the more tightly the nucleons are held together.

Moving farther to the right, the binding energy per nucleon begins to level off. It reaches a maximum when the atomic mass number, *A,* is around 55, as seen with iron, cobalt, and nickel. The most stable nuclei are $^{56}_{26}$Fe and $^{58}_{28}$Ni. These isotopes are relatively abundant in the universe, and they are the major components of the Earth's core.

Beyond these elements, the nucleus is too large for added nucleons to increase the overall attraction among the particles. As you move even farther to the right, repulsions become more significant, and the binding energy per nucleon decreases gradually. Beyond mass number 209, no stable nuclide exists.

CONCEPT CHECK

1. How do the nuclides $^{16}_{8}$O, $^{15}_{8}$O, and $^{15}_{7}$N differ?
2. Why do nuclei not fly apart as a result of electrostatic repulsion?
3. How do stable nuclides with very low mass numbers differ from those with high mass numbers?

SECTION 18-1

VISUAL STRATEGY

Figure 18-4   Emphasize that what is being shown is binding energy *per nucleon,* not total binding energy. Elements above Fe-56 still increase in binding energy but at a slower rate than the number of nucleons increases. Therefore, binding energy per nucleon begins to decrease.

COMMON MISCONCEPTION

Some students may already realize that isotopes, whether naturally occurring or artificially produced, are classified simply as nonradioactive (stable) or radioactive (unstable). Students may not realize that different levels of nuclear stability are affected by temperature and pressure. Inform students that stable atomic nuclei occur under the conditions of temperature and pressure that prevail on Earth. However, the stability of nuclei can vary under the conditions that exist in stars, including novae and supernovae.

ANSWERS

CONCEPT CHECK

1. Nuclides $^{16}_{8}$O and $^{15}_{8}$O are isotopes of the same element, oxygen. They have the same atomic number (number of protons) but different mass numbers (number of protons and neutrons). The different mass numbers indicate $^{15}_{8}$O has one fewer neutron than $^{16}_{8}$O. Nuclides $^{15}_{8}$O and $^{15}_{7}$N are isobars with the same mass number but different atomic numbers.

2. The nucleons exert a strong nuclear force on one another that overcomes electrostatic repulsion. This force keeps the nuclei from flying apart.

3. Stable nuclides with low atomic numbers have a low binding energy per nucleon, but stable nuclides with higher atomic numbers generally have a higher binding energy per nucleon.

VISUAL STRATEGY

Figure 18-5 Students should note that vertical columns of dots represent a series of stable isotopes of the same element. Point out that nuclei with a low atomic number lie close to the line representing a neutron-proton ratio of 1:1. At the upper end, the ratio has increased to nearly 1.5:1. Ask students what this graph shows about the composition of stable nuclei as atomic number increases. As atomic number increases, the number of neutrons increases more rapidly than the atomic number, thus increasing the neutron-proton ratio.

COMMON MISCONCEPTION

The term *magic number* is misleading. As with all natural phenomena, there is no magical explanation for the stability of nuclei having a "magic number" of particles.

The current model of the nucleus is based on quantum mechanics. Like electrons, nuclear particles are thought to have spin, exist in shells or in energy levels, and have ground states and excited states. It is thought that the so-called magic numbers correspond to stable nucleon arrangements similar to the stable electron arrangements of the noble gases.

band of stability

the area on a graph of neutron number versus proton number in which all stable nuclei lie

▼ **FIGURE 18-5**

The graph below shows the number of protons and neutrons for all 256 of the known stable nuclei.

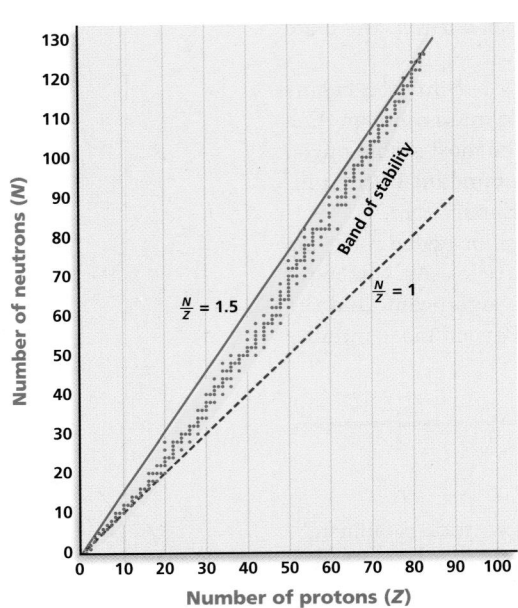

Neutron-Proton Ratios of Stable Nuclei

Predicting nuclear stability

What other factors affect nuclear stability? Look at the graph in **Figure 18-5.** It shows all 256 of the known stable nuclei represented by red dots. Here the number of neutrons, N, of each stable nucleus is plotted against the number of protons (atomic number Z). The pattern formed by plotting these stable nuclei is called the **band of stability.** The maroon line shows where the data would lie for $N/Z = 1$. For lighter nuclei, the data fall near the maroon line. As nuclei become heavier, N/Z approaches 1.5, and the data lie nearer the green line. The band of stability is shown in yellow.

The graph in Figure 18-5 reveals additional rules for nuclear stability.

1. **Except for the smallest nuclei, $_1^1H$ and $_2^3He$, all stable nuclei contain a number of neutrons that is equal to or greater than the number of protons.**

2. **A nucleus with too many or too few neutrons is unstable.** For small atoms, the ratio of neutrons, N, to protons, Z, is very close to one. As the nuclei get larger, this ratio increases gradually until it is near 1.5 for the largest atoms.

The following rules are not obvious at first on the graph, but they become clear when Figure 18-5 is viewed carefully.

3. **Nuclei with even numbers of nucleons are more stable.** Almost 60% of all stable nuclei have even numbers of both protons and neutrons. From this fact, it is safe to assume that an even-even combination is particularly stable. Of the four odd-odd nuclei, all are small, with a N/Z ratio equal to one. Of the 50 odd-even nuclei, 20 are nuclei of elements that have only one stable nuclide.

4. **Nuclei with so-called *magic numbers* of protrons and *magic numbers* of neutrons tend to be more stable than others.** These numbers—2, 8, 20, 28, 50, 82, and 126—apply to the number of protons or the number of neutrons. Notice in Figure 18-4 the large binding energy of $_2^4He$. This is a very small even-even nucleus with two protons and two neutrons. This extra stability also shows up in the element calcium, which has six stable isotopes ranging from $_{20}^{40}Ca$ to $_{20}^{48}Ca$. All have 20 protons, and the two shown have 20 and 28 neutrons, respectively. Tin, with the magic number of

50 protons, has 10 stable isotopes, the greatest number of any element. The heaviest stable element, bismuth, with only one stable isotope, has the magic number of 126 neutrons in $^{209}_{83}$Bi.

5. Of two neighboring isobars, at least one is unstable. Refer to the three examples of isobars at the beginning of this section. Notice that the nuclei of atomic numbers 51 and 53 are missing. These two missing isobars are nuclei, $^{124}_{51}$Sb and $^{124}_{53}$I. They are the neighboring isobars of the stable nuclides; therefore, they are unstable.

SECTION REVIEW

Total recall

1. What are the nucleons of an atom?
2. What role does the strong nuclear force play in the structure of an atom?
3. What is the band of stability?
4. Explain the difference between isotopes and isobars.
5. What is mass defect?
6. What is the nuclear binding energy?
7. Why is bismuth, $^{209}_{83}$Bi, stable?
8. Which is more stable, nuclei with an even number of nucleons or nuclei with an odd number of nucleons?

Critical thinking

9. Which is generally more stable, a small nucleus or a large nucleus? Explain.
10. How does nuclear binding energy relate to the stability of an atom?
11. Which is expected to be more stable, $^{6}_{3}$Li or $^{9}_{3}$Li?
12. **a.** What creates the electrostatic repulsion in the nucleus of an atom?
    b. How is the repulsive force overcome?
    c. What would happen if this force were not overcome?

13. **Interpreting Graphics** Use Figure 18-5 and the rules for predicting nuclear stability to determine whether the following isotopes are stable or unstable.
    a. $^{32}_{15}$P   **d.** $^{24}_{12}$Mg
    b. $^{14}_{6}$C   **e.** $^{97}_{43}$Tc
    c. $^{51}_{23}$V

14. Why are certain numbers referred to as magic numbers in terms of atomic nuclei?

15. **Story Clue** What element is the basis of all of the organic substances found in living things?

16. **Interpreting Graphics** Use Figure 18-4 to answer the following:
    a. For the elements shown, what happens to the binding energy as the mass number for the nucleus increases?
    b. Which is more stable, the hydrogen isotope or the helium isotope?

17. Which elements have no stable isotopes? (Examine Figure 18-5 carefully)

LESSON WARM-UP

Alchemy and Transmutations
Start by asking students to recall anything they have heard about the ancient alchemists. Two of their goals were to discover the "elixir of life" and to find a way to turn base metals into gold. The alchemists searched for the "philosopher's stone," a substance that, when mixed with the base metals, would change them to gold by chemical means. Ask students why this transmutation was an impossible goal.

💡 DID YOU KNOW?

It is thought by chemistry historians that most alchemists after about A.D. 1400 no longer believed that transmutation was possible. Many were charlatans who took advantage of rich people seeking more money and power.

HISTORICAL CONNECTION

When Henri Becquerel (1852–1908) discovered that uranium ore gave off penetrating radiation, he intended to determine whether the sun emitted X rays. The uranium ore was supposed to absorb solar X rays and re-emit the energy at longer wavelengths. On an overcast day, Becquerel placed a photographic plate and uranium in a drawer. When the plate was developed, it looked the same as the plates that had been exposed to sunlight, indicating that uranium is a source of energy similar to sunlight.

What kinds of nuclear change occur?

OBJECTIVES

▶ **Describe** the particles and electromagnetic waves that make up radioactive emissions.

▶ **Distinguish** between radioactive decay, fission, fusion, and transmutation.

▶ **Balance** nuclear equations.

▶ **Classify** nuclear reactions from their equations.

▶ **Describe** the characteristics of a chain reaction.

Radioactive processes

You could say that nuclear changes are easier to understand than chemical changes because only four classes of nuclear changes occur. The first class is the spontaneous change of an unstable nucleus to form a more stable one. This change involves the emission of particles or electromagnetic rays, or both, and is generally called radioactivity. We now know that **radioactivity** is the breakdown (decay) of unstable nuclei to produce alpha particles, beta particles, and, almost always, gamma rays. Before examining the four classes of nuclear changes, look at the properties of the particles summarized in **Table 18-1**.

radioactivity

the process during which unstable nuclei undergo spontaneous nuclear decay and emit particles and electromagnetic waves

| TABLE 18-1 | Characteristics of Nuclear Particles and Rays | | | |

Particle	Mass (amu)	Charge	Symbol	Stopped by
proton	1.007 276 47	+1	p, p^+, ^1_1H	a few sheets of paper
neutron	1.008 664 90	0	n, n^0, ^1_0n	a few centimeters of Pb
β particle (electron)	0.000 548 580	−1	β, β^-, $^0_{-1}e*$	a few sheets of aluminum foil
positron†	0.000 548 580	+1	β^+, $^0_{-1}e*$	same as electron
alpha particle (He-4 nucleus)	4.001 506 17	+2	α, α^{2+}, ^4_2He	skin or one sheet of paper
gamma ray	0	0	γ	several centimeters of Pb

*The superscript zero in the symbols for electron and positron does not mean that they have zero mass. It means their *mass number* is zero.

†The positron is the *antiparticle* of the electron. Each particle has an antiparticle, but only the positron is important here.

internetconnect

SC**LINKS**
NSTA
TOPIC: Radioactive emissions
GO TO: www.scilinks.org
KEYWORD: HW181

DEMONSTRATION 2

Detecting and Measuring Radiation

Approximate time: 10 minutes

1. Obtain a beta source in a sealed container from a scientific supply company.

2. Use a Geiger counter that is equipped with a loudspeaker or a large meter visible from a distance of 30 m. Be sure the radiation source is at least 30 m away from the students and from the counter.

3. Take a reading of background radiation. Measure the radiation by placing the Geiger tube 5 cm away from the beta source.

4. Measure the radiation again at distances of 10 cm, 30 cm, and 1 m away from the beta source.

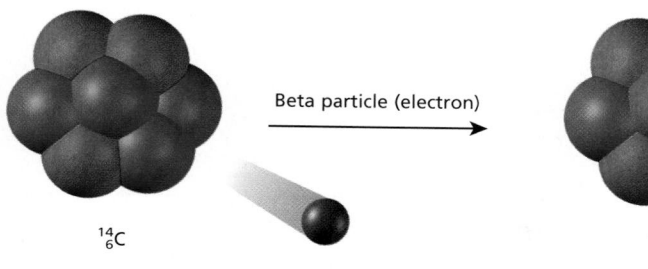

Beta particle (electron)

$^{14}_{6}C$ $^{14}_{7}N$

FIGURE 18-6

When the unstable carbon-14 nucleus emits a beta particle, it changes into a nitrogen-14 nucleus.

Stabilizing nuclei by converting neutrons into protons

Recall from Section 18-1 that the stability of a nucleus depends on the ratio of neutrons to protons, the N/Z ratio. If the number of neutrons is too great for a particular atomic number, the nucleus will decay and emit radiation.

It is possible for a neutron in an unstable nucleus to emit a high-energy electron, called a **beta particle** (β particle), and change to a proton. This process is called *beta decay* and is the usual process by which nuclei with too many neutrons become more stable.

$$^{1}_{0}n \xrightarrow{\text{beta decay}} {}^{1}_{+1}p + {}^{0}_{-1}e$$

Because this process changes a neutron to a proton, the atomic number of the nucleus increases by one, as you can see in **Figure 18-6.** In other words, through beta decay, carbon can become a different element, nitrogen. However, the mass number does not change because the total number of nucleons does not change.

$$^{14}_{6}C \longrightarrow {}^{14}_{7}N + {}^{0}_{-1}e$$

Stabilizing nuclei by converting protons into neutrons

A second reason for nuclear instability is that a nucleus has too few neutrons. There are two ways that a nucleus with too few neutrons can become more stable.

1. **Electron capture** In this process, the nucleus merely absorbs one of the atom's electrons, usually from the 1*s* orbital. This changes a proton into a neutron, thereby decreasing the atomic number by one but keeping the mass number the same.

$$^{1}_{+1}p + {}^{0}_{-1}e \xrightarrow{\text{electron capture}} {}^{1}_{0}n$$
orbital
electron

A typical nucleus that decays by this process is chromium-51. This unstable nuclide has a neutron-to-proton ratio that is too low; therefore, it needs a larger number of neutrons. The change that occurs as it converts a proton into a neutron is shown in the following equation.

$$^{51}_{24}Cr + {}^{0}_{-1}e \xrightarrow{\text{electron capture}} {}^{51}_{23}V + \gamma$$

beta particle
a high-energy electron emitted from the nucleus when a neutron changes to a proton

---

SECTION 18-2

VISUAL STRATEGY

Figure 18-6 Stress that transmutation always consists of either a proton in the atomic nucleus changing into a neutron or a neutron in the nucleus changing into a proton. The total number of nucleons remains unchanged. Although many nuclei are unstable and therefore decay, the sum of mass and energy is conserved.

VOCABULARY STRATEGY

Ernest Rutherford named the three types of radioactive emission after the first three letters of the Greek alphabet—alpha, beta, and gamma (α, β, and γ, respectively).

HISTORICAL CONNECTION

Marie Sklodowska Curie (1867–1934) and her husband, Pierre, discovered the elements radium and polonium, the latter of which was named for Marie's homeland, Poland (*Polonia* in Latin). She also determined that the only radioactive parts of uranium and thorium compounds were the uranium and thorium atoms.

TEACHING TIP

Beta Particles Make students aware that $^{0}_{-1}e$ is the symbol for a beta particle. Beta particles are high-energy electrons that result from the decay of a neutron into a proton. In this decay process, the total number of nucleons doesn't change, so the atomic number increases while the mass number stays the same.

DID YOU KNOW?

Some older references refer to electron capture as K-capture because the first energy level was once known as the K level.

---

5. Place a piece of paper between the source and the Geiger tube, and measure the radiation. You can repeat this shielding technique with a piece of plywood 1 cm thick, a piece of aluminum 1 cm thick, or a piece of plexiglass 1 cm thick.

Safety

Safety glasses and a lab apron must be worn. Students must be 30 m or more from the demonstration. Be certain that the Geiger tube has a metal or hard-plastic mounting.

Obtain isotopes from a scientific supply company in quantities that do not require licensing. Sources not among those listed above or not in sealed containers should not be used.

Even when using small amounts of isotopes in sealed cases, gloves should be worn. Students should not handle the isotopes or the Geiger counter under any circumstances.

If the counter has a power supply that operates on AC, be certain that there are no

CONTINUED ON PAGE 666

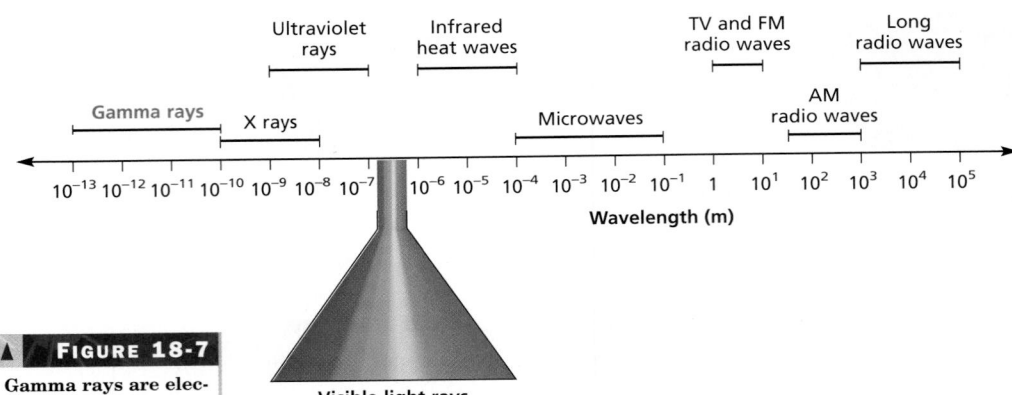

VISUAL STRATEGY

Figure 18-7 Make students aware that visible light makes up a very small portion of the entire electromagnetic spectrum. Ask the class to imagine what our vision would be like if we were able to see other forms of electromagnetic radiation, such as radio waves, microwaves, or infrared waves. Night-vision devices detect infrared radiation. Mention that some insects, such as bees, see primarily in the ultraviolet segment of the spectrum.

TEACHING TIP

Designing a Model Have each student construct a physical model that can be used to demonstrate the hypothetical changes in the Mg-28 nucleus mentioned in the Alternative Assessment on page 667. Students could represent protons and neutrons with balls of modeling clay of two different colors. Electrons and positrons could be small, hard balls or beads of contrasting colors.

HISTORICAL CONNECTION

In 1932, the American physicist Carl David Anderson discovered the first example of antimatter, the positron. A positron has properties similar to those of an electron, except that its charge is positive. For this reason, a positron in a magnetic field is deflected in a direction opposite that of an electron.

▲ **FIGURE 18-7**

Gamma rays are electromagnetic waves emitted by decaying nuclei. Gamma rays are at the high-energy, short-wavelength end of the electromagnetic spectrum.

gamma ray

high-energy electromagnetic radiation produced by decaying nuclei

annihilation of matter

the event that occurs when a particle collides with its antiparticle and both are changed into electromagnetic energy

The final symbol in the equation, γ, indicates the emission of gamma radiation. Many nuclear changes leave the nucleus in an energetic, or excited, state. When the nucleus stabilizes, this energy is given off in the form of **gamma rays.** This electromagnetic radiation has high energy and a short wavelength, as shown by **Figure 18-7.** Gamma rays are emitted in almost every radioactive disintegration.

2. **Positron emission** Nuclei that are further out of balance in favor of protons can become stable by emitting positrons, the *antiparticles* of electrons. The process is similar to *beta* emission, but in this case, a positron is emitted by a proton instead of an electron being emitted by a neutron. As in electron capture, the proton is also changed into a neutron.

$$_{+1}^{1}p \xrightarrow{\text{positron emission}} {}_{0}^{1}n + {}_{+1}^{0}e$$

Note that the mass number stays the same but the atomic number decreases by one. The isotope chromium-49 decays by this process, as shown below.

$$_{24}^{49}\text{Cr} \longrightarrow {}_{23}^{49}\text{V} + {}_{+1}^{0}e$$

The positron is a beta antiparticle, but unlike a beta particle, a positron seldom makes it into the surroundings. Instead, the positron usually collides with its antiparticle, the electron. Any time a particle collides with its antiparticle, all of the mass of the two particles is converted entirely into electromagnetic energy—two gamma rays going in opposite directions. This process is called **annihilation of matter.**

$$_{-1}^{0}e + {}_{-1}^{0}e \xrightarrow{\text{annihilation}} 2\gamma$$

The gamma rays from electron-positron annihilation have a characteristic wavelength and identify decay by positron emission. Such gamma rays have been detected coming from the center of the Milky Way galaxy.

DEMONSTRATION 2 *CONTINUED*

bare wires, that all connections are covered with "friction" tape, that the power supply is equipped with a three-wire cord and a three-prong plug, and that the three-slot outlet is protected with a ground fault interrupter. Be sure that the equipment is off before plugging it in (and before unplugging it) and that the polarity is correct. Any adjustments to the wiring must be made when the unit is unplugged. Be certain that the area under

the wires is dry (as are your hands) and that the wires do not dangle and are kept dry.

Disposal

None. Save all materials for future demonstrations. Unplug and disconnect all wires from the detector when finished.

Stabilizing nuclei by losing alpha particles

If a nucleus is very large and has too few neutrons, it can decay in another way—by emitting alpha particles. None of the elements above atomic number 83 and mass number 126 have stable isotopes, and many decay by emitting alpha particles as well as by electron capture. Look at the following example.

$$^{238}_{92}\text{U} \xrightarrow{\text{alpha decay}} {}^{234}_{90}\text{Th} + {}^{4}_{2}\text{He}$$

The atomic number decreases by two, and the mass number decreases by four. Alpha particles have very low penetrating ability, as shown in Table 18-1, because they are large and soon collide with other matter. Exposure to external sources of alpha radiation is usually of little consequence. However, if substances that undergo alpha decay are ingested or inhaled, the radiation can be quite damaging.

Many heavy nuclei go through a series of reactions called a *decay series* before they reach a stable state. The decay series for uranium-238 is shown in **Figure 18-8.** After the $^{238}_{92}\text{U}$ nucleus decays to $^{234}_{90}\text{Th}$, the nucleus is still unstable because it has too many neutrons. This nucleus undergoes beta decay to produce an isotope of protactinium.

By another beta decay, $^{234}_{91}\text{Pa}$ changes to $^{234}_{92}\text{U}$. These nuclides, which have too few neutrons, undergo a sequence of five alpha decays. You

FIGURE 18-8 ▼

Uranium-238 decays to lead-206 in a radioactive series.

Uranium-238 Decay Series

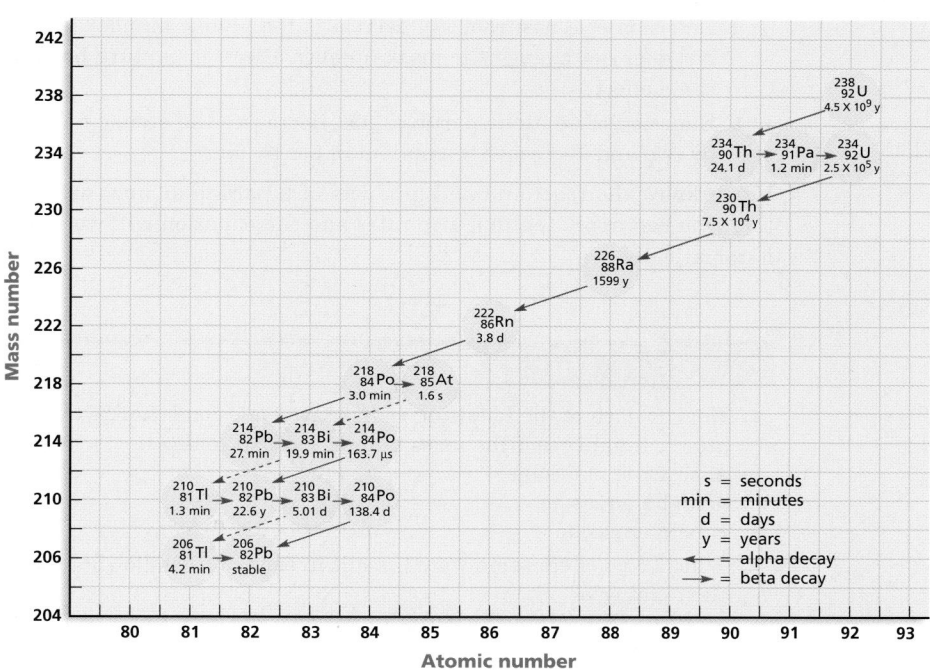

TEACHING TIP

Alpha Decay Point out to students that alpha decay is a common decay mode only in the heavier elements beyond bismuth. Below bismuth, $Z = 83$, alpha decay usually occurs only in the lightest isotopes of an element. Below hafnium, $Z = 72$, there are few examples of initial alpha decay.

VISUAL STRATEGY

Figure 18-8 Stress that the U-238 nucleus does not decay directly into Pb-206. Draw students' attention to the alternative pathways of disintegration after the decay series reaches Po-218. Ask students how they could determine the decay mode of each isotope if there were no color-coded arrows. An alpha decay is indicated by a decrease of four in the mass number and a decrease of two in the atomic number. A beta decay is indicated by an increase of one in the atomic number and no change in the mass number.

Remind students that most processes in chemistry, including nuclear processes, proceed to products that are more stable than the reactants. A decay series proceeds until a stable (nonradioactive) nucleus is achieved.

ALTERNATIVE ASSESSMENT

Writing Nuclear Equations

Write the isotope $^{28}_{12}\text{Mg}$ on the board. Inform students that this isotope always undergoes beta decay but that they should assume it can decay by all four principal decay modes—alpha decay, beta decay, positron emission, and electron capture. Their job is to write a nuclear equation for each type of decay showing the product that would form.

Alpha decay: $^{24}_{10}\text{Ne}$

Beta decay: $^{28}_{13}\text{Al}$

Positron emission: $^{28}_{11}\text{Na}$

Electron capture: $^{28}_{11}\text{Na}$

Follow up by having students determine the products that result from the decay noted for several of the following isotopes:

Alpha decay: Am-243, U-230, Ra-223, Cm-245

Beta decay: Rb-87, Al-28, As-76, Au-198

Positron emission: Au-188, Ba-125, Cu-61, K-38

Electron capture: Ar-37, Co-57, Sr-82, U-231

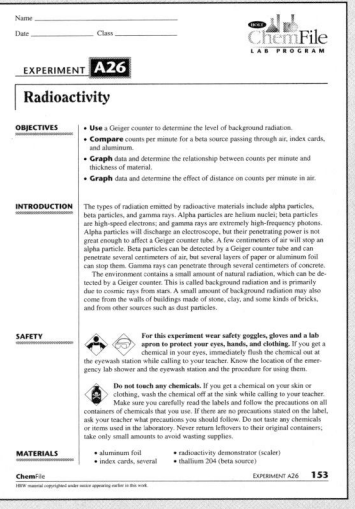
will learn more about the concept of nuclear decay as it relates to half-life in section 18-3. After several more decays (and after perhaps millions of years), the nucleus finally becomes a stable isotope, $^{206}_{82}Pb$. Figure 18-8, on page 667, shows the complete sequence of reactions.

Nuclear equations are also balanced

Look back at all of the nuclear equations that have appeared so far in this chapter. Notice that the total of the mass numbers (superscripts) on one side of the equation always equals the total of the mass numbers on the other side of the equation. Likewise, the totals of the atomic numbers (subscripts) on each side of the equation are equal. Look at the following nuclear equations, and notice that they balance in terms of both mass and charge.

$$^{234}_{90}Th \longrightarrow\ ^{234}_{91}Pa +\ ^{0}_{-1}e \quad \begin{array}{l}[234 = 234 +\ \ 0 \text{ mass balance}]\\ [\ \ 90 =\ \ 91 + (-1) \text{ charge balance}]\end{array}$$

$$^{238}_{92}U \longrightarrow\ ^{234}_{90}Th +\ ^{4}_{2}He \quad \begin{array}{l}[238 = 234 + 4 \text{ mass balance}]\\ [\ \ 92 =\ \ 90 + 2 \text{ charge balance}]\end{array}$$

When you write and balance a nuclear equation, keep the following rules in mind.

1. The total of the mass numbers is the same on both sides of the equation.

2. The total nuclear charge is the same on both sides of the equation.

3. Emission of a beta particle, $^{0}_{-1}e$, increases the atomic number by one but does not change the mass number.

4. Emission of a positron, $^{0}_{+1}e$, decreases the atomic number by one but does not change the mass number. Electron capture has the same effect.

5. Emission of an alpha particle, $^{4}_{2}He$, decreases the atomic number by two and decreases the mass number by four.

If you know the reactants and products of a particular nuclear reaction, you can apply the first two rules and the equation will work out automatically.

CONCEPT CHECK

1. How do each of the following radioactive emissions change the atomic number and the mass number of a nucleus?
   a. positron emission
   b. alpha emission
   c. beta emission

2. Which type of emission would result in each of the following nuclear changes?
   a. $^{15}_{6}C \longrightarrow\ ^{15}_{7}N$ **b.** $^{147}_{62}Sm \longrightarrow\ ^{143}_{60}Nd$

GRAPHIC ORGANIZER

Decay mode	*Detected as	Result	Example
Alpha emission	alpha particles and gamma rays	$^{A}_{Z}X \longrightarrow\ ^{A-4}_{Z-2}X =\ ^{4}_{2}He$	$^{232}_{90}TH \longrightarrow\ ^{228}_{88}Ra +\ ^{4}_{2}He$
Beta emission	beta particles and gamma rays	$^{A}_{Z}X \longrightarrow\ ^{A}_{Z+1}X +\ ^{0}_{-1}e$	$^{32}_{15}P \longrightarrow\ ^{32}_{16}S +\ ^{0}_{-1}e$
Positron emission	gamma rays from annihilation	$^{A}_{Z}X \longrightarrow\ ^{A}_{Z-1}X +\ ^{0}_{+1}e$ $^{0}_{+1}e +\ ^{0}_{+1}e \longrightarrow 2\lambda$	$^{15}_{8}O \longrightarrow\ ^{15}_{7}N +\ ^{0}_{+1}e$
Electron capture	gamma rays	$^{A}_{Z}X +\ ^{0}_{-1}e \longrightarrow\ ^{A}_{Z-1}X$	$^{53}_{25}Mn +\ ^{0}_{-1}e \longrightarrow\ ^{53}_{24}Cr$

*Gamma rays are usually emitted in alpha decay, beta decay, and electron capture.

Artificial transmutations

At the beginning of this section you read that there are four classes of nuclear changes. So far you have learned about one class in which a nucleus decays by adding or losing particles. Two other types of nuclear changes are fission and fusion. These are classified as artificial transmutations because they usually do not occur naturally on Earth. In recent years, however, scientists have discovered natural deposits of uranium that show signs of having undergone fission reactions in the geological past.

Large unstable nuclei can split in two

Observe what is happening to the single-celled organism shown in **Figure 18-9.** The organism is dividing in two by a process called cell division, or fission. Large, unstable atomic nuclei can also undergo fission. **Nuclear fission** refers to a nuclear reaction in which a very heavy nucleus splits into two smaller nuclei, each having a higher binding energy per nucleon than the original nucleus. There are two kinds of fission: spontaneous and induced. A very small fraction of naturally occurring uranium atoms are of the isotope $^{235}_{92}U$, which undergoes spontaneous fission. However, most fission reactions are induced artificially by bombarding nuclei with neutrons.

The energy yield of fission reactions is very high. For example, the fission of 1 g of uranium-235 generates as much energy as the combustion of 2700 kg of coal. Fission reactions are the source of energy used to generate electricity in nuclear power plants. Uranium-235 and plutonium-239 are the main radioactive isotopes used in these reactors. In one possible fission reaction, the uranium-235 nucleus absorbs a neutron. Then the uranium-236 nucleus splits in two, forming two smaller nuclides. In the process a few neutrons are ejected. The product nuclei have far too many neutrons, and are intensely radioactive, emitting

nuclear fission

a nuclear reaction in which a very heavy nucleus splits into two smaller nuclei of approximately equal mass

internet**connect**

SC*i*LINKS.
NSTA
TOPIC: Fission
GO TO: www.scilinks.org
KEYWORD: HW182

FIGURE 18-9 ▼

a The single-celled paramecium is about to undergo fission, a process of reproduction. The term *fission* has nearly the same meaning in biology as it does in chemistry.

b The paramecium has fissioned, or divided, into two smaller organisms, just as a nucleus divides into smaller nuclei during nuclear fission.

TEACHING TIP
Vocabulary Strategy   The word *fission* is applied to the splitting process of cell reproduction and the splitting of a nucleus into two smaller parts. The word is derived from *fissus,* a form of the Latin verb *findere,* which means "to split." The word *fissure* is derived from the same root.

HISTORICAL CONNECTION
The German physicist Lise Meitner was the first to use the word *splitting* to describe the breaking of the nucleus. She used the term in 1939 when suggesting a reason for the formation of barium atoms in an experiment in which uranium nuclei were bombarded with neutrons.

VISUAL STRATEGY

Figure 18-9   Fission of cells and fission of atomic nuclei both involve splitting. Beyond that, the cell analogy does not work because the two daughter cells are identical to the original cells, whereas the two nuclei from atomic fission are not identical to the parent nucleus nor (usually) to each other.

DISCUSSION STRATEGY
Have students quickly scan through the descriptions of atomic fission and fusion. Then ask them to tell how fission is similar to cell division and how it is different. Also ask them to compare atomic fusion and the term *fusion* as they have heard it applied to music.

On December 2, 1942, physicist Enrico Fermi and his colleagues at the University of Chicago demonstrated that a self-sustaining nuclear fission reaction could be produced in a few lumps of natural uranium shielded by blocks of graphite. Although the reactor produced only a few watts of power, this was sufficient to show that nuclear fission could be used to produce energy.

VISUAL STRATEGY

Figure 18-10 Make sure students understand that in this figure, the ratio of neutron release is actually 1:3:9:27:81:243, and so on, and that the picture has been simplified for easier study. The escaping neutrons will continue to bombard other nearby atoms unless they encounter absorbing material, such as graphite, europium, or cobalt.

chain reaction

a nuclear reaction that sustains itself because the particles produced in the reaction, which go on to initiate the same reaction in other nuclei, are the same as the particles that started the reaction

critical mass

the smallest mass of radioactive material needed to sustain a chain reaction

beta particles. This is the "nuclear waste". The following equation represents the first reaction shown in **Figure 18-10,** in which three neutrons are emitted.

$$^{235}_{92}\text{U} + ^{1}_{0}n \longrightarrow \left[^{236}_{92}\text{U}\right] \xrightarrow{\text{nuclear fission}} ^{93}_{36}\text{Kr} + ^{140}_{56}\text{Ba} + 3\,^{1}_{0}n$$

temporary
nuclide

As you can see in Figure 18-10, each of the three neutrons emitted by the fission of one nucleus can cause the fission of another uranium-235 nucleus. Again some neutrons are emitted. These reactions continue one after another as long as a sufficient concentration of uranium-235 remains. This process is called a **chain reaction.** One characteristic of a chain reaction is that the particle (neutron) that starts the reaction is also produced in the reaction. A minimum quantity of radioactive material is needed to sustain a chain reaction. The amount must be sufficient for most neutrons to be captured by other nuclei before they leave the material. The smallest mass of radioactive material needed to sustain a chain reaction is known as the **critical mass.**

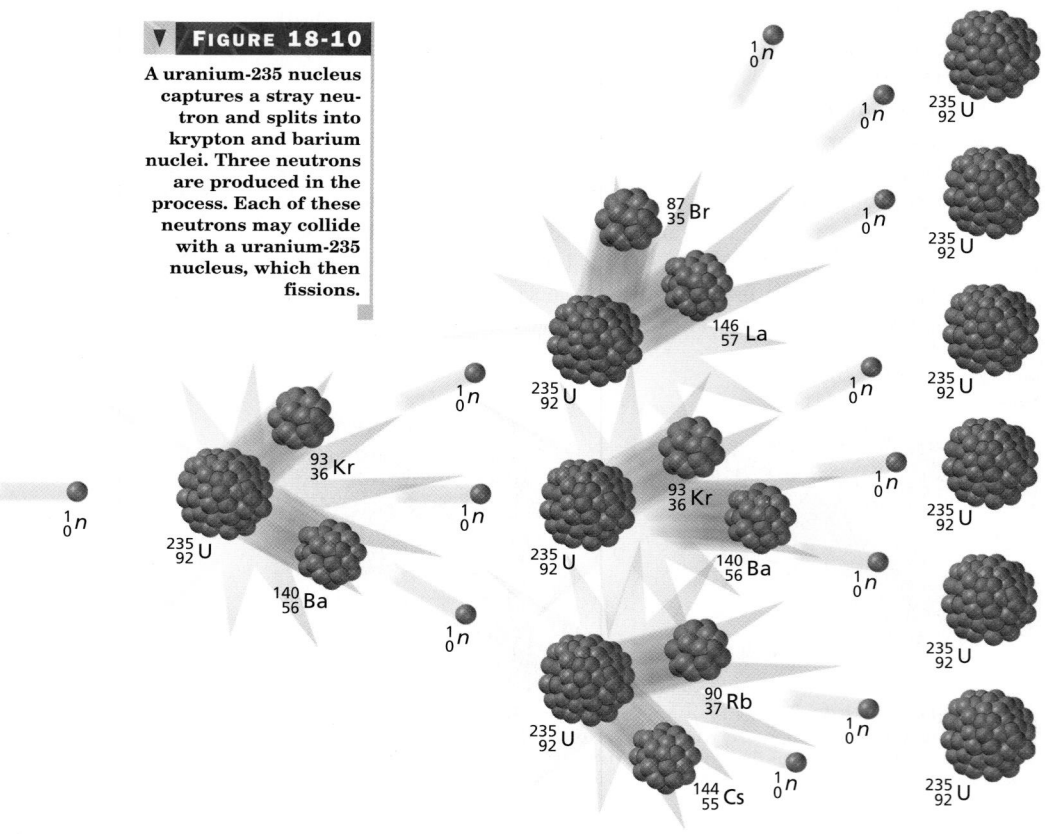

▼ **FIGURE 18-10**

A uranium-235 nucleus captures a stray neutron and splits into krypton and barium nuclei. Three neutrons are produced in the process. Each of these neutrons may collide with a uranium-235 nucleus, which then fissions.

ALTERNATIVE ASSESSMENT

Chain Reaction

Model a chain reaction and fission with the following activity:

1. Prepare 40 or more envelopes with the following written on the outside of each envelope: uranium-235, $p = 92$, $n = 143$.

2. Inside each envelope, place five cards with the following words written on them: energy, krypton-93, neutron, barium-140, and neutron. The envelopes should be

folded, not sealed, so that they can be reused.

3. Give each student an envelope. If your class is small, give each student two or three envelopes.

4. Instruct students not to open the envelope until they are given a neutron card.

5. Neutron cards must be given to anyone with an unopened uranium-235 envelope.

Water heated by nuclear reactor
Water converted to steam
Water used to condense steam

Containment structure

Nuclear reactor

Control rod

Uranium fuel rod

Moderator and coolant (liquid water under high pressure)

Pump

Steam generator

Steam turbine

Electric generator

Electric current

Condenser

Pump

Cool water

Warm water

FIGURE 18-11 ▲

This model of a nuclear power plant shows a pressurized light-water reactor, the type most often used to generate electricity in the United States. The rate of the chain reaction is controlled by moving the control rods in and out. Note that each of the three water systems is isolated from the others for safety reasons.

In a nuclear reactor, represented in **Figure 18-11,** the fuel rods are surrounded by a *moderator,* a substance that slows down neutrons. Graphite and ordinary water are effective moderators. Heavy water, deuterium oxide, $^{2}_{1}H_2O$, is a more efficient moderator.

Control rods are used to adjust the rate of the chain reactions. These rods absorb some of the free neutrons produced by fission. Moving these rods into and out of the reactor controls the number of neutrons that are available to continue the chain reaction. If these control rods were removed, an uncontrolled chain reaction would occur. The heat from an uncontrolled reaction, in the worst case, could cause a *meltdown* of the reactor. A failure of control systems followed by fire, explosion, and meltdown occurred at Chernobyl, Ukraine, in 1986, killing many people and poisoning the environment for many years with radioactive elements.

Some small nuclei can join to form heavier nuclei

Fusion is the third class of nuclear change. As the term suggests, **nuclear fusion** occurs when two small nuclei combine, or fuse, to form a larger, more stable nucleus. The new nucleus has a higher binding energy, and energy is released as it forms. This results in a more stable nucleus. In fact, fusion releases tremendous amounts of energy. It is the process by which the sun produces energy and the process that occurs in the explosion of a hydrogen bomb, shown in **Figure 18-12.**

internet**connect**

SCI**LINKS**

NSTA

TOPIC: Fusion
GO TO: www.scilinks.org
KEYWORD: HW183

nuclear fusion

the combining of two small nuclei to form a larger, more stable nucleus with the release of energy

NUCLEAR CHEMISTRY **671**

6. Start the chain reaction by handing your neutron card to a student. You should be the only one with a neutron card.

7. That student will open an envelope, take out the five cards, and distribute the three neutron cards (the one received plus the two in the envelope) to three other students.

8. Each of those students will then open an envelope, take out the five cards, and distribute the three neutron cards to any students with unopened envelopes. The entire supply of uranium-235 will be quickly exhausted as the chain reaction proceeds.

The number of fission reactions is represented by the number of neutron cards distributed each time, that is, 1, 3, 9, 27, 81, 243, and so on. The students should note that new fission products, the barium-140 and krypton-93 cards, have formed as a result of the reaction. The matter and energy of the uranium-235 have not simply disappeared.

▲ FIGURE 18-12

The hydrogen bomb uses nuclear fusion. As a result, an exploding hydrogen bomb has even greater destructive power than the first nuclear bombs, which were fission bombs.

transmutation

creating new nuclei by bombarding a nucleus with energetic particles

In the sun, fusion combines four hydrogen nuclei to form a single ${}_2^4$He nucleus. The temperature of the sun's core, where some of the fusion reactions occur, is about $1.5 \times 10^7 °$C. Very high pressures and very high temperatures are required to bring the nuclei together. When the hydrogen nuclei are fused to form a larger nucleus, some mass is lost and converted to energy. Even more energy is released per gram of reactant in fusion than in fission.

Fusion reactions are hard to contain

Currently, scientists are investigating ways to control fusion reactions so that they may be used for both energy generation and research. If fusion reactions are ever to become a practical source of energy, the energy given off must be greater than the energy required to start them. At the moment, scientists are near the break-even point.

In fusion reactions, the reactants are in the form of a *plasma,* a random mixture of positive nuclei and electrons. The biggest problem scientists must overcome is containing this plasma at the tremendous temperatures required for fusion to occur. No form of solid matter can withstand such conditions. Scientists currently use extremely strong magnetic fields to suspend the charged plasma particles in space. In this way, the plasma can be kept from contacting the container walls. Scientists have also experimented with high-powered laser light to start the fusion process.

The following is a typical fusion reaction.

$${}_1^3H + {}_1^2H \longrightarrow {}_2^4He + {}_0^1n + 1.7 \times 10^{12} \text{ J/mol of He}$$

Sea water is the source for the deuterium, ${}_1^2$H. Tritium, ${}_1^3$H, must be produced in a nuclear reactor, often by bombarding lithium-6 atoms with neutrons from the fission reaction in progress.

$${}_3^6Li + {}_0^1n \longrightarrow {}_1^3H + {}_2^4He + 4.3 \times 10^{11} \text{ J/mol of } {}_1^3H$$

New nuclides can be produced by nuclear bombardment

The three types of nuclear change that you have read about so far are spontaneous processes in which unstable nuclides move toward stability. It is also possible to create new nuclides by bombarding a nucleus with other particle nuclei. This process is called **transmutation** and is the modern-day equivalent of the early alchemists' attempts to turn lead into gold. In 1919, Rutherford became the first to recognize a transmutation while experimenting with how far alpha particles travel in various gases. When he used air or nitrogen, a reaction occurred that yielded two products. Careful study identified these products as hydrogen and an isotope of oxygen. The alpha particle is absorbed into the nitrogen nucleus, and then the energetic *compound nucleus* emits a proton to stabilize itself.

$$^{14}_{7}\text{N} + ^{4}_{2}\text{He} \longrightarrow [^{18}_{9}\text{F}] \longrightarrow ^{17}_{8}\text{O} + ^{1}_{1}\text{H}$$
$\llcorner$—— Unstable compound nucleus

When the discovery of transmutation became known, scientists began to bombard almost every known element with alpha particles, producing hundreds of new radioactive nuclides. The yields were very low because the nucleus of a target atom strongly repels the positively charged alpha particle. Therefore, very few alpha particles have enough kinetic energy to overcome this repulsion. Refer to Chapter 4 for information on particle acceleration.

SECTION REVIEW

Total recall

1. What is the name given to a high-energy electron that is emitted from an unstable nucleus?

2. Write the nuclear equation that shows how electron capture by a nucleus changes a proton into a neutron.

3. How is critical mass related to a chain reaction?

4. What is transmutation?

5. What was the first artificial transmutation carried out by scientists?

6. Describe what happens when a positron and electron collide.

7. **a.** What is nuclear fission?
   b. How does it differ from nuclear fusion?

Critical thinking

8. Write the balanced equations for the following nuclear reactions:
   a. Uranium-233 undergoes alpha decay.
   b. Copper-66 undergoes beta decay.
   c. Beryllium-9 and an alpha particle combine to form carbon-13. The carbon-13 nucleus then emits a neutron.
   d. Uranium-238 absorbs a neutron. The product then undergoes successive beta emissions to become plutonium-239.

9. **Interpreting Graphics** Write a possible fission reaction for uranium-235 producing isotopes of Sr and Xe. The equation should show that two neutrons are emitted. Divide the remaining neutrons between Sr and Xe roughly in proportion to their atomic numbers.

10. A fusion reaction that takes place in the sun is the combination of two helium-3 nuclei to form two hydrogen atoms and one other atom. Write the balanced nuclear equation for this fusion reaction. Be sure to include both products that are formed.

11. What happens to a nucleus that is very large and has too few neutrons?

12. **Story Clue** Assume that some of the carbon atoms in the Iceman's body are $^{14}_{6}\text{C}$ atoms. What will happen to these atoms as time passes?

NUCLEAR CHEMISTRY   673

SECTION 18-2

ANSWERS

SECTION REVIEW

Total recall

1. a beta particle

2. $^{1}_{+1}p + ^{0}_{-1}e \xrightarrow{\text{electron capture}} ^{1}_{0}n$

3. Chain reactions can occur only when a certain minimum mass of the fissionable element is present. This mass is called the critical mass.

4. Transmutation is the process by which new nuclides are created when a nucleus is bombarded with energetic particles.

5. $^{14}_{7}\text{N} + ^{4}_{2}\text{He} \longrightarrow [^{18}_{9}\text{F}] \longrightarrow ^{17}_{8}\text{O} + ^{1}_{1}\text{H}$

6. They annihilate each other and are converted to energy in the form of gamma rays.

7. **a.** Fission is the splitting of an atomic nucleus into two smaller nuclei.
   b. Fusion is the combining of two small nuclei to make one larger nucleus. It is the opposite of fission.

Critical thinking

8. **a.** $^{233}_{92}\text{U} \longrightarrow ^{229}_{90}\text{Th} + ^{4}_{2}\text{He}$
   b. $^{66}_{29}\text{Cu} \longrightarrow ^{66}_{30}\text{Zn} + ^{0}_{-1}e$
   c. $^{9}_{4}\text{Be} + ^{4}_{2}\text{He} \longrightarrow ^{13}_{6}\text{C}$
   $^{13}_{6}\text{C} \longrightarrow ^{12}_{6}\text{C} + ^{1}_{0}n$
   d. $^{238}_{92}\text{U} + ^{1}_{0}n \longrightarrow ^{239}_{92}\text{U}$
   $^{239}_{92}\text{U} \longrightarrow ^{239}_{93}\text{Np} + ^{0}_{-1}e$
   $^{239}_{93}\text{Np} \longrightarrow ^{239}_{94}\text{Np} + ^{0}_{-1}e$

9. The following is one possibility:
   $^{235}_{92}\text{U} + ^{1}_{0}n \longrightarrow ^{96}_{38}\text{Sr} + ^{137}_{54}\text{Xe} + 3^{1}_{0}n$
   The three neutrons shown on the right side of the equation account for the colliding neutron and the two neutrons emitted by the fission.

10. $2^{3}_{2}\text{He} \longrightarrow 2^{1}_{1}\text{H} + ^{4}_{2}\text{He}$

11. If a nucleus is too large and has too few neutrons, it can decay by emitting alpha particles.

12. They will undergo beta decay to form nitrogen-14 atoms.

673

Positron Emission Tomography (PET) is another application of nuclear decay that is an important diagnostic tool in medicine. It allows medical personnel to observe images of internal organs and their activities without invading the body. In PET, an isotope such as C-11, N-13, O-15, or one of several isotopes of Tc decays by positron emission. Positron emission results in the annihilation of the positron and an electron that produces gamma rays. These rays are detected and measured, and the data are used by a computer to generate an image.

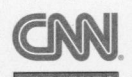

Science in the News

PRESENTS **Feature story 32**
Radioisotopes in Medicine See the Science in the News video guide for more details.

RADIOACTIVITY

Historical Perspective

In 1903, Marie Curie, her husband, Pierre, and Henri Becquerel were jointly awarded a Nobel Prize for their discovery of radioactivity. They had observed that compounds of the elements uranium and thorium gave off an unusual energy, causing the surrounding air to become slightly warmer. This energy also exposed photographic paper and killed small organisms in the vicinity. Marie Curie called these energy-producing elements *radioactive*, which describes a substance that has undergone nuclear decay and emits radiation.

Marie Curie and her husband, Pierre

Unfortunately, the harmful effects of radiation were not realized until much later, after both Marie and Pierre suffered permanent physical damage as a result of their scientific research.

Radiology: A New Medical Field World War I marked the first medical use of radiation. During that war, Marie Curie took charge of the Military Radiological Service, where she taught military doctors about *radiology,* the branch of medicine that uses ionizing radiation for diagnosis and treatment. During the war, X rays were used mostly to locate fractures and to detect the position of bullets. Early radiology relied heavily on the use of X rays.

Advances in Radiological Technology

CAT Scan During a computerized axial tomography (CAT) scan, a computer monitors the body's reaction to X rays directed at the body from a number of different angles. The computer then assembles images of many different cross sections of the body. CAT scans enable doctors to see the features of organs with similar densities. It is especially helpful in the diagnosis of problems with the brain and spinal cord.

MRI and NMR Magnetic resonance imaging (MRI) relies on the body's absorption of radio waves in a magnetic field. Nuclear magnetic resonance (NMR) is a process in which a computer depicts an image from inside the body by reading the body's absorption of radio waves. NMR aids doctors in the early detection of heart disease, multiple sclerosis, and cancer.

PET Scan Positron emission tomography (PET) scans detects gamma rays from positron-electron annihilation. For example, a patient is given glucose, some of whose molecules contain carbon-11, a positron emitter. A gamma-ray detector measures the gamma rays from various regions of the brain, determing the rate of glucose metabolism. Doctors have found this procedure helpful in diagnosing brain disorders. For example, schizophrenics metabolize much less glucose in the brain than normal.

The bones in the right hand and wrist of this patient are visible in this Xray.

CAREER APPLICATION

What would it be like to . . .
▸ operate technologically advanced computer equipment?
▸ perform radiological procedures?
▸ help to diagnose patients?

Science/Math Career Preparation	
High School	**College**
Mathematics	Mathematics
Biology	Biology
Chemistry	Chemistry
Physics	Physics

Radiological Technician

An important career in the radiology industry is that of a radiological, or X-ray, technician. A radiological technician makes sure that patients are ready for the imaging process. Technicians administer substances, such as barium sulfate, that make internal body parts visible to X rays. They also provide patients with safety equipment to protect them from high doses of radiation, and they operate the radiological equipment. The equipment ranges from X-ray machines to computer-aided imaging equipment necessary for CAT scans or PET scans.

People who choose the career of a radiological technician generally study mathematics, biology, chemistry, and physics in high school. These courses prepare them for American Medical Association (AMA)–approved professional or academic programs that range in duration from 1 to 4 years. These programs are available at vocational schools, hospitals, colleges and universities, and in the armed forces. Radiological technicians must usually be licensed in the state where they work.

How is nuclear chemistry used?

OBJECTIVES

▶ **Define** the half-life of a radioactive nuclide.

▶ **Describe** how the half-life of a radioactive isotope is used to determine the age of an object.

▶ **Describe** how the process of neutron activation is used to analyze objects.

▶ **Identify** possible health hazards of radiation exposure.

Half-life

At the beginning of this chapter, you read that an archaeologist estimated the Iceman died about 4000 years ago. From the shape and composition of the Iceman's ax, the archaeologist reasoned that the Iceman lived during the early Bronze Age, which began around 2200 B.C. However, the ax blade was found to be made of pure copper and not bronze. This indicates that the Iceman must have been older, because the Age of Copper began around 4000 B.C. and lasted until the start of the Bronze Age. But rather than determining the Iceman's age solely on the basis of objects found with him, scientists also calculated his age by analyzing radioactive isotopes in his body.

Radioactive isotopes decay at definite rates

The rate of nuclear decay is usually given in terms of the half-life. One **half-life** is the time that it takes for half a sample of a particular radioactive isotope to decay. This half-life is a constant value and is not influenced by any external conditions, such as temperature and pressure. The use of radioactive isotopes to determine the age of an object is called *radioactive dating*. It is based on the fact that each radioactive nuclide has a characteristic half-life. Radioactive dating can be used to establish the age of ancient objects, as shown in **Figure 18-13.**

Although this rule does not always hold true, in general, the more unstable a nuclide is, the shorter its

half-life
the time required for half of a sample of radioactive atoms to decay

▶ **FIGURE 18-13**

Using radioactive dating techniques, scientists determined this Incan vessel to be about 550 years old.

TABLE 18-2 Half-Lives of Some Radioactive Isotopes

Isotope	Half-life	Radiation emitted
Carbon-14	5.715×10^3 years	β^-
Potassium-40	1.28×10^9 years	β^-, electron capture, γ
Radon-222	3.82 days	α, γ
Radium-226	1.60×10^3 years	α, γ
Thorium-230	7.54×10^4 years	α, γ
Thorium-234	24.10 days	β^-, γ
Uranium-235	7.04×10^8 years	α, γ
Uranium-238	4.47×10^9 years	α, γ
Plutonium-239	2.41×10^4 years	α, γ

internet connect

SCI LINKS
NSTA

TOPIC: Radioactive dating
GO TO: www.scilinks.org
KEYWORD: HW184

half-life is and the faster it decays. Protium and deuterium are examples of unstable nuclei that have infinite half-lives. **Figure 18-14** shows another example of a radioactive isotope with a short half-life, iodine-131. **Table 18-2** lists the half-lives for a few radioactive isotopes. For example, the half-life of the radioactive isotope carbon-14 provides the key to the age of the Iceman. Nearly all of the carbon on Earth is present as the stable isotope carbon-12; less than one-millionth of one percent of the carbon in Earth's atmosphere is the radioactive isotope carbon-14. This minute amount of carbon-14 is continuously formed by cosmic rays in the Earth's atmosphere striking nitrogen-14 atoms. Because carbon-12 and carbon-14 have the same electron configuration, they react chemically in an identical fashion. Both of these carbon isotopes combine with oxygen to form carbon dioxide, which is taken in by plants and used in photosynthesis. Therefore, all plants on Earth contain carbon compounds with a small amount of carbon-14.

Photosynthetic organisms, such as plants, are the basis of Earth's food chain. As a result, all animals that eat plants contain the same

FIGURE 18-14 ▼

The radioactive isotope $^{131}_{53}$I has a half-life of 8.07 days. In each successive 8.07-day period, half the atoms of $^{131}_{53}$I in the original sample decay to $^{131}_{54}$Xe.

1.00 mg $^{131}_{53}$I	0.500 mg $^{131}_{53}$I	0.250 mg $^{131}_{53}$I	0.125 mg $^{131}_{53}$I
Original sample of radioactive isotope $^{131}_{53}$I	Amount of $^{131}_{53}$I remaining after 1 half-life (8.07 days)	Amount of $^{131}_{53}$I remaining after 2 half-lives (16.14 days)	Amount of $^{131}_{53}$I remaining after 3 half-lives (24.21 days)

NUCLEAR CHEMISTRY 677

HISTORICAL CONNECTION

Carbon-14 dating (radiocarbon dating) was invented in 1946 by Willard F. Libby, an American chemist. Libby was awarded the Nobel Prize in chemistry in 1960 for his discovery. He also worked on the Manhattan Project to develop the atomic (fission) bomb.

In 1907, an American radiochemist, B. R. Boltwood, first used the decay of uranium into lead to date rocks.

TEACHING TIP

Half-life Analogy Select one student to be a millionaire. He or she has $1 000 000 in a bank account. The only stipulation is that every 2 seconds the amount of money will decrease by half. Ask the class: How long will it be until the millionaire is penniless? (In 52 seconds, or 26 half-lives, the $1 000 000 will have "decayed" to 1.5 cents. The millionaire will be broke before 1 minute has elapsed.)

RESOURCE LINK

ChemFile Lab A
Skills Development
Have students do Experiment A27: *Detecting Radioactivity.*

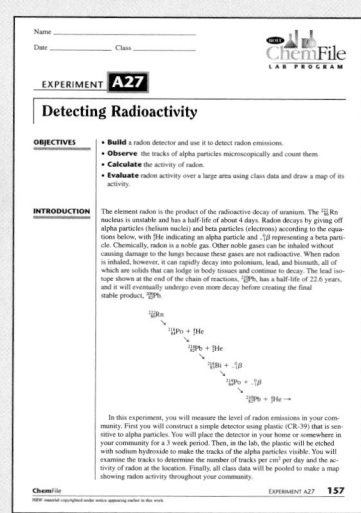

6. Place the pennies from the "tails" pile back in the box, and shake the contents again. Repeat step 3 with this set of pennies, and record the number of heads from the second count (half-lives = 2).

7. Continue this process until all of the pennies have "decayed." Students should graph the data to show the rate of decay.

8. Have the groups compare their data with data from other groups. Students should note that the pattern of decay becomes less predictable as the number of "unde-

cayed" pennies decreases. Finally, pool all of the data, and make a graph based on the total number of pennies used.

Safety
None.

Disposal
None.

ratio of carbon-14 to carbon-12 as the plants. Other animals eat those animals, and so on up the food chain, so all animals contain radioactive carbon-14. These atoms of carbon-14 undergo radioactive decay to become N-14, emitting beta particles in the process.

$$^{14}_6C \longrightarrow {}^{14}_7N + {}^{0}_{-1}e$$

Plants take in carbon dioxide throughout their lives. Therefore, they constantly replenish lost carbon-14. Animals also maintain a constant level of carbon-14. But when a plant or animal dies, it stops taking in fresh supplies of carbon-containing substances, so replenishment of carbon-14 stops. The half-life of carbon-14 is 5715 years. So from the time an organism dies, the amount of carbon-14 in its body decays by half every 5715 years. In other words, half of the carbon-14 atoms now present in a living plant or animal will have decayed 5715 years after its death. In another 5715 years, half of the remaining carbon-14 atoms will have decayed, leaving one-fourth of the original amount.

Once an archaeologist has measured the amounts of carbon-12 and carbon-14 in a fossil or other object, the ratio of carbon-14 to carbon-12 is compared with the ratio of these isotopes in a sample of similar material whose age is known. Using this technique of radioactive dating with carbon-14, scientists have concluded that the Iceman lived about 5000 years ago, between 3500 and 3000 B.C.

Radioactive dating is used to measure geologic time

Scientists' ability to date objects using carbon-14, as shown in Figure 18-15, is limited by two factors. The first limitation is that C-14 cannot be used to date objects composed of material that was never alive, such as clay or rocks. The second limitation is that after four half-lives, the amount of radioactive C-14 remaining in an object is too small to give

▶ **Figure 18-15**

Scientists determined the age of this cave painting, from the Cosquer cave, in France, to be approximately 16 500 years old. Carbon-14 was used to date the painting because organic materials were used in the paint.

678 **Chapter 18**

Alternative Assessment

Half-Life

Ask students to determine how long it would take for 1 mol of a radioactive nuclide to decay if its half-life is 1 minute. Can you predict the point at which no undecayed nuclei would remain? Theoretically, after 79 half-lives (79 minutes) of continuous decay, only one atom should remain. It is not possible to predict when all of a nuclide will have decayed because half-life is a statistical average based on the decay of a large number of nuclei. When only a few atoms remain, it is impossible to predict when any one of them will decay.

If there is one atom left and n = the number of half lives, the following solution can be used:

$$1 \text{ atom} = \frac{6.02 \times 10^{23} \text{ atoms}}{2^n}$$

$$2^{79} = 6.04 \times 10^{23}$$

Rate of Decay

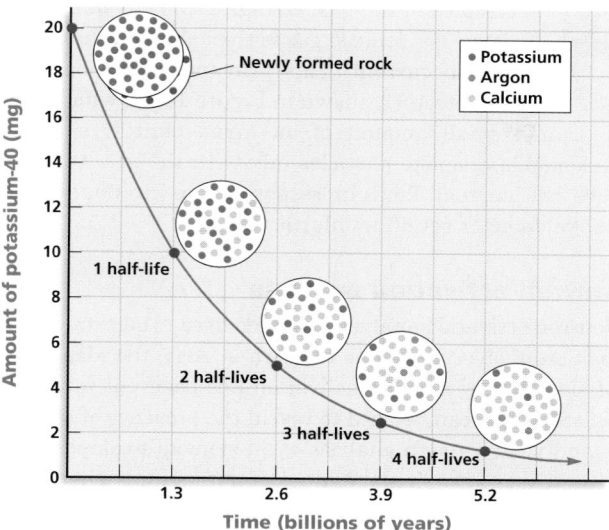

Newly formed rock

- Potassium
- Argon
- Calcium

1 half-life

2 half-lives

3 half-lives

4 half-lives

Amount of potassium-40 (mg)

Time (billions of years)

FIGURE 18-16 ◀

Potassium-40 decays to argon-40 and calcium-40, but scientists monitor only the ratio of potassium-40 to argon-40 to determine the age of the object.

reliable data. Consequently, C-14 is not useful for dating specimens that are more than about 25 000 years old. Anything older must be dated on the basis of a radioactive isotope that has a half-life longer than that of carbon-14.

Potassium-40, with a half-life of 1.28 billion years, represents only about 0.012% of the potassium present in the earth today. Potassium-40 is useful in dating ancient rocks and minerals. Potassium-40 produces two different isotopes in its radioactive decay. About 11% of the potassium-40 in a mineral decays to argon-40, which may remain in the sample. The remaining 89% of potassium-40 decays to calcium-40, which is not useful for radioactive dating because it cannot be distinguished from other calcium in the rock. The argon-40, however, can be measured. **Figure 18-16** shows the decay of potassium-40 through four half-lives. The amount of argon detected, relative to the potassium-40, shows the age of a mineral.

Other isotopes with even longer half-lives than potassium-40 have been used to determine the age of the Earth. By measuring these isotopes, scientists have estimated Earth to be an impressive 4.5 billion years old.

Smoke detectors contain sources of alpha particles

How does a smoke detector, like the one shown in **Figure 18-7,** work? Alpha particles travel only short

FIGURE 18-17 ▼

This smoke detector contains a minute amount of $^{241}_{95}Am$, an alpha emitter. These ionized alpha particles allow a steady current to flow between two electrodes. When smoke particles interrupt the current, an alarm sounds.

NUCLEAR CHEMISTRY 679

TEACHING TIP

Carbon Dating Students should understand that an ancient object that contains carbon and was once living cannot always be carbon dated. Ask students if they think C-14 dating could be used to determine the age of a lump of coal, which is mostly carbon. Lead them to understand that C-14 dating of coal would not be possible because the organisms that formed it lived too long ago, about 300 million to 350 million years ago.

ADDITIONAL APPLICATION

Potassium-40 dating was used to date moon rocks. The results of the dating determined that the moon formed at about the same time as Earth.

VISUAL STRATEGY

Figure 18-17 Emphasize that ionizing smoke detectors usually carry a label explaining where and how to dispose of the unit when it no longer functions. The long half-lives of the isotopes (432 years for americium-241 and 2.14 million years for neptunium-237) will pose long-term environmental problems if the detector is disposed of in a landfill.

$$\frac{6.02 \times 10^{23} \text{ atoms}}{6.04 \times 10^{23}} = 1$$

$n = 79$ half-lives

680

TEACHING TIP

Conservation of Matter Point out to students that even though a nucleus decays, matter does not disappear. Stress that nuclear decay is the transformation of one element, whose radioactive emissions are being measured, into another element, which may or may not be radioactive. The change in overall mass over time is very small.

ADDITIONAL APPLICATION

Scientists use neutron activation analysis to analyze a specimen that is rare or valuable, or one that cannot be damaged. In this technique, the sample to be analyzed is exposed to a beam of neutrons from a nuclear reactor. When the nuclei of the sample absorb these neutrons, some of the nuclei become radioactive isotopes. Each element in the sample can then be identified and its mass calculated based on the type and energy of radioactivity it emits.

HISTORICAL CONNECTION

An unusual application of neutron activation analysis involved the 12th president of the United States, Zachary Taylor. On July 4, 1850, President Taylor dedicated the cornerstone for the Washington Monument. Five days later, he became seriously ill and died. Some historians believed that Taylor had been poisoned with arsenic. To settle the issue, forensic scientists opened Taylor's sealed, lead coffin almost 150 years after his death and took small samples of his hair, nails and body tissues. Neutron activation analysis revealed that arsenic was present but only in levels that are normally present in the human body. The scientists concluded that President Taylor had not been poisoned.

▲ **FIGURE 18-18**

This worker wears a radiation detector to monitor the level of nuclear radiation to which she is exposed.

distances, even in gases. When alpha particles travel through a gas, they attract electrons from molecules of the gas, changing the gas molecules to ions. The ionized gas is then able to conduct an electrical current. This principle is the basis of smoke detectors, shown in Figure 18-17, which contain a small amount of an alpha emitter such as $^{241}_{95}Am$. When smoke particles mix with the gas, they reduce the current flow. In response, the circuits of the smoke detector set off an alarm.

Neutron activation analysis

Neutron activation analysis has been used to determine the composition of objects such as meteorites. Also, the identification of elements by neutron activation has been put to use in forensic science. It can be used to reveal the presence of certain elements and yield a rough analysis of an element's composition. Firing a gun leaves very small residues of antimony, barium, and copper on a person's hand. Neutron activation analysis can reveal the presence of these elements on residues taken from a suspect's hand.

Exposure to radiation must be monitored

The effects of nuclear radiation on the body are cumulative. Repeated exposure to small doses of radiation over a long period of time can be as dangerous as a single large dose if the total amount of radiation received is equal. People working with radioactivity, whether in medicine or industry, must therefore monitor the amount of radiation to which they are exposed. The woman in **Figure 18-18** is wearing a simple device to monitor her exposure to radiation—a film badge. Remember that Becquerel discovered radioactivity when it fogged his sealed photographic plates. This film badge works on exactly the same principle. Every week or so, the film from the badge is developed. Any darkening

TABLE 18-3 Effect of Whole-Body Exposure to a Single Dose of Radiation

Dose (rems)	Probable effect
0–25	no observable effect
25–50	slight decrease in white blood cell count
50–100	marked decrease in white blood cell count
100–200	nausea, loss of hair
200–500	ulcers, internal bleeding
>500	death

ALTERNATIVE ASSESSMENT

Group Strategy

Divide the class into pairs, and have one student in each pair solve the problem for the odd-numbered isotopes while the other student solves the problem for the even-numbered isotopes. Have team members check each other's work.

How long does it take 400 g of each carbon isotope listed in the table to decay to less than 0.001 g?

Isotope	Half-life	(Answers)
Carbon-9	0.1265 s	2.404 s
Carbon-10	19.2 s	6.08 min
Carbon-11	20.38 min	6.454 h
Carbon-12	stable	no decay
Carbon-13	stable	no decay
Carbon-14	5715 y	108 600 y
Carbon-15	2.449 s	46.53 s
Carbon-16	0.75 s	14 s

of the film indicates that the badge wearer was exposed to radiation, and the degree of darkening indicates the total amount of exposure.

The biological effect of exposure to nuclear radiation is expressed in a unit known as a *rem*. **Table 18-3** on page 680, lists the effects of exposure to various doses of radiation. People who work with radioactive isotopes are advised to limit their exposure to 5 rems per year. This exposure is 1000 times higher than the recommended exposure level for most people, including you.

SECTION REVIEW

Total recall

1. What does neutron activation analysis reveal about a sample?
2. Identify three practical applications of nuclear chemistry.
3. What is a rem?
4. Identify the radioactive nuclide used to date ancient rocks and minerals.
5. What does PET stand for?
6. Why do workers exposed to radiation wear film badges?
7. What is meant by "the half-life of a radioactive nuclide"?

Critical thinking

8. Explain how carbon-14 is used to determine the age of an object.
9. Airline crews are exposed to between 0.5 and 0.7 rems of radiation per year, which is a higher exposure than most people receive. What do you think causes this higher exposure?
10. **Interpreting Tables** A practical rule is that a radioactive nuclide is essentially gone after 10 half-lives. What percentage of the original radioactive nuclide is left after 10 half-lives? How long will it take for 10 half-lives to pass for plutonium-239? Refer to Table 18-2 on page 677.
11. **Interpreting Tables** Give two reasons why uranium-235 is considered a greater health threat than radon-222. Refer to Table 18-2 on page 677.
12. Why would carbon-14 not be a good choice to use in smoke detectors?
13. No observable effects are noted in a person exposed to a single dose of 0–25 rems. So why are people who work with radioactive isotopes advised to limit their exposure to only 5 rems per year?
14. **Story Clue** If the Iceman's body has a carbon-14 to carbon-12 ratio of one-half times that found in a living organism, how old is the Iceman? How old would he be if the carbon-14 to carbon-12 ratio were one-quarter times that found in a living organism?
15. What fraction of an original sample of a radioactive isotope remains after three half-lives?
16. How many half-lives of radon-222 have passed in 11.46 days? If 5.2×10^{-8} g of radon-222 remain in a sealed box after 11.46 days, how much was present in the box initially? Refer to Table 18-2 on page 677.
17. Would an emitter of alpha particles be useful in measuring the thickness of a sheet of steel? Explain your answer.

NUCLEAR CHEMISTRY 681

(The 400 g decays to 200 g after one half-life, to 100 g after two half-lives, and so on. It decays for 19 half-lives, when the amount of radioactive material remaining is 7.63×10^{-4} g, less than 0.001 g. Therefore, the time required for 400 g of each isotope to decay to this amount is equal to the isotope's half-life multiplied by 19.)

SECTION 18-3

ANSWERS

SECTION REVIEW

Total recall

1. the sample's elemental composition
2. Answers may include radioactive dating, smoke detectors, elemental analysis, and medical treatment.
3. A rem is the unit used to measure the biological effect of radiation.
4. potassium-40
5. Positron Emission Tornography
6. The film is exposed by nuclear radiation. When the film is developed, its level of darkness indicates the amount of radiation the wearer was exposed to during the time he or she wore the badge.
7. Half-life is the time required for half of the nuclei of a radioactive element to decay.

Critical thinking

8. The object must have come from a living thing. The amounts of C-12 and C-14 in the sample are measured. The fraction of C-14 remaining tells how many half-lives have passed since the carbon was incorporated into the object.
9. Flying high in Earth's atmosphere causes airline crews to be exposed to more cosmic rays than people at ground level are exposed to. These rays are usually absorbed as they pass through the lower atmosphere.
10. The percentage remaining is 0.0098%. The half-life of Pu-239 is 2.41×10^4 years. Ten half-lives would pass in 2.41×10^5 years.
11. The half-life of Rn-222 is only 3.28 days; the half-life of U-235 is 24 100 years. Radon will decay rapidly to a harmless state.

Answers continue on page 687A.

681

You began your study of nuclear reactions by reading about the Iceman. Now that you have completed your study of nuclear chemistry, reconsider the questions that were asked at the beginning of the chapter.

LOOKING BACK

Exactly when did the Iceman die?

By radioactive dating with carbon-14 scientists have determined that the Iceman lived sometime between 3500 and 3000 B.C., during the Age of Copper. The Age of Copper lasted from about 4000 to 2200 B.C. It was the Iceman's ax blade of copper that helped scientists focus on that time period. The blade was originally thought to be bronze, which looks similar to copper. Analysis revealed its true chemical identity.

How did scientists determine what the Iceman looked like when he was alive?

To reconstruct the Iceman's face, scientists used nuclear imaging techniques on the Iceman's skull to generate three-dimensional computer images. Based on these images, and tables of anatomical data scientists built a three-dimensional model of the Iceman's skull. They then used clay to duplicate his muscles and soft polyurethane to reconstruct his skin. The completed model showed that the Iceman had distinctive features—a broad nose, a protruding lower lip, and a prominent chin.

How did the Iceman die?

Nuclear imaging techniques provided the key to answering this question. Scientists believe that the Iceman died from exhaustion, per-haps from being exposed too long to adverse weather conditions. In this state of exhaustion, the Iceman lay down on his left side in a small depression in the mountain, where he froze to death. His body was gradually covered with snow, which eventually turned into the hard ice coffin in which the Iceman lay buried for the next 5000 years.

A sculpted model of the Iceman's skull was reconstructed using measurements, three-dimensional computer images, x-rays, and CT scans.

Soft urethane was used to reconstruct the facial features of the Iceman.

KEY TERMS

18-1
band of stability
mass defect
nuclear binding energy
nucleon

nuclide
strong nuclear force

18-2
annihilation of matter
beta particle

chain reaction
critical mass
gamma ray
nuclear fission
nuclear fusion

radioactivity
transmutation

18-3
half-life

KEY CONCEPTS

18-1 Why are some atomic nuclei stable?

▶ The strong nuclear force overcomes the repulsive force between protons to keep a nucleus intact.

▶ The energy released when nucleons form a nucleus is known as the nuclear binding energy.

▶ The mass that is converted to energy when nucleons form a nucleus is known as the mass defect.

▶ If the mass defect is known, the nuclear binding energy can be calculated by using the equation $E = mc^2$.

▶ The ratio of neutrons to protons in stable nuclei defines a band of stability that includes the stable nuclei.

18-2 What kinds of nuclear change occur?

▶ Unstable nuclei are radioactive and can emit radiation in the form of alpha particles, beta particles, and gamma rays.

▶ Unstable nuclei with too many neutrons usually emit beta particles.

▶ Unstable nuclei with too few neutrons can undergo either electron capture or positron emission, emitting gamma rays in the process.

▶ Large nuclei with too few neutrons frequently emit alpha particles.

▶ Nuclear equations are balanced in terms of mass and charge.

▶ In nuclear fission, a heavy nucleus splits into two smaller nuclei; in nuclear fusion, two smaller nuclei combine to form one larger nucleus.

▶ Nuclear fission reactions that cause other fissions are chain reactions. Sustained chain reactions must be controlled to avoid a nuclear explosion.

▶ Nuclear reactions result in a transmutation.

18-3 How is nuclear chemistry used?

▶ Half-life is the time required for one half of the mass of a radioactive isotope to decay.

▶ The half-life of the carbon-14 isotope can be used to date organic material that is up to 20 000 years old. Other radioactive isotopes are used to date older rock and mineral formations.

▶ Radioactive isotopes have a number of practical applications in industry, medicine, and chemical analysis.

▶ The biological effects of radiation are measured in units called rems.

KEY SKILLS

Before your exam be sure you understand the concept of a half-life. Also be sure you understand the rules for predicting nuclear stability and for balancing nuclear equations.

REVIEW & ASSESS

TERM REVIEW

1. nuclear binding energy
2. nucleon
3. gamma ray
4. nuclear fusion
5. transmutation
6. radioactivity
7. critical mass
8. half-life

CONCEPT & SKILLS REVIEW

1. The strong nuclear force is an attractive force that acts among all protons and neutrons in a nucleus. It acts only at the very close distances that exist in nuclei and is much stronger than the electrostatic repulsion between protons.

2. Unstable nuclei decay in a variety of ways, eventually forming stable nuclei.

3. a. In small, stable nuclei, the numbers of neutrons and protons are approximately equal.
   b. In large, stable nuclei, the numbers of neutrons and protons approach a ratio of 1.5:1.

4. When a nucleus forms from protons and neutrons separated by large distances, energy is given off as the particles come together because the nucleus has greater stability than the separated particles. This energy is the binding energy for that nucleus.

5. The mass defect is the mass equivalent of the binding energy as given by Einstein's equation $E = mc^2$. It is the difference between the sum of the separate masses of the nucleons of the atom and the mass of the formed atom.

6. Smaller nuclei have a lower binding energy than do larger nuclei because they have fewer particles. Calculating binding energy per nucleon ignores the size of the nucleus and allows us to compare the stability of all nuclei with one another.

TERM REVIEW

1. The energy emitted when a nucleus forms is known as the _____.
   (strong nuclear force, nuclear binding energy)

2. A _____ can be either a proton or a neutron.
   (beta particle, nucleon, gamma ray)

3. The high-energy electromagnetic radiation produced by decaying nuclei is known as a(n) _____.
   (gamma ray, alpha particle)

4. When two smaller nuclei have combined, _____ has occurred.
   (nuclear fission, nuclear fusion)

5. The creation of a new nuclei as a result of bombarding the nucleus with other nuclei is called a _____.
   (chain reaction, transmutation)

6. When an unstable nucleus decays, emitting particles and energy, the process is called _____.
   (annihilation of matter, radioactivity)

7. _____ is the smallest mass of radioactive material needed to sustain a chain reaction.
   (mass defect, critical mass)

8. The time required for 50% of a sample of a radioactive isotope to decay is known as its _____.
   (half-life, radioactivity)

CONCEPT & SKILLS REVIEW

NUCLEAR STABILITY

1. Explain how the strong nuclear force holds a nucleus together despite the repulsive forces between protons.

2. Describe what happens to unstable nuclei.

3. a. What is the relationship among number of protons, number of neutrons, and the stability of the nucleus for small atoms?
   b. What is the relationship among number of protons, number of neutrons, and the stability of the nucleus for large atoms?

4. What is the relationship between binding energy and the formation of a nucleus from protons and neutrons?

5. What is the relationship between mass defect and binding energy?

6. Why is nuclear stability better indicated by binding energy per nucleon than by total binding energy per nucleus?

7. Medium-mass nuclei have larger binding energies per nucleon than heavier nuclei. What can you conclude from this fact?

NUCLEAR CHANGES

8. What is the relationship between an alpha particle and a helium nucleus?

9. The decay of uranium-238 results in the spontaneous ejection of an alpha particle. Write the nuclear equation that describes this process.

10. Compare the penetrating powers of alpha particles, beta particles, and gamma rays.

11. What type of radiation is emitted in the decay described by the following equation?
    $$^{43}_{19}K \longrightarrow\, ^{43}_{20}Ca + ?$$

12. Is the decay of an unstable isotope into a stable isotope always a one-step process? Explain.

13. How does artificial transmutation differ from natural radioactive decay?

14. a. What role does the neutron serve in starting a nuclear chain reaction and in keeping it going?

b. Why must neutrons in a chain reaction be controlled?

c. Why must there be a minimum mass of material in order to sustain a chain reaction?

15. a. Describe the similarities and differences between fusion and fission.

b. Under what conditions does fusion occur?

16. What difficulties must be overcome before fusion can be used as a practical source of energy?

17. The plutonium isotope $^{239}_{94}$Pu is sometimes detected in nuclear reactors. Consider that nuclear fuel contains a large portion of the common uranium isotope $^{238}_{92}$U in addition to fissionable $^{235}_{92}$U. Describe a process by which $^{239}_{94}$Pu might form in a nuclear reactor.

18. What is the difference between a moderator and a control rod in a nuclear reactor?

19. Why are elevated temperatures necessary to initiate fusion reactions but not fission reactions?

20. Why do lighter elements undergo fusion more readily than heavier elements?

21. The release of radioactive strontium into the atmosphere was once a major concern, especially for infants whose main food source was milk. Why were scientists concerned about radioactive strontium? **(Hint: Check a periodic table for the members of the group that include strontium.)**

22. Plutonium is one of the most toxic substances known to humans. Once inside the body, plutonium ions are easily oxidized to form Pu^{4+} ions. These Pu^{4+} ions behave chemically much like Fe^{3+} ions. What effect would these Pu^{4+} ions have on the body? **(Hint: What role does Fe play in the body?)**

23. Concerns have recently been raised about the levels of radon gas in homes. Although radon is a noble gas and is therefore chemically inert, it is unstable and radioactive. When a radon-222 nucleus decays, an alpha particle is emitted. Write the nuclear equation to show what happens when a radon-222 nucleus decays. What is the other product that forms?

24. Why do positron emission and electron capture have the same effect on a nucleus?

USING NUCLEAR REACTIONS

25. The radiation given off by iodine-131 in the form of beta particles is used to treat cancer of the thyroid gland. Write the nuclear equation to show what happens when an iodine-131 nucleus decays.

26. Why is the constant rate of decay of radioactive nuclei so important in radioactive dating?

27. The Environmental Protection Agency has been concerned about the levels of radon gas in homes. The half-life of one radon isotope is 3.8 days. If a sample of gas taken from a basement contains 4.38 μg of radon-222, how much radon will remain in the sample after 15.2 days?

28. A pathologist working in a police laboratory wants to analyze a small sample of blood from a crime scene. He cannot damage the blood sample because it will be used in court as evidence. What kind of radioactive analysis should he use? Why?

29. Many cancer patients lose their hair during radiation therapy. How is this hair loss related to rem exposure?

30. Describe a situation outside of chemistry that illustrates the concept of half-life.

31. Why would someone working around radioactive waste in a landfill use a radiation monitor instead of a watch to determine when the workday is over? At what point would that person decide to stop working?

32. Radioactive isotopes are often used as "tracers" to follow the path of an element through a chemical reaction. For example, the oxygen atoms in O_2 produced by a plant during photosynthesis come from the oxygen in H_2O and not the oxygen in carbon dioxide, CO_2. Explain how you could use a radioactive isotope of oxygen to identify the source of the oxygen atoms in the O_2 produced during photosynthesis.

33. Phosphorus-32 is used to treat a certain form of leukemia. Starting with 10.0 mg of phosphorus-32, how many milligrams would be left after 57 days? The half-life of phosphorus-32 is 14.3 days.

7. Medium-mass nuclei are more stable than heavier nuclei.

8. An alpha particle is a helium-4 nucleus.

9. $^{238}_{92}\text{U} \longrightarrow {}^{234}_{90}\text{Th} + {}^{4}_{2}\text{He}$

10. Alpha particles have very low penetrating power because they are large, charged, massive, and slow. Beta particles have greater penetrating power because they have little mass and a much higher velocity than alpha particles. Gamma rays have high penetrating power because they are massless, travel at the velocity of light, and have no charge.

11. a beta particle ($^{0}_{-1}e$)

12. No. Often, the nucleus decays to another nucleus that is also unstable.

13. In transmutation, a nucleus is bombarded with particles from a particle accelerator. Natural decay occurs spontaneously because a nucleus is unstable.

14. a. A neutron begins the reaction by colliding with a nucleus. Additional neutrons are ejected from the fissioning nucleus and go on to collide with other nuclei, continuing the reaction.

b. Neutrons must be controlled in order to control the rate of the chain reaction and, consequently, the rate of energy output of a reactor. Without control, the temperature of the material would keep increasing until a meltdown occurred.

c. The chain reaction occurs only when enough nuclei are present so that the neutrons from each fission will collide with unsplit nuclei, thus sustaining the reaction. The critical mass is the minimum mass that provides this concentration of nuclei.

15. a. A great amount of energy is released in both processes. Fission occurs when a nucleus splits into smaller nuclei. Fusion occurs when nuclei collide and merge into larger nuclei.

   b. Fusion occurs only at extremely high temperatures and pressures.

16. The problems involve providing the conditions needed for controlled fusion. The temperature required for this process is so great that no solid form of matter can be used as a container to hold the nuclear reaction. A magnetic field must be used to contain the plasma in which fusion occurs.

17. Answers may vary. The most common pathway that occurs is the following:

$$^{238}_{92}U + ^{1}_{0}n \longrightarrow ^{239}_{92}U$$
$$^{239}_{92}U \longrightarrow ^{239}_{93}Np + ^{0}_{-1}e$$
$$^{239}_{93}Np \longrightarrow ^{239}_{94}Pu + ^{0}_{-1}e$$

18. Control rods absorb neutrons, thereby controlling the chain reaction. A moderator slows down the neutrons, allowing collisions between neutrons and nuclei to be more effective.

19. In order for fusion to occur, nuclei must collide with a great amount of energy. Such energy is present only at very high temperatures.

20. When light elements fuse, the nuclei formed are likely to have a higher binding energy per nucleon and thus be more stable.

21. Strontium is chemically similar to calcium and can replace calcium ions in bones and teeth. Milk is rich in calcium, so strontium could become concentrated in milk produced by grazing animals that have consumed strontium-contaminated foliage.

Answers continue on page 687A.

34. Copper-64 is used to study brain tumors. Assume that the original mass of a sample of copper-64 is 26.00 g. After 64 hours, all that remains is 0.8125 g of copper-64. What is the half-life of this radioactive isotope?

LINKING CHAPTERS

1. Structure of the nucleus
Compare the behavior of nucleons in a nuclear reaction with the behavior of nucleons in a chemical reaction.

2. Theme: Classification and trends
Explain the relationship among atomic number, size of the nucleus, and stability.

3. Density
Calculate the density in g/cm^3 of uranium-235 if $8.0 \ m^3$ has a mass of 1.5×10^5 kg.

4. Writing equations
One radioactive decay series that begins with uranium-235 and ends with lead-207 shows the following sequence of emissions: alpha, beta, alpha, beta, alpha, alpha, alpha, alpha, beta, beta, and alpha. Write an equation for each reaction in the series.

ALTERNATIVE ASSESSMENTS

Performance assessment

1. Your teacher will give you an index card listing the name of a radioactive isotope. Predict what type of emission this isotope will give off when it decays. Write a balanced nuclear equation that shows the decay process.

2. Design an experiment that uses 128 pennies to illustrate the concept of half-life.

Portfolio projects

1. Chemistry and you
Your local grocery store may sell perishable foods that have been irradiated. Find out what stores in your area sell irradiated foods,

and determine the shelf life of these foods. What are the shelf lives of the same foods without irradiation? Do research to identify foods that are routinely irradiated even though their label may not indicate. Report your findings to the class.

2. Research and communication
   a. Research some important historical findings that have been validated through radioactive dating. Report your findings to the class.
   b. You have made an important archaeological or geological find. Describe how you will determine which method of radioactive dating to use.

3.

| TOPIC: Radiation effects on humans |
| GO TO: www.scilinks.org |
| KEYWORD: HW185 |

Research and communication
Compare the physiological effects on humans of the different kinds of radiation. Find out if any adults you know are exposed to radiation at work. Ask about the kind of radiation involved and what precautions they take to avoid the harmful effects of radiation. Report your findings to the class.

4.

| TOPIC: Nuclear power |
| GO TO: www.scilinks.org |
| KEYWORD: HW186 |

Research and communication
Find out about the use of nuclear power in this country. How many plants are currently supplying power? How many are in the construction stage? How does the use of nuclear power in the United States compare with that in Europe?

1. Atoms with the same mass number but different atomic numbers are known as _____.

   a. isotopes   c. nucleons

   b. alpha particles   d. isobars

2. When protons and neutrons form a nucleus,
   a. some mass is gained.
   b. energy is absorbed.
   c. some mass is converted to energy.
   d. electrons are captured by the nucleus that forms.

3. Which of the following combinations of proton number and neutron number yields a nucleus that is least stable?
   a. even/even   c. odd/even
   b. even/odd   d. odd/odd

4. When smaller nuclei contain too few neutrons, they _____.
   a. tend to emit beta particles
   b. emit positrons or capture electrons
   c. undergo a chain reaction
   d. cannot undergo a transmutation

5. Which of the following nuclear equations is correctly balanced?
   a. $^{37}_{18}\text{Ar} + ^{0}_{-1}e \longrightarrow ^{37}_{17}\text{Cl}$
   b. $^{6}_{3}\text{Li} + 2^{1}_{0}n \longrightarrow ^{4}_{2}\text{He} + ^{3}_{1}\text{H}$
   c. $^{254}_{99}\text{Es} + ^{4}_{2}\text{He} \longrightarrow ^{258}_{101}\text{Md} + 2^{1}_{0}n$
   d. $^{14}_{7}\text{N} + ^{4}_{2}\text{He} \longrightarrow ^{17}_{8}\text{O} + ^{2}_{1}\text{H}$

6. Gamma rays _____.
   a. have the same energy as beta particles
   b. are not produced during a transmutation
   c. have no charge and no mass
   d. are not a form of electromagnetic radiation

7. Combining a nucleus of curium-246 with a nucleus of carbon-12 will produce a nucleus of _____.
   a. einsteinium-254
   b. nobelium-258
   c. fermium-254
   d. mendelevium-256

8. The half-life of thorium-234 is 24 days. If you start with a 42.0 g sample of thorium-24, how much will remain after 72 days?
   a. 42.0 g   c. 10.5 g
   b. 21.0 g   d. 5.25 g

9. Alpha particles can safely be used in smoke detectors because they _____.
   a. are not a form of radiation
   b. cannot even penetrate paper
   c. are harmless even if swallowed
   d. combine with beta particles to produce a neutron

10. Every radioactive isotope _____.
   a. emits an alpha particle
   b. has a characteristic half-life
   c. exists as an isobar
   d. has an atomic number greater than 92

Assign prior to chapter test.

1. d
2. c
3. d
4. b
5. a
6. c
7. b
8. d
9. b
10. b

Continuation of Answers

Answers from page 663

11. Lithium-6 is more stable because the smallest nuclei are more stable with neutrons and protons in a ratio near 1:1. Lithium-6 has three neutrons and three protons.

12. a. Positively charged protons repel each other.
   b. The strong nuclear force overcomes electrostatic repulsion at the very small distances of nucleons in a nucleus.
   c. The nucleus would come apart as a result of electrostatic repulsion.

13. a. unstable
   b. unstable
   c. stable
   d. stable
   e. unstable

14. A nucleus with a magic number of protons, neutrons, or total nucleons tends to be stable. The numbers are 2, 8, 20, 28, 50, 82, and 126.

15. carbon

16. a. According to Figure 18-4, binding energy increases rapidly for the lighter elements then levels off to a maximum at mass number 55. Binding energies gradually decrease for nuclei with high mass numbers.
   b. The helium isotope is more stable than the oxygen isotope.

17. Elements with too few or too many neutrons have no stable nuclei.

Answers from page 681

12. Carbon-14 decays by emitting beta particles, which are more penetrating than the alpha particles emitted by the isotopes that are usually used.

13. Biological effects are related to cumulative exposure to radiation. A person who works with radioactivity can accumulate a dangerous level of biological damage in a few years.

14. If 0.50 of the C-14 remains, one half-life has passed, and the Iceman is about 5700 years old. If 0.25 of the C-14 remains, two half-lives have passed, and the Iceman is about 11 400 years old.

15. After three half-lives, 0.125 of the original radioactive sample remains.

16. After 11.43 days, 3 half-lives for radon-222 have passed. If 5.2×10^{-8} g of radon-222 are left after 11.46 days, then the original sample contained 4.16×10^{-7} g of radioactive material.

17. No. Alpha particles are relatively slow, have a large mass, and can be stopped by a sheet of paper. Therefore, they will not penetrate a sheet of metal.

Answers from page 686

CONCEPT & SKILLS REVIEW

22. Most iron in the body is found in the heme groups of hemoglobin in red blood cells. The incorporation of plutonium in place of iron would kill red blood cells and other cells as the cells pass through capillaries.

23. $^{222}_{86}\text{Rn} \longrightarrow {}^{218}_{84}\text{Po} + {}^{4}_{2}\text{He}$

24. Both result in the change of a proton to a neutron, thereby reducing the atomic number by one without changing the mass number.

25. $^{131}_{53}\text{I} \longrightarrow {}^{131}_{54}\text{Xe} + {}^{0}_{-1}e$

26. Radiometric dating can work only if the decay rates of radioisotopes were the same in the past as they are today.

27. 15.2 days is four half-lives, so one-sixteenth of the original quantity will remain. 0.274 µg of radon–222 will remain.

28. He would have to use neutron activation analysis because this technique is used in forensic science.

29. Loss of hair occurs after a single radiation dose of 100 to 200 rem.

30. Answers will vary. For example, a pelican depletes a pond of half its fish population each day. If the pond starts with 200 fish, 100 would remain after one day, 50 after the next day, and so on.

31. Workers will have decided on a safe daily dose of radiation. The dose will depend on the number of days a worker is likely to be exposed. When that dose is reached, the worker must leave the job.

32. Set up an experiment in which one group of plants is supplied with water in which some O-16 atoms have been replaced by O-15, the radioactive isotope that has the longest half-life, 122 seconds. The other group would be supplied with ordinary water and O-15 labeled "CO_2." After both groups have photosynthesized for a time, the atmosphere inside the growing chambers is tested for the presence of O-15.

33. 0.625 mg would remain after 57 days (four half-lives).

34. The quantity 0.8125 g is 1/32 of the original quantity, 26.00 g, so five half-lives have passed ($2^5 = 32$). The half-life is 64/5 = 12.8 hours.

LINKING CHAPTERS

1. In nuclear reactions, for example, radiactive decay, neutrons are sometimes converted into protons and protons are sometimes converted into neutrons. Artificial transmutation also changes the number of nucleons in the nuclei. In chemical reactions, the nucleons do not undergo any changes. The electronic distribution of atoms is altered while the nucleus remains intact.

2. As atomic number increases, the mass of the nucleus also increases. The mass of the nucleus increases more rapidly than the atomic number, however, because additional neutrons are required to stabilize the nucleus as the number of protons increases.

3. $150\,000 \text{ kg} \times \dfrac{1000 \text{ g}}{1 \text{ kg}} = 1.5 \times 10^8 \text{ g}$

$8.0 \text{ m}^3 \times \dfrac{1\,000\,000 \text{ cm}^3}{1 \text{ m}^3} = 8.0 \times 10^6 \text{ cm}^3$

$1.5 \times 10^8 \text{ g} \div 8.0 \times 10^6 \text{ cm}^3 = 19 \text{ g/cm}^3$

4. $^{235}_{92}\text{U} \longrightarrow {}^{231}_{90}\text{Th} + {}^{4}_{2}\text{He}$

$^{231}_{90}\text{Th} \longrightarrow {}^{231}_{91}\text{Pa} + {}^{0}_{-1}e$

$^{231}_{91}\text{Pa} \longrightarrow {}^{227}_{89}\text{Ac} + {}^{4}_{2}\text{He}$

$^{227}_{89}\text{Ac} \longrightarrow {}^{227}_{90}\text{Th} + {}^{0}_{-1}e$

$^{227}_{90}\text{Th} \longrightarrow {}^{223}_{88}\text{Ra} + {}^{4}_{2}\text{He}$

$^{223}_{88}\text{Ra} \longrightarrow {}^{219}_{86}\text{Rn} + {}^{4}_{2}\text{He}$

$^{219}_{86}\text{Rn} \longrightarrow {}^{215}_{84}\text{Po} + {}^{4}_{2}\text{He}$

$^{215}_{84}\text{Po} \longrightarrow {}^{211}_{82}\text{Pb} + {}^{4}_{2}\text{He}$

$$^{211}_{82}\text{Pb} \longrightarrow {}^{211}_{83}\text{Bi} + {}^{0}_{-1}e$$

$$^{211}_{83}\text{Bi} \longrightarrow {}^{211}_{84}\text{Po} + {}^{0}_{-1}e$$

$$^{211}_{84}\text{Po} \longrightarrow {}^{207}_{82}\text{Pb} + {}^{4}_{2}\text{He}$$

ALTERNATIVE ASSESSMENTS

Performance assessment

1. Students should use the guidelines in Section 18-2 to determine the likely decay mode. Choose isotopes from a table such as the Table of the Isotopes that appears in the *CRC Handbook of Chemistry and Physics* or the Table of Radioactive Isotopes in *The Merck Index*. Refer students to these resources in order to verify the decay mode they choose.

2. Students should devise a method in which the coins "decay" by turning up tails when the coins are dumped on a table.

3. Experimental designs should be based on the differences in penetrability of the three types of radiation.

Portfolio projects

1. Responses will vary. Students should discover that irradiation increases the shelf life of foods. Unlabeled irradiated foods might include potatoes, onions, dry beans, and similar items.

2. Answers will vary. For item 2b, students should understand that isotopes used in dating should have a half-life that corresponds to no more than about one-eighth of the suspected age of the object being dated.

3. Responses will vary. Students should learn that physiological effects depend on the type of radiation and the duration of exposure. Students could bring in film badges, dosimeters, and other devices that are used to measure radiation exposure.

4. Responses will vary. Students should research the latest decisions regarding nuclear waste storage and its effect on plant operations. Economic, regulatory, and environmental aspects of plant construction, operation, and decommissioning should be included in the report.

LABORATORY PROGRAM

EXPLORATION TECHNIQUE BUILDER

INVESTIGATION PROBLEM SOLVING

WORKING IN THE WORLD OF A CHEMIST

Each lab exercise takes place in the context of a real-world situation. All students will experience what it is like to be an employee, to follow directions, and to apply creative thinking to solve problems with available resources. As a result, students will be able to see how the techniques and concepts they are learning in the lab and classroom can relate to problems in the real world. Even students who may not become scientists will gain valuable insight into the application of science and how it can both create and solve problems in today's world.

TWO TYPES OF LABS

The lab exercises in the textbook are divided into two types.

EXPLORATIONS: TECHNIQUE BUILDERS WITH PROCEDURES

Explorations provide students complete procedures, along with thorough questions designed to help them make sense of what they observe in the lab. In this way, each Exploration follows the format of a traditional lab and helps students focus on meaningful measurements and results.

INVESTIGATIONS: OPEN-ENDED PROBLEM SOLVING

Investigations are complete scenarios that encourage student-designed procedures and open-minded lab work. All Investigations are preceded by an Exploration, which serves as a prerequisite, and a Technique Builder. The Investigation gives students a chance to use their problem-solving skills as they examine another aspect of the technique, reaction, or concept they encountered in the Exploration.

Meeting today's challenges

Even though you have already taken science classes with lab work, you will find the two types of laboratory experiments in this book organized differently from those you have done before. The first type of lab is called an Exploration. Each *Exploration* helps you gain skills in lab techniques that you will use to solve a real problem presented in the second type of lab, which is called an Investigation. The *Exploration* serves as a *Technique Builder*, and the *Investigation* is presented as an exercise in *Problem Solving*.

Both types of labs refer to you as an employee of a professional company, and your teacher has the role of supervisor. Lab situations are given for real-life circumstances to show how chemistry fits into the world outside of the classroom. This will give you valuable practice with skills that you can use in chemistry and in other careers, such as creating a plan with available resources, developing and following a budget, and writing business letters.

As you work in these labs, you will better understand how the concepts you studied in the chapters are used by chemists to solve problems that affect life for everyone.

Explorations

The Explorations provide step-by-step procedures for you to follow, encouraging you to make careful observations and interpretations as you progress through the lab session. Each Exploration gives you an opportunity to practice and perfect a specific lab technique or concept that will be needed later in an Investigation.

What you should do before an Exploration

Preparation will help you work safely and efficiently. The evening before a lab, be sure to do the following:

▶ **Read the lab procedure** to make sure you understand what you will do.

▶ **Read the safety information** that begins on page 693, as well as any safety information provided in the lab procedure itself.

▶ **Write down any questions** you have in your lab notebook so that you can ask your teacher about them before the lab begins.

▶ **Prepare all necessary data tables** so that you will be able to concentrate on your work when you are in the lab.

What you should do after an Exploration

Most teachers require a lab report as a way of making sure that you understand what you are doing. Your teacher will give you specific details about how to organize your lab reports, but most lab reports will include the following:

▶ **title** of the lab

▶ **summary paragraph(s)** describing the purpose and procedure

▶ **data tables and observations** that are organized and comprehensive

STUDENTS EXPLORE SCIENCE AND CAREERS

Most lab programs are organized in ways that do not reflect how scientists actually work. Usually, students merely repeat some work that was first done by scientists several hundred years ago who used techniques unlike those used today. The various challenges in this lab program allow students to conduct lab activities that relate to modern testing and research and development. They also provide valuable insight for students who might consider becoming scientists.

- **worked-out calculations** with proper units
- **answers that are,** boxed, circled, or highlighted for items in the *Analysis and Interpretation, Conclusions,* and *Extensions* sections

Investigations

The Investigations differ from Explorations because they do not provide step-by-step instructions. In each Investigation, you are required to develop your own procedure to solve a problem presented to your company by a client. You must decide how much money to spend on the project and what equipment to use. Although this may seem difficult, the Investigations contain a number of clues about how to successfully solve the problem.

What you should do before an Investigation

Before you will be allowed to work on the lab, you must turn in a preliminary report. Usually, you must describe in detail the procedure you plan to use, provide complete data tables for the data and observations you will collect, and list exactly what equipment you will need and the costs. Only after your teacher, acting as your supervisor, approves your plans are you allowed to proceed. Before you begin writing a preliminary report, follow these steps.

- **Read the Investigation thoroughly,** and search for clues.
- **Jot down notes** in your lab notebook as you find clues.
- **Consider what you must measure** or observe to solve the problem.

- **Think about Explorations** you have done that used a similar technique or reaction.
- **Imagine working through a procedure,** keeping track of each step, and determining what equipment you need.
- **Carefully consider** whether your approach is the best, most efficient one.

What you should do after an Investigation

After you finish, organize a report of your data as described in the Memorandum. This is usually in the form of a one- or two-page letter to the client. Your teacher may have additional requirements for your report. Carefully consider how to convey the information the client needs to know. In some cases, a graph or diagram can communicate information better than words can. As a part of your report, you must include an invoice for the client that explains how much the client owes and how much you charged for each part of the procedure. Remember to include the cost of your work in the analysis.

If you need help with graphing or with using significant figures, ask your teacher.

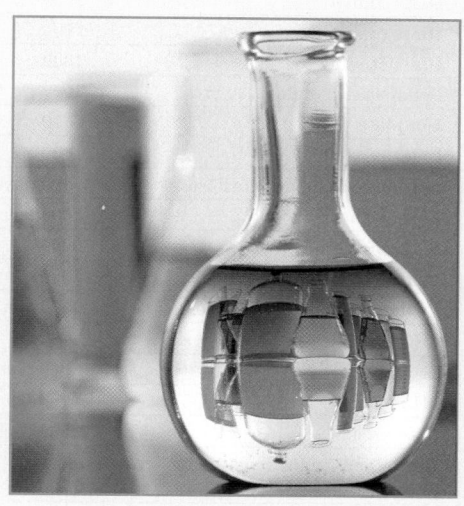

Instead of instructions, students are given a business letter from a "client" that outlines a problem and a memo from their supervisor that offers further suggestions. Using the problem as their basis, students must create a plan for their procedure, select equipment from a list of available materials, and attempt to stay within a budget. Student plans are reviewed by you, the teacher, for practicality and safety before students enter the lab. Upon completion of the lab, instead of writing a traditional lab report, students write a business letter to the "client" explaining their results and submit a bill for their services.

LABS THAT MEET THE NEEDS OF ALL STUDENTS

Along with encouraging a thorough development of scientific-process skills, the Investigations provide sensible opportunities for students to sharpen their critical-thinking skills regardless of whether they pursue science as a career.

STUDENTS TAKE RESPONSIBILITY FOR THEIR LEARNING

By designing their own procedures for the Investigations, students will feel they have solved a problem by using their own ingenuity. They are given the freedom to make their own mistakes; this enables them to learn from their mistakes rather than obsess over whether they are performing a lab skill the "right way." All of the Investigations require students to plan a budget and factor in costs for equipment. If students make a mistake in the process, they may lose money on paper, but they do not need to be punished with a lower grade.

 ## CRITICAL THINKING SKILLS

When performing an Investigation, students will have an opportunity to sharpen the following critical-thinking skills:

- applying abstract concepts to specific situations
- deciding what equipment and materials are necessary to carry out the procedure
- developing and following a budget

- finding information in a business letter, memo, or reference work
- identifying problems
- identifying the measurements that must be made in order to draw conclusions
- planning a procedure to solve the problem
- writing a business letter that organizes the results

Extending the Consulting-Firm Scenario

When performing an Investigation, students may use the additional suggestions listed below to expand the scope of their work.

 SAFETY AND WASTE MANAGEMENT

▸ Develop a complete safety plan for the lab in the event of accidents, such as chemical spills, fires, and natural disasters, including earthquakes, tornadoes, hurricanes, and floods.

▸ Develop a plan for hazardous-waste management and disposal.

▸ Create a floor plan for lab facilities that takes safety, efficiency, and cost into account.

 FINANCE AND MARKETING

▸ Develop a plan for creating a business.

▸ Create financial statements.

▸ Develop a marketing strategy.

▸ Develop promotional materials.

▸ Fill out copies of business-loan forms from local banks.

▸ Fill out copies of government forms, such as incorporation papers or corporate registrations, business licenses, applications for lab permits or chemical licenses, corporate tax forms, and EPA hazardous-waste management forms.

▸ Develop a plan for using profits to reinvest in personnel, equipment, and marketing. (Some teachers allow profitable lab groups to become "venture capitalists," who loan money to other lab groups that have made costly mistakes in planning their procedures and use of resources.)

Materials list for Investigations

Refer to the Equipment and Chemical lists below when planning your procedure for the Investigation labs. Include in your budget only the items you will need to solve the problem presented to your company by the client. Remember, you must always include the cost of lab space and the standard disposal fee in your budget.

Equipment	Cost per item/unit
Aluminum foil	1000/cm^2
Balance	5000
Beaker, 250 mL	1000
Beaker, 400 mL	2000
Beaker tongs	1000
Büchner funnel	2000
Bunsen burner/related equipment	10 000
Buret	5000
Cobalt glass plate	2000
Crucible and cover	5000
Crucible tongs	2000
Desiccator	3000
Drying oven	5000
Erlenmeyer flask, 250 mL	1000
Evaporating dish	1000
Filter flask with sink attachment	2000
Filter paper	500/piece
Flame-test wire	2000
Glass funnel	1000
Glass plate	1000
Glass stirring rod	1000
Graduated cylinder, 100 mL	1000
Hot plate	8000
Index card (3 × 5 in.)	1000
Lab space/fume hood/utilities	15 000/day
Litmus paper	1000/piece
Magnetic stirrer	5000
Mortar and pestle	2000
Paper clips	500/box
pH meter	3000
pH paper	2000/piece
pH probe	5000
Plastic bags	500/each
Ring stand/ring/wire gauze or pipe-stem triangle	2000

Equipment	Cost per item/unit
Ring stand with buret clamp	2000
Rubber policeman	500
Spatula	500
Spectroscope	15 000
Standard disposal fee	2000/g of product
Stopwatch	5000
6 test tubes/holder/rack	2000
Thermistor probe	2000
Thermometer	2000
Wash bottle	500
Watch glass	1000
Weighing paper	500/piece

FINES

OSHA safety violation	2000/incident

REAGENTS and ADDITIONAL MATERIALS

Chemical	Cost per item/unit
0.02 M KMnO$_4$	1000/mL
1.0 M H$_2$SO$_4$	1000/mL
0.5 M HCl for titration	500/mL
0.5 M NaOH for titration	500/mL
0.5 M Na$_2$CO$_3$ solution	1000/mL
1.0 M CuCl$_2$	1000/mL
1 M HCl	500/mL
Gypsum sample	500/g
Ice	500
MgCl$_2$	500/g
Mossy zinc, Zn	500/g
NaCl	500/g
Phenolphthalein	2000
Plaster of Paris sample	500/g
Rock salt	2000
Zn(NO$_3$)$_2$	500/g

* No refunds on returned chemicals or unused equipment.

 TEACHER SUPPORT

To help you prepare for each lab, the following support notes are outlined in the margins of the teacher's edition.

Planning helps you prepare the time, materials, and solutions that are needed to perform the lab.

Pre-lab Discussion is designed to help students understand how their work relates to the chemistry concepts they are studying.

Techniques to Demonstrate frees students' time so they can spend it performing the lab instead of trying to figure out how to operate equipment.

Required Precautions helps keep you and your students safe.

Sample Data helps you evaluate students' work.

Disposal offers guidelines for properly disposing of each reactant and product from the lab.

Answers provide full responses to the items in the Analysis and Interpretation, Conclusions, and Extensions sections, so you can spend your time evaluating students' work rather than performing the calculations.

SAFETY IN THE CHEMISTRY LABORATORY

Any chemical can be dangerous if it is misused. Always follow the instructions for the experiment. Pay close attention to the safety notes. Do not do anything differently unless you are instructed to do so by your teacher.

Chemicals, even water, can cause harm. The challenge is to know how to use chemicals correctly. If you follow the rules stated below, pay attention to your teacher's directions, and follow the precautions on chemical labels and in the experiments, then you will be using chemicals correctly.

THESE SAFETY RULES ALWAYS APPLY IN THE LAB

1. **Always wear a lab apron and safety goggles.**
Laboratories contain chemicals that can damage your clothing even if you aren't working on an experiment at the time. Keep the apron strings tied.

Some chemicals can cause eye damage and even blindness. If your safety goggles are uncomfortable or if they cloud up, ask your teacher for help. Try lengthening the strap, washing the goggles with soap and warm water, or using an anti-fog spray.

2. **Do not wear contact lenses in the lab.**
Even if you wear safety goggles, chemicals can get between contact lenses and your eyes and cause irreparable eye damage. If your doctor requires you to wear contact lenses instead of glasses, then you should wear eye-cup safety goggles in the lab. Ask your doctor or your teacher how to use this very important and special eye protection.

3. **NEVER WORK ALONE IN THE LABORATORY.**
Do lab work only under the supervision of your teacher.

4. **Wear the right clothing for lab work.**
Necklaces, neckties, dangling jewelry, long hair, and loose clothing can knock things over or catch on fire. Tuck in neckties, or take them off. Do not wear a necklace or other dangling jewelry, including hanging earrings. It also might be a good idea to remove your wristwatch so that it is not damaged by a chemical splash.

Pull back long hair, and tie it in place. Wear cotton clothing if you can. Nylon and polyester fabrics burn and melt more readily than cotton does. It's best to wear fitted garments, but if your clothing is loose or baggy, tuck it in or tie it back so that it does not get in the way or catch on fire. It is also important to wear pants, not shorts or skirts.

Wear shoes that will protect your feet from chemical spills. Do not wear open-toed shoes or sandals or shoes with woven leather straps. Shoes made of solid leather or polymer are preferred over shoes made of cloth.

5. **Only books and notebooks needed for the experiment should be in the lab.**
Do not bring textbooks, purses, bookbags, backpacks, or other items into the lab; keep these things in your desk or locker.

COMPLETE SAFETY AND DISPOSAL

Complete safety information is provided for each lab. In addition, disposal instructions for all chemicals and all combinations of products are included in the Teacher's Notes that appear on the same page as the lab. This eliminates guesswork and ensures that you are using appropriate and environmentally sound disposal practices. For more discussion on disposal issues, see the Teacher's Notes on pages 694–695.

DO YOU REALLY KNOW HOW TO OPERATE AN EYEWASH STATION?

Make sure you know exactly how to use an eyewash station. It could save someone's eyesight. Be sure to instruct everyone working in the lab in the proper use of the eyewash fountain, as outlined below.

▸ If your eyes are exposed to chemicals, walk immediately to an eyewash fountain, preferably within 15 seconds of exposure.

▸ Immediately start flushing your eyes; continue for at least 5 minutes while someone else calls a doctor.

▸ Keep your eyes wide open; use your fingers to lift your upper and lower lids away from the eyeball so that the flowing water washes across it.

▸ Continually move your eyeball up, down, left, right, and in a circle. This will help the flowing water get inside the eyeball socket and wash out any chemicals that could enter from behind the eyeball.

ELECTRICAL SAFETY

The following safety precautions must be followed any time electrical equipment is present in the lab to avoid electric shocks.

▸ Each electrical socket in the laboratory must be a three-hole socket and must be protected with a GFI (ground fault interrupter) circuit.

▸ First check the polarity of all circuits by using a polarity tester from an electronics supply store. Repair any incorrectly wired sockets.

▸ Use only electrical equipment equipped with a three-wire cord and three-prong plug.

▸ Be sure all electrical equipment is turned off before being plugged into a socket. Turn off electrical equipment before it is unplugged.

▸ Wiring hookup should be made or altered only when apparatus is disconnected from the power source and the power switch is turned off.

▸ Do not let electrical cords dangle from workstations; dangling cords are a tripping and shock hazard.

693

- Do not use electrical equipment with frayed or twisted cords.
- The area under and around electrical equipment should be dry, and cords should not lie in puddles of liquid.
- Your hands should be dry when you use electrical equipment.
- Do not use electrical equipment powered by 110–115 V alternating current for "conductivity" demonstrations or for any other use in which bare wires are exposed, even if the current is connected to a lower-voltage AC or DC connection.
- Use dry cells or NiCad rechargeable batteries as DC sources. Do not use automobile storage batteries or AC-to-DC converters; they can cause serious shock.

6. Read the entire experiment before entering the lab.
Memorize the safety precautions. Be familiar with the instructions for the experiment. Only materials and equipment authorized by your teacher should be used. When you do your lab work, follow the instructions and safety precautions described in the experiment.

7. Read chemical labels.
Follow the instructions and safety precautions stated on the labels.

8. Walk with care in the lab.
Sometimes you will have to carry chemicals from the supply station to your lab station. Avoid bumping into other students and spilling the chemicals. Stay at your lab station at other times.

9. Food, beverages, chewing gum, cosmetics, and smoking are NEVER allowed in the lab.
(You should already know this.)

10. NEVER taste chemicals or touch them with your bare hands.
Keep your hands away from your face and mouth while working, even if you are wearing gloves.

11. Use a sparker to light a Bunsen burner.
Do not use matches. Be sure that all gas valves are turned off and that all hot plates are turned off and unplugged when you leave the lab.

12. Be careful with hot plates, Bunsen burners, and other heat sources.
Keep your body and clothing away from flames. Do not touch a hot plate after it has just been turned off because it is probably still hot. The same is true of glassware, crucibles, and other things that have been removed from the flame of a Bunsen burner or from a drying oven.

13. Do not use electrical equipment with frayed or twisted wires.

14. Be sure your hands are dry before you use electrical equipment.
Before plugging an electrical cord into a socket, be sure the equipment is turned off. When you are finished with the equipment, turn it off. Before you leave the lab, unplug the equipment, but be sure to turn it off FIRST.

15. Do not let electrical cords dangle from work stations.
Dangling cords can cause tripping or electrical shocks. The area under and around electrical equipment should be dry, and cords should not lie in puddles of spilled liquid.

16. Know fire-drill procedures and the locations of exits.

 ## DISPOSAL OF CHEMICALS

Only a small percentage of waste chemicals are classified as hazardous by the Environmental Protection Agency. The EPA regulations are derived from two acts (as amended) passed by the United States Congress: the Resource Conservation and Recovery Act (RCRA) and the Comprehensive Environmental Response, Compensation, and Liability Act (CERCLA).

Some states have enacted legislation governing the disposal of hazardous waste that differs from the federal legislation. The disposal procedures described in this book have been designed to comply with the federal legislation. In most cases, these disposal procedures will probably comply with your state's disposal requirements as well. However, check with your state's environmental agency to be sure. If a particular disposal procedure does not comply with your state's requirements, ask that office to assist you in devising a procedure that is compliant.

17. **Know the location and operation of safety showers and eyewash stations.**

18. **If your clothes catch on fire, walk to the safety shower, stand under it, and turn it on.**

19. **If you get a chemical in your eyes, walk immediately to the eyewash station, turn it on, and lower your head so that your eyes are in the running water.**
Hold your eyelids open with your thumbs and fingers, and roll your eyeballs around. Flush your eyes continuously for at least 15 minutes. Call out to your teacher as you do this.

20. **If you spill anything on the floor or lab bench, call your teacher rather than trying to clean it up by yourself.**
Your teacher will tell you if it is OK for you to do the cleanup; if not, your teacher will know how the spill should be cleaned up safely.

21. **If you spill a chemical on your skin, wash the chemical off at the sink and call your teacher.**
If you spill a solid chemical on your clothing, brush it off carefully without scattering it onto somebody else, and call your teacher. If you get liquid on your clothing, wash it off right away using the faucet at the sink, and call your teacher. If the spill is on your pants or somewhere else that will not fit under the sink faucet, use the safety shower. Remove the pants or other affected clothing while you are under the shower, and call your teacher. (It may be temporarily embarrassing to remove pants or other clothing in front of your class, but failing to flush that chemical off your skin could cause permanent damage.)

22. **The best way to prevent an accident is to stop it before it happens.**
If you have a close call, tell your teacher so that you and your teacher can find a way to prevent it from happening again. Otherwise, the next time, it could be a harmful accident instead of just a close call. If you get a head-

ache, feel sick to your stomach, or feel dizzy, tell your teacher immediately.

23. **All accidents, no matter how minor, should be reported to your teacher.**

24. **For all chemicals, take only what you need.**
If you take too much and have some left over, DO NOT put it back in the bottle. If a chemical is accidently put into the wrong bottle, the next person to use it will have a contaminated sample. Ask your teacher what to do with leftover chemicals.

25. **NEVER take any chemicals out of the lab.**

26. **Horseplay and fooling around in the lab are very dangerous.**
NEVER be a clown in the laboratory.

27. **Keep your work area clean and tidy.**
After your work is done, clean your work area and all equipment.

28. **Always wash your hands with soap and water before you leave the lab.**

29. **All of these rules apply all of the time you are in the lab.**

The following general practices are recommended:

▸ Except when otherwise specified in the disposal procedures, neutralize acidic and basic wastes with 1.0 M sodium hydroxide, NaOH, or 1.0 M sulfuric acid, H_2SO_4, added slowly while stirring.

▸ When working with a waste-disposal contractor, prepare a complete list of the chemicals you want to dispose of. Classify each chemical in your disposal list as a hazardous or nonhazardous waste

chemical. Check with your local environmental agency for the details of such classification.

▸ Unlabeled chemicals must be classified as hazardous or nonhazardous waste. Some landfills will analyze unknown substances for a fee if the substance is shipped to the landfill in a separate package and labeled as a sample and if it includes instructions to analyze the contents well enough to determine its proper disposal method.

SAFETY SYMBOLS

To highlight specific types of precautions, the following symbols are used throughout the lab program. Remember that no matter what safety symbols you see in the lab instructions, all 29 of the safety rules previously described should be followed at all times.

CLOTHING PROTECTION

▶ Wear laboratory aprons in the laboratory. Keep the apron strings tied so that they do not dangle.

EYE SAFETY

▶ Wear safety goggles in the laboratory at all times. Know how to use the eyewash station.

CLEAN UP

▶ Keep your hands away from your face and mouth.

▶ Always wash your hands before leaving the laboratory.

CHEMICAL SAFETY

▶ Never taste, eat, or swallow any chemicals in the laboratory. Do not eat or drink any food from laboratory containers. Beakers are not cups, and evaporating dishes are not bowls.

▶ Never return unused chemicals to their original containers.

▶ It helps to label the beakers and test tubes containing chemicals. (This is not a new rule, just a good idea.)

▶ Never transfer substances by sucking on a pipet or straw; use a suction bulb.

WASTE DISPOSAL

▶ Some chemicals are harmful to our environment. You can help protect the environment by following the instructions for proper disposal.

GLASSWARE SAFETY

▶ Never place glassware, containers of chemicals, or anything else near the edges of a lab bench or table.

HAND SAFETY

▶ If a chemical gets on your skin or clothing or in your eyes, rinse it immediately, and alert your teacher.

CAUSTIC SAFETY

▶ If a chemical is spilled on the floor or lab bench, tell your teacher, but do not clean it up yourself unless your teacher says it is OK to do so.

HEATING SAFETY

▶ When heating a chemical in a test tube, always point the open end of the test tube away from yourself and other people.

Refer to the list of rules on pages 693–695, and identify whether a specific rule applies or whether the rule presented is a new rule.

1. Tie back long hair, and confine loose clothing.
   (Rule ? applies.)

2. Never reach across an open flame.
   (Rule ? applies.)

3. Use proper procedures when lighting Bunsen burners. Turn off hot plates, Bunsen burners, and other heat sources when they are not in use.
   (Rule ? applies.)

4. Heat flasks or beakers on a ring stand with wire gauze between the glass and the flame.
   (Rule ? applies.)

5. Use tongs when heating containers. Never hold or touch containers while heating them. Always allow heated materials to cool before handling them.
   (Rule ? applies.)

6. Turn off gas valves when they are not in use.
   (Rule ? applies.)

7. Use flammable liquids only in small amounts.
   (Rule ? applies.)

8. When working with flammable liquids, be sure that no one else is using a lit Bunsen burner or plans to use one.
   (Rule ? applies.)

9. What additional rules apply to every lab?
   (Rule ? applies.)

10. Check the condition of glassware before and after using it. Inform your teacher of any broken, chipped, or cracked glassware because it should not be used.
    (Rule ? applies.)

11. Do not pick up broken glass with your bare hands. Place broken glass in a specially designated disposal container.
    (Rule ? applies.)

12. Never force glass tubing into rubber tubing, rubber stoppers, or wooden corks. To protect your hands, wear heavy cloth gloves or wrap toweling around the glass and the tubing, stopper, or cork, and gently push in the glass.
    (Rule ? applies.)

13. Do not inhale fumes directly. When instructed to smell a substance, use your hand to wave the fumes toward your nose, and inhale gently.
    (Rule ? applies.)

14. Keep your hands away from your face and mouth.
    (Rule ? applies.)

15. Always wash your hands before leaving the laboratory.

Finally, if you are wondering how to answer the question that asks what additional rules apply to every lab, here is the correct answer.

Any time you see any of the safety symbols, you should remember that all 29 of the numbered laboratory rules always apply.

USING THE CBL™ IN THE EXPLORATIONS AND INVESTIGATIONS

Many of the Explorations and Investigations featured in this textbook contain procedures for the Texas Instruments Calculator-Based Laboratory™ (CBL) System. These CBL procedures are written for use with the CHEMBIO™ program, designed by Vernier Software. The step-by-step instructions for Technology Procedure Options 1 and 2 refer specifically to the menus that will appear on your calculator screen when you use this program.

The lab procedures in this book are written specifically for use with TI-83 and TI-82 calculators. Although the procedures can be followed to work with all TI calculations, some minor adaptations may be necessary.

HOW TO SET UP CHEMBIO

1. Open the folder called "Vernier" on the *Holt Chemistry: Visualizing Matter Test Generator with TestBuilder Software for Macintosh® and Windows®* CD-ROM. The folder contains a text file that gives more information on using the CHEMBIO programs. You can also access this information through Holt's Web site at go.hrw.com. The keyword can be found in the Internet Connect box below.

 internet connect

Holt Chemistry: Visualizing Matter

 On-Line Resources
go.hrw.com
Visit the HRW web site for a variety of resources related to the labs. Just type in the keyword HW0 Lab.

Different calculator versions of the software are included for the different CBL-compatible TI graphing calculators; make sure you use the correct version for your calculators.

 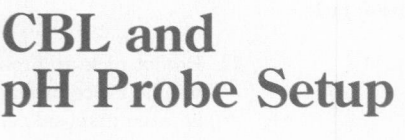

CBL and pH Probe Setup

MATERIALS

▶ **CBL**
▶ **graphing calculator with link cable**
▶ **Vernier pH amplifier and pH electrode**
▶ **Vernier adapter cable**

SETUP

1. Connect the CBL to the graphing calculator. Use the unit-to-unit link cable and the input/output ports located at the base of each unit.

2. Plug the pH amplifier into the Vernier adapter cable. The adapter cable should be connected to CH1 of the CBL system. (*Note: the pH electrode should be connected to the pH amplifier.*)

3. Firmly press in all cable ends.

4. Turn on the CBL unit and the graphing calculator.

5. **To start the CHEMBIO program:**
   ▶ Press the PRGM key on the graphing calculator.
   ▶ Select the CHEMBIO option from the list.
   ▶ Press ENTER after PrgmCHEMBIO appears on the screen.

   ▶ When the Vernier Software introduction screen appears, press enter to continue.

6. **To set up the graphing calculator and CBL unit for pH measurement:**
   ▶ Select the SET UP PROBES option from the MAIN MENU.
   ▶ Enter the number of probes.
   ▶ Select the pH option from the SELECT PROBES menu.
   ▶ Enter the channel number.
   ▶ Select the USE STORED option from the CALIBRATION menu.

7. **To set up the graphing calculator and CBL unit for data collection:**
   ▶ Select the COLLECT DATA option from the MAIN MENU.
   ▶ Select the MONITOR INPUT option from the DATA COLLECTION menu.

8. Allow the system to warm up for 30 seconds before continuing. Refer to the Exploration for lab setup. When you are ready to measure the pH, press ENTER on the graphing calculator. The pH reading is displayed on the screens of the CBL unit and the graphing calculator.

   (Note: No readings are stored when the INPUT mode is in use.)

9. When you are finished with the lab, rinse the pH probe with distilled water. Press the + key on the graphing calculator to quit MONITOR INPUT.

10. If you are setting up the CBL unit and graphing-calculator system to take pH readings over a specific interval of time, replace steps 5–6 with steps 11–12.

11. **To set up the calculator and CBL unit for timed data collection:**

    ‣ Select COLLECT DATA from the MAIN MENU.

    ‣ Select TIME GRAPH from the DATA COLLECTION menu. Follow the directions on the calculator screen to allow the system to warm up, then press enter.

    ‣ Enter the time interval between samples in seconds.

    ‣ Enter the number of samples and press ENTER.

    ‣ Select USE TIME SETUP to continue. If you want to change the sample time or sample number, select MODIFY SETUP.

    ‣ Enter the minimum pH on the (Y min) line.

    ‣ Enter the maximum pH on the (Y max) line.

    ‣ Enter the number of pH increments on the (Y scl) line.

12. Refer to the Exploration for lab setup. When you are ready to begin monitoring data, press ENTER on the graphing calculator. After data collection stops, press ENTER to display a graph of pH-versus-time. Examine the data points along the curve. As you move the cursor to the right or left, the time (X) and pH (Y) values of each data point are displayed below the graph. Determine the initial pH and final pH, and record these values in your data table.

13. To print a copy of the graph use the TI-Graph Link cable and program to transfer the graph of pH-versus-time from the graphing calculator to a Macintosh or IBM-compatible computer.

Battery acid · Stomach acid · Apple juice · Black coffee · Pure water · Antacid · Baking soda · Hand soap · Household ammonia · Drain cleaner

more acidic ← NEUTRAL → more basic

2. To download the CHEMBIO group file from your computer to your calculator, refer to the manual that comes with the TI-GRAPH LINK, and follow the directions.

   When the transfer is complete, a set of programs will appear on your graphing calculator; this will include the program titled "CHEMBIO" and a list of subprograms that are used by the main CHEMBIO program.

3. Use the link-to-link cable to copy your programs to your students' calculators. Refer to page 700 for system requirements.

   Because of the size of the CHEMBIO program group, it is recommended that you remove all other programs before loading CHEMBIO onto a calculator. The CHEMBIO programs are locked, so students will not be able to change the programs on their calculators. Students should keep all the programs so they can use them throughout the year.

4. To use the CHEMBIO program with a pH probe, refer to page 698 for equipment setup, then simply follow the instructions given in the lab procedure.

   The CHEMBIO program can calibrate sensors, collect data, and perform data analysis. This allows you to use the CBL to its full potential with many Vernier probes in your classroom without writing your own programs or using many different interfaces.

How to set up CHEMBIO

1. Open the folder called "Vernier" on the *Holt Chemistry: Visualizing Matter Test Generator with TestBuilder Software for Macintosh® and Windows®* CD-ROM. The folder contains a text file that gives more information on using the CHEMBIO programs. You can also access this information through Holt's Web site at go.hrw.com. The keyword can be found in the Internet Connect box below.

internetconnect

Holt Chemistry: Visualizing Matter

On-Line Resources
go.hrw.com
Visit the HRW web site for a variety of resources related to the labs. Just type in the keyword HW0 Lab.

Different calculator versions of the software are included for the different CBL-compatible TI graphing calculators; make sure you use the correct version for your calculators.

2. To download the CHEMBIO group file from your computer to your calculator, refer to the manual that comes with the TI-GRAPH LINK, and follow the directions.

When the transfer is complete, a set of programs will appear on your graphing calculator; this will include the program titled "CHEMBIO" and a list of subprograms that are used by the main CHEMBIO program.

CBL and Temperature Probe Setup

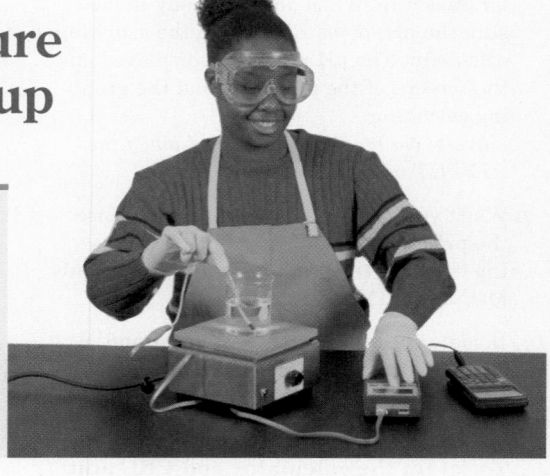

MATERIALS

▶ **CBL**
▶ **graphing calculator with link cable**
▶ **temperature probe**

SETUP

1. Connect the CBL to the graphing calculator. Use the unit-to-unit link cable and the input/output ports located at the base of each unit.

2. Connect the temperature probe to the CH1 port of the CBL system. Firmly press in all cable ends. Turn on the CBL unit and the graphing calculator.

3. **To start the CHEMBIO program:**
   ▶ Press the PRGM key on the graphing calculator.
   ▶ Select the CHEMBIO option from the list.
   ▶ Press ENTER after PrgmCHEMBIO appears on the screen.
   ▶ Press ENTER after the Vernier Software introduction screen appears.

4. **To set up the graphing calculator and CBL unit for temperature measurement:**
   ▶ Select option SET UP PROBES from the MAIN MENU.

Trigger Mode

The Trigger mode on the graphing calculator and CBL unit may be used in laboratory exercises that require recording measurements until a constant temperature is reached or that require recording untimed temperature measurements. A stopwatch will be necessary to record the time interval in lab exercises using this method.

   ▶ Enter 1 for the number of probes.
   ▶ Select TEMPERATURE from the list.
   ▶ Enter 1 for the channel number.

1. **To setup data collection using trigger mode:**
   ▶ Select the COLLECT DATA option from the MAIN MENU.
   ▶ Select the TRIGGER option from the DATA COLLECTION menu.

2. Refer to the Exploration for lab setup.

SYSTEM REQUIREMENTS

You will need TI-GRAPH LINK™ software and a TI-GRAPH LINK computer-interface cable to get started using these programs with your TI graphing calculator and CBL. These are available from CENCO, Vernier, or educational- and office-supply companies.

Contact TI for information and technical support.
email: ti-cares@ti.com
address: Texas Instruments
         Customer Support Line
         P. O. Box 650311, MS 3962
         Dallas, TX 75265

Information
Customer Support
phone: 1-800-TI-CARES

Programming Assistance
Technical Support
phone: (972) 917-8324

For more information on Vernier products:
email: info@vernier.com
address: Vernier Software
         8565 S.W. Beaverton-Hillsdale Hwy.
         Portland, OR 97225-2429
phone: (503) 297-5317

3. To collect a temperature reading:

▶ Press TRIGGER on the CBL.

▶ Select the MORE DATA option from the TRIGGER menu to take another temperature reading.

4. When constant temperature is reached or you are through recording, select STOP from the TRIGGER menu. Press ENTER to continue. *(Note: make sure to record all temperature readings in your data table.)*

5. To view a graph of temperature versus time:

▶ Select the COLLECT DATA option from the MAIN MENU.

▶ Select the option TIME GRAPH from the DATA COLLECTION menu.

▶ Enter the time interval between each temperature reading.

▶ Enter the number of samples taken. Press ENTER to continue.

▶ Select the USE TIME SETUP option to continue.

▶ Enter the minimum temperature on the (Y min) line. If the value is a negative number, remember to use the (–), and not the – option.

▶ Enter the maximum temperature on the (Y max) line. Enter the temperature increment on the (Y scl) line.

▶ Press ENTER. The calculator should plot your data. Press ENTER again to see the line graph. Use the arrow keys to trace the graph. Time in seconds is graphed on the *x*-axis, and the temperature readings are graphed on the *y*-axis.

Timed Graph Mode

1. To setup data collection using the timed graph mode:

▶ Select the COLLECT DATA option from the MAIN MENU.

▶ Select the option TIME GRAPH from the DATA COLLECTION menu.

▶ Enter the time interval between each temperature reading. If this number is not outlined in the Exploration, ask your teacher what time interval is appropriate for the lab.

▶ Enter the number of samples the CBL should record. (If this number is not given, it can be calculated by multiplying the total time in minutes by 60 seconds, then dividing by the time interval). Press ENTER.

▶ Select the USE TIME SETUP to continue.

▶ Enter the minimum temperature on the (Y min) line. If the value is a negative number, remember to use the (–), and not the – option.

▶ Enter the maximum temperature on the (Y max) line. Enter the temperature increment on the (Y scl) line.

2. The CBL and graphing calculator are now set up for data collection. Refer to the Exploration before you begin collecting data.

3. Press ENTER on the graphing calculator when you are ready to begin temperature readings.

4. When the CBL screen changes from SAMPLING to DONE, use the arrow keys to trace the graph. Time in seconds is graphed on the *x*-axis, and the temperature readings are graphed on the *y*-axis.

5. If your teacher allows, you may print a copy of the temperature-versus-time graph by transferring the graph from the calculator to a Macintosh or IBM-compatible computer using the TI-Graph Link cable and program.

3. Use the link-to-link cable to copy your programs to your students' calculators.

Because of the size of the CHEMBIO program group, it is recommended that all other programs be removed before loading CHEMBIO onto a calculator. The CHEMBIO programs are locked, so students will not be able to change the programs on their calculators. Students should keep all the programs so they can use them throughout the year.

4. To use the CHEMBIO program with a temperature probe, refer to page 700 for equipment setup, then simply follow the instructions given in the lab procedure.

The CHEMBIO program can calibrate sensors, collect data, and perform data analysis. This allows you to use the CBL to its full potential with many Vernier probes in your classroom without writing your own programs or using many different interfaces.

OBJECTIVES

Students will:

▶ use appropriate lab safety procedures.

▶ use a Bunsen burner.

▶ determine the most efficient setting for the burner's fuel-air ratio.

▶ use a laboratory balance to measure mass.

▶ demonstrate appropriate technique in transferring solids.

▶ use a graduated cylinder to measure volume.

▶ collect, organize, and graph data.

RECOMMENDED TIME:

1 lab period

MATERIALS

(for each lab group)

▶ 250 mL beakers, 2

▶ balance

▶ Bunsen burner with gas tubing and striker

▶ crucible tongs (Do not use beaker tongs)

▶ copper wire, 18 gauge, 10 cm

▶ evaporating dish

▶ NaCl crystals, about 5 g

▶ spatula

▶ wax paper or weighing paper

PRE-LAB DISCUSSION

Thoroughly discuss all safety precautions outlined in this laboratory and in the safety section. Because this laboratory will be one of the first ones of the year, be sure to make safety a priority.

Point out the location and demonstrate the operation of all of the safety equipment, especially the lab shower, eyewash station, and fire blankets. Be sure students know what steps to follow in an emergency. Demonstrate the proper use of safety goggles and a lab apron. If students think that the lab equipment and chemicals used in this Exploration are not particularly dangerous, remind them that other items in the lab may be dangerous, so safety precautions must be taken. Explain

1A | Laboratory Techniques

OBJECTIVES

▶ **Demonstrate proficiency in using a Bunsen burner, a triple-beam balance, and a graduated cylinder.**

▶ **Demonstrate proficiency in handling solid and liquid chemicals.**

▶ **Develop proper safety techniques for all lab work.**

▶ **Apply data-collecting techniques.**

▶ **Use graphing techniques to plot data.**

MATERIALS

▶ **100 mL graduated cylinder**

▶ **250 mL beakers, 2**

▶ **Bunsen burner and related equipment**

▶ **copper wire**

▶ **crucible tongs**

▶ **evaporating dish**

▶ **heat-resistant mat**

▶ **NaCl**

▶ **spatula**

▶ **test tube**

▶ **triple-beam balance**

▶ **wax paper or weighing paper**

Situation

You have applied to work at a company that does research, development, and analysis work. Although the company does not require employees to have extensive chemical experience, all applicants are tested for their ability to follow directions, heed safety precautions, perform simple laboratory procedures, clearly and concisely communicate results, and make logical inferences.

The company will consider your performance on the test in deciding whether to hire you and what your initial salary will be.

Always wear safety goggles and a lab apron to protect your eyes and clothing. If you get a chemical in your eyes, immediately flush the chemical out at the eyewash station while calling to your teacher. Know the location of the emergency lab shower and eyewash station and the procedures for using them.

Do not touch any chemicals. If you get a chemical on your skin or clothing, wash the chemical off at the sink while calling to your teacher. Make sure you carefully read the labels and follow the precautions on all containers of chemicals that you use. If no precautions are stated on the label, ask your teacher what precautions to follow. Do not taste any chemicals or items used in the laboratory. Never return leftover chemicals to their original containers; take only small amounts to avoid wasting supplies.

 When using a Bunsen burner, confine long hair and loose clothing. If your clothing catches fire, WALK to the emergency lab shower and use it to put out the fire. Do not heat glassware that is broken, chipped, or cracked. Use tongs or a hot mitt to handle heated glassware and other equipment; heated glassware does not always look hot.

Background

Pay close attention to the procedures and safety precautions because you will continue to use them throughout your work if you are hired by this company. In addition, you will need to pay attention to what is happening around you, make careful observations, and keep a clear and legible record of these observations in your lab notebook.

Problem

This laboratory orientation session will teach you some of the following techniques:

▶ how to use a Bunsen burner
▶ how to handle solids and liquids
▶ how to use a triple-beam balance
▶ how to practice basic safety techniques in lab work

Preparation

1. Organizing Data
   Copy the data tables in your lab notebook.

2. Record in your lab notebook where the following items are located and how each item is used: emergency lab shower, eyewash station, and emergency telephone numbers.

3. Check to be certain that the gas valve at your lab station and at the nearest lab station are turned off. Notify your teacher immediately if a valve is on because the fumes must be cleared before any work continues.

Data Table 1

Material	Mass (g)
Weighing paper	
Weighing paper + NaCl	

Data Table 2

Material	Mass (g)—step 11	Mass (g)—step 12
Empty beaker		
Beaker + 50 mL of water		
50 mL of water		
Beaker + 100 mL of water		
100 mL of water		
Beaker + 150 mL of water		
150 mL of water		

REQUIRED PRECAUTIONS

▶ Read all safety precautions, and discuss them with your students.

▶ Safety goggles and a lab apron must be worn at all times.

▶ Long hair and loose clothing must be tied back.

▶ If students find a gas valve that has not been turned off properly, the room must be thoroughly ventilated—using the fume hood and windows—in order to prevent a fire hazard.

the need to tie back loose clothing and long hair when working in the lab. Emphasize the need to wear appropriate clothing, as outlined in the safety section.

Have students make the data tables before they enter the lab.

Remind students to make very careful observations, especially for the portion of the lab using the copper wire and the Bunsen burner.

TECHNIQUES TO DEMONSTRATE

Bunsen burners tend to vary in design; therefore, show students exactly how to light the Bunsen burners used in your lab. Tell students that the burner flame is a chemical reaction in which methane and oxygen react to form carbon dioxide and water vapor.

Lighting Bunsen burners with a match can be dangerous, especially if the matches are not safety matches. It is best to use a striker.

Be sure to demonstrate the proper technique for measuring mass with a balance. Make sure students know how to help keep the lab equipment in good shape. Be certain that neither chemicals nor hot objects are put directly on the balance pan. Students may also have difficulty understanding how to use the Vernier scale on the triple-beam balance unless they can see a demonstration. If you are using another kind of balance, explain how it works.

Show students how to read volume from the meniscus. This can be demonstrated with a quick sketch on the board or on an overhead projector. Remind students to keep their eyes at the same level as the top of the fluid when reading volume.

SAMPLE DATA

When the burner's ports are closed, the flame is bright yellow, and it makes a roaring noise. When the ports are open, the flame is blue, dim, and quiet. Answers will vary for the mass measurements involving NaCl. Be sure students measure the mass with the correct precision for your lab equipment and that they measure the mass of the weighing paper alone first.

Figure A

Technique

4. Compare the Bunsen burner in **Figure A** with your burner. Construction may vary, but the air and methane gas, CH_4, always mix in the barrel, the vertical tube in the center of the burner.

5. Partially close the air ports at the base of the barrel, turn the gas on full, hold the sparker about 5 cm above the top of the barrel, and proceed to light. Adjust the gas valve until the flame extends about 8 cm above the barrel. Adjust the air supply until you have a quiet, steady flame with a sharply defined, light-blue inner cone. **If an internal flame develops, turn off the gas valve and let the burner cool down. Otherwise, the metal of the burner can get hot enough to set fire to anything nearby that is flammable. Before you relight the burner, partially close the air ports.**

6. Using crucible tongs, hold a 10 cm piece of copper wire for 2–3 seconds in the part of the flame labeled *a* in **Figure B.** Repeat for the parts of the flame labeled *b* and *c.* Record your observations in your lab notebook.

7. Experiment with the flame by completely closing the air ports at the base of the burner. Observe and record the color of the flame and the sounds made by the burner. Using crucible tongs, hold an evaporating dish in the tip of the flame for about 3 minutes. Place

the dish on a heat-resistant mat, and shut off the burner. After the dish cools, examine its underside, and record your observations.

8. Before using the triple-beam balance, make sure that it is level and that the pointer rests at zero. If all slider masses are set at zero but the pointer is not at zero, adjust the calibration knob. To avoid discrepancies, use the same balance for all measurements during a lab activity. **Never put chemicals directly on the balance pan.**

9. Place a piece of weighing paper on the balance pan. Determine the mass of the paper by adjusting the masses on the various sliding scales. Record this mass to the nearest 0.01 g in your data table. Then move the 10 g slide to the 10 g position, and move the 1 g slide to the 3.00 g position. Put a small quantity of NaCl on a separate piece of weighing paper. Then transfer some of the NaCl to the weighing paper on the balance pan until you nearly balance the pointer. Slide the masses until the pointer is exactly balanced, and record the exact mass to the nearest 0.01 g in your data table.

10. Remove the weighing paper and NaCl from the balance pan. Lay the test tube flat on the table, and transfer the NaCl into the tube by rolling the weighing paper and sliding it into the test tube. As you lift the test tube to a vertical position, tap the

Figure B

SAMPLE DATA

MATERIALS	MASS (g)—STEP 11	MASS (g)—STEP 12
250 mL beaker	104.10	101.20
250 mL beaker + 50 mL water	154.40	151.53
50 mL of water	50.30	50.33
250 mL beaker + 100 mL water	205.23	201.17

SAMPLE DATA

MATERIALS	MASS (g)—STEP 11	MASS (g)—STEP 12
100 mL water	101.13	99.97
250 mL beaker + 150 mL water	255.92	252.01
150 mL water	151.82	150.81

*Note: This data was collected with a centigram balance. Some triple-beam balances do not have the same precision.

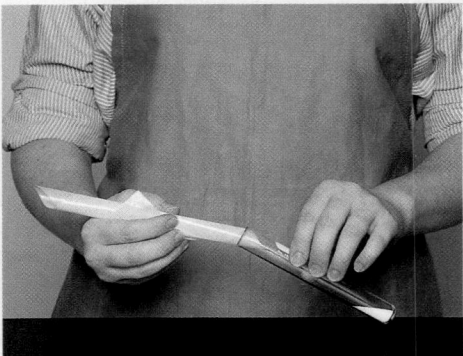

Figure C

paper gently, and the solid will slip into the test tube, as shown in **Figure C**.

11. Measure the mass of a dry 250 mL beaker, and record it in your data table. Add water up to the 50 mL mark, determine the new mass, and record it in your data table. Repeat the procedure by filling the beaker to the 100 mL mark and then to the 150 mL mark, and record the mass each time. Subtract the mass of the empty beaker from the other measurements to determine the masses of the water.

12. Repeat step 11 with a second dry 250 mL beaker, but use a graduated cylinder to measure the volumes of water to the nearest 0.1 mL before pouring the water into the beaker. Read the volumes using the bottom of the meniscus, the curve formed by the water's surface.

Cleanup and Disposal

13. Clean all apparatus and your lab station. Put the wire, NaCl, and weighing paper in the containers designated by your teacher. Pour the water from the beakers into the sink. Scrub the cooled evaporating dish with soap, water, and a scrub brush. Be certain that the gas valves at your lab station and the nearest lab station are turned off. Be sure lab equipment is completely cool before storing it. Always wash your hands thoroughly after all lab work is finished and before you leave the lab.

Analysis and Interpretation

1. **Organizing Ideas**
   Based on your observations, which type of flame is hotter: the flame formed when the air ports are open or the flame formed when they are closed? What is the hottest part of the flame? (Hint: The melting point of copper is 1083°C.)

2. **Analyzing Information**
   Which of the following measurements could have been made by your balance: 3.42 g of glass, 5.666 72 g of aspirin, or 0.000 017 g of paper?

3. **Organizing Data**
   Make a graph of mass versus volume for data from steps 11 and 12. The mass of water (g) should be graphed along the y-axis as the dependent variable, and the volume of water (mL) should be graphed along the x-axis as the independent variable.

Conclusions

4. **Relating Ideas**
   When methane is burned, it usually produces carbon dioxide and water. If there is a shortage of oxygen, the flame is not as hot, and black carbon solid is formed. Which steps in the lab demonstrate these flames?

5. **Inferring Conclusions**
   Which is the most accurate method for measuring volumes of liquids, a beaker or a graduated cylinder? Explain why.

Extensions

1. **Resolving Discrepancies**
   In Mandeville High School, Jarrold got only partway through step 7 of this experiment when he had to put everything away. Soon after Jarrold left, his lab drawer caught on fire. How did this happen?

2. **Relating Ideas**
   The density of water is equal to its mass divided by its volume. Calculate the density of water using your data from step 11. Then calculate the density of water using your data from step 12.

LABORATORY TECHNIQUES   705

OBJECTIVES

Students will:

▸ use a laboratory balance.

▸ use a Bunsen burner.

▸ perform multiple trials.

▸ calculate averages of data.

▸ design and implement their own procedure.

▸ relate their results to the law of conservation of mass.

RECOMMENDED TIME:

1–2 lab periods

MATERIALS

(for each pair of students)

▸ 1 sheet of aluminum foil

▸ 80 kernels of popcorn for each of the three brands

▸ 250 mL beaker

▸ Bunsen burner with gas tubing and striker

▸ oil (to coat the bottom of the beaker)

▸ ring stand, iron ring, and wire gauze

ESTIMATED COST OF MATERIAL:
$65 000

PRE-LAB DISCUSSION

You may ask some of the following questions for the students to consider as they make their plans:

▸ How will you keep the popcorn from flying out of the beaker as it pops?

▸ Is it best to use all of the popcorn at once or to do several smaller trials?

▸ How often should you measure the mass of the popcorn?

▸ Will you need to measure the mass of any other objects or containers?

TIPS FOR EVALUATING THE PRE-LAB REQUIREMENTS

Some students will want to pop all their kernels on the first trial. Encourage them to save some for a second and third trial. Other students may plan to pop one kernel at a time.

1A | Conservation of Mass
Percentage of Water in Popcorn

THE PROBLEM

Juliette Brand Foods

January 9, 1999

Director of Research
CheMystery Labs, Inc.
52 Fulton Street
Springfield, VA 22150

Dear Director of Research:

Juliette Brand Foods is preparing to enter the rapidly expanding popcorn market with a new popcorn product. As you may know, the key to making popcorn pop is the amount of water contained within the kernel.

Thus far, the product development division has created three different production techniques for the popcorn, each of which creates popcorn with differing amounts of water. We need an independent lab such as yours to measure the percentage of water contained in each sample and to determine which technique produces the best-popping popcorn.

I've enclosed samples from each of the three techniques, labeled "technique beta," "technique gamma," and "technique delta." Please bill us when the work is complete.

Sincerely,

Mary Biedenbecker

Mary Biedenbecker
Director
Product Development Division

References

Popcorn "pops" because of the natural moisture inside each kernel. When the internal water is heated above 100°C, the kernel expands rapidly and the liquid water changes to a gas, which takes up much more room than the liquid.

The percentage of water in popcorn can be determined by the following equation.

$$\frac{mass_{before} - mass_{after}}{mass_{before}} \times 100$$

$$= \% \, H_2O \text{ in unpopped popcorn}$$

The popping process works best when the kernels are first coated with a small amount of vegetable oil. Be certain you account for the presence of this oil when measuring masses.

SOLUTION/MATERIAL PREPARATION

1. Kernels for "technique beta" require no preparation.

2. Kernels for "technique gamma" should be soaked for approximately 1 hour prior to use.

3. Kernels for "technique delta" should be soaked overnight prior to use.

4. Be sure to pat the popcorn dry before giving the treated kernels to the students.

REQUIRED PRECAUTIONS

▸ Safety goggles and a lab apron must be worn at all times.

▸ Long hair and loose clothing must be tied back.

▸ Remind students to use beaker tongs to handle heated glassware; heated glass does not always look hot.

▸ Remind students that the popcorn is for testing only and must not be eaten.

CheMystery Labs, Inc.
52 Fulton Street
Springfield, VA 22150

MEMORANDUM

Date: January 11, 1999

To: Leon Fuller
From: Martha Li-Hsien

We have a budget of $250,000 for this project to take care of equipment, lab space, and labor costs. It is important that we use these funds conservatively and obtain quality results.

Your team needs to design a procedure for determining the percentage of water in three samples of popcorn. Some of the popcorn was damaged in mailing, so each team will have only 80 kernels of popcorn per technique. Be sure to use your samples carefully!

Before you begin the lab work, I must approve your procedure. Give me the following items as soon as possible:
- detailed one-page plan for your procedure, including any necessary data tables
- detailed list of the equipment and materials you will need with itemized and total costs for the accounting department. (Remember, coming in under the $250,000 budget increases our profits, so don't order all the equipment available; order just what you need to get the job done right!)

When finished, prepare a report in the form of a two-page letter to Mary Biedenbecker that includes the following:
- paragraph summarizing how you analyzed the samples
- your findings about the percentage of water in each sample, including calculations and a discussion of the multiple trials
- detailed and organized data table
- graph comparing your findings with those of the other teams
- detailed invoice showing all costs, services, and employee hours spent on this project
- suggestions for reducing costs and improving the analysis procedure

For prices of materials, see Page 692.

Required Precautions

Safety goggles and a lab apron must be worn at all times. Confine long hair and loose clothing.

Do not eat the popcorn; it is for testing purposes only.

Remember, hot glass does not look hot. Be sure to use beaker tongs when handling glassware.

Spill Procedures/ Waste-Disposal Methods

- The popped popcorn should be disposed of in the designated waste container.
- Clean the area and all equipment after use.

SAMPLE DATA

	TECHNIQUE BETA	TECHNIQUE GAMMA	TECHNIQUE DELTA
20 kernels	2.47 g	2.93 g	3.76 g
250 mL beaker	101.40 g	101.40 g	101.40 g
Beaker + oil	101.50 g	101.50 g	101.50 g
Beaker + oil + 20 kernels (before)	103.97 g	104.43 g	105.26 g
Beaker + oil + 20 kernels (after)	103.50 g	103.50 g	103.80 g
Mass of water in 20 kernels	0.47 g	0.93 g	1.46 g
% water in popcorn	19%	32%	39%

Popcorn prepared by technique delta pops very poorly.

Encourage these students to use at least 10 kernels at a time. You may need to explain that for each technique the percentage of water in a sample should be about the same, regardless of the size of the sample.

Be certain students' plans account for measuring the mass of the beaker after oil has been added.

Students often wonder what the foil is for. Remind them of stove-top style popcorn tins. The foil is used to keep the popcorn from being lost, and holes are made in it to allow the water vapor from the popcorn to escape.

TECHNIQUES TO DEMONSTRATE

Review how to use the balance. Students often have difficulty reading the balance to 0.01 g precision. In addition, students often forget to use weighing paper and to measure the mass of the empty glassware.

Review how to use a Bunsen burner. Remind students to close the ports at the end of the barrel on the Bunsen burner before lighting it.

PROPOSED PROCEDURE

Cover the beaker in which the popcorn is being popped with foil. Put holes in the foil to allow the water vapor to escape.

Measure the mass of the unpopped kernels. (Twenty kernels work well.)

Measure the mass of the beaker.

Measure the mass of the beaker with the uncooked popcorn and vegetable oil coating.

Heat the popcorn until the majority of the kernels have popped. The popcorn pops more efficiently if the beaker is held firmly with tongs and gently shaken side to side on the wire gauze.

Allow the beaker to cool for 5 minutes. Measure the mass of the beaker, popped corn, and vegetable oil. Subtract the "before" and "after" masses of the popcorn to determine the mass of water in the kernels.

DISPOSAL

There are no special disposal requirements, but provide a waste container for the popcorn to emphasize that it is not to be eaten.

2A

OBJECTIVES

Students will:

▸ use appropriate lab safety procedures.

▸ use a laboratory balance to measure mass.

▸ use a graduated cylinder to measure volume.

▸ use a ruler to measure length.

▸ relate the increment used on a measuring tool to the precision of measurements made with the tool.

▸ collect and organize data.

▸ calculate values from experimental measurements.

▸ relate accuracy to calculations of percentage error.

▸ relate precision to calculations of absolute deviation, average deviation, and uncertainty.

▸ calculate an average value from class data and use it to calculate absolute deviation and average deviation.

RECOMMENDED TIME:

1 lab period

MATERIALS

(for each lab group)

▸ 15 cm plastic ruler

▸ 20 g metal shot (Any type of metal shot will do, but aluminum and copper are recommended.)

▸ 25 mL graduated cylinder (for best results, marked in 0.2 mL or 0.5 mL increments)

▸ 100 mL graduated cylinder

▸ 250 mL beaker

▸ balance (Centigram balances will give best results, but less precise balances are acceptable.)

▸ Celsius thermometer, nonmercury type, with a range from −10°C to 120°C (Students should use only nonmercury thermometers. If a mercury thermometer breaks, the droplets that are not cleaned up will quickly evaporate, creating toxic mercury vapors.)

2A | Accuracy and Precision

OBJECTIVES

▸ Use experimental measurements in calculations.

▸ Demonstrate proficiency in measuring masses and volumes.

▸ Organize data by compiling it in tables.

▸ Calculate an average value from class data.

▸ Relate absolute deviation, average deviation, uncertainty, and percentage error, and use them as methods for gauging accuracy and precision.

MATERIALS

▸ 15 cm plastic ruler

▸ 25 mL graduated cylinder

▸ 100 mL graduated cylinder

▸ 250 mL beaker

▸ balance

▸ chemical handbook or other source of density values for water and metals

▸ distilled water

▸ metal shot

▸ nonmercury thermometer

▸ stopwatch or clock with a second hand

OPTIONAL EQUIPMENT

▸ CBL unit

▸ graphing calculator with link cable

▸ Vernier temperature probe

Situation

As part of your orientation as a new employee at a chemical firm, you must participate in an assessment of your lab skills. This survey will help you evaluate the accuracy of your equipment and the precision of your lab technique.

Background

Accuracy is how close to the actual value a measurement is; *precision* is how close each measurement is to others in the set.

The accuracy of a measurement can be determined only if you have some way of knowing what the measurement should be. One indicator of accuracy is the percentage error, which can be calculated using the following equation.

$$\frac{\text{value}_{\text{accepted}} - \text{value}_{\text{measured}}}{\text{value}_{\text{accepted}}} \times 100 = \text{percentage error}$$

REQUIRED PRECAUTIONS

▸ Safety goggles and a lab apron must be worn at all times.

▸ Confine loose clothing and long hair.

▸ Read all safety precautions, and discuss them with your students.

Precision indicates whether the experimental data are consistent. Three common statistical tools used to check precision are *absolute deviation, average deviation,* and *uncertainty in measurement.* Absolute deviation is the difference between a single experimental value and the average of all values. Average deviation is the sum of the absolute deviations for an entire data set divided by the total number of measurements. The uncertainty of a measurement is expressed as plus or minus one unit of the last significant digit, indicating the last digit is an estimate. The percentage uncertainty is determined by dividing the uncertainty by the measurement and multiplying this value by 100, as shown.

$$\frac{\pm\,0.01\ cm}{24.65\ cm} \times 100 = \pm\,0.04\%$$

Problem

You will use measurement and analysis skills to evaluate measurements of length, volume, mass, and temperature. You will also determine the identity of a metal sample by calculating its density and comparing the result to density values for various metals found in chemical handbooks.

Data Table 1

Measuring tool	Smallest division
Ruler	
100 mL graduated cylinder	
25 mL graduated cylinder	
Balance	

Data Table 2

Inside diameter of 100 mL cylinder		Mass of 25 mL cylinder with water and metal	
Height of 50 mL mark on 100 mL cylinder		Temperature of water (after 2 min)	
Mass of dry 25 mL cylinder		(after 4 minutes)	
Volume of water added to 25 mL cylinder		(after 6 minutes)	
Mass of 25 mL cylinder with water		(after 8 minutes)	
Volume of metal shot and water		Density of water at above temperature from handbook	

- chemical handbook with density values for water and various metals (for example, *CRC Handbook of Chemistry and Physics,* or *Lange's Handbook of Chemistry*)
- distilled water

OPTIONAL EQUIPMENT
- CBL unit
- graphing calculator with link cable
- Vernier temperature probe (If your students are using the Vernier probe to take temperature measurements, refer to page 700 for equipment setup.)

PRE-LAB DISCUSSION
Review the terms *accuracy, precision,* and *uncertainty.* For most students, this may be their first exposure to the concept of uncertainty in measurements. Students frequently equate science with absolute certainty, rather than with measurements of definite uncertainty.

TECHNIQUES TO DEMONSTRATE
Review the use of the analytical balance. Remind the students to check that the balance is properly calibrated before making a measurement, and be certain that students use the same balance for each measurement.

Remind students to measure volumes from the bottom of the meniscus.

DISPOSAL
There are no special disposal guidelines. The metal shot can be reused for each class.

SAMPLE DATA

MEASURING TOOL	SMALLEST DIVISION
Ruler	1 mm (0.1 cm)
100 mL graduated cylinder	1 mL
25 mL graduated cylinder	0.2 mL
Balance	0.01 g

SAMPLE DATA

MEASUREMENTS OF **100 mL** GRADUATED CYLINDER	
Inside diameter	2.5 cm
Inside height of 50 mL mark	9.3 cm

Preparation

1. Organizing Data
Copy the data tables on page 709 in your lab notebook.

2. Locate a handbook for finding densities of metals and for determining the density of water at various temperatures.

3. If you are using the Vernier temperature probe and CBL units, refer to pages 700–701 for equipment setup.

Technique

4. Record in your data table the smallest division on the ruler and the smallest division on the 100 mL graduated cylinder.

5. Measure the inside diameter of the 100 mL graduated cylinder using the ruler. Measure the height of the cylinder's 50 mL mark. Record these measurements in your data table.

6. Examine the 25 mL graduated cylinder. What is the smallest division? Examine the scale on the balance. What is the smallest division? Record the answers with units in your data table.

7. Using the balance, determine the mass of the dry 25 mL cylinder to the nearest 0.1 g. Record this mass in your data table.

8. Fill the 250 mL beaker half-full with water. Using a thermometer or a Vernier temperature probe, determine the temperature of the water to the nearest 0.1°C. To do this, gently put the thermometer or probe in the water, being careful not to break it. Wait 2 minutes before recording the temperature of the water in your lab notebook. After another 2 minutes, record the temperature again. Repeat this process every 2 minutes until two consecutive temperature measurements are the same. In a handbook, look up the density of water at that temperature, and record it in your data table. **Never use a thermometer to stir anything. It will break easily. The glass wall surrounding the bulb must be very thin to**

Figure A

provide quick and accurate temperature readings.

9. Pour between 10 mL and 15 mL of water from the beaker into the 25 mL graduated cylinder. Read the volume to the nearest 0.1 mL, and record it in your data table. Determine the combined mass of the water and the cylinder to the nearest 0.1 g, as shown in **Figure A.** Record this value in your data table. Keep the water in the cylinder for the next step.

10. Add enough of the sample of metal shot to the cylinder to increase the volume by at least 5 mL. Determine the volume and the mass of the water and shot together in the graduated cylinder, and record your measurements.

Cleanup and Disposal

11. Clean all apparatus and your lab station. Remove the metal shot from the cylinder, and place it in the container designated by your teacher. Pour the water down the sink. Wash your hands thoroughly after cleaning up the lab area and equipment.

Analysis and Interpretation

1. Organizing Data
What is the uncertainty in a measurement made by each of these devices: the ruler, the

SAMPLE DATA	
MEASUREMENTS WITH 25 mL GRADUATED CYLINDER	
Mass of empty cylinder	42.39 g
Volume of H_2O	13.8 mL
Mass of cylinder + H_2O	55.98 g
Volume of metal + H_2O	20.2 mL
Mass of metal + H_2O + cylinder	73.98 g

Temperature of H_2O: 25°C
Density of H_2O from handbook: 0.997 g/mL

100 mL graduated cylinder, the 25 mL graduated cylinder, and the balance?

2. Organizing Data

Calculate the volume of the 100 mL graduated cylinder up to its 50 mL mark. (Hint: $V = \pi r^2 h$ for a cylinder.)

3. Analyzing Data

Assume the accepted value for the volume of a graduated cylinder up to the 50 mL mark is 50.00 mL. Calculate the percentage error in your calculations from item 2.

4. Organizing Data

Calculate the mass of water as determined by the balance. Calculate the mass of water from its measured volume and its known density. Using the mass obtained by the balance as the accepted value and the value calculated from the density as the experimental value, calculate the percentage error. Be sure to follow significant-figure rules in your calculations.

5. Organizing Data

Subtract the volume of the water from the combined volume of the metal and the water to calculate the volume of the metal alone. Subtract the mass of the water and cylinder from the mass of the metal, water, and cylinder to determine the mass of the metal; then calculate its density. Show all your work.

6. Evaluating Data

Record the metal-density calculations made by the other teams, and calculate the average density of the unknown metal. Calculate the average deviation for the measurements.

Conclusions

7. Inferring Conclusions

Compare your value and the class average of the unknown metal's density with the densities for metals given in the handbook. Determine the identity of the metal.

8. Evaluating Methods

Calculate the percentage error by comparing your experimental value with the value you found in the handbook. Then calculate percentage error for the class average. Which is more accurate, the class average or your value?

Extensions

1. Evaluating Conclusions

Marie and Jason determined the density of a liquid three times. The values they obtained were 2.84 g/mL, 2.85 g/mL, and 2.80 g/mL. The accepted value is 2.40 g/mL. Are the values that Marie and Jason determined precise? Are the values accurate? Explain your answers. Calculate the percentage error and uncertainty of each measurement.

2. Applying Ideas

When you are cutting the legs of a table to make them shorter, precision is more important than accuracy. Explain why.

3. Applying Ideas

A store has a balance with a scale marked in gram units, and each unit is divided in half by a smaller mark. A student working in the store after school measured a sample mass as 5.367 g using this balance. What is wrong with this measurement?

4. Applying Ideas

It is said that the ancient Greek mathematician and scientist Archimedes used density to determine that a goldsmith had cheated when making a crown for the king. Explain what steps you would take to alter this lab procedure to check a metal's purity.

The uncertainty of each measurement is ±0.005 mL. Calculations for percent error are shown below.

$$\frac{2.40 \text{ mL} - 2.84 \text{ g/mL}}{2.40 \text{ g/mL}} \times 100 = -18\% \text{ error}$$

$$\frac{2.40 \text{ mL} - 2.85 \text{ g/mL}}{2.40 \text{ g/mL}} \times 100 = -19\% \text{ error}$$

$$\frac{2.40 \text{ mL} - 2.80 \text{ g/mL}}{2.40 \text{ g/mL}} \times 100 = -17\% \text{ error}$$

2. If the precision is poor, the legs will be of unequal length, and the table will wobble.

3. This measurement is reported with the wrong number of significant figures for the precision of the measuring tool. If the balance's uncertainty is ±0.5 g, the most precise measurement would be 5.5 g.

4. The purity of the metal could be checked by comparing the volume and mass of a container of water before and after the crown was added. Then the density of the metal could be compared with the density of an object known to be pure gold. It would be necessary to choose a container large enough for the crown and the water.

ANSWERS

ANALYSIS AND INTERPRETATION

1. ruler: ±0.5 mm (0.05 cm)
    100 mL graduated cylinder: ±0.5 mL
    25 mL graduated cylinder: ±0.1 mL
    balance: ±0.005 g

2. $V = (3.14)\left(\dfrac{2.5 \text{ cm}}{2}\right)^2 (9.3 \text{ cm})$
    $V = 46 \text{ cm}^3 = 46 \text{ mL}$

3. $\dfrac{50.00 \text{ mL} - 46 \text{ mL}}{50 \text{ mL}} \times 100 = 8\% \text{ error}$

4. 55.98 g – 42.39 g = 13.59 g
    0.997 g/mL × 13.8 mL = 13.8 g
    $\dfrac{13.59 \text{ g} - 13.8 \text{ g}}{13.59 \text{ g}} \times 100 = -2\% \text{ error}$

5. 20.2 mL – 13.8 mL = 6.4 mL
    73.98 g – 55.98 g = 18.00 g
    $\dfrac{18.00 \text{ g}}{6.4 \text{ mL}} = 2.8 \text{ g/mL}$

6. Answers will vary depending on the data for the rest of the class. Be certain that calculations follow rules for significant figures.

CONCLUSIONS

7. Answers will vary depending upon which type of metal shot was used for analysis. The sample data represents values taken for aluminum.

8. Answers will vary. A sample calculation for aluminum is shown below. For most values, the class average will be more accurate.
    $$\frac{2.7 \text{ mL} - 2.8 \text{ g/mL}}{2.7 \text{ g/mL}} \times 100 = -4\% \text{ error}$$

EXTENSIONS

1. The measurements described are precise because they are all close to each other. However, they are far from the accepted value, so they are not accurate.

2B | Separation of Mixtures

OBJECTIVES

Students will:

▶ use appropriate lab safety procedures.

▶ interpret a temperature–solubility graph.

▶ measure temperature.

▶ use a Bunsen burner and an ice bath to control temperature.

▶ use a laboratory balance to measure mass.

▶ demonstrate appropriate technique in transferring liquids.

▶ demonstrate appropriate technique in filtering.

RECOMMENDED TIME:

2 lab periods if filtering is done once (includes overnight drying time)

MATERIALS

(for each lab group)

▶ 20 g rock salt

▶ 50 mL NaCl-KNO₃ solution

▶ 100 mL graduated cylinder

▶ 150 mL beakers, 4

▶ beaker tongs or hot mitt

▶ centigram balance

▶ Celsius thermometer, nonmercury type, with a range from –10°C to 120°C

▶ hot plate or Bunsen burner with gas tubing and striker

▶ ice, about 1.5 L

▶ ring stand, ring, and wire gauze (nonasbestos)

▶ rubber policeman and glass stirring rod

▶ spatula

▶ tray, tub, or pneumatic trough for ice bath

GRAVITY FILTRATION OPTION

▶ glass funnel

▶ filter paper

OBJECTIVES

▶ Recognize how the solubility of a salt varies with temperature.

▶ Demonstrate proficiency in fractional crystallization and in vacuum filtration or gravity filtration.

▶ Determine the percentage of two salts recovered by fractional crystallization.

MATERIALS

▶ 50 mL NaCl–KNO₃ solution

▶ 100 mL graduated cylinder

▶ 150 mL beakers, 4

▶ balance

▶ beaker tongs or hot mitt

▶ Bunsen burner and related equipment or hot plate

▶ distilled water

▶ filter paper

▶ glass stirring rod

▶ ice

▶ nonmercury thermometer

▶ ring and wire gauze

▶ ring stand

▶ rock salt

▶ rubber policeman

▶ spatula

▶ tray, tub, or pneumatic trough

▶ vacuum filtration setup with Büchner funnel, one-hole rubber stopper, filter flask, and tubing; or gravity-filtration setup with glass funnel, ring, and ring stand

OPTIONAL EQUIPMENT

▶ CBL unit

▶ graphing calculator with link cable

▶ Vernier temperature probe

Situation

Your company has been contacted by a firework factory. A mislabeled container of sodium chloride, NaCl, was accidentally mixed with potassium nitrate, KNO₃. KNO₃ is used as an oxidizer in fireworks to ensure that the fireworks burn thoroughly. The fireworks company wants your company to investigate ways they could separate the two compounds. They have provided an aqueous solution of the mixture for you to work with.

SOLUTION/MATERIAL PREPARATION

1. For every liter of solution, add about 140 g of NaCl and 320 g of KNO₃. It is necessary to stir and gently heat the solution to completely dissolve the salts. A hot-plate stirrer is a valuable tool.

2. Students should use only nonmercury thermometers. If a mercury thermometer breaks, the droplets that are not cleaned up will quickly evaporate, creating toxic mercury vapors.

3. Centigram balances will give best results, but less precise balances are acceptable.

Always wear safety goggles and a lab apron to protect your eyes and clothing. If you get a chemical in your eyes, immediately flush the chemical out at the eyewash station while calling to your teacher. Know the location of the emergency lab shower and eyewash station and the procedures for using them.

Do not touch any chemicals. If you get a chemical on your skin or clothing, wash the chemical off at the sink while calling to your teacher. Make sure you carefully read the labels and follow the precautions on all containers of chemicals that you use. If no precautions are stated on the label, ask your teacher what precautions to follow. Do not taste any chemicals or items used in the laboratory. Never return leftover chemicals to their original containers; take only small amounts to avoid wasting supplies.

When using a Bunsen burner, confine long hair and loose clothing. If your clothing catches on fire, WALK to the emergency lab shower and use it to put out the fire. Do not heat glassware that is broken, chipped, or cracked. Use tongs or a hot mitt to handle heated glassware and other equipment; heated glassware does not always look hot.

Background

The substances in a mixture can be separated by physical means. For example, if one substance dissolves in a liquid solvent but another does not, the mixture can be filtered. The substance that dissolved will be carried through the filter by the solvent, but the other substance will not. Because both NaCl and KNO_3 dissolve in water, filtering alone cannot separate them. However, there are differences in the way they dissolve. The graph in Figure A shows the same amount of sodium chloride dissolving in water regardless of the temperature of the water. On the other hand, potassium nitrate is very soluble in warm water but much less soluble at 0°C.

Problem

You will make use of the differences in solubility to separate the two salts. This technique is known as fractional crystallization. If the water solution of NaCl and KNO_3 is cooled from room temperature to a temperature near 0°C, some KNO_3 will crystallize. This KNO_3 residue can then be separated from the NaCl solution by filtration. The NaCl can be isolated from the filtrate by evaporation of the water. To determine whether this method is efficient, you will measure the mass of each of the recovered substances. Then your client can decide whether this method is cost-effective.

Figure A This graph shows the relationship between temperature and the solubility of NaCl and KNO_3.

VACUUM FILTRATION OPTION

▸ aspirator for spigot
▸ Büchner funnel (either ceramic or plastic)
▸ filter paper
▸ one-hole rubber stopper or sleeve
▸ vacuum flask (sidearm flask) and tubing

OPTIONAL EQUIPMENT

▸ CBL unit
▸ graphing calculator with link cable
▸ Vernier temperature probe (If your students are using the Vernier probe to take temperature measurements, refer to page 700 for equipment setup.)

PRE-LAB DISCUSSION

Thoroughly discuss the procedure used in this lab. Students need to work quickly and efficiently in order to complete this lab in one lab period. If students work in a step-by-step process, the lab may take too long. Instead, encourage them to perform multiple tasks simultaneously through teamwork. While one partner is cooling the solution, the other lab partner could be cleaning, drying, and measuring the mass of the other beakers.

Students may have difficulty reading the solubility graph. It is not necessary for students to understand all aspects of solutions and solubility, but an understanding of this graph is important to understanding the concept of fractional crystallization; therefore, explain the graph thoroughly. Practice taking several readings from the graph, asking students how many grams of each salt would dissolve in 100 g of water at a given temperature. Relate the results to the cycles of cooling and heating in the procedure.

Results are greatly improved if a second filtration step is performed after a little water has evaporated, but this takes more time.

Students get very frustrated when their results do not match calculated ideal values. Students should realize when they answer Conclusions item 9 that it is impossible to achieve a perfect separation using this technique.

REQUIRED PRECAUTIONS

▸ Safety goggles and a lab apron must be worn at all times.

▸ Read all safety precautions, and discuss them with your students.

▸ Remind students that when equipment has been heated, it should be handled with tongs or a hot mitt; heated glassware does not always look hot.

This exploration provides an opportunity for discussions about the uncertain nature of science and the constant need to improve on lab techniques at all levels of science.

TECHNIQUES TO DEMONSTRATE

Be sure to review the vocabulary associated with filtration, especially the difference between the filtrate and the residue.

Review the vacuum filtration setup if your students are using this technique. This method speeds up the lab considerably. (Plastic Büchner funnels are far less prone to breakage than glass funnels or ceramic Büchner funnels.)

Review the gravity filtration, especially folding the filter paper, if your students are using this technique.

You will also need to show students how to use a rubber policeman to collect crystals. Remind students to evaporate the water gradually to avoid violent bubbling and loss of product.

DISPOSAL

Potassium nitrate, KNO_3, cannot be disposed of in any manner because it is a strong oxidizer. However, it can be reused the next time you do this lab. Dry the crystals in a separate disposal container, and then store the dried crystals in sealed, labeled glass bottles completely away from the bottles of reducing substances, especially those that can burn. Reuse the crystals the following year instead of ordering more. Because this is a separation exercise, it does not matter if impurities are present.

FILTRATION-TECHNIQUE OPTION

Figure B   Vacuum filtration

Figure C   Gravity filtration

Vacuum-Filtration Setup

1. To set up a vacuum filtration, screw an aspirator nozzle onto the faucet. Attach the other end of the plastic tubing to the side arm of the filter flask.

2. Place a one-hole rubber stopper on the stem of the funnel, and fit the stopper snugly in the neck of the filter flask, as shown in **Figure B.**

3. Place a piece of filter paper on the bottom of the funnel so that it is flat and covers all of the holes in the funnel.

4. When you are ready, turn on the water at the faucet that has the aspirator nozzle attached. This creates a vacuum, which helps the filtering process go much faster. If the suction is working properly, the filter paper should be pulled against the bottom of the funnel, covering all of the holes. If the filter paper appears to have bubbles of air under it or is not centered well, turn the water off, reposition the filter paper, and begin again.

Gravity-Filtration Setup

1. Set up a ring stand with a ring. Gently rest a glass funnel inside the ring, and place a beaker under the glass funnel, as shown in **Figure C.**

2. Fold a piece of filter paper in half along its diameter, and then fold it again to

form a quadrant, as shown in **Figure D.** Separate the folds of the filter paper so that three thicknesses are on one side and one thickness is on the other.

3. Fit the filter paper in the funnel, and wet it with a little water so that it will adhere to the sides of the funnel. Gently but firmly press the paper against the sides of the funnel so that no air is between the funnel and the filter paper. Be certain that the filter paper does not extend above the sides of the funnel.

(a)   (b)

(c)   (d)

Figure D   Filter paper

Preparation

1. Organizing Data

Copy the data table below in your lab notebook.

2. Obtain four clean, dry 150 mL beakers, and label them 1, 2, 3, and 4.

3. If you are using the Vernier temperature probe and CBL unit, refer to pages 700–701 for equipment setup.

4. Set up your filtering apparatus. If you are using a Büchner funnel for vacuum filtration or a glass funnel for gravity filtration, follow the setup procedure on page 714.

Technique

5. Measure the mass of beaker 1 to the nearest 0.01 g, and record the mass in your data table.

6. Measure about 50 mL of the NaCl–KNO$_3$ solution into a graduated cylinder. Record the exact volume in your data table. Pour this mixture into beaker 1.

7. Using a thermometer or a temperature probe, measure the temperature of the mixture. Record this temperature in your data table.

8. Measure the mass of a piece of filter paper to the nearest 0.01 g, and record the mass in your data table.

Data Table
Mass of beaker 1
Volume of NaCl–KNO$_3$ solution in beaker 1
Temperature of mixture before cooling
Mass of the filter paper
Mass of beaker 4
Mass of beaker 4 with NaCl
Mass of beaker 1 with filter paper and KNO$_3$
Temperature of mixture after cooling

9. Make an ice bath by filling a tray, tub, or trough half-full with ice. Add a handful of rock salt. The salt lowers the freezing point of water so that the ice bath can cool to a lower temperature. Fill the ice bath with water until it is three-quarters full.

10. Using a fresh supply of ice and distilled water, fill beaker 2 half-full with ice, and add water. Do not add rock salt to this ice-water mixture. You will use this water to wash your purified salt.

11. Put beaker 1 with your NaCl–KNO$_3$ solution into the ice bath. Place a thermometer or a temperature probe in the solution to monitor the temperature. Stir the solution with a stirring rod while it cools. The lower the temperature of the mixture is, the more KNO$_3$ that will crystallize out of solution. When the temperature nears 4°C, proceed with step 11a if you are using the Büchner funnel or step 11b if you are using a glass funnel. **Never stir a solution with a thermometer; the bulb is very fragile.**

a. Vacuum filtration

Prepare the filtering apparatus by pouring approximately 50 mL of ice-cold distilled water from beaker 2 through the filter paper. After the water has gone through the funnel, empty the filter flask into the sink. Reconnect the filter flask, and pour the salt-and-water mixture in beaker 1 into the funnel. Use the rubber policeman to transfer all of the cooled mixture into the funnel, especially any crystals that are visible. It may be helpful to add small amounts of ice-cold water from beaker 2 to beaker 1 to wash any crystals onto the filter paper. After all of the solution has passed through the funnel, wash the KNO$_3$ residue by pouring a very small amount of ice-cold water from beaker 2 over it. When this water has passed through the filter paper, turn off the faucet and carefully remove the tubing from the aspirator. Empty the filtrate, which has passed through the filter paper and is now in the filter flask, into beaker 3. When finished, continue with step 12.

SAMPLE DATA	
Volume of solution added to beaker 1	46.5 mL
Mass of beaker 1	65.80 g
Mass of filter paper	0.40 g
Mass of beaker 1, filter paper, and KNO$_3$ (Day 2)	78.22 g

SAMPLE DATA	
Mass of beaker 4	66.25 g
Mass of beaker 4 with NaCl	72.37 g
Temperature before cooling	25°C
Temperature after cooling	–2°C

b. Gravity filtration

Place beaker 3 under the glass funnel. Prepare the filtering apparatus by pouring approximately 50 mL of ice-cold water from beaker 2 through the filter paper. The water will pass through the filter paper and drip into beaker 3. When the dripping stops, empty beaker 3 into the sink. Place beaker 3 back under the glass funnel so that it will collect the filtrate from the funnel. Pour the salt-water mixture into the funnel. Use the rubber policeman to transfer all of the cooled mixture into the funnel, especially any visible crystals. It may be helpful to add small amounts of ice-cold water from beaker 2 to beaker 1 to wash any crystals onto the filter paper. After all of the solution has passed through the funnel, wash the KNO_3 by pouring a very small amount of ice-cold water from beaker 2 over it.

12. After you have finished filtering, use either a hot plate or a Bunsen burner, ring stand, ring, and wire gauze to heat beaker 3. When the liquid in beaker 3 begins to boil, continue heating gently until enough water has vaporized to decrease the volume to approximately 25–30 mL. **Be sure to use beaker tongs. Remember that hot glassware does not always look hot.**

13. Allow the solution in beaker 3 to cool. Then set it in the ice bath and stir until the temperature is approximately 4°C.

14. Measure the mass of beaker 4, and record the mass in your data table.

15. Repeat step 11a or step 11b, pouring the solution from beaker 3 onto the filter paper and using beaker 4 to collect the filtrate that passes through the filter.

16. Wash and dry beaker 1. Carefully remove the filter paper with the KNO_3 from the funnel, and put it in the beaker. Avoid spilling the crystals. Place the beaker in a drying oven overnight.

Figure E Use beaker tongs to move a beaker that has been heated, even if you believe that the beaker is cool.

17. Heat beaker 4 with a hot plate or Bunsen burner until the water begins to boil. Continue to heat the beaker gently until all of the water has vaporized and the salt appears dry. Turn off the hot plate or burner, and allow the beaker to cool. Use beaker tongs to move the beaker, as shown in **Figure E.** Measure the mass of beaker 4 with the NaCl to the nearest 0.01 g, and record the mass in your data table.

18. The next day, use beaker tongs to remove beaker 1 with the filter paper and KNO_3 from the drying oven. Allow the beaker to cool. Measure the mass using the same balance you used to measure the mass of the empty beaker. Record the new mass in your data table. **Be sure to use beaker tongs. Remember that hot glassware does not always look hot.**

Cleanup and Disposal

19. Clean all apparatus and your lab station. Once the mass of the NaCl has been determined, add water to dissolve the NaCl, and rinse the solution down the drain. Do not wash KNO_3 down the drain. Dispose of the KNO_3 in the waste container designated by your teacher. Wash your hands thoroughly after all lab work is finished and before you leave the lab.

Analysis and Interpretation

1. Organizing Data
Find the mass of NaCl in your 50 mL sample by subtracting the mass of the empty beaker 4 from the mass of beaker 4 with NaCl.

2. Organizing Data
Find the mass of KNO_3 in your 50 mL sample by subtracting the mass of beaker 1 and the mass of the filter paper from the mass of beaker 1 with the filter paper and KNO_3.

3. Organizing Data
Determine the total mass of the two salts.

4. Analyzing Information
How many grams of KNO_3 and NaCl would be found in a 1.0 L sample of the solution? (Hint: For each substance, make a conversion factor using the mass of the compound and the volume of the solution.)

5. Interpreting Graphics
Use the graph at the beginning of this exploration to determine how much of each compound would dissolve in 100 g of water at room temperature and at the temperature of your ice-water bath.

Conclusions

6. Inferring Conclusions
Calculate the percentage by mass of NaCl in the salt mixture. Calculate the percentage by mass of KNO_3 in the salt mixture. Assume that the density of your 50 mL solution is 1.0 g/mL.

7. Applying Conclusions
The fireworks company has another 55 L of the salt mixture dissolved in water just like the sample you worked with. How many kilograms of each compound can the company expect to recover from this sample? (Hint: Use your answer from item 4 to help you answer this question.)

8. Evaluating Methods
Use the graph shown at the beginning of this exploration to estimate how much KNO_3 could still be contaminating the NaCl you recovered.

9. Relating Ideas
Use the graph shown at the beginning of this exploration to explain why it is impossible to completely separate the two compounds by fractional crystallization.

10. Evaluating Methods
Why was it important to use ice-cold water to wash the KNO_3 after filtration?

11. Evaluating Methods
If it was important to use very cold water to wash the KNO_3, why wasn't the salt-and-ice-water mixture from the bath used? After all, it had a lower temperature than the ice and distilled water from beaker 2. (Hint: Consider what is contained in rock salt.)

12. Evaluating Methods
Why was it important to keep the amount of cold water used to wash the KNO_3 as small as possible?

Extensions

1. Interpreting Graphics
Using the graph shown at the beginning of this exploration, determine the minimum mass of water necessary to dissolve the amounts of each compound from Analysis and Interpretation items 1 and 2. Calculate the mass dissolved at room temperature and at 4°C. What volumes of water would be necessary? (Hint: The density of water is about 1.0 g/mL.)

2. Designing Experiments
Describe how you could use the properties of the compounds to test the purity of your recovered samples. If your teacher approves your plan, use it to check your separation of the mixtures. (Hint: Check a chemical handbook for more information about the properties of NaCl and KNO_3.)

3. Designing Experiments
How could you improve the yield or the purity of the compounds you recovered? If you can think of ways to modify the procedure, ask your teacher to approve your plan, and run the procedure again.

ANALYSIS AND INTERPRETATION

1. 72.37 g − 66.25 g = 6.12 g NaCl

2. 78.22 g − 65.80 g = 12.42 g KNO_3

3. 12.42 g + 6.12 g = 18.54 g total

4. $1.0 \text{ L} \times \dfrac{6.12 \text{ g NaCl}}{46.5 \text{ mL}} \times$
   $\dfrac{1000 \text{ mL}}{1 \text{ L}} = 132 \text{ g NaCl}$

   $1.0 \text{ L} \times \dfrac{12.42 \text{ g } KNO_3}{46.5 \text{ mL}} \times$
   $\dfrac{1000 \text{ mL}}{1 \text{ L}} = 267 \text{ g } KNO_3$

5. At room temperature, 25°C, about 32 g of KNO_3 and 35 g of NaCl will dissolve in 100 g of water. At −2°C, 15 g of KNO_3 and 33 g of NaCl will dissolve in 100 g of water.

CONCLUSIONS

6. $\dfrac{6.12 \text{ g NaCl}}{18.56 \text{ g total}} \times 100 = 33.0\% \text{ NaCl}$

   $\dfrac{12.42 \text{ g } KNO_3}{18.56 \text{ g total}} \times 100 = 66.92\% \text{ } KNO_3$

7. $55 \text{ L} \times \dfrac{132 \text{ g NaCl}}{1 \text{ L}} \times \dfrac{1 \text{ kg}}{1000 \text{ g}} = 7.3 \text{ kg}$

   $55 \text{ L} \times \dfrac{267 \text{ g } KNO_3}{1 \text{ L}} \times \dfrac{1 \text{ kg}}{1000 \text{ g}} = 15 \text{ kg}$

8. As much as 7 g of KNO_3 could still be contaminating the NaCl if the solution was filtered only once.

9. Because the solubility of KNO_3 is never 0.0 g, it is always possible that some of the KNO_3 is dissolved in the solution after filtration.

10. Because the water was ice cold, the KNO_3 did not dissolve very well in it. But if there was any NaCl mixed with the KNO_3 crystals, the NaCl would have dissolved in the ice-cold water and passed through the filter paper.

11. Although the rock salt and ice mixture was cooler, it contained NaCl and would have contaminated the KNO_3 crystals if it had been used in the rinsing step.

12. By using a small amount of water to wash the crystals, students kept the amount of KNO_3 that redissolved in the water to a minimum.

EXTENSIONS

1. 17.5 g H_2O to dissolve 6.12 g NaCl at 25°C

   38.8 g H_2O to dissolve 12.42 g KNO_3 at 25°C

   18.5 g H_2O to dissolve 6.12 g NaCl at −2°C

   82.8 g H_2O to dissolve 12.42 g KNO_3 at −2°C

2. Suggestions for determining purity will vary but could include measuring the density or testing the melting point. The latter would require special equipment.

3. Suggestions for improving purity will vary. Be sure answers are safe and include carefully planned procedures.

2B | Separation of Mixtures
Mining Contract

OBJECTIVES

Students will:

▶ use appropriate lab safety procedures.

▶ measure temperature.

▶ use a Bunsen burner and an ice bath to control temperature.

▶ use a laboratory balance to measure mass.

▶ demonstrate appropriate technique in transferring liquids.

▶ demonstrate appropriate technique in filtering.

▶ design and implement their own procedure.

RECOMMENDED TIME:
2 lab periods

PREREQUISITE:
Exploration 2B

MATERIALS

(for each pair of students)

▶ 1.5 mL ice

▶ 20 g rock salt

▶ 50 mL $Cu(NO_3)_2 \cdot KNO_3$ solution

▶ 100 mL graduated cylinder

▶ 250 mL beakers, 2

▶ balance

▶ Celsius thermometer, nonmercury type, with a range from −10°C to 120°C

▶ hot plate or Bunsen burner with gas tubing and striker

▶ plastic bags, 2

▶ ring stand, ring, and wire gauze (nonasbestos)

▶ rubber policeman and glass stirring rod

▶ spatula

▶ tray, tub, or pneumatic trough for ice bath

ESTIMATED COST OF MATERIALS:
$100 000–$107 500

THE PROBLEM

GOLDSTAKE MINING COMPANY

January 20, 1999

George Taylor
Director of Analytical Services
CheMystery Labs, Inc.
52 Fulton Street
Springfield, VA 22150

Dear George:

I thought of your new company when a problem came up here at Goldstake. I think I have a job for you. While performing exploratory drilling for natural gas near Afton in western Wyoming, our engineers encountered a new subterranean geothermal aquifer. We estimate the size of the aquifer to be 1×10^{12} liters.

The Bureau of Land Management advised us to alert the Environmental Protection Agency. Preliminary qualitative test of the water identified two dissolved salts: potassium nitrate and copper nitrate.

The EPA is concerned that a full-scale mining operation may harm the environment if the salts are present in large quantities. They're requiring us to halt all operations while we obtain more information for an environmental impact statement. We need your firm to separate, purify, and make a determination of the amounts of the two salts in the Afton Aquifer.

Sincerely,

Lynn L. Brown

Lynn L. Brown
Director of Operations
Goldstake Mining Corporation

718   INVESTIGATION 2B

References

The procedure for this Investigation is similar to one your team recently completed involving the separation of sodium chloride, NaCl and potassium nitrate, KNO_3 in Exploration 2B.

SOLUTION/MATERIAL PREPARATION

1. To prepare the unknown solution for 15 lab groups, dissolve 300 g of KNO_3 and 150 g of $Cu(NO_3)_2 \cdot 3H_2O$ in 900 mL of water. Slowly heat the solution while stirring until the two salts are completely dissolved. Each 50 mL sample should contain approximately 15 g of KNO_3 and 7.5 g of $Cu(NO_3)_2$. There is no need to reheat the solution before the lab.

REQUIRED PRECAUTIONS

▶ Safety goggles and a lab apron must be worn at all times.

▶ Read all safety precautions, and discuss them with your students.

▶ Remind students to use beaker tongs or a hot mitt when handling glassware that has been heated.

▶ If a hot plate is used, the precautions listed on page 693 must be followed to prevent electric shock.

THE PLAN

CheMystery Labs, Inc.
52 Fulton Street
Springfield, VA 22150

MEMORANDUM

Date: January 23, 1999
To: Andre Kalaviencz
From: George Taylor

We received this contract because the D.O. at Goldstake is an old friend of mine. She knows we're a new company and hungry for work. It's important that we get her an answer quickly and accurately. We can't afford to fail.

Because this is our first mining-industry contract, we need to plan carefully to get good results at minimum cost. Each research team will receive a 50.0 mL sample of the aquifer water, but that's all.

I'd like the following information from each analytical team before the work begins.
- detailed one-page plan for the procedure that you will use to accomplish the analysis, including all necessary data tables
- list of the materials and supplies you will need and their individual and total costs
(Remember, with all the costs associated with starting the company, we don't have much money—you've got to keep your cost under $200 000)

Goldstake would like the following information presented in a two-page report after the completion of all lab work.
- mass of potassium nitrate, KNO_3, and copper nitrate, $Cu(NO_3)_2$, in the 50.0 mL sample
- extrapolated mass of KNO_3 and $Cu(NO_3)_2$, in the Afton Aquifer
- summary paragraph describing the procedure used
- detailed and organized data and analysis section showing your calculations and explanations of any possible sources of error
- detailed invoice for the services rendered and the expenses incurred
Doing this job well could mean a long term contract with Goldstake.

For prices of materials, see page 692.

Required Precautions

Safety goggles and lab aprons must be worn at all times.

Before lighting the burner, remember to confine long hair and loose clothing. Use tongs at all times because heated glassware does not always look hot.

Do not touch or taste any chemicals. Wash your hands thoroughly when finished.

Spill Procedures/Waste-Disposal Methods

- Do not try to rinse the $Cu(NO_3)_2$ and KNO_3 down the drain. Dispose of each substance in separate waste containers designated by your teacher.

719

SAMPLE DATA			
Volume of solution	46.50 mL	Mass of beaker 2	66.25 g
Mass of beaker 1	65.80 g	Mass of beaker 2 with $Cu(NO_3)_2$	72.37 g
Mass of filter paper	0.40 g	Temperature before cooling	25°C
Mass of beaker 1 with filter paper and KNO_3 (Day 2)	78.22 g	Temperature after cooling	–2°C

Most students will recover approximately 12 g of KNO_3 and 7 g of $Cu(NO_3)_2$ from 50 mL of solution. Given this data, the aquifer would contain 2.4×10^{14} g of KNO_3 and 1.4×10^{14} g of $Cu(NO_3)_2$.

3A

3A | Flame Tests

OBJECTIVES

Students will:

▸ use appropriate lab safety procedures.

▸ use a Bunsen burner.

▸ perform flame tests with a variety of metal compounds.

▸ identify an unknown based on its flame test.

RECOMMENDED TIME:

1–2 lab periods

MATERIALS

(for each lab group)

▸ 3 g NaCl crystals

▸ 5 cm flame test wire

▸ 5 mL 1.0 M HCl solution

▸ 250 mL beaker

▸ Bunsen burner with gas tubing and striker

▸ CaCl₂ solution

▸ cobalt glass plate

▸ crucible tongs

▸ distilled water

▸ glass plate (a 7 cm × 15 cm plate or a microchemistry well plate)

▸ K₂SO₄ solution

▸ Li₂SO₄ solution

▸ Na₂SO₄ solution

▸ NaCl solution

▸ SrCl₂ solution

▸ unknown solution

OPTIONAL EQUIPMENT

▸ spectroscope

▸ wooden splints

OBJECTIVES

▸ Identify a set of flame-test color standards for selected metal ions.

▸ Relate the colors of a flame test to the behavior of excited electrons in a metal ion.

▸ Identify an unknown metal ion by using a flame test.

▸ Demonstrate proficiency in performing a flame test and in using a spectroscope.

MATERIALS

▸ 1.0 M HCl solution

▸ 250 mL beaker

▸ Bunsen burner and related equipment

▸ CaCl₂ solution

▸ cobalt glass plates

▸ crucible tongs

▸ distilled water

▸ flame-test wire

▸ glass test plate, or a microchemistry plate with wells

▸ K₂SO₄ solution

▸ Li₂SO₄ solution

▸ NaCl crystals

▸ NaCl solution

▸ Na₂SO₄ solution

▸ SrCl₂ solution

▸ spectroscope

▸ unknown solution

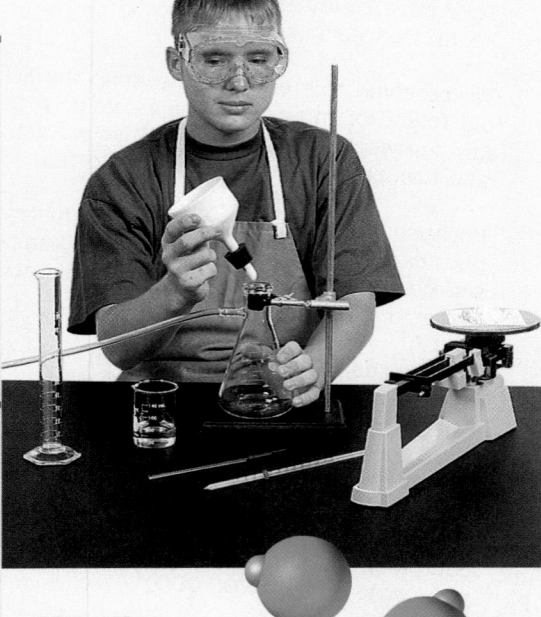

Situation

Your company has been contacted by Julius and Annette Benetti. They are worried about some abandoned, rusted barrels of chemicals that their daughter found while playing in the vacant lot behind their home. The barrels have begun to leak a colored liquid that flows through their property before emptying into a local sewer. The Benettis want your company to identify the compound in the liquid. Earlier work indicates that it is a dissolved metal compound. Many metals, such as lead, have been determined to be hazardous to our health. Many compounds of these metals are often soluble in water and are therefore easily absorbed into the body.

SOLUTION/MATERIAL PREPARATION

1. To prepare 1.0 M HCl, observe the required precautions. Add 83 mL of concentrated HCl to enough distilled water to make 1.00 L of solution. Add the acid slowly while stirring to avoid overheating.

2. To prepare 0.5 M CaCl₂, dissolve 55 g of CaCl₂ in enough water to make 1.00 L of solution.

3. To prepare 0.5 M K₂SO₄, dissolve 87 g of K₂SO₄ in enough water to make 1.00 L of solution.

4. To prepare 0.5 M Li₂SO₄, dissolve 64 g of Li₂SO₄•H₂O in enough water to make 1.00 L of solution.

5. To prepare 0.5 M Na₂SO₄, dissolve 71 g of Na₂SO₄ in enough water to make 1.00 L of solution.

6. To prepare 0.5 M NaCl, dissolve 29 g of NaCl in enough water to make 1.00 L of solution.

7. To prepare 0.5 M SrCl₂, dissolve 133.3 g of SrCl₂•6H₂O in enough water to make 1.00 L of solution.

8. For the unknown solution, any of the above solutions can be used. Mixtures may prove to be too complicated for students to analyze. Excess solutions can be stored and used next year.

9. For flame-test wire, use either number 24 platinum wire or nichrome wire. Some teachers prefer to use wooden splints for the flame

Always wear safety goggles and a lab apron to protect your eyes and clothing. If you get a chemical in your eyes, immediately flush the chemical out at the eyewash station while calling to your teacher. Know the location of the emergency lab shower and eyewash station and the procedures for using them.

Do not touch any chemicals. If you get a chemical on your skin or clothing, wash the chemical off at the sink while calling to your teacher. Make sure you carefully read the labels and follow the precautions on all containers of chemicals that you use. If no precautions are stated on the label, ask your teacher what precautions to follow. Do not taste any

chemicals or items used in the laboratory. Never return leftover chemicals to their original containers; take only small amounts to avoid wasting supplies.

When using a Bunsen burner, confine long hair and loose clothing. If your clothing catches fire, WALK to the emergency lab shower and use it to put out the fire. Do not heat glassware that is broken, chipped, or cracked. Use tongs or a hot mitt to handle heated glassware and other equipment; heated glassware does not always look hot.

Call your teacher in the event of an acid or base spill. Acid or base spills should be cleaned up promptly according to your teacher's instructions.

Background

Electrons in atoms jump from their ground state to excited states by absorbing energy. Eventually these electrons fall back to their ground state, re-emitting the absorbed energy in the form of light. Because each atom has a unique structure and arrangement of electrons, each atom emits a unique type of light. This characteristic light is the basis for the chemical test known as a flame test. In this test the atoms are excited by being placed within a flame. As they re-emit the absorbed energy in the form of light, the color of the flame changes. For most metals, these changes are easily visible. However, even the presence of a tiny speck of another substance can interfere with the identification of the true color of a particular type of atom.

Problem

To determine what metal is contained in the barrels behind the Benettis' house, you must first perform flame tests with a variety of standard solutions of different metal compounds. Then you will perform a flame test with the unknown sample from the site to see if it matches any of the solutions you've used as standards. Be sure to keep your equipment very clean, and perform multiple trials to check your work.

Preparation

1. Organizing Data

Copy the data table below in your lab notebook. Be sure that you have plenty of room for observations about each test.

Data Table		
Metal compound	**Color of flame**	**Wavelengths (nm)**
CaCl$_2$ solution		
K$_2$SO$_4$ solution		
Li$_2$SO$_4$ solution		
Na$_2$SO$_4$ solution		
SrCl$_2$ solution		
Na$_2$SO$_4$ (cobalt glass)		
K$_2$SO$_4$ (cobalt glass)		
Na$_2$SO$_4$ and K$_2$SO$_4$		
Na$_2$SO$_4$ and K$_2$SO$_4$ (cobalt glass)		
NaCl solution		
NaCl crystals		
Unknown solution		

This identification technique can be used to introduce concepts that provide information about the behavior and arrangement of electrons in atoms. To emphasize this point, apply high voltage to a gas-discharge tube containing helium or neon, and place a few crystals of sodium chloride on the grating of a lit Fisher burner. Explain that the colored lights are actually a combination of several very specific wavelengths of light. Each wavelength of light corresponds to excited electrons moving from a different energy level to their ground state, emitting light in the process.

TECHNIQUES TO DEMONSTRATE

Demonstrate the flame-test technique, including how to clean the flame-test wire. Point out that because the color lasts briefly, several trials may be necessary. If you have spectroscopes, each pair of students can use one to identify the specific lines in the spectra of the light emitted in the flame test. One student can view through the spectroscope while the other performs the flame test. Be sure you explain how to use the spectroscope.

DISPOSAL

Set out a disposal container for the students. After all of the waste beakers have been emptied, neutralize the resulting solution with 0.1 M NaOH. When the solution's pH is between 5 and 9, pour it down the drain. If you use wooden splints, collect them after they have been labeled, and reuse them next year for the same compounds.

Solution/Material Preparation continued

tests. If the splints are soaked in the appropriate solutions overnight, the splints provide a colored flame that is longer lasting and easier to view with the spectroscope. If this is done, however, each splint should be extinguished in the waste beaker. Be sure to label the splints with the compound they were soaked in so that they can be reused. The sodium content of the splint may interfere with some flame tests.

REQUIRED PRECAUTIONS

▶ Read all safety precautions, and discuss them with your students.

▶ Safety goggles and a lab apron must be worn at all times.

▶ Tie back long hair and loose clothing when working in the lab.

▶ Wear goggles, a face shield, impermeable gloves, and a lab apron when you prepare the HCl. Work in a hood known to be in good

operating condition, and have another person standing by to call for help in case of an emergency. Work within a 30 second walk of a safety shower and eyewash station.

▶ Students should not handle concentrated acid solutions. In case of an acid spill, dilute the spill with water. Then mop up the spill with wet cloths or a wet cloth mop designated for spill cleanup. Wear disposable plastic gloves while cleaning spills.

ANSWERS

ANALYSIS AND INTERPRETATION

(Note: Assign only items 1–3 if spectroscopes are unavailable.)

1. See the sample data table below.

2. Answers will vary. Some students may have had difficulty cleaning the wire properly, so the first test of a new compound may have had traces of the previous compound.

3. The flame color of potassium is purple, but it is so weak that it can be overpowered by the yellow sodium light if a mixture is tested. The cobalt glass screens out the yellow sodium light.

4. Each line in the spectroscope represented the energy emitted as excited electrons moved from a specific high-energy orbital back to their ground state.

5. Answers will vary, but students should realize that the colors seen by the eye were the result of combining the colors of light seen in the line spectra.

Figure A Be sure that you record the position of the various metal ion solutions in each well of the well strip.

2. Label a beaker "Waste." Thoroughly clean and dry a well strip. Fill the first well one-fourth full with 1.0 M HCl. Clean the test wire by first dipping it in the HCl and then holding it in the flame of the Bunsen burner. Repeat this procedure until the flame is not colored by the wire. When the wire is ready, rinse the well with distilled water, and collect the rinse water in the waste beaker.

3. Put 10 drops of each metal ion solution listed in the materials list except NaCl in a row in each well of the well strip. Put a row of 1.0 M HCl drops on a glass plate across from the metal ion solutions. Record the position of all of the chemicals placed in the wells. The wire will need to be cleaned thoroughly with HCl between each test solution to avoid contamination from the previous test.

Technique

4. Dip the wire into the $CaCl_2$ solution, as shown in **Figure A,** and then hold it in the Bunsen burner flame. Observe the color of the flame, and record it in the data table. Repeat the procedure again, but this time look through the spectroscope to view the results. Record the wavelengths you see

from the flame. Perform each test three times. Clean the wire with the HCl as you did in step 2.

5. Repeat step 4 with the K_2SO_4 and with each of the remaining solutions in the well strip. For each solution that you test, record the color of each flame and the wavelength observed with the spectroscope. After the solutions are tested, clean the wire thoroughly, rinse the well strip with distilled water, and collect the rinse water in the waste beaker.

6. Test another drop of Na_2SO_4, but this time view the flame through two pieces of cobalt glass. Clean the wire, and repeat the test using the K_2SO_4. View the flame through the cobalt glass. Record in your data table the colors and wavelengths of the flames. Clean the wire and the well strip, and rinse the well strip with distilled water. Pour the rinse water into the waste beaker.

7. Put a drop of K_2SO_4 in a clean well. Add a drop of Na_2SO_4. Flame-test the mixture. Observe the flame without the cobalt glass. Repeat the test, this time observing the flame through the cobalt glass. Record the colors and wavelengths of the flames in the data table. Clean the wire, and rinse the well strip with distilled water. Pour the rinse water into the waste beaker.

8. Test a drop of the NaCl solution in the flame, and then view it through the spectroscope. (Do not use the cobalt glass.) Record your observations. Clean the wire, and rinse the well strip with distilled water. Pour the rinse water into the waste beaker. Place a few crystals of NaCl in a clean well, dip the wire in the crystals, and do the flame test once more. Record the color of the flame test. Clean the wire, and rinse the well strip with distilled water. Pour the rinse water into the waste beaker.

SAMPLE DATA

METAL COMPOUND	COLOR OF FLAME	WAVELENGTH DETECTED (nm)
$CaCl_2$	yellowish red (orange)	420, 445, 460, 485, 610, 645, 650
K_2SO_4	violet (purple)	405, 408, 695, 700
Li_2SO_4	red (carmine)	462, 498, 612, 670
Na_2SO_4	yellow	590, 595
$SrSO_4$	scarlet	405, 420, 460, 485, 490, 500, 665, 685, 710

Note: Students' data tables should show three trials for each compound.

Figure B Flame test

9. Dip the wire into the unknown solution; then hold it in the Bunsen burner flame, as shown in **Figure B.** Perform flame tests for it, both with and without the cobalt glass. Record your observations. Clean the wire, and rinse the well strip with distilled water. Pour the rinse water into the waste beaker.

 Cleanup and Disposal

10. Clean all apparatus and your lab station. Dispose of the contents of the waste beaker in the container designated by your teacher. Wash your hands thoroughly after cleaning up the lab area and equipment.

Analysis and Interpretation

1. Organizing Data
Examine your data table, and create a summary of the flame test for each metal ion.

2. Analyzing Data
Account for any differences in the individual trials for the flame tests for the metal ions.

3. Organizing Ideas
Explain how viewing the flame through cobalt glass can make it easier to analyze the ions being tested.

4. Relating Ideas
Explain how the lines seen in the spectroscope relate to the position of electrons in the metal atom.

5. Relating Ideas
For three of the metal ions tested, explain how the flame color you saw relates to the lines of color you saw when you looked through the spectroscope.

Conclusions

6. Inferring Conclusions
What metal ions are in the unknown solution from the barrels on the vacant lot?

7. Evaluating Methods
How would you characterize the flame test with respect to its sensitivity? What difficulties could there be when identifying ions by the flame test?

8. Evaluating Methods
Explain how you can use a spectroscope to identify the components of solutions containing several different metal ions.

Extensions

1. Inferring Conclusions
A student performed flame tests on several unknowns and observed that they all were shades of red. What should the student do to correctly identify these substances? Explain your answer.

2. Applying Ideas
During a flood, the labels from three bottles of chemicals were lost. The three unlabeled bottles of white solids were known to contain the following: strontium nitrate, ammonium carbonate, and potassium sulfate. Explain how you could easily test the substances, and relabel the three bottles. (Hint: Ammonium ions do not provide a distinctive flame color.)

3. Applying Ideas
Some stores sell jars of "fireplace crystals." When sprinkled on a log, these crystals make the flames blue, red, green, and violet. Explain how these crystals can change the flame's color. What ingredients would you expect them to contain?

FLAME TESTS   723

SAMPLE DATA		
METAL COMPOUND	**COLOR OF FLAME**	**WAVELENGTHS DETECTED (nm)**
NaCl solution	yellow	590, 595
NaCl crystals	yellow	590, 595
Na only (cobalt glass)	only the cobalt glass is visible	n/a
K only (cobalt glass)	violet (purple)	n/a
Na and K	yellow	n/a
Na and K (cobalt glass)	violet	n/a
Unknown	Answers will vary.	Answers will vary.

3A | Spectroscopy and Flame Tests
Identifying Materials

OBJECTIVES

Students will:

▸ use appropriate lab safety procedures.

▸ use a Bunsen burner.

▸ identify an unknown based on its flame test.

▸ design and implement their own procedure.

RECOMMENDED TIME:
1 lab period

PREREQUISITE:
Exploration 3A

MATERIALS

(for each lab group)

▸ 5 mL 1.0 M HCl solution

▸ 5 cm flame-test wire

▸ 250 mL beaker

▸ Bunsen burner, gas tubing, and striker

▸ cobalt glass plate

▸ crucible tongs

▸ glass plate (a 7 cm × 15 cm plate or a microchemistry well plate)

▸ unknown solution (0.5 M Li_2SO_4 is recommended)

OPTIONAL EQUIPMENT

▸ spectroscope

▸ wooden splints

ESTIMATED COST OF MATERIALS:
$86 000
($101 000 with spectroscope)

PRE-LAB DISCUSSION

Begin by discussing the results and procedure used in Exploration 3A, especially any errors in lab technique that occurred. Discuss any disparity between the students' results and the expected flame colors and wavelengths.

If students are uncertain how to begin planning, encourage them to start by reviewing the procedure and results from the Exploration.

THE PROBLEM

E·T·A
Experimental Testing Agency

January 27, 1999

Director of Investigations
CheMystery Labs, Inc.
52 Fulton Street
Springfield, VA 22150

Dear Director:

As you may have seen in news reports, one of our freelance pilots, Davin Matthews, was killed in a crash of an experimental airplane that was struck by lightning.

What the reports did not mention was that Matthews's airplane was a recently perfected new design that he'd been developing for us. The notes he left behind indicate that the coating on the nose cone was the key to the plane's speed and maneuverability. Unfortunately, he did not reveal what substances he used, and we were able to recover only flakes of material from the nose cone after the accident.

We have sent you samples of these flakes dissolved in a solution. Please identify the material Matthews used so that we can duplicate his prototype. We will pay $200,000 for this work, provided that you can identify the material within three days.

Sincerely,

Jared MacLaren

Jared MacLaren
Experimental Testing Agency

References

Review information about spectroscopic analysis. The procedure is similar to one your team recently completed to identify an unknown metal in a solution. As before, use small amounts, and clean equipment carefully to avoid contamination. Perform multiple trials for each sample.

The following information is the bright-line emission data (in nm) for the four possible metals.

• Lithium: 670, 612, 498, 462

• Potassium: 700, 695, 408, 405

• Strontium: 710, 685, 665, 500, 490, 485, 460, 420, 405

• Calcium: 650, 645, 610, 485, 460, 445, 420

SOLUTION/MATERIAL PREPARATION

1. See the Teachers' Notes for Exploration 3A for information on preparing 1.0 M HCl.

2. To prepare 0.5 M Li_2SO_4, dissolve 64 g of $Li_2SO_4 \cdot H_2O$ in enough water to make 1.00 L of solution. (Other solutions from Exploration 3A can be used as the unknown if preferred.)

3. If wooden splints will be used instead of flame-test wire, remember to soak them overnight in the ion solution.

REQUIRED PRECAUTIONS

▸ Read all safety precautions, and discuss them with your students.

▸ Safety goggles and a lab apron must be worn.

▸ Tie back long hair and loose clothing.

▸ Students should not handle concentrated acid solutions. In case of an acid spill, dilute the spill with water. Then mop up the spill with wet cloths or a wet cloth mop designated for spill cleanup. Wear disposable gloves while cleaning spills.

THE PLAN

MEMORANDUM

CheMystery Labs, Inc.
52 Fulton Street
Springfield, VA 22150

Date: January 28, 1999
To: Edwin Thien
From: Marissa Bellinghausen

We have narrowed down the material used to four possibilities. It is a compound of either lithium, potassium, strontium, or calcium. Using flame tests and the wavelengths of spectroscopic analysis, you should be able to identify which of these is in the sample.

Because our contract depends on timeliness, give me a preliminary report that includes the following as soon as possible:
• detailed one-page summary of your plan for the procedure
• itemized list of equipment with total costs (Remember, the less you spend, the more profit for the company—provided you can get accurate results!)

After you complete your analysis, prepare a report in the form of a two-page letter to MacLaren. It must include the following:
• identity of the metal in the sample
• summary of your procedure
• detailed and organized analysis and data sections showing tests and results
• detailed invoice for all expenses and services

For prices of materials, see page 692.

Required Precautions

Safety goggles and a lab apron must be worn at all times.

Do not touch or taste any chemicals. Wash your hands thoroughly before you leave the lab.

Confine long hair and loose clothing.

If you get acid or base on your skin or clothing, wash the chemical off at the sink while calling to your teacher. If you get acid or base in your eyes, immediately flush it out at the eyewash station while calling to your teacher.

Spill Procedures/ Waste-Disposal Methods

• In case of spills, follow your teacher's instructions.
• Place all remaining solutions in separate disposal containers as indicated by your teacher.
• Clean the area and all equipment after use.

725

SAMPLE DATA

SUBSTANCE	Unknown
FLAME COLOR	red (carmine)
WAVELENGTHS (nm)	462, 498, 612, 670

Student data should have multiple trials. Data is shown for Li_2SO_4. Data will vary if a different unknown is chosen.

TIPS FOR EVALUATING THE PRE-LAB REQUIREMENTS

Students may want to test the labeled solutions from Exploration 3A again. This is not recommended. Forcing students to rely on their records of the results gained in the Exploration or on the wavelengths given in the Investigation helps them learn to relate the recorded data given in different situations.

Be certain students remember to use a waste beaker to collect all rinsings. If students suggest that they will need more than 5 mL of 1 M HCl, have them reconsider their procedure.

TECHNIQUES TO DEMONSTRATE

Review the proper way to clean the wire and glass plate. Emphasize that all rinses should be made with distilled water and collected in a waste beaker for disposal. If students will be using spectroscopes, review the techniques for viewing with a spectroscope.

PROPOSED PROCEDURE

Place three drops of the unknown solution and several drops of 1.0 M HCl on a glass plate. Dip the flame-test wire in a drop of HCl to clean it. Dip the flame-test wire into the first drop of unknown solution. Hold the wire in a Bunsen burner flame, and record the color. (Record the wavelength as well if a spectroscope is available.) Clean the wire in another drop of HCl, and repeat the process. When finished, rinse the plate with distilled water, and collect the rinse water in a waste beaker.

DISPOSAL

Set out a disposal container for the students. When all of the waste beakers have been emptied, neutralize the resulting solution with 0.1 M NaOH. When the solution's pH is between 5 and 9, pour it down the drain. If you use wooden splints, collect them after they have been labeled. Store the labeled splints for reuse for the same compounds next year.

OBJECTIVES

Students will:

▸ observe the physical properties of common elements.

▸ observe the properties and trends in the elements on the periodic table.

▸ identify unknown elements based on observed trends in properties.

RECOMMENDED TIME:

1–2 lab periods

MATERIALS

(for each lab group)

▸ 3 × 5 in. note cards (about 30 per group)

▸ blank periodic table

▸ elemental property cards that list 7 different properties for each element

▸ elemental samples

   copper: electrical wire or pre-1982 United States pennies

   carbon: pencil lead

   tin: sheet metal from a hardware store

   lead: fishing sinkers

   argon: gas inside a light bulb

▸ periodic table

*Li, He, Na, Ca, Ne, Br$_2$, K, I$_2$, Si, Ge, and Mg can be added if available.

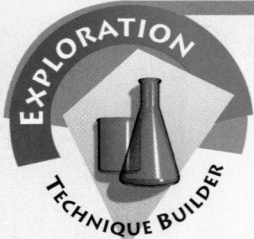

4A | The Mendeleev Lab of 1869

OBJECTIVES

▸ **Observe the physical properties of common elements.**

▸ **Observe the properties and trends in the elements on the periodic table.**

▸ **Identify unknown elements based on observed trends in properties.**

MATERIALS

▸ **blank periodic table**

▸ **elemental samples* of Ar, C, Cu, Sn, and Pb**

▸ **note cards (3 × 5)**

▸ **periodic table**

Background

Russian chemist Dmitri Mendeleev is generally credited as being the first chemist to observe that patterns emerge when the elements are arranged according to their properties. Mendeleev's arrangement of the elements was unique because he left blank spaces for elements that he claimed were undiscovered as of 1869. Mendeleev was so confident that he even predicted the properties of these undiscovered elements. His predictions were eventually proven to be quite accurate, and these new elements fill the spaces that originally were blank in his table.

SOLUTION/MATERIAL PREPARATION

1. When you are ready to begin the lab, place the element cards of the knowns and unknowns around the classroom. Give the students blank note cards so that they can write down the properties of each element. Elements that are present in samples require students to make observations about their physical state or color. These observations should be written on the students' note cards. The other information can be copied directly from the element cards.

2. When all of the element cards have been copied, the students should organize the known elements. The cards can be organized in the form of a periodic table, shown at the bottom of page 728. Photocopy this model for each group and have the groups use it as a guide for arranging the elements. For example, the cards for lithium, sodium, and potassium should be arranged in a vertical column so students can observe the trends in their properties. While this organizational strategy seems effective, the students may wish to create their own methods. This is fine as long as students make progress toward identifying the unknowns. Students should note that the elements highlighted in red are radioactive.

3. To save time, an alternate procedure may be used. Instead of placing element cards around the classroom, photocopy

Always wear safety goggles and lab apron to protect your eyes and clothing. If you get a chemical in your eyes, immediately flush the chemical out at the eyewash station while calling to your teacher. Know the location of the emergency lab shower and eyewash station and the procedure for using them.

 Some samples may be hazardous to humans. Do not open or touch any sample unless directed to do so by your teacher.

Call you teacher in the event of a spill. Spills should be cleaned up promptly according to your teacher's directions.

Problem

Use your knowledge of the periodic table to determine the identity of each of the nine unknown elements in this activity.

▶ The unknown elements are from the following groups in the periodic table. *Each group listed below contains at least one unknown.*

    1   2   11   13   14   17   18

▶ None of the known elements serves as one of the nine unknowns.

▶ No radioactive elements are used during this experiment. The relevant radioactive elements include Fr, Ra, At, and Rn.

▶ You may not use your textbook or other reference materials. You have been provided with enough information to determine each of the unknown elements.

Preparation

1. Organizing Data

Copy the data table below in your laboratory notebook. Be sure to add enough space for all the unknown elements.

Data Table

Unknown	Element
1	
2	
3	
4	

Technique

2. Use the note cards to copy the information listed on each of the sample cards on page 728 and 729. If the word *observe* is listed, you will need to visually inspect the sample and then write the observation in the appropriate space.

3. Arrange the note cards of the known elements in a crude representation of the periodic table. In other words, all of the known elements from Group 1 should be arranged in the appropriate order. Arrange all of the other cards accordingly.

4. Once the cards of the known elements are in place, inspect the properties of the unknowns to see where their properties would best "fit" the trends of the elements of each group.

5. Assign the proper element name to each of the unknowns. Add the symbol for each one of the "unknowns" to your data table.

Cleanup and Disposal

6. Clean up your lab station, and return the leftover note cards and samples of the elements to your teacher. Do not pour any of the samples down the drain or in the trash unless your teacher directs you to do so. Wash your hands thoroughly before you leave the lab and after all your work is finished.

Conclusion

1. Summarize your group's reasoning for the assignment of each unknown. Explain in a few sentences exactly how you predicted the identity of the nine unknowns.

PRE-LAB DISCUSSION

Discuss the work of Dmitri Mendeleev and the concept of periodicity with your students before starting this activity. In your discussion, emphasize the trends among the groups of elements in the periodic table, but do not explain the chemical basis for these trends, because doing so might distract the students from observing the various patterns and trends in the properties.

This experiment can seem overwhelming to students because of the large number of elements and properties. Students should work in groups of 3–4 students, where they can verbalize their reasoning as they attempt to identify the unknowns. Encourage students to divide the experiment into smaller tasks such as data collection, organization of the known elements, and identification of the unknowns. Minimize some of the initial frustration by directing students' attention to the trends in the properties among the known alkali metals. Seeing the trends in the properties of lithium, sodium, and potassium should help students as they try to identify the nine unknown elements.

TECHNIQUES TO DEMONSTRATE

Introduce this activity by referring to Figure 4–21, which shows small pieces of the active metals lithium, sodium, and potassium being added to water. Additionally, you may wish to perform a similar demonstration involving magnesium and calcium. (See Demonstration 3 on page 114.)

DISPOSAL

None. The samples and the set of element cards can be kept for future use.

CONCLUSION

1.

Unknown #	Element
1	Si
2	F
3	Rb
4	Kr
5	Au
6	Sr
7	Ge
8	Mg
9	Tl

Solution/Material Preparation continued

pages 728–729 and distribute one copy to each group. Designate one person from each group to cut the pages into individual element cards. When all of the element cards have been cut out, the students should organize the known elements in the form of a periodic table showing elements with similar properties in the same group.

REQUIRED PRECAUTIONS

▶ Read all safety precautions, and discuss them with your students.

▶ Safety goggles, gloves, and a lab apron must be worn at all times.

▶ Students should wash their hands immediately and avoid touching their eyes if they accidentally touch the tin or lead samples. These elements pose a health risk if they enter a student's body.

Li	
Physical state	solid
Density	0.534 g/cm³
Hardness	soft, claylike
Conductivity	good
Melting point	180°C
Solubility (H₂O)	reacts with water
Color	silver

Ag	
Physical state	solid
Density	10.50 g/cm³
Hardness	somewhat soft
Conductivity	excellent
Melting point	961°C
Solubility (H₂O)	none
Color	silver

Cu	
Physical state	(observe)
Density	8.96 g/cm³
Hardness	somewhat soft
Conductivity	excellent
Melting point	1083°C
Solubility (H₂O)	none
Color	(observe)

C	
Physical state	(observe)
Density	2.10 g/cm³
Hardness	soft yet brittle
Conductivity	good
Melting point	3550°C
Solubility (H₂O)	negligible
Color	(observe)

Cl₂	
Physical state	gas
Density	0.00321 g/cm³
Hardness	none
Conductivity	very poor
Melting point	−101°C
Solubility (H₂O)	slight
Color	greenish yellow

He	
Physical state	gas
Density	0.00018 g/cm³
Hardness	none
Conductivity	very poor
Melting point	−272°C
Solubility (H₂O)	none
Color	colorless

Na	
Physical state	solid
Density	0.971 g/cm³
Hardness	soft, claylike
Conductivity	good
Melting point	98°C
Solubility (H₂O)	reacts rapidly
Color	silver

Ca	
Physical state	solid
Density	1.57 g/cm³
Hardness	medium
Conductivity	good
Melting point	845°C
Solubility (H₂O)	reacts
Color	silvery white

Be	
Physical state	solid
Density	1.85 g/cm³
Hardness	brittle
Conductivity	excellent
Melting point	1287°C
Solubility (H₂O)	none
Color	gray

Sn	
Physical state	(observe)
Density	7.31 g/cm³
Hardness	somewhat soft
Conductivity	good
Melting point	232°C
Solubility (H₂O)	none
Color	(observe)

Ne	
Physical state	gas
Density	0.00090 g/cm³
Hardness	none
Conductivity	very poor
Melting point	−249°C
Solubility (H₂O)	none
Color	colorless

Br₂	
Physical state	liquid
Density	3.12 g/cm³
Hardness	none
Conductivity	very poor
Melting point	−7.2°C
Solubility (H₂O)	negligible
Color	reddish brown

K	
Physical state	solid
Density	0.86 g/cm³
Hardness	soft, claylike
Conductivity	good
Melting point	63°C
Solubility (H₂O)	reacts rapidly
Color	silver

Ba	
Physical state	solid
Density	3.6 g/cm³
Hardness	soft
Conductivity	good
Melting point	710°C
Solubility (H₂O)	reacts strongly
Color	silvery white

Xe	
Physical state	gas
Density	0.00585 g/cm³
Hardness	none
Conductivity	very poor
Melting point	−111.9°C
Solubility (H₂O)	none
Color	colorless

In			I₂			Pb	

In

Physical state...............solid
Density.......................7.31 g/cc
Hardness......................very soft
Conductivity.................medium
Melting point ....157°C
Solubility (H₂O)............none
Color ....silvery white

I₂

Physical state...............solid
Density.......................4.93 g/cm³
Hardness......................soft
Conductivity.................very poor
Melting point...............113.5°C
Solubility (H₂O).............negligible
Color.............................bluish-black

Pb

Physical state...............(observe)
Density.......................11.35 g/cm³
Hardness......................somewhat soft
Conductivity.................poor
Melting point...............327.5°C
Solubility (H₂O).............none
Color.............................(observe)

Ar

Physical state...............(observe)
Density.......................0.00178 g/cm³
Hardness......................none
Conductivity.................very poor
Melting point...............−189.2°C
Solubility (H₂O)............none
Color ....(observe)

Ga

Physical state...............solid
Density ....5.904 g/cc
Hardness......................soft
Conductivity.................medium
Melting point ....30°C
Solubility (H₂O)............none
Color ....silvery

Cs

Physical state...............solid
Density ....1.87 g/cm³
Hardness......................soft
Conductivity.................good
Melting point ....29°C
Solubility (H₂O).............reacts violently
Color ....silvery white

Unknown #1

Physical state...............solid
Density.......................2.33 g/cm³
Hardness......................brittle
Conductivity.................intermediate
Melting point...............1410°C
Solubility (H₂O)............none
Color ....gray

Unknown #2

Physical state...............gas
Density.......................0.00170 g/cm³
Hardness......................none
Conductivity.................very poor
Melting point...............−219.6°C
Solubility (H₂O)............slight
Color ....pale yellow

Unknown #3

Physical state ....solid
Density.......................1.53 g/cm³
Hardness......................soft
Conductivity.................good
Melting point...............39°C
Solubility (H₂O).............reacts violently
Color.............................silvery white

Unknown #4

Physical state..........gas
Density.......................0.00374 g/cm³
Hardness......................none
Conductivity..............very poor
Melting point.............−156.6°C
Solubility (H₂O)........none
Color.............................colorless

Unknown #5

Physical state...............solid
Density.......................19.3 g/cm³
Hardness......................soft
Conductivity.................excellent
Melting point...............1064°C
Solubility (H₂O).............none
Color.............................gold

Unknown #6

Physical state...............solid
Density.......................2.54 g/cm³
Hardness......................somewhat soft
Conductivity.................good
Melting point...............769°C
Solubility (H₂O)..............reacts rapidly
Color.............................silvery white

Unknown #7

Physical state...............solid
Density.......................5.32 g/cm³
Hardness......................fairly brittle
Conductivity.................fair to poor
Melting point...............937°C
Solubility (H₂O).............none
Color.............................gray

Unknown #8

Physical state...............solid
Density.......................1.74 g/cm³
Hardness......................medium
Conductivity.................good
Melting point...............651°C
Solubility (H₂O).............reacts slowly
Color.............................silvery white

Unknown #9

Physical state...............solid
Density.......................11.85 g/cc
Hardness......................very soft
Conductivity.................medium
Melting point...............303°C
Solubility (H₂O).............none
Color.............................silvery white

OBJECTIVES

Students will:

▶ use appropriate lab safety procedures.

▶ use a laboratory balance to measure mass.

▶ use a Bunsen burner to evaporate a substance's water of crystallization.

▶ collect data and organize it in a table.

▶ calculate molar amounts from mass values.

▶ determine the empirical formula for a hydrated compound.

▶ determine the percentage of water in a hydrated compound.

▶ determine how much water can be absorbed by 25 g of an anhydrous compound.

RECOMMENDED TIME:

1 lab period

MATERIALS

(for each lab group)

▶ balance (may be shared among lab groups)

▶ Bunsen burner with gas tubing and striker

▶ crucible and cover

▶ crucible tongs (Do not use beaker tongs.)

▶ $CuSO_4 \cdot 5H_2O$, about 5 g

▶ desiccator

▶ distilled water

▶ dropper or micropipet

▶ glass stirring rod

▶ ring and pipe-stem triangle

▶ ring stand

▶ spatula

▶ weighing paper

OPTIONAL EQUIPMENT

▶ wing top for burner

5A | Percent Composition of Hydrates

OBJECTIVES

▶ Demonstrate proficiency in using the balance and the Bunsen burner.

▶ Determine that all the water has been driven from a hydrate by heating a sample to constant mass.

▶ Relate results to the law of conservation of mass and the law of multiple proportions.

▶ Perform calculations using the molar mass.

▶ Determine the empirical formula of the hydrate and its percentage by mass of water.

MATERIALS

▶ balance

▶ Bunsen burner

▶ crucible and cover

▶ crucible tongs

▶ $CuSO_4$, hydrated crystals

▶ desiccator

▶ distilled water

▶ dropper or micropipet

▶ glass stirring rod

▶ ring and pipe-stem triangle

▶ ring stand

▶ spatula

▶ weighing paper

Situation

You are a research chemist working for a company that is developing a new chemical moisture absorber and indicator. The company plans to seal the moisture absorber into a transparent porous pouch attached to a cellophane window on the inside of packages for compact disc players. This way, moisture within the packages will be absorbed, and any package that has too much moisture can be quickly detected and dried out. Your company's efforts have focused on copper(II) sulfate, $CuSO_4$, which can absorb water to become a hydrate that shows a distinctive color change.

SOLUTION/MATERIAL PREPARATION

1. If you do not have a desiccator, you can use a jar with a lid or a similar container. To make a resting place for a crucible within the jar, use a pipe-stem triangle. Bend the ends of the pipe-stem triangle down to form legs. Fill the bottom of the jar with granular anhydrous $CaCl_2$.

Always wear safety goggles and a lab apron to protect your eyes and clothing. If you get a chemical in your eyes, immediately flush the chemical out at the eyewash station while calling to your teacher. Know the location of the emergency lab shower and eyewash station and the procedures for using them.

 Do not touch any chemicals. If you get a chemical on your skin or clothing, wash the chemical off at the sink while calling to your teacher. Make sure you carefully read the labels and follow the precautions on all containers of chemicals that you use. If no precautions are stated on the label, ask your teacher what precautions to follow. Do not taste any chemicals or items used in the laboratory. Never return leftover chemicals to their original containers; take only small amounts to avoid wasting supplies.

 When using a Bunsen burner, confine long hair and loose clothing. If your clothing catches fire, WALK to the emergency lab shower and use it to put out the fire. Do not heat glassware that is broken, chipped, or cracked. Use tongs or a hot mitt to handle heated glassware and other equipment; heated glassware does not always look hot.

 Never put broken glass or ceramics in a regular waste container. Broken glass and ceramics should be disposed of in a separate container designated by your teacher.

Background

When many ionic compounds are crystallized from a water solution, they include individual water molecules as part of their crystalline structure. If the substances are heated, this water of crystallization may be driven off, leaving behind the pure anhydrous form of the compound. Because the law of multiple proportions also applies to crystalline hydrates, the number of moles of water driven off per mole of the anhydrous compound should be a simple whole number ratio. You can use this information to help you determine the formula of the hydrate.

Problem

To help your company decide whether $CuSO_4$ is the right substance for the moisture absorber and indicator, you will need to examine the hydrated and anhydrous forms of the compound and determine the following:

▸ the empirical formula of the hydrate, including its water of crystallization
▸ if the compound is useful as an indicator when it changes from the hydrated to the anhydrous form
▸ the mass of water absorbed by the 25 g of anhydrous compound that the company proposes to use

Even if you can guess what the formula for the hydrate should be, carefully perform this exploration so that you know how well your company's supply of $CuSO_4$ absorbs moisture.

Preparation

1. Organizing Data

Copy the data table below in your lab notebook. Leave room for observations about the procedure.

2.
Make sure that your equipment and tongs are very clean so that you will get the best possible results. Remember that you will need to cool the heated crucible in the desiccator before measuring its mass. **Never put a hot crucible on a balance; it will damage the balance.**

Data Table 1

Mass of empty crucible and cover
Initial mass of sample, crucible, and cover
Mass of sample, crucible, and cover after first heating
Mass of sample, crucible, and cover after second heating
Constant mass of sample, crucible, and cover

PERCENT COMPOSITION OF HYDRATES 731

Students should be familiar with the concepts of empirical formula and percentage by mass as well as the process of mass-mole conversions. Remind students that the symbol in a hydrate is not a multiplication symbol.

To review the law of conservation of mass and the law of multiple proportions, write the following reaction on the board.

$$CuSO_4 \cdot nH_2O \longrightarrow CuSO_4 + nH_2O$$

According to the law of conservation of mass, the mass will be the same on both sides of the equation. This allows the mass of water to be calculated by comparing the mass of the substance before and after the reaction. According to the law of multiple proportions, n, the number of water molecules per formula unit of $CuSO_4$, should be a small whole number.

TECHNIQUES TO DEMONSTRATE

Students will need to be given detailed instructions on how to use a crucible; how to set it on the pipe-stem triangle; and how to place the crucible lid on top of the crucible, leaving a small opening. Be certain they realize that they should always use crucible tongs to touch the crucible, even when the crucible is cool. If they touch the crucible, oils from their hands can contribute to errors in mass measurements. Remind students to gently break up the crystals with a stirring rod after placing them in the crucible. This will prevent the crucible from cracking and breaking as it is heated.

Students should use the same balance throughout this lab. Remind students not to put hot crucibles on balances.

Emphasize the need to heat the copper sulfate very slowly. If it is heated too rapidly, it may splatter or decompose. As noted in the procedure, any yellowish color that persists after the cooling is a sign of decomposition of the sulfate due to overheating.

▸ Read all safety precautions, and discuss them with your students.
▸ Safety goggles and a lab apron must be worn at all times.
▸ Remind students to confine long hair and loose clothing before lighting a burner.
▸ Remind students that heated objects can be hot enough to burn even if they look cool. Students should always use crucible tongs to handle crucibles and crucible covers.

The crystals may turn slightly yellow when heated, but this color should not remain after cooling. A wing top on the burner will produce a steady, warm flame that can help prevent decomposition.

DISPOSAL

Provide a labeled container for the disposal of the rehydrated and anhydrous copper sulfate and any excess of the original compound. Later, redissolve the contents of the container in distilled water. Let the solution evaporate, and then recover the crystals for reuse next year. Do not dispose of copper sulfate in a landfill or an incinerator, and do not pour it down a drain.

Figure A

Technique

3. Place the crucible and cover on the triangle with the lid slightly tipped, as shown in **Figure A.** The small opening will allow gases to escape. Heat the crucible and cover until the crucible glows slightly red. Use the tongs to transfer the crucible and cover to the desiccator, and allow them to cool for 5 minutes. Determine the mass of the crucible and cover to the nearest 0.01 g, and record the mass in your data table.

4. Using a spatula, add approximately 5 g of copper sulfate hydrate crystals to the crucible. Break up any large crystals before placing them in the crucible. Determine the mass of the covered crucible and crystals to the nearest 0.01 g, and record the mass in your data table.

5. Place the crucible with the copper sulfate hydrate on the triangle, and again position the cover so there is only a small opening. If the opening is too large, the crystals may spatter as they are heated. Heat the crucible very gently on a low flame to avoid spattering. Increase the temperature gradually for 2 or 3 minutes, and then heat until the crucible glows red for at least 5 minutes. Be very careful not to raise the temperature of the crucible and its contents too suddenly.

You will observe a color change, which is normal, but if the substance remains yellow after cooling, it was overheated and has begun to decompose. Allow the crucible, cover, and contents to cool for 5 minutes in the desiccator, and then measure their mass. Record the mass in your data table.

6. Heat the covered crucible and contents to redness again for 5 minutes. Allow the crucible, cover, and contents to cool in the desiccator, and then determine their mass and record it in the data table. If the two mass measurements differ by no more than 0.01 g, you may assume that all of the water has been driven off. Otherwise, repeat the process until the mass no longer changes, indicating that all of the water has evaporated. Record this constant mass in your data table.

7. After recording the constant mass, set aside a part of your sample on a piece of weighing paper. Using the dropper or pipet, as shown in **Figure B,** put a few drops of water onto this sample to rehydrate the crystals. Record your observations in your lab notebook.

Cleanup and Disposal

8. Clean all apparatus and your lab station. Make sure to completely shut off the gas valve before leaving the laboratory. Remember to wash your hands thoroughly. Place the rehydrated and anhydrous chemicals in the disposal containers designated by your teacher.

Figure B

SAMPLE DATA	
Mass of empty crucible and cover	32.18 g
Mass of crucible, cover, and copper sulfate hydrate	37.18 g
Mass of crucible, cover, and anhydrous copper sulfate after first heating	36.08 g

SAMPLE DATA	
Mass of crucible, cover, and anhydrous copper sulfate after second heating	35.43 g
Mass of crucible, cover, and anhydrous copper sulfate after third heating	35.42 g

Students should reheat the crucible, cover, and anhydrous copper sulfate until successive masses are within 0.02 g.

Analysis and Interpretation

1. Analyzing Methods

Why do you need to heat the clean crucible before using it in this lab? Why do the tongs used throughout this lab need to be especially clean?

2. Analyzing Methods

Why do you need to use a cover for the crucible? Could you leave the cover off each time you measure the mass of the crucible and its contents and still get accurate results? Explain your answer.

3. Analyzing Information

Calculate the mass of anhydrous copper sulfate (the residue that remains after heating to constant mass) by subtracting the mass of the empty crucible and cover from the mass of the crucible, cover, and heated $CuSO_4$. Use the molar mass for $CuSO_4$, determined from the periodic table, to calculate the number of moles present.

4. Resolving Discrepancies

Explain why the mass of the sample decreased after it was heated, despite the law of conservation of mass.

5. Analyzing Information

Calculate the mass and moles of water originally present in the hydrate using the molar mass determined from the periodic table.

Conclusions

6. Analyzing Information

Using your answers from items 3 and 5, determine the empirical formula for the copper sulfate hydrate.

7. Analyzing Information

What is the percentage by mass of water in the original hydrated compound?

8. Organizing Conclusions

How much water could 25 g of anhydrous $CuSO_4$ absorb?

9. Evaluating Conclusions

When you rehydrated the small amount of anhydrous copper sulfate, what were your observations? Explain whether this substance would make a good indicator of moisture.

Extensions

1. Applying Conclusions

Some cracker tins include a glass vial of drying material in the lid. This is often a mixture of magnesium sulfate and cobalt chloride. As the mixture absorbs moisture to form hydrated compounds, the cobalt chloride changes from blue-violet $CoCl_2 \cdot 2H_2O$ to pink $CoCl_2 \cdot 6H_2O$. When this hydrated mixture becomes totally pink, it can be restored to the dihydrate form by being heated in the oven. Write equations for the reactions that occur when this mixture is heated.

2. Applying Ideas

Three pairs of students obtained the following results when they heated a solid. In each case, the students observed that when they began to heat the solid, drops of a liquid formed on the sides of the test tube.

a. Could the solid be a hydrate? Explain how you could find out.

b. If the solid has a molar mass of 208 g/mol after heating and a formula of XY, how many formula units of water are there in one formula unit of the unheated compound?

Data Table 2

Sample number	Mass before heating (g)	Constant mass after heating (g)
1	1.92	1.26
2	2.14	1.40
3	2.68	1.78

2. a. The solid could be a hydrate, because it has less mass after heating. If the ratio of the amount of the water apparently lost to the amount of the apparently anhydrous compound is a small, whole-number ratio that remains constant with different samples, the solid is a hydrate.

b. sample 1: $1.26 \text{ g } XY \times \dfrac{1 \text{ mol}}{208 \text{ g}} = 6.06 \times 10^{-3} \text{ mol } XY$

$0.66 \text{ g } H_2O \times \dfrac{1 \text{ mol}}{18.02 \text{ g}} = 3.7 \times 10^{-2} \text{ mol } H_2O$

$\dfrac{3.7 \times 10^{-2} \text{ mol } H_2O}{6.06 \times 10^{-3} \text{ mol } XY} = \dfrac{6.1 \text{ mol } H_2O}{1.0 \text{ mol } XY}$

sample 2:

$\dfrac{4.1 \times 10^{-2} \text{ mol } H_2O}{6.73 \times 10^{-3} \text{ mol } XY} = \dfrac{6.1 \text{ mol } H_2O}{1.0 \text{ mol } XY}$

sample 3:

$\dfrac{5.0 \times 10^{-2} \text{ mol } H_2O}{8.56 \times 10^{-3} \text{ mol } XY} = \dfrac{5.8 \text{ mol } H_2O}{1.0 \text{ mol } XY}$

empirical formula: $XY \cdot 6H_2O$

5A

OBJECTIVES

Students will:

▶ use appropriate lab safety procedures.

▶ use a laboratory balance to measure mass.

▶ use a Bunsen burner to evaporate a substance's water of crystallization.

▶ collect and organize data.

▶ calculate molar amounts from mass values.

▶ determine the empirical formula for two hydrates of a compound.

▶ design and implement their own procedure.

RECOMMENDED TIME:
1–2 lab periods

PREREQUISITE:
Exploration 5A

MATERIALS

(for each lab group)

▶ 5 g gypsum sample

▶ 5 g plaster of Paris sample

▶ balance (0.01 g accuracy if possible)

▶ Bunsen burner with gas tubing and striker

▶ crucibles and covers, 2

▶ crucible tongs (not beaker tongs)

▶ desiccator

▶ mortar and pestle

▶ ring stand, ring, pipe-stem triangle

▶ spatula

ESTIMATED COST OF MATERIALS:
$75 500 (will vary depending on sample size and disposal needs)

ANALYSIS

$$3.90 \text{ g} \times \frac{1 \text{ mol CaSO}_4}{136.15 \text{ g}} = 2.86 \times 10^{-2} \text{ mol}$$

$CaSO_4$ in gypsum sample

$$1.10 \text{ g} \times \frac{1 \text{ mol H}_2O}{18.02 \text{ g}} = 6.10 \times 10^{-2} \text{ mol}$$

H_2O in gypsum sample

February 9, 1999

Director of Research
CheMystery Labs, Inc.
52 Fulton Street
Springfield, VA 22150

Dear Sir:

Lost Art Gypsum Mine previously sold its raw gypsum to a manufacturing company that used it to make anhydrous calcium sulfate, $CaSO_4$ (a desiccant), and plaster of Paris. That firm has now gone out of business, and we are currently negotiating the purchase of the firm's equipment to process our own gypsum into anhydrous calcium sulfate and plaster of Paris.

Your company has been recommended to plan the large-scale industrial process for our new plant. We will need a detailed report on the development of the process and formulas for these products. This report will be presented to the bank handling our loan for the new plant. As we discussed on the telephone today, we are willing to pay you $250,000 for the work, with the contract papers arriving under separate cover today.

Sincerely,

Alex Farros

Alex Farros
Vice President
Lost Art Gypsum Mine

References

Review information about hydrates and water of crystallization. Gypsum and plaster of Paris are hydrated forms of $CaSO_4$. One of the largest gypsum mines in the world is located outside Paris, France. Plaster of Paris has less water of crystallization than gypsum. Plaster of Paris is commonly used in plaster walls and art sculptures.

SOLUTION/MATERIAL PREPARATION

1. Gypsum and plaster of Paris are available at most hardware and art-supply stores. Several days before the lab, prepare the plaster of Paris according to the package directions. Allow it to dry thoroughly in the open air or in a drying oven set on low temperature. To distribute the gypsum and plaster of Paris, chip off a 5 g chunk for each lab group.

2. See the Teacher's Notes for Exploration 5A for instructions on making your own desiccator.

REQUIRED PRECAUTIONS

▶ Read all safety precautions, and discuss them with your students.

▶ Safety goggles and a lab apron must be worn at all times.

▶ Remind students to confine long hair and loose clothing before lighting a burner.

▶ Remind students that heated objects can be hot enough to burn even if they look cool. Students should always use crucible tongs to handle crucibles and crucible covers.

THE PLAN

CheMystery Labs, Inc.
52 Fulton Street
Springfield, VA 22150

MEMORANDUM

Date: February 10, 1999
To: Kenesha Smith
From: Martha Li-Hsien

Your team needs to develop a procedure to experimentally determine the correct empirical formulas for both hydrates of this anhydrous compound. You will use gypsum samples from the mine and samples of the plaster of Paris product; both are available at a cost.

Once this work is complete, our chemical engineering division will examine the most efficient way to implement the procedures for manufacturing. We're getting $250,000 from Lost Art. Your part of the job must cost less than $125,000 so that the chemical engineering division has enough money to do its job.

As soon as possible, I need a preliminary report from you that includes the following:

- detailed one-page summary of your plan for the procedure with all necessary data tables
- itemized list of equipment with total costs (Remember to keep costs under $125,000)

After you complete the analysis, prepare a two-page report for the chemical engineering division that includes the following information:

- formulas for anhydrous calcium sulfate, plaster of Paris, and gypsum
- summary of your procedure
- detailed and organized data and analysis sections that show calculations, along with estimates and explanations of any possible sources of error
- detailed invoice of all expenses and services

This report will become Chapter 2 of our final report to Mr. Farros.

For prices of materials, see page 692.

$$\frac{6.10 \times 10^{-2} \text{ mol } H_2O}{2.86 \times 10^{-2} \text{ mol } CaSO_4} = \frac{2.13 \text{ mol } H_2O}{1.00 \text{ mol Ca } SO_4}$$

gypsum: $CaSO_4 \cdot 2H_2O$

$$4.71 \text{ g} \times \frac{1 \text{ mol } CaSO_4}{136.15 \text{ g}} = 3.46 \times 10^{-2} \text{ mol}$$
$CaSO_4$ in plaster of Paris sample

$$0.29 \text{ g} \times \frac{1 \text{ mol } H_2O}{18.02 \text{ g}} = 1.6 \times 10^{-2} \text{ mol } H_2O$$
in plaster of Paris sample

$$\frac{1.6 \times 10^{-2} \text{ mol } H_2O}{3.46 \times 10^{-2} \text{ mol } CaSO_4} = \frac{0.46 \text{ mol } H_2O}{1.00 \text{ mol } CaSO_4}$$

plaster of Paris: $CaSO_4 \cdot \frac{1}{2}H_2O$

PRE-LAB DISCUSSION

Make sure students understand that fractional coefficients represent a fraction of a molar amount, not a fraction of a molecule.

Remind students to heat the empty crucible before measuring its mass at the very beginning. Students should heat samples of both plaster of Paris and gypsum separately until anhydrous $CaSO_4$ is formed.

TECHNIQUES TO DEMONSTRATE

Review proper use of the mortar and pestle and the proper technique and safety procedures for heating a crucible.

PROPOSED PROCEDURE

Heat a crucible and lid, cool them, and measure their mass. Add some crushed crystals of gypsum. Measure the mass, and then heat gently. Cool and measure the new mass. Keep reheating until the mass is fairly constant. Repeat for the plaster of Paris.

DISPOSAL

Provide a labeled container for students to dispose of all forms of $CaSO_4$. Pour the contents of the waste container onto several layers of newspaper to absorb excess water. Roll up the newspaper, and discard it in the trash can. Do not pour the contents of the waste container down the drain.

Required Precautions

Safety goggles and a lab apron must be worn at all times in the laboratory.

Confine long hair and loose clothing.

Do not touch or taste any chemicals. Always wash your hands thoroughly when finished in the lab.

Spill Procedures/ Waste-Disposal Methods

- Solids must go in the designated waste containers.
- Clean the lab area and all equipment after use.

735

SAMPLE DATA		
	GYPSUM	**PLASTER OF PARIS**
Mass of empty crucible and lid	32.18 g	32.18 g
Mass of crucible, lid, and compound	37.18 g	37.18 g
Mass of crucible, lid, and compound after first heating	36.10 g	36.91 g
Mass of crucible, lid, and compound after second heating	36.08 g	36.89 g

7A

OBJECTIVES

Students will:

▶ use appropriate lab safety procedures.

▶ use polymers to make a latex rubber ball and an ethanol-silicate polymer ball ("super ball").

▶ observe similarities and differences in the properties of the two balls.

▶ measure the bounce height of the two types of polymer balls.

▶ calculate volume from measurements of ball diameter.

▶ use a laboratory balance to measure mass.

▶ calculate the density of each type of ball.

RECOMMENDED TIME:

1 lab period

MATERIALS

(for each lab group)

▶ 2 L beaker, plastic bucket, or tub

▶ 3 mL of a 50% ethanol solution

▶ 5 oz paper cups, 2

▶ 10 mL of a 5% acetic acid solution (vinegar)

▶ 10 mL graduated cylinder

▶ 10 mL liquid latex

▶ 12 mL sodium silicate solution

▶ 25 mL graduated cylinder

▶ distilled water

▶ paper towels

▶ wooden stick

7A | Polymers and Toy Balls

OBJECTIVES

▶ **Synthesize two different polymers.**

▶ **Prepare a small toy ball from each polymer.**

▶ **Observe the similarities and differences between the two types of balls.**

▶ **Measure the density of each polymer.**

▶ **Compare the bounce height of the two balls.**

MATERIALS

▶ **2 L beaker, or plastic bucket or tub**

▶ **3 mL 50% ethanol solution**

▶ **5 oz paper cups, 2**

▶ **10 mL 5% acetic acid solution (vinegar)**

▶ **10 mL graduated cylinder**

▶ **10 mL liquid latex**

▶ **12 mL sodium silicate solution**

▶ **25 mL graduated cylinder**

▶ **distilled water**

▶ **gloves**

▶ **meterstick**

▶ **paper towels**

▶ **wooden stick**

Situation

Your company has been contacted by a toy company that specializes in toy balls made from vulcanized rubber. Recent environmental legislation has increased the cost of disposing of the sulfur and other chemical byproducts of the manufacturing process for this type of rubber. The toy company wants you to research some other materials.

SOLUTION/MATERIAL PREPARATION

1. For 5% acetic acid, use white vinegar. Do not dilute glacial acetic acid.

2. Liquid latex may be purchased from Flinn Scientific, Inc., in Batavia, IL. The following catalog numbers can be used: L0004—500 mL; L0110—1.00 L; L0222—4.00 L.

3. Sodium silicate solution, also known as water glass, can be purchased ready to use from many scientific supply companies.

4. Keep the bottles of latex and acetic acid solution in an operating hood because the vapors are unpleasant. Keep the bottle of ethanol in an operating fume hood because the vapors are flammable. Remind students to keep all three containers closed when not in use.

5. If balls need to be kept overnight, place them in plastic bags. If the ethanol-silicate polymer ball crumbles, add a few drops of water to it.

Always wear safety goggles and a lab apron to protect your eyes and clothing. If you get a chemical in your eyes, immediately flush the chemical out at the eyewash station while calling to your teacher. Know the location of the emergency lab shower and eyewash station and the procedures for using them.

Do not touch any chemicals. If you get a chemical on your skin or clothing, wash the chemical off at the sink while calling to your teacher. Make sure you carefully read the labels and follow the precautions on all containers of chemicals that you use. If no precautions are stated on the label, ask

your teacher what precautions to follow. Do not taste any chemicals or items used in the laboratory. Never return leftover chemicals to their original containers; take only small amounts to avoid wasting supplies.

Wear disposable plastic gloves; the sodium silicate solution and the alcohol silicate polymer are irritating to your skin.

Ethanol is flammable. Make sure there are no flames anywhere in the laboratory when you are using it. Also, keep it away from other sources of heat.

Background

Rubber is a polymer of covalently bonded atoms. When rubber is vulcanized, it is heated with sulfur. The sulfur atoms form bonds between adjacent molecules of rubber, increasing its strength and making it more elastic.

Latex rubber is a colloidal suspension that can be made synthetically or found naturally in plants such as the para rubber tree *(Hevea brasiliensis),* in which it dries to form a waterproof layer for protection. Latex is composed of approximately 60% water, 35% hydrocarbon monomers, 2% proteins, and some sugars and inorganic salts. Commercial latex is preserved with ammonia so that it remains a liquid until it can be molded or stretched into its final form. Latex is used in paints and disposable gloves.

The polymer formed from ethanol, C_2H_5OH, and a solution of sodium silicate, mostly in the form of $Na_2Si_3O_7$, also has covalent bonds. It is known as water glass because it dissolves in water. When the polymer is formed, water is also a product.

Problem

Latex rubber and the ethanol–sodium silicate polymer are the two materials you will become familiar with as you do the following:

▸ Synthesize each polymer.

▸ Make a ball 2–3 cm in diameter from each polymer.
▸ Make observations about the physical properties of each polymer.
▸ Measure how well each ball bounces.

Preparation

1. Organizing Data
Copy the data table below in your lab notebook. Prepare one table for each polymer. Leave space to record observations about the balls.

Technique

2. Fill the 2 L beaker, bucket, or tub about half-full with distilled water.

3. Using a clean 25 mL graduated cylinder, measure 10 mL of liquid latex and pour it into one of the paper cups.

Data Table 1			
Trial	Height (cm)	Mass (g)	Diameter (cm)
1			
2			
3			

PRE-LAB DISCUSSION

Review the material on polymers in Chapter 7. Be certain students understand the differences between a monomer and a polymer. Be sure to relate the properties of these polymers, such as strength, flexibility, and elasticity, to the nature of the covalent bonds holding them together.

TECHNIQUES TO DEMONSTRATE

Show students how to roll the latex and the ethanol-silicate polymer into a ball. Students will have difficulty making a perfect sphere, but they should try to make it as regular as possible. The more irregular the shape is, the more difficulty students will have calculating the volume and determining the bounce height because the ball will not bounce straight up.

To determine the volume of the balls, students should use mathematical calculations and measurements of the diameters. Instruct students not to measure the volumes by water displacement. The ethanol-silicate polymer will dissolve in water.

Remind students to be patient with the ethanol-silicate polymer, which tends to crumble. If it crumbles too much, a few drops of water will rehydrate it so it can be reshaped into a ball.

DISPOSAL

Paper cups, paper towels, disposable gloves, latex, and ethanol-silicate polymer balls and fragments should be thrown in the trash can. Waste liquids from this lab can be poured down the drain.

REQUIRED PRECAUTIONS

▸ Wear safety goggles and a lab apron during the lab.

▸ Read all safety precautions, and discuss them with your students.

▸ Promptly clean up all spills with paper towels.

▸ Ethanol is flammable. Ensure that there are no flames anywhere in the room when an alcohol is present. Keep the alcohol in a hood, use a container with a lid, and restrict the amount

kept in the hood to the minimum needed by the students.

▸ Do not allow students to take any ethanol-silicate polymer from the laboratory.

ANALYSIS AND INTERPRETATION

1. isoprene monomer: C_5H_8; ethanol-silicate monomer: $SiC_4H_{10}O_3$

2. Answers will vary but could include the following: The latex ball is more opaque, less smooth, and less crumbly than the ethanol-silicate polymer ball. The ethanol-silicate polymer ball breaks down after a period of time. Both balls bounce.

3. Ionic substances are not crumbly nor do they tend to bounce.

4. average bounce height for latex ball:

$$\frac{50 + 50 + 55}{3} = 52 \text{ cm}$$

average bounce height for ethanol-silicate polymer ball:

$$\frac{58 + 60 + 50}{3} = 56 \text{ cm}$$

5. volume for latex ball:

$$\frac{4}{3}(3.14)(3.0)^3 = 113 \text{ cm}^3$$

volume for ethanol-silicate polymer ball:

$$\frac{4}{3}(3.14)(3.5)^3 = 180 \text{ cm}^3$$

6. density for latex ball:

$$\frac{45.20 \text{ g}}{110 \text{ cm}^3} = 0.41 \text{ g/cm}^3$$

density for ethanol-silicate polymer ball:

$$\frac{84.03 \text{ g}}{180 \text{ cm}^3} = 0.47 \text{ g/cm}^3$$

4. Thoroughly clean the 25 mL graduated cylinder with soap and water, and then rinse it with distilled water.

5. Measure 10 mL of distilled water. Pour it into the paper cup with the latex.

6. Measure 10 mL of the 5% acetic acid solution, and pour it into the paper cup with the latex and water.

7. Immediately stir the mixture with the wooden stick.

8. As you continue stirring, a polymer "lump" will form around the wooden stick. Pull the stick with the polymer lump from the paper cup and immerse the lump in the 2 L beaker, bucket, or tub.

9. While wearing gloves, gently pull the lump from the wooden stick. Be sure to keep the lump immersed in the water, as shown in **Figure A.**

10. Keep the latex rubber underwater, and use your gloved hands to mold the lump into a ball, as shown in **Figure B.** Squeeze the lump several times to remove any unused chemicals. You may remove the latex rubber from the water as you roll it in your hands to smooth the ball.

11. Set aside the latex-rubber ball to dry. While it is drying, begin to make a ball from the ethanol and sodium silicate solutions.

12. In a clean 25 mL graduated cylinder, measure 12 mL of sodium silicate solution, and pour it into the other paper cup.

13. In a clean 10 mL graduated cylinder, measure 3 mL of 50% ethanol. Pour the ethanol into the paper cup with the sodium silicate, and mix with the wooden stick until a solid substance is formed.

14. While wearing gloves, remove the polymer that forms and place it in the palm of one hand, as shown in **Figure C.** Gently press it with the palms of both your hands until a ball that does not crumble is formed. This takes a little time and patience. The liquid that comes out of the ball is a combination of ethanol and water. Occasionally moisten the ball by letting a small amount of water from a faucet run over it. When the ball no longer crumbles, you are ready to go on to the next step.

15. Observe as many physical properties of the balls as possible, and record your observations in your lab notebook.

16. Drop each ball several times, and record your observations.

17. Drop each ball from a height of 1 m, and measure its bounce. Perform three trials for each ball, and record the values in your data table.

18. Measure the diameter and the mass of each ball, and record the values in your data table.

Figure A

Figure B

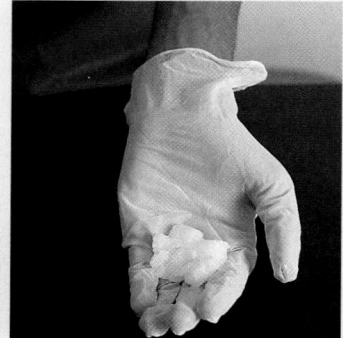

Figure C

SAMPLE DATA

BOUNCE HEIGHT	LATEX RUBBER	ETHANOL-SILICATE POLYMER
Trial 1	50. cm	58. cm
Trial 2	50. cm	60. cm
Trial 3	55. cm	50. cm

Cleanup and Disposal

19. Clean all apparatus and your lab station. Dispose of any extra solutions in the containers indicated by your teacher. Clean up your lab area. Remember to wash your hands thoroughly when your lab work is finished.

Analysis and Interpretation

1. Analyzing Information
Give the chemical formula for the latex (isoprene) monomer and the ethanol–sodium silicate polymer.

2. Analyzing Information
List at least three observations you made of the properties of the two different balls.

3. Applying Models
Explain how your observations in item 2 indicate that the polymers in each ball are not ionically bonded.

4. Organizing Data
Calculate the average height of the bounce for each type of ball.

5. Organizing Data
Calculate the volume for each ball. Even though the balls may not be perfectly spherical, assume that they are. (Hint: The volume of a sphere is equal to $4/3 \times \pi \times r^3$, where r is the radius of the sphere, which is one-half of the diameter.)

6. Organizing Data
Using your measurements for the volumes from item 5 and the recorded mass, calculate the density of each ball.

Conclusions

7. Inferring Conclusions
Which polymer would you recommend for the toy company's new toy balls? Explain your reasoning.

8. Evaluating Viewpoints
Using the table shown below, calculate the unit cost, that is, the amount of money it costs to make a single ball. (Hint: Calculate how much of each reagent is needed to make a single ball.)

Data Table 2	
Reagent	**Price (dollars per liter)**
Acetic acid solution	1.50
Ethanol solution	9.00
Latex solution	20.00
Sodium silicate solution	10.00

9. Evaluating Viewpoints
What are some other possible practical applications for each of the polymers you made?

Extensions

1. Research and Communication
Polymers are used in our daily lives. Describe or list the polymers you come into contact with during a one-day period in your life.

2. Designing Experiments
Design a mold for a polymer ball that will make it symmetrical and smooth. If your teacher approves of your design, try the procedure again with the mold.

3. Predicting Outcomes
When a ball bounces up, kinetic energy of motion is converted into potential energy. With this in mind, explain which will bounce higher, a perfectly symmetrical, round sphere or an oblong shape that vibrates after it bounces.

4. Predicting Outcomes
Explain why you didn't measure the volume of the balls by submerging them in water.

CONCLUSIONS

7. Answers will vary but should be based on the properties of the ball. Students may argue that because the ethanol-silicate polymer ball crumbles in time, it would be a poor candidate for a toy.

8. To make a latex ball you need 0.010 L of liquid latex and 0.010 L of acetic acid. The cost per liter of these combined substances is $21.50. The unit cost for a latex ball is $0.215. To make an ethanol-silicate polymer ball you need 0.012 L of sodium silicate solution and 0.003 L of 50% ethanol. The cost per liter of sodium silicate is $0.12. The cost per liter of 50% ethanol is $0.027. The unit cost for an ethanol-silicate polymer ball is $0.147.

9. Answers will vary but should be based on the properties of each substance.

EXTENSIONS

1. Answers will vary. Some possible polymers include rubber, proteins, cellulose, nylon, polyester, polyurethane, etc.

2. Suggestions for a mold will vary. Be sure students choose a material that will not dissolve in the solvents used in this process.

3. A ball with an oblong shape will not bounce as high because some of the kinetic energy will be transferred into the energy of vibration, leaving less to be transferred into gravitational potential energy. A sphere that bounces will transfer nearly all of its kinetic energy into gravitational potential energy.

4. The ethanol-silicate polymer ball would break down in the water, so density had to be calculated from measurements of diameter.

SAMPLE DATA		
	LATEX RUBBER	**ETHANOL-SILICATE POLYMER**
Mass	45.20 g	84.03 g
Diameter	6.00 cm	7.00 cm
Other observations	does not crumble very easily; seems more opaque	tends to bounce higher than other balls; crumbles easily; seems translucent

OBJECTIVES

Students will:

▸ write the proper chemical formulas for each reactant and product.

▸ balance each of the three possible equations.

▸ use appropriate lab safety procedures.

▸ assemble a ring stand.

▸ use a laboratory balance to measure mass.

▸ perform an experiment using a crucible.

▸ use a Bunsen burner.

▸ collect and organize data.

▸ use mass-mass stoichiometry to determine which chemical reaction has occurred.

RECOMMENDED TIME:
1 lab period

MATERIALS

(for each lab group)

▸ 2.5 g of baking soda

▸ balance (can be shared among lab groups)

▸ Bunsen burner

▸ crucible and cover

▸ crucible tongs (Do not use beaker tongs.)

▸ ignitor

▸ pipe-stem triangle

▸ ring stand

▸ ring clamp

▸ spatula

▸ weighing boat

10A | Decomposition of Baking Soda

OBJECTIVES

▸ Observe the thermal decomposition reaction of baking soda.

▸ Measure the mass of the remaining material after the reaction is complete.

▸ Calculate the expected masses of the solid products for each potential decomposition reaction.

▸ Compare the experimental mass to stoichiometric predictions to determine which reaction occurred.

MATERIALS

▸ baking soda
▸ balance
▸ Bunsen burner and sparker
▸ crucible and cover
▸ crucible tongs

▸ pipestem triangle
▸ ring clamp
▸ ring stand
▸ spatula
▸ weighing boats

Situation

You are a food chemist working for a company that makes boxed cake mix. Your company is trying to formulate a new recipe for Black Forest cake, and every ingredient needed in the powdered cake mix has been added except sodium bicarbonate (commonly called baking soda). Sodium bicarbonate is used to ensure that breads and cakes rise during baking. Your company wants you to determine the correct decomposition reaction that baking soda undergoes. This will determine what quantity to use in the mix.

REQUIRED PRECAUTIONS

▸ If students find a gas valve that has not been turned off properly, the room must be thoroughly ventilated—using the fume hood and windows—in order to prevent a fire hazard.

▸ Safety goggles and a lab apron must be worn throughout this activity.

▸ Long hair and loose clothing should be tied back.

SAMPLE DATA

Mass of empty crucible (g)	9.33 g
Mass of baking soda (g)	2.00 g
Mass of crucible and baking soda (g)	11.33 g
Mass of crucible and product (g)	10.58 g

Background

Due to the widespread use of sodium bicarbonate in many food products, the thermal decomposition reaction has been studied extensively by food chemists. Baking soda is used to prepare cakes in order to ensure that cakes rise as they bake.

As the temperature of the cake batter reaches approximately 50°C, the baking soda decomposes and carbon dioxide is released. The use of baking soda is especially popular in pancakes and waffles because the high cooking temperatures of 350–450°F (175–230°C) cause the carbon dioxide to be liberated before the dough sets. Thus, the batter rises before it sets, and we get a light and tasty finished product.

Problem

The goal of this lab is for you to experimentally determine which of three possible reactions is correct. All of these equations appear to be reasonable, but only one actually occurs. On the basis of stoichiometry, you can eliminate reactions that do not fit your experimental results when you conduct the thermal decomposition of baking soda.

Possible Decomposition Reactions

sodium bicarbonate (solid) $\longrightarrow$
sodium hydroxide (solid) + carbon dioxide (gas)

sodium bicarbonate (solid) $\longrightarrow$
sodium oxide (solid) + carbon dioxide (gas)
+ water (gas)

sodium bicarbonate (solid) $\longrightarrow$
sodium carbonate (solid) + carbon dioxide (gas)
+ water (gas)

Preparation

1. **Organizing Data**
   Copy the data table below in your lab notebook.

2. Set up the ring stand, ring clamp and Bunsen burner setup. Place the pipestem triangle on the ring clamp.

Data Table

Mass of empty crucible (g)	
Mass of baking soda (g)	
Mass of crucible and baking soda (g)	
Mass of crucible and product (g)	

The overall stoichiometry problems are shown. Analysis and Interpretation items 3–5 at the end of this lab ask students to perform each mathematical step separately. Teachers who use a multi-step approach may wish to have their students skip these items.

First possible reaction

$$2.00 \text{ g NaHCO}_3 \times \frac{1 \text{ mol NaHCO}_3}{84.0 \text{ g NaHCO}_3} \times \frac{1 \text{ mol NaOH}}{1 \text{ mol NaHCO}_3} \times \frac{40.0 \text{ g NaOH}}{1 \text{ mol NaOH}} = 0.952 \text{ g NaOH}$$

Second possible reaction

$$2.00 \text{ g NaHCO}_3 \times \frac{1 \text{ mol NaHCO}_3}{84.0 \text{ g NaHCO}_3} \times \frac{1 \text{ mol Na}_2\text{O}}{2 \text{ mol NaHCO}_3} \times \frac{62.0 \text{ g Na}_2\text{O}}{1 \text{ mol Na}_2\text{O}} = 0.738 \text{ g Na}_2\text{O}$$

Third possible reaction

$$2.00 \text{ g NaHCO}_3 \times \frac{1 \text{ mol NaHCO}_3}{84.0 \text{ g NaHCO}_3} \times \frac{1 \text{ mol Na}_2\text{O}}{2 \text{ mol NaHCO}_3} \times \frac{106 \text{ g Na}_2\text{CO}_3}{1 \text{ mol Na}_2\text{CO}_3} = 1.26 \text{ g Na}_2\text{CO}_3$$

Figure A

Technique

3. Measure the mass of the empty crucible. Record this measurement in your data table.

4. Obtain 2.0 g of baking soda in a clean, dry plastic weighing boat, as shown in **Figure A.** Record the exact mass, and include all decimal places. Record this measurement in your data table.

5. Transfer the solid material to the crucible, being careful to ensure the complete transfer to the small crucible, as shown in **Figure B.**

Figure B

6. Measure the total mass of the crucible and the baking soda. Record this measurement in your data table.

7. Place the crucible directly into the small pipestem triangle.

8. Heat the crucible and its contents with the Bunsen burner for 10 minutes. The bottom of the crucible should become bright orange, as shown in **Figure C.** Use a spatula to carefully break up any clumps that form as the heating proceeds.

9. Once the crucible has cooled to room temperature, measure the mass of the crucible and the remaining solid material. Record this measurement in your data table.

◆ ◆ Cleanup and Disposal

10. Clean all apparatus and your lab station. Return equipment to its proper place. Dispose of chemicals and solutions in the containers designated by your teacher. Do not pour any chemicals down the drain or in the trash unless your teacher directs you to do so. Wash your hands thoroughly after all work is finished and before you leave the lab.

Figure C

Analysis and Interpretation

1. Organizing Ideas
   Translate each of the three possible word equations in the Problem section of the lab into balanced chemical equations.

2. Organizing Ideas
   What was the mass of the remaining solid product that was formed in this chemical reaction?

3. Applying Ideas
   Calculate the number of moles of baking soda that were present in your crucible.

4. Applying Ideas
   Look at each of your balanced chemical equations. How many moles of the three different solid products would be formed from the number of moles of baking soda? (Hint: Use the mole ratios.)

5. Applying Ideas
   How are most decomposition reactions initiated?

Conclusions

6. Applying Conclusions
   Use your answers from item 4 to determine the predicted mass of the solid product in each of the three possible chemical reactions.

7. Applying Conclusions
   Which chemical reaction occurred inside the crucible?

8. Evaluating Methods
   If the crucible were not heated long enough, would you expect the mass of the solid material inside the crucible to have a higher or lower mass than what stoichiometry would predict?

9. Apply Ideas
   A student adds 0.40 g of sodium hydroxide to a clean, dry 250 mL beaker and leaves the beaker on the lab table. The mass of the empty beaker is 112.58 g. After 24 hours, the student observes that the beaker contains a dry, solid white residue. The total mass of the beaker and its contents is 113.16 g. Following are three possible chemical reactions that could have occurred:

Reaction A
sodium hydroxide (s) + carbon dioxide (g) $\longrightarrow$ sodium bicarbonate (s)

Reaction B
sodium hydroxide (s) + carbon dioxide (g) $\longrightarrow$ sodium bicarbonate (s) + water (g)

Reaction C
sodium hydroxide (s) $\longrightarrow$ sodium oxide (s) + water (g)

Use your knowledge of stoichiometry to determine which chemical reaction occurred. Show your work, and explain your reasoning whenever needed.

Extensions

1. Designing Experiments
   What possible sources of error can you identify with this procedure? If you can think of ways to eliminate them, ask your teacher to approve your plans, and run the procedure again.

9. The mass of the dry solid residue left over in the beaker is 0.58 g. Of the three possible reactions, Reaction B can be eliminated automatically because the students cannot balance the equation. The predicted mass for the product, sodium oxide, in Reaction C is 0.31 g; therefore, Reaction C did not occur either. According to the balanced chemical equation $NaOH + CO_2 \longrightarrow NaHCO_3$, 0.40 g NaOH reacts with CO_2 to produce 0.84 g $NaHCO_3$. Therefore, Reaction A is the reaction that occurred because it is closer to the actual mass.

$$0.40 \text{ g NaOH} \times \frac{1 \text{ mol NaOH}}{39.997 \text{ g NaOH}} \times \frac{1 \text{ mol NaHCO}_3}{1 \text{ mol NaOH}} \times$$
$$\frac{84.007 \text{ g NaHCO}_3}{1 \text{ mol NaHCO}_3} = 0.84 \text{ g NaHCO}_3$$

EXTENSION

1. Answers will vary.

OBJECTIVES

Students will:

▶ use appropriate lab safety procedures.

▶ observe the double-displacement reaction between solutions of strontium chloride and sodium carbonate.

▶ use a laboratory balance to measure mass.

▶ demonstrate appropriate technique in transferring liquids and filtering.

▶ perform stoichiometric calculations to determine the mass of sodium carbonate present in the solution.

RECOMMENDED TIME:

2 lab periods (includes overnight drying time)

MATERIALS

(for each lab group)

▶ 0.3 M $SrCl_2$ solution, 50 mL

▶ 15 mL Na_2CO_3 solution (unknown concentration)

▶ 100 mL graduated cylinder

▶ 250 mL beakers, 2

▶ balance

▶ beaker tongs

▶ distilled water

▶ drying oven

▶ glass stirring rod

▶ paper towels

▶ pipe-stem triangle

▶ ring and ring stand

▶ spatula

▶ water bottle

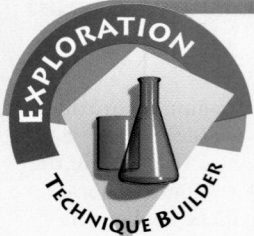

10B | Stoichiometry and Gravimetric Analysis

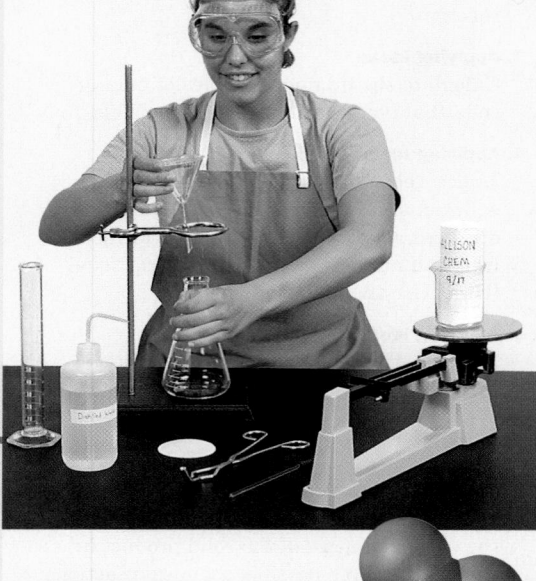

OBJECTIVES

▶ **Observe the double-displacement reaction between solutions of strontium chloride and sodium carbonate.**

▶ **Demonstrate proficiency with gravimetric methods.**

▶ **Measure the mass of insoluble precipitate formed.**

▶ **Relate the mass of precipitate formed to the mass of reactants before the reaction.**

▶ **Calculate the mass of sodium carbonate in a solution of unknown concentration.**

MATERIALS

▶ **0.30 M $SrCl_2$ solution, 45 mL**

▶ **15 mL Na_2CO_3 solution of unknown concentration**

▶ **100 mL graduated cylinder**

▶ **250 mL beakers, 3**

▶ **balance**

▶ **beaker tongs**

▶ **distilled water**

▶ **drying oven**

▶ **filter paper**

▶ **glass funnel or Büchner funnel with related equipment**

▶ **glass stirring rod**

▶ **paper towels**

▶ **ring and ring stand**

▶ **rubber policeman**

▶ **spatula**

▶ **water bottle**

Situation

You are working for a company that makes water-softening agents for homes with hard water. Recently, there was a mix-up on the factory floor, and sodium carbonate solution was mistakenly mixed in a vat with an unknown quantity of distilled water. You must determine the amount of Na_2CO_3 in the vat in order to properly predict the percentage yield of the water-softening product. You have been given a small sample from the 575 L of new solution.

SOLUTION/MATERIAL PREPARATION

1. To prepare 0.3 M $SrCl_2$, dissolve 80.0 g of $SrCl_2 \cdot 6H_2O$ in enough H_2O to make 1.00 L of solution.

2. For the unknown, 0.5 M Na_2CO_3 is recommended. To prepare 0.5 M Na_2CO_3, dissolve 53.0 g of Na_2CO_3 in enough H_2O to make 1.00 L of solution.

Always wear safety goggles and a lab apron to protect your eyes and clothing. If you get a chemical in your eyes, immediately flush the chemical out at the eyewash station while calling to your teacher. Know the locations of the emergency lab shower and eyewash and the procedure for using them.

Do not touch any chemicals. If you get a chemical on your skin or clothing, wash the chemical off at the sink while calling to your teacher. Make sure you carefully read the labels and follow the precautions on all containers of chemicals that you use. If there are no precautions stated on the

label, ask your teacher what precautions to follow. Do not taste any chemicals or items used in the laboratory. Never return leftovers to their original containers; take only small amounts to avoid wasting supplies.

Use tongs or a hot mitt to handle heated glassware or other equipment; heated glassware does not always look hot.

MATERIALS CONTINUED

GRAVITY-FILTRATION OPTION
▸ glass funnel
▸ filter paper

VACUUM-FILTRATION OPTION
▸ aspirator for spigot
▸ Büchner funnel (ceramic or plastic)
▸ filter paper
▸ one-hole rubber stopper or sleeve
▸ vacuum flask (sidearm flask) and tubing

Background

When chemists are faced with problems that require them to determine the quantity of a substance by mass, they often use a technique called gravimetric analysis. In this technique, a small sample of the material undergoes a reaction with an excess of another reactant. The chosen reaction is one that almost always provides a yield near 100%. In other words, all of the reactant of unknown amount will be converted into product. If the mass of the product is carefully measured, you can use stoichiometry calculations to determine how much of the reactant of unknown amount was involved in the reaction. Then by comparing the size of the analysis sample with the size of the original material, you can determine exactly how much of the substance is present.

This procedure involves a double-displacement reaction between strontium chloride, $SrCl_2$, and sodium carbonate, Na_2CO_3. In general, this reaction can be used to determine the amount of any carbonate compound in a solution.

Problem

Remember that accurate results depend on precise mass measurements, so keep all glassware very clean and do not lose any reactants or products during your lab work. You will react an unknown amount of sodium carbonate with an excess of strontium chloride. After purifying the product, you will determine the following:

▸ how much product is present
▸ how much Na_2CO_3 must have been present to produce that amount of product
▸ how much Na_2CO_3 is contained in the 575 L of solution

Preparation

1. **Organizing Data**
   Copy the data table below in your lab notebook.

2. Clean all of the necessary lab equipment with soap and water. Rinse each piece of equipment with distilled water.

3. Measure the mass of a piece of filter paper to the nearest 0.01 g, and record this value in your data table.

Data Table

Volume of Na_2CO_3 solution added	
Volume of $SrCl_2$ solution added	
Mass of dry filter paper	
Mass of beaker with paper towel	
Mass of beaker with paper towel, filter paper, and precipitate	

PRE-LAB DISCUSSION

Thoroughly discuss mass-mass stoichiometry and its application in the laboratory. It would be useful to perform calculations with sample data before performing the lab.

TECHNIQUES TO DEMONSTRATE

Review the procedures for the filtration technique your students will be using.

Remind students of the importance of using clean glassware and avoiding loss of product.

DISPOSAL

Be sure to set out two disposal containers, one for solids and another for liquids. The solids can be disposed of in the trash. The liquids can be washed down the drain with plenty of water.

REQUIRED PRECAUTIONS

▸ Read all safety precautions, and discuss them with your students.
▸ Safety goggles and a lab apron must be worn at all times.
▸ Remind students that heated objects can be hot enough to burn even if they look cool. Students should always use beaker tongs to place samples in a drying oven.

4. Refer to page 714 to set up a filtering apparatus, either a Büchner funnel or a gravity filtration, depending on what equipment is available.

5. Label a paper towel with your name, your class, and the date. Place the towel in a clean, dry 250 mL beaker, and measure and record the mass of the towel and beaker to the nearest 0.01 g.

Technique

6. Measure about 15 mL of the Na_2CO_3 solution into the graduated cylinder. Record this volume to the nearest 0.5 mL in your data table. Pour the Na_2CO_3 solution into a clean, empty 250 mL beaker. Carefully wash the graduated cylinder, and rinse it with distilled water.

7. Measure about 25 mL of the 0.30 M $SrCl_2$ solution into the graduated cylinder. Record this volume to the nearest 0.5 mL in your data table. Pour the $SrCl_2$ solution into the beaker with the Na_2CO_3 solution, as shown in **Figure A.** Gently stir the solution and precipitate with a glass stirring rod.

8. Carefully measure another 10 mL of $SrCl_2$ into the graduated cylinder. Record the volume to the nearest 0.5 mL in your data table. Slowly add it to the beaker. Repeat this step until no more precipitate forms.

Figure B

9. Once the precipitate has settled, slowly pour the mixture into the funnel. Be careful not to overfill the funnel because some of the precipitate could be lost between the filter paper and the funnel. Use the rubber policeman to transfer as much of the precipitate into the funnel as possible.

10. Rinse the rubber policeman into the beaker with a small amount of distilled water, and pour this solution into the funnel. Rinse the beaker several more times with small amounts of distilled water, as shown in **Figure B.** Pour the rinse water into the funnel each time.

11. After all of the solution and rinses have drained through the funnel, slowly rinse the precipitate on the filter paper in the funnel with distilled water to remove any soluble impurities.

12. Carefully remove the filter paper from the funnel, and place it on the paper towel that you have labeled with your name. Unfold the filter paper, and place the paper towel, filter paper, and precipitate in the rinsed beaker. Then place the beaker in the drying oven. For best results, allow the precipitate to dry overnight.

13. Using beaker tongs, remove your sample from the drying oven, and allow it to cool.

Figure A

SAMPLE DATA	
Volume of 0.3 M $SrCl_2$	35 mL
Volume of Na_2CO_3	15 mL
Mass of filter paper	0.30 g
Mass of filter paper + $SrCO_3$	1.36 g

Measure and record the mass of the beaker with paper towel, filter paper, and precipitate to the nearest 0.01 g.

 Cleanup and Disposal

14. Dispose of the precipitate in a designated waste container. Pour the filtrate in the other 250 mL beaker into the designated waste container. Clean up the lab and all equipment after use, and dispose of substances according to your teacher's instructions. Wash your hands thoroughly after all lab work is finished and before you leave the lab.

Analysis and Interpretation

1. Organizing Ideas
Write a balanced equation for the reaction. What is the precipitate? Write its empirical formula. (Hint: It was a double-displacement reaction.)

2. Applying Ideas
Calculate the mass of the dry precipitate. Calculate the number of moles of precipitate produced in the reaction. (Hint: Use the results from step 13.)

3. Applying Ideas
How many moles of Na_2CO_3 were present in the 15 mL sample?

4. Evaluating Methods
There was 0.30 mol of $SrCl_2$ in every liter of solution. Calculate the number of moles of $SrCl_2$ that were added. Determine whether $SrCl_2$ or Na_2CO_3 was the limiting reactant. Would this experiment have worked if the other reactant had been chosen as the limiting reactant? Explain why or why not.

5. Evaluating Methods
Why was the precipitate rinsed in step 11? What soluble impurities could have been on the filter paper along with the precipitate? How would the calculated results vary if the precipitate had not been completely dry? Explain your answer.

Conclusions

6. Inferring Conclusions
How many grams of Na_2CO_3 were present in the 15 mL sample?

7. Applying Conclusions
How many grams of Na_2CO_3 are present in the 575 L? (Hint: Create a conversion factor to convert from the sample, with a volume of 15 mL, to the entire solution, with a volume of 575 L.)

Extensions

1. Evaluating Methods
Ask your teacher for the theoretical mass of Na_2CO_3 in the sample, and calculate your percentage error.

2. Designing Experiments
What possible sources of error can you identify with your procedure? If you can think of ways to eliminate them, ask your teacher to approve your plan, and run the procedure again.

10B | Gravimetric Analysis
Hard Water Testing

OBJECTIVES

Students will:

▶ use appropriate lab safety procedures.

▶ observe the double-displacement reaction between sodium carbonate and calcium compounds containing water.

▶ use a laboratory balance to measure mass.

▶ demonstrate appropriate technique in transferring liquids.

▶ demonstrate appropriate technique in filtering.

▶ perform stoichiometric calculations to determine the mass of calcium ions present in the solution.

▶ determine whether or not a water sample should be classified as hard water.

▶ design and implement their own procedure.

RECOMMENDED TIME:
2 lab periods (includes overnight drying time)

PREREQUISITE:
Exploration 10B

MATERIALS

(for each lab group)

▶ 20 mL of CaCl₃ solution

▶ 75 mL or less of 0.5 M Na₂CO₃

▶ 100 mL graduated cylinder

▶ 250 mL beakers, 2

▶ balance

▶ beaker tongs

▶ drying oven

▶ pipe-stem triangle

▶ ring and ring stand

See the Teachers' Notes for Exploration 10B for information on materials for filtration options.

ESTIMATED COST OF MATERIALS:
$78 500–$143 000, depending on the amount of Na₂CO₃ and the filtration technique used.

March 3, 1999

George Taylor, Director of Analysis
CheMystery Labs, Inc.
52 Fulton Street
Springfield, VA 22150

Dear Mr. Taylor:

The city's Public Works Department is investigating new sources of water. One proposal involves drilling wells into a nearby aquifer that is protected from brackish water by a unique geological formation. Unfortunately, this formation is made of calcium minerals. If the concentration of calcium ions in the water is too high, the water will be "hard," and treating it to meet local water standards would be too expensive for us.

Water containing more than 120 mg of calcium per liter is considered hard. Enclosed is a sample that has been distilled from 1.0 L to its present volume. Please determine whether it is of suitable quality.

We are seeking a firm to be our consultant for the entire testing process. Interested firms will be evaluated based on this analysis. We look forward to receiving your report.

Sincerely,

Dana Rubio

Dana Rubio
City Manager

References

Review Chapter 10 for information about mass-mass stoichiometry. In this investigation, you will use a double-displacement reaction, but Na₂CO₃ will be used as a reagent to identify how much calcium is present in a sample. Like strontium and other Group 2 metals, calcium salts react with carbonate-containing salts to produce an insoluble precipitate.

SOLUTION/MATERIAL PREPARATION

1. To prepare 0.5 M Na₂CO₃, dissolve 53.0 g of Na₂CO₃ in enough distilled water to make 1.00 L of solution.

2. For the water sample, use 0.001 M CaCl₂ if you want students to find that the water is not hard. To prepare the 0.001 M CaCl₂, dissolve 0.147 g of CaCl₂•2H₂O in enough distilled water to make 1.00 L of solution. Use 0.5 M CaCl₂ if you want students to discover that

the water is hard. To prepare the 0.5 M CaCl₂, dissolve 73.5 g of CaCl₂•2H₂O in enough distilled water to make 1.00 L of solution.

3. To improve the results and reduce the time needed for this lab, the calcium carbonate can be centrifuged instead of filtered and then dried with a burner. The heat must be applied slowly to avoid decomposition.

THE PLAN

CheMystery Labs, Inc.
52 Fulton Street
Springfield, VA 22150

MEMORANDUM

Date: March 4, 1999
To: Shane Thompson
From: George Taylor

We must do a very accurate and efficient job on this analysis because this contract could be valuable for us in terms of both income and prestige. Besides, losing the contract to some out-of-town analysis firm would be awful!

We still don't have any capital expenditure funds for elaborate equipment purchases, but we can solve the city's problem with some careful gravimetric analysis because calcium salts and carbonate compounds undergo double-displacement reactions to give insoluble calcium carbonate as a precipitate.

Before you begin your work, I will need the following information from you so that I can put together our bid:
- detailed one-page summary of your plan for the procedure along with all necessary data tables
- description of necessary calculations
- itemized list of equipment with total costs. (Our financial planner tells me that even though we will bill the city for this work, we can afford to spend only $200,000 on this project.)

After you complete the analysis, prepare a two-page report for Dana Rubio. Remember that this report will be seen by a variety of city officials, so be certain it projects the image we want to present. Make sure the following items are included:
- calculation of calcium concentration in mg/L for the aquifer water
- explanation of how you determined the amount of calcium in the sample, including measurements and calculations
- balanced chemical equation for the reaction
- explanations and estimations for any possible sources of error
- detailed invoice for services rendered and expenses incurred

For prices of materials, see page 692.

Required Precautions

 Safety goggles and a lab apron must be worn at all times.

 Do not touch or taste any chemicals. Wash your hands thoroughly when finished.

 Use beaker tongs to remove glassware from the drying oven.

Spill Procedures/ Waste-Disposal Methods

- **Solids must go in the trash can. Do not wash them down the sink.**
- **Liquids may be washed down the sink with an excess of water.**
- **Clean the area and all equipment after use.**

749

SAMPLE DATA

Volume of water sample	20.00 mL
Volume of 0.5 M Na_2CO_3	40.00 mL
Mass of 150 mL beaker	65.80 mL
Mass of filter paper	0.31 g
Mass of beaker, filter paper, and $CaCO_3$	67.07 g

PRE-LAB DISCUSSION

Discuss any disparity between results in Exploration 10B and the actual amount of Na_2CO_3. Remind students that no reaction produces a 100% yield but that results should be close.

Encourage students to start planning by writing the balanced chemical equation for the reaction.

TIPS FOR EVALUATING THE PRE-LAB REQUIREMENTS

If students plan to use more than 75 mL of either reactant, have them reconsider their procedures. Students' plans should include measuring the mass of the filter paper and beaker before work begins.

Be certain that the description of necessary calculations is accurate. Students should calculate the mass of calcium present, not the mass of $CaCO_3$. Check that each student's data table contains the same headings as those shown in the sample data table below.

TECHNIQUES TO DEMONSTRATE

Discuss any errors in lab technique that you witnessed during Exploration 10B, and demonstrate the correct technique. Demonstrate the filtering technique students will use. Vacuum filtration is recommended because it is faster than gravity filtration.

ANALYSIS

Mass of Ca = 0.96 g $CaCO_3$ ×

$$\frac{40.08 \text{ g Ca}}{100.09 \text{ g } CaCO_3} \times \frac{1000 \text{ mg}}{1 \text{ g}} =$$

380 mg Ca

380 mg of Ca/L > 120 mg of Ca/L

The sample is hard water.

PROPOSED PROCEDURE

Measure the mass of a piece of filter paper and a beaker. Add an excess of Na_2CO_3 solution of known concentration to a carefully measured volume of a solution containing calcium ions. Filter and dry the $CaCO_3$ precipitate that forms. Measure its mass.

DISPOSAL

Students may dispose of solids in the trash can. Students may wash liquids down the drain with plenty of water.

EXPLORATION
TECHNIQUE BUILDER
10C

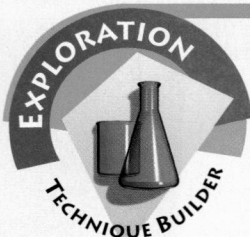

EXPLORATION
TECHNIQUE BUILDER

10C | Stoichiometry of Reactions

OBJECTIVES

Students will:

▸ use appropriate lab safety procedures.

▸ observe the double-displacement reaction between CH_3COOH and $NaHCO_3$ and the subsequent decomposition of H_2CO_3.

▸ use a laboratory balance to measure mass.

▸ determine the mole ratio of reactants and products.

▸ calculate the number of moles of reactants and products.

RECOMMENDED TIME:

1 lab period

MATERIALS

(for each lab group)

▸ 3 g of $NaHCO_3$

▸ 50 mL of 1.0 M acetic acid

▸ beaker tongs

▸ centigram balance

▸ dropper or pipet

▸ evaporating dish

▸ spatula

▸ watch glass

HOT-PLATE OPTION

▸ hot plate

BUNSEN BURNER OPTION

▸ Bunsen burner with gas tubing and striker

▸ ring stand and ring

▸ wire gauze with ceramic center

OBJECTIVES

▸ Demonstrate proficiency in measuring masses.

▸ Determine the number of moles of reactants and products in a reaction experimentally.

▸ Use the mass and mole relationships of a chemical reaction in calculations.

▸ Perform calculations that involve density and stoichiometry.

MATERIALS

▸ 1.0 M acetic acid

▸ 2–3 g $NaHCO_3$

▸ 100 mL graduated cylinder

▸ balance

▸ beaker tongs

▸ Bunsen burner and related equipment, or hot plate

▸ dropper or pipet

▸ evaporating dish

▸ ring stand and ring (for use with Bunsen burner)

▸ spatula

▸ watch glass

▸ wire gauze with ceramic center (for use with Bunsen burner)

Situation

Your company has a contract to determine the reaction requirements for a large-scale baking operation. The bakery purchases large quantities of ingredients and needs to know the correct proportions to avoid waste or inferior quality. The bakery needs to produce 425 mL of carbon dioxide, CO_2, for every cake during the rising step, which takes place just before baking. The bakery needs you to determine the exact amount of ingredients necessary to provide this amount of CO_2.

SOLUTION/MATERIAL PREPARATION

1. To prepare 1.0 M CH_3COOH, observe the required precautions. Add 87 mL of glacial CH_3COOH to enough distilled water to make 1.00 L of solution.

2. Better results are obtained using hot plates instead of Bunsen burners.

Background

Some recipes use baking soda, $NaHCO_3$, to make cakes rise. When you add a weak acid, such as vinegar, which contains acetic acid, CH_3COOH, or buttermilk, which contains lactic acid, CH_3COOH, to baking soda, bubbles of carbon dioxide gas are produced. The word equation for the reaction with vinegar is as follows: acetic acid and sodium hydrogen carbonate yields sodium acetate, water, and carbon dioxide. But you can't merely add an excess of baking soda to be sure enough CO_2 is formed because too much baking soda can make the cakes crumbly and bitter. Similarly, too much acid can cause a cake to taste sour. The amount of each reactant must be perfectly measured to produce the correct amount of CO_2, which has a density of 1.25 g/L at baking temperature.

Problem

To figure out the solution for the bakery, you will need to do the following:

▸ React a carefully measured mass of the reactant, $NaHCO_3$.
▸ Measure the mass of the product, $NaCH_3COOH$.

▸ Determine the mass and mole relationships for the other reactants and products.
▸ Calculate the number of moles and mass of each reactant required to produce 425 mL of CO_2.

Preparation

1. Organizing Data

Copy the data table below in your lab notebook.

Data Table	
Material	**Mass (g)**
Empty evaporating dish and watch glass	
Empty evaporating dish, watch glass, and $NaHCO_3$	
Heating 1, evaporating dish, watch glass, and $NaCH_3COO$	
Heating 2, evaporating dish, watch glass, and $NaCH_3COO$	
Heating 3, evaporating dish, watch glass, and $NaCH_3COO$	

ANALYSIS AND INTERPRETATION

1. $NaHCO_3(s) + CH_3COOH(aq) \longrightarrow$
   $CO_2(g) + H_2O(l) + CH_3COONa(aq)$

2. $NaHCO_3$ molar mass: 84.01 g/mol
   CH_3COOH molar mass: 60.06 g/mol
   CO_2 molar mass: 44.01 g/mol
   H_2O molar mass: 18.02 g/mol
   CH_3COONa molar mass:
   82.04 g/mol

3. The bubbling was caused by the formation of carbon dioxide gas.

4. The residue is entirely CH_3COONa because CH_3COOH was added in excess to be certain that the reaction went to completion.

5. $NaHCO_3$: 2.10 g

   $2.10 \text{ g NaHCO}_3 \times \dfrac{1 \text{ mol NaHCO}_3}{84.01 \text{ g NaHCO}_3} =$

   $2.50 \times 10^{-2} \text{ mol NaHCO}_3$

   CH_3COONa: 2.03 g

   $2.03 \text{ g CH}_3\text{COONa} \times$
   $\dfrac{1 \text{ mol CH}_3\text{COONa}}{82.04 \text{ g CH}_3\text{COONa}} =$
   $2.47 \times 10^{-2} \text{ mol CH}_3\text{COONa}$

6. Theoretical yield of CH_3COONa:
   $2.50 \times 10^{-2} \text{ mol NaHCO}_3 \times$
   $\dfrac{1 \text{ mol CH}_3\text{COONa}}{1 \text{ mol NaHCO}_3} \times$
   $\dfrac{82.04 \text{ g CH}_3\text{COONa}}{1 \text{ mol CH}_3\text{COONa}} =$
   $2.05 \text{ g CH}_3\text{COONa}$

Technique

2. Measure the mass of a clean, dry evaporating dish and watch glass to the nearest 0.01 g. Record this mass in your data table.

3. Add 2–3 g $NaHCO_3$ to your evaporating dish. Measure the exact mass, with the cover glass, to the nearest 0.01 g. Record this mass in your data table.

4. Slowly add 30 mL of the acetic acid solution to the $NaHCO_3$ in the evaporating dish. Add more acetic acid with a dropper or pipet until the bubbling stops.

5. If you are using a Bunsen burner, place the evaporating dish and its contents on a ceramic-centered wire gauze placed on an iron ring attached to the ring stand, as shown in **Figure A**. Place the watch glass, concave side up, on top of the dish, making sure that there is a slight opening for steam to escape. If you are using a hot plate, position the watch glass the same way.

6. Gently heat the evaporating dish until only a dry solid remains. Make sure that no water droplets remain on the underside of the watch glass. **Do not heat too rapidly, or the material will boil, and the product will spatter out of the evaporating dish.**

Figure A

Figure B

7. Turn off the gas burner or hot plate. Allow the apparatus to cool for at least 15 minutes. Determine the mass of the cooled equipment to the nearest 0.01 g, as shown in **Figure B**. Record the mass of the dish, residue, and watch glass in your data table.

8. If time permits, reheat the evaporating dish and contents for 2 minutes. Let it cool, and measure its mass again. The sample will be dry when you can make two successive measurements within 0.02 g of each other.

Cleanup and Disposal

9. Clean up the lab and all equipment after use. Dispose of any unused chemicals in the containers designated by your teacher. Wash your hands thoroughly before you leave the lab and after all lab work is finished. Make sure to turn off all gas valves.

Analysis and Interpretation

1. **Analyzing Results**
   Write a balanced equation for the reaction of baking soda and acetic acid. Be sure to include states of matter for all of the reactants and products.

2. **Organizing Data**
   Use the periodic table to calculate the molar mass for each of the reactants and products.

SAMPLE DATA	
Mass of dish and glass	71.17 g
Mass of dish, glass, and $NaHCO_3$	73.27 g
Mass of dish, glass, and residue (CH_3COONa) after first heating	73.22 g
Mass of dish, glass, and residue (CH_3COONa) after second heating	73.20 g

3. Analyzing Results

Explain what caused the bubbling when the reaction took place.

4. Analyzing Methods

How do you know that all of the residue is actually sodium acetate rather than a mixture of sodium bicarbonate and sodium acetate?

5. Organizing Data

Calculate the mass of $NaHCO_3$, the number of moles of $NaHCO_3$, the mass of $NaC_2H_3O_2$, and the number of moles of $NaC_2H_3O_2$.

6. Evaluating Data

Using the balanced equation and the amount of $NaHCO_3$, determine the theoretical yield of $NaC_2H_3O_2$ in moles and grams. (Hint: See Chapter 10 for a discussion of theoretical yield, and assume the acetic acid was present in excess.)

Conclusions

7. Analyzing Conclusions

What is the percentage yield for your reaction? (Hint: See Chapter 10 for a discussion of percentage yield.)

8. Inferring Conclusions

What is the theoretical yield for CO_2? Using the density value given, 1.25 g/L, calculate the volume of CO_2 that would be produced by this reaction in an oven. Show your calculations.

9. Applying Conclusions

How many moles of $NaHCO_3$ and CH_3COOH are necessary to produce 425 mL of CO_2 at baking temperature? Show your calculations. (Hint: Be sure to include your percentage yield for this reaction in your calculations.)

Extensions

1. Designing Experiments

If your percentage yield is less than 100%, explain why. If you can think of ways to eliminate any problems, ask your teacher to approve your plan, and run the procedure again.

2. Research and Communication

Many recipes for breads use yeast instead of baking soda as a source of CO_2. Research the use of yeast, and explain what ingredients are necessary for the yeast to produce carbon dioxide. What is the balanced chemical equation for the reaction that yeast use to produce CO_2?

CONCLUSIONS

7. Percentage yield: $\dfrac{2.03 \text{ g actual}}{2.05 \text{ g theoretical}} \times 100 = 99.0\%$

8. Theoretical yield of CO_2:

$2.50 \times 10^{-2} \text{ mol NaHCO}_3 \times \dfrac{1 \text{ mol CO}_2}{1 \text{ mol NaHCO}_3} \times \dfrac{44.01 \text{ g}}{1 \text{ mol CO}_2} = 1.10 \text{ g CO}_2$

$1.10 \text{ g CO}_2 \times \dfrac{1 \text{ L}}{1.25 \text{ g CO}_2} = 0.880 \text{ L CO}_2$

9. mol of $NaHCO_3$ = mol of CH_3COOH

$425 \text{ mL CO}_2 \times \dfrac{1 \text{ L}}{1000 \text{ mL}} \times \dfrac{1.25 \text{ g CO}_2}{1 \text{ L CO}_2} \times \dfrac{1 \text{ mol CO}_2}{44.01 \text{ g CO}_2} \times \dfrac{1 \text{ mol NaHCO}_3}{1 \text{ mol CO}_2} = 0.0121 \text{ mol of NaHCO}_3$

EXTENSIONS

1. Suggestions for sources of error and plans for improving the procedure will vary. Possible suggestions could include improving technique, using larger quantities, or performing multiple trials. Be sure students' suggestions for improvements are safe and include carefully planned procedures.

2. Yeast use the cellular respiration reaction to produce CO_2. This process requires oxygen and sugar, usually in the form of glucose.

$$C_6H_{12}O_6 + 6O_2 \longrightarrow 6CO_2 + 6H_2O$$

10C | Stoichiometry
Viral Disease Alert

OBJECTIVES

Students will:

▶ use appropriate lab safety procedures.

▶ choose appropriate reactants to synthesize $ZnCl_2$.

▶ determine proper molar and mass amounts of reactants.

▶ use a laboratory balance to measure mass.

▶ design and implement their own procedure.

RECOMMENDED TIME:
2 lab periods

PREREQUISITE:
Exploration 10C

MATERIALS

(for each lab group)

▶ 2.0 g of mossy zinc

▶ 25 mL of 1.0 M HCl

▶ 100 mL graduated cylinder

▶ 250 mL beaker

▶ balance, centigram

▶ Bunsen burner with gas tubing and striker or hot plate

▶ drying oven

▶ ring stand, ring, and wire gauze

▶ weighing paper

ESTIMATED COST OF MATERIALS:
$63 000–$65 000

PRE-LAB DISCUSSION

Begin by discussing the results and procedure used in Exploration 10C, especially any errors in lab technique that occurred. To help students, you may offer the following leading questions for them to consider as they make their plans:

▶ Are you given amounts of reactants or products?

▶ Which reactants will react to provide $ZnCl_2$?

▶ What amounts of the reactants will you need?

▶ Which reactant should be in excess?

THE PROBLEM

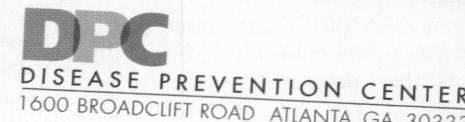

DPC
DISEASE PREVENTION CENTER
1600 BROADCLIFT ROAD ATLANTA, GA 30333

March 7, 1999

Ms. Sandra Fernandez
Director of Development
CheMystery Labs, Inc.
52 Fulton Street
Springfield, VA 22150

Dear Ms. Fernandez:

The DPC has been monitoring reports of a cluster of illnesses near the town of Grover's Corner, New Jersey. Toxicology reports indicate that the disease is spread much like viral meningitis, only more quickly. We estimate that irreparable harm to the nervous system occurs in victims approximately 12 hours after their initial exposure to the virus. It is imperative that we find a treatment soon.

Preliminary research indicates that zinc chloride acts as an inhibitor to the reproduction of this unidentified virus. For this reason, several companies, including yours, have been contacted to produce a large quantity of zinc chloride quickly and economically.

Sincerely,

Rhonda Baclig

Rhonda Baclig, M.D.
Disease Prevention Center
Special Pathogens Branch

References

Review Chapter 10 for information on stoichiometric calculations. You will also need to review theoretical yield, actual yield, and percentage yield. The methods used in this procedure are very dependent on using clean and dry equipment. Remember that 1.0 M HCl contains 1.0 mol of HCl formula units in every liter.

SOLUTION/MATERIAL PREPARATION

1. To prepare 1.0 M HCl, take these precautions. Wear goggles, a face shield, impermeable gloves, and a lab apron. Work in a hood known to be in good operating condition, and have another person standing by to call for help in case of an emergency. Be sure you are within a 30 second walk of a safety shower and eyewash station. Add 83 mL of concentrated HCl to enough distilled water to make 1.00 L of solution. Add the acid slowly while stirring to avoid overheating.

REQUIRED PRECAUTIONS

▶ Read all safety precautions, and discuss them with your students.

▶ Safety goggles and a lab apron must be worn at all times.

▶ Students should not handle concentrated acids. In case of an acid spill, dilute the spill with water. Then mop up the spill with wet cloths or a cloth mop designated for spill cleanup. Wear disposable plastic gloves while cleaning spills.

THE PLAN

MEMORANDUM

CheMystery Labs, Inc.
52 Fulton Street
Springfield, VA 22150

Date: March 8, 1999
To: Michael Belan
From: Sandra Fernandez

A rush job! If the disease spreads past this town and toward larger cities, an uncontrollable situation will develop very soon. Dr. Baclig has asked several companies to develop procedures for making small amounts of $ZnCl_2$ for $200,000. Based on the DPC's evaluation, a primary subcontractor will be chosen to prepare the inhibitor in bulk. She needs a preliminary report tomorrow that includes the following:

- detailed one-page summary of your plan for the procedure, including a suggested synthesis reaction
- itemized list of equipment with total costs

After you receive her approval, go ahead. When the work is complete, prepare a two-page letter and a minimum sample of 1.5 g of the inhibitor to go to Dr. Baclig. She will present them at a joint Disease Prevention Center/New Jersey Health Department meeting. Your letter must include the following:

- balanced chemical equation of the reaction you chose for producing the antidote
- molar masses and moles of the reactants and products
- theoretical and actual yield of the product
- percentage yield for your antidote, along with a discussion of what you did to keep the yield as high as possible and the cost as low as possible
- description of a procedure and cost for producing 37.50 kg of $ZnCl_2$
- detailed analysis and data sections showing calculations along with estimates and explanations of any possible sources of error
- detailed invoice for all expenses and services

For prices of materials, see page 692.

Required Precautions

Safety goggles and a lab apron must be worn at all times.

Do not touch or taste any chemicals. Always wash your hands thoroughly when finished.

If you get acid or base on your skin or clothing, wash it off at the sink while calling to your teacher. If you get acid or base in your eyes, immediately flush it out at the eyewash station while calling to your teacher.

Spill Procedures/ Waste-Disposal Methods

- In case of spills, follow your teacher's instructions.
- Dispose of all solid and liquid wastes in the containers designated by your teacher.
- Clean the area and all equipment after use.
- Wash your hands when you are finished working in the lab.

755

SAMPLE DATA

Mass of 250 mL beaker	99.43 g
Mass of zinc added	2.00 g
Volume of 1.0 M HCl	25.0 mL
Mass of 250 mL beaker and $ZnCl_2$	101.11 g
Mass of $ZnCl_2$	1.68 g

TIPS FOR EVALUATING THE PRE-LAB REQUIREMENTS

Be certain students have chosen the right reactants. Although $CuCl_2$ and Zn will react to form $ZnCl_2$, this reaction is more expensive than the reaction of Zn and HCl. No other combination of reactants will react.

Students should also designate the necessary amounts. Zn should be the excess reactant because it can be removed more easily from the $ZnCl_2$ solution than HCl can. To ensure at least 1.5 g of $ZnCl_2$ is produced, react about 25 mL of HCl with 2.0 g of Zn. Do not allow students to use more than 50 mL of 1.0 M HCl.

PROPOSED PROCEDURE

Measure the mass of a clean, dry 250 mL beaker. Pour 25 mL of 1.0 M HCl into the beaker. Add an excess of Zn. When the reaction stops, remove any remaining Zn. The resulting solution contains only water and $ZnCl_2$. Evaporate the water with a Bunsen burner, and dry the crystals overnight. Remind students to heat the solution gently when they are evaporating the water.

DISPOSAL

Set out three disposal containers. One is for unreacted zinc metal, which can be rinsed and reused next year. The second container is for the $ZnCl_2$ that is produced. The third is for any liquid waste produced.

If you can use the $ZnCl_2$, evaporate the liquid portion of the $ZnCl_2$ waste container and store the $ZnCl_2$ crystals in a labeled sealed container.

To dispose of the contents of the liquid and $ZnCl_2$ waste containers, combine the contents and treat them in a working fume hood with Na_2S solution. The ZnS precipitate formed should be filtered, dried in the hood, and placed in the trash. Treat the filtrate with 1.0 M acid or base until its pH is between 5 and 9, and pour it down the drain with plenty of water.

OBJECTIVES

Students will:

▸ use appropriate lab safety procedures.

▸ use a laboratory balance to measure mass.

▸ use a graduated cylinder to measure volume.

▸ use a thermometer or the Vernier probe to measure temperature.

▸ determine the maximum temperature attained by a mixture of reactants.

▸ use a calorimeter to determine the heat of reaction for various combinations of an acid and a base.

▸ use measured heats of reaction in energy-stoichiometry calculations.

RECOMMENDED TIME:

1 lab period

MATERIALS

(for each lab group)

▸ 4 g of NaOH pellets

▸ 50 mL of 1.0 M HCl

▸ 50 mL of 1.0 M NaOH

▸ 100 mL of 0.50 M HCl

▸ 100 mL graduated cylinder

▸ balance, centigram

▸ Celsius thermometer, nonmercury type, with a range from −10°C to 120°C

▸ distilled water

▸ glass stirring rod

▸ plastic-foam cups or calorimeters

▸ spatula

▸ watch glass

OPTIONAL EQUIPMENT

(Refer to page 700 for equipment set up.)

▸ CBL unit

▸ graphing calculator with link cable

▸ Vernier temperature probe

EXPLORATION
TECHNIQUE BUILDER

11A | Calorimetry and Hess's Law

OBJECTIVES

▸ **Demonstrate proficiency in the use of calorimeters and related equipment.**

▸ **Relate temperature changes to enthalpy changes.**

▸ **Determine the heat of reaction for several reactions.**

▸ **Demonstrate that the heat of reaction can be additive.**

MATERIALS

▸ **0.50 M HCl solution, 100 mL**

▸ **1.0 M HCl solution, 50 mL**

▸ **1.0 M NaOH solution, 50 mL**

▸ **4 g NaOH pellets**

▸ **100 mL graduated cylinder**

▸ **balance**

▸ **distilled water**

▸ **glass stirring rod**

▸ **plastic-foam cups (or calorimeters)**

▸ **spatula**

▸ **thermometer**

▸ **watch glass**

OPTIONAL EQUIPMENT

▸ **CBL unit**

▸ **graphing calculator with link cable**

▸ **Vernier temperature probe**

Situation

A man working for a cleaning firm was told by his employer to pour some old cleaning supplies into a glass container for disposal. Some of the supplies included muriatic (hydrochloric acid), HCl(*aq*), and a drain cleaner containing lye, NaOH(*s*). When the substances were mixed, the container shattered, spilling the contents onto the worker's arms and legs. The worker claims that the hot spill caused burns, and he is therefore suing his employer. The employer claims that the worker is lying because the solutions were at room temperature before they were mixed. The employer says that a chemical burn is unlikely because tests after the accident revealed that the mixture had a neutral pH, indicating that the HCl and NaOH were neutralized. The court has asked you to evaluate whether the worker's story is supported by scientific evidence.

SOLUTION/MATERIAL PREPARATION

1. To prepare 0.50 M HCl, observe the required precautions. Add 42 mL of concentrated HCl to enough distilled water to make 1.00 L of solution. Add the acid slowly while stirring to avoid overheating.

2. To prepare 1.0 M HCl, add 83 mL of concentrated HCl to enough distilled water to make 1.00 L of solution. Add the acid slowly while stirring to avoid overheating.

3. To prepare 1.00 L of 1.0 M NaOH, dissolve 40.0 g of NaOH in enough water to make 1.00 L of solution.

4. To prevent the hygroscopic NaOH pellets from absorbing too much water, keep them in a reagent bottle with a stopper. Instruct students to replace the stopper after they have obtained what they need.

Always wear safety goggles and a lab apron to protect your eyes and clothing. If you get a chemical in your eyes, immediately flush the chemical out at the eyewash station while calling to your teacher. Know the locations of the emergency lab shower and eyewash station and the procedure for using them.

Do not touch any chemicals. If you get a chemical on your skin or clothing, wash the chemical off at the sink while calling to your teacher. Make sure you carefully read the labels and follow the precautions on all containers of chemicals that you use. If there are no precautions stated on the label, ask

your teacher what precautions to follow. Do not taste any chemicals or items used in the laboratory. Never return leftovers to their original containers; take only small amounts to avoid wasting supplies.

Never put broken glass in a regular waste container. Broken glass should be disposed of separately in the container designated by your teacher.

Call your teacher in the event of an acid or base spill. Acid or base spills should be cleaned up promptly according to your teacher's instructions.

Background

Chemicals can be dangerous because of their special storage needs. Acids cannot be stored in metal containers, and organic solvents cannot be kept in plastic ones. Chemicals that are mixed and react are even more dangerous because many reactions release large amounts of heat. Glass, although relatively nonreactive with solutions of pure substances, is heat-sensitive and can shatter if there is a sudden change in temperature due to a reaction. Some glassware, such as Pyrex, is heat-conditioned but can still fracture under extreme heat conditions, especially if scratched.

Problem

You will measure the amount of heat released by mixing the chemicals in two ways. First you will break the reaction into steps and measure the heat change of each step. Then you will

measure the heat change of the reaction when it takes place all at once. When you are finished, you will be able to use the calorimetry equation from Chapter 11 to determine the following:

- the amount of heat evolved during the overall reaction
- the amount of heat for each step
- the amount of heat for the reaction in kilojoules per mole
- whether this heat could have raised the temperature of the water in the solution high enough to cause a burn

Preparation

1. Organizing Data

Copy the data table below in your lab notebook. Reactions 1 and 3 will each require two additional spaces to record the mass of the empty watch glass and the mass of the watch glass with NaOH.

Data Table

	Reaction 1	Reaction 2	Reaction 3
Total volumes of liquid(s)			
Initial temperature			
Final temperature			
Mass of empty watch glass			
Mass of watch glass with NaOH			

Figure A

2. If you are not using a plastic-foam cup as a calorimeter, ask your teacher for instructions on using the calorimeter. At various points in steps 3 through 13, you will need to measure the temperature of the solution within the calorimeter.

3. Measure the temperature by gently inserting the thermometer or Vernier temperature probe into the hole in the calorimeter lid, as shown in **Figure A.** If you are using the Vernier probe and CBL unit, refer to page 700 for equipment setup. The thermometer takes time to reach the same temperature as the solution inside the calorimeter, so wait to be sure you have an accurate reading. **Thermometers break easily, so be careful with them, and do not use them to stir a solution.**

Technique

Reaction 1: Dissolving NaOH

4. Pour about 100 mL of distilled water into a graduated cylinder. Measure and record the volume of the water to the nearest 0.1 mL. Pour the water into your calorimeter. Measure and record the water temperature to the nearest 0.1°C.

5. Determine and record the mass of a clean and dry watch glass to the nearest 0.01 g. Remove the watch glass from the balance. While wearing gloves, obtain about 2 g of NaOH pellets, and put them on the watch glass. Use forceps when handling NaOH pellets. Measure and record the mass of the watch glass and the pellets to the nearest 0.01 g. **It is important that this step be done quickly because NaOH is hygroscopic. It absorbs moisture from the air, and increases its mass as long as it remains exposed to the air.**

6. Immediately place the NaOH pellets in the calorimeter cup, and gently stir the solution with a stirring rod. **Do not stir with a thermometer.** Place the lid on the calorimeter. Watch the thermometer or CBL unit, and record the highest temperature in the data table. When the reaction is finished, pour the solution into the container designated by your teacher for disposal of basic solutions.

7. Be sure to clean all equipment and rinse it with distilled water before continuing with the next procedure.

Reaction 2: NaOH and HCl in solution

8. Pour about 50 mL of 1.0 M HCl into a graduated cylinder. Measure and record the volume of the HCl solution to the nearest 0.1 mL. Pour the HCl solution into your calorimeter. Measure and record the temperature of the HCl solution to the nearest 0.1°C.

9. Pour about 50 mL of 1.0 M NaOH into a graduated cylinder. Measure and record the volume of the NaOH solution to the nearest 0.1 mL. **For this step only, rinse the thermometer or probe in distilled water, and measure the temperature of the NaOH solution in the graduated cylinder to the nearest 0.1°C. Record the temperature in your data table, and then replace the thermometer in the calorimeter.**

10. Pour the NaOH solution into the calorimeter cup, and stir gently. Place the lid on the calorimeter. Watch the thermometer or CBL unit, and record the highest temperature in the data table. When finished with

SAMPLE DATA			
	REACTION 1	**REACTION 2**	**REACTION 3**
Volume of fluid (mL)	100.0	100.0	100.0
Initial temperature (°C)	21.5	22.0	22.0
Highest temperature (°C)	26.5	28.1	33.0

this reaction, pour the solution into the container designated by your teacher for disposal of mostly neutral solutions.

11. Clean and rinse all equipment before continuing with the next procedure.

Reaction 3: Solid NaOH and HCl in solution

12. Pour about 100 mL of 0.50 M HCl into a graduated cylinder. Measure and record the volume to the nearest 0.1 mL. Pour the HCl solution into your calorimeter, as shown in **Figure B**. Measure and record the temperature of the HCl solution to the nearest 0.1°C.

13. Measure the mass of a clean and dry watch glass, and record it in your data table. Obtain approximately 2 g of NaOH. Place it on the watch glass, and record the total mass to the nearest 0.01 g. **It is important that this step be done quickly because NaOH is hygroscopic.**

14. Immediately place the NaOH pellets in the calorimeter, and gently stir the solution. Place the lid on the calorimeter. Watch the thermometer, and record the highest temperature in the data table. When finished with this reaction, pour the solution into the container designated by your teacher for disposal of mostly neutral solutions.

Figure B

◆ ◆ Cleanup and Disposal

15. Clean all apparatus and your lab station. Check with your teacher for the proper disposal procedures. Any excess NaOH pellets should be disposed of in the designated container. Always wash your hands thoroughly after cleaning up the lab area and equipment.

Analysis and Interpretation

1. **Organizing Ideas**
Write a balanced chemical equation for each of the three reactions that you performed. (Hint: Be sure to include states of matter for all substances in each equation.)

2. **Organizing Ideas**
Find a way to get the equation for the total reaction by adding two of the equations from Analysis and Interpretation item 1 and then canceling out substances that appear in the same form on both sides of the new equation. (Hint: Start with the equation whose product is a reactant in a second equation. Add those two equations together.)

3. **Analyzing Methods**
Explain why a plastic-foam cup makes a better calorimeter than a paper cup does.

4. **Organizing Data**
Calculate the change in temperature (Δt) for each of the reactions.

5. **Organizing Data**
Assuming that the density of the water and the solutions is 1.00 g/mL, calculate the mass, m, of liquid present for each of the reactions.

6. **Analyzing Results**
Using the calorimeter equation, calculate the heat released by each reaction. (Hint: Use the specific heat capacity of water in your calculations; $c_{p,\mathrm{H_2O}} = 4.180$ J/g•°C.)

$$\text{Heat} = m \times \Delta t \times c_{p,\mathrm{H_2O}}$$

ANALYSIS AND INTERPRETATION

1. $NaOH(s) \longrightarrow NaOH(aq)$

$NaOH(aq) + HCl(aq) \longrightarrow$
$\qquad H_2O(l) + NaCl(aq)$

$NaOH(s) + HCl(aq) \longrightarrow$
$\qquad H_2O(l) + NaCl(aq)$

2. $NaOH(s) \longrightarrow \overline{NaOH(aq)}$
$\overline{NaOH(aq)} + HCl(aq) \longrightarrow$
$\qquad \underline{H_2O(l) + NaCl(aq)}$
$NaOH(s) + HCl(aq) \longrightarrow$
$\qquad H_2O(l) + NaCl(aq)$

3. A good calorimeter must insulate; any heat created by the reaction should be absorbed by the water instead of the surroundings. Plastic-foam cups insulate better than paper cups and therefore make better calorimeters.

4. $\Delta t_1 = 26.5°C - 21.5°C = 5.0°C$

$\Delta t_2 = 28.1°C - 22.0°C = 6.1°C$

$\Delta t_3 = 33.0°C - 22.0°C = 11.0°C$

5. $m = 100.0$ mL $H_2O \times \dfrac{1.00 \text{ g } H_2O}{1 \text{ mL } H_2O} =$
100.0 g H_2O for all three reactions

6. heat of reaction 1:

100.0 g $H_2O \times 5.0°C \times \dfrac{4.180 \text{ J}}{1 \text{ g•°C}} =$
2100 J $= 2.1$ kJ

heat of reaction 2:

100.0 g $H_2O \times 6.1°C \times \dfrac{4.180 \text{ J}}{1 \text{ g•°C}} =$
2500 J $= 2.5$ kJ

heat of reaction 3:

100.0 g $H_2O \times 11.0°C \times \dfrac{4.180 \text{ J}}{1 \text{ g•°C}} =$
4600 J $= 4.6$ kJ

7. moles NaOH for reaction 1:

2.00 g NaOH $\times \dfrac{1 \text{ mol NaOH}}{40.00 \text{ g NaOH}} =$
5.00×10^{-2} mol NaOH

moles NaOH for reaction 2:

50 mL $\times \dfrac{1 \text{ L}}{1000 \text{ mL}} \times$
$\dfrac{1.00 \text{ mol NaOH}}{1 \text{ L NaOH}} =$
5.00×10^{-2} mol NaOH

moles NaOH for reaction 3:

2.01 g NaOH $\times \dfrac{1 \text{ mol NaOH}}{40.00 \text{ g NaOH}} =$
5.02×10^{-2} mol NaOH

SAMPLE DATA

	REACTION 1	REACTION 2
Mass of empty watch glass (g)	30.15	30.15
Mass of watch glass + NaOH (g)	32.15	32.16

8. Enthalpy changes should be negative because the reactions are exothermic.

$$\Delta H_1 = \frac{-2.1 \text{ kJ}}{5.00 \times 10^{-2} \text{ mol NaOH}} = -42 \text{ kJ/mol NaOH}$$

$$\Delta H_2 = \frac{-2.5 \text{ kJ}}{5.00 \times 10^{-2} \text{ mol NaOH}} = -50. \text{ kJ/mol NaOH}$$

$$\Delta H_3 = \frac{-4.6 \text{ kJ}}{5.00 \times 10^{-2} \text{ mol NaOH}} = -92 \text{ kJ/mol NaOH}$$

9. The sum of the heats of the first two reactions should equal the heat of the third reaction.

10. Reaction 1 involved heat of solution. Reaction 2 involved heat of reaction. Reaction 3 involved heat of solution and heat of reaction.

CONCLUSIONS

11. By direct measurement, ΔH should be −92 kJ/mol. By indirect calculation, it is also −92 kJ/mol (−50. kJ/mol − 42 kJ/mol).

12. molar amount of NaOH:

$$55 \text{ g NaOH} \times \frac{1 \text{ mol NaOH}}{40.00 \text{ g NaOH}} = 1.4 \text{ mol NaOH}$$

molar amount of HCl: 1.35 mol

heat of dissolution:

$$1.4 \text{ mol NaOH} \times \frac{-42 \text{ kJ}}{1 \text{ mol NaOH}} = -59 \text{ kJ}$$

heat of reaction:

$$1.35 \text{ mol NaOH} \times \frac{-50 \text{ kJ}}{1 \text{ mol NaOH}} = -67.5 \text{ kJ}$$

(The remaining NaOH is an excess reactant that remains unreacted.)

total heat of reaction:

−59 kJ − 67.5 kJ = −126 kJ

$$\Delta t_{\text{H}_2\text{O}} = 126\,000 \text{ J} \times \frac{1 \text{ g} \cdot ^\circ\text{C}}{4.180 \text{ J}} \times \frac{1}{450. \text{ g H}_2\text{O}} = 67^\circ\text{C}$$

final temperature = 25°C + 67°C = 92°C

The mixture is likely to cause a burn because the temperature would be much higher than 60°C.

13. HCl is the limiting reactant. There was 0.05 mol NaOH left unreacted.

---

7. **Organizing Data**
   Calculate the moles of NaOH used in each of the reactions. (Hint: To find the number of moles in a solution, multiply the volume in liters by the molar concentration.)

8. **Analyzing Results**
   Calculate the ΔH value in terms of kilojoules per mole of NaOH for each of the three reactions.

9. **Organizing Ideas**
   Using your answer to Analysis and Interpretation item 2 and your knowledge of Hess's law from Chapter 11, explain how the enthalpies for the three reactions should be mathematically related.

10. **Organizing Ideas**
    Which of the following types of heat of reaction apply to the enthalpies calculated in Analysis and Interpretation item 8: heat of combustion, heat of solution, heat of reaction, heat of fusion, heat of vaporization, and heat of formation?

Conclusions

11. **Evaluating Methods**
    Use your answers from Analysis and Interpretation items 7 and 8 to determine the ΔH value for the reaction of solid NaOH with HCl solution by direct measurement and by indirect calculation.

12. **Inferring Conclusions**
    Third-degree burns can occur if skin comes into contact for more than 4 seconds with water that is hotter than 60°C (140°F). Suppose someone accidentally poured hydrochloric acid into a glass-disposal container that already contained the drain cleaner NaOH and the container shattered. The solution in the container was approximately 55 g of NaOH and 450 mL of muriatic acid solution containing 1.35 mol of HCl (a 3.0 M HCl solution). If the initial temperature of the solutions was 25°C, could a mixture hot enough to cause burns have resulted?

---

13. **Applying Conclusions**
    For the reaction between the drain cleaner and HCl described in item 12, which chemical is the limiting reactant? How many moles of the other reactant remained unreacted?

Extensions

1. **Applying Ideas**
   When chemists make solutions from NaOH pellets, they often keep the solution in an ice bath. Explain why.

2. **Applying Ideas**
   When a strongly acidic or basic solution is spilled on a person, the first step is to dilute it by washing the area of the spill with a lot of water. Explain why adding an acid or base to neutralize the solution immediately is not a good idea.

3. **Evaluating Methods**
   You have worked with heats of solution for exothermic reactions. Could the same type of procedure be used to determine the temperature changes for endothermic reactions? How would the procedure stay the same? What would change about the procedure and the data?

4. **Applying Ideas**
   A chemical supply company is going to ship NaOH pellets to a very humid place, and you have been asked to give advice on packaging. Design a package for the NaOH pellets. Explain the advantages of your package's design and materials. (Hint: Remember that the reaction in which NaOH absorbs moisture from the air is exothermic and that NaOH reacts exothermically with other compounds as well.)

5. **Inferring Conclusions**
   Which is more stable, solid NaOH or NaOH solution? Explain your answer.

EXTENSIONS

1. The chemists use an ice bath because the heat of solution for NaOH pellets is high enough to make the solution dangerously hot.

2. If acid or base spills are neutralized instead of diluted, the heat of reaction for the neutralization could cause a heat burn. In addition, the acid or base could cause a chemical burn.

3. The same procedure could be used for endothermic reactions. However, the temperature of the water will decrease, and the enthalpy change for the reaction will have a positive value.

4. Suggestions for package design will vary. Be sure each design addresses the dangers of moisture, breakage, and spills.

5. NaOH solution is more stable than solid NaOH. The products of an exothermic reaction are more stable than the reactants.

11B | Kitchen Calorimetry

OBJECTIVES

▶ Construct a functional calorimeter from an empty soda can.

▶ Observe the combustion of several different food samples.

▶ Apply the law of conservation of energy to a simple heat-exchange process.

▶ Measure the change in temperature of the water inside the calorimeter.

▶ Measure the change in mass caused by the burning process.

▶ Calculate the heat energy lost by the burning food sample.

▶ Evaluate the experimental design to identify sources of heat loss.

MATERIALS

▶ 100 mL graduated cylinder

▶ balance

▶ empty soda can

▶ food samples*

▶ large cork

▶ large paper clips, 4

▶ matches

▶ ring stand

▶ small nail

▶ small ring clamp

▶ tap water

▶ thermometer

▶ weighing boats

* Potato chips, tortilla chips, walnuts, pecans, and peanuts are suggested for this activity.

OBJECTIVES

Students will:

▶ construct a functional calorimeter from an empty soda can.

▶ observe the combustion of several different food samples.

▶ apply the law of conservation of energy to a simple heat-exchange process.

▶ measure the change in temperature of the water inside the calorimeter.

▶ measure the change in mass caused by the burning process.

▶ calculate the heat energy lost by the burning food sample.

▶ evaluate the experimental design to identify sources of heat loss.

RECOMMENDED TIME:
1–2 lab periods

MATERIALS

(for each group)

▶ 100 mL graduated cylinder

▶ empty soda can

▶ food samples *, 4

▶ large cork

▶ large paper clips, 4

▶ matches

▶ ring stand

▶ small nail

▶ small ring clamp

▶ tap water

▶ thermometer

▶ tongs

▶ weighing boats

*Potato chips, tortilla chips, walnuts, pecans, and peanuts are suggested for this activity.

Background

The law of conservation of energy states that energy cannot be created or destroyed. Energy can, however, be transferred from one object to another. This experiment involves the transfer of energy from a given food sample to a known quantity of water.

heat lost by the food sample =
heat gained by the water

All of the food samples chosen for this experiment can be ignited with a match. Once they begin burning, they will continue to burn for several minutes, causing the temperature of the water in the calorimeter to rise. Knowing the mass of the water, the water's specific heat capacity, and the change in temperature of the

PRE-LAB DISCUSSION

Thoroughly discuss the important concepts involved in this lab. Students should recognize the importance of the law of conservation of energy. It is recommended that students are comfortable with the heat equation and its respective variables.

TECHNIQUES TO DEMONSTRATE

Perform a similar calorimetry experiment with a candle. Assemble the soda-can calorimeter in advance so that the demonstration can be initiated with a simple question—"How much heat energy is released from a burning candle in 5 minutes?"

Add a known mass of water to the calorimeter. The specific heat of water is 1.00 cal/g•°C. The initial temperature of the water can be measured with a thermometer. The candle is lit, and the final temperature is recorded after 5 minutes. After blowing out the candle, the teacher can walk the students through the appropriate calculations on the board.

DISPOSAL

The burned food samples should be discarded in a metal waste can. Be certain the food samples have been extinguished. The soda-can calorimeters, paper clips, and corks can be reused by the next class.

water will allow you to calculate the amount of heat energy that was released from the burning food sample.

$$\text{heat gained by the water} =$$
$$\text{temperature change of water} \times \text{mass of}$$
$$\text{water} \times \text{specific heat capacity of water}$$

The calorimeter that will be used in this experiment will be constructed from an empty soda can. Due to heat loss to the surroundings, the heat-transfer process will not be perfect, but good results can still be obtained.

Problem

You will burn four different food samples in this activity. Your goal is to measure the change in temperature of the water inside the calorimeter.

To do this, you will need to know the initial and final temperatures of the water. Because the masses of the food samples are different, the mass of each food sample must be measured. The residual mass of the food sample (ash) will also be measured. To determine the mass of the food sample that actually burned, you can subtract the residual mass from the initial mass of the food sample.

Preparation

1. Organizing Data
Copy the data table below in your lab notebook.

2. If you are using the Vernier probe and CBL unit refer to page 700 for equipment setup.

Data Table

Food sample	Initial mass (g)	Final mass (g)	Initial temp (°C)	Final temp (°C)	Mass of water (g)

(Note: If the known density of water is 1.00 g/mL, what will be the mass of the 200.0 mL of water that is used in each trial? You can add this value to your data table for the mass of the water.)

REQUIRED PRECAUTIONS

▶ Read all safety precautions, and discuss them with your students

▶ Safety goggles and a lab apron must be worn at all times. Black soot will form on the underside of the calorimeter.

▶ Caution students to avoid moving the food samples while samples are burning; they tend to fall off the paper clip stand. Once the food samples have burned out, allow them to cool completely before attempting to measure their residual masses.

▶ Paper or paper towels should be removed from the calorimeter setup before igniting the food sample. These items can easily ignite if a burning food sample falls on them.

▶ Students should never leave a burning food sample unattended. Do not put hot food samples on the balance. Damage to the laboratory balances can occur if hot food samples come into contact with the pan of a balance.

▶ Remind students that heated objects can be hot enough to burn even though they look cool. Students should always use tongs when handling heated equipment.

Figure A

Figure B

Assembly of Calorimeter

3. To prepare a calorimeter using a soda can, as shown in **Figure A,** start by removing the tab from the top of the empty soda can.

4. Use a small nail to poke four holes into the sides of the can near the top. From the top of the can, the holes should appear in the 3, 6, 9, and 12 o'clock positions.

5. Straighten two large paper clips, and insert them into the can's holes. The wires should form a cross hair in the center of the can with the wires extending from the can.

6. Suspend the calorimeter from a ring clamp that has been fastened to a ring stand.

7. Make a stand for the food sample by straightening all but one section of another paper clip. Bend the straightened section downward, and insert it into the cork. Some food samples may need a second paper clip for more support. The food sample should now rest easily on this paper-clip stand.

Technique

8. Slowly add exactly 200.0 mL of water to the calorimeter.

9. Carefully lower the thermometer or temperature probe into the can.

10. Read the initial temperature of the water. Record this in your data table.

11. Measure the mass of the food sample. Record this in your data table.

12. Place the sample to be burned on the paper clip stand.

13. Ignite the sample with a match, as shown in **Figure B.** Be patient, and avoid moving the cork even slightly to prevent the sample from falling off.

14. Monitor the change in temperature of the water. You are measuring in the *highest temperature* of the water. Record this in your data table.

15. Allow the sample to burn out. After it has cooled to room temperature, measure its *final mass*. (Not all of the sample will have burned.) Do not place the burned sample directly on the balance. Record this in your data table.

16. After all measurements have been recorded, discard the burned sample in the wastebasket. **After each trial, pour the water from the calorimeter down the drain.**

17. Repeat with a different food sample.

SAMPLE DATA					
FOOD SAMPLE	INITIAL MASS (g)	FINAL MASS (g)	INITIAL TEMP (°C)	FINAL TEMP (°C)	MASS OF WATER (g)
Potato chip	1.377	0.143	20.0	24.1	200.0
Walnut	1.086	0.078	23.6	31.0	200.0
Tortilla chip	1.084	0.093	23.4	30.1	200.0

ANSWERS

1. Answers will vary for each sample. The temperature change calculation for a potato chip is shown.

   potato chip: $24.1°C - 20.0°C = 4.1°C$

2. Answers will vary for each sample. The mass calculation for a potato chip is shown.

   potato chip: $1.377\ g - 0.143\ g = 1.234\ g$

3. Answers will vary for each sample. The amount of heat energy for a potato chip is shown.

   potato chip: $(200.0\ g)(1.00\ cal/g°C)(4.1°C) = 820\ calories$

4. $$\frac{\text{calories of energy released from the food sample}}{\text{mass of sample that was actually burned}}$$

   potato chip: $\dfrac{820\ cal}{1.234\ g} = 660\ cal/g$

CONCLUSIONS

5. The position of the calorimeter is important. If the calorimeter is too far from the burning sample, the majority of the heat from the burning food sample will be lost to the air. Therefore, the temperature change of the water inside the calorimeter will be much smaller.

6. The heat lost by the food sample is equal to the heat gained by the water inside the calorimeter. We assume that no heat energy was absorbed by the aluminum can, paper clips, and air.

7. Heat energy is lost to the aluminum can, paper clips, and the air. There may also be problems obtaining an accurate final mass of the ashes of the food samples.

8. All of the heat energy from the burning food sample was not transferred to the water inside the calorimeter. The heat values we obtained do not account for the lost heat. The heat energy values account for only the heat that reached the calorimeter.

✦ ✦ Cleanup and Disposal

18. Clean all apparatus and your lab station. Return equipment to its proper place. The used soda cans can be recycled. The corks and paper clips can be kept for future use. Dispose of items in the containers designated by your teacher. Wash your hands thoroughly after all work is finished and before you leave the lab.

Analyzing Data

1. Analyzing Results
Calculate the change in temperature of the water for each sample tested.

2. Analyzing Results
Determine the mass of the sample that actually burned in each trial you conducted.

3. Applying Ideas
Use the heat equation to determine the amount of heat energy (calories) that was absorbed by the water in each trial.

4. Applying Ideas
Consider two potato chips: one is large, and the other is small. If used in this experiment, the larger chip will contain more energy. Therefore, the mass of the food samples must also be considered. For each trial, determine the number of calories per gram of food sample. Use the formula listed below.

$$\frac{\text{calories of energy released from the food sample}}{\text{mass of sample that was actually burned}}$$

Conclusions

5. Evaluating Methods
Would you expect the vertical distance from the burning food sample to the calorimeter to be important? Predict what would happen if the calorimeter were placed too far above the burning sample. Explain.

6. Applying Ideas
Explain how the conservation of energy relates to this activity. Be specific.

7. Evaluating Methods
What are several sources of error in this experiment? Be specific.

8. Applying Conclusions
Why are the experimental heat energy values (calories) for these food products always lower than what the food companies list? Explain why we never obtain experimental values that exceed the food companies' values.

9. Applying Ideas
How do food Calories differ from the calorie units that scientists use? What is the connection between these two similar units of measurement?

Extension

1. Designing Experiments
Refer to your answer for Conclusions item 6. Can you think of a way to eliminate your sources of error? If so, ask your teacher to approve your plan and run the procedure again.

9. One food Calorie is equal to 1000 calories. Food Calories, also called kilocalories, are spelled with an uppercase C.

EXTENSION

1. Answers will vary.

13A | Paper Chromatography of Colored Markers

OBJECTIVES

▸ Design a successful method to ensure that the chromatography paper remains vertical throughout the experiment.

▸ Conduct a paper chromatography experiment with three different water-soluble colored markers.

▸ Observe the dye components of three different water-soluble markers.

MATERIALS

▸ 10 mL graduated cylinder

▸ 250 mL beaker

▸ chromatography paper

▸ developing solution: NaCl solution (0.1% by mass)

▸ hot plate

▸ markers

▸ paper clips

▸ pencils

▸ ruler

▸ scissors

Background

There is a wide variety of marker products on the market today ranging in color and function. All of these markers contain different dye components that are responsible for their color.

Paper chromatography is an analytical technique that uses paper as a medium to separate the different dye components dissolved in a mixture. In this process, the mixture to be separated is placed on a piece of chromatography paper. A solvent is then allowed to soak up into the paper. As the solvent travels across the paper, some of the components of the mixture are carried with it. Particles of the same component group together. The components that are

SOLUTION/MATERIAL PREPARATION

1. To prepare the NaCl solution, dissolve 10 g of NaCl in enough water to make 1.00 L of solution.

OBJECTIVES

Students will:

▸ design a successful method to ensure that the chromatography paper remains vertical throughout the experiment.

▸ conduct a paper chromatography experiment with three different water-soluble colored markers.

▸ observe the dye components of three different water-soluble markers.

RECOMMENDED TIME:

1 lab period

MATERIALS

(for each lab group)

▸ 10 mL graduated cylinder

▸ 250 mL beaker

▸ chromatography paper

▸ developing solution: NaCl solution (0.1% by mass)

▸ hot plate

▸ markers

▸ paper clips

▸ pencils

▸ ruler

▸ scissors

▸ tape

PRE-LAB DISCUSSION

Before beginning the lab, students should review basic information about chromatography and look at a developed chromatogram. Direct the students' attention to the fact that they will have to design a method for the chromatography paper to remain vertical as it develops. Encourage the students to create their own method to achieve this task.

Stress that the initial spots on the chromatography paper must remain above the liquid in the beaker. Some students may have the misconception that their experiment was unsuccessful if an orange marker does not reveal a mixture of yellow and red dyes. One often overlooked explanation is that the orange marker is composed only of orange dyes. The lack of color separation could be attributed to the presence of a single dye.

Use this activity as an introduction to chromatography. This experiment serves as a good foundation for the open-ended mini-lab "The Color of M&M® Candies," on page 477.

TECHNIQUES TO DEMONSTRATE

Refer the students to the chromatogram shown in Figure 13-4, on page 477. You may wish to hold a piece of chromatography paper in a beaker to show students the basic idea of this experiment. However, avoid recommending specific methods to keep the chromatography paper vertical inside the developing chamber.

most soluble and least attracted to the paper travel farther than others. A color band is created and the different components can be seen separated on the paper. The success of chromatography hinges on the slight difference in the physical properties of the individual components.

In this activity you will use a paper chromatography to determine the components of the dyes found in water-soluble markers.

Problem

Your goal is to use paper chromatography to determine the dye components of three different water-soluble markers. You will also need to design a simple method that will keep the chromatography paper vertical while it is in the developing solution.

Preparation

1. Organizing Data

Copy the data table below in your lab notebook.

Data Table

Marker color	Dye components

2. Obtain a clean 250 mL beaker and a 7.0 × 2.5 cm piece of chromatography paper.

3. Choose three different markers for this activity. Write the color of each marker in your data table.

4. Using a ruler, draw a horizontal line in pencil approximately 1.0 cm from one of the ends of the paper. Mark three small dots on this line, using a different marker for each dot.

5. Using a pencil, label each of the dots on the chromatography paper according to the color of the markers.

Technique

6. Measure out 7.0 mL of the developing solution in a 10 mL graduated cylinder.

7. Pour the 7.0 mL of solution in a 250 mL beaker, as shown in **Figure A** on the next page. Make sure the bottom of the beaker is completely covered. **The level of the liquid must be below the marks on your chromatography paper.**

8. You will need to design an experimental technique to ensure that your paper sample does not slide into the developing solution. The chromatography paper must remain vertical as the developing solution rises into the paper.

REQUIRED PRECAUTIONS

▶ Read all safety precautions, and discuss them with your students.

▶ Always wear safety goggles and a lab apron to protect your eyes and clothing. The developing solution could irritate the eyes and other exposed skin.

▶ If a hot plate is used, it should be equipped with a three-prong plug. Each electrical socket in the laboratory must have three holes, with a GFI (ground-fault interrupter) circuit. Check the polarity of the circuit with a polarity tester from an electronics supply store. Repair any incorrectly wired sockets.

▶ Be certain electrical equipment is turned off before plugging it in. Turn it off again before unplugging it. Wiring hookups should be made or altered only when the apparatus is disconnected from the power source and the power switch is in the "off" position.

▶ Do not let electrical cords dangle from work stations; dangling cords are a tripping and shock hazard.

▶ Do not use electrical equipment with frayed or kinked cords.

▶ Be certain the area under and around electrical equipment is dry.

▶ Cords should not lie in puddles or spilled liquids. Students should have dry hands when they are using electrical equipment.

Figure A

Figure B

9. Carefully place your paper (with the dots at the bottom) into the liquid, as shown in **Figure B.**

10. When the level of the liquid has advanced through most of the paper, remove the paper from the developing solution. Hold up the paper and observe the colors.

11. The chromatography samples can be carefully dried on a hot plate.

12. You may repeat this process using overwrite or color-change markers.

 Cleanup and Disposal

13. Clean all apparatus and your lab station. Return equipment to its proper place. Dispose of chemicals and solutions in the containers designated by your teacher. Do not pour any chemicals down the drain or in the trash unless your teacher directs you to do so.

Analysis and Interpretation

1. **Organizing Ideas**
   What was the purpose of this experiment?

2. **Evaluating Methods**
   Why shouldn't you use a ballpoint pen when marking the initial line and spots on the chromatography paper? Explain.

3. **Evaluating Methods**
   Why were only water-soluble markers used in this experiment? Could permanent markers be used?

4. **Evaluating Methods**
   Why must the spotted marks remain above the level of the liquid in the beaker?

Conclusions

5. **Interpreting Results**
   Make observations about the dye components (colors) of each marker based on your results.

6. **Applying Conclusions**
   Explain how law enforcement officials could use paper chromatography to identify a pen that was used in a ransom note.

7. List some other applications for using paper chromatography.

Extensions

1. **Evaluating Methods**
   Compare your results with those of another lab group. Were the dye components found in other markers different from those found in yours?

PAPER CHROMATOGRAPHY OF COLORED MARKERS **767**

Required Precautions continued

▸ Turn off and unplug all electrical equipment before leaving the laboratory.

▸ Remind students that heated objects can be hot enough to burn even though they look cool. Students should always use tongs when handling heated equipment.

13B

OBJECTIVES

Students will:

◗ use appropriate lab safety procedures.

◗ measure mass with a laboratory balance.

◗ measure volume with a graduated cylinder.

◗ measure the boiling point of water without a solute and with three non-volatile solutes (NaCl, sucrose, and MgSO$_4$).

◗ calculate boiling-point elevation for solutes.

◗ calculate molal concentration of solutions.

◗ identify an unknown using boiling-point-elevation data.

◗ calculate the molecular mass of three solutes using boiling-point-elevation data.

RECOMMENDED TIME:

1 lab period
(for each lab group)

MATERIALS

◗ 10.0 g of MgSO$_4$•7H$_2$O

◗ 10.0 g of NaCl

◗ 10.0 g of sucrose

◗ 10.0 g of unknown

◗ 125 mL Erlenmeyer flask

◗ balance

◗ beaker tongs

◗ Bunsen burner, gas tubing, striker

◗ Celsius thermometer, nonmercury type with 0.01°C markings

◗ distilled water

◗ glass stirring rod

◗ ring stand and iron ring

◗ thermometer clamp

◗ wire gauze with ceramic center

13B | Boiling-Point Elevation and Molar Mass

OBJECTIVES

◗ Demonstrate proficiency in measuring masses, temperatures, and boiling points.

◗ Relate the concentration of a solution to boiling-point elevation data.

◗ Determine the molar mass of a solute from experimental data.

MATERIALS

◗ distilled water

◗ MgSO$_4$•7H$_2$O, 10.0 g

◗ NaCl, 10.0 g

◗ sucrose, 10.0 g

◗ unknown sample, 10.0 g

◗ balance

◗ beaker tongs

◗ Bunsen burner and related equipment, or hot plate

◗ 125 mL Erlenmeyer flask

◗ ring stand and ring

◗ thermometer (nonmercury with 0.1°C markings) or Vernier temperature probe

◗ thermometer clamp

◗ wire gauze with ceramic center

Situation

Your company needs to determine the identity of a white powder that a young boy has swallowed. Doctors need to know the powder's identity to treat him. The substance must be one of the following: sodium chloride, NaCl; sugar (sucrose), C$_{12}$H$_{22}$O$_{11}$; or hydrated magnesium sulfate (Epsom salts), MgSO$_4$•7H$_2$O. Along with the unknown, you have pure samples of the three substances.

Background

The boiling point of a solution is always higher than that of a pure liquid because the attraction of the solute for individual water molecules hinders their ability to move into the gaseous state. *Colligative properties* are properties of solutes that affect solutions. When dealing with

SOLUTION/MATERIAL PREPARATION

1. Give some groups NaCl, some groups sucrose, and some groups MgSO$_4$.

2. If you do not have access to thermometers with 0.01°C markings, increase the mass of the solutes to 15 g. (This will change the sample results and calculations.)

Always wear safety goggles and a lab apron to protect your eyes and clothing. If you get a chemical in your eyes, immediately flush the chemical out at the eyewash station while calling to your teacher. Know the locations of the emergency lab shower and eyewash station and the procedure for using them.

Do not touch any chemicals. If you get a chemical on your skin or clothing, wash the chemical off at the sink while calling to your teacher. Make sure you carefully read the labels and follow the precautions on all containers of chemicals that you use. If there are no precautions stated on the label, ask

your teacher what precautions to follow. Do not taste any chemicals or items used in the laboratory. Never return leftovers to their original containers; take only small amounts to avoid wasting supplies.

When you use a Bunsen burner, confine any long hair and loose clothing. If your clothing catches on fire, WALK to the emergency lab shower, and use it to put out the fire. Do not heat glassware that is broken, chipped, or cracked. Use tongs or a hot mitt to handle heated glassware and other equipment because hot glassware does not always look hot.

colligative properties, the concentration units of *molality* (*m*) are used instead of *molarity* (M). Molality is defined as the number of moles of solute per kilogram of the solvent.

$$m = \frac{\text{moles solute}}{\text{kilograms solvent}}$$

Experiments have determined that the boiling-point elevation of a 1.00 *m* solution for any molecular solute in water is 0.51°C. This value is known as the molal boiling-point constant, K_b. The constant has the units °C/*m*.

Problem

To identify the unknown, you must do the following.

▶ make solutions using the same solute mass for each standard and for the unknown

▶ compare the boiling points of the resulting solutions to determine which matches that of the unknown

Calculate the molality of each solution based on the value of the boiling point. Then use the amount of solute you added and the number of moles (from the molality) to determine the molar mass.

$$\begin{array}{l}\text{molar mass} \\ \text{of solute}\end{array} = \frac{\text{g of solute}}{\text{kg of solvent} \times \text{molal conc.}}$$

Preparation

1. Organizing Data
   Prepare a data table in your lab notebook like the one below.
2. Measure the mass of the Erlenmeyer flask. Record this mass in your lab notebook.

Data Table

Solution	Mass of solute (g)	Mass of flask and water (g)	Boiling point
Water			
NaCl			
Sucrose			
$MgSO_4 \cdot 7H_2O$			
Unknown			

PRE-LAB DISCUSSION

Students may initially have difficulty understanding the difference between molality and molarity and wonder why it is necessary to have different units of concentration. Point out that molarity is a measure of molar amount per liter of solution, while molality is a measure of molar amount per kilogram of solvent. Because colligative properties depend on interactions between the solute and solvent, molality is the concentration unit required for this lab.

It may help to work through the following calculations with some sample data.

Δt_b = molal concentration of particles × 0.51°C/*m*

Therefore, molal concentration of particles

$$= \frac{\text{moles of particles}}{\text{kilograms of solvent}} = \frac{\Delta t_b}{0.51°C/m}$$

Once the molal concentration has been determined, multiply by the mass of solvent to determine the number of particles. By comparing the mass of the particles with the number of particles, students can calculate the molar mass.

TECHNIQUES TO DEMONSTRATE

Demonstrate how to recognize the boiling point of a solution. If necessary, review the use of thermometers.

DISPOSAL

Students should wash any solutions down the sink. Set out a disposal container for excess solids. Dissolve the solids in 20 times as much water, and wash them down the sink.

REQUIRED PRECAUTIONS

▶ Read all safety precautions, and discuss them with your students.

▶ Safety goggles and a lab apron must be worn at all times.

▶ Tie back long hair and loose clothing when working in the lab.

▶ Remind students to wash their hands thoroughly when they are finished in the lab.

ANALYSIS AND INTERPRETATION

1. Δt_b for NaCl = 3.5°C

Δt_b for sucrose = 0.3°C

Δt_b for MgSO$_4$ = 1.8°C

Δt_b for unknown = 1.9°C

2. The data for the unknown most closely matches those for MgSO$_4$.

3. molality for particles,

$$NaCl = \frac{3.5°C}{0.51°C/m} = 6.9\ m$$

molality for particles,

$$sucrose = \frac{0.3°C}{0.51°C/m} = 0.6\ m$$

molality for particles,

$$MgSO_4 = \frac{0.9°C}{0.51°C/m} = 2\ m$$

molality for particles,

$$unknown = \frac{1.0°C}{0.51°C/m} = 2.0\ m$$

4. $50.0\ g\ H_2O \times \dfrac{1\ kg}{1000\ g} = 5.00 \times 10^{-2}\ kg$

H$_2$O in flask

5. $\dfrac{10.0\ g}{5.000 \times 10^{-2}\ kg\ H_2O} \times$

$\dfrac{1\ kg\ H_2O}{6.9\ mol\ particles} \times \dfrac{2\ mol\ particles}{1\ mol\ NaCl} =$

58 g/mol for NaCl

$\dfrac{9.91\ g}{5.003 \times 10^{-2}\ kg\ H_2O} \times$

$\dfrac{1\ kg\ H_2O}{0.6\ mol\ particles} \times \dfrac{1\ mol\ particles}{1\ mol\ sucrose} =$

330 g/mol for sucrose

$\dfrac{9.98\ g}{4.985 \times 10^{-2}\ kg\ H_2O} \times$

$\dfrac{1\ kg\ H_2O}{2\ mol\ particles} \times \dfrac{2\ mol\ particles}{1\ mol\ MgSO_4}$

= 200 g/mol for MgSO$_4$•7H$_2$O

$\dfrac{10.01\ g}{4.997 \times 10^{-2}\ kg\ H_2O} \times$

$\dfrac{1\ kg\ H_2O}{2.0\ mol\ particles} \times \dfrac{2\ mol\ particles}{1\ mol\ unknown} =$

200 g/mol for unknown

CONCLUSIONS

6. Percent error is zero because of rounding for significant figures.

$$\frac{200\ g/mol - 200\ g/mol}{200\ g/mol} \times 100 =$$

0% error

Figure A

3. If you are using the Vernier temperature probe and CBL unit refer to pages 698–699 for equipment setup.

Technique

4. Add distilled water to the Erlenmeyer flask until the total mass is as close as possible to 50.0 g more than the amount recorded in your lab notebook for the mass of the flask. Record this mass in your data table.

5. Place the flask of water on the wire gauze on the ring stand. Using the thermometer clamp, suspend the thermometer or probe in the water so that it does not touch the sides or bottom of the flask as shown in **Figure A.** Do not use a one-hole stopper to hold the thermometer or probe because the solution will be boiled.

6. Heat the water until it boils vigorously and the temperature remains constant. This temperature is the boiling point. Record it in your data table. (Note: Leave the box in your data table for *Mass of solute* (g) blank for this trial involving only water.)

7. Pour the contents of the flask into the sink. Then add distilled water to the flask until the total mass is as close as possible to 50.0 g more than the mass of the flask. Record this mass in your data table. Add 10.0 g of NaCl to this water, and swirl the flask gently until the salt dissolves completely. Record the mass of solute in your data table. **Do not allow the water to splash out of the flask because it will cause inaccuracy in your results.**

8. Place your flask on the wire gauze, and suspend the thermometer or probe in the water as before. Heat the solution to boiling, and record the boiling point in your data table.

9. Pour the contents of the flask into the sink. Rinse the flask three times with distilled water. Repeat steps 7 and 8 for sucrose, MgSO$_4$•7H$_2$O, and for the unknown sample.

Cleanup and Disposal

10. Clean all apparatus and your lab station. Solutions may be rinsed down the sink. Check with your teacher for the proper disposal of other chemicals. Be certain all gas valves are turned off. Wash your hands thoroughly after cleaning up the area and equipment.

Analysis and Interpretation

1. Organizing Data

For the trials with solutes including the unknown, calculate the solution's change in boiling point, Δt_b. (Hint: Use the boiling point you measured for the pure water as the solvent's boiling point.)

SAMPLE DATA

SOLUTION	MASS OF SOLUTE (g)	MASS OF FLASK AND WATER (g)	BOILING POINT (°C)
H$_2$O	n/a	112.04	100.0
NaCl	10.00	112.12	103.5
Sucrose	9.91	112.07	100.3
MgSO$_4$•7H$_2$O	9.98	111.89	100.9
Unknown	10.01	112.01	101.0

Mass of empty Erlenmeyer flask: 62.04 g

2. Analyzing Information

Given that similar masses of each substance were used, do the data for the unknown most closely match NaCl, sucrose, or $MgSO_4 \cdot 7H_2O$?

3. Analyzing Data

Calculate the approximate molalities of dissolved particles for the known and unknown solutes using the following equation and your answers to item 1. (Hint: $K_b = 0.51°C/m$)

$$m = \frac{\Delta t_b}{K_b}$$

4. Organizing Data

For each trial, calculate the mass of water in the flask in kilograms.

5. Analyzing Data

Using your answers from Analysis and Interpretation items 3 and 4 and your data, calculate an experimental value for the molar mass of each solute.

Conclusions

6. Evaluating Conclusions

How close is the estimated molar mass of the unknown solute to the estimated molar mass of the solute chosen in Analysis and Interpretation item 2? Calculate the percentage error using the unknown solute's molar mass estimate as the experimental value.

7. Evaluating Methods

Determine the molar mass of NaCl, sucrose, and $MgSO_4 \cdot 7H_2O$ from the periodic table. Calculate the percentage error for your experimental molar-mass values.

8. Evaluating Methods

How accurate do you think it is to identify the unknown substance using this procedure? Can you explain any deviations that occur?

9. Applying Ideas

Explain in your own words why adding a solute raises the temperature at which a substance boils. (Hint: Consider what you know about bonding, phase changes, and kinetic-molecular theory.)

10. Analyzing Methods

Why do you need to determine the boiling point of water without a solute dissolved in it? Explain your answer.

Extensions

1. Designing Experiments

Obtain a water-soluble unknown from your teacher, and determine whether it is NaCl, sucrose, or $MgSO_4 \cdot 7H_2O$ by using the freezing-point depression method. (As determined by experimentation, the freezing-point depression of a 1.00 m solution of any molecular solute in water is $-1.86°C$.)

2. Research and Communication

Consult chemical handbooks and other reference works to determine the possible health hazards of these solutes. For each solute, what should be done if someone swallows it?

3. Applying Ideas

Find out how much and what type of salt a large northern city such as New York or Chicago uses on icy roads in the winter. What problems result from use of this salt? What salt substitutes can melt ice and snow? Which would be safest for our environment?

4. Research and Communication

What are some of the primary uses of $MgSO_4 \cdot 7H_2O$, and how is it produced for commercial use?

7. $\dfrac{58.44 \text{ g/mol} - 58 \text{ g/mol}}{58.44 \text{ g/mol}} \times 100 =$
0.75% error for NaCl

$\dfrac{342.34 \text{ g/mol} - 300 \text{ g/mol}}{342.34 \text{ g/mol}} \times 100 =$
12% error for sucrose

$\dfrac{246.51 \text{ g/mol} - 200 \text{ g/mol}}{246.51 \text{ g/mol}} \times 100 =$
19% error for $MgSO_4$

8. This method is accurate if the choice is limited to several very different options. The larger the molar mass of the substance is, the greater the possibility for error.

9. When a substance dissolves in water, the substance forms attractions with the water molecules, making it harder for individual molecules to enter the gas phase.

10. The boiling point of water is not 100°C at every location and under every condition. In order to be sure of the precision, students must make the measurement of the pure solvent's boiling point with the same instrument.

EXTENSIONS

1. Suggestions for improving the procedure will vary. Be sure answers included safe, carefully planned procedures. Possibilities include using larger amounts of solute so that boiling-point elevation will be greater.

2. Sucrose and NaCl pose no health hazard. $MgSO_4$ is moderately toxic.

3. Answers may vary but should show a recognition that salt contributes to automobile rusting and the breakdown of the pavement.

4. Magnesium sulfate is also known as Epsom salt. It is used in the bleaching, dyeing, and fire-proofing of fabrics and in the manufacture of explosives and matches. It is also used to treat some infections.

SAMPLE DATA			
SOLUTION	SOLUTE MASS (g)	MASS OF FLASK + WATER (g)	BOILING POINT (°C)
$MgSO_4 \cdot 7H_2O$	9.98	111.89	100.9
Unknown	10.01	112.01	101.0

Mass of empty Erlenmeyer flask: 62.04 g

OBJECTIVES

Students will:

▶ use appropriate lab safety procedures.

▶ use a buret to dispense an accurate volume of two acid solutions.

▶ translate word equations into chemical formulas.

▶ count the number of drops of NaOH needed to completely react with different acid samples.

▶ calculate the average number of drops of NaOH needed for each acid.

▶ relate the number of drops to the coefficients in the balanced chemical equations.

RECOMMENDED TIME:

1 lab period

MATERIALS

(for each lab group)

▶ 0.10 M HCl

▶ 0.10 M H_2SO_4

▶ 0.30 M NaOH

▶ burets, 2

▶ buret clamp

▶ phenolphthalein indicator

▶ pipets

▶ ring stands

▶ test tubes

▶ test-tube rack

15A | Drip-Drop Acid-Base Experiment

OBJECTIVES

▶ Translate word equations into chemical formulas.

▶ Count the number of drops of sodium hydroxide needed to completely react with different acid samples.

▶ Calculate the average number of drops of sodium hydroxide needed for each acid.

▶ Relate the number of drops to the coefficients in the balanced chemical equations.

MATERIALS

▶ 0.1 M H_2SO_4

▶ 0.1 M HCl

▶ 0.3 M NaOH

▶ burets, 2

▶ buret clamps

▶ phenolphthalein indicator

▶ pipets

▶ ring stands

▶ test-tube rack

▶ test tubes

Background

The purpose of this lab is to investigate the simple reaction between two different acids and a base. We will be counting the number of drops of sodium hydroxide that are needed to react completely with all of the acid. The starting acid and base solutions are colorless and clear, and the final products are colorless and clear. To monitor the progress of the chemical reaction, the acid-base indicator phenolphthalein will be used. Phenolphthalein is colorless when acidic and pink in color when neutral or basic. In this activity, we will know that all of the acid has been consumed by the base when the test-tube solution starts to turn pink. We can monitor the progress of the reaction so that a single drop of the base results in a sudden change from colorless to pink. At that point, we will know that all of the acid has reacted with the base.

SOLUTION/MATERIAL PREPARATION

1. To prepare 0.10 M HCl, dissolve 8.3 mL of concentrated HCl in enough water to make 1.00 L of solution.

2. To prepare 0.10 M H_2SO_4, dissolve 5.6 mL of concentrated H_2SO_4 in enough water to make 1.00 L of solution.

3. To prepare 0.30 M NaOH, dissolve 12 g of solid NaOH in enough water to make 1.00 L of solution.

Always wear safety goggles and a lab apron to protect your eyes and clothing. If you get a chemical in your eyes, immediately flush the chemical out at the eyewash station while calling to your teacher. Know the location of the emergency lab shower and eyewash station and the procedure for using them.

Do not touch any chemicals. If you get a chemical on your skin or clothing, wash the chemical off at the sink while calling to your teacher. Make sure you carefully read the labels and follow the precautions on all containers of chemicals that you use.

If there are no precautions, ask your teacher what precautions to follow. Do not taste any chemicals or items used in the laboratory. Never return leftovers to their original containers; take only small amounts to avoid wasting supplies.

Never put broken glassware in a regular waste container. Broken glass should be disposed of separately in a container designated by your teacher.

Call your teacher in the event of an acid or base spill. Acid or base spills should be cleaned up promptly according to your teacher's instructions.

Problem

You will need to count the number of drops of sodium hydroxide that are necessary to neutralize two different acids. Find the relationship between the sodium hydroxide drops necessary and the coefficients in the balanced chemical equation.

Preparation

1. Translate each of the word equations shown below into chemical equations.

hydrochloric acid + sodium hydroxide $\longrightarrow$
  sodium chloride + water

sulfuric acid + sodium hydroxide $\longrightarrow$
  sodium sulfate + water

2. Organizing Data
Copy the two data tables in your laboratory notebook.

3. Clean six test tubes, and rinse them with distilled water. They do not need to be dry.

4. Obtain approximately 10 mL of sodium hydroxide solution in a small beaker.

Technique

Part I

5. Use a buret to put exactly 2.00 mL of hydrochloric acid directly into your test tube, as shown in **Figure A** on the next page.

6. Add two drops of phenolphthalein indicator solution to the test tube.

7. Use a pipet to add the sodium hydroxide solution dropwise to the test tube. Count the number of drops of sodium hydroxide as you add them. Gently shake the test tube from side to side after adding each drop. **Continue adding drops until the color just changes from colorless to pink.**

8. Record in your data table the total number of drops of sodium hydroxide needed to reach the color change. To obtain consistent results, repeat this trial.

Part II

9. Use a buret to add exactly 4.00 mL of hydrochloric acid directly into a clean test tube.

Data Table 1	
HCl volume (mL)	**NaOH (drops)**
2.00	
2.00	
4.00	
4.00	

Data Table 2	
H_2SO_4 Volume (mL)	**NaOH (drops)**
2.00	
2.00	

PRE-LAB DISCUSSION

Make sure you have discussed the nomenclature of ionic compounds with your students before allowing them to perform this experiment. Have each student translate the word equations shown in the Preparation section. Before the students begin the experiment, check their chemical formulas.

If you do not have enough burets for each group, simply set up the acids from four different "buret stations" placed around the room. Each buret station should consist of two labeled burets on a ring stand. Fill one buret with hydrochloric acid, and fill the other with sulfuric acid. Using four buret stations helps to avoid congestion as students measure their acids directly into their test tubes. With four small dropper bottles of the phenolphthalein indicator solution available, the students progress quickly through the lab.

TECHNIQUES TO DEMONSTRATE

Demonstrate how to use burets to ensure the accuracy of the volume measurements. It may be a good time to remind students about the importance of reading the meniscus and measuring the height of the liquids at eye level. Using colored water generally improves the effectiveness of this demonstration because the students can easily observe the buret's contents and see that turning the stopcock changes the contents.

Also demonstrate the pink color of the end point. A highly effective technique is to demonstrate how the addition of one drop of NaOH can produce the desired end point. Also demonstrate that additional drops of base do not change the color of the indicator.

DISPOSAL

The contents of the test tubes can be poured down the sink with plenty of water. The stock solutions of HCl, H_2SO_4, and NaOH can be kept for other experiments.

REQUIRED PRECAUTIONS

▸ Read all safety precautions, and discuss them with your students.

▸ Safety goggles and lab aprons should be worn at all times.

▸ Wash hands with water if the chemicals in this experiment come in contact with your skin.

▸ Be sure to completely close the stopcock valve on the burets.

Figure A

10. Add two drops of phenolphthalein indicator solution to the test tube.

11. Using a pipet, add one drop of sodium hydroxide solution at a time to the test tube. Count the number of drops of sodium hydroxide as you add them. Gently swirl the test tube after adding each drop. **Continue adding drops until the color just changes from colorless to a pink.**

12. Record in your data table the total number of drops of sodium hydroxide needed to reach the color change. Repeat this trial.

Part III: Sulfuric Acid

13. Use a buret to add exactly 2.00 mL of sulfuric acid directly into your test tube.

14. Add two drops of phenolphthalein indicator solution to the test tube.

15. Using a pipet, add one drop of sodium hydroxide solution at a time to the test tube. Count the number of drops of sodium hydroxide as you add them. Gently swirl the test tube after adding each drop. **Continue adding drops until the color just changes from colorless to pink.**

16. Record in your data table the total number of drops of sodium hydroxide needed to reach the color change. Repeat this trial.

Cleanup and Disposal

17. Clean all apparatus and your lab station. Return equipment to its proper place. Dispose of chemicals and solutions in the containers designated by your teacher. Do not pour any chemicals down the drain or in the trash unless your teacher directs you to do so. Wash your hands thoroughly after all work is finished and before you leave the lab.

Analysis and Interpretation

1. **Analyzing Results**
   What was the average number of drops of sodium hydroxide required to consume 2.00 mL of HCl? Show your work. 4.00 mL of HCl? Show your work.

2. **Analyzing Results**
   What was the average number of drops of sodium hydroxide required to consume 2.00 mL of H_2SO_4? Show your work.

3. **Analyzing Results**
   Compare your responses to Analysis and Interpretation items 1 and 2. Is there a difference in the average number of drops? What is the ratio between these two numbers? Is it 1:1, 1:2, 2:1, or 1:3? Explain the "chemistry" behind this ratio.

4. **Analyzing Results**
   Now compare your responses to Analysis and Interpretation items 1 and 2. Is there a difference in the average number of drops? What is the ratio between these two numbers? Is it 1:1, 1:2, 1:3, etc? Explain the "chemistry" behind this ratio.

Conclusion

5. **Applying Conclusions**
   Based on your observed results, how many drops of sodium hydroxide would be needed to react completely with a 2.00 mL sample of HNO_3?

$$HNO_3 + NaOH \longrightarrow NaNO_3 + H_2O$$

SAMPLE DATA	
HCl VOLUME (mL)	**NaOH (DROPS)**
2.00	16
2.00	16
2.00	16
4.00	32
4.00	33

SAMPLE DATA	
H_2SO_4 VOLUME (mL)	**NaOH (DROPS)**
2.00	33
2.00	32

15B | Acid-Base Titration of an Eggshell

CONSUMER ACTIVITY

15B

OBJECTIVES

- Determine the amount of calcium carbonate present in an eggshell.
- Relate experimental titration measurements to a balanced chemical equation.
- Infer a conclusion from experimental data.
- Apply reaction-stoichiometry concepts.

MATERIALS

- 1.00 M HCl
- 1.00 M NaOH
- 10 mL graduated cylinder
- 50 mL bottle or small Erlenmeyer flask
- 100 mL beaker
- balance
- desiccator (optional)
- distilled water
- drying oven
- eggshell
- forceps
- mortar and pestle
- medicine droppers or thin-stemmed pipets, 3
- phenolphthalein solution
- weighing paper
- white paper or white background

Situation

You are a research scientist working with the Department of Agriculture. A farmer from a nearby ranch has brought a problem to you. In the past 10 years, his hens' eggs have become increasingly fragile. So many of them have been breaking that he is beginning to lose money on the operation. The farmer believes his problems are linked to a landfill upstream, which is being investigated for illegal dumping of PCBs and other hazardous chemicals. Your job is to find out if the PCBs are the cause of the hens' fragile eggs.

OBJECTIVES

Students will:

- use appropriate lab safety procedures.
- measure volume and mass.
- use a buret or a dropper calibrated to measure the number of drops per milliliter.
- observe the reaction of $CaCO_3$ with a carefully measured excess of acid.
- perform a back-titration (titrating the excess acid with base).
- apply solution-stoichiometry concepts to determine the amount of each reactant required for the neutralization reaction and for the $CaCO_3$ reaction.

RECOMMENDED TIME:
1–2 lab periods

MATERIALS

(for each lab group)

- 1 mL of phenolphthalein solution
- 10 mL graduated cylinder
- 50 mL bottle or small Erlenmeyer flask
- 100 mL beaker
- balance
- desiccator (optional)
- distilled water
- drying oven
- eggshell
- forceps
- mortar and pestle
- weighing paper
- white paper for background

SOLUTION/MATERIAL PREPARATION

1. Desiccators are optional. Less equipment will be required if students share.

2. If droppers or pipets are labeled as "acid," "base," and "indicator," these can be reused from class to class. For drops of equal size, place the pipet or dropper bulb in a tubing screw-clamp. Each turn of the screw will force out a drop of equal size.

3. To prepare 1.00 M HCl, follow the required precautions. Add 82.6 mL of concentrated HCl to enough distilled water to make 1.00 L of solution. Add the acid slowly while stirring to avoid overheating.

4. To prepare 1.00 M NaOH, dissolve 40.0 g of NaOH pellets in enough distilled water to make 1.00 L of solution. Add a few pellets at a time while stirring to avoid overheating.

5. To prepare phenolphthalein solution, dissolve 1.00 g phenolphthalein in 50.0 mL of denatured alcohol, and add 50.0 mL of distilled water.

6. A Vernier pH probe can be used to monitor the titration and its end point.

7. Provide miscellaneous shells (such as clam, oyster, and snail shells) for Extension 3. Alternatively, students could determine the amount of $CaCO_3$ contained in pieces of chalk.

- 15 mL of 1.00 M NaOH
- 15 mL of 1.00 M HCl
- medicine droppers or thin-stemmed pipets, 3

FULL-SCALE OPTION

- 100 mL of 1.00 M NaOH
- 100 mL of 1.00 M HCl
- burets

OPTIONAL EQUIPMENT

(Refer to page 698 for equipment setup.)

- CBL unit
- graphing calculator with link cable
- Vernier pH probe with amplifier

PRE-LAB DISCUSSION

Be sure to explain the nature of a back-titration. Students may not realize that the amount of CaCO₃ is being measured indirectly.

PROCEDURAL CHANGES FOR FULL-SCALE OPTION

Prepare burets for titrations.

Delete the first data table and the "number of drops" entries in the second data table.

Omit steps 3–6 for calibrating droppers.

Use a sample size near 1.00 g instead of 0.10 g in step 8.

Rinse burets in the same way that droppers are rinsed in step 9.

Instead of 150 drops, use 50.0 mL of HCl from the acid buret to react with the CaCO₃ in step 10.

Titrate the mixture with NaOH from the base buret until the phenolphthalein changes color in step 11.

Omit item 3 in the Analysis and Interpretation section.

SAFETY

 Always wear safety goggles and a lab apron to protect your eyes and clothing. If you get a chemical in your eyes, immediately flush the chemical out at the eyewash station while calling to your teacher. Know the locations of the emergency lab shower and eyewash station and the procedure for using them.

 Do not touch any chemicals. If you get a chemical on your skin or clothing, wash the chemical off at the sink while calling to your teacher. Make sure you carefully read the labels and follow the precautions on all containers of chemicals that you use. If no precautions are stated on the label, ask your teacher what precautions to follow. Do not taste any chemicals or items used in the laboratory. Never return leftovers to their original containers; take only small amounts to avoid wasting supplies.

 The oven used in this Exploration is hot; use tongs to remove beakers from the oven because heated glassware does not always look hot.

 Call your teacher in the event of an acid or base spill. Acid or base spills should be cleaned up promptly according to your teacher's instructions.

Background

Birds have evolved a chemical process that allows them to rapidly produce the calcium carbonate, CaCO₃, required for eggshell formation. The shell provides a strong protective covering for the developing embryo. Research has shown that some chemicals, like DDT and PCBs, can decrease the amount of calcium carbonate in the eggshell, resulting in shells that are thin and fragile.

Problem

You need to determine how much calcium carbonate is in sample eggshells from chickens that were not exposed to PCBs. The farmer's eggshells contain about 78% calcium carbonate. The calcium carbonate content of eggshells can easily be determined by means of an acid-base back-titration. A carefully measured excess of a strong acid will react with the calcium carbonate. Because the acid is in excess, there will be some left over at the end of the reaction. The resulting solution will be titrated with a strong base to determine how much acid remained unreacted. Phenolphthalein will be used as an indicator to signal the endpoint of the titration. From this measurement, you can determine the following:

- the amount of excess acid that reacted with the eggshell
- the amount of calcium carbonate that was present to react with this acid

776 EXPLORATION 15B

Preparation

1. Organizing Data

Make data and calculation tables like those below and on page 777 in your lab notebook.

Data Table 1

Total volume of acid drops	
Average volume of each drop	
Total volume of base drops	
Average volume of each drop	

Data Table 2

Titration steps	
Mass of entire eggshell	
Mass of ground eggshell sample	
Number of drops of 1.00 M HCl added	150
Volume of 1.00 M HCl added	
Number of drops of 1.00 M NaOH added	
Volume of 1.00 M NaOH added	
Volume of 1.00 HCl reacting with NaOH	
Volume of 1.00 HCl reacting with eggshell	
Number of moles of HCl reacting with eggshell	
Number of moles of CaCO₃ reacting with HCl	
Mass of CaCO₃ in eggshell sample	
Percentage of CaCO₃ in eggshell sample	

REQUIRED PRECAUTIONS

- Read all safety precautions, and discuss them with your students.
- Safety goggles and a lab apron must be worn at all times.
- Wear goggles, a face shield, impermeable gloves, and a lab apron when you prepare the HCl and NaOH. Work in a hood known to be in good operating condition, and have a another person standing standing by to call for help in case of an emergency. Be sure you are within a 30 second walk of a safety shower and eyewash station.
- Students should not handle concentrated acid solutions.
- In case of an acid or base spill, dilute the spill with water. Then mop up the spill with wet cloths or a wet cloth mop designated for spill cleanup. Wear disposable plastic gloves while cleaning up spills.
- Remind students to use tongs to remove beakers from the oven because the beakers will be hot.

Figure A

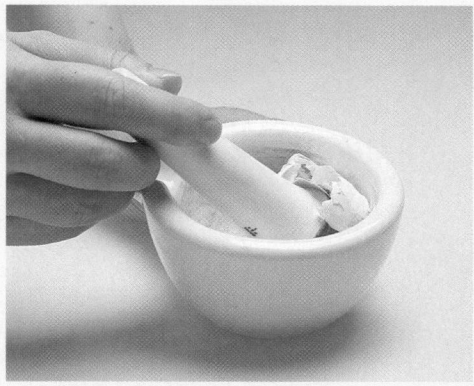

Figure B

2. Remove the white and the yolk from the egg, as shown in **Figure A.** Dispose of these according to your teacher's directions. Wash the shell with distilled water, and carefully peel all the membranes from the inside of the shell. Discard the membranes. Place ALL of the shell in a premassed beaker, and dry the shell in the drying oven at 110°C for about 15 minutes.

3. Put exactly 5.0 mL of water in the 10.0 mL graduated cylinder. Record this volume in the data table in your lab notebook. Fill the first dropper or pipet with water. This dropper should be labeled "Acid." **Do not use this dropper for the base solution.** Holding the dropper vertical, add 20 drops of water to the cylinder. **For the best results, keep the sizes of the drops as even as possible throughout this investigation.** Record the new volume of water in the first data table as Trial 1.

4. Without emptying the graduated cylinder, add an additional 20 drops from the dropper,

as you did in step 3, and record the new volume as the final volume for Trial 2. Repeat this procedure once more for Trial 3.

5. Repeat steps 3 and 4 for the second thin-stemmed dropper. Label this dropper "Base." **Do not use this dropper for the acid solution.**

6. Make sure that the three trials produce data that are similar to each other. If one is greatly different from the others, perform steps 3–5 over again. If you're still waiting for the eggshell in the drying oven, calculate and record in the first data table the total volume of the drops and the average volume per drop.

7. Remove the eggshell and beaker from the oven. Cool them in a desiccator. Record the mass of the entire eggshell in the second data table. Place half the shell in a clean mortar, and grind it to a very fine powder, as shown in **Figure B.** This will save time when dissolving the eggshell. (If time permits, dry the crushed eggshell again, and cool it in the desiccator.)

TECHNIQUES TO DEMONSTRATE

Demonstrate titration procedures, showing the proper way to add drops from burets or droppers and showing the proper way to swirl the flask after adding each drop. Show the end point of the titration. Remind students that the pink color that first appears often disappears when the flask is swirled.

DISPOSAL

Set out three disposal containers: one for unused acid solutions, one for unused base solutions, and one for partially neutralized substances and the contents of the waste beaker. While stirring, slowly combine the solutions one at a time. Adjust the pH of the final waste liquid with 1.0 M acid or base until the pH is between 5 and 9. Pour the neutralized liquid down the drain.

Graduated Cylinder Readings (Pipet Calibration: Steps 3–5)				
Trial	Initial acid pipet	Final acid pipet	Initial base pipet	Final base pipet
1				
2				
3				

SAMPLE DATA	
Mass of entire eggshell (g)	5.27
Mass of ground eggshell sample (g)	0.11
Number of drops of 1.00 M HCl added	150
Number of drops of 1.00 M NaOH added	99

Figure C

Figure D

Technique

8. Measure the mass of a piece of weighing paper. Transfer about 0.1 g of ground eggshell to a piece of weighing paper, and measure the eggshell's mass as accurately as possible. Record the mass in the second data table. Place this eggshell sample in a clean 50 mL bottle or Erlenmeyer flask. A flask will make it easier to swirl the mixture when needed.

9. Fill the acid dropper with the 1.00 M HCl acid solution, and then empty the dropper into an extra 100 mL beaker. Label the beaker "Waste." Fill the base dropper with the 1.00 M NaOH base solution, and then empty the dropper into the 100 mL beaker.

10. Fill the acid dropper once more with 1.00 M HCl. Using the acid dropper, add exactly 150 drops of 1.00 M HCl to the bottle (or flask) with the eggshell, as shown in **Figure C.** Swirl gently for 3–4 minutes. Rinse the sides of the flask with about 10 mL of distilled water. Using a third dropper, add two drops of phenolphthalein solution. Record the number of drops of HCl used in the second data table.

11. Fill the base dropper with the 1.00 M NaOH. Slowly add NaOH from the base dropper into the bottle or flask with the eggshell mixture until a faint pink color persists, even after it is swirled gently, as shown in **Figure D.** It may help to use a white piece of paper as a background so you will be able to see the color as soon as possible. **Be sure to add the base drop by drop, and be certain the drops end up in the reaction mixture and not on the side of the bottle or flask. Keep a careful count of the number of drops used.** Record the number of drops of base used in the second data table.

 ## Cleanup and Disposal

12. Clean all apparatus and your lab station. Return the equipment to its proper place. Dispose of chemicals and solutions in the containers designated by your teacher. Do not pour any chemicals down the drain or in the trash unless your teacher directs you to do so. Wash your hands thoroughly before you leave the lab and after all work is finished.

Analysis and Interpretation

1. Organizing Ideas
The calcium carbonate in the eggshell sample undergoes a double-replacement reaction with the hydrochloric acid in step 10. Then the carbonic acid that was formed decomposes. Write a balanced chemical equation for these reactions. (Hint: The gas observed was carbon dioxide.)

2. Organizing Ideas
Write the balanced chemical equation for the acid-base neutralization of the excess unreacted HCl with the NaOH.

3. Organizing Data
Make the necessary calculations from the first data table to find the number of milliliters in each drop. Using this milliliter/drop ratio, convert the number of drops of each solution in the second data table to volumes in milliliters.

4. Organizing Data
Using the relationship between the molarity and volume of acid and the molarity and volume of base needed to neutralize the acid, calculate the volume of the HCl solution that was neutralized by the NaOH. Then subtract this amount from the initial volume of HCl to determine how much HCl reacted with $CaCO_3$.

Conclusions

5. Organizing Data
Use the stoichiometry of the reaction in Analysis and Interpretation item 1 to calculate the number of moles of $CaCO_3$ that reacted with the HCl, and record this number in your table.

6. Evaluating Methods
Workers in a lab in another city have also tested eggs, and they found that a normal eggshell is about 97% $CaCO_3$. Calculate the percent error for your measurement.

Extensions

1. Inferring Conclusions
Calculate an estimate of the mass of $CaCO_3$ present in the entire eggshell, based on your results. (Hint: Apply the percent composition of your sample to the mass of the entire eggshell.)

2. Designing Experiments
What possible sources of error can you identify in this procedure? If you can think of ways to eliminate them, ask your teacher to approve your plan, and run the procedure again.

OBJECTIVES

Students will:

▸ use appropriate lab safety procedures.

▸ measure the pH of a solution using pH paper or a pH meter.

▸ choose the proper reagent for titrating a solution.

▸ measure volume with a buret or with a dropper calibrated to measure the number of drops per milliliter.

▸ perform a titration and recognize the end point.

▸ use solution stoichiometry calculations to determine the concentration of an unknown solution.

▸ design and implement their own procedure.

RECOMMENDED TIME:
1 lab period

PREREQUISITE:
Exploration 15B

MATERIALS

(for each lab group)

▸ 1 mL of phenolphthalein solution

▸ 50 mL of 0.5 M NaOH

▸ 50 mL unknown solution (0.20 M HCl)

▸ 250 mL Erlenmeyer flask

▸ 250 mL beaker

▸ buret tubes, 2

▸ double buret clamp

▸ index card

▸ pH paper

▸ ring stand

▸ wash bottle

OPTIONAL EQUIPMENT

(Refer to page 698 for equipment setup.)

▸ CBL unit

▸ graphing calculator with link cable

▸ Vernier pH probe with amplifier

▸ stopwatch

ESTIMATED COST OF MATERIALS:
$260 000–$268 000

15B | Acid-Base Titration
Industrial Spill

THE PROBLEM

BLEACHEX

Vacaville Bleachex Production Facility
3617 Industrial Parkway
Vacaville, CA 90627

DELIVER BY OVERNIGHT COURIER
Date: April 21, 1999
To: EPA National Headquarters
From: Anthony Wong, Plant Supervisor
Re: Vacaville Bleachex Corp. Plant Spill

As a result of last night's earthquake, the Bleachex plant in the industrial park south of Vacaville was severely damaged. The safety control measures failed because of the magnitude of the earthquake.

Bleachex manufactures a variety of products using concentrated acids and bases. Plant officials noticed a large quantity of liquid, believed to be either sodium hydroxide or hydrochloric acid solution, flowing through the loading bay doors. An Emergency Toxic Spill Response Team attempted to determine the source and identity of the unknown liquid. A series of explosions and the presence of chlorine gas forced the team to abandon their efforts. The unknown liquid continues to flow into the nearly full containment ponds.

We are sending a sample of the liquid to you by overnight courier and hope that you can quickly and accurately identify the liquid and notify us of the proper method for cleanup and disposal. We need your answer as soon as possible.

Anthony Wong

Anthony Wong

References

Review titration methods using a buret. Before filling the buret, be sure it is clean. Then rinse the buret three times with 5 mL of the standard solution each time before filling the buret. The equivalence point of the titration can be determined using an indicator or pH probe. This is a simple titration, not a back-titration, in which the unknown reacts with an excess of acid and the excess acid is titrated to determine how much must have reacted.

SOLUTION/MATERIAL PREPARATION

1. To prepare the unknown (0.20 M HCl is recommended), follow the precautions in the Teacher's Notes for Exploration 15B. Add 16.5 mL of concentrated HCl to enough distilled water to make 1.00 L of solution. Add the acid slowly to avoid overheating. (NaOH requires another indicator, so it is not recommended as the unknown.)

2. To prepare 0.50 M NaOH, dissolve 20.0 g of NaOH pellets in enough distilled water to

make 1.00 L of solution. Add a few pellets at a time while stirring to avoid overheating.

3. To prepare phenolphthalein solution, dissolve 1.00 g phenolphthalein in 50.0 mL of denatured alcohol, and add 50.0 mL of distilled water.

4. A CBL unit, a Vernier pH probe, and a graphing calculator can be used to monitor the titration and its end point.

MEMORANDUM

CheMystery Labs, Inc.
52 Fulton Street
Springfield, VA 22150

Date: April 22, 1999
To: Cicely Jackson
From: Marissa Bellinghausen

This is a rush job from the EPA. We have been promised $300,000, three times their normal fee of $100,000, so give this project top priority!

First we must determine the pH of the unknown so that we know whether it is an acid or a base. Then titrate the unknown using a standard solution to determine its concentration so that we can advise Bleachex on the amount of neutralizing agents that will be needed for the three 1.75×10^7 L containment ponds.

Because we have a limited sample, I need to approve your plans before you begin your lab work. Therefore, I need the following items:
- detailed one-page plan for your procedure with all necessary data tables (include multiple trials)
- detailed list of the equipment and materials you will need with itemized and total costs

When you are finished, prepare a report in the form of a two-page letter that we can fax to Anthony Wong. The letter must include the following:
- identity of the unknown and its concentration
- pH of the unknown and how you determined it
- paragraph summarizing how you titrated the sample to determine its concentration
- detailed and organized data table
- detailed analysis section with calculations, a discussion of the multiple trials, and a statistical analysis of your precision
- your proposed method for cleanup and disposal, including amount of neutralizing agents necessary
- detailed invoice showing all costs, services, and time for this work

For prices of materials, see page 692.

Required Precautions

Safety goggles and a lab apron must be worn at all times.

Do not touch or taste any chemicals. Always wash your hands thoroughly when finished.

If you get acid or base on your skin or clothing, wash the chemical off at the sink while calling to your teacher. If you get acid or base in your eyes, immediately flush it out at the eyewash station while calling to your teacher.

Spill Procedures/ Waste-Disposal Methods

- In case of a spill, follow your teacher's instructions.
- Put excess chemicals and solutions in the containers designated by your teacher. Do not pour them down the sink or place them in the trash can.

REQUIRED PRECAUTIONS

▶ Read all safety precautions, and discuss them with your students.

▶ Safety goggles and a lab apron must be worn.

▶ Students should not handle concentrated acids.

▶ In case of an acid or base spill, dilute the spill with water. Then mop up the spill with wet cloths or a wet cloth mop designated for spill cleanup. Wear disposable plastic gloves while cleaning up spills.

SAMPLE DATA

SOLUTION	TRIAL 1	TRIAL 2
Unknown (HCl)	25.0 mL	25.0 mL
0.5 M NaOH	9.9 mL	10.0 mL

ANALYSIS

The unknown is HCl.

$$10.0 \times 10^{-3}\ \text{L} \times \frac{0.500\ \text{mol NaOH}}{1\ \text{L NaOH}} \times$$

$$\frac{1\ \text{mol HCl}}{1\ \text{mol NaOH}} \times \frac{1\ \text{mol HCl}}{25.0 \times 10^{-3}\ \text{L}} =$$

$$0.200\ \text{M HCl}$$

$$3\ \text{ponds} \times \frac{1.75 \times 10^7\ \text{L}}{1\ \text{pond}} \times \frac{0.200\ \text{mol HCl}}{1\ \text{L HCl}} \times$$

$$\frac{1\ \text{mol NaOH}}{1\ \text{mol HCl}} = 1.05 \times 10^7\ \text{mol NaOH}$$

(4.21×10^5 kg NaOH for neutralization)

PRE-LAB DISCUSSION

Refer students to Exploration 15C for ideas on how to proceed, but make it clear that procedures must be adjusted.

TIPS FOR EVALUATING THE PRE-LAB REQUIREMENTS

If students plan to use more than 50 mL of the unknown or of the titrating solution, have them reconsider their procedure.

TECHNIQUES TO DEMONSTRATE

Demonstrate the titration technique to be used. Remind students to swirl the flask after each addition.

PROPOSED PROCEDURE

The unknown can be identified as an acid with phenolphthalein, pH paper, or a pH probe. Place 25.0 mL of unknown in a flask. After cleaning and rinsing a buret with 0.50 M NaOH, fill the buret with NaOH. Transfer small amounts of NaOH from the buret to the flask, swirling the flask after each addition, until the end point is reached. Repeat the procedure with 25.0 mL of unknown.

DISPOSAL

Set out three disposal containers— one for unused acid solutions, one for unused base solutions, and one for partially neutralized substances and the contents of the waste beaker. One at a time, slowly combine the solutions while stirring. Adjust the pH of the final waste liquid with 1.0 M acid or base until the pH is between 5 and 9. Pour the neutralized liquid down the drain.

OBJECTIVES

Students will:

▸ use appropriate lab safety procedures.
▸ use litmus paper to determine pH.
▸ use a pH probe.
▸ measure the pH of household solutions.
▸ determine whether household solutions are acidic or basic.

RECOMMENDED TIME:

1 lab period

MATERIALS

(for each lab group)
▸ blue litmus paper
▸ CBL unit
▸ eye droppers, 10
▸ red litmus paper
▸ graphing calculator with link cable
▸ test solutions, 10
   1.0 M NaOH
   apple juice
   baking soda
   cola
   drain cleaner
   lemon juice
   dishwashing liquid
   milk
   vinegar
   water
▸ test tube, 10
▸ test-tube rack
▸ Vernier pH probe with amplifier
▸ wash bottle

PRE-LAB DISCUSSION

Students should be familiar with the concept of acids and bases and pH. Make sure students refer to page 698 for CBL, pH probe, and graphing calculator setup.

15C | Measuring the pH of Household Products

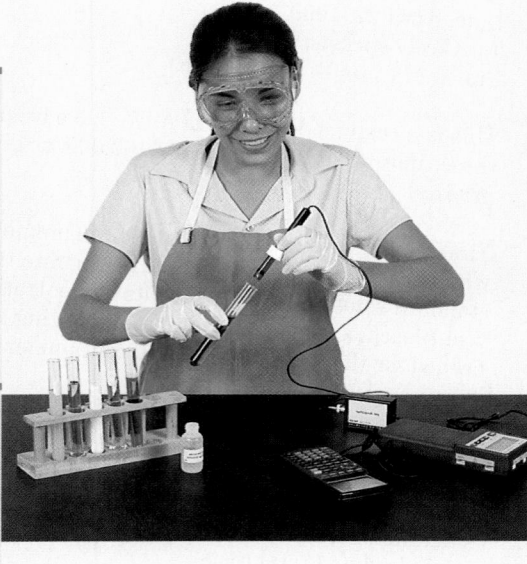

OBJECTIVES

▸ Relate the concepts of acid and base to household products.
▸ Determine if a solution is an acid or a base.
▸ Determine the pH of a solution.
▸ Demonstrate proficiency in the using litmus paper and a pH probe.

MATERIALS

▸ blue litmus paper
▸ distilled water
▸ large test tubes, 10
▸ red litmus paper
▸ small microtip pipets, 10
▸ test-tube rack
▸ wash bottle

TEST SOLUTIONS, 10

▸ 1.0 M NaOH
▸ apple juice
▸ baking soda
▸ clear soft drink

▸ detergent
▸ drain cleaner
▸ lemon juice
▸ milk
▸ vinegar
▸ tap water

OPTIONAL EQUIPMENT

▸ CBL
▸ graphing calculator with link cable
▸ Vernier pH probe with amplifier

Background

Have you ever wondered how many household products contain an acid or a base? A simple pH test can determine whether something is acidic or basic. A pH of 7 indicates a solution is neutral. Acidic solutions have pH values less than 7, and basic solutions have pH values greater than 7.

Problem

You will use what you know about acids and bases to predict which household solutions from the materials list are acidic and which are basic. Then you will measure the pH value of the 10 household solutions. To be sure your results are accurate, you will measure the pH value in two ways. First you will test each solution with a strip of red litmus paper and a strip of blue litmus paper. Then you will measure the pH value with a pH probe.

SOLUTION/MATERIAL PREPARATION

1. To prepare 1 M NaOH, dissolve 40.0 g of NaOH pellets in enough distilled water to make 1.00 L of solution. Add a few pellets at a time, and stop to stir in order to avoid overheating.

REQUIRED PRECAUTIONS

▸ Read all safety precautions, and discuss them with your students.
▸ Safety goggles and a lab apron must be worn at all times.
▸ In case of an acid or base spill, dilute the spill with water. Then mop up the spill with wet cloths or a wet cloth mop designated for spill cleanup. Wear disposable plastic gloves while cleaning up spills.

Preparation

1. Predict which solutions are acidic and which are basic, and write your predictions in your data table.

2. Obtain samples of each solution from your teacher, and label the test tubes 1–10. Label the pipets 1–10.

3. Fill each test tube with 3 mL of a different solution. Be sure to record the position of each solution in your data table.

Technique

pH test with litmus paper

4. Use pipet 1 to transfer one drop of Solution 1 to a strip of blue litmus paper. Record the result in your data table.

5. Using the same pipet, transfer one drop of Solution 1 to a strip of red litmus paper. Record the result in your data table.

6. Repeat steps 4 and 5 with the remaining solutions. Use the appropriate pipet for each pH test.

pH probe

7. Refer to page 698 for pH probe, CBL, and graphing calculator setup.

8. When you are ready to use the Vernier pH probe, take it out of the electrode solution. Rinse the probe thoroughly with distilled water, and pour the water in a waste beaker.

9. Insert the pH probe into solution 1, and swirl the solution around the probe. When the reading on the CBL unit remains constant, record this value in your data table.

10. Rinse the probe with distilled water, and then place the pH probe in the electrode solution. Make sure you swirl the solution around the probe.

11. Repeat steps 9 and 10 with the remaining solutions.

Cleanup and Disposal

12. Clean all apparatus and your lab station. Return equipment to its proper place. Dispose of chemicals and solutions in the containers designated by your teacher. Do not pour any chemicals down the drain or in the trash unless your teacher directs you to do so. Wash your hands thoroughly.

Analysis and Interpretation

1. Organizing Data

List the acidic solutions in order of decreasing acid strength. List the basic solutions in order of decreasing base strength.

2. Evaluating Methods

Explain why it was important to rinse the probe after measuring the pH of each solution. What would have happened to the pH value if the probe had not been rinsed with distilled water?

ANSWERS

ANALYSIS AND INTERPRETATION

1. acids: lemon juice, vinegar, cola, apple juice
   bases: NaOH, drain cleaner, detergent, baking soda, milk

2. Rinsing the probe with distilled water prevents one solution from being contaminated by another. Accurate pH measurements cannot be given for contaminated solutions.

SAMPLE DATA

TEST TUBE	SOLUTION	BLUE LITMUS PAPER	RED LITMUS PAPER	pH	PREDICTION
1	NaOH	blue	blue	14.00	basic
2	apple juice	red	red	3.30	acidic
3	baking soda	blue	blue	8.32	basic
4	cola	red	red	3.26	acidic
5	drain cleaner	blue	blue	13.42	basic
6	lemon juice	red	red	2.87	acidic
7	detergent	blue	blue	8.50	basic
8	milk	blue	blue	6.60	basic
9	vinegar	red	red	3.04	acidic
10	water	blue	red	7.00	neutral

OBJECTIVES

Students will:

▶ use appropriate lab safety procedures.

▶ prepare reaction mixtures of several different concentrations.

▶ observe chemical processes and interactions.

▶ measure time elapsed before the appearance of an indicator.

▶ relate measurements of time elapsed to reaction rates.

▶ define the relationship between reaction rate and concentration.

RECOMMENDED TIME:

1 lab period

MATERIALS

(for each lab group)

▶ 5 mL clock solution A (1.0 M H_2SO_4, $Na_2S_2O_5$, and soluble starch)

▶ 5 mL clock solution B (KIO_3)

▶ distilled or deionized water

▶ eight-well microscale reaction strips, 2

▶ fine-tipped dropper bulbs or small microtip pipets, 3

▶ stopwatch or clock with second hand

OBJECTIVES

▶ **Prepare and observe several different reaction mixtures.**

▶ **Demonstrate proficiency in measuring reaction rates.**

▶ **Relate experimental results to a rate law that you can use to predict the results of various combinations of reactants.**

MATERIALS

▶ **8-well microscale reaction strips, 2**

▶ **distilled or deionized water**

▶ **fine-tipped dropper bulbs or small microtip pipets, 3**

▶ **solution A**

▶ **solution B**

▶ **stopwatch or clock with second hand**

Situation

Executive "toys" are a big business. Your company has been contacted by a toy company that wants technical assistance in designing a new executive desk gadget. The company wants to investigate a reaction that turns a distinctive color in a specific amount of time. Although it will not be easy to determine the precise combination of chemicals that will work, the profit the company stands to make would be worthwhile in the end.

SOLUTION/MATERIAL PREPARATION

1. To prepare clock solution A, make a paste of 1 g of water-soluble starch and about 10 mL of water. Add 225 mL of boiling distilled water. Reheat and boil the solution for a few minutes. After the solution has cooled, add 0.05 g of sodium metabisulfate, $Na_2S_2O_5$, and 1.3 mL of 1.0 M H_2SO_4. Dilute with enough distilled water to make 250 mL of solution. (Note: This solution should be prepared within months of its use.)

2. To prepare 10 mL of 1.0 M H_2SO_4, observe the required precautions. Add 0.6 mL of concentrated H_2SO_4 to 9.4 mL of distilled water. Add the acid slowly while stirring to avoid overheating.

3. To prepare clock solution B, dissolve 1.07 g KIO_3 in enough distilled water to make 250 mL of solution.

4. If the reaction suggested here is too slow, add a few milligrams of $Na_2S_2O_5$ to Solution A. If it is too fast, add some distilled water to clock solution B to dilute the KIO_3 solution.

5. Test the reaction before students begin. Make certain you are familiar with proper disposal methods for the reactants and products.

SAFETY

 Always wear safety goggles and a lab apron to protect your eyes and clothing. If you get a chemical in your eyes, immediately flush the chemical out at the eyewash station while calling to your teacher. Know the location of the emergency lab shower and eyewash station and the procedure for using them.

 Do not touch any chemicals. If you get a chemical on your skin or clothing, wash the chemical off at the sink while calling to your teacher. Make sure you carefully read the labels and follow the precautions on all containers of chemicals that you use.

If no precautions are stated on the label, ask your teacher what precautions to follow. Do not taste any chemicals or items used in the laboratory. Never return leftovers to their original containers; take only small amounts to avoid wasting supplies.

 Always clean up the lab and all equipment after use, and dispose of substances according to proper disposal methods. Wash your hands thoroughly before you leave the lab and after all lab work is finished.

Background

In this experiment you will determine the rate of an *oxidation-reduction,* or *redox,* reaction. Reactions of this type will be discussed in Chapter 17. The net equation for the reaction you will study is as follows:

$$3Na_2S_2O_5(aq) + 2KIO_3(aq) + 3H_2O(l) \xrightarrow{H^+}$$
$$2KI(aq) + 6NaHSO_4(aq)$$

One way to study the rate of this reaction is to observe how fast $Na_2S_2O_5$ is used up. After all the $Na_2S_2O_5$ solution has reacted, the concentration of iodine, I_2, an intermediate in the reaction, builds up. A starch indicator solution added to the reaction mixture will signal when this happens. The colorless starch will change to a blue-black color in the presence of I_2.

In the experiment, the concentrations of the reactants are given in terms of drops of Solution A and drops of Solution B. Solution A contains $Na_2S_2O_5$, the starch-indicator solution, and dilute sulfuric acid to supply the hydrogen ions needed to catalyze the reaction. Solution B

contains KIO_3. You will run the reaction with several different concentrations of the reactants and record the time it takes for the blue-black color to appear.

Problem

To determine the best conditions and concentrations for the reaction, you will determine the following:

▶ how changes in reactant concentrations affect the reaction outcome
▶ how much time elapses for each reaction
▶ a rate law for the reaction that will allow you to predict the results with other combinations

Preparation

1. Organizing Data
Copy the data table below in your lab notebook.

Data Table

	Well 1	Well 2	Well 3	Well 4	Well 5
Time reaction began					
Time reaction stopped					
Drops of A					
Drops of B					
Drops of H_2O					

REACTION RATES 785

PRE-LAB DISCUSSION

Thoroughly discuss the concept of rate. Work through a calculation with sample data, relating time elapsed to rate and the resulting rate data to a rate expression that involves concentration.

TECHNIQUES TO DEMONSTRATE

Point out that holding the dropper bottles vertically will help ensure consistently sized drops.

DISPOSAL

Set out one container for disposal. Treat the waste with 1.0 M $Na_2S_2O_3$ solution to be certain all iodine is reduced to iodide. Neutralize the solution with 1.0 M acid or base, and pour it down the drain.

Solution/Material Preparation continued

6. Fine-tipped dropper bulbs can be made out of thin-stem pipets. Stretch the pipets by hand, narrowing the tube near the bulb, and then cut off the excess tube.

REQUIRED PRECAUTIONS

▶ Read all safety precautions, and discuss them with your students.
▶ Safety goggles and a lab apron must be worn at all times.
▶ Students should not handle concentrated acid solutions.
▶ In case of an acid or base spill, dilute the spill with water. Then mop up the spill with wet cloths or a wet cloth mop designated for spill

cleanup. Wear disposable plastic gloves while cleaning up spills.
▶ Wear safety goggles, a face shield, impermeable gloves, and a lab apron when you prepare the HCl. Work in a fume hood known to be in good operating condition, and have another person standing by to call for help in case of an emergency. Be sure you are within a 30 second walk of a safety shower and eyewash station.

785

ANALYSIS AND INTERPRETATION

1. Students will need to convert from minutes and seconds to just seconds.

   well 1: 143 s   well 2: 67 s
   well 3: 43 s   well 4: 35 s
   well 5: 26 s

2.

   x-axis: Number of drops of Solution B
   y-axis: Time elapsed (s)

   x-axis: Number of drops of Solution B
   y-axis: Rate (1/s)

3. The most concentrated solution (5 drops of B) had the fastest reaction time. The least concentrated solution (1 drop of B and 4 drops of water) had the slowest reaction time.

4. The total number of drops for each well should be the same to make valid comparisons of different concentrations.

CONCLUSIONS

5. The reactions began at the same time because the shake-start mixes all of the solutions at once. In this way, all the reactions take place at the same time and under the same conditions.

6. The effect of reactant concentration (for Solution B) on reaction rate is being measured in this experiment.

7. The rate of the reaction is directly proportional to the concentration of Solution B. $R = k[B]$ or $R \propto [B]$

Figure A

2. Obtain three dropper bulbs or small microtip pipets, and label them "A," "B," and "H_2O."

3. Fill bulb or pipet A with solution A, fill bulb or pipet B with solution B, and fill the bulb or pipet for H_2O with distilled water.

Technique

4. Using the first 8-well strip, place five drops of Solution A into each of the first five wells, as shown in **Figure A.** (Disregard the remaining three wells.) Record the number of drops in the appropriate places in your data table. **For best results, try to make all of the drops about the same size.**

5. In the second 8-well reaction strip, place one drop of Solution B in the first well, two drops in the second well, three drops in the third well, four drops in the fourth well, and five drops in the fifth well. Record the number of drops in the appropriate places in your data table.

6. In the second 8-well strip that contains drops of Solution B, add four drops of water to the first well, three drops to the second well, two drops to the third well, and one drop to the fourth well. Do not add any water to the fifth well.

7. Carefully invert the second strip. The surface tension should keep the solutions from falling out of the wells. Place the second strip well-to-well on top of the first strip, as shown in **Figure B.**

8. Holding the strips tightly together, record the exact time or set the stopwatch as you shake the strips. This procedure should effectively mix the upper solutions with each of the corresponding lower ones.

9. Observe the lower wells. Note the sequence in which the solutions react, and record the number of seconds it takes for each solution to turn a blue-black color.

Cleanup and Disposal

10. Dispose of the solutions in the container designated by your teacher. Wash your hands thoroughly after cleaning up the area and equipment.

Analysis and Interpretation

1. **Organizing Data**
   Calculate the time elapsed for the complete reaction of each combination of Solution A and Solution B.

Figure B

SAMPLE DATA

	WELL 1	WELL 2	WELL 3	WELL 4	WELL 5
Time reaction began	00:00:00	00:00:00	00:00:00	00:00:00	00:00:00
Time reaction stopped	00:02:23	00:01:07	00:00:43	00:00:35	00:00:26
Drops of Solution A	5	5	5	5	5
Drops of Solution B	1	2	3	4	5
Drops of H_2O	4	3	2	1	0

2. Evaluating Data

Make a graph of your results. Label the x-axis "Number of drops of Solution B." Label the y-axis "Time elapsed." Make a similar graph for drops of Solution B versus rate (1/time elapsed).

3. Analyzing Information

Which mixture reacted the fastest? Which mixture reacted the slowest?

4. Evaluating Methods

Why was it important to add the drops of water to the wells that contained fewer than five drops of Solution B? (Hint: Figure out the total number of drops in each of the reaction wells.)

Conclusions

5. Analyzing Methods

How can you be sure that each of the chemical reactions began at about the same time? Why is this important?

6. Evaluating Conclusions

Of the following variables that can affect the rate of a reaction, which is tested in this experiment: temperature, catalyst, concentration, surface area, or nature of reactants? Explain your answer.

7. Applying Ideas

Use your data and graphs to determine the relationship between the concentration of Solution B and the rate of the reaction. Describe this relationship in terms of a rate law.

Extensions

1. Evaluating Data

Share your data with other lab groups, and calculate a class average for the rate of the reaction for each concentration of B. Compare the results from other groups with your results. Explain why there are differences in the results.

2. Analyzing Methods

What are some possible sources of error in this procedure? If you can think of ways to

eliminate them, ask your teacher to approve your plan and run your procedure again.

3. Predicting Outcomes

What combination of drops of Solutions A and B would you use if you wanted the reaction to last exactly 2.5 minutes? Design an experiment to test your answer. If your teacher approves your plan, perform the experiment, and record these results. Make another graph that includes both the old and new data.

4. Predicting Outcomes

How would your data be different if the experiment were repeated but Solution A was diluted with one part solution for every seven parts distilled water?

5. Designing Experiments

How would you determine the smallest interval of time during which you could distinguish a clock reaction? Design an experiment to find out. If your teacher approves your plan, perform your experiment.

6. Designing Experiments

How would the results of this experiment be affected if the reaction took place in a cold environment? Design an experiment to test your answer using materials available. If your teacher approves your plan, perform your experiment and record the results. Make another graph, and compare it with your old data.

7. Designing Experiments

Devise a plan to determine the effect of Solution A on the rate law. If your teacher approves your plan, perform your experiment, and determine the rate law for this reaction.

8. Relating Ideas

If Solution B contains 0.02 M KIO_3, calculate the value for the constant, k, in the expression below. (Hint: Remember that Solution B is diluted when it is added to Solution A.)

$$\text{rate} = k[KIO_3]$$

1. Answers will vary because of variations in drop size.

2. Suggestions for improving the procedure will vary. Possibilities may include minimizing error by performing multiple trials or keeping the drop size standard. Be sure answers include safe, carefully planned procedures.

3. Answers will vary depending on the conditions in your lab. For the sample data, it would require a mixture close to 4 drops A:25 drops B:21 drops H_2O. Students may need to use a different reaction vessel if this is too much for the micro-well strips. Be sure answers include safe, carefully planned procedures.

4. Suggestions will vary. Be sure answers include safe, carefully planned procedures. Students should find that the rate is seven times slower.

5. Answers may vary. Determine the difference in time for the smallest difference in the amounts of the reactants. Be sure answers include safe, carefully planned procedures.

6. Answers will vary. Be sure students' suggestions are safe and include carefully planned procedures. The rate is slower at lower temperatures.

7. Students may suggest using drops of water and Solution A and keeping the amount of Solution B constant. Another linear relationship is involved.

$R = k[A][B]$

8. well 1: $k = \dfrac{6.99 \times 10^{-3}}{0.0020 \text{ M}} = 3.5$

well 2: $k = \dfrac{0.015}{0.0040 \text{ M}} = 3.8$

well 3: $k = \dfrac{0.023}{0.0060 \text{ M}} = 3.8$

well 4: $k = \dfrac{0.029}{0.0080 \text{ M}} = 3.6$

well 5: $k = \dfrac{0.038}{0.0010 \text{ M}} = 3.8$

average value for $k = 3.7$

OBJECTIVES

Students will:

▸ use appropriate lab safety procedures.

▸ measure volume using burets.

▸ perform a redox titration.

▸ recognize the end point of a redox reaction.

▸ write a balanced oxidation-reduction reaction.

▸ determine the concentration of a solution using stoichiometry and titration data.

RECOMMENDED TIME:

1 lab period

MATERIALS

(for each lab group)

▸ 5 mL of 1.0 M H_2SO_4

▸ 50 mL of 0.0200 M $KMnO_4$

▸ 50 mL of unknown (0.15 M $FeSO_4$ solution)

▸ 100 mL graduated cylinder

▸ 125 mL Erlenmeyer flasks, 4

▸ 250 mL beakers, 2

▸ 400 mL beaker

▸ burets, 2

▸ distilled water

▸ double buret clamp

▸ ring stand

▸ wash bottle

17A | Redox Titration

OBJECTIVES

▸ Demonstrate proficiency in performing redox titrations and recognizing the end point of a redox reaction.

▸ Determine the concentration of a solution using stoichiometry and volume data from a titration.

MATERIALS

▸ 0.0200 M $KMnO_4$

▸ 1.0 M H_2SO_4

▸ 100 mL graduated cylinder

▸ 125 mL Erlenmeyer flask, 4

▸ 250 mL beaker, 2

▸ 400 mL beaker

▸ burets, 2

▸ distilled water

▸ double buret clamp

▸ $FeSO_4$ solution

▸ ring stand

▸ wash bottle

Situation

You are a chemist working for a chemical analysis firm. A large pharmaceutical company has hired you to help salvage some products that were damaged by a small fire in their warehouse. Although there was only minimal smoke and fire damage to the warehouse and products, the sprinkler system ruined the labeling on many of the pharmaceuticals. The firm's best-selling products are iron tonics used to treat low-level anemia. The tonics are produced from hydrated iron(II) sulfate, $FeSO_4 \cdot 7H_2O$. The different types of tonics contain different concentrations of $FeSO_4$. You have been hired to help the pharmaceutical company figure out the proper label for each bottle of tonic.

SOLUTION/MATERIAL PREPARATION

1. To prepare 0.0200 M $KMnO_4$, dissolve 3.16 g of $KMnO_4$ in enough distilled water to make 1.00 L of solution. For best results, this solution must be prepared shortly before the lab.

2. To prepare 0.15 M $FeSO_4$, dissolve 41.70 g of $FeSO_4 \cdot 7 H_2O$ in enough distilled water to make 1.00 L of solution.

3. To prepare 1.00 L of 1.0 M H_2SO_4, observe the required precautions. Slowly add 56 mL of

concentrated H_2SO_4 to enough distilled water to make 1.00 L of solution. Add the acid slowly while stirring to avoid overheating.

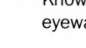

Always wear safety goggles and a lab apron to protect your eyes and clothing. If you get a chemical in your eyes, immediately flush the chemical out at the eyewash station while calling to your teacher. Know the location of the emergency lab shower and eyewash station and the procedure for using them.

Do not touch any chemicals. If you get a chemical on your skin or clothing, wash the chemical off at the sink while calling to your teacher. Make sure you carefully read the labels and follow the precautions on all containers of chemicals that you use. If no precautions are stated on the label, ask your teacher what precautions to follow. Do not taste any chemicals or items used in the laboratory.

Never return leftovers to their original containers; take only small amounts to avoid wasting supplies.

Never put broken glass in a regular waste container. Broken glass should be disposed of separately in a container designated by your teacher.

Call your teacher in the event of an acid, base, or potassium permanganate spill. Such spills should be cleaned up promptly according to your teacher's instructions. Acids and bases are corrosive. Avoid breathing fumes; $KMnO_4$ is a strong oxidizer. If any of the oxidizer spills on you, immediately flush the area with water and notify your teacher.

Background

In Chapter 15 you studied acid-base titrations in which an unknown amount of acid is titrated with a carefully measured amount of base. In this procedure a similar approach called a redox titration is used. In a redox titration, the reducing agent, Fe^{2+}, is oxidized to Fe^{3+} by the oxidizing agent, MnO_4^-. When this process occurs, the Mn in MnO_4^- changes from a +7 to a +2 oxidation state and has a noticeably different color. You can use this color change in the same way that you used the color change of phenolphthalein in acid-base titrations—to signify a redox reaction end point. When the reaction is complete, any excess MnO_4^- added to the reaction mixture will give the solution a pink or purple color. The volume data from the titration, the known molarity of the $KMnO_4$ solution, and the mole ratio from the following balanced redox equation will give you the information you need to calculate the molarity of the $FeSO_4$ solution.

$$5Fe^{2+} + MnO_4^- + 8H^+ \longrightarrow 5Fe^{3+} + Mn^{2+} + 4H_2O$$

Problem

To determine how to label the bottles, you must determine the concentration of iron(II) ions in the sample from an unlabeled bottle from the warehouse by answering the following questions:

▶ How can the volume data obtained from the titration and the mole ratios from the balanced redox reaction be used to determine the concentration of the sample?
▶ Which tonic is in the sample, given information about the concentration of each tonic?

Preparation

1. Organizing Data
   Copy the data table below in your lab notebook.

2. Clean two 50 mL burets with a buret brush and distilled water. Rinse each buret at least three times with distilled water to remove any contaminants.

Data Table

Trial	Initial KMnO₄ volume	Final KMnO₄ volume	Initial FeSO₄ volume	Final FeSO₄ volume
1				
2				
3				

REDOX TITRATION   789

PRE-LAB DISCUSSION
Thoroughly discuss the concept of oxidation-reduction and how this type of reaction can result in a color change. Review the concept of molar ratios and balancing redox equations.

TECHNIQUES TO DEMONSTRATE
At this point, students should have had plenty of practice in operating burets with acid-base titrations. Remind students to create the end-point standard in step 7.

DISPOSAL
Set out one container for disposal. The mixture that results should be acidic. If the mixture is purple, add $FeSO_4$ solution slowly while stirring until the color is gone. Precipitate the iron by adding 1.0 M NaOH. Filter the iron, and put the precipitate in the trash. Neutralize the filtrate with 1.0 M acid or base until its pH is between 5 and 9, and pour it down the drain.

REQUIRED PRECAUTIONS

▶ Read all safety precautions, and discuss them with your students.

▶ Safety goggles and a lab apron must be worn at all times.

▶ Students should not handle concentrated acid solutions. In case of an acid spill, dilute the spill with water. Then mop up the spill with wet cloths or a wet cloth mop designated for spill cleanup. Wear disposable plastic gloves while cleaning up spills.

▶ Wear safety goggles, a face shield, impermeable gloves, and a lab apron when you prepare the HCl. Work in a fume hood known to be in good operating condition, and have another person standing by to call for help in case of an emergency. Be sure you are within a 30 second walk of a safety shower and eyewash station.

ANALYSIS AND INTERPRETATION

1. trial 1: 15.0 mL KMnO$_4$ ×

$$\frac{1 \text{ L}}{1000 \text{ mL}} \times \frac{0.020 \text{ mol KMnO}_4}{1 \text{ L}} =$$

$$3.0 \times 10^{-4} \text{ mol KMnO}_4$$

trial 2: 14.5 mL KMnO$_4$ ×

$$\frac{1 \text{ L}}{1000 \text{ mL}} \times \frac{0.020 \text{ mol KMnO}_4}{1 \text{ L}} =$$

$$2.9 \times 10^{-4} \text{ mol KMnO}_4$$

trial 3: 15.5 mL KMnO$_4$ ×

$$\frac{1 \text{ L}}{1000 \text{ mL}} \times \frac{0.020 \text{ mol KMnO}_4}{1 \text{ L}} =$$

$$3.1 \times 10^{-4} \text{ mol KMnO}_4$$

2. The ratio of Fe^{2+} to MnO$_4^-$ is 5:1.

trial 1: 3.0×10^{-4} mol MnO$_4^-$ ×

$$\frac{5 \text{ mol Fe}^{2+}}{1 \text{ mol KMnO}_4} =$$

$$1.5 \times 10^{-3} \text{ mol Fe}^{2+}$$

trial 2: 2.9×10^{-4} mol MnO$_4^-$ ×

$$\frac{5 \text{ mol Fe}^{2+}}{1 \text{ mol KMnO}_4} =$$

$$1.5 \times 10^{-3} \text{ mol Fe}^{2+}$$

trial 3: 3.1×10^{-3} mol MnO$_4^-$ ×

$$\frac{5 \text{ mol Fe}^{2+}}{1 \text{ mol KMnO}_4} =$$

$$1.6 \times 10^{-3} \text{ mol Fe}^{2+}$$

3. average molarity =

$$\frac{1.5 \times 10^{-3} \text{ mol Fe}^{2+}}{10.0 \text{ mL}} \times \frac{1000 \text{ mL}}{1 \text{ L}} =$$

$$0.15 \text{ M Fe}^{2+}$$

4. The concentrations of each solution is very important. If you rinse the buret only with distilled water, the solutions might be diluted if there was any water left in the buret. By using the solution being measured to rinse the buret, you can be sure any solution left behind will not dilute the solution added.

3. Label two 250 mL beakers "0.0200 M KMnO$_4$," and "FeSO$_4$ solution." Label three of the flasks 1, 2, and 3. Label the 400 mL beaker "Waste." Label one buret "KMnO$_4$" and the other "FeSO$_4$."

4. Measure approximately 75 mL of 0.0200 M KMnO$_4$, and pour it into the appropriately labeled beaker. Obtain approximately 75 mL of FeSO$_4$ solution, and pour it into the appropriately labeled beaker.

5. Rinse one buret three times with a few milliliters of 0.0200 M KMnO$_4$ from the appropriately labeled beaker. Collect these rinses in the waste beaker. Rinse the other buret three times with small amounts of FeSO$_4$ solution from the appropriately labeled beaker. Collect these rinses in the waste beaker.

6. Set up the burets as shown in **Figure A.** Fill one buret with approximately 50 mL of the 0.0200 M KMnO$_4$ from the beaker, and fill the other buret with approximately 50 mL of the FeSO$_4$ solution from the other beaker.

7. With the waste beaker underneath its tip, open the KMnO$_4$ buret long enough to be

Figure A

Figure B

sure the buret tip is filled. Repeat for the FeSO$_4$ buret.

8. Add 50 mL of distilled water to one of the 125 mL Erlenmeyer flasks, and add one drop of 0.0200 M KMnO$_4$ to the flask. Set this aside to use as a color standard, as shown in **Figure B,** to compare with the titration and to determine the end point.

Technique

9. Record the initial buret readings for both solutions in your data table. Add 10.0 mL of the hydrated iron(II) sulfate, FeSO$_4$•7H$_2$O, solution to flask 1. Add 5 mL of 1.0 M H$_2$SO$_4$ to the FeSO$_4$ solution in this flask. The acid will help keep the Fe^{2+} ions in the reduced state, allowing you time to titrate.

10. Slowly add KMnO$_4$ from the buret to the FeSO$_4$ in the flask while swirling the flask, as shown in **Figure C.** When the color of the solution matches the color standard you prepared in step 8, record the final readings of the burets in your data table.

11. Empty the titration flask into the waste beaker. Repeat the titration procedure in steps 9 and 10 with flasks 2 and 3.

SAMPLE DATA				
TRIAL	INITIAL KMnO$_4$ VOLUME (mL)	FINAL KMnO$_4$ VOLUME (mL)	INITIAL FeSO$_4$ VOLUME (mL)	FINAL FeSO$_4$ VOLUME (mL)
1	50.0	35.0	50.0	40.0
2	35.0	20.5	40.0	30.0
3	20.5	5.0	30.0	20.0

Figure C

 Cleanup and Disposal

12. Always clean up the lab and all equipment after use. Dispose of the contents of the waste beaker in the container designated by your teacher. Also pour the contents of the color-standard flask into this container. Wash your hands thoroughly after cleaning up the area and equipment.

Analysis and Interpretation

1. Evaluating Data
Calculate the number of moles of MnO_4^- reduced in each trial.

2. Analyzing Information
Calculate the number of moles of Fe^{2+} oxidized in each trial.

3. Applying Conclusions
Calculate the average concentration (molarity) of the iron tonic.

4. Analyzing Methods
Explain why it was important to rinse the burets with $KMnO_4$ or $FeSO_4$ before adding the solutions. (Hint: Consider what would happen to the concentration of each solution

if it were added to a buret that had been rinsed only with distilled water.)

Conclusions

5. Inferring Conclusions
The company makes three different types of iron tonics: Feravide A, with a concentration of 0.145 M $FeSO_4$; Feravide Extra-Strength, with 0.225 M $FeSO_4$; and Feravide Jr., with 0.120 M $FeSO_4$. Which tonic is your sample?

Extensions

1. Evaluating Methods
What possible sources of error can you identify with this procedure? If you can think of ways to eliminate them, ask your teacher to approve your plan, and run the procedure again.

2. Research and Communication
Blueprints are based on a photochemical reaction. The paper is treated with a solution of iron(III) ammonium citrate and potassium hexacyanoferrate(III) and dried in the dark. When a tracing-paper drawing is placed on the blueprint paper and exposed to light, Fe^{3+} ions are reduced to Fe^{2+} ions, which react with hexacyanoferrate(III) ions in the moist paper to form the blue color on the paper. The lines of the drawing block the light and prevent the reduction of Fe^{3+} ions, resulting in white lines. Find out how sepia prints are made, and report on this information.

3. Relating Ideas
Electrochemical cells are based on the process of electron flow in a system with varying potential differences. Batteries are composed of such systems and contain different chemicals for different purposes and price ranges. You can make simple experimental batteries using metal wires and items such as lemons, apples, and potatoes. What are some other "homemade" battery sources, and what is the role of these food items in producing electrical energy that can be measured as battery power? Explain your answers.

CONCLUSION

5. The sample tonic is most likely Feravide A, 0.145 M $FeSO_4$.

EXTENSIONS

1. Suggestions for improving the procedure will vary. Possible suggestions include performing repeated trials or using larger volumes for the titration. Be sure answers include safe, carefully planned procedures.

2. Sepia printing is similar to blueprint printing. In sepia printing, the potassium hexacyanoferrate(III) oxidizes the crystals of silver in the print so that they become silver ions again. Then the print is redeveloped in sodium sulfide.

3. Answers will vary. The food is the conductor that completes the circuit between the two metals, each of which has a different reduction potential. In terms of a traditional cell, the food acts as both the porous barrier that separates the metal and the solution of aqueous ions that completes the circuit.

OBJECTIVES

Students will:

▸ use appropriate lab safety procedures.

▸ measure volume using burets.

▸ perform a redox titration.

▸ recognize the end point of a redox reaction.

▸ write a balanced oxidation-reduction reaction.

▸ determine the concentration of a solution using stoichiometry and titration data.

▸ design and implement their own procedure.

RECOMMENDED TIME:
1 lab period

PREREQUISITE:
Exploration 17A

MATERIALS

(for each lab group)

▸ 5 mL of 1.0 M H_2SO_4

▸ 50 mL of unknown solution (0.25 M $FeSO_4$)

▸ 100 mL of 0.0200 M $KMnO_4$

▸ 100 mL graduated cylinder

▸ 125 mL Erlenmeyer flasks, 4

▸ 250 mL beakers, 2

▸ 400 mL beaker

▸ burets, 2

▸ distilled water

▸ double buret clamp

▸ ring stand

▸ wash bottle

ESTIMATED COST OF MATERIALS:
$158 000

ANALYSIS

$$25.0 \text{ mL} \times \frac{1 \text{ L}}{1000 \text{ mL}} \times \frac{0.020 \text{ mol } KMnO_4}{1 \text{ L}} =$$
$$5 \times 10^{-4} \text{ mol } KMnO_4$$

$$5 \times 10^{-4} \text{ mol } KMnO_4 \times \frac{5 \text{ mol } FeSO_4}{1 \text{ mol } KMnO_4} =$$
$$2.5 \times 10^{-3} \text{ mol } FeSO_4 \text{ (also the amount of Fe)}$$

mass $FeSO_4$ = 0.38 g $FeSO_4$;
   mass Fe = 0.14 g Fe

17A | Redox Titration
Mining Feasibility Study

THE PROBLEM

GOLDSTAKE
MINING
COMPANY

May 11, 1999

George Taylor
Director of Analytical Services
CheMystery Labs, Inc.
52 Fulton Street
Springfield, VA 22150

Dear Mr. Taylor:

Because of the high quality of your firm's work in the past, Goldstake is again asking that you submit a bid for a mining feasibility study. A study site in New Mexico has yielded some promising iron ore deposits, and we are evaluating the potential yield.

Your bid should include the cost of evaluating the sample we're sending with this letter and the fees for 20 additional analyses to be completed over the next year. The sample is a slurry extracted from the mine using a special process that converts the iron ore into $FeSO_4$ dissolved in water. The mine could produce up to 1.0×10^5 L of this slurry daily, but we need to know how much iron is in that amount of slurry before we proceed.

The contract for the other analyses will be awarded based on the accuracy of this analysis and the quality of the accompanying report. Your report will be used for two purposes: to evaluate the site for quantity of iron and to determine who our analytical consultant will be if the site is developed into a mining operation. I look forward to reviewing your bid proposal.

Sincerely,

Lynn L. Brown

Lynn L. Brown
Director of Operations
Goldstake Mining Company

792   INVESTIGATION 17A

References

Review more information on redox reactions. Remember to add a small amount of H_2SO_4 so the iron will stay in the Fe^{2+} form. Calculate your disposal costs based on the mass of $KMnO_4$ and $FeSO_4$ in your solutions, plus the mass of the H_2SO_4 solution.

SOLUTION/MATERIAL PREPARATION

1. See the Teacher's Notes for Exploration 17A for information on preparing 0.0200 M $KMnO_4$ and 1.0 M H_2SO_4.

2. To prepare 0.25 M $FeSO_4$, dissolve 69.51 g of $FeSO_4\cdot 7H_2O$ to enough distilled water to make 1.00 L of solution.

REQUIRED PRECAUTIONS

▸ Safety goggles and a lab apron must be worn at all times.

▸ Read all safety precautions, and discuss them with your students.

▸ Students should not handle concentrated acids. In case of an acid spill, dilute the spill with water. Then mop up the spill with wet cloths or a wet cloth mop designated for spill cleanup. Wear disposable plastic gloves while cleaning up spills.

THE PLAN

MEMORANDUM

CheMystery Labs, Inc.
52 Fulton Street
Springfield, VA 22150

Date: May 12, 1999
To: Crystal Sievers
From: George Taylor

Good news! It looks as though the quality of our work has earned us a repeat customer, Goldstake Mining Company. We've done work for them in the past, and they pay their bills on time. This analysis could turn into a long-term arrangement, so when bonus time arrives, I'll be looking favorably on lab teams that produce accurate, high-quality reports for this job. Perform the analysis more than once so that we can be confident of our accuracy.

Before you begin, send Ms. Brown the following items:

- detailed one-page plan for the procedure and all necessary data tables
- detailed bid sheet that lists all of the equipment and materials you plan to use, including individual and total costs

As soon as you have completed the laboratory work, please prepare a report in the form of a two-page letter to Ms. Brown, and include the following information.

- moles and grams of $FeSO_4$ in 10 mL of sample
- moles, grams, and percentage of iron(II) in 10 mL of the sample
- kilograms of iron that the company could extract from the mine each year, assuming that 1.0×10^5 L of slurry could be mined per day, year round
- balanced equation for the redox equation
- detailed and organized data and analysis section showing calculations of how you determined the moles, grams, and percentage of iron(II) in the sample (include calculations of the mean, or average, of the multiple trials)
- detailed invoice for this analysis that includes our equipment and labor costs (and a small amount of profit)
- bid for 20 additional analyses based on the costs incurred for this one

For prices of materials, see page 692.

Required Precautions

Safety goggles and lab aprons must be worn at all times.

If you get acid, base, or permanganate on your skin or clothing, wash the chemical off at the sink while calling to your teacher. If you get acid, base, or permanganate in your eyes, immediately flush it out at the eyewash station while calling to your teacher.

Do not touch or taste any chemicals. Wash your hands thoroughly when finished.

Spill Procedures/ Waste-Disposal Methods

- In case of spills, follow your teacher's instructions.
- Dispose of solutions from the waste beaker and other leftover reagents in the disposal container designated by your teacher.

793

$$\text{percentage Fe} = \frac{55.85 \text{ g Fe}}{151.91 \text{ g FeSO}_4} \times$$
$$100 = 36.77\%$$

$$\text{annual yield: } \frac{0.15 \text{ g}}{10 \text{ mL}} \times \frac{1000 \text{ mL}}{1 \text{ L}} \times$$
$$\frac{1 \text{ kg}}{1000 \text{ g}} \times \frac{1 \times 10^5 \text{ L}}{1 \text{ day}} \times \frac{365 \text{ days}}{1 \text{ year}} =$$
$$5.5 \times 10^5 \text{ kg/year}$$

PRE-LAB DISCUSSION

The process is very similar to that of Exploration 17A. Encourage students to use 10 mL samples of the solution, so the amounts of $KMnO_4$ necessary are not excessive.

TIPS FOR EVALUATING PRE-LAB REQUIREMENTS

If students plan to use more than 100 mL of either the unknown or potassium permanganate, have them reconsider their procedures.

TECHNIQUES TO DEMONSTRATE

Remind students to create an end-point standard to compare with as they titrate.

PROPOSED PROCEDURE

Prepare the burets for the titration using $KMnO_4$ in one buret and $FeSO_4$ in the other. Put a drop of $KMnO_4$ in one Erlenmeyer flask to serve as a color standard to recognize the end point.

Put 10.0 mL of the $FeSO_4$ solution in an Erlenmeyer flask. Add 5 mL of 1.0 M H_2SO_4. Slowly add $KMnO_4$ from the buret. Swirl after each drop is added. When the color matches the standard, record the final volumes of the burets. Repeat the titration procedure twice.

DISPOSAL

Set out one container for disposal. The mixture that results should be acidic. If the mixture is purple, add $FeSO_4$ solution slowly while stirring until the color is gone. Precipitate the iron by adding 1.0 M NaOH. Filter the iron, and put the precipitate in the trash. Neutralize the filtrate with 1.0 M acid or base until its pH is between 5 and 9, and pour it down the drain.

SAMPLE DATA

TRIAL	INITIAL FeSO₄ VOLUME (mL)	FINAL FeSO₄ VOLUME (mL)	INITIAL KMnO₄ VOLUME (mL)	FINAL KMnO₄ VOLUME (mL)
1	50.0	40.0	50.0	25.0
2	40.0	30.0	50.0	25.2
3	30.0	20.0	50.0	24.8

REFERENCE TABLES

TABLE A-1   SI Measurements

Metric Prefixes

Prefix	Symbol	Factor of base unit
giga-	G	1 000 000 000
mega-	M	1 000 000
kilo-	k	1 000
hecto-	h	100
deka-	da	10
deci-	d	0.1
centi-	c	0.01
milli-	m	0.001
micro-	μ	0.000 001
nano-	n	0.000 000 001
pico-	p	0.000 000 000 001

Mass

1 kilogram (kg)	= SI base unit of mass
1 gram (g)	= 0.001 kg
1 milligram (mg)	= 0.000 001 kg
1 microgram (μg)	= 0.000 000 001 kg

Lengths

1 kilometer (km)	= 1000 m
1 meter (m)	= SI base unit of length
1 centimeter (cm)	= 0.01 m
1 millimeter (mm)	= 0.001 m
1 micrometer (μm)	= 0.000 001 m
1 nanometer (nm)	= 0.000 000 001 m
1 picometer (pm)	= 0.000 000 000 001 m

Area

1 square kilometer (km^2)	= 100 hectares (ha)
1 hectare (ha)	= 10 000 square meters (m^2)
1 square meter (m^2)	= 10 000 square centimeters (cm^2)
1 square centimeter (cm^2)	= 100 square millimeters (mm^2)

Volume

1 liter (L)	= common unit for liquid volume (not SI)
1 cubic meter (m^3)	= 1000 L
1 kiloliter (kL)	= 1000 L
1 milliliter (mL)	= 0.001 L
1 milliliter (mL)	= 1 cubic centimeter (cm^3)

TABLE A-2   Abbreviations

amu	= atomic mass unit (mass)		**mol**	= mole (quantity)
atm	= atmosphere (pressure, non-SI)		**M**	= molarity (concentration)
Bq	= becquerel (nuclear activity)		**N**	= newton (force)
°C	= degree Celsius (temperature)		**Pa**	= pascal (pressure)
J	= joule (energy)		**s**	= second (time)
K	= kelvin (temperature, thermodynamic)		**V**	= volt (electric potential difference)

TABLE A-3 Symbols

Symbol	Meaning
α	= helium nucleus (also ^4_2He) emission from radioactive materials
β	= electron (also $^0_{-1}e$) emission from radioactive materials
γ	= high-energy photon emission from radioactive materials
Δ	= change in a given quantity (e.g., ΔH for change in enthalpy)
c	= speed of light in a vacuum
c_p	= specific heat capacity (at constant pressure)
D	= density
E_a	= activation energy
E^0	= standard electrode potential
G	= Gibbs free energy
ΔG^0	= standard free energy of reaction
ΔG^0_f	= standard molar free energy of formation
H	= enthalpy
ΔH^0	= standard enthalpy of reaction

Symbol	Meaning
ΔH^0_f	= standard molar enthalpy of formation
K_a	= ionization constant (acid)
K_{eq}	= equilibrium constant
K_{sp}	= solubility-product constant
KE	= kinetic energy
m	= mass
N_A	= Avogadro's number
n	= number of moles
P	= pressure
pH	= measure of acidity ($-\log[\text{H}_3\text{O}^+]$)
R	= ideal gas law constant
S	= entropy
S^0	= standard molar entropy
T	= temperature (thermodynamic, in kelvins)
t	= temperature ($\pm$ degrees Celsius)
V	= volume
v	= velocity

TABLE A-4 Water-Vapor Pressure

Temperature (°C)	Pressure (mm Hg)	Pressure (kPa)	Temperature (°C)	Pressure (mm Hg)	Pressure (kPa)	Temperature (°C)	Pressure (mm Hg)	Pressure (kPa)
0.0	4.6	0.61	19.5	17.0	2.27	27.0	26.7	3.57
5.0	6.5	0.87	20.0	17.5	2.34	28.0	28.3	3.78
10.0	9.2	1.23	20.5	18.1	2.41	29.0	30.0	4.01
12.5	10.9	1.45	21.0	18.6	2.49	30.0	31.8	4.25
15.0	12.8	1.71	21.5	19.2	2.57	35.0	42.2	5.63
15.5	13.2	1.76	22.0	19.8	2.64	40.0	55.3	7.38
16.0	13.6	1.82	22.5	20.4	2.72	50.0	92.5	12.34
16.5	14.1	1.88	23.0	21.1	2.81	60.0	149.4	19.93
17.0	14.5	1.94	23.5	21.7	2.90	70.0	233.7	31.18
17.5	15.0	2.00	24.0	22.4	2.98	80.0	355.1	47.37
18.0	15.5	2.06	24.5	23.1	3.10	90.0	525.8	70.12
18.5	16.0	2.13	25.0	23.8	3.17	95.0	633.9	84.53
19.0	16.5	2.19	26.0	25.2	3.36	100.0	760.0	101.32

TABLE A-5 The Elements—Symbols, Atomic Numbers, and Atomic Masses

Name of element	Symbol	Atomic number	Atomic mass	Name of element	Symbol	Atomic number	Atomic mass
actinium	Ac	89	[227.0278]	holmium	Ho	67	164.93032
aluminum	Al	13	26.981539	hydrogen	H	1	1.00794
americium	Am	95	[243.0614]	indium	In	49	114.818
antimony	Sb	51	121.757	iodine	I	53	126.90447
argon	Ar	18	39.948	iridium	Ir	77	192.22
arsenic	As	33	74.92159	iron	Fe	26	55.847
astatine	At	85	[209.9871]	krypton	Kr	36	83.80
barium	Ba	56	137.327	lanthanum	La	57	138.9055
berkelium	Bk	97	[247.0703]	lawrencium	Lr	103	[262.11]
beryllium	Be	4	9.012182	lead	Pb	82	207.2
bismuth	Bi	83	208.98037	lithium	Li	3	6.941
bohrium	Bh	107	[262.12]	lutetium	Lu	71	174.967
boron	B	5	10.811	magnesium	Mg	12	24.3050
bromine	Br	35	79.904	manganese	Mn	25	54.93805
cadmium	Cd	48	112.411	meitnerium	Mt	109	[266]
calcium	Ca	20	40.078	mendelevium	Md	101	[258.10]
californium	Cf	98	[251.0796]	mercury	Hg	80	200.59
carbon	C	6	12.011	molybdenum	Mo	42	95.94
cerium	Ce	58	140.115	neodymium	Nd	60	144.24
cesium	Cs	55	132.90543	neon	Ne	10	20.1797
chlorine	Cl	17	35.4527	neptunium	Np	93	[237.0482]
chromium	Cr	24	51.9961	nickel	Ni	28	58.6934
cobalt	Co	27	58.93320	niobium	Nb	41	92.90638
copper	Cu	29	63.546	nitrogen	N	7	14.00674
curium	Cm	96	[247.0703]	nobelium	No	102	[259.1009]
dubnium	Db	105	[262.114]	osmium	Os	76	190.23
dysprosium	Dy	66	162.50	oxygen	O	8	15.9994
einsteinium	Es	99	[252.083]	palladium	Pd	46	106.42
erbium	Er	68	167.26	phosphorus	P	15	30.973762
europium	Eu	63	151.965	platinum	Pt	78	195.08
fermium	Fm	100	[257.0951]	plutonium	Pu	94	[244.0642]
fluorine	F	9	18.9984032	polonium	Po	84	[208.9824]
francium	Fr	87	[223.0197]	potassium	K	19	39.0983
gadolinium	Gd	64	157.25	praseodymium	Pr	59	140.90765
gallium	Ga	31	69.723	promethium	Pm	61	[144.9127]
germanium	Ge	32	72.61	protactinium	Pa	91	231.03588
gold	Au	79	196.96654	radium	Ra	88	[226.0254]
hafnium	Hf	72	178.49	radon	Rn	86	[222.0176]
hassium	Hs	108	[265]	rhenium	Re	75	186.207
helium	He	2	4.002602	rhodium	Rh	45	102.90550

A value given in brackets denotes the mass number of the most stable or most common isotope. The atomic masses of most of these elements are believed to have an error no greater than ±1 in the last digit given.

TABLE A-5 CONTINUED The Elements—Symbols, Atomic Numbers, and Atomic Masses

Name of element	Symbol	Atomic number	Atomic mass	Name of element	Symbol	Atomic number	Atomic mass
rubidium	Rb	37	85.4678	thallium	Tl	81	204.3833
ruthenium	Ru	44	101.07	thorium	Th	90	232.0381
rutherfordium	Rf	104	[261.11]	thulium	Tm	69	168.93421
samarium	Sm	62	150.36	tin	Sn	50	118.710
scandium	Sc	21	44.955910	titanium	Ti	22	47.88
seaborgium	Sg	106	[263.118]	tungsten	W	74	183.84
selenium	Se	34	78.96	ununnilium	Uun	110	[269]
silicon	Si	14	28.0855	unununium	Uuu	111	[272]
silver	Ag	47	107.8682	uranium	U	92	238.0289
sodium	Na	11	22.989768	vanadium	V	23	50.9415
strontium	Sr	38	87.62	xenon	Xe	54	131.29
sulfur	S	16	32.066	ytterbium	Yb	70	173.04
tantalum	Ta	73	180.9479	yttrium	Y	39	88.90585
technetium	Tc	43	[97.9072]	zinc	Zn	30	65.39
tellurium	Te	52	127.60	zirconium	Zr	40	91.224
terbium	Tb	65	158.92534				

A value given in brackets denotes the mass number of the most stable or most common isotope. The atomic masses of most of these elements are believed to have an error no greater than ±1 in the last digit given.

TABLE A-6 Physical Constants

Quantity	Symbol	Value
Atomic mass unit	amu	$1.660\,5402 \times 10^{-27}$ kg
Avogadro's number	N_A	$6.022\,137 \times 10^{23}$/mol
Electron rest mass	m_e	$9.109\,3897 \times 10^{-31}$ kg 5.4858×10^{-4} amu
Ideal gas law constant	R	8.314 L•kPa/mol•K 0.0821 L•atm/mol•K
Molar volume of ideal gas at STP	V_M	22.414 10 L/mol
Neutron rest mass	m_n	$1.674\,9286 \times 10^{-27}$ kg 1.008 665 amu
Normal boiling point of water	T_b	373.15 K = 100.0°C
Normal freezing point of water	T_f	273.15 K = 0.00°C
Planck's constant	h	$6.626\,076 \times 10^{-34}$ J•s
Proton rest mass	m_p	$1.672\,6231 \times 10^{-27}$ kg 1.007 276 amu
Speed of light in a vacuum	c	$2.997\,924\,58 \times 10^8$ m/s
Temperature of triple point of water		273.16 K = 0.01°C

TABLE A-7 Properties of Common Elements

Name	Form/color at room temperature	Density† (g/cm³)	Melting point (°C)	Boiling point (°C)	Common oxidation states
aluminum	silver metal	2.702	660.37	2467	3+
antimony	blue-white metalloid	6.684^{25}	630.5	1750	3−, 3+, 5+
argon	colorless gas	1.784*	−189.2	−185.7	0
arsenic	gray metalloid	5.727^{14}	817 (28 atm)	613 (*sublimes*)	3−, 3+, 5+
barium	bluish white metal	3.51	725	1640	2+
beryllium	gray metal	1.85	1278 ± 5	2970 (0.0066 atm)	2+
bismuth	white metal	9.80	271.3	1560 ± 5	3+
boron	black metalloid	2.34	2300	2550	3+
bromine	red-brown liquid	3.119	−7.2	58.78	1−, 1+, 3+, 5+, 7+
calcium	silver metal	1.54	839 ± 2	1484	2+
carbon	diamond	3.51	3500 (63.5 atm)	3930	2+, 4+
	graphite	2.25	3652 (*sublimes*)	—	
chlorine	green-yellow gas	3.214*	−100.98	−34.6	1−, 1+, 3+, 5+, 7+
chromium	gray metal	7.2028	1857 ± 20	2672	2+, 3+, 6+
cobalt	gray metal	8.9	1495	2870	2+, 3+
copper	red metal	8.92	1083.4 ± 0.2	2567	1+, 2+
fluorine	yellow gas	1.69‡	−219.62	−188.14	1−
germanium	gray metalloid	5.323^{25}	937.4	2830	4+
gold	yellow metal	19.31	1064.43	2808 ± 2	1+, 3+
helium	colorless gas	0.1785*	−272.2 (26 atm)	−268.9	0
hydrogen	colorless gas	0.0899*	−259.34	−252.8	1−, 1+
iodine	blue-black solid	4.93	113.5	184.35	1−, 1+, 3+, 5+, 7+
iron	silver metal	7.86	1535	2750	2+, 3+
lead	bluish white metal	11.3437^{16}	327.502	1740	2+, 4+
lithium	silver metal	0.534	180.54	1342	1+
magnesium	silver metal	1.74^{5}	648.8	1107	2+
manganese	gray-white metal	7.20	1244 ± 3	1962	2+, 3+, 4+, 6+, 7+
mercury	silver liquid metal	13.5462	−38.87	356.58	1+, 2+
neon	colorless gas	0.9002*	−248.67	−245.9	0
nickel	silver metal	8.90	1455	2730	2+, 3+
nitrogen	colorless gas	1.2506*	−209.86	−195.8	3−, 3+, 5+
oxygen	colorless gas	1.429*	−218.4	−182.962	2−
phosphorus	yellow solid	1.82	44.1	280	3−, 3+, 5+
platinum	silver metal	21.45	1772	3827 ± 100	2+, 4+
plutonium	silver metal	19.84	641	3232	3+, 4+, 5+, 6+
potassium	silver metal	0.86	63.25	760	1+
radon	colorless gas	9.73*	−71	−61.8	0
silicon	gray metalloid	2.33 ± 0.01	1410	2355	2+, 4+
silver	white metal	10.5	961.93	2212	1+
sodium	silver metal	0.97	97.8	882.9	1+

†Densities obtained at 20°C unless otherwise noted (superscript)
‡Density of fluorine given in g/L at 1 atm and 15°C
*Densities of gases given in g/L at STP

TABLE A-7 *CONTINUED*   Properties of Common Elements

Name	Form/color at room temperature	Density† (g/cm³)	Melting point (°C)	Boiling point (°C)	Common oxidation states
strontium	silver metal	2.6	769	1384	2+
sulfur	yellow solid	1.96	119.0	444.674	2−, 4+, 6+
tin	white metal	7.28	231.88	2260	2+, 4+
titanium	white metal	4.5	1660 ± 10	3287	2+, 3+, 4+
tungsten	gray metal	19.35	3410 ± 20	5660	6+
uranium	silver metal	19.05 ± 0.0225	1132.3 ± 0.8	3818	3+, 4+, 6+
zinc	blue-white metal	7.14	419.58	907	2+

†Densities obtained at 20°C unless otherwise noted (superscript)

TABLE A-8   Common Ions

Cation	Symbol
aluminum	Al^{3+}
ammonium	NH_4^+
arsenic(III)	As^{3+}
barium	Ba^{2+}
calcium	Ca^{2+}
chromium(II)	Cr^{2+}
chromium(III)	Cr^{3+}
cobalt(II)	Co^{2+}
cobalt(III)	Co^{3+}
copper(I)	Cu^+
copper(II)	Cu^{2+}
hydronium	H_3O^+
iron(II)	Fe^{2+}
iron(III)	Fe^{3+}
lead(II)	Pb^{2+}
magnesium	Mg^{2+}
mercury(I)	Hg_2^{2+}
mercury(II)	Hg^{2+}
nickel(II)	Ni^{2+}
potassium	K^+
silver	Ag^+
sodium	Na^+
strontium	Sr^{2+}
tin(II)	Sn^{2+}
tin(IV)	Sn^{4+}
titanium(III)	Ti^{3+}
titanium(IV)	Ti^{4+}
zinc	Zn^{2+}

Anion	Symbol
acetate	CH_3COO^-
bromide	Br^-
carbonate	CO_3^{2-}
chlorate	ClO_3^-
chloride	Cl^-
chlorite	ClO_2^-
chromate	CrO_4^{2-}
cyanide	CN^-
dichromate	$Cr_2O_7^{2-}$
fluoride	F^-
hexacyanoferrate(II)	$Fe(CN)_6^{4-}$
hexacyanoferrate(III)	$Fe(CN)_6^{3-}$
hydride	H^-
hydrogen carbonate	HCO_3^-
hydrogen sulfate	HSO_4^-
hydroxide	OH^-
hypochlorite	ClO^-
iodide	I^-
nitrate	NO_3^-
nitrite	NO_2^-
oxide	O^{2-}
perchlorate	ClO_4^-
permanganate	MnO_4^-
peroxide	O_2^{2-}
phosphate	PO_4^{3-}
sulfate	SO_4^{2-}
sulfide	S^{2-}
sulfite	SO_3^{2-}

TABLE A-9 Densities of Gases at STP

Gas	Density (g/L)	Gas	Density (g/L)
air, dry	1.293	hydrogen	0.0899
ammonia	0.771	hydrogen chloride	1.639
carbon dioxide	1.997	hydrogen sulfide	1.539
carbon monoxide	1.250	methane	0.7168
chlorine	3.214	nitrogen	1.2506
dinitrogen monoxide	1.977	nitrogen monoxide (at 10°C)	1.340
ethyne (acetylene)	1.165	oxygen	1.429
helium	0.1785	sulfur dioxide	2.927

TABLE A-10 Density of Water

Temperature (°C)	Density (g/cm³)	Temperature (°C)	Density (g/cm³)
0	0.999 84	25	0.997 05
2	0.999 94	30	0.995 65
3.98 (maximum)	0.999 973	40	0.992 22
4	0.999 97	50	0.988 04
6	0.999 94	60	0.983 20
8	0.999 85	70	0.977 77
10	0.999 70	80	0.971 79
14	0.999 24	90	0.965 31
16	0.998 94	100	0.958 36
20	0.998 20		

TABLE A-11 Solubilities of Gases in Water

Volume of gas (in L) at STP that can be dissolved in 1 L of water at the temperature indicated.

Gas	0°C	10°C	20°C	60°C
air	0.029 18	0.022 84	0.018 68	0.012 16
ammonia	1130	870	680	200
carbon dioxide	1.713	1.194	0.878	0.359
carbon monoxide	0.035 37	0.028 16	0.023 19	0.014 88
chlorine	—	3.148	2.299	1.023
hydrogen	0.021 48	0.019 55	0.018 19	0.016 00
hydrogen chloride	512	475	442	339
hydrogen sulfide	4.670	3.399	2.582	1.190
methane	0.055 63	0.041 77	0.033 08	0.019 54
nitrogen*	0.023 54	0.018 61	0.015 45	0.010 23
nitrogen monoxide	0.073 81	0.057 09	0.047 06	0.029 54
oxygen	0.048 89	0.038 02	0.031 02	0.019 46
sulfur dioxide	79.789	56.647	39.374	—

*Atmospheric nitrogen—98.815% N_2, 1.185% inert gases

TABLE A-12 Solubilities of Compounds

Solubilities are given in grams of solute dissolved in 100 g of water at the temperature indicated.

Compound	Formula	0°C	20°C	60°C	100°C
aluminum sulfate	$Al_2(SO_4)_3$	31.2	36.4	59.2	89.0
ammonium chloride	NH_4Cl	29.4	37.2	55.3	77.3
ammonium nitrate	NH_4NO_3	118	192	421	871
ammonium sulfate	$(NH_4)_2SO_4$	70.6	75.4	88	103
barium carbonate	$BaCO_3$	—*	$0.0022^{18°}$	—*	0.0065
barium hydroxide	$Ba(OH)_2$	1.67	3.89	20.94	$101.40^{80°}$
barium nitrate	$Ba(NO_3)_2$	4.95	9.02	20.4	34.4
barium sulfate	$BaSO_4$	—*	$0.000\,246^{25°}$	—*	0.000\,413
cadmium sulfate	$CdSO_4$	75.4	76.6	81.8	60.8
calcium carbonate	$CaCO_3$	—*	$0.0014^{25°}$	—*	$0.0018^{75°}$
calcium fluoride	CaF_2	$0.0016^{18°}$	$0.0017^{26°}$	—*	—*
calcium hydrogen carbonate	$Ca(HCO_3)_2$	16.15	16.60	17.50	18.40
calcium hydroxide	$Ca(OH)_2$	0.189	0.173	0.121	0.076
calcium sulfate	$CaSO_4$	—*	$0.209^{30°}$	—*	0.1619
copper(II) chloride	$CuCl_2$	68.6	73.0	96.5	120
copper(II) sulfate pentahydrate	$CuSO_4 \bullet 5H_2O$	23.1	32.0	61.8	114
lead(II) chloride	$PbCl_2$	0.67	1.00	1.94	3.20
lead(II) nitrate	$Pb(NO_3)_2$	37.5	54.3	91.6	133
lithium chloride	$LiCl$	69.2	83.5	98.4	128
lithium sulfate	Li_2SO_4	36.1	34.8	32.6	$30.9^{90°}$
magnesium hydroxide	$Mg(OH)_2$	—*	$0.0009^{18°}$	—*	0.004
magnesium sulfate	$MgSO_4$	22.0	33.7	54.6	68.3
mercury(I) chloride	Hg_2Cl_2	—*	$0.000\,20^{25°}$	$0.001^{43°}$	—*
mercury(II) chloride	$HgCl_2$	3.63	6.57	16.3	61.3
potassium aluminum sulfate	$KAl(SO_4)_2$	3.00	5.90	24.8	$109^{90°}$
potassium bromide	KBr	53.6	65.3	85.5	104
potassium chlorate	$KClO_3$	3.3	7.3	23.8	56.3
potassium chloride	KCl	28.0	34.2	45.8	56.3
potassium chromate	K_2CrO_4	56.3	63.7	70.1	$74.5^{90°}$
potassium iodide	KI	128	144	176	206
potassium nitrate	KNO_3	13.9	31.6	106	245
potassium permanganate	$KMnO_4$	2.83	6.34	22.1	—*
potassium sulfate	K_2SO_4	7.4	11.1	18.2	24.1
silver acetate	$AgC_2H_3O_2$	0.73	1.05	1.93	$2.59^{80°}$
silver chloride	$AgCl$	$0.000\,089^{10°}$	—*	—*	0.0021
silver nitrate	$AgNO_3$	122	216	440	733
sodium acetate	$NaC_2H_3O_2$	36.2	46.4	139	170
sodium chlorate	$NaClO_3$	79.6	95.9	137	204
sodium chloride	$NaCl$	35.7	35.9	37.1	39.2
sodium nitrate	$NaNO_3$	73.0	87.6	122	180
sucrose	$C_{12}H_{22}O_{11}$	179.2	203.9	287.3	487.2

*Dashes indicate that values are not available.

TABLE A-13 Standard Thermodynamic Properties

Substance	Standard enthalpy of formation ΔH_f^o(kJ/mol)	Standard entropy S^o (J/mol•K)	Substance	Standard enthalpy of formation ΔH_f^o(kJ/mol)	Standard entropy S^o (J/mol•K)
Aluminum			**Copper**		
Al(s)	0.0	28.3	Cu(s)	0.0	33.2
AlCl$_3$(s)	−705.6	110.7	CuCl$_2$(s)	−220.1	108.1
Al$_2$O$_3$(s, corundum)	−1676.0	51.0	CuSO$_4$(s)	−770.0	109.3
Bromine			**Fluorine**		
Br$_2$(l)	0.0	152.2	F$_2$(g)	0.0	202.8
Br$_2$(g)	30.9	245.5	HF(g)	−272.5	173.8
HBr(g)	−36.4	198.6	**Hydrogen**		
Calcium			H$_2$(g)	0.0	130.7
Ca(s)	0.0	41.6	H$_2$O(l)	−285.8	70.0
CaCO$_3$(s, calcite)	−1206.9	92.9	H$_2$O(g)	−241.8	188.7
CaCl$_2$(s)	−795.8	108.4	H$_2$O$_2$(l)	−187.8	109.6
CaO(s)	−634.9	38.2	HCN(g)	135.1	201.7
Ca(OH)$_2$(s)	−985.2	83.4	**Iron**		
Carbon			Fe(s)	0.0	27.3
C(s, graphite)	0.0	5.7	FeCl$_3$(s)	−399.4	142.3
C(s, diamond)	1.9	2.4	Fe$_2$O$_3$(s, hematite)	−825.5	87.4
CCl$_4$(l)	−132.8	216.2	Fe$_3$O$_4$(s, magnetite)	−1120.9	145.3
CCl$_4$(g)	−95.8	309.9	**Lead**		
CH$_4$(g)	−74.9	186.3	Pb(s)	0.0	64.8
CH$_3$OH(l)	−239.1	127.2	PbCl$_2$(s)	−359.4	136.2
C$_2$H$_2$(g)	228.2	201.0	PbO(s)	−219.4	66.3
C$_2$H$_4$(g)	52.5	219.3	**Lithium**		
C$_2$H$_6$(g)	−83.8	229.1	Li(s)	0.0	29.1
C$_2$H$_5$OH(l)	−277.0	161.0	LiOH(s)	−484.9	42.8
C$_3$H$_8$(g)	−104.7	270.2	LiCl(s)	−408.6	59.3
C$_4$H$_{10}$(g, n-butane)	−125.6	310.1	**Magnesium**		
C$_4$H$_{10}$(g, isobutane)	−134.2	294.6	Mg(s)	0.0	32.7
C$_6$H$_6$(l)	49.0	173.4	MgCl$_2$(s)	−641.6	89.6
C$_6$H$_{12}$O$_6$(s)	−1273.3	212.1	**Mercury**		
C$_6$H$_{14}$(g, n-hexane)	−167.1	388.4	Hg(l)	0.0	76.0
C$_7$H$_{16}$(g, n-heptane)	−187.7	427.9	Hg$_2$Cl$_2$(s)	−264.2	192.5
C$_8$H$_{18}$(g, n-octane)	−208.6	466.7	HgO(s)	−90.8	70.3
C$_8$H$_{18}$(g, isooctane)	−224.0	423.2	**Nitrogen**		
CO(g)	−110.5	197.6	N$_2$(g)	0.0	191.6
CO$_2$(g)	−393.5	213.8	NH$_3$(g)	−45.9	192.8
CS$_2$(g)	117.1	237.8	NH$_4$Cl(s)	−314.4	94.6
HCOOH(l)	−425.1	129.0	NO(g)	90.3	210.8
Chlorine			NO$_2$(g)	33.1	240.0
Cl$_2$(g)	0.0	223.1	N$_2$O(g)	82.4	220.0
HCl(g)	−92.3	186.8			

TABLE A-13 CONTINUED Standard Thermodynamic Properties

Substance	Standard enthalpy of formation ΔH_f^0 (kJ/mol)	Standard entropy S^0 (J/mol·K)	Substance	Standard enthalpy of formation ΔH_f^0 (kJ/mol)	Standard entropy S^0 (J/mol·K)
$N_2O_4(g)$	9.1	304.4	**Sodium**		
$HNO_3(g)$	−134.3	266.4	$Na(s)$	0.0	51.5
Oxygen			$NaCl(s)$	−411.2	72.1
$O_2(g)$	0.0	205.1	$NaOH(s)$	−425.9	64.4
$O_3(g)$	142.7	238.9	**Sulfur**		
Potassium			$S(s)$	0.0	32.1
$K(s)$	0.0	64.7	$SO_2(g)$	−296.8	248.1
$KCl(s)$	−436.7	82.6	$SO_3(g)$	−395.8	256.8
$KNO_3(s)$	−494.6	133.0	$H_2S(g)$	−20.5	205.7
$KOH(s)$	−424.7	78.9	$H_2SO_4(l)$	−814.0	156.9
Silicon			**Tin**		
$Si(s)$	0.0	18.8	$Sn(s, \text{white})$	0.0	51.6
$SiCl_4(g)$	−657.0	330.9	$Sn(s, \text{gray})$	−2.1	44.1
$SiO_2(s, \text{quartz})$	−910.9	41.5	$SnCl_4(l)$	−511.3	258.6
Silver			**Zinc**		
$Ag(s)$	0.0	42.7	$Zn(s)$	0.0	41.6
$AgCl(s)$	−127.1	96.2	$ZnCl_2(s)$	−415.0	111.5
$AgNO_3(s)$	−124.4	140.9	$ZnO(s)$	−348.3	43.6

TABLE A-14 Heat of Combustion

Substance	Formula	State	ΔH_c	Substance	Formula	State	ΔH_c
hydrogen	H_2	g	−285.8	propene (propylene)	C_3H_6	g	−2058.0
graphite	C	s	−393.5	ethyne (acetylene)	C_2H_2	g	−1301.1
carbon monoxide	CO	g	−283.0	benzene	C_6H_6	l	−3267.6
methane	CH_4	g	−890.8	toluene	C_7H_8	l	−3910.3
ethane	C_2H_6	g	−1560.7	naphthalene	$C_{10}H_8$	s	−5156.3
propane	C_3H_8	g	−2219.2	anthracene	$C_{14}H_{10}$	s	−7076.5
butane	C_4H_{10}	g	−2877.6	methanol	CH_3OH	l	−726.1
pentane	C_5H_{12}	g	−3535.6	ethanol	C_2H_5OH	l	−1366.8
hexane	C_6H_{14}	l	−4163.2	ether	$(C_2H_5)_2O$	l	−2751.1
heptane	C_7H_{16}	l	−4817.0	formaldehyde	CH_2O	g	−570.7
octane	C_8H_{18}	l	−5470.5	glucose	$C_6H_{12}O_6$	s	−2803.0
ethene (ethylene)	C_2H_4	g	−1411.2	sucrose	$C_{12}H_{22}O_{11}$	s	−5640.9

ΔH_c = heat of combustion of the given substance. All values of ΔH_c are expressed as kJ/mol of substance oxidized to $H_2O(l)$ and/or $CO_2(g)$ at constant pressure and 25°C.
s = solid, l = liquid, g = gas

TABLE A-15 Comparison of Ionic and Atomic Radii

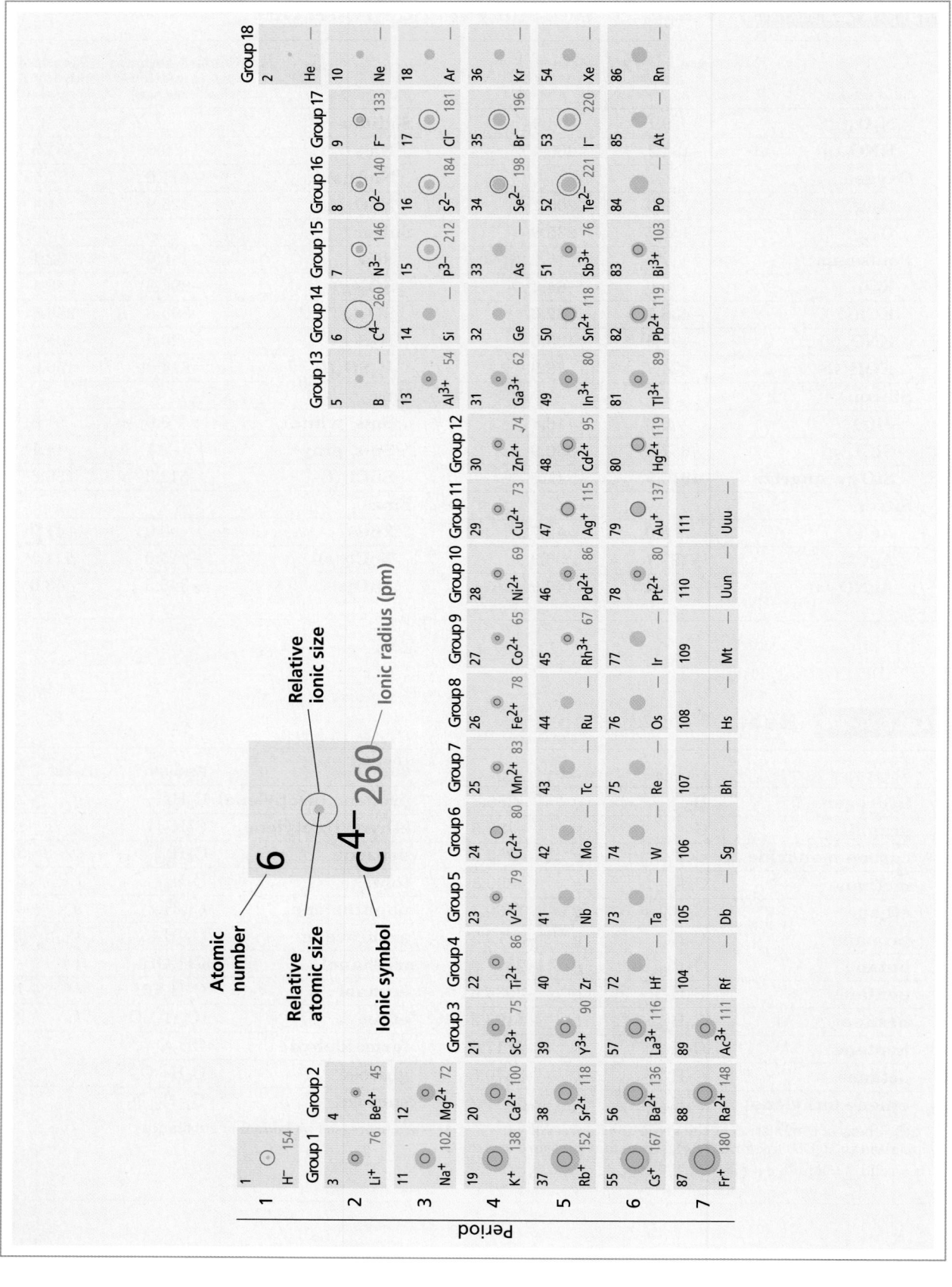

TABLE A-16 Agencies Regulating Chemicals in the United States

Agency	Purpose	Significant activities related to chemistry
Food and Drug Administration (FDA)	develops and enforces regulations regarding impurities and other hazards in foods, drugs, and cosmetics	▶ approves new drugs for public release ▶ sets labeling standards for drugs and food (except meat and poultry) ▶ sets regulations for the use of additives ▶ inspects food manufacturers for sanitary conditions ▶ validates product claims
Environmental Protection Agency	works with state and local governments to enforce laws enacted by Congress regarding control of air and water pollution, solid wastes, pesticides, radiation, and toxic substances	▶ sets limits for pollutants ▶ sets restrictions on use of hazardous substances ▶ sets tolerance levels for pesticides in foods; monitors those levels in humans, animals, and food plants
Occupational Health and Safety Administration (OSHA)	develops and enforces regulations regarding safe and healthy work environments	▶ conducts site inspections to ensure safe conditions ▶ imposes citations and penalties for noncompliance
Agency for Toxic Substances and Disease Registry	works with state and federal information regarding adverse agencies to collect and disseminate health effects of hazardous substances in storage or of accidental release of hazardous substances through fire, explosions, or transportation accidents	▶ maintains list of areas closed because of toxic contamination ▶ assists in treatment of individuals exposed to hazardous substances
Consumer Product Safety Commission	evaluates safety of consumer products	▶ enforces labeling of hazards on products ▶ bans highly hazardous products
Department of Agriculture	works to maintain and improve agricultural productivity while protecting natural resources; ensures quality of food supply	▶ analyzes foods for contaminants and pesticides ▶ provides information on nutrient values in foods

READING AND STUDY SKILLS

How To	Make power notes

Power notes help you organize the chemical concepts you are studying by distinguishing main ideas from details. Similar to outlines, power notes are linear in form and provide you with a framework of important concepts. Power notes are easier to use than outlines because their structure is simpler. Using the power notes numbering system you assign a *1* to each main idea and a *2, 3,* or *4* to each detail.

Power notes are an invaluable asset to the learning process, and they can be used frequently throughout your chemistry course. You can use power notes to organize ideas while reading your text or to restructure your class notes for studying purposes.

To learn to make power notes, practice first by using single-word concepts and a subject you are especially interested in, such as animals, sports, or movies. As you become comfortable with structuring power notes, integrate their use into your study of chemistry. For an easier transition, start with a few boldfaced vocabulary terms. Later you can strengthen your notes by expanding these single-word concepts into more-detailed phrases and sentences. Use the following general format to help you structure your power notes.

Power 1: Main idea

  Power 2: Detail or support for power 1

    Power 3: Detail or support for power 2

      Power 4: Detail or support for power 3

1 Pick a Power 1 word from the text

The text you choose does not have to come straight from your chemistry textbook. You may be making power notes from your lecture notes or from an outside source. We'll use the italicized term *electrode* found in Section 3-2 of this book.

Power 1: Electrode

2 Using the text, select some Power 2 words to support your Power 1 word

We'll use the boldfaced terms *anode* and *cathode,* which are two types of electrodes.

Power 1: Electrode

  Power 2: Anode

  Power 2: Cathode

3 Select some Power 3 words to support your Power 2 words

We'll use the terms *oxidation* and *reduction,* two terms that describe the Power 2 words.

Power 1: Electrode
 Power 2: Anode
  Power 3: Oxidation
 Power 2: Cathode
  Power 3: Reduction

4 **Continue to add powers to support and detail the main idea as necessary**

There are no restrictions on how many power numbers you can use in your notes. If you have a main idea that requires a lot of support, add more powers to help you extend and organize your ideas. Be sure that words having the same power number have a similar relationship to the power above. Power 1 terms do not have to be related to each other. You can use power notes to organize the material in an entire section or chapter of your text. Doing so will provide you with an invaluable study guide for your classroom quizzes and tests.

Power 1: Electrode
 Power 2: Anode
  Power 3: Oxidation
   Power 4: Lose electrons
 Power 2: Cathode
  Power 3: Reduction
   Power 4: Gain electrons

PRACTICE

1. Use a periodic table and the power notes structure below to organize the following terms: *alkaline-earth metals, nonmetals, calcium, sodium, halogens, metals, alkali metals, chlorine, barium,* and *iodine.*

1 _____
 2 _____
  3 _____
 2 _____
  3 _____
  3 _____
1 _____
 2 _____
  3 _____
  3 _____

You can use pattern puzzles to help you remember sequential information. Pattern puzzles are not just a tool for memorization. They also promote a greater understanding of a variety of chemical processes, from the steps in solving a mass-mass stoichiometry problem to the procedure for making a solution of specified molarity.

1   **Write down the steps of a process in your own words**

We'll use the How To feature on preparing a 0.5000 M solution from Section 13-1. On a sheet of notebook paper, write down one step per line, and do not number the steps. Also, do not copy the process straight from your text. Copying encourages strict memorization, whereas writing the steps in your own words promotes a more thorough understanding of the process. You may want to divide the longer steps into two or three shorter steps.

- Calculate the mass of solute needed to make 1 L of a 0.5000 M solution.
- Measure out the correct mass of solute in a beaker.
- Add some of the solvent to the beaker in order to dissolve the solute.
- Pour the solute/solvent mixture into a 1 L volumetric flask.
- Rinse the beaker with more solvent and pour it into the flask until the solution nears the neck of the flask.
- Stopper the flask and gently swirl the mixture.
- Fill the flask to its mark with solvent.
- Stopper the flask and invert it several times to ensure complete mixing.

2   **Cut the sheet of paper into strips with only one step per strip of paper**

Shuffle the strips of paper so that they are out of sequence.

- Rinse the beaker with more solvent and pour it into the flask until the solution nears the neck of the flask.

- Measure out the correct mass of solute in a beaker.

- Fill the flask to its mark with solvent.

- Calculate the mass of solute needed to make 1 L of a 0.5000 M solution.

- Pour the solute/solvent mixture into a 1 L volumetric flask.

- Stopper the flask and and invert it several times to ensure complete mixing.

- Stopper the flask and gently swirl the mixture.

- Add some of the solvent to the beaker in order to dissolve the solute.

3 Place the strips in their proper sequence

Confirm the order of the process by checking your text or your class notes.

- Calculate the mass of solute needed to make 1 L of a 0.5000 M solution.

- Measure out the correct mass of solute in a beaker.

- Add some of the solvent to the beaker in order to dissolve the solute.

- Pour the solute/solvent mixture into a 1 L volumetric flask.

- Rinse the beaker with more solvent and pour it into the flask until the solution nears the neck of the flask.

- Stopper the flask and gently swirl the mixture.

- Fill the flask to its mark with solvent.

- Stopper the flask and and invert it several times to ensure complete mixing.

Pattern puzzles are especially helpful when you are studying for your chemistry tests. Before tests, use your puzzles to practice sequencing and to review the steps of chemistry processes. You and a classmate can also take turns creating your own pattern puzzles of different chemical processes and putting each other's puzzles in the correct sequence. Studying with a class-mate in this manner will help make studying fun and will enable you to help each other.

PRACTICE

1. Rewrite the following sentences, which describe the process of making pattern puzzles, in the correct order.

Place the strips in their proper sequence.

Write down the steps of the process in your own words.

Shuffle the strips of paper.

Choose a multiple-step process from your text.

Using your text, confirm the order of the process.

Cut the paper into strips so that there is one step per strip.

Make KWL notes

The KWL strategy, an exciting and helpful approach to learning, is somewhat different from the other learning strategies you have seen in this appendix. This strategy, which stands for "what I **K**now–what I **W**ant to know–what I **L**earned," differs in that it prompts you to brainstorm about the subject matter before reading the assigned material. Relating your new ideas and concepts with those you have previously learned will help you to more readily understand and apply the new knowledge you obtain in this course. The section objectives throughout your text are ideal for using the KWL strategy. Just read the objectives before reading each section, and follow the instructions in the example below.

1 **Read the section objectives**

You may also want to scan headings, boldface terms, and illustrations in the section. We'll use a few of the objectives from Section 12-1.

- ▶ Describe the general properties of gases.
- ▶ Define pressure, and give the SI unit for pressure.
- ▶ Describe the causes of global warming.

2 **Divide a sheet of paper into three columns, and label the columns "What I know," "What I want to know," and "What I learned"**

What I know	What I want to know	What I learned

3 **Brainstorm about what you know about the information in the objectives, and write these ideas in the first column**

Because this chart is designed primarily to help you integrate your own knowledge with new information, it is not necessary to write complete sentences.

4 **Think about what you want to know about the information in the objectives, and write these ideas in the second column**

You'll want to know the information you will be tested over, so include information from both the section objectives and any other objectives your teacher has given you.

5 **While reading the section or afterwards, use the third column to write down the information you learned**

While reading, pay close attention to any information about the topics you wrote in the "What I want to know" column. If you do not find all of the answers you are looking for, you may need to reread the section or reference a second source. Be sure to ask your teacher if you still cannot find the information after reading the section a second time.

It is also important to review your brainstormed ideas when you have completed reading the section. Compare your ideas in the first column with the information you wrote down in the third column. If you find that some of your brainstormed ideas are incorrect, cross them out. It is extremely important to identify and correct any misconceptions you had prior to reading before you begin studying for your test.

What I know	What I want to know	What I learned
▶ gases are invisible and flow through the air easily ▶ gases don't have a definite volume	▶ general properties of gases	▶ gases are fluids ▶ gas molecules are in constant motion ▶ collisions between gas molecules are elastic ▶ low densities ▶ highly compressible ▶ made of tiny particles far apart from each other ▶ fill the entire container ▶ exert pressure equally in all directions
▶ pressure is when one thing pushes on something else ▶ you apply pressure to stop a wound from bleeding	▶ definition of pressure and SI unit of pressure	▶ pressure is the force on a surface divided by the area of that surface ▶ SI pressure unit is pascal
▶ CFCs in atmosphere from aerosol cans, refrigerators, and air conditioners ▶ hole in the ozone layer above Antarctica ▶ car pollution ▶ temperatures get warmer ▶ skin cancer gets worse	▶ causes of global warming	▶ increase in concentration of greenhouse gases (gases in the atmosphere that reflect infrared radiation back to Earth's surface) ▶ increased levels of carbon dioxide from fuels for driving cars and using electricity ▶ increase in artificial greenhouse gases (CFCs from air conditioning)

PRACTICE

1. Use column 3 from the table above to identify and correct any misconceptions in the following brainstorm list.

    a. The gasoline used in cars is in a gaseous state.

    b. Car pooling may help reduce global warming.

    c. The SI unit of pressure is the pascal.

    d. Global warming is solely caused by the accumulation of CFCs in the atmosphere.

    e. Gases are extremely dense.

Two-column notes can be used to learn and review definitions of vocabulary terms, examples of multiple-step processes, or details of specific concepts. The two-column-note strategy is simple: write the term, main idea, step-by-step process, or concept in the left-hand column, and the definition, example, or detail on the right.

One strategy for using two-column notes is to organize main ideas and their details. The main ideas from your reading are written in the left-hand column of your paper and can be written as questions, key words, or a combination of both. Details describing these main ideas are then written in the right-hand column of your paper.

1 Identify the main ideas

The main ideas for a chapter are listed in the section objectives. However, you decide which ideas to include in your notes. Here are the main ideas from the objectives in Section 4-1 as an example.

Describe characteristic properties of the alkali metals, alkaline-earth metals, halogens, noble gases, lanthanides, and actinides.

2 Divide a blank sheet of paper into two columns, and write the main ideas in the left-hand column

Remind yourself that your two-column notes are precisely that—notes. Do not copy ideas straight out of the book or waste your time writing them in complete sentences. Summarize your ideas using quick phrases that are easy for you to understand and remember. Decide how many details you need for each main idea, and write that number in parentheses under the main idea. Using the example from Section 4–1, you will list the number of characteristic properties you need to know for each group of the periodic table.

Main idea	
▶ Alkali metals (3 characteristic properties)	
▶ Alkaline-earth metals (2 characteristic properties)	
▶ Halogens (2 characteristic properties)	
▶ Noble gases (2 characteristic properties)	
▶ Lanthanides (2 characteristic properties)	
▶ Actinides (2 characteristic properties)	

3 Write the detail notes in the right-hand column

Be sure you list as many details as you designated in the main-idea column.

Main idea	Detail notes
▷ Alkali metals (3 characteristic properties)	▷ highly reactive ▷ good conductors of electricity ▷ soft
▷ Alkaline-earth metals (2 characteristic properties)	▷ reactive ▷ harder than alkali metals
▷ Halogens (2 characteristic properties)	▷ reactive ▷ nonmetallic
▷ Noble gases (2 characteristic properties)	▷ low reactivity ▷ gaseous
▷ Lanthanides (2 characteristic properties)	▷ reactive ▷ metallic
▷ Actinides (2 characteristic properties)	▷ radioactive ▷ metallic

The two-column method of review is perfect whether you use it to study for a short quiz or for a test on the material in an entire chapter. Just cover the information in the right-hand column with a sheet of paper, and after reciting what you know, uncover the notes to check your answers. Then ask yourself what else you know about that topic. Linking ideas in this way will help you to gain a more complete picture of chemistry.

PRACTICE

1. Make your own two-column notes using the periodic table. Your notes should include details such as the symbol and the atomic number of each of the following elements.

   a. neon   **c.** calcium   **e.** oxygen

   b. lead   **d.** copper   **f.** sodium

Making concept maps can help you decide what material in a chapter is important and how to efficiently learn that material. A concept map presents key ideas, meanings, and relationships for the concepts being studied. It can be thought of as a visual road map of the chapter. Learning happens efficiently when you use concept maps because you work with only the key ideas and how they fit together.

The concept map shown as **Map A** was made from vocabulary terms in Chapter 1. Vocabulary terms are generally labels for concepts, and concepts are generally nouns. Linking words are used to form propositions that connect concepts and give them meaning in context. For example, on the map below, "matter is described by physical properties" is a proposition.

Studies show that people are better able to remember materials presented visually. The concept map is better than an outline because you can see the relationships among many ideas. Because outlines are linear, there is no way of linking the ideas from various sections of the outline. Read through the map to become familiar with the information presented. Then look at the map in relation to all of the text pages in Chapter 1; which gives a better picture of the important concepts—the map or the full chapter?

Map A

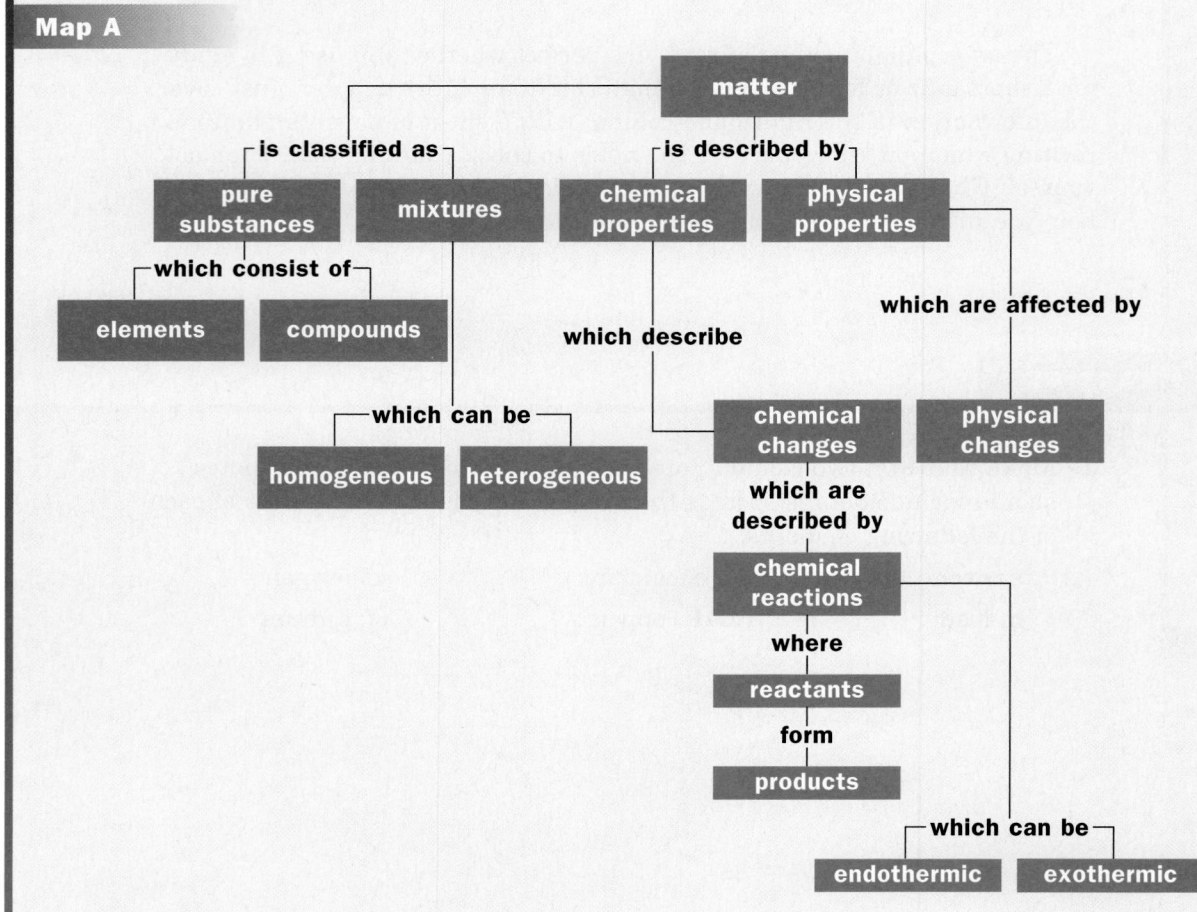

1 List all the important concepts

We'll use some of the boldface terms in Chapter 1.

allotropes
compound
element
heterogeneous mixture
homogenous mixture

inorganic compound
mixture
organic compound
pure substance

▶ From this list, group similar concepts together. For example, one way to group these concepts would be into two groups—one that is related to mixtures and one that is related to pure substances.

mixture
heterogeneous mixture
homogenous mixture

pure substance
compound
element
allotrope
inorganic compound
organic compound

2 Select a main concept for the map

We will use *matter* as the main concept for this map.

3 Build the map by placing the concepts according to their importance under the main concept, *matter*

One way of arranging the concepts is shown in **Map B.**

Map B

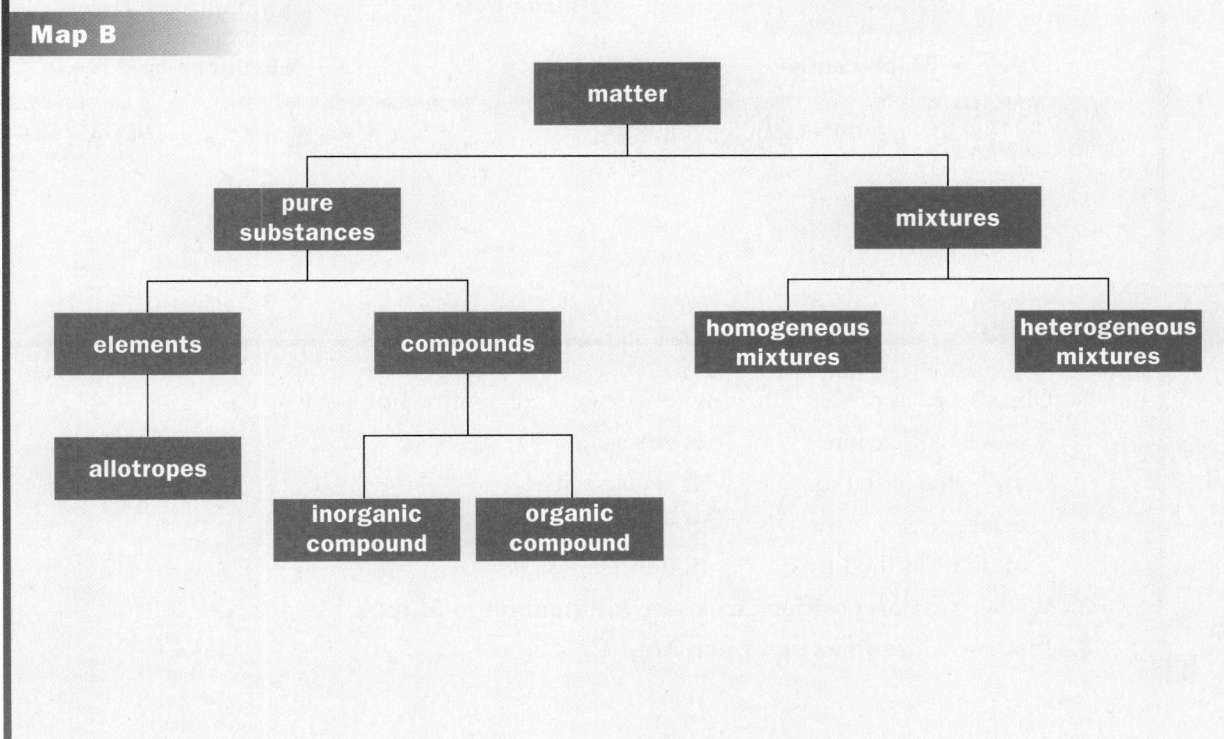

4 Add linking words to give meaning to the arrangement of concepts

When adding the links, be sure that each proposition makes sense. To distinguish concepts from links, place your concepts in circles, ovals, or rectangles, as shown in the maps. Then make cross-links. Cross-links are made of propositions and lines connecting concepts across the map. Links that apply in only one direction are indicated with an arrowhead. **Map C** is a finished map covering the main ideas found in the vocabulary listed in Step 1.

Making maps might seem difficult at first, but the process forces you to think about the meanings and relationships among the concepts. If you do not understand those relationships, you can get help early on.

Practice mapping by making concept maps about topics you know. For example, if you know a lot about a particular sport, such as basketball, or if you have a particular hobby, such as playing a musical instrument, you can use that topic to make a practice map. By perfecting your skills with information that you know very well, you will begin to feel more confident about making maps from the information in a chapter.

Remember, the time you devote to mapping will pay off when it is time to review for an exam.

Map C

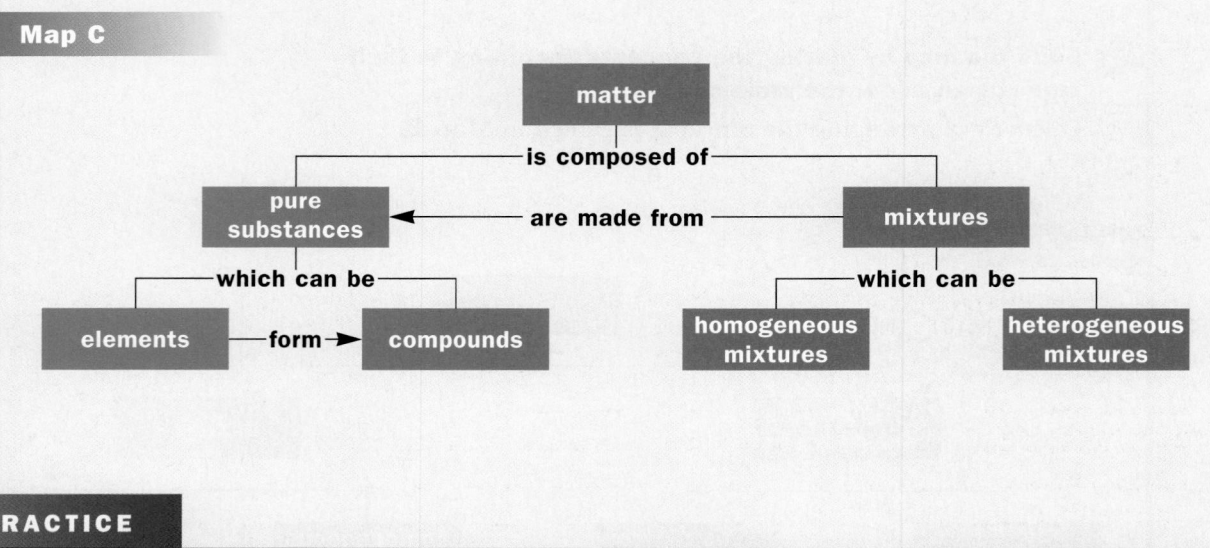

PRACTICE

1. Classify each of the following as either a concept or linking word(s).

    a. classification   **e.** reaction

    b. is classified as   **f.** reacts with

    c. forms   **g.** metal

    d. is described by   **h.** defines

2. Write three propositions from the information in **Map A.**

3. List two cross-links shown on **Map C.**

ANSWERS TO SELECTED PROBLEMS

CHAPTER 1

Practice problems, page 19

8. a. $21.59 \text{ L} \times \dfrac{1000 \text{ mL}}{1 \text{ L}} = 21\,590 \text{ mL}$, or $2.159 \times 10^4 \text{ mL}$

 b. 162 cm, or 1.62×10^2 cm

 c. 6.4×10^4 nm   d. 0.02648 kg, or 2.648×10^{-2} kg

CHAPTER 2

Practice problems, page 47

9. a. $T(\text{K}) = 373$ K   c. $T(\text{K}) = 273$ K
 b. $T(\text{K}) = 1058$ K   d. $T(\text{K}) = 236$ K

10. a. $t(^\circ\text{C}) = 0^\circ\text{C}$ c. $t(^\circ\text{C}) = -273^\circ\text{C}$
 b. $t(^\circ\text{C}) = 927^\circ\text{C}$ d. $t(^\circ\text{C}) = -173^\circ\text{C}$

11. $KE = \dfrac{(1300 \text{ kg})(50 \text{ m/s})^2}{2} = 1\,625\,000 \text{ J}$

Practice problems, page 64

8. a. 3   c. 6   e. unlimited
 b. 3   d. 4

9. a. 47.10 g   c. 3.424×10^5 g   e. 28.62 mi/h
 b. 32.86 L   d. 0.123 cm^2

10. a. $\dfrac{129 \text{ g}}{29.2 \text{ mL}} = 4.42 \text{ g/mL}$

 b. $(1.551 \text{ mm})(3.260 \text{ mm})(4.9001 \text{ mm}) = 24.78 \text{ mm}^3$

 c. 1.4×10^5 kJ/s   d. 0.367 L + 2.51 L + 1.6004 L = 4.48 L

11. 4593 kJ/min

12. a. $277\,088\,000\,000\,000$ atoms $= 2.770\,88 \times 10^{14}$ atoms
 b. $0.000\,000\,000\,000\,839\,602$ g $= 8.396\,02 \times 10^{-13}$ g
 c. $700\,004$ mm $= 7.000\,04 \times 10^5$ mm

13. $2300 \text{ metric tons} \times \dfrac{1000 \text{ kg}}{1 \text{ metric ton}} \times \dfrac{1000 \text{ g}}{1 \text{ kg}} = 2.3 \times 10^9 \text{ g}$

CHAPTERS 3, 4, 5

CHAPTER 6

Practice problems, page 201

6. a. ionic   d. polar covalent
 b. nonpolar covalent   e. nonpolar covalent
 c. ionic   f. polar covalent

7. a. Br   c. O   e. neither
 b. S   d. Cl   f. Br

8. polar covalent; electronegativity difference = 1.2

Practice problems, page 213

7. a. 2   b. 5   c. 4   d. 1
8. a. Be·   b. ·N·   c. ·Si·   d. K·

9. a. :Br—Br: e. :Br—F:

 b.
H H H—C—H H
H—C—N—C—H
  H   H

 f.
H H
:N—N:
H H

 c. O=O—O: ⟷ :O—O=O

 d. $\left[\text{H—O—H} \right]^+$ g. $\left[\text{O=N—O:} \right]^- \longleftrightarrow \left[:\text{O—N=O} \right]^-$

10. a. silicon dioxide   c. tin tetraiodide
 b. phosphorus tribromide   d. dinitrogen trioxide

11. a. PBr_5 b. B_5H_9 c. P_2O_3 d. N_2O_4

12. H—O—H

Practice problems, page 217

1. a. trigonal pyramidal   b. bent

:Cl:
H—N—H

O=N—Cl:

2. a. trigonal planar

$\left[\text{O=N—O:} \right]^- \longleftrightarrow \left[:\text{O—N—O:} \right]^- \longleftrightarrow \left[:\text{O—N=O} \right]^-$

 b. tetrahedral

$\left[\begin{array}{c} \text{H} \\ \text{H—N—H} \\ \text{H} \end{array} \right]^+$

Practice problems, page 218

5. Both are linear. Br_2 is nonpolar. HBr is polar because H and Br have an electronegativity difference of 0.8.

6. SCl_2 is bent.
 PF_3 is trigonal pyramidal.
 NCl_3 is trigonal pyramidal.
 PF_3 is the most polar. The electronegativity difference is greatest between P and F, and the bond angles of all three molecules are similar.

CHAPTER 7

Practice problems, page 243

9. a. $-\overset{\text{O}}{\overset{\|}{\text{C}}}-\text{H}$ b. $-\text{OH}; -\overset{\text{O}}{\overset{\|}{\text{C}}}-\text{OH}$

10. a. carboxylic acid   c. ketone   e. halide
 b. ether   d. amine

11. in order: alkane, alcohol, carboxylic acid, ketone, ether

Practice problems, page 252

11. a.
$$\text{Cl}-\overset{\displaystyle H}{\underset{\displaystyle H}{C}}-\overset{\displaystyle H}{\underset{\displaystyle H}{C}}-\overset{\displaystyle H}{\underset{\displaystyle H}{C}}-\overset{\displaystyle H}{\underset{\displaystyle Cl}{C}}-\overset{\displaystyle H}{\underset{\displaystyle H}{C}}-\overset{\displaystyle H}{\underset{\displaystyle H}{C}}-H$$

b.
$$\text{H}-\overset{\displaystyle H}{\underset{\displaystyle H}{C}}-\overset{\displaystyle O}{\overset{\displaystyle \|}{C}}-\overset{\displaystyle H}{\underset{\displaystyle H}{C}}-\overset{\displaystyle H}{\underset{\displaystyle H}{C}}-\overset{\displaystyle H}{\underset{\displaystyle H}{C}}-H$$

c.
$$\text{H}-\overset{\displaystyle H}{\underset{\displaystyle H}{C}}-\overset{\displaystyle Br}{\underset{\displaystyle H}{C}}-\overset{\displaystyle H}{\underset{\displaystyle H}{C}}-\overset{\displaystyle H}{\underset{\displaystyle Cl}{C}}-\overset{\displaystyle H}{\underset{\displaystyle H}{C}}-\overset{\displaystyle H}{\underset{\displaystyle H}{C}}-\overset{\displaystyle H}{\underset{\displaystyle H}{C}}-H$$

d.
$$\text{H}-\overset{\displaystyle Cl}{\underset{\displaystyle H}{C}}-\overset{\displaystyle H}{\underset{\displaystyle H}{C}}-C\equiv C-\overset{\displaystyle H}{\underset{\displaystyle H}{C}}-\overset{\displaystyle H}{\underset{\displaystyle H}{C}}-\overset{\displaystyle H}{\underset{\displaystyle H}{C}}-\overset{\displaystyle H}{\underset{\displaystyle H}{C}}-H$$

12. a. 2, 4-dimethylpentane   b. 1, 2-dibromobutane

CHAPTER 8

Practice problems, page 278

1. $3.7 \text{ mol Na} \times \dfrac{6.022 \times 10^{23} \text{ Na atoms}}{\text{mol}} = 2.2 \times 10^{24} \text{ Na atoms}$

2. 9.33×10^{25} As atoms

3. $5.66 \times 10^{26} \text{ Xe atoms} \times \dfrac{1 \text{ mol Xe}}{6.022 \times 10^{23} \text{ Xe atoms}} = 940. \text{ mol Xe}$

4. 4.796×10^{-9} mol Ag

Practice problems, page 279

1. $(27.98 \text{ amu})(0.9221) + (28.98 \text{ amu})(0.047) +$
$\qquad\qquad (29.97 \text{ amu})(0.0309) = 28.09 \text{ amu}$

2. 15.99 amu   **3.** 55.84 amu

Practice problems, page 283

9. $8.6 \text{ mol Br} \times \dfrac{79.90 \text{ g Br}}{\text{mol Br}} = 690 \text{ g Br}$ **10.** 212 g Si

11. $38 \text{ g C} \times \dfrac{1 \text{ mol C}}{12.01 \text{ g C}} = 3.2 \text{ mol C}$ **12.** 2.0 mol H

13. a. 0.0100 mol Cl   c. 0.005 mol Cu
b. 8.012 mol Na   d. 5.056 mol Fe

14. $(0.20)(10 \text{ amu}) + (0.80)(11 \text{ amu}) = 10.8 \text{ amu, 5, boron}$

15. a. $1.38 \text{ mol N} \times \dfrac{14.01 \text{ g N}}{\text{mol N}} = 19.3 \text{ g N}$
b. 6.022×10^{23} Ag atoms = 1 mol Ag = 107.9 g Ag
c. 8.24×10^{9} g S
d. 3.19×10^{-8} g O

16. a. $2 \text{ mol Fe} \times \dfrac{6.022 \times 10^{23} \text{ Fe atoms}}{\text{mol Fe}} = 1 \times 10^{24} \text{ atoms}$

b. $40.1 \text{ g Ca} \times \dfrac{1 \text{ mol Ca}}{40.08 \text{ g Ca}} \times \dfrac{6.022 \times 10^{23} \text{ atoms Ca}}{\text{mol Ca}} =$
$\qquad\qquad\qquad\qquad\qquad\qquad\qquad 6.02 \times 10^{23} \text{ atoms}$
c. 2.7×10^{24} atoms   d. 4.825×10^{24} atoms

17. a. $\dfrac{1.01 \text{ g H}}{6.022 \times 10^{23} \text{ H atoms}} = 1.68 \times 10^{-24} \text{ g/H atoms}$
b. 2.523×10^{-22} g/Eu atom   c. 3.239×10^{-22} g/Pt atom

Practice problems, page 288

1. a. 122.55 g/mol   e. 60.06 g/mol   i. 131.07 g/mol
b. 234.06 g/mol   f. 74.14 g/mol   j. 92.15 g/mol
c. 158.04 g/mol   g. 206.31 g/mol   k. 300.06 g/mol
d. 72.17 g/mol   h. 58.32 g/mol

2. a. $NaHCO_3$, 84.01 g/mol   e. $Fe(OH)_3$, 106.88 g/mol
b. $K_2Cr_2O_7$, 294.20 g/mol   f. $SnCl_2$, 189.61 g/mol
c. $Mg(ClO_4)_2$, 223.20 g/mol   g. $HClO_4$, 100.46 g/mol
d. $Al_2(SO_4)_3$, 342.17 g/mol   h. $NiCl_2 \cdot 6H_2O$, 237.71 g/mol

Practice problems, page 292

1. $70.0 \text{ g Mn} \times \dfrac{1 \text{ mol Mn}}{54.94 \text{ g Mn}} = 1.27 \text{ mol Mn}$

$30.0 \text{ g O} \times \dfrac{1 \text{ mol Cl}}{16.00 \text{ g O}} = 1.875 \text{ mol O}$

$\dfrac{1.27 \text{ mol Mn}}{1.27} = 1 \times 2 = 2$

$\dfrac{1.875 \text{ mol O}}{1.27} = 1.56 \times 2 \approx 3, \ Mn_2O_3$

2. Cl_2O_7

Practice problems, page 294

1. $\dfrac{78 \text{ g/mol}}{13.02 \text{ g/mol}} = 6, \ C_6H_6$ **2.** $\dfrac{214 \text{ g/mol}}{70.11 \text{ g/mol}} = 3.1, \ C_9H_{18}N_6$

Practice problems, page 295

1. $\dfrac{72.06 \text{ g C}}{180.18 \text{ g C}_6\text{H}_{12}\text{O}_6} \times 100 = 39.99\% \text{ C}$

$\dfrac{12.12 \text{ g H}}{180.18 \text{ g C}_6\text{H}_{12}\text{O}_6} \times 100 = 6.73\% \text{ H}$

$\dfrac{96.00 \text{ g O}}{180.18 \text{ g C}_6\text{H}_{12}\text{O}_6} \times 100 = 53.28\% \text{ O}$

2. 42.10% C, 6.49% H, 51.41% O

Practice problems, page 297

7. a. 158.18 g/mol   c. 183.2 g/mol   e. 86.20 g/mol
b. 357.49 g/mol   d. 180.17 g/mol

8. a. $\dfrac{87.42 \text{ g N}}{14.01 \text{ g/mol}} = 6.24 \text{ mol N}$ $\dfrac{12.58 \text{ g H}}{1.01 \text{ g/mol}} = 12.46 \text{ mol H}$
$\dfrac{6.24 \text{ mol N}}{6.24} = 1$ $\dfrac{12.46 \text{ mol H}}{6.24} = 2$
NH_2
b. BCl_2 c. CO_2F_2 d. $ZnMn_2O_8$ e. $C_5H_{14}N_2$

9. a. $\dfrac{116.1 \text{ g/mol}}{29.02 \text{ g/mol}} = 4, \ C_4H_4O_4$ b. B_2Cl_4 c. $N_3P_3Cl_6$

10. a. 35.41% Sr, 64.59% Br
b. 29.44% Ca, 23.55% S, 47.01% O
c. 31.83% Mg, 31.46% C, 36.70% N
d. 63.70% Pb, 14.77% C, 1.86% H, 19.67% O

11. a. SrS, 119.69 g/mol   c. $Zn(CH_3COO)_2$, 183.49 g/mol
b. NH_4F, 37.05 g/mol   d. $Hg(BrO_3)_2$, 456.39 g/mol

12. a. 55.39% Pb, 18.95% Cl, 25.66% O
    b. 25.94% N, 74.06% O
    c. 27.93% Fe, 24.05% S, 48.00% O
    d. 25.45% Cu, 12.84% S, 57.66% O, 4.04% H
    e. 68.27% C, 5.74% H, 25.98% O

13. $\dfrac{33.5 \text{ g H}_2\text{O}}{18.02 \text{ g/mol}} = 1.86 \text{ mol H}_2\text{O}$

$1.86 \text{ mol H}_2\text{O} \times \dfrac{1 \text{ mol CaCl}_2}{6 \text{ mol H}_2\text{O}} = 0.310 \text{ mol CaCl}_2$

$0.310 \text{ mol CaCl}_2 \times \dfrac{110.98 \text{ g CaCl}_2}{1 \text{ mol}} = 34.4 \text{ g CaCl}_2$

CHAPTER 9

Practice problems, page 316

1. a. $2\text{ZnS} + 3\text{O}_2 \longrightarrow 2\text{ZnO} + 2\text{SO}_2$ c. $\text{CS}_2 + 3\text{O}_2 \longrightarrow \text{CO}_2 + 2\text{SO}_2$
   b. $2\text{C}_2\text{H}_2 + 5\text{O}_2 \longrightarrow 4\text{CO}_2 + 2\text{H}_2\text{O}$ d. $\text{N}_2\text{O}_5 + \text{NO} \longrightarrow 3\text{NO}_2$

Practice problems, page 317

7. a. hydrogen + chlorine $\longrightarrow$ hydrogen chloride;
      $\text{H}_2 + \text{Cl}_2 \longrightarrow \text{HCl}$
   b. aluminum + iron(III) oxide $\longrightarrow$ aluminum oxide + iron;
      $\text{Al} + \text{Fe}_2\text{O}_3 \longrightarrow \text{Al}_2\text{O}_3 + \text{Fe}$
   c. potassium chlorate $\longrightarrow$ potassium chloride + oxygen;
      $\text{KClO}_3 \longrightarrow \text{KCl} + \text{O}_2$
   d. calcium hydroxide + hydrochloric acid $\longrightarrow$
      calcium chloride + water;
      $\text{Ca(OH)}_2 + \text{HCl} \longrightarrow \text{CaCl}_2 + \text{H}_2\text{O}$

8. a. $\text{H}_2 + \text{Cl}_2 \longrightarrow 2\text{HCl}$ c. $2\text{KClO}_3 \longrightarrow 2\text{KCl} + 3\text{O}_2$
   b. $2\text{Al} + \text{Fe}_2\text{O}_3 \longrightarrow \text{Al}_2\text{O}_3 + 2\text{Fe}$
   d. $\text{Ca(OH)}_2 + 2\text{HCl} \longrightarrow \text{CaCl}_2 + 2\text{H}_2\text{O}$

9. a. $3\text{CaSi}_2 + 2\text{SbCl}_3 \longrightarrow 6\text{Si} + 2\text{Sb} + 3\text{CaCl}_2$
   b. $2\text{Al} + 6\text{CH}_3\text{OH} \longrightarrow 2(\text{CH}_3\text{O})_3\text{Al} + 3\text{H}_2$
   c. $\text{P}_4 + 5\text{O}_2 \longrightarrow 2\text{P}_2\text{O}_5$ d. $4\text{Fe} + 3\text{O}_2 \longrightarrow 2\text{Fe}_2\text{O}_3$

10. a. $2\text{Cu} + \text{O}_2 \longrightarrow 2\text{CuO}$ b. $2\text{Fe} + \text{O}_2 \longrightarrow 2\text{FeO}$

Practice problems, page 324

8. a. 16 mol of KCl, 24 mol of O_2 b. 6 mol of CaO, 6 mol of CO_2
   c. 7 mol of N_2O, 14 mol of H_2O
   d. 6 mol of NH_3, assuming sufficient N_2 is present

9. a. $16.0 \text{ mol KClO}_3 \times \dfrac{78 \text{ kJ}}{2 \text{ mol KClO}_3} = +624 \text{ kJ}$; endothermic
   b. +1070 kJ; endothermic
   c. –252 kJ; exothermic   d. –276 kJ; exothermic

Practice problems, page 328

1. copper, iron, zinc, aluminum, barium

2. a. $\text{Cu}(s) + \text{Zn}^{2+}(aq)$ c. no reaction
   b. $\text{Pb}(s) + \text{Mg}^{2+}(aq)$ d. $\text{Ag}(s) + \text{Cu}^{2+}(aq)$

Practice problems, page 330

8. a. $\text{H}_2\text{O}(l) + \text{SO}_3(g) \longrightarrow \text{H}_2\text{SO}_4(aq)$
   b. $2\text{C}_4\text{H}_{10}(g) + 13\text{O}_2(g) \longrightarrow 8\text{CO}_2(g) + 10\text{H}_2\text{O}(l)$
   c. $2\text{KClO}_3(s) \longrightarrow 2\text{KCl}(g) + 3\text{O}_2(g)$
   d. $\text{Zn}(s) + \text{CuSO}_4(aq) \longrightarrow \text{ZnSO}_4(aq) + \text{Cu}(s)$
   e. $\text{Ag}^+(aq) + \text{Cl}^-(aq) \longrightarrow \text{AgCl}(s)$

9. a. no reaction
   b. $\text{Mg}(s) + \text{Cu}^{2+}(aq) \longrightarrow \text{Mg}^{2+}(aq) + \text{Cu}(s)$
   c. $2\text{Ba}(s) + \text{O}_2(g) \longrightarrow 2\text{BaO}(s)$
   d. $\text{H}^+(aq) + \text{OH}^-(aq) \longrightarrow \text{H}_2\text{O}(l)$

CHAPTER 10

Practice problems, page 351

1. $55.0 \text{ g HF} \times \dfrac{1 \text{ mol HF}}{20.01 \text{ g HF}} \times \dfrac{1 \text{ mol SnF}_2}{2 \text{ mol HF}} \times \dfrac{156.7 \text{ g SnF}_2}{1 \text{ mol SnF}_2} =$

   215 g SnF_2

2. $57.6 \text{ g C}_6\text{H}_5\text{Cl}$

3. $38.00 \text{ kg C}_{20}\text{H}_{12}\text{O}_5$

Practice problems, page 353

1. $0.0103 \text{ mol O}_2 \times \dfrac{31.999 \text{ g O}_2}{1 \text{ mol O}_2} = 0.3296 \text{ g O}_2$

   $0.3296 \text{ g O}_2 \times \dfrac{1 \text{ mol O}_2}{31.999 \text{ g O}_2} \times \dfrac{6 \text{ mol CO}_2}{6 \text{ mol O}_2} \times \dfrac{44.01 \text{ g CO}_2}{1 \text{ mol CO}_2} =$

   0.453 g CO_2

2. $0.186 \text{ g H}_2\text{O}$

3. $6 \text{ mol CH}_3\text{COOH} \times \dfrac{60.05 \text{ g CH}_3\text{COOH}}{1 \text{ mol CH}_3\text{COOH}} = 360.3 \text{ g CH}_3\text{COOH}$

   $360.3 \text{ g CH}_3\text{COOH} \times \dfrac{1 \text{ mol CH}_3\text{COOH}}{60.05 \text{ g CH}_3\text{COOH}} \times$

   $\dfrac{6 \text{ mol CH}_3\text{COOC}_5\text{H}_{11}}{6 \text{ mol CH}_3\text{COOH}} \times \dfrac{130.2 \text{ g CH}_3\text{COOC}_5\text{H}_{11}}{1 \text{ mol CH}_3\text{COOC}_5\text{H}_{11}} =$

   $781 \text{ g CH}_3\text{COOC}_5\text{H}_{11}$

Practice problems, page 355

1. $1.5 \text{ L H}_2\text{O} \times \dfrac{1000 \text{ mL}}{1 \text{ L}} \times \dfrac{1.00 \text{ g H}_2\text{O}}{1 \text{ mL H}_2\text{O}} \times \dfrac{1 \text{ mol H}_2\text{O}}{18.015 \text{ g H}_2\text{O}} \times$

   $\dfrac{2 \text{ mol LiOH}}{1 \text{ mol H}_2\text{O}} \times \dfrac{23.95 \text{ g LiOH}}{1 \text{ mol LiOH}} = 4.0 \times 10^3 \text{ g LiOH}$

2. $15 \text{ g NaHCO}_3 \times \dfrac{1 \text{ mol NaHCO}_3}{84.01 \text{ g NaHCO}_3} \times \dfrac{1 \text{ mol CO}_2}{1 \text{ mol NaHCO}_3} \times$

   $\dfrac{44.01 \text{ g CO}_2}{1 \text{ mol CO}_2} \times \dfrac{1 \text{ L CO}_2}{1.10 \text{ g CO}_2} = 7.14 \text{ L CO}_2$

Practice problems, page 360

1. No, there is not enough Al(OH)_3.

   $34.0 \text{ g HCl} \times \dfrac{1 \text{ mol HCl}}{36.46 \text{ g HCl}} \times \dfrac{1 \text{ mol Al(OH)}_3}{1 \text{ mol HCl}} \times$

   $\dfrac{78.004 \text{ g Al(OH)}_3}{1 \text{ mol Al(OH)}_3} = 78.0 \text{ g Al(OH)}_3$

2. N_2 is the limiting reactant.

   $92.7 \text{ kg N}_2 \times \dfrac{1000 \text{ g}}{1 \text{ kg}} \times \dfrac{1 \text{ mol N}_2}{28.01 \text{ g N}_2} = 3.31 \times 10^3 \text{ mol N}_2$

   $265.8 \text{ kg H}_2 \times \dfrac{1000 \text{ g}}{1 \text{ kg}} \times \dfrac{1 \text{ mol H}_2}{2.0159 \text{ g H}_2} = 1.319 \times 10^5 \text{ mol H}_2$

   $131\,900 \text{ mol H}_2 \times \dfrac{1 \text{ mol N}_2}{3 \text{ mol H}_2} = 4.397 \times 10^4 \text{ mol N}_2 \text{ needed}$

1. $550 \text{ g C}_7\text{H}_8 \times \dfrac{1 \text{ mol C}_7\text{H}_8}{92.141 \text{ g C}_7\text{H}_8} \times \dfrac{1 \text{ mol C}_7\text{H}_7\text{NO}_2}{1 \text{ mol C}_7\text{H}_8} \times$

$\dfrac{137.14 \text{ g C}_7\text{H}_7\text{NO}_2}{1 \text{ mol C}_7\text{H}_7\text{NO}_2} = 818.6 \text{ g C}_7\text{H}_7\text{NO}_2$

$\dfrac{305 \text{ g actual}}{819 \text{ g theoretical}} \times 100 = 37.2\% \text{ yield}$

2. 51.7% yield

Practice problems, page 366

4. a. TiCl_4 is the limiting reactant.
O_2 is the excess reactant.

$4.5 \text{ mol O}_2 \times \dfrac{1 \text{ mol TiCl}_4}{1 \text{ mol O}_2} = 4.5 \text{ mol TiCl}_4$

b. 992 mol O_2 will remain.

$3.5 \text{ mol TiCl}_4 \times \dfrac{189.7 \text{ g TiCl}_4}{1 \text{ mol TiCl}_4} = 663.95 \text{ g TiCl}_4$

$663.95 \text{ g TiCl}_4 \times \dfrac{1 \text{ mol TiCl}_4}{189.69 \text{ g TiCl}_4} \times \dfrac{1 \text{ mol O}_2}{1 \text{ mol TiCl}_4} \times$

$\dfrac{32.100 \text{ g O}_2}{1 \text{ mol O}_2} = 112.36 \text{ g O}_2$

$4.5 \text{ mol O}_2 \times \dfrac{31.999 \text{ g O}_2}{1 \text{ mol O}_2} = 144.10 \text{ g O}_2$

$144.10 \text{ g O}_2 - 112.35 \text{ g O}_2 = 31.75 \text{ g O}_2$

$31.75 \text{ g O}_2 \times \dfrac{1 \text{ mol O}_2}{31.999 \text{ g O}_2} = 0.992 \text{ mol O}_2$

c. $3.5 \text{ mol TiCl}_4 \times \dfrac{1 \text{ mol O}_2}{1 \text{ mol TiCl}_4} = 3.5 \text{ mol O}_2$

$3.5 \text{ mol TiCl}_4 \times \dfrac{2 \text{ mol Cl}_2}{1 \text{ mol TiCl}_4} = 7 \text{ mol Cl}_2$

5. a. $\text{P}_4\text{O}_{10}(g) + 6\text{H}_2\text{O}(l) \longrightarrow 4\text{H}_3\text{PO}_4(aq)$

b. $100 \text{ g P}_4\text{O}_{10} \times \dfrac{1 \text{ mol P}_4\text{O}_{10}}{283.9 \text{ g P}_4\text{O}_{10}} \times \dfrac{4 \text{ mol H}_3\text{PO}_4}{1 \text{ mol P}_4\text{O}_{10}} \times$

$\dfrac{97.995 \text{ g H}_3\text{PO}_4}{1 \text{ mol H}_3\text{PO}_4} = 138.1 \text{ g H}_3\text{PO}_4 \text{ theoretical yield}$

c. $\dfrac{126.2 \text{ g H}_3\text{PO}_4 \text{ actual}}{138.1 \text{ g H}_3\text{PO}_4 \text{ theoretical}} \times 100 = 91.4\% \text{ yield}$

6. 93.8%

7. $\text{Al}(s) + 3\text{CuSO}_4(aq) \longrightarrow 3\text{Cu}(s) + \text{Al(SO}_4)_3(aq)$

$1.85 \text{ g Al} \times \dfrac{1 \text{ mol Al}}{26.981 \text{ g Al}} \times \dfrac{3 \text{ mol Cu}}{1 \text{ mol Al}} \times \dfrac{65.546 \text{ g Cu}}{1 \text{ mol Cu}} = 13.5 \text{ g Cu}$

$13.5 \text{ g Cu} \times \dfrac{56.6\%}{100\%} = 7.64 \text{ g Cu}$

8. $58.8 \text{ g C}_9\text{H}_8\text{O}$

9. $10.1 \text{ g Mg} \times \dfrac{1 \text{ mol Mg}}{24.31 \text{ g Mg}} \times \dfrac{2 \text{ mol H}_2\text{O}}{1 \text{ mol Mg}} \times \dfrac{18.02 \text{ g H}_2\text{O}}{1 \text{ mol H}_2\text{O}} \times$

$\dfrac{1 \text{ mL H}_2\text{O}}{1.0 \text{ g H}_2\text{O}} = 15.0 \text{ mL H}_2\text{O}$

10. Mg is the limiting reactant.

$10.1 \text{ g Mg} \times \dfrac{1 \text{ mol Mg}}{24.31 \text{ g Mg}} = 0.415 \text{ mol Mg}$

$15.0 \text{ g H}_2\text{O} \times \dfrac{1 \text{ mol H}_2\text{O}}{18.02 \text{ g H}_2\text{O}} = 0.832 \text{ mol H}_2\text{O}$

$0.832 \text{ mol H}_2\text{O} \times \dfrac{1 \text{ mol Mg}}{2 \text{ mol H}_2\text{O}} = 0.416 \text{ mol Mg}$

Practice problems, page 369

1. $65.1 \text{ L N} \times \dfrac{0.916 \text{ g N}_2}{1 \text{ L N}_2} \times \dfrac{1 \text{ mol N}_2}{28.02 \text{ g N}_2} \times \dfrac{2 \text{ mol Na}}{3 \text{ mol N}_2} \times$

$\dfrac{22.9898 \text{ g Na}}{1 \text{ mol Na}} = 32.6 \text{ g Na}$

$32.6 \text{ g Na} \times \dfrac{1 \text{ mol Na}}{22.9898 \text{ g Na}} \times \dfrac{1 \text{ mol Fe}_2\text{O}_3}{6 \text{ mol Na}} \times$

$\dfrac{159.89 \text{ g Fe}_2\text{O}_3}{1 \text{ mol Fe}_2\text{O}_3} = 37.8 \text{ g Fe}_2\text{O}_3$

2. $32.6 \text{ g Na} \times \dfrac{1 \text{ mol Na}}{22.9898 \text{ g Na}} \times \dfrac{3 \text{ mol Na}_2\text{O}}{6 \text{ mol Na}} \times$

$\dfrac{61.98 \text{ g Na}_2\text{O}}{1 \text{ mol Na}_2\text{O}} = 43.9 \text{ g Na}_2\text{O}$

$43.9 \text{ g Na}_2\text{O} \times \dfrac{1 \text{ mol Na}_2\text{O}}{61.98 \text{ g Na}_2\text{O}} \times \dfrac{2 \text{ mol NaHCO}_3}{1 \text{ mol Na}_2\text{O}} \times$

$\dfrac{84.007 \text{ g NaHCO}_3}{1 \text{ mol NaHCO}_3} = 119 \text{ g NaHCO}_3$

3. $119 \text{ g NaHCO}_3 \times \dfrac{1 \text{ mL NaHCO}_3}{2.20 \text{ g NaHCO}_3} = 54.1 \text{ mL NaHCO}_3$

4. $325 \text{ g CH}_3\text{COONa}$

Practice problems, page 371

1. a. $3.00 \text{ L C}_8\text{H}_{18} \times \dfrac{1000 \text{ mL}}{1 \text{ L}} \times \dfrac{0.692 \text{ g C}_8\text{H}_{18}}{1 \text{ mL C}_8\text{H}_{18}} = 2076 \text{ g C}_8\text{H}_{18}$

$2076 \text{ g C}_8\text{H}_{18} \times \dfrac{1 \text{ mol C}_8\text{H}_{18}}{114 \text{ g C}_8\text{H}_{18}} = 18.21 \text{ mol C}_8\text{H}_{18}$

$35\,000 \text{ L air} \times \dfrac{21 \text{ L O}_2}{100 \text{ L air}} \times \dfrac{1.33 \text{ g O}_2}{1 \text{ L O}_2} = 9775.5 \text{ g O}_2$

$9775.5 \text{ g O}_2 \times \dfrac{1 \text{ mol O}_2}{31.999 \text{ g O}_2} = 305 \text{ mol O}_2$

$305 \text{ mol O}_2 \times \dfrac{2 \text{ mol C}_8\text{H}_{18}}{25 \text{ mol O}_2} \times \dfrac{114 \text{ g C}_8\text{H}_{18}}{1 \text{ mol C}_8\text{H}_{18}} \times$

$\dfrac{1 \text{ mL C}_8\text{H}_{18}}{0.692 \text{ g C}_8\text{H}_{18}} \times \dfrac{1 \text{ L}}{1000 \text{ mL}} = 3.95 \text{ L C}_8\text{H}_{18}$

$3.95 \text{ L C}_8\text{H}_{18} - 3.00 \text{ L C}_8\text{H}_{18} = 9.50 \times 10^{-1} \text{ L C}_8\text{H}_{18}$

b. $1.5 \times 10^4 \text{ L air}$

c. 98.4 L air

2. $984 \text{ g H}_2\text{O}$

Practice problems, page 374

4. $22.4 \text{ g NaN}_3 \times \dfrac{1 \text{ mol NaN}_3}{65.01 \text{ g NaN}_3} \times \dfrac{3 \text{ mol N}_2}{2 \text{ mol NaN}_3} \times \dfrac{28.01 \text{ g N}_2}{1 \text{ mol N}_2} \times$

$\dfrac{1 \text{ L N}_2}{0.916 \text{ g N}_2} = 15.8 \text{ L N}_2$

5. $18.3 \text{ g O} \times \dfrac{1 \text{ mol O}}{15.999 \text{ g O}} \times \dfrac{1 \text{ mol O}_2}{1 \text{ mol O}} \times \dfrac{31.999 \text{ g O}_2}{1 \text{ mol O}_2} = 36.6 \text{ g O}_2$

6. $25 \text{ mol NH}_3 \times \dfrac{4 \text{ mol NO}}{4 \text{ mol NH}_3} \times \dfrac{30.01 \text{ g NO}}{1 \text{ mol NO}} = 750 \text{ g NO}$

$750 \text{ g NO} \times \dfrac{1 \text{ L NO}}{1.340 \text{ g NO}} = 560 \text{ L NO}$

7. $74.0 \text{ g C}_8\text{H}_{18} \times \dfrac{1 \text{ mol C}_8\text{H}_{18}}{114 \text{ g C}_8\text{H}_{18}} \times \dfrac{16 \text{ mol CO}}{2 \text{ mol C}_8\text{H}_{18}} \times$

$\dfrac{28.01 \text{ g CO}}{1 \text{ mol CO}} = 145 \text{ g CO}$

CHAPTER 11

Practice problems, page 388

1. $90.0 \text{ g H}_2\text{O} \times \dfrac{1 \text{ mol H}_2\text{O}}{18.02 \text{ g H}_2\text{O}} \times \dfrac{76 \text{ J}}{\text{mol} \cdot \text{K}} \times 10 \text{ K} = 3800 \text{ J}$

2. 530 J

Practice problems, page 391

12. The value will be approximately 4×25 J/K•mol, or 100 J/K•mol.

13. $142 \text{ kJ/g} \times \dfrac{2.20 \text{ g H}_2}{1 \text{ mol H}_2} = 286.84 \text{ kJ}$

14. $260 \text{ g Al} \times \dfrac{1 \text{ mol Al}}{26.98 \text{ g Al}} \times \dfrac{24.2 \text{ J}}{\text{mol} \cdot \text{K}} \times 125 \text{ K} = 29\,000 \text{ J, or } 29 \text{ kJ}$

15. 15 000 J, or 15 kJ

Practice problems, page 394

1. $100. \text{ g H}_2\text{O} \times \dfrac{1 \text{ mol}}{18.02 \text{ g H}_2\text{O}} \times \dfrac{75.3 \text{ J}}{\text{K} \cdot \text{mol}} \times 34.5 \text{ K} = 14.4 \text{ kJ}$

2. $1 \text{ mol Al} \times \dfrac{24.2 \text{ J}}{\text{K} \cdot \text{mol}} \times -105.9 \text{ K} = -2.56 \text{ kJ}$

3. $\dfrac{618 \text{ J}}{\text{mol}} \times \dfrac{1 \text{ K} \cdot \text{mol}}{420 \text{ J}} = 1.47 \text{ K}$

Practice problems, page 395

8. $\Delta T = -9.6 \,^\circ\text{C} = -9.6 \text{ K}$

9. $80.2 \text{ g H}_2\text{O} \times \dfrac{1 \text{ mol H}_2\text{O}}{18.02 \text{ g H}_2\text{O}} \times \dfrac{37.4 \text{ J}}{\text{K} \cdot \text{mol}} \times 3.2 \text{ K} = 0.533 \text{ kJ}$

10. −2.17 kJ   **11.** 0.727 kJ

12. $\dfrac{-186.9 \text{ J}}{\text{mol}} \times \dfrac{1 \text{ K} \cdot \text{mol}}{172 \text{ J}} = -1.09\,^\circ\text{C}$

13. $1 \text{ mol H}_2 \times \dfrac{28.8 \text{ J}}{\text{K} \cdot \text{mol}} \times 25 \text{ K} = 0.72 \text{ kJ}$

Practice problem, page 401

17. $\dfrac{29.5 \text{ kJ}}{\text{mol}} \times \dfrac{1 \text{ mol}}{88.6 \text{ J} \cdot \text{K}} \times \dfrac{1000 \text{ J}}{1 \text{ kJ}} = 333 \text{ K}$

Practice problem, page 405

1. $[(-241.8 \text{ kJ} \cdot \text{mol}) + (-1206.9 \text{ kJ} \cdot \text{mol})] - [(-986.1 \text{ kJ} \cdot \text{mol}) +$
$(-393.5 \text{ kJ} \cdot \text{mol})] = -69.1 \text{ kJ/mol}$

Practice problems, page 406

1. 146.1 J/K   **2.** 159.1 J/K

3. ΔS for the conversion of 1 mol of C_{diamond} to 1 mol of C_{graphite} is 3.3 J/K. You cannot determine that the reaction is spontaneous from entropy data alone. You must also know the enthalpy change and calculate the Gibbs energy change to determine spontaneity. In this case, ΔG is negative, and the reaction is spontaneous.

Practice problems, page 408

1. $\Delta G = -58.0$ kJ The reaction is spontaneous.

2. $\Delta G = -39.0$ kJ at 900°C

3. $T = 911 \text{ K} = 638\,^\circ\text{C}$

Practice problems, page 413

3. Reaction 1: $\Delta G = 115$ kJ, not spontaneous
Reaction 2: $\Delta G = -244$ kJ, spontaneous
Reaction 3: $\Delta G = -623$ kJ, spontaneous

4. The reaction using H_2O is not spontaneous at 25°C because $\Delta G = 474$ kJ. The reaction using HCl is likewise not spontaneous at 25°C because $\Delta G = 134$ kJ. It would be spontaneous at temperatures above 830°C.

CHAPTER 12

Practice problems, page 436

1. $P_2 = \dfrac{(22.5 \text{ kPa})(155 \text{ cm}^3)}{90.0 \text{ cm}^3} = 38.8 \text{ kPa}$

2. $V_2 = \dfrac{(0.500 \text{ atm})(300.0 \text{ mL})}{0.750 \text{ atm}} = 200. \text{ mL}$

3. 10. L   **4.** 142 mL

Practice problems, page 440

1. $V_2 = \dfrac{(80.0 \text{ K})(2.5 \text{ L})}{300.0 \text{ K}} = 0.67 \text{ L}$

2. $P_2 = \dfrac{(325 \text{ K})(3.00 \text{ atm})}{298 \text{ K}} = 3.27 \text{ atm}$

Practice problems, page 444

5. $V_2 = \dfrac{(101\,325 \text{ Pa})(30.0 \text{ m}^3)}{2.87 \times 10^2 \text{ Pa}} = 1.06 \times 10^4 \text{ m}^3$

6. $v_{\text{SO}_2} = 0.380 \text{ km/s} \sqrt{\dfrac{70.90 \text{ g/mol}}{64.07 \text{ g/mol}}} = 0.400 \text{ km/s}$

7. 471 m/s   **8.** 397 m/s

9. $\dfrac{v_{\text{H}_2\text{O}}}{v_{\text{CO}_2}} = \sqrt{\dfrac{44.01 \text{ g/mol}}{18.02 \text{ g/mol}}} = 1.56$

Molecules of water vapor effuse at 1.56 times the rate that carbon dioxide molecules do.

10. $M_{\text{H}_2\text{S}} = (2 \times 1.01 \text{ g/mol}) + 32.07 \text{ g/mol} = 34.09 \text{ g/mol}$
$M_{\text{C}_7\text{H}_6\text{O}} = (7 \times 12.01 \text{ g/mol}) + (6 \times 1.01 \text{ g/mol}) + 16.00 \text{ g/mol} = 106.13 \text{ g/mol}$
$M_{\text{C}_8\text{H}_{10}\text{O}_3} = (8 \times 12.01 \text{ g/mol}) + (10 \times 1.01 \text{ g/mol}) + (3 \times 16.00 \text{ g/mol}) = 154.18 \text{ g/mol}$
H_2S is the lightest molecule, so you would smell it first.

Practice problems, page 447

1. $500. \text{ g CO}_2 \times \dfrac{1 \text{ mol CO}_2}{44.01 \text{ g CO}_2} = 11.36 \text{ mol CO}_2$

$V = \dfrac{(11.36 \text{ mol CO}_2)\left(8.314\dfrac{\text{L} \cdot \text{kPa}}{\text{mol} \cdot \text{K}}\right)(298 \text{ K})}{975 \text{ kPa}} = 28.9 \text{ L CO}_2$

2. 22.4 L CO_2

3. $n = \dfrac{(110 \text{ kPa})(4.0 \text{ L})}{\left(8.314\dfrac{\text{L} \cdot \text{kPa}}{\text{mol} \cdot \text{K}}\right)(310 \text{ K})} = 0.17 \text{ mol O}_2$

4. 101 g Cl_2

Practice problems, page 449

1. $V_2 = \dfrac{(400.0 \text{ K})(2.0 \text{ m}^3)(100.0 \text{ kPa})}{(100.0 \text{ K})(200.0 \text{ kPa})} = 4.0 \text{ m}^3$

2. $6.06 \times 10^3 \text{ kPa}$ 3. 164.7 K 4. 81 m^3

Practice problems, page 451

5. $35.0 \text{ g CO}_2 \times \dfrac{1 \text{ mol CO}_2}{44.01 \text{ g CO}_2} = 0.7953 \text{ mol CO}_2$

$P = \dfrac{(0.7953 \text{ mol CO}_2)\left(8.314\dfrac{\text{L} \cdot \text{kPa}}{\text{mol} \cdot \text{K}}\right)(400 \text{ K})}{2.5 \text{ L}} = 1100 \text{ kPa}$

6. 0.39 L N_2

7. a. $n = \dfrac{(2.5 \text{ atm})(1 \text{ L})}{\left(0.0821\dfrac{\text{L} \cdot \text{atm}}{\text{mol} \cdot \text{K}}\right)(250 \text{ K})} = 0.122 \text{ mol N}_2$

$0.122 \text{ mol N}_2 \times \dfrac{28.02 \text{ g N}_2}{1 \text{ mol N}_2} = 3.4 \text{ g N}_2$

$D = \dfrac{m}{V} = \dfrac{3.4 \text{ g N}_2}{1 \text{ L}} = 3.4 \text{ g/L}$

b. 1.3 g/L

8. $5.3 \times 10^{-3} \text{ mol SO}_2$

9. $400 \text{ psi} \times \dfrac{6.892\,86 \times 10^3 \text{ Pa}}{1 \text{ psi}} \times \dfrac{1 \text{ kPa}}{1000 \text{ Pa}} = 2757 \text{ kPa}$

$V_2 = \dfrac{(2757 \text{ kPa})(10.0 \text{ L He})}{100 \text{ kPa}} = 275.7 \text{ L He}$

$275.7 \text{ L He} \times \dfrac{1 \text{ balloon}}{4 \text{ L He}} = 68.9 \text{ balloons}$

You could fill 68 balloons.

10. $2\text{Fe(OH)}_3 \xrightarrow{\Delta} \text{Fe}_2\text{O}_3 + 3\text{H}_2\text{O}$

a. $n = \dfrac{(1 \text{ atm})(0.75 \text{ L})}{\left(0.0821\dfrac{\text{L} \cdot \text{atm}}{\text{mol} \cdot \text{K}}\right)(500 \text{ K})} = 0.0183 \text{ mol H}_2\text{O}$

$0.0183 \text{ mol H}_2\text{O} \times \dfrac{2 \text{ mol Fe(OH)}_3}{3 \text{ mol H}_2\text{O}} \times \dfrac{106.88 \text{ g Fe(OH)}_3}{1 \text{ mol Fe(OH)}_3} =$
1.3 g Fe(OH)_3

b. $0.0183 \text{ mol H}_2\text{O} \times \dfrac{1 \text{ mol Fe}_2\text{O}_3}{3 \text{ mol H}_2\text{O}} \times \dfrac{159.70 \text{ g Fe}_2\text{O}_3}{1 \text{ mol Fe}_2\text{O}_3} =$
$0.97 \text{ g Fe}_2\text{O}_3$

11. $3.0 \text{ L H}_2 \times \dfrac{2 \text{ L HCl}}{1 \text{ L H}_2} = 6.0 \text{ L HCl}$

Assume that the volume of HCl is measured at the same conditions of temperature and pressure under which the H_2 was measured.

12. $15 \text{ L NH}_3 \times \dfrac{5 \text{ L O}_2}{4 \text{ L NH}_3} = 19 \text{ L O}_2$

13. $V = 4.0 \times 10^2 \text{ cm} \times 2.5 \times 10^2 \text{ cm} \times 8.0 \times 10^2 \text{ cm} =$
$8.0 \times 10^7 \text{ cm}^3$

$8.0 \times 10^7 \text{ cm}^3 \times \dfrac{1 \text{ mL}}{1 \text{ cm}^3} \times \dfrac{1 \text{ L}}{1000 \text{ mL}} = 8.0 \times 10^4 \text{ L}$

$n = \dfrac{(5.0 \text{ kPa})(8.0 \times 10^4 \text{ L})}{\left(8.314\dfrac{\text{L} \cdot \text{kPa}}{\text{mol} \cdot \text{K}}\right)(288 \text{ K})} = 167 \text{ mol CO}_2$

$167 \text{ mol CO}_2 \times \dfrac{2 \text{ mol LiOH}}{1 \text{ mol CO}_2} \times \dfrac{23.95 \text{ g LiOH}}{1 \text{ mol LiOH}} = 8.0 \times 10^3 \text{ g LiOH}$

CHAPTER 13

Practice problems, page 475

1. $\dfrac{125 \text{ g}}{2.0 \text{ L}} \times \dfrac{1 \text{ mol NaClO}}{74.44 \text{ g}} = 0.840 \text{ M NaClO}$

2. $\dfrac{1 \text{ L}}{0.375 \text{ mol}} \times \dfrac{1 \text{ mol}}{84.01 \text{ g NaHCO}_3} \times 15.3 \text{ g NaHCO}_3 \times$

$\dfrac{1000 \text{ mL}}{\text{L}} = 486 \text{ mL}$

3. 1.70 L

4. $\dfrac{0.2500 \text{ mol}}{\text{L}} \times 0.0750 \text{ L} \times \dfrac{249.72 \text{ g CuSO}_4 \cdot 5\text{H}_2\text{O}}{\text{mol}} =$
$4.68 \text{ g CuSO}_4 \cdot 5\text{H}_2\text{O}$

5. $1.38 \text{ kg C}_{12}\text{H}_{22}\text{O}_{11}$

6. $\dfrac{5.00 \text{ mol H}_3\text{PO}_4}{\text{L}} \times 7.5 \text{ L} \times \dfrac{1 \text{ mol Ca}_3(\text{PO}_4)_2}{2 \text{ mol H}_3\text{PO}_4} \times$

$\dfrac{310.18 \text{ g}}{\text{mol Ca}_3(\text{PO}_4)_2} = 5.8 \times 10^3 \text{ g Ca}_3(\text{PO}_4)_2$

$\dfrac{5.00 \text{ mol H}_3\text{PO}_4}{\text{L}} \times 7.5 \text{ L} \times \dfrac{6 \text{ mol H}_2\text{O}}{2 \text{ mol H}_3\text{PO}_4} \times \dfrac{18.02 \text{ g}}{\text{mol H}_2\text{O}} =$
$2.0 \times 10^3 \text{ g H}_2\text{O}$

7. 0.571 M HCl

8. $0.0100 \text{ M C}_4\text{H}_4\text{Au}_2\text{CaO}_4\text{S}_2 \times \dfrac{1 \text{ L}}{1000 \text{ mL}} \times 10.0 \text{ mL} \times$

$\dfrac{614.24 \text{ g}}{\text{mol}} \times \dfrac{1000 \text{ mg}}{\text{g}} = 61.4 \text{ mg}$

9. 0.28 M KI

10. a. $2.2 \text{ M NaOH} \times 65.0 \text{ mL} \times \dfrac{1 \text{ L}}{1000 \text{ mL}} = 0.14 \text{ mol}$

b. $0.143 \text{ mol (from calculator)} \times \dfrac{40.00 \text{ g}}{\text{mol}} = 5.7 \text{ g}$

11. $146.3 \text{ g NaCl} \times \dfrac{1 \text{ mol}}{58.44 \text{ g}} \times \dfrac{1 \text{ L}}{1.50 \text{ mol}} = 1.67 \text{ L}$

12. 0.0846 M

Practice problems, page 478

6. a. $\dfrac{0.0750 \text{ mol}}{115 \text{ mL}} \times \dfrac{1000 \text{ mL}}{\text{L}} = 0.652$ M   b. 6.52 M

7. a. 1.5 M   b. $1.5 \text{ M} \times 350 \text{ mL} \times \dfrac{1 \text{ L}}{1000 \text{ mL}} = 0.525$ mol

8. 0.282 M

9. Weigh a clean empty beaker, and record its mass. Pour NaCl into the beaker until the mass is increased by 49.7 g, the mass of 0.85 mol of sodium chloride. Use a funnel to pour the salt into a 1 L volumetric flask. Rinse the beaker and funnel with plenty of distilled water. Add more distilled water to the beaker and swirl until thoroughly dissolved. Add more water one drop at a time until the flask is filled to the mark. Invert the flask, and swirl several times to ensure thorough mixing.

10. $35 \text{ g bear fat} \times \dfrac{8 \text{ g PCB}}{10^6 \text{ g bear fat}} \times \dfrac{1000 \text{ mg}}{\text{g}} = 0.28$ mg

CHAPTER 14

Practice problems, page 526

1. $K_{eq} = \dfrac{[CO][H_2O]}{[CO_2][H_2]} = \dfrac{(0.019)^2}{(0.012)(0.014)} = 2.1$

2. 2.0   3. 1.28×10^4

Practice problems, page 527

1. $K_{eq} = 290 = \dfrac{[CH_3OH]}{[CO][H_2]^2}$; $[CH_3OH]$
   $= (290)(0.025)(0.080)^2 = 0.046$ mol/L

2. 3.5×10^{-5} mol/L   3. 0.59 mol/L

Practice problems, page 532

1. $K_{sp} = [Ca^{2+}]^3[PO_4^{3-}]^2 = (3.42 \times 10^{-7})^3(2.28 \times 10^{-7})^2$
   $= 2.08 \times 10^{-33}$

2. 2.6×10^{-4} M   4. 1.43×10^{-2} M   6. 4.15×10^{-4} M

3. 6.2×10^{-9} 5. 2.9×10^{-3} g Ag^+

Practice problems, page 533

6. $K_{sp} = 1.3 \times 10^{-36} = [Cu^{2+}][S^{2-}]$; $[Cu^{2+}] = 1.1 \times 10^{-18}$ M

7. $K_{eq} = 54.3 = \dfrac{[HI]^2}{[H_2][I_2]}$; $[HI]^2 = (54.3)(4.79 \times 10^{-4})^2$;
   $[HI] = 3.53 \times 10^{-3}$ M

8. 2.5×10^{-2}

CHAPTER 15

Practice problems, page 549

7. $[H_3O^+] = \dfrac{86.5 \text{ g}}{2.3 \text{ L}} \times \dfrac{1 \text{ mol}}{63.02 \text{ g}} = 0.60$ M;
   $[OH^-] = \dfrac{K_w}{[H_3O^+]} = 1.7 \times 10^{-14}$ M

8. $[H_3O^+] = [OH^-] = \sqrt{2.50 \times 10^{-14}} = 1.58 \times 10^{-7}$ M

Practice problems, page 562

1. a. pH = $-\log 0.010 = 2.00$ c. 2.41
   b. 1.33   d. 3.26

2. $10^{-2.50} = 0.0032$ M HNO_3

3. $[H_3O^+] = \dfrac{10.0 \text{ mL} \times 2.00 \text{ M}}{500.0 \text{ mL}} = 0.0400$ M;
   pH = $-\log 0.0400 = 1.398$

Practice problems, page 563

1. pH = $-\log\left(\dfrac{1.00 \times 10^{-14}}{0.00256}\right) = 11.408$

2. $[OH^-] = 0.0350$ M; pH = 12.544   3. 7.415

Practice problems, page 567

7. Solution 1: pH = 8; $[OH^-] = 10^{-6}$ M; $[H_3O^+] = 10^{-8}$ M
   Solution 2: pH = 11; $[OH^-] = 10^{-3}$ M; $[H_3O^+] = 10^{-11}$ M

8. pH = 3.10; $[H_3O^+] = 7.9 \times 10^{-4}$ M; $[OH^-] = 1.3 \times 10^{-11}$ M

9. 3×10^{-8} M   10. 3.51

Practice problems, page 577

9. $\dfrac{20.6 \text{ mL} \times 0.010 \text{ M HCl}}{30.0 \text{ mL}} = 0.0069$ M NaOH

10. 0.585 M NaOH

11. $\dfrac{46.0 \text{ mL} \times 0.407 \text{ M HClO}_4}{0.256 \text{ M Ba(OH)}_2} \times \dfrac{1 \text{ mol Ba(OH)}_2}{2 \text{ mol HClO}_4} = 36.6$ mL

12. $\dfrac{2.00 \text{ g} \times \dfrac{1 \text{ mol}}{204.23 \text{ g}}}{0.0347 \text{ L}} = 0.282$ M

CHAPTER 16

Practice problems, page 596

1. $\dfrac{rate_1}{rate_2} = \dfrac{3.3 \times 10^{-2} \text{ M/s}}{8.2 \times 10^{-3} \text{ M/s}} = \dfrac{k[0.020 \text{ M}]^n}{k[0.010 \text{ M}]^n} = 4.0 = 2^n$
   rate = $k[HI]^2$

2. a. $k[2x]^0 = 2^0 k[x]^0 = 1k[x]^0 = 1 \times$ rate
   b. $k[2x]^3 = 2^3 k[x]^3 = 8k[x]^3 = 8 \times$ rate
   c. $k[2x]^4 = 2^4 k[x]^4 = 16k[x]^4 = 16 \times$ rate

Practice problems, page 598

7. a. rate = $\dfrac{-1}{4} \times \dfrac{\Delta[PH_3]}{\Delta t} = \dfrac{\Delta[P_4]}{\Delta t} = \dfrac{1}{6} \times \dfrac{\Delta[H_2]}{\Delta t}$
   b. rate = $\dfrac{-1}{1} \times \dfrac{\Delta[S^{2-}]}{\Delta t} = \dfrac{-1}{1} \dfrac{\Delta[I_3^-]}{\Delta t} = \dfrac{\Delta[S]}{\Delta t} = \dfrac{1}{3} \dfrac{\Delta[I^-]}{\Delta t}$
   c. rate = $\dfrac{-1}{1} \times \dfrac{\Delta[C_2H_4]}{\Delta t} = \dfrac{-1}{1} \dfrac{\Delta[Br_2]}{\Delta t} = \dfrac{\Delta[C_2H_4Br_2]}{\Delta t}$

8. a. $\dfrac{5}{4} rate_{NH_3} = rate_{O_2} = \dfrac{5}{4}(0.80 \text{ M/min}) = 1.0$ M/min
   b. $rate_{NO} = 0.80$ M/min
      $rate_{H_2O} = 1.2$ M/min

9. with respect to NO: second order; with respect to Cl_2: first order; overall: third order

10. $k[1.41 \times B]^2 = 1.41^2 k[B]^2 = 1.99k[B]^2 \approx 2 \times$ rate
    $k[0.5 \times B]^2 = 0.5^2 k[B]^2 = 0.25k[B]^2 = \dfrac{1}{4} \times$ rate

CHAPTER 17

Practice problems, page 626

1. energy $= (0.25 \text{ V})(3.037 \times 10^6 \text{ C}) = 7.6 \times 10^5 \text{ J}$

2. $30.0 \text{ min} \times \dfrac{1.50 \text{ C}}{1 \text{ s}} \times \dfrac{60 \text{ s}}{1 \text{ min}} \times \dfrac{1 \text{ mol } e^-}{96\,485 \text{ C}} \times \dfrac{1 \text{ mol Ag}}{1 \text{ mol } e^-} \times$
$\dfrac{107.87 \text{ g Ag}}{1 \text{ mol Ag}} = 3.02 \text{ g Ag}$

Practice problems, page 627

5. $2.5 \text{ mol } e^- \times \dfrac{96\,485 \text{ C}}{1 \text{ mol } e^-} = 2.4 \times 10^5 \text{ C}$

6. $1.0 \text{ min} \times \dfrac{60 \text{ s}}{1 \text{ min}} \times \dfrac{5.0 \text{ C}}{1 \text{ s}} = 3.0 \times 10^2 \text{ C}$
energy $= (12.0 \text{ V})(3.0 \times 10^2 \text{ C}) = 3.6 \times 10^3 \text{ J}$

7. a. $Pt^{2+} + 2e^- \longrightarrow Pt$ d. $Br_2 + 2e^- \longrightarrow 2Br^-$
   b. $Fe^{2+} \longrightarrow Fe^{3+} + e^-$ e. $Au \longrightarrow Au^{3+} + 3e^-$
   c. $S + 2e^- \longrightarrow S^{2-}$

8. $\dfrac{1.00 \text{ C}}{1 \text{ s}} \times \dfrac{1 \text{ s}}{300 \text{ discharges}} = 3.33 \times 10^{-3} \text{ C}$
energy $= (0.1000 \text{ V})(3.33 \times 10^{-3} \text{ C}) = 3.33 \times 10^{-4} \text{ J}$

9. $600.0 \text{ V} \times \dfrac{1 \text{ plate}}{0.1500 \text{ V}} = 4.000 \times 10^3 \text{ plates}$

Practice problems, page 631

1. $n = \dfrac{(101 \text{ kPa})(1.000 \text{ L})}{(8.314 \text{ kPa} \cdot \text{L/K} \cdot \text{mol})(298 \text{ K})} = 4.08 \times 10^{-2} \text{ mol O}_2$

charge $= 4.08 \times 10^{-2} \text{ mol O}_2 \times \dfrac{4 \text{ mol } e^-}{1 \text{ mol O}_2} \times \dfrac{96\,485 \text{ C}}{1 \text{ mol } e^-} = 1.57 \times 10^4 \text{ C}$
energy $= (2.0 \text{ V})(1.57 \times 10^4 \text{ C}) = 3.1 \times 10^4 \text{ J}$

2. $1.0 \text{ h} \times \dfrac{3600 \text{ s}}{1 \text{ h}} \times \dfrac{3.0 \times 10^4 \text{ C}}{1 \text{ s}} \times \dfrac{1 \text{ mol } e^-}{96\,485 \text{ C}} \times \dfrac{1 \text{ mol Cl}_2}{2 \text{ mol } e^-} = 560 \text{ mol Cl}_2$

Practice problem, page 633

6. $100.0 \text{ g Al} \times \dfrac{1 \text{ mol Al}}{26.98 \text{ g Al}} \times \dfrac{12 \text{ mol } e^-}{4 \text{ mol Al}} \times \dfrac{96\,485 \text{ C}}{1 \text{ mol } e^-} = 1.07 \times 10^6 \text{ C}$
energy $= (6.2 \text{ V})(1.07 \times 10^6 \text{ C}) = 6.7 \times 10^6 \text{ J}$

Practice problems, page 639

1. $1.33 \times 10^5 \text{ C} \times \dfrac{1 \text{ mol } e^-}{96\,485 \text{ C}} \times \dfrac{1 \text{ mol Pb}}{2 \text{ mol } e^-} \times \dfrac{207.2 \text{ g}}{1 \text{ mol Pb}} = 140 \text{ g Pb}$

2. charge $= \dfrac{1300 \text{ J}}{1.54 \text{ V}} = 844 \text{ C}$
$844 \text{ C} \times \dfrac{1 \text{ mol } e^-}{96\,485 \text{ C}} \times \dfrac{1 \text{ mol Zn(OH)}_2}{2 \text{ mol } e^-} \times \dfrac{99.41 \text{ g Zn(OH)}_2}{1 \text{ mol Zn(OH)}_2} = 0.43 \text{ g}$

Practice problems, page 648

6. Magnesium has a greater tendency to give up electrons than does lead. Therefore, only the reverse reaction will occur spontaneously.

7. $Ce^{4+}(aq) + Ag(s) + Cl^-(aq) \longrightarrow Ce^{3+}(aq) + AgCl(s)$

8. Yes; calcium has a greater tendency to give up electrons than does lead sulfate.

9. $I_2(s) + Pb(s) \longrightarrow 2I^-(aq) + Pb^{2+}(aq)$

10. $2Fe^{3+}(aq) + 3H_2(g) + 6OH^-(aq) \longrightarrow 2Fe(s) + 6H_2O(l)$

CHAPTER 18
none

APPENDIX B

Practice, page 807

1. **1** metals   **1** nonmetals
      2 alkali metals   **2** halogens
         3 sodium   **3** chlorine
      2 alkaline-earth metals   **3** iodine
         3 calcium
         3 barium

Practice, page 809

1. Choose a multiple-step process from your text.

   Write down the steps of the process in your own words.
   Cut the paper into strips so that there is one step per strip.
   Shuffle the strips of paper.
   Place the strips in their proper sequence.
   Using your text, confirm the order of the process.

Practice, page 811

1. a. The gasoline used in cars is not in a gaseous state; it is a liquid.
   b. no misconception
   c. no misconception
   d. Global warming is not solely caused by the accumulation of CFCs in the atmosphere. It is also caused by the increased levels of carbon dioxide from the combustion of fossil fuels.
   e. Gases are the least dense of the three states of matter.

Practice, page 813

1.

Main idea	Detail notes
▶ neon	▶ Ne, 10
▶ lead	▶ Pb, 82
▶ calcium	▶ Ca, 20
▶ copper	▶ Cu, 29
▶ oxygen	▶ O, 8
▶ sodium	▶ Na, 11

Practice, page 816

1. a. concept   d. linking words   g. concept
   b. linking words   e. concept   h. linking word
   c. linking word   f. linking words

2. Some possible responses are the following: *matter is described by chemical properties,* and *matter is classified as mixtures.*

3. *mixtures are made from pure substances,* and *elements form compounds*

A

accuracy: the extent to which a measurement approaches the true value of a quantity **(57)**

acid: a class of compounds whose water solutions taste sour, turn blue litmus paper red, and react with bases to form salts **(26)**

acid-ionization constant: the equilibrium constant for a reaction in which an acid donates a proton to water **(556)**

actinides: shiny, metallic transition metals with atomic numbers 90 through 103 in which electrons are added to $5f$ orbitals **(121)**

activated complex: a temporary combination of high-energy reactant atoms or molecules that decomposes into products; also called a transition state **(602)**

activation energy: the least amount of energy needed to permit a particular chemical reaction **(602)**

activity series: an arrangement of elements in the order of their tendency to react with water and acids **(327)**

actual yield: the measured amount of product experimentally produced from a given amount of reactant **(361)**

addition polymer: a polymer formed by chain addition reactions between monomers that contain a double bond **(256)**

adiabatic calorimetry: a method of measuring the heat absorbed or released in a chemical or physical change in which no heat is allowed to enter or leave the system **(403)**

alkali metals: highly reactive metallic elements in Group 1 that react rapidly with water to form hydrogen and alkaline solutions and that burn in air **(119)**

alkaline-earth metals: reactive metallic elements in Group 2 with two electrons in the outermost energy level **(120)**

alkane: a hydrocarbon that contains only single bonds **(236)**

alkene: a hydrocarbon that contains one or more double bonds **(237)**

alkyne: a hydrocarbon with one or more triple bonds **(238)**

allotrope: one of a number of different molecular or crystalline forms of an element **(23)**

alloy: a solid or liquid solution of two or more metals **(129)**

alpha particle: a positively charged particle produced by some nuclear disintegrations **(84)**

amine: an organic compound that contains a nitrogen atom and that can be considered a derivative of ammonia **(547)**

ampere: the SI unit of electric current; equal to 1 C/s **(621)**

amphoteric: any molecule or ion that can act either as an acid or as a base **(553)**

anhydrous: without water **(183)**

anion: an ion that has a negative charge **(159)**

annihilation of matter: the event that occurs when a particle collides with its antiparticle and both are changed into electromagnetic energy **(666)**

anode: an electrode through which electrons enter a metal **(82)**

antioxidant: a substance that can prevent chain reactions involving O_2 and O_3 **(608)**

aqueous: describing a solution in which the solvent is water **(470)**

aromatic compound: a compound containing a ring of carbon atoms pictured with alternating single and double bonds with delocalized electrons that provide great stability **(239)**

atom: the basic unit of matter **(20)**

atomic mass: the mass of an atom in atomic mass units **(80)**

atomic mass unit: one-twelfth the mass of the carbon-12 isotope **(80)**

atomic number: the number of protons in the nucleus of an atom **(86)**

atomic theory: the theory that all matter is composed of indivisible particles called atoms **(74)**

aufbau principle: electrons in an atom will occupy the lowest-energy orbitals available **(99)**

average rate: the change in a measured property (usually concentration) divided by the total time elapsed **(590)**

Avogadro's constant: the number of particles in 1 mol, 6.022×10^{23}/mol **(81)**

Avogadro's law: equal volumes of different gases under the same conditions of temperature and pressure have the same number of molecules **(441)**

B

band of stability: the area on a graph of neutron number versus proton number in which all stable nuclei lie **(662)**

base: a class of compounds that taste bitter, feel slippery in water solution, turn red litmas to blue, and react with acids to form salts **(27)**

battery: a group of self-contained galvanic cells that convert chemical energy into electrical energy **(636)**

benzene: a six-membered ring of carbon atoms pictured with alternating double and single bonds, indicating delocalized electrons **(238)**

beta particle: a high-energy electron emitted from the nucleus when a neutron changes to a proton **(665)**

binary ionic compound: an ionic compound that consists of the cations of one element and the anions of another element **(162)**

boiling-point elevation: the difference between the boiling point of a solution and that of the pure solvent **(495)**

bond energy: the energy required to break a chemical bond between two atoms and separate them **(197)**

bond length: the distance between two bonded atoms at their minimum potential energy; the average distance between two bonded atoms **(196)**

bond radius: one-half the distance from center to center of two like atoms bonded together **(135)**

Boyle's law: the volume of a given amount of gas at constant temperature is inversely proportional to the pressure **(435)**

Brønsted-Lowry acid: any ion or molecule that can donate a proton to another species **(550)**

Brønsted-Lowry base: any atom, ion, or molecule that can accept a proton from another species **(552)**

buffer solution: a solution that resists changes in pH **(565)**

C

calorimeter: a device used to measure the heat absorbed or released in a chemical or physical change **(402)**

carboxylic acid: an organic compound that contains the carboxyl functional group **(545)**

catalysis: the process by which reaction rates are increased by the addition of a catalyst **(604)**

catalyst: a substance added to a chemical reaction to increase the rate that is not itself changed in the reaction **(604)**

cathode: an electrode through which electrons leave a metal **(82)**

cation: an ion that has a positive charge **(159)**

chain reaction: a self-sustaining nuclear or chemical reaction in which the product from one step acts as a reactant for the next step **(431)**

Charles's law: the volume of a sample of gas at constant pressure is directly proportional to the absolute temperature **(438)**

chemical: any substance with a definite composition **(4)**

chemical bond: a mutual attraction between different atoms that binds the atoms together **(40)**

chemical change: a change that produces one or more new substances **(18)**

chemical energy: the energy that matter possesses because of its chemical makeup **(40)**

chemical equation: an expression showing the formulas and the relative amounts of the reactants and products in a chemical reaction **(312)**

chemical equilibrium: a condition where the forward reaction occurs at the same speed as the reverse reaction, and all reactants and products are present **(361)**

chemical kinetics: the branch of chemistry concerned with reaction rates and how reactions occur **(589)**

chemical property: a property of matter that can be observed only when substances interact with one another **(18)**

chemical reaction: the process by which elements and/or compounds interact with one another to form new substances **(7)**

chromatography: a technique for separating components of a mixture by placing the mixture in a mobile phase that is passed over a stationary phase **(477)**

coefficient: a numeral used in a chemical equation to indicate relative amounts of reactants or products **(313)**

colligative property: a physical property that is dependent on the number of solute particles present rather than on the identity of those particles **(496)**

colloid: a mixture in which small particles are suspended throughout a solvent **(469)**

combined gas law: the gas law for a given quantity of gas that is changed from one set of P, V, or T conditions to another **(448)**

combustion: a violently exothermic reaction with oxygen to form oxide(s) **(325)**

common ion: an ion that is present in two or more substances involved in an ionic chemical equilibrium **(533)**

common ion effect: the reduction in the solubility of an ionic compound by the addition of a soluble compound that provides an ion in common with it **(533)**

complex ion: an ion that has a structure in which a central atom or ion is bonded by coordinate covalent bonds to other ions or molecules **(519)**

compound: the product that results when two or more different elements are chemically combined **(26)**

concentration: the quantity of solute in a specific quantity of solvent or solution **(470)**

condensation: the process by which a gas changes to a liquid **(455)**

condensation polymer: a polymer formed by reactions in which water or another small molecule is a byproduct **(258)**

conduction band: a band within (or into which) electrons must move to allow electrical conduction **(127)**

conductivity: the ability to conduct an electric current **(487)**

conjugate acid: the acid formed when a base accepts a proton **(554)**

conjugate base: the base formed when an acid donates a proton **(554)**

conversion factor: a mathematical expression that relates two units **(13)**

corrosion: the deterioration of metals due to oxidation reactions with their environment **(640)**

coulomb: the SI unit of electric charge **(621)**

coulombic force: the attraction or repulsion between two objects that have electric charges **(168)**

Coulomb's law: the force between two charged particles is inversely proportional to the square of the distance between them **(88)**

covalent bond: the bond formed when two or more valence electrons are attracted by the positively charged nuclei of two atoms and are thus shared between both atoms **(195)**

covalent network solid: a solid composed of atoms covalently bonded in a network in two or three dimensions **(235)**

critical mass: the smallest mass of radioactive material needed to sustain a chain reaction **(670)**

critical point: the temperature and pressure at and above which the properties of the vapor phase of a substance cannot be distinguished from those of the liquid phase **(458)**

crystal: a substance in which the atoms or molecules are arranged in an orderly, geometric, repeating pattern **(126)**

crystal lattice: a repetitive geometric arrangement of points in space about which atoms, ions, or molecules are arranged to form a crystal structure **(168)**

D

Dalton's law of partial pressures: the total pressure in a gas mixture is the sum of the partial pressures of the individual components, each behaving as if the other gases were absent **(436)**

decomposition: a chemical reaction in which a single compound is broken down to produce two or more simpler substances **(327)**

density: the ratio of mass to volume **(16)**

detergent: a surfactant other than soap **(501)**

diffusion: the process by which particles mix by dispersing from regions of higher concentration to regions of lower concentration **(443)**

dipole: a molecule in which one end has a partial positive charge and the other end has a partial negative charge **(200)**

diprotic acid: an acid that can donate two hydrogen ions per molecule **(551)**

displacement reaction: a chemical reaction in which one element replaces another element in a compound that is in solution **(327)**

dissociation: a process in which a compound separates into fragments, such as simpler molecules, atoms, radicals, or ions **(491)**

distillation: a separation process in which a liquid component is evaporated from a solution and the vapor is condensed to liquid, usually for the purpose of purification **(478)**

double-displacement reaction: a chemical reaction in which ions from two compounds interact in solution to form a product **(329)**

Downs cell: an electrolytic cell that uses a graphite anode and an iron cathode to produce sodium metal **(629)**

E

effusion: the motion of a gas through a small opening **(442)**

elastomer: a polymer that has elastic properties similar to rubber **(259)**

electrochemical cell: an apparatus through which electricity can flow that includes at least two electrodes and at least one electrolyte solution **(624)**

electrochemical series: a table in which the elements are listed in order of increasing standard electrode potential **(646)**

electrode: the junction between a metallic conductor and an ionic conductor, often an electrolyte solution **(622)**

electrolysis: the decomposition of a substance by an electric current **(630)**

electrolyte: a substance that, when dissolved in a solvent, increases the solvent's conductivity **(488)**

electrolytic cell: an electrochemical cell in which electrical energy is used to drive two electrode reactions and bring about chemical changes **(625)**

electromagnetic spectrum: the total range of electromagnetic radiation, ranging from the longest radio waves to the shortest gamma waves **(93)**

electron: a small, negatively charged particle found in atoms **(83)**

electron affinity: the energy emitted upon the addition of an electron to an atom or group of atoms while in the gas phase **(139)**

electron configuration: a description of the occupied electron orbitals in an atom **(98)**

electron shielding: the reduction of the attractive force between a posi-

tively charged nucleus and its outermost electrons due to the cancellation of some of the positive charge by the negative charge of the other electrons **(136)**

electronegativity: the tendency of an atom to attract bonding electrons to itself when it bonds with another atom **(198)**

electroneutrality: the condition of having an equal number of positive and negative charges **(159)**

electroplating: an electrochemical process in which a metal ion is reduced and solid metal is deposited on a surface **(622)**

electrosynthesis: a synthesis reaction that is carried out in an electrochemical cell using an electric current **(630)**

element: one of the 111 simplest substances from which more complex materials are made **(20)**

elementary step: a single step in the mechanism of a reaction **(597)**

empirical formula: a formula that represents the simplest ratio among the elements in a compound **(289)**

emulsifier: a substance that stabilizes an emulsion by forming a molecular layer between two immiscible liquids **(499)**

emulsion: colloidal-sized droplets (about 100 nm wide) of one liquid suspended in another liquid **(498)**

end point: the point in a titration at which the indicator changes color **(573)**

endothermic reaction: a reaction in which energy is absorbed **(8)**

energy: the capacity to do work **(42)**

enthalpy: the total energy content of a system **(322)**

entropy: a measure of the randomness or disorder of a system **(390)**

enzyme: a large protein molecule that catalyzes chemical reactions in living things **(606)**

equilibrium cell: an electrochemical cell in which no electric current flows **(627)**

equilibrium constant: for a reversible reaction in equilibrium, an expression that relates the concentrations of the reactants and products at a specific temperature to a constant **(524)**

equilibrium voltage: the voltage of a cell as measured by a voltmeter when no current is flowing **(644)**

equivalence point: the point in a titration when the amount of added base or acid exactly equals the amount of acid or base originally in solution **(571)**

ester: an organic compound often responsible for the aromas and flavors of fruits **(345)**

evaporation: the process by which molecules in a nonboiling liquid escape the liquid surface and enter the gas phase **(399)**

excess reactant: a reactant that will not be used up in a reaction that goes to completion **(358)**

excited state: the condition of an atom in a state higher than the ground state **(94)**

exothermic reaction: a reaction in which energy is released **(8)**

extensive property: a property that depends on the amount of material present **(392)**

— **F** —

fiber: a polymer that has a thread-like structure and is highly resistant to being stretched **(259)**

formula unit: the unit of an ionic compound that represents the simplest ratio of cations to anions **(286)**

free radical: an atom or molecule that has one or more unpaired electrons and is therefore very reactive **(431)**

freezing-point depression: the difference between the freezing point of a pure solvent and that of a solution **(495)**

fuel cell: a galvanic cell in which electricity is produced using reactants supplied from outside the cell **(635)**

functional group: a group of atoms that give characteristic properties to organic compounds **(239)**

— **G** —

galvanic cell: an electrochemical cell in which two electrode reactions occur spontaneously and produce electric energy **(625)**

gamma ray: high-energy electro-magnetic radiation produced by decaying nuclei **(666)**

Gay-Lussac's law of combining volumes: at constant temperature and pressure, gases react in volume proportions that are whole numbers (equivalent to the coefficients in the balanced chemical equation) **(441)**

Gibbs energy: a thermodynamic property incorporating both enthalpy and entropy **(400)**

Graham's law of effusion: the rates of effusion for two gases are inversely proportional to the square roots of their molar masses at the same temperature and pressure **(443)**

greenhouse effect: an increase in the temperature of Earth caused by reflected solar radiation that is trapped in the atmosphere **(430)**

ground state: the lowest energy state of a quantized system **(94)**

group: a series of elements that form a vertical column in the periodic table **(117)**

— **H** —

half-life: the time required for half of a sample of radioactive atoms to decay **(676)**

halide: a salt that is composed of cations combined with anions of one of the halogen elements **(168)**

halogen: a nonmetallic element in Group 17 of the periodic table that has seven electrons in the outermost energy level and that combines with many metals to form salts **(121)**

heat: the sum total of kinetic energy of the particles in a sample of matter **(43)**

Henry's law: the solubility of a gas in a liquid is directly proportional to the partial pressure of that gas on the surface of the liquid **(481)**

Hess's law: the overall enthalpy change in a reaction is equal to the sum of the enthalpy changes of the individual steps in the process **(403)**

heterogeneous catalyst: a catalyst whose phase is different from that of the reactants **(605)**

heterogeneous mixture: a mixture containing substances that are not uniformly distributed **(29)**

homogeneous catalyst: a catalyst that is in the same phase as all of the reactants and products in a system **(605)**

homogeneous mixture: a mixture containing substances that are uniformly distributed **(29)**

Hund's rule: the most stable arrangement of electrons is that with the maximum number of unpaired electrons, all with the same spin quantum number **(100)**

hydrate: an ionic compound that contains precise numbers of water molecules in its crystal lattice **(183)**

hydration: the process by which water molecules surround each ion as it moves into solution **(491)**

hydrocarbon: the simplest class of organic compounds, consisting of only hydrogen and carbon atoms **(236)**

hydrogen bond: a form of dipole attraction in which a hydrogen atom bonded to a strongly electro-negative atom is attracted to another electron-rich atom **(221)**

hydronium ion: a hydrogen ion covalently bonded to a water molecule, written as H_3O^+ **(489)**

hypothesis: a reasonable and testable explanation of observations **(52)**

— **I** —

ideal gas: a model that effectively describes the behavior of gases under most conditions **(424)**

ideal gas law: the equation of state for an ideal gas in which the product of the pressure and volume is proportional to the product of the absolute temperature and the amount of gas expressed in moles **(446)**

immiscible: describes liquids that will not dissolve appreciably in each other **(482)**

indicator: a dye that changes to different colors in solutions of different pH **(563)**

inhibitor: a substance added to a chemical reaction to slow the reaction down **(608)**

inorganic compound: all compounds outside the organic family of compounds **(28)**

insoluble: does not dissolve appreciably in a particular solvent **(480)**

intensive property: a property that does not depend on the amount of material present **(393)**

intermediate: a structure formed in one elementary step but consumed in a later step of a mechanism **(597)**

intermolecular force: an attraction that exists between molecules **(220)**

ion: an atom or group of atoms with an electrical charge **(26)**

ionic bond: the coulombic force of attraction between ions of opposite charge **(167)**

ionic compound: chemical compound composed of oppositely charged ions **(162)**

ionization energy: the amount of energy needed to remove an outer electron from a specific atom or ion in its ground state and in the gas phase **(137)**

isoelectronic: having the same electron configuration as another atom **(160)**

isomers: compounds with the same number and types of atoms but differing geometric arrangements **(237)**

isotope: one of two or more atoms of the same element with different numbers of neutrons **(89)**

──────── **K** ────────

kinetic energy: the energy a moving object has because of its motion **(41)**

kinetic-molecular theory: the theory that explains the behavior of gases at the molecular level **(424)**

──────── **L** ────────

lanthanides: shiny, metallic transition metals with atomic numbers 58 through 71 in which electrons are added to $4f$ orbitals **(120)**

lattice energy: the energy released when well-separated atoms, ions, or molecules come together to form a crystal **(172)**

law of conservation of energy: in any chemical or physical process, energy is neither created nor destroyed **(42)**

law of conservation of mass: the products of a chemical reaction have the same mass as the reactants **(54)**

law of definite proportions: any sample of a compound always has the same composition **(75)**

law of multiple proportions: the mass ratio for one of the elements that combines with a fixed mass of another element can be expressed in small whole numbers **(77)**

Le Châtelier's principle: if a system at equilibrium is disturbed by applying stress, the system attains a new equilibrium position to accommodate the change and tends to relieve the stress **(516)**

Lewis structure: a structure in which atomic symbols represent nuclei and inner-shell electrons, and dots are used to represent valence electrons **(203)**

ligand: a molecule or ion that is bonded to the central atom of a complex ion **(520)**

limiting reactant: a reactant that is consumed completely in a reaction that goes to completion **(358)**

line-emission spectrum: distinct lines of colored light that are produced when the light produced by excited atoms of an element is passed through a prism **(94)**

London force: an attraction between atoms and molecules caused by the formation of instantaneous dipoles in the atoms and molecules **(223)**

──────── **M** ────────

main-group elements: elements belonging to Groups 1 and 2 and Groups 13–18 in the periodic table and having very regular electron configurations **(118)**

mass: the quantity of matter in an object **(11)**

mass defect: the mass lost by conversion to energy when a nucleus forms from separated nucleons **(659)**

mass number: the total number of protons and neutrons in the nucleus of an atom **(87)**

matter: anything that has mass and volume **(10)**

mechanism: a proposed sequence of steps that describes how reactants are changed into products **(597)**

metal: any element that is a good conductor of electricity **(117)**

micelle: a spherical arrangement formed by molecules of fat or fat-like substances in an aqueous environment **(500)**

mineral: a naturally occurring inorganic substance that has a definite composition and an ordered structure **(182)**

miscible: describes liquids that will dissolve in each other **(482)**

mixture: a collection of two or more pure substances physically mixed together **(29)**

molar enthalpy of fusion: the heat absorbed when 1 mol of a substance melts **(397)**

molar enthalpy of vaporization: the heat absorbed when 1 mol of a liquid vaporizes **(397)**

molar heat capacity: the heat required to increase the temperature of 1 mol of a substance by 1 K **(387)**

molar mass: the mass in grams equal to the sum of all the atomic masses of the component atoms of a substance **(280)**

molarity: a concentration unit expressed as moles of solute per liter of solution **(470)**

mole: the SI unit for measuring the amount of a substance **(81)**

mole fraction: the number of moles of one component compared with the total number of moles in the mixture expressed as a ratio **(437)**

molecular formula: the type and actual number of atoms in a covalent compound **(292)**

molecular orbital: a region where an electron pair is most likely to exist as it travels in the three-dimensional space around two nuclei **(195)**

molecule: a neutral group of atoms held together by chemical bonds **(23)**

monomer: the small unit from which polymers form **(256)**

monoprotic acid: an acid that can donate one hydrogen ion per molecule **(551)**

N

net ionic equation: an equation that includes only those compounds and ions that are involved in a chemical change in a reaction **(330)**

neutral: describes a solution that contains equal concentrations of hydronium ions and hydroxide ions **(560)**

neutralization reaction: a reaction in which hydronium ions from an acid and hydroxide ions from a base react to produce water molecules **(548)**

neutron: a particle with no electric charge found in atomic nuclei **(86)**

newton: the force that will increase the speed of a 1 kg mass by 1 m/s each second that force is applied **(427)**

noble gas: elements in Group 18 of the periodic table that are characterized by low reactivity **(122)**

nonelectrolyte: a substance that, when dissolved in a solvent, will not enhance that solvent's conductivity **(489)**

nonmetal: an element that is a poor conductor of electricity **(117)**

nonpolar covalent bond: an attraction between two atoms in which bonding electrons are shared equally between the atoms **(198)**

normal boiling point: the temperature at which a substance boils at 1.0000 atm of pressure **(457)**

nuclear binding energy: the energy emitted when nucleons come together to form a nucleus; also the energy needed to break a nucleus into individual separated nucleons **(660)**

nuclear fission: a nuclear reaction in which a very heavy nucleus splits into two smaller nuclei of approximately equal mass **(669)**

nuclear fusion: the combining of two small nuclei to form a larger, more stable nucleus with the release of energy **(671)**

nuclear reaction: a reaction that involves a change in the composition of the nucleus of an atom **(144)**

nucleons: the protons and neutrons that make up the nucleus of an atom **(658)**

nucleus: the central region of an atom; made up of protons and neutrons **(84)**

nuclide: any combination of protons and neutrons in a nucleus **(658)**

O

octet rule: the tendency of atoms of elements to gain or lose electrons so that their outer *s* and *p* orbitals are full with eight electrons **(161)**

orbital: a region of an atom in which there is a high probability of finding one or more electrons **(96)**

order: the exponent on the concentration for a specified reactant in a rate law expression **(594)**

organic compound: any covalently bonded compound containing carbon (except carbonates and oxides) **(28)**

overall reaction order: the sum of all the exponents in a rate law expression **(596)**

oxidation: any chemical reaction in which the reactant loses electrons **(623)**

oxidation number: a number assigned to an atom in a polyatomic ion or molecular compound based on the assumption of complete transfer of electrons **(180)**

oxyanion: a negative polyatomic ion containing oxygen **(177)**

P

partial pressure: the pressure of an individual gas in a gas mixture that contributes to the total pressure of the mixture **(436)**

pascal: a unit of pressure equal to the force of 1 N on 1 m^2 **(427)**

Pauli exclusion principle: a maximum of two electrons can occupy each orbital, and these electrons must have different spin quantum numbers **(98)**

peptide bond: the bond formed between the carboxylic acid group of one amino acid and the amine group of another amino acid **(258)**

percentage composition: the percentage by mass of each element in a compound **(289)**

percentage yield: the ratio of actual yield to theoretical yield, multiplied by 100 **(362)**

period: a series of elements that form a horizontal row in the periodic table **(117)**

periodic law: the physical and chemical properties of elements are periodic functions of their atomic numbers **(116)**

pH: the negative logarithm of the hydronium ion concentration in a solution **(27)**

pH meter: an electronic device that measures pH **(564)**

phase: any part of a system that has uniform composition and properties **(457)**

phase diagram: a graphic representation of the relationships between the physical states (phases) of a substance at different pressures and temperatures **(457)**

physical change: a change that affects only physical properties **(17)**

physical property: any property of matter that can be measured without changing its chemical nature **(17)**

physical state: the form matter takes as a result of the arrangement of its particles **(6)**

plasma: a gas composed of ions, electrons, and neutral particles **(119)**

plastic: a polymer that is able to be shaped or molded without destroying the molecule **(259)**

polar covalent bond: an attraction between two atoms in which bonding electrons are localized on the more electronegative atom **(199)**

polyatomic ion: an electrically charged group of two or more chemically bonded atoms that function as a single ion **(176)**

polymer: a large organic molecule composed of smaller units bonded together **(51)**

potential energy: the energy an object has because of its position **(41)**

precision: the extent to which a series of measurements of the same quantity made in the same way agree with one another **(57)**

pressure: the force exerted per unit area **(427)**

primary cell: a galvanic cell that converts chemical energy to electrical energy; cannot be recharged **(635)**

product: a chemical produced as a result of a chemical reaction **(7)**

proton: a particle with a positive charge; found in atomic nuclei **(85)**

Q

quantity: something that has magnitude or size **(12)**

quantum number: a number with certain definite values **(95)**

R

radioactivity: the process during which unstable nuclei undergo spontaneous nuclear decay and emit particles and electromagnetic waves **(664)**

radioisotope: an unstable atom that undergoes radioactive decay **(90)**

rate-determining step: the slowest elementary step in a reaction mechanism **(597)**

rate law: an expression for the rate of a reaction as a function of the concentration of one or more reactants **(594)**

reactant: a chemical that is present at the beginning of a chemical reaction and that takes part in the reaction **(7)**

reaction rate: the decrease in reactant concentration or increase in product concentration per unit of time as a reaction proceeds **(589)**

redox reaction: any chemical process in which both oxidation and reduction occur **(623)**

reduction: a chemical reaction in which the reactant gains electrons **(622)**

resonance structure: a possible Lewis dot structure of a molecule for which more than one Lewis structure can be written **(208)**

S

sacrificial anode: metal attached to a metallic structure that serves as an anode preventing the corrosion of the structural metal **(641)**

salt: an ionic compound that is composed of cations bonded to anions, other than oxide or hydroxide anions; arranged in a regular three-dimensional pattern **(121)**

saturated: containing the amount of solute specified by the solubility **(481)**

saturated fat: a fat primarily containing saturated fatty acids **(249)**

scientific law: a description of the natural world that has proven reliable over time **(54)**

secondary cell: an electrochemical cell that can act as a galvanic cell or, on recharge as an electrolytic cell **(635)**

semiconductor: a crystalline material with intermediate electrical conductivity **(118)**

significant figure: any digit in a measurement that is known with certainty plus one final digit, which is somewhat uncertain or estimated **(58)**

silicate: any of the compounds containing silicon, oxygen, one or more metals, and possibly hydrogen **(182)**

single bond: a covalent bond in which one pair of electrons is shared between two atoms **(204)**

soap: a sodium or potassium salt of a long-chain fatty acid **(500)**

solubility: the maximum amount of a chemical that will dissolve in a given quantity of a solvent at a specified temperature while the solution is in contact with undissolved solute **(479)**

solubility product constant: the equilibrium constant for a slightly soluble ionic solid in equilibrium with its ions in a saturated solution **(529)**

soluble: can be dissolved in a particular solvent **(480)**

solute: the substance dissolved in a solution **(470)**

solvent: the substance in which the solute dissolves to make the solution **(470)**

specific heat capacity: the amount of heat energy required to raise the temperature of 1 g of a substance by 1 K **(45)**

spectator ion: an ion that remains unchanged in a chemical reaction (330)

standard electrode potential: the measured voltage when an electrode under standard conditions of temperature, pressure, and concentration is paired with a standard hydrogen electrode in an equilibrium cell (645)

standard enthalpy of formation: the amount of heat released or absorbed when 1 mol of compound is made from its elements under standard conditions (404)

standard hydrogen electrode: an electrode used as a reference for measuring other electrode potentials; it is arbitrarily assigned an electrode potential of 0.00 V (645)

standard solution: a solution whose concentration is accurately known (571)

standard temperature and pressure (STP): standard conditions for a gas at 0°C and 1 atm (428)

stoichiometry: mass and amount relationships between reactants and products in a chemical reaction (344)

strong acid: an acid that ionizes completely in aqueous solution (542)

strong nuclear force: the force of attraction among the particles of a nucleus that overcomes electrostatic repulsion and holds the nucleus together (659)

sublimation: a change of state in which a solid is transformed directly to a gas without going through the liquid state (458)

subscript: a whole number written below and to the right of an element's symbol that is used to denote the number of atoms in a formula (163)

substrate: the molecule or molecules with which an enzyme interacts (606)

superheavy element: an element with an atomic number greater than 106 (148)

supersaturated: containing more than the standard amount of

solute specified by the solubility at a given set of conditions (481)

surfactant: a class of salts, valued for their cleansing properties, whose anions possess a negatively charged "head" and a long nonpolar "tail" (500)

suspension: a mixture that appears uniform while being stirred but separates into different phases when agitation ceases (468)

synthesis: a chemical reaction in which atoms or simple molecules combine to form a compound that is more complex (326)

system: a specific portion of matter in a given region of space that has been selected for study during an experiment or observation (43)

— T —

temperature: a measure of the average kinetic energy of the particles in a sample of matter (44)

theoretical yield: the calculated maximum amount of product possible from a given amount of reactant (361)

theory: a well-tested explanation of observations (53)

thermodynamics: the branch of science concerned with the energy changes that accompany physical and chemical processes (390)

titrant: the solution added to another solution in a titration (571)

titration: the operation of gradually adding one solution to another to reach an equivalence point (571)

transition metals: elements in Groups 3 through 12 (117)

transition range: the pH range through which an indicator changes color (572)

transmutation: the process of changing one nucleus into another by radioactive disintegration or bombardment with other particles (145)

triple point: the temperature and pressure at which three phases of a substance exist in equilibrium (458)

triprotic acid: an acid that can donate three hydrogen ions per molecule (551)

— U —

unit: a standard used when measuring a quantity (12)

unit cell: the simplest repeating unit of a crystal lattice (169)

unsaturated fat: a fat primarily containing unsaturated fatty acids (249)

unsaturated hydrocarbon: a hydrocarbon that has at least one double or triple bond between carbon atoms (245)

unshared pair: a pair of valence electrons not involved in bonding to another atom (203)

— V —

valence electron: an electron in the outermost energy level of an atom, where it can participate in bonding (202)

van der Waals radius: half the distance between the nuclei in adjacent non-bonded molecules (135)

vapor pressure: the pressure exerted by a vapor in equilibrium with its liquid state at a given temperature (455)

volt: the SI unit of voltage (620)

voltage: an electric potential difference (620)

volume: the amount of space an object occupies (10)

VSEPR (valence shell electron pair repulsion) theory: a simple model that predicts the general shape of a molecule based on the repulsion between both bonding and nonbonding electron clouds (215)

— W —

weak acid: an acid that is a weak electrolyte (542)

weight: the force produced by gravity acting on mass (11)

——————— **T** ———————

ART CREDITS

Abbreviated as follows: (t) top; (b) bottom; (l) left; (r) right; (c) center.

All art, unless otherwise noted, by Holt, Rinehart, and Winston.

Front Cover and Master Items: Leslie Kell. **Front Matter:** Page II, (tl), J/B Woolsey Associates; V (tl) J/B Woolsey Associates; V (cl), David Uhl Studio; VIII (bl), Michael Morrow; XV (tl), David Uhl Studio. **Chapter One:** 5, (br), Leslie Kell; 24, (tl), J/B Woolsey Associates; 28, (tl), J/B Woolsey Associates; 28, (tc), J/B Woolsey Associates; 28, (c), J/B Woolsey Associates; 33, (br), J/B Woolsey Associates. **Chapter Two:** Page 40, (br), J/B Woolsey Associates; 45, (tr), Foca; 48, (b) Leslie Kell; 57, (t) David Uhl Illustrations. **Chapter Three:** Page 75, (br), Leslie Kell; 77, (t) Stephen Durke/Dick Washington; 78, (cl), J/B Woolsey Associates; 82, (b) David Uhl Studio; 84, (bl) David Uhl Studio; 92, (b) David Uhl Studio; 98, (tl), J/B Woolsey Associates; 98, (tr), J/B Woolsey Associates; 98, (cr) J/B Woolsey Associates; 106, (tl), Foca; 106, (tr), Foca; 106, (tr), Foca; 107, (tl), Foca. **Chapter Four:** Page 113, (c), Jack Scott; 126, (bl) J/B Woolsey Associates; 126, (br), J/B Woosley Associates. **Chapter Five:** Page 171, (all) Leslie Kell; 173, (tl), David Uhl Studio. **Chapter Six:** Page 195, (tl), J/B Woolsey Associates; 216, (tr), J/B Woolsey Associates; 217, (bc) J/B Woolsey Associates; 217, (c), J/B Woolsey Associates; 218, (tl), J/B Woolsey Associates; 223, (b) J/B Woolsey Asociates. **Chapter Seven:** Page 234, (tr), J/B Woolsey Associates; 235 (tl), J/B Woolsey Associates. **Chapter Eight:** Page 285, (t) Kristy Sprott; 286, (b) Kristy Sprott; 286 (b) Kristy Sprott; 286, (b) Kristy Sprott; 293, (tr), J/B Woolsey Associates. **Chapter Nine:** Page 333, (tr), Morgan Cain Associates. **Chapter Ten:** Page 358, (t) Leslie Kell; 368, (t) Kristy Sprott; 370, (cl), Peter Bollinger; 370, (c), Peter Bollinger; 370, (cr) Peter Bollinger. **Chapter Eleven:** Page 385, (bl) Leslie Kell; 402, (b) David Uhl Illustrations; 410, (t) Kristy Sprott. **Chapter Twelve:** Page 429, (tl) David Uhl Studio; 430, (bl) J/B Woolsey Associates; 430, (br), J/B Woolsey Associates; 435, (b) David Uhl Studio; 435, (b) David Uhl Studio; 445, (tr), David Uhl Studio; 452, (b) David Uhl Studio; 455, (tr), Stephen Durke/Dick Washington. **Chapter Thirteen:** Page 469, (c), Stephen Durke/Dick Washington; 469, (c), Stephen Durke/Dick Washington; 469, (br), Stephen Durke/Dick Washington; 488, (tc), Stephen Durke/Dick Washington; 488, (tc), Stephen Durke/Dick Washington; 489, (b) Stephen Durke/Dick Washington; 491, (b) Stephen Durke/Dick Washington; 497, (bc) Stephen Durke/Dick Washington; 497, (br), Stephen Durke/Dick Washington; 498, (bl) Stephen Durke/Dick Washington; 499, (tr), Stephen Durke/Dick Washington; 500, (br), Stephen Durke/Dick Washington. **Chapter Fourteen:** Page 518, (b) Christy Krames. **Chapter Fifteen:** Page 546, (bl) Kristy Sprott; 547, (tr), J/B Woolsey Associates; 550, (b) Kristy Sprott; 552 (bl) Kristy Sprott; 552, (t) Kristy Sprott; 552, (cr) Kristy Sprott; 553, (t) Leslie Kell; 578, (br), Leslie Kell. **Chapter Sixteen:** Page 589, (b) Stephen Durke/Dick Washington; 589, (b) Stephen Durke/Dick Washington; 589, (b) Stephen Durke/Dick Washington; 606, (bc) Christy Krames; 606, (bc) Christy Krames. **Chapter Seventeen:** Page 620, (b) David Uhl Studio; 623, (tr), Kristy Sprott; 623, (tr), Kristy Sprott; 624, (tr), David Uhl Studio; 624, (bl) David Uhl Studio; 629, (b) David Uhl Studio; 632, (br), David Uhl Studio; 635, (b) David Uhl Studio; 637, (bl) David Uhl Studio; 637, (br), David Uhl Studio; 638, (b) David Uhl Studio; 640, (b) David Uhl Studio; 640, (br), Kristy Sprott; 644 (bl) David Uhl Studio; 644, (bl) David Uhl Studio; 644, (br) David Uhl Studio; 645, (tr), David Uhl Studio; 645, (br), David Uhl Studio. **Chapter Eighteen:** Page 671, (t) David Uhl Studio; 677, (b) Leslie Kell; 714, (tl), David Uhl Studio; 756, (tr), David Uhl Studio; 780, (tl), David Uhl Studio.

PHOTO CREDITS

Abbreviated as follows: (t) top; (b) bottom; (l) left; (r) right; (c) center.

All photos, unless otherwise noted, by HRW Staff Photographer, Sam Dudgeon. Acknowledgments:

Quick Lab Icon (watch) - Image copyright © 2000 Photodisc, Inc.

Inquiry Lab Icon (glassware) - Image copyright © 1997 Photodisc, Inc.

Table of Contents: II (br) Dennis Fagan/HRW; III (br) Charlie Winters; IV (tr) Douglas Struthers/Tony Stone Images; (bl) Tony Freeman/PhotoEdit; V (tr) EdPritchard/Tony Stone Images; (br) Charlie Winters; VI (tc) Andrew Syred/Tony Stone Images; (cl) Manfred Kage/Peter Arnold, Inc.; VII (tr) Charlie Westerman/Liaison International; (cl) Ken Whitmore/Tony Stone Images; (bl) John Langford/HRW Photo; VIII (tr) Vladimir Pcholkin/FPG International; (cl) Charlie Winters; (cr) Sergio Purtell/Foca; (bl) Matthew Stockman/Allsport; (br) Courtesy of Ford Motor Co.; IX (tr) Jenny Hager/Adventure Photo; (bl) Ozone Processing Team Code 916/NASA Goddard Space Flight Center; (tl) Westlight; X (tc) Dr. E.R. Degginger; (bl) Peter Van Steen/HRW Photo; (br, bc, c) Charlie Winters; XI (tr) Tony Stone Images; (c) Sergio Purtell/Foca; (bl) Rod Planck/Photo Researchers, Inc.; (cl) Randal Alhadeff/HRW Photo; XII (t) William Warren/Westlight; (cl) Peter Van Steen/HRW Photo; (bl) Frank Rossotto/The Stock Market; XIII (tr) Sergio Purtell/Foca; (cl) Dennis Fagan/HRW Photo; XIV (bl) Phil Degginger/Bruce Coleman, Inc.; XV (t) Harry Giglio Photography, Inc.; XVI (tr) Sergio Purtell/Foca. **Chapter 1:** 2 (all) SuperStock; 4 (b) Image Bank; 6 (br) Randal Alhadeff/HRW Photo; 7 (bc) Charlie Winters; 8 (tr) Charlie Winters; (tc) Richard Megna/Fundamental Photographs; 11 (tr) Charlie Winters; 12 (tl) Andrew Brookes Creative/The Stock Market; 16 (bl) Dennis Fagan/HRW Photo; 18 (bc) Charlie Winters; 19 (all) Sergio Purtell/Foca; 23 (tl) Sergio Purtell/Foca; 24 (tr) John Neubauer/Rainbow, Inc.; 25 (cr) Tom Pantages Photography; 26 (b) Peter Van Steen/HRW Photo; 27 (tl, tc) Charlie Winters; 29 (bl) Neal Mishler/FPG International; (br) Sergio Purtell/Foca; (tr) Jenny Hager/Adventure Photo; 31 (all) Charlie Winters; 33 (br) Sergio Purtell/Foca. **Chapter 2:** 38 (all) Paul & Lindamarie/FPG International; 41 (tc) Visuals Unlimited; 42 (bc) Tony Freeman/PhotoEdit; 43 (tl) Peter Van Steen/HRW Photo; (tc) Sergio Purtell/Foca/Prism Technologies, Inc.; 44 (tl) Sergio Purtell/Foca; 50 (b) Andre Jenny/Stock South/PNI; 52 (tl, br) Sergio Purtell/Foca; (bc) Digital Stock Corp.; 53 (tr) © 1994 by The New York Times Co. Reprinted by Permission.; 54 (tr) Image Copyright © 1996 Photodisc, Inc.; (tl) Sergio Purtell/Foca; 56 (all) Kristen Brochmann/Fundamental Photographs; 65 (tr) Scoones/SIPA Press; 66 (tr) Corbis-Bettmann. **Chapter 3:** 72 (all) Ed Pritchard/Tony Stone Images; 74 (br) Giraudon/Art Resource/NY; 75 (bl) Peter Van Steen/HRW Photo; 77 (tr) Sergio Purtell/Foca; 81 (tr) Corbis-Bettmann; 83 (br) Richard Megna/Fundamental Photographs; (tr) Sergio Purtell/Foca; 85 (tl) David Sailors/The Stock Market; (tr) Sergio Purtell/Foca; 96 (bl) Image used with permission of IMS Properties, Inc.; 102 (br) Ed Pritchard/Tony Stone Images; 103 (cr) Dr. E.R. Degginger; (c) Carl Frank/Photo Researchers, Inc. **Chapter 4:** 110 (all) Charlie Winters; 112 (all) Charlie Winters; 117 (bl, bc) Charlie Winters; (br) Dr. E.R. Degginger; 120 (bl) Vanni/Art Resource/NY; 124 (cr) Terry Donnelly/Tony Stone Images; 125 (br) Bruce Iverson; 126 (bl) J & L Weber/Peter Arnold, Inc.; (br) Charles D. Winters; 128 (bl) Telegraph Colour Library/FPG International; 132 (cr) Wesley Hitt/Tony Stone Images; 133 (tr) Gabe Palmer/The Stock Market; 134 (b) Peter Cade/Tony Stone Images; (all others) Charlie Winters/HRW Photo; 143 (br) HST image: Hui Yang (U. of Illinois Jeff J. Hester and NASA); 144 (tl) Roger Ressmeyer/Corbis; 149 (tr) Alfred Pasieka/Peter Arnold, Inc. **Chapter 5:** 156 (all) Manfred Kage/Peter Arnold, Inc.; 163 (all) Charlie Winters; 165 (tr) Rick Lance/PhotoTake; 166 (bl) Charlie Winters; (bc) Andrew Syred/Tony Stone Images; 169 (c) Paul Silverman/Fundamental Photographs; 170 (bl) Charlie Winters; 174 (all) Charlie Winters; 182 (bc) Tom Pantages Photography; (br) Lafaille/Gamma Liaison; 183 (tl) Sergio Purtell/Foca; (tc, tr) Charlie Winters. **Chapter 6:** 192 (all) Douglas Struthers/Tony Stone Images; 194 (bc) T. McCarthy/Custom Medical Stock Photo; 195 (bc) Victoria Smith/HRW Photo; 206 (all) Sergio Purtell/Foca; 208 (br)

Periodic Table of the Elements

Key:

6	Atomic number
C	Symbol
Carbon	Name
12.011	Average atomic mass
[He]$2s^2 2p^2$	Electron configuration

Period

Period 1

1
H
Hydrogen
1.00794
$1s^1$

Group 1

3
Li
Lithium
6.941
[He]$2s^1$

11
Na
Sodium
22.989768
[Ne]$3s^1$

19
K
Potassium
39.0983
[Ar]$4s^1$

37
Rb
Rubidium
85.4678
[Kr]$5s^1$

55
Cs
Cesium
132.90543
[Xe]$6s^1$

87
Fr
Francium
(223.0197)
[Rn]$7s^1$

Group 2

4
Be
Beryllium
9.012182
[He]$2s^2$

12
Mg
Magnesium
24.3050
[Ne]$3s^2$

20
Ca
Calcium
40.078
[Ar]$4s^2$

38
Sr
Strontium
87.62
[Kr]$5s^2$

56
Ba
Barium
137.327
[Xe]$6s^2$

88
Ra
Radium
(226.0254)
[Rn]$7s^2$

Group 3

21
Sc
Scandium
44.955910
[Ar]$3d^1 4s^2$

39
Y
Yttrium
88.90585
[Kr]$4d^1 5s^2$

57
La
Lanthanum
138.9055
[Xe]$5d^1 6s^2$

89
Ac
Actinium
(227.0278)
[Rn]$6d^1 7s^2$

Group 4

22
Ti
Titanium
47.88
[Ar]$3d^2 4s^2$

40
Zr
Zirconium
91.224
[Kr]$4d^2 5s^2$

72
Hf
Hafnium
178.49
[Xe]$4f^{14} 5d^2 6s^2$

104
Rf
Rutherfordium
(261.11)
[Rn]$5f^{14} 6d^2 7s^2$

Group 5

23
V
Vanadium
50.9415
[Ar]$3d^3 4s^2$

41
Nb
Niobium
92.90638
[Kr]$4d^4 5s^1$

73
Ta
Tantalum
180.9479
[Xe]$4f^{14} 5d^3 6s^2$

105
Db
Dubnium
(262.114)
[Rn]$5f^{14} 6d^3 7s^2$

Group 6

24
Cr
Chromium
51.9961
[Ar]$3d^5 4s^1$

42
Mo
Molybdenum
95.94
[Kr]$4d^5 5s^1$

74
W
Tungsten
183.84
[Xe]$4f^{14} 5d^4 6s^2$

106
Sg
Seaborgium
(263.118)
[Rn]$5f^{14} 6d^4 7s^2$

Group 7

25
Mn
Manganese
54.93805
[Ar]$3d^5 4s^2$

43
Tc
Technetium
(97.9072)
[Kr]$4d^6 5s^1$

75
Re
Rhenium
186.207
[Xe]$4f^{14} 5d^5 6s^2$

107
Bh
Bohrium
(262.12)
[Rn]$5f^{14} 6d^5 7s^2$

Group 8

26
Fe
Iron
55.847
[Ar]$3d^6 4s^2$

44
Ru
Ruthenium
101.07
[Kr]$4d^7 5s^1$

76
Os
Osmium
190.23
[Xe]$4f^{14} 5d^6 6s^2$

108
Hs
Hassium
(265)†
[Rn]$5f^{14} 6d^6 7s^2$

Group 9

27
Co
Cobalt
58.93320
[Ar]$3d^7 4s^2$

45
Rh
Rhodium
102.906
[Kr]$4d^8 5s^1$

77
Ir
Iridium
192.22
[Xe]$4f^{14} 5d^7 6s^2$

109
Mt
Meitnerium
(266)†
[Rn]$5f^{14} 6d^7 7s^2$

† Estimated from currently available IUPAC data.

* The systematic names and symbols for elements greater than 109 will be used until the approval of trivial names by IUPAC.

58
Ce
Cerium
140.115
[Xe]$4f^1 5d^1 6s^2$

59
Pr
Praseodymium
140.908
[Xe]$4f^3 6s^2$

60
Nd
Neodymium
144.24
[Xe]$4f^4 6s^2$

61
Pm
Promethium
(144.9127)
[Xe]$4f^5 6s^2$

62
Sm
Samarium
150.36
[Xe]$4f^6 6s^2$

90
Th
Thorium
232.0381
[Rn]$6d^2 7s^2$

91
Pa
Protactinium
231.03588
[Rn]$5f^2 6d^1 7s^2$

92
U
Uranium
238.0289
[Rn]$5f^3 6d^1 7s^2$

93
Np
Neptunium
(237.0482)
[Rn]$5f^4 6d^1 7s^2$

94
Pu
Plutonium
244.0642
[Rn]$5f^6 7s^2$